D1541704

SRA®

MATH

Explorations and Applications

Make thinking a basic skill on the road of life.

Solve the persistent problems of teaching elementary mathematics by teaching children how to *think* mathematically.

REPORT CARD
Subjects
1 2 3 4
Math
Knows and uses basic facts
Demonstrates understanding of the math concepts using manipulatives and abstract thinking
Solves word problems
Uses problem-solving strategies to solve real-world problems
Language Arts

Visit our website
www.SRA-4KIDS.com

Introducing

SRA MATH

Explorations and Applications

Take the right path to teaching mathematics.

This comprehensive, research-based program challenges students to think every day, on every page, at every juncture. It's the answer that teachers need to make math instruction effective and math learning enjoyable.

Level K

Level 1

Level 2

Level 3

Level 4

Level 5

Level 6

Also Available

- **Professional Development Handbook**
- **Program Guide**
- **Test Preparation Practice Workbook**
- **Lesson Plans**
- ***Minds on Math***
- ***Math CrossSections***
- ***Science, Math & YOU***
- ***Cooperate 1, 2, and 3***
- ***Junior Thinklab™***
- ***Thinklab™***
- ***Scoring High in Math***

Take along the essentials for the journey.

Core Materials

- Student Editions (K–2) in consumable format that introduce, integrate, and practice concepts and skills
- Student Editions (3–6) in hardbound format filled with lessons that integrate concept development, practice, and problem solving
- Thinking Story Books (Levels 1–3) for teachers to read to the class
- Teacher's Guides that provide the road map along with practice, reteaching, and enrichment support
- Basic Manipulative Kits needed for Cube Games and Mental Math Activities

Lesson Support Materials

- Practice Activities in Workbook and Blackline Master formats
- Enrichment Activities in Workbook and Blackline Master formats
- Reteaching Activities in Workbook and Blackline Master formats
- Assessment Masters
- Home Connections Masters
- Literature Library (K–3)

Manipulative Support Materials

- Game Mat Packages (K–6) for skill practice and problem solving
- Primary Manipulative Kit (K–2) to introduce basic concepts
- Primary Overhead Manipulative Kit (K–2)
- Intermediate Manipulative Kit (3–6) for variety in concept presentation
- Intermediate Overhead Manipulative Kit (3–6)
- Teacher Manipulative Kit for classroom demonstrations

Technology Support Materials

- *Math Explorations and Applications* Software (1–6) provides extra skill practice for every lesson.
- *The Cruncher* (4–6) offers a student-friendly spreadsheet application for appropriate lessons.
- *My Silly CD of Counting* CD-ROM (K) helps build the concept of counting.
- TI-108™ Calculator Package (K–3)
- Math Explorer™ Calculator Package (4–6)
- Primary Overhead Calculator (K–3)
- Intermediate Overhead Calculator (4–6)

Professional Development

- Professional Development Handbook

It's mathematics, taken off the beaten path.

Math Explorations and Applications **helps students learn the real basics: traditional arithmetic skills, computation, and problem solving.**

- **Concept Integration.** The program's organization, scope, and sequence allow integration and thorough study of math concepts.
- **In-Depth Study.** Lessons devote the number of pages needed to teach a concept, not artificially dividing every topic into the same lesson length. Sometimes it takes more than two pages to effectively cover the important points in a lesson.
- **Concepts in Context.** Skills and concepts are taught and retaught in different contexts—never in isolation.

- **Variety of Presentations.** Explore, Practice, Problem Solving, and Projects address a variety of learning styles so that students stay interested and motivated as they learn to think.
- **Cumulative Review of Content.** Once a skill has been introduced, it is integrated, practiced, and reviewed in mixed practice and in context throughout the grade level. Lesson by lesson, students accumulate the skills they need to master more complicated math concepts, as they continually review previously introduced skills.
- **Life-Long Learning.** As they see mathematics used to solve realistic problems, students begin to view strong math skills as useful, lifelong tools they can use both inside and outside the classroom.
- **Focus on Computation *and* Problem Solving.** *Math Explorations and Applications* develops and provides practice of traditional skills in problem-solving settings such as games. This makes efficient use of teacher and student time and effort.

Developing concepts in context paves the road to understanding.

Math Explorations and Applications **introduces and integrates concepts so that students make connections and build on what they already know.**

- **Early Introduction of Concepts.** An early age-appropriate introduction to concepts such as algebra, geometry, multiplication, and division builds understanding and connections from the very beginning. Because most students actually begin to use the principles of more advanced math concepts like algebra long before the eighth grade, *Math Explorations and Applications* helps students feel comfortable with these concepts from the very start.

- **Core Concept Development at Every Level.** Operations, thinking skills, problem solving, mental math, estimation, data organization, geometry, probability, and statistics are emphasized at all grade levels.

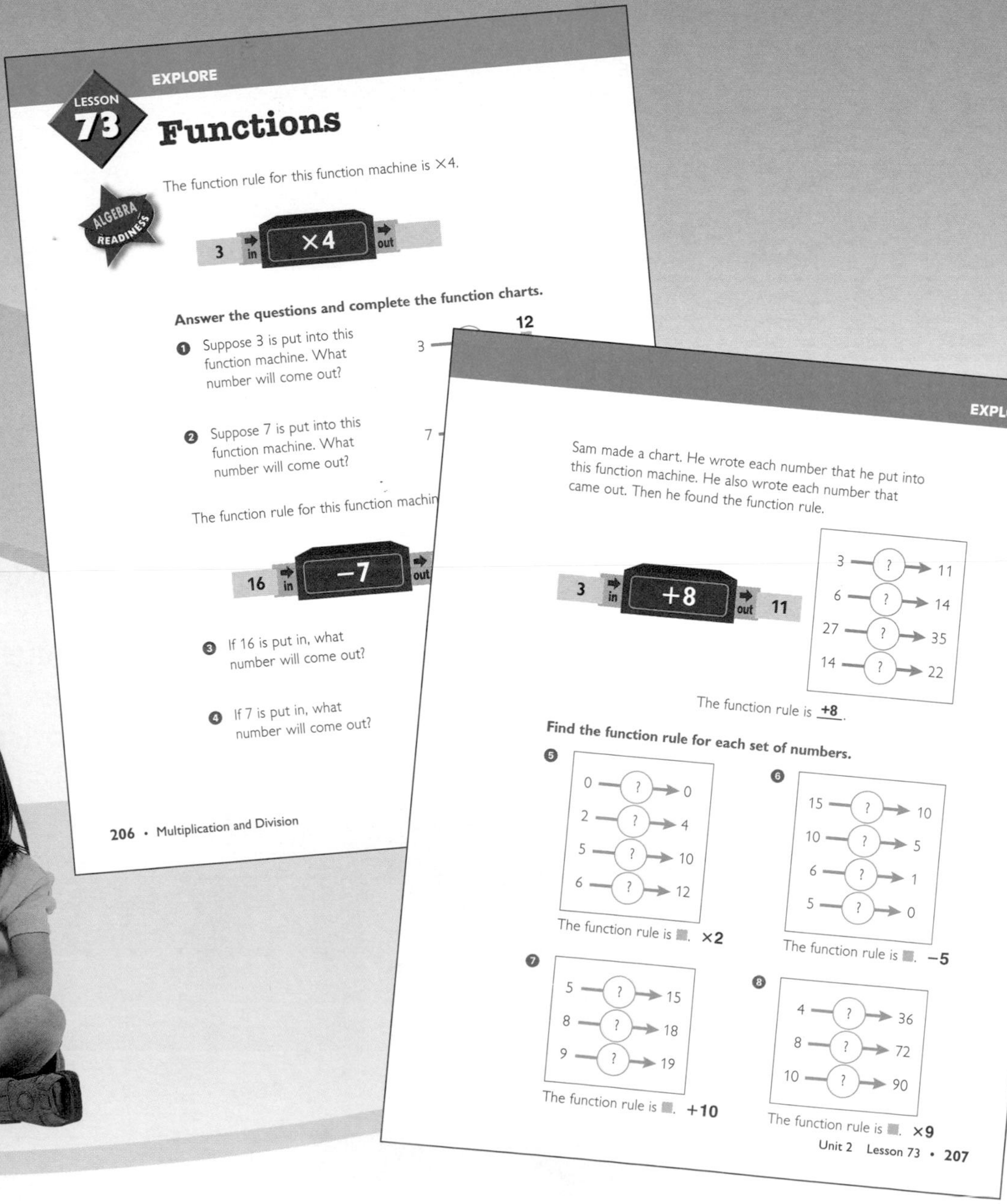
EXPLORE

LESSON 73

Functions

ALGEBRA READINESS

The function rule for this function machine is ×4.

3 in ×4 out

Answer the questions and complete the function charts.

1. Suppose 3 is put into this function machine. What number will come out? 3 — 12

2. Suppose 7 is put into this function machine. What number will come out? 7 —

The function rule for this function machin

16 in −7 out

3. If 16 is put in, what number will come out?

4. If 7 is put in, what number will come out?

206 • Multiplication and Division

EXPLORE

Sam made a chart. He wrote each number that he put into this function machine. He also wrote each number that came out. Then he found the function rule.

3 in +8 out 11

in		out
3	?	11
6	?	14
27	?	35
14	?	22

The function rule is +8.

Find the function rule for each set of numbers.

5.

in		out
0	?	0
2	?	4
5	?	10
6	?	12

The function rule is ■. ×2

6.

in		out
15	?	10
10	?	5
6	?	1
5	?	0

The function rule is ■. −5

7.

in		out
5	?	15
8	?	18
9	?	19

The function rule is ■. +10

8.

in		out
4	?	36
8	?	72
10	?	90

The function rule is ■. ×9

Unit 2 Lesson 73 • 207

Level 3

◆ **Concepts in Context.** Concepts are developed in different contexts to help students recognize their natural connections. For example, the concept of fractions is developed in relation to time, money, and measurement.

◆ **Intelligent Use of Manipulatives.** Intelligent use of hands-on activities and manipulatives establishes concepts in the concrete, showing students a variety of ways to solve a problem. Students are encouraged to use these tools where appropriate, then to move beyond these tools as quickly as possible toward the goal of abstract thinking.

◆ **Realistic Problem-Solving Models.** Exciting **Act It Out** lessons model problem-solving strategies by having students physically work through new concepts.

◆ **Emphasizing Natural Concept Relationships** By drawing on the natural relationships that exist among concepts, students learn to make connections between concepts so that they can understand them more effectively.

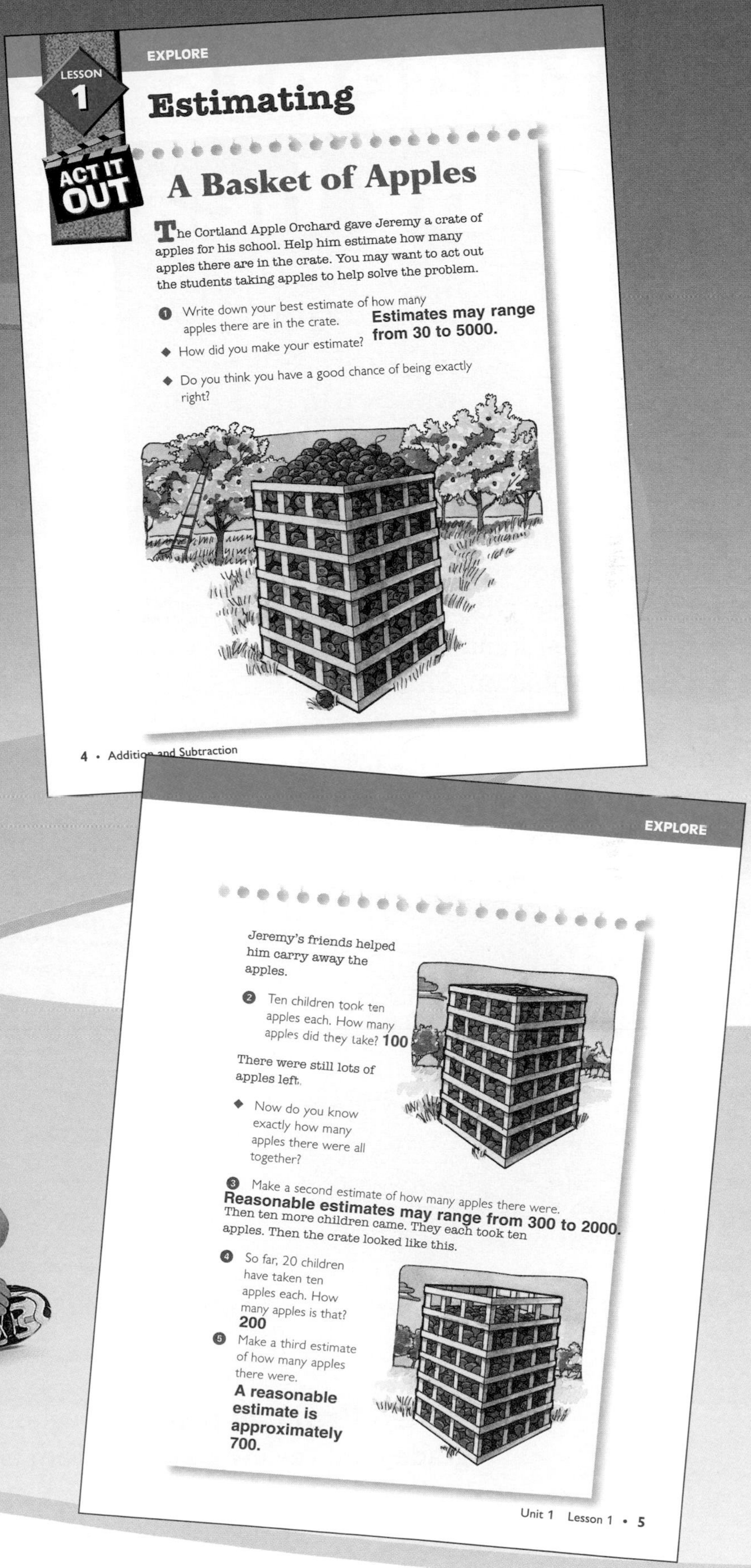
LESSON 1
ACT IT OUT
EXPLORE

Estimating

A Basket of Apples

The Cortland Apple Orchard gave Jeremy a crate of apples for his school. Help him estimate how many apples there are in the crate. You may want to act out the students taking apples to help solve the problem.

1. Write down your best estimate of how many apples there are in the crate. **Estimates may range from 30 to 5000.**

◆ How did you make your estimate?

◆ Do you think you have a good chance of being exactly right?

4 • Addition and Subtraction

EXPLORE

Jeremy's friends helped him carry away the apples.

2. Ten children took ten apples each. How many apples did they take? **100**

There were still lots of apples left.

◆ Now do you know exactly how many apples there were all together?

3. Make a second estimate of how many apples there were. **Reasonable estimates may range from 300 to 2000.**

Then ten more children came. They each took ten apples. Then the crate looked like this.

4. So far, 20 children have taken ten apples each. How many apples is that? **200**

5. Make a third estimate of how many apples there were. **A reasonable estimate is approximately 700.**

Unit 1 Lesson 1 • 5

Level 4

Step by step, students learn the basics by heart and mind.

Computational skills are essential for efficient mathematical thinking. But skill practice can be enjoyable and is one more opportunity to challenge students to think mathematically.

- **Practice** pages often have hidden patterns that help students understand number relationships and encourage mathematical thinking on every problem on every page.

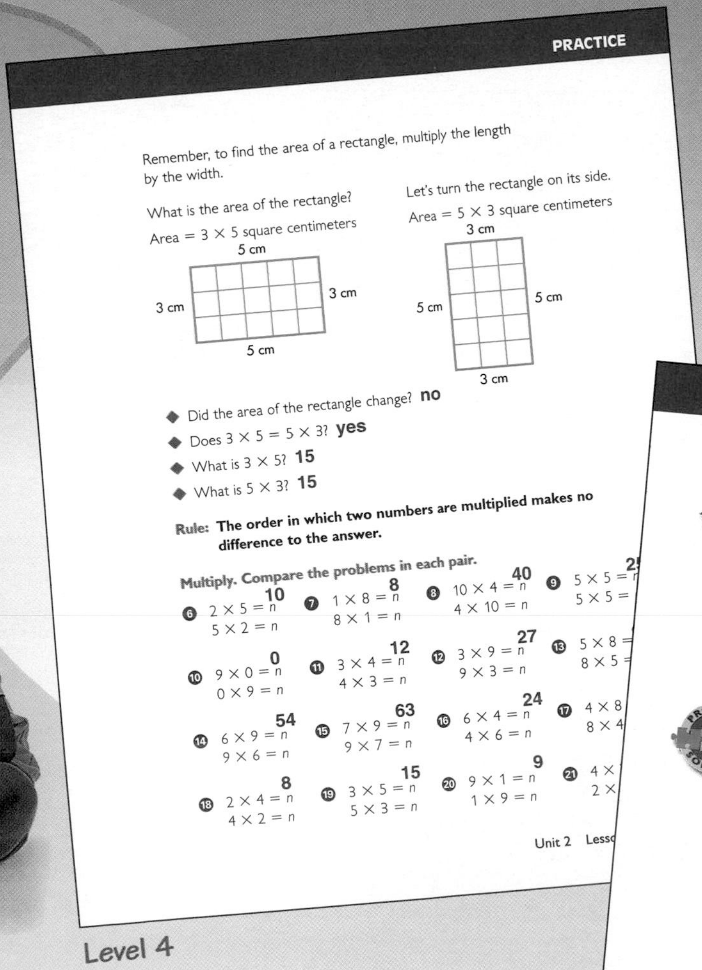

PRACTICE

Remember, to find the area of a rectangle, multiply the length by the width.

What is the area of the rectangle?
Area = 3 × 5 square centimeters

Let's turn the rectangle on its side.
Area = 5 × 3 square centimeters

- Did the area of the rectangle change? **no**
- Does 3 × 5 = 5 × 3? **yes**
- What is 3 × 5? **15**
- What is 5 × 3? **15**

Rule: The order in which two numbers are multiplied makes no difference to the answer.

Multiply. Compare the problems in each pair.

6. 2 × 5 = n **10**; 5 × 2 = n
7. 1 × 8 = n **8**; 8 × 1 = n
8. 10 × 4 = n **40**; 4 × 10 = n
9. 5 × 5 = n **25**; 5 × 5 = n
10. 9 × 0 = n **0**; 0 × 9 = n
11. 3 × 4 = n **12**; 4 × 3 = n
12. 3 × 9 = n **27**; 9 × 3 = n
13. 5 × 8 = ; 8 × 5 =
14. 6 × 9 = n **54**; 9 × 6 = n
15. 7 × 9 = n **63**; 9 × 7 = n
16. 6 × 4 = n **24**; 4 × 6 = n
17. 4 × 8; 8 × 4
18. 2 × 4 = n **8**; 4 × 2 = n
19. 3 × 5 = n **15**; 5 × 3 = n
20. 9 × 1 = n **9**; 1 × 9 = n
21. 4 ×; 2 ×

Unit 2 Lesso

Level 4

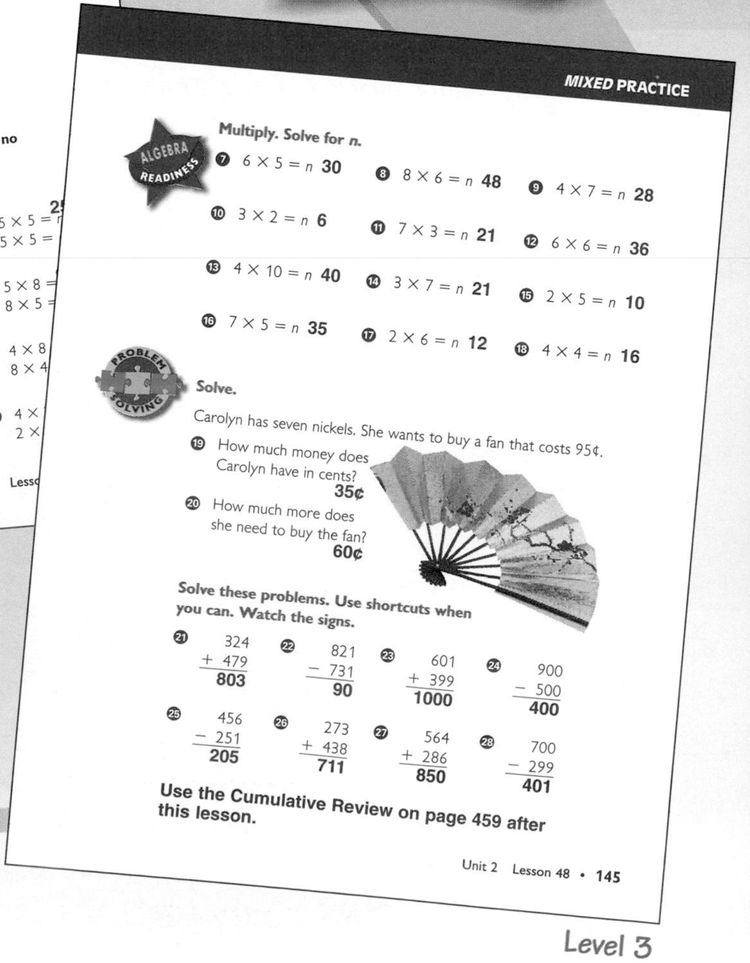

MIXED PRACTICE

ALGEBRA READINESS

Multiply. Solve for *n*.

7. 6 × 5 = n **30**
8. 8 × 6 = n **48**
9. 4 × 7 = n **28**
10. 3 × 2 = n **6**
11. 7 × 3 = n **21**
12. 6 × 6 = n **36**
13. 4 × 10 = n **40**
14. 3 × 7 = n **21**
15. 2 × 5 = n **10**
16. 7 × 5 = n **35**
17. 2 × 6 = n **12**
18. 4 × 4 = n **16**

PROBLEM SOLVING

Solve.

Carolyn has seven nickels. She wants to buy a fan that costs 95¢.

19. How much money does Carolyn have in cents? **35¢**
20. How much more does she need to buy the fan? **60¢**

Solve these problems. Use shortcuts when you can. Watch the signs.

21. 324 + 479 = **803**
22. 821 − 731 = **90**
23. 601 + 399 = **1000**
24. 900 − 500 = **400**
25. 456 − 251 = **205**
26. 273 + 438 = **711**
27. 564 + 286 = **850**
28. 700 − 299 = **401**

Use the Cumulative Review on page 459 after this lesson.

Unit 2 Lesson 48 • 145

Level 3

- **Mixed Practice** pages throughout each grade level review concepts from all lessons and encourage students to think about what they're doing and how they do it.

Multiplication Table Game
Math Focus:
•Practicing basic facts–multiplying two factors of 5 or less
•Using a multiplication table
Object of the Game: To have more counters at the end of the game
Players: Two
MATERIALS
Two cubes
36 counters or pennies
SET UP
Every circle on the mat must be covered with a counter.
Players roll the 0-5 number cube. The person who rolls the higher number goes first.
HOW TO PLAY
1 Players take turns rolling both cubes and making multiplication sentences out of the numbers. For example, if a 4 and a 2 are rolled, the player could say either "4 times 2 equals 8" or "2 times 4 equals 8."
2 After giving the multiplication sentence, players check their answers by looking under the appropriate counter. If correct, the player keeps the counter; if incorrect, the player replaces the counter.
3 Once the counter on a circle has been won, the circle remains empty. A player who cannot make a multiplication sentence that applies to a covered circle cannot win a counter that turn.
4 The player with more counters at the end of the game wins.
Multiplication Table Game
Multiplication Table Game

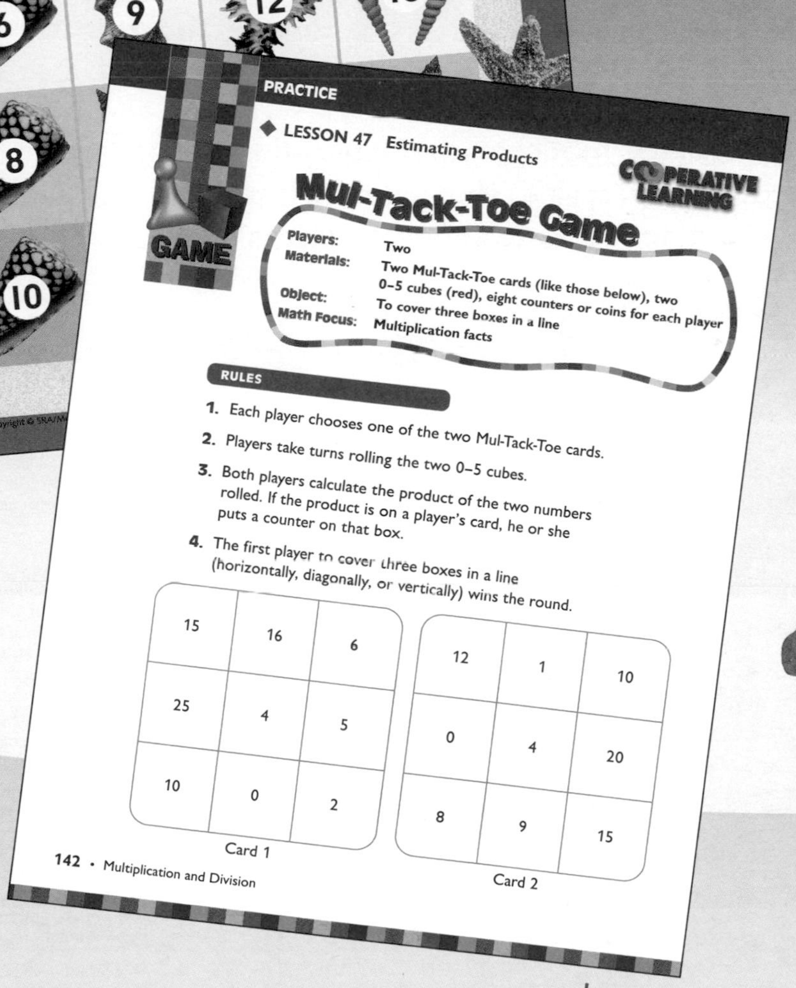

PRACTICE

◆ LESSON 47 Estimating Products

COOPERATIVE LEARNING

GAME

Mul-Tack-Toe Game

Players: Two
Materials: Two Mul-Tack-Toe cards (like those below), two 0–5 cubes (red), eight counters or coins for each player
Object: To cover three boxes in a line
Math Focus: Multiplication facts

RULES

1. Each player chooses one of the two Mul-Tack-Toe cards.
2. Players take turns rolling the two 0–5 cubes.
3. Both players calculate the product of the two numbers rolled. If the product is on a player's card, he or she puts a counter on that box.
4. The first player to cover three boxes in a line (horizontally, diagonally, or vertically) wins the round.

15	16	6
25	4	5
10	0	2

Card 1

12	1	10
0	4	20
8	9	15

Card 2

142 • Multiplication and Division

Level 3

◆ **Games** are not just for fun. Throughout the program, games provide extensive, serious practice with traditional arithmetic. They also offer opportunities to identify and solve interesting problems. Students don't even realize how much math they're practicing!

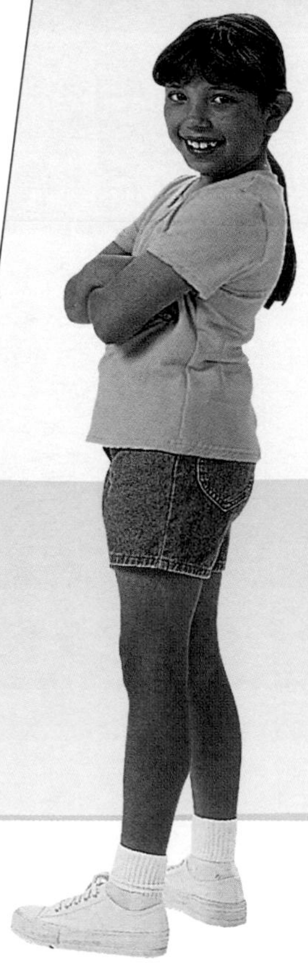

MENTAL MATH

Interactive **Mental Math** activities in every lesson in the Teacher's Guide help students develop the ability to manipulate numbers in their minds, easily and with common sense.

Children learn to solve problems by solving problems.

Problem-solving strategies are integrated throughout *SRA Math Explorations and Applications,* never taught in isolation. Instead of memorizing rote strategies, students learn to:

- **recognize a problem,**
- **select an appropriate strategy,**
- **solve the problem, and**
- **reflect on their reasoning.**

◆ **Thinking Stories** model mathematical thinking and problem-solving strategies. They demonstrate that real-life "problems" can appear in unexpected places.

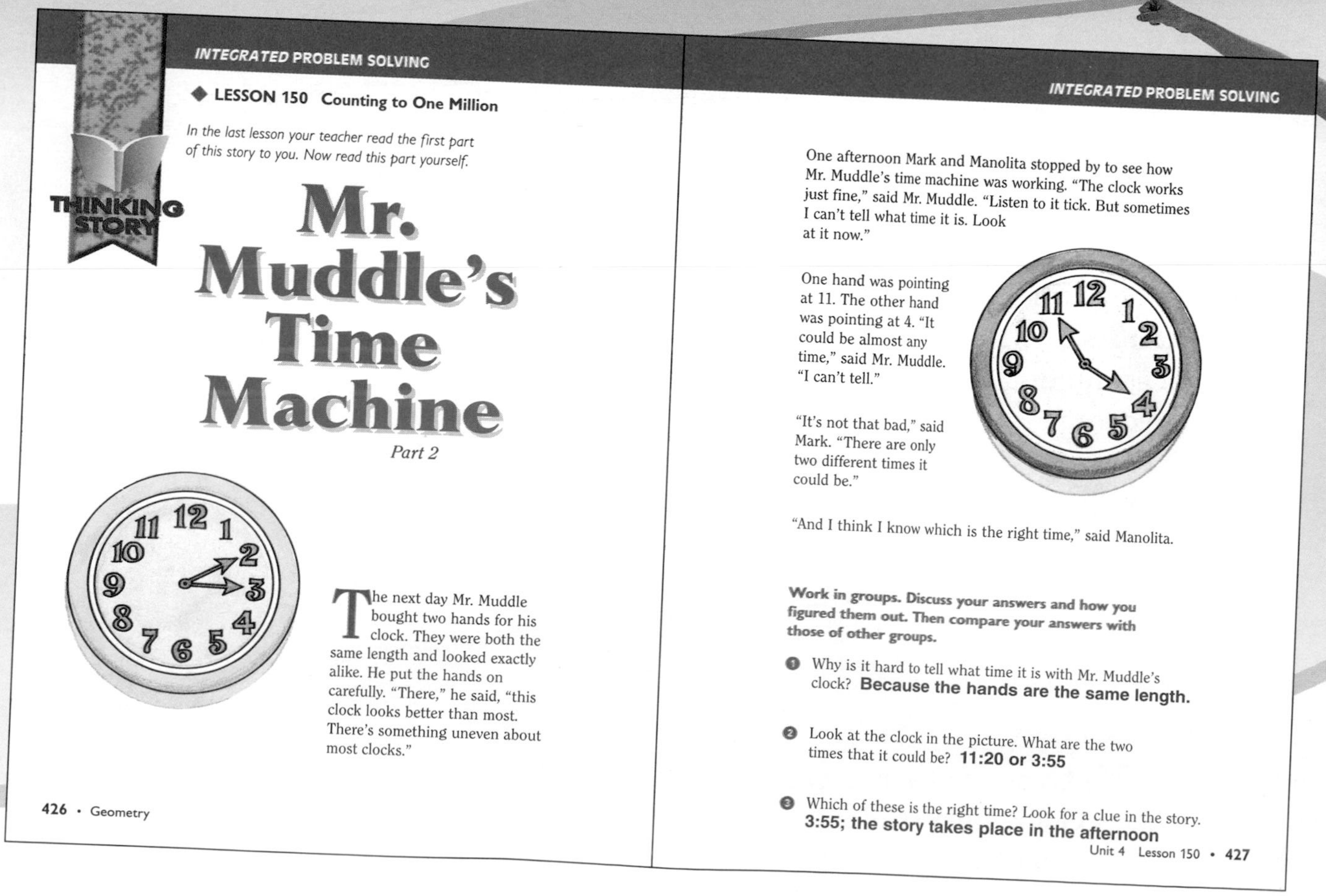

INTEGRATED PROBLEM SOLVING

◆ LESSON 150 Counting to One Million

In the last lesson your teacher read the first part of this story to you. Now read this part yourself.

THINKING STORY

Mr. Muddle's Time Machine

Part 2

The next day Mr. Muddle bought two hands for his clock. They were both the same length and looked exactly alike. He put the hands on carefully. "There," he said, "this clock looks better than most. There's something uneven about most clocks."

426 • Geometry

INTEGRATED PROBLEM SOLVING

One afternoon Mark and Manolita stopped by to see how Mr. Muddle's time machine was working. "The clock works just fine," said Mr. Muddle. "Listen to it tick. But sometimes I can't tell what time it is. Look at it now."

One hand was pointing at 11. The other hand was pointing at 4. "It could be almost any time," said Mr. Muddle. "I can't tell."

"It's not that bad," said Mark. "There are only two different times it could be."

"And I think I know which is the right time," said Manolita.

Work in groups. Discuss your answers and how you figured them out. Then compare your answers with those of other groups.

1. Why is it hard to tell what time it is with Mr. Muddle's clock? **Because the hands are the same length.**
2. Look at the clock in the picture. What are the two times that it could be? **11:20 or 3:55**
3. Which of these is the right time? Look for a clue in the story. **3:55; the story takes place in the afternoon**

Unit 4 Lesson 150 • 427

Level 3

◆ **Word Problems** throughout the student books are carefully crafted to involve multiple operations, cumulative content, and sometimes, insufficient information so that students always have to think.

◆ **Games** provide lots of opportunities for students to identify problems and develop strategies for their solution.

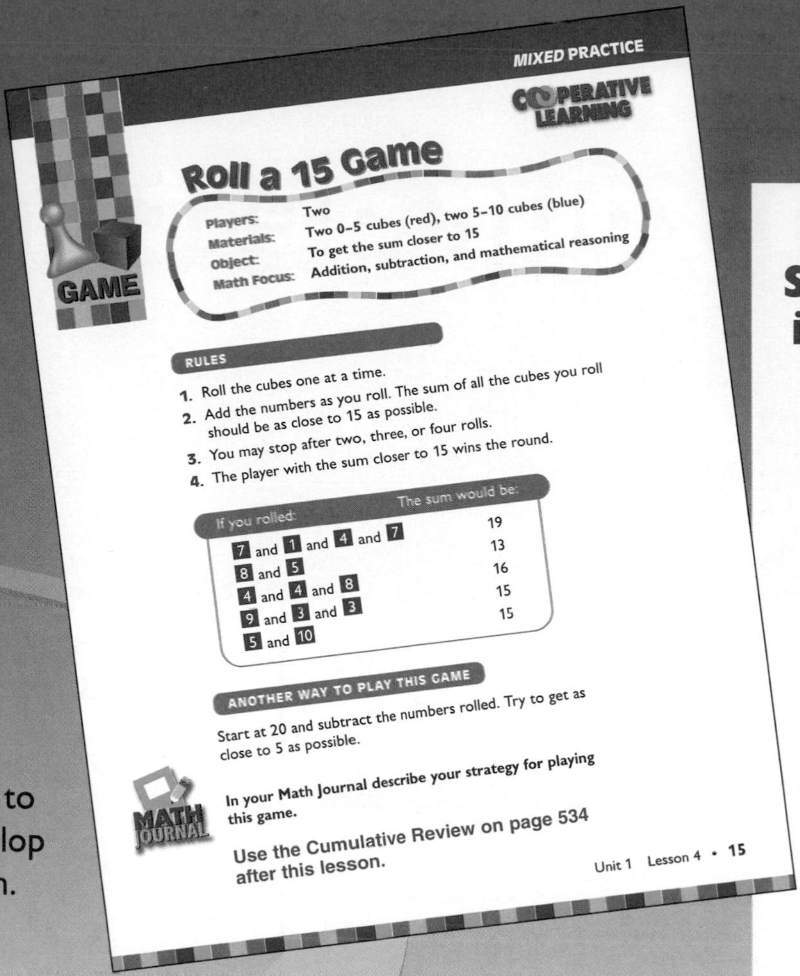

MIXED PRACTICE

COOPERATIVE LEARNING

GAME

Roll a 15 Game

Players: Two
Materials: Two 0–5 cubes (red), two 5–10 cubes (blue)
Object: To get the sum closer to 15
Math Focus: Addition, subtraction, and mathematical reasoning

RULES

1. Roll the cubes one at a time.
2. Add the numbers as you roll. The sum of all the cubes you roll should be as close to 15 as possible.
3. You may stop after two, three, or four rolls.
4. The player with the sum closer to 15 wins the round.

If you rolled:	The sum would be:
7 and 1 and 4 and 7	19
8 and 5	13
4 and 4 and 8	16
9 and 3 and 3	15
5 and 10	15

ANOTHER WAY TO PLAY THIS GAME

Start at 20 and subtract the numbers rolled. Try to get as close to 5 as possible.

MATH JOURNAL In your Math Journal describe your strategy for playing this game.

Use the Cumulative Review on page 534 after this lesson.

Unit 1 Lesson 4 • 15

Level 4

◆ **Projects** at the end of each unit allow students to solve complex problems, many of which require outside research and data analysis.

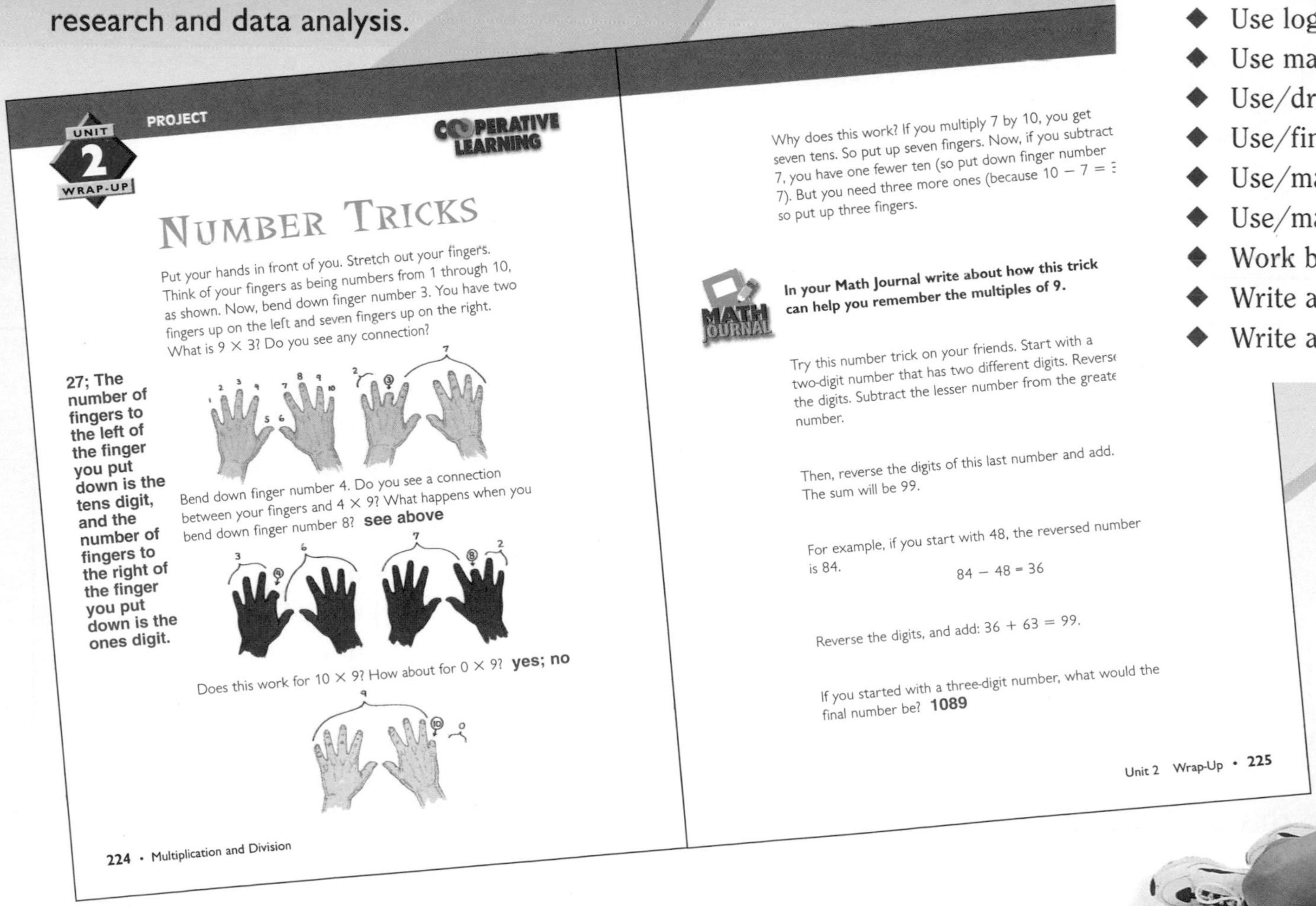

UNIT 2 WRAP-UP PROJECT

COOPERATIVE LEARNING

Number Tricks

Put your hands in front of you. Stretch out your fingers. Think of your fingers as being numbers from 1 through 10, as shown. Now, bend down finger number 3. You have two fingers up on the left and seven fingers up on the right. What is 9 × 3? Do you see any connection?

27; The number of fingers to the left of the finger you put down is the tens digit, and the number of fingers to the right of the finger you put down is the ones digit.

Bend down finger number 4. Do you see a connection between your fingers and 4 × 9? What happens when you bend down finger number 8? **see above**

Does this work for 10 × 9? How about for 0 × 9? **yes; no**

224 • Multiplication and Division

Why does this work? If you multiply 7 by 10, you get seven tens. So put up seven fingers. Now, if you subtract 7, you have one fewer ten (so put down finger number 7). But you need three more ones (because 10 − 7 = 3) so put up three fingers.

MATH JOURNAL **In your Math Journal write about how this trick can help you remember the multiples of 9.**

Try this number trick on your friends. Start with a two-digit number that has two different digits. Reverse the digits. Subtract the lesser number from the greater number.

Then, reverse the digits of this last number and add. The sum will be 99.

For example, if you start with 48, the reversed number is 84. 84 − 48 = 36

Reverse the digits, and add: 36 + 63 = 99.

If you started with a three-digit number, what would the final number be? **1089**

Unit 2 Wrap-Up • 225

Level 3

Problem-Solving Strategies and Methods integrated throughout the program

- Act it out
- Check reasonableness
- Choose a strategy
- Choose the appropriate operation
- Choose the method
- Conduct an experiment
- Eliminate possibilities
- Identify extra information
- Identify needed information
- Interpret data
- Interpret the quotient and remainder
- Make an organized list
- Solve a simpler/similar problem
- Solve multistep problems
- Use a formula
- Use estimation
- Use guess and check/test
- Use logical reasoning
- Use manipulatives
- Use/draw a picture or diagram
- Use/find a pattern
- Use/make a model
- Use/make a table
- Work backwards
- Write a number sentence
- Write an equation

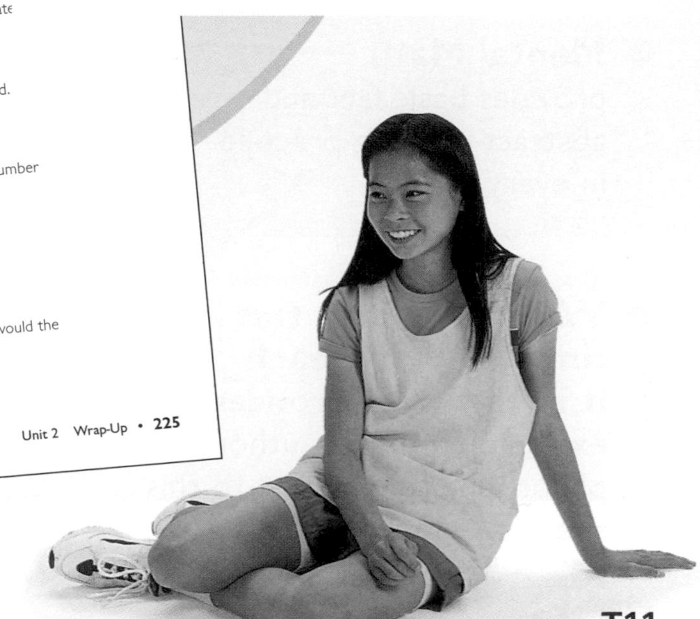

To reach your destination,

Math Explorations and Applications **gives teachers the support they need to challenge students to think mathematically, not to just complete exercises.**

- **Lesson Planner** offers a quick overview of the lesson objectives, materials, and resources.
- **Context of the Lesson** explains how this lesson fits into sequence with others.
- A clear, three-step lesson plan lays out how to **Warm-Up, Teach,** and **Wrap-Up** each lesson.
- **Problem of the Day** presents an interesting problem for students to ponder in every lesson.
- **Mental Math** provides basic fact and abstract-thinking practice in every lesson.
- **Why teach it at this time?** or **Why teach it in this way?** provides an explanation of the authors' philosophy as it relates to this specific lesson.

LESSON 106

Student Edition pages 298–299

Practicing Basic Operations

LESSON PLANNER

Objectives

✓ to assess mastery of students' ability to add and subtract decimals (with up to two decimal places)

▶ to provide practice in adding and subtracting decimals

Context of the Lesson This is the 15th of 15 lessons on decimals. This lesson also contains the 22nd of 24 Mastery Checkpoints.

Materials	Program Resources
graph paper (optional)	Thinking Story Book, pages 88–89
play money (optional)	Practice Master 106
	Enrichment Master 106
	Assessment Master
	For extra practice: CD-ROM* Lesson 106

1 Warm-Up

5 MINUTES

Problem of the Day Present this problem: Fay called her friend Samir and asked him to meet her at the library. Fay lives 3.4 kilometers away from the library, while Samir lives 1.62 kilometers away. Who must travel farthest to the library? (Fay: 3.4 > 1.62) How much farther? (1.78 km: 3.40 – 1.62 = 1.78)

MENTAL MATH Review addition and subtraction of decimals. On the chalkboard write: 4.2 - 1.14 = ____. Show that the problem can be done by changing 4.2 to the equivalent 4.20 and then subtracting. Then have students respond quickly by writing their answers on paper as you read the following problems aloud.

a. 3.57 – 2.4 = (1.17) **b.** 15.63 – 4.7 = (10.93)
c. 5.3 – 2.02 = (3.28) **d.** 9.1 + 6.04 = (15.14)
e. 8.35 + 3.2 = (11.55) **f.** 7.06 – 1.3 = (5.76)

298 Fractions and Decimals

MIXED PRACTICE

LESSON 106

Practicing Basic Operations

Solve these problems. Watch the signs.

1. 5.3 − 2.1 **3.2**
2. 5.47 − 3.6 **1.87**
3. 2.4 − 1.87 **0.53**
4. 4.71 + 5.62 **10.33**
5. 5.62 + 4.71 **10.33**
6. 5.62 − 4.71 **0.91**
7. 3.8 + 1.2 **5.0**
8. 4.07 − 3.7 **0.37**
9. 12.13 − 8.6 **3.53**
10. 5.81 − 3.28 = ■ **2.53**
11. 9.03 + 9.3 = ■ **18.33**
12. 2.66 − 1.7 = ■ **0.96**
13. 7.56 + 9.33 = ■ **16.89**
14. 4.2 − 1.75 = ■ **2.45**
15. 3.44 − 2.07 = ■ **1.37**
16. 5.4 + 8.17 = ■ **13.57**
17. 12.1 + 4.79 = ■ **16.89**

Number correct ■

298 • Fractions and Decimals

RETEACHING

Students who fall short of the mastery objective should be checked to determine the nature of the difficulty. If the trouble lies with multidigit addition and subtraction of whole numbers, reteach the appropriate algorithms using concrete materials. If the difficulty is adding and subtracting decimals, have students solve problems both with and without concrete objects such as play money*. Use graph paper if students have difficulty lining up the decimal points and columns.

PRACTICE p. 106

LESSON 106 PRACTICE Name ____________

Solve. Watch the signs.

1. 16.24 − 9.3 6.94
2. 8.9 + 4.1 13.0
3. 13.5 − 7.86 5.64
4. 6.47 + 8.64 15.11
5. 4.7 + 10.53 15.23
6. 7.13 + 8.89 16.02
7. 11.21 − 4.6 6.61
8. 9.37 − 8.59 0.78
9. 6.4 + 7.32 = 13.72
10. 3.76 – 1.8 = 1.96
11. 7.3 – 1.45 = 5.85
12. 4.53 – 3.67 = 0.86
13. 5.25 + 1.75 = 7.00
14. 1.9 + 3.8 = 5.7
15. 4.47 + 1.3 = 5.77
16. 3.7 – 1.25 = 2.45

Solve these problems.

17. Maxine rode her bike 4.5 miles on Saturday and 6.8 miles on Sunday. How far did she ride over the weekend? 11.3 miles
18. Today Pete walked 1.75 miles to school, 0.8 miles to his friend's house, and 2.1 miles back home. How far did Pete walk all together today? 4.65 miles

106 • *Math Explorations and Applications* Level 3

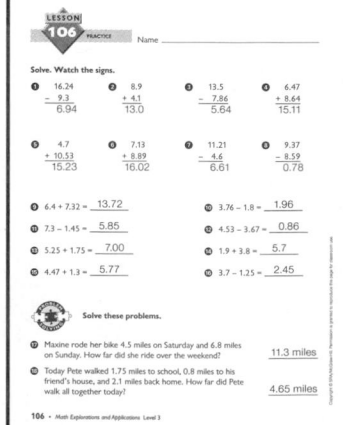

*available separately

you need a clear road map.

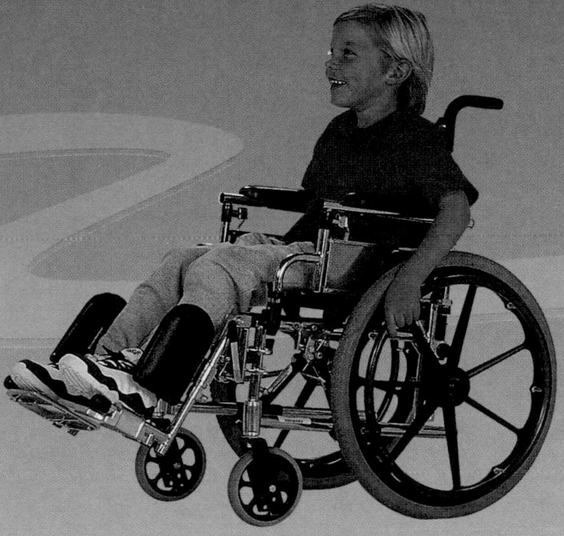

PROBLEM SOLVING

Solve.

18 Each time Amy adds a book to her bookshelf, she records how much room is left on the shelf. All her books are the same thickness. Copy and complete Amy's table.

Space on Amy's Bookshelf

Number of Books	5	6	7	8	9	10	11	12	13
Space Used	1.03	0.99	0.95	0.91	0.87	0.83	0.79	0.75	0.71

MATH JOURNAL

Make up five problems using the map below and solve them. Write your problems in your Math Journal and explain how to solve them.

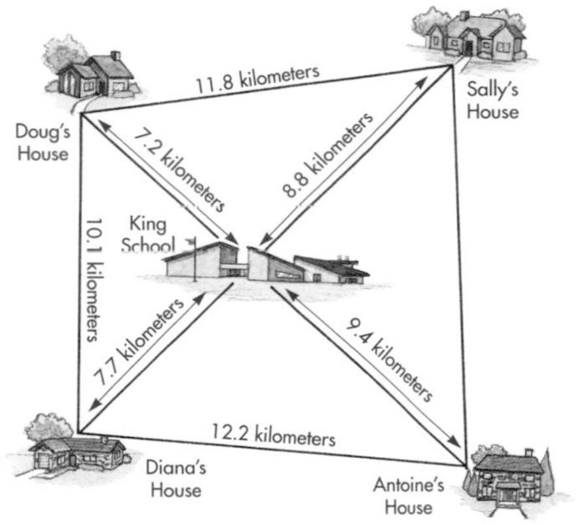

Unit 3 Lesson 106 • 299

❷ Teach

Using the Student Pages Tell students that the problems on page 298 are a test. Allow students enough time to finish. When all students have finished, have them proofread their papers as a group. Remember to focus attention on the number of correct rather than the number of incorrect answers. Then have students complete page 299.

Using the Thinking Story Have students complete three problems from among those following "Mosquito Lake" on pages 88–89 of the Thinking Story Book.

❸ Wrap-Up

5 MINUTES

In Closing Ask students what they must remember to do when adding or subtracting numbers with decimals. Students should say they must write more zeros as necessary so that each number in the problem has the same number of decimal places.

Mastery Checkpoint 22

Students should demonstrate mastery of the addition and subtraction of decimals (with up to two decimal places) by correctly answering 12 of the 17 problems on page 298. The results of this assessment may be recorded on the Mastery Checkpoint Chart. You may also wish to assign the Assessment Master on page 41 to determine mastery.

Assessment Criteria

Did the student . . .

- ✓ make up at least five word problems with solutions based on page 299?
- ✓ demonstrate mastery of the addition and subtraction of decimals?

Homework To reinforce the lesson concept, have students play the "Harder Rummage Sale" game with a household member.

Unit 3 Lesson 106 **299**

ENRICHMENT p. 106

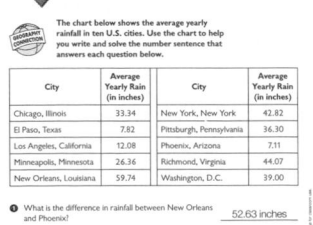

LESSON 106 ENRICHMENT Name ____________

The chart below shows the average yearly rainfall in ten U.S. cities. Use the chart to help you write and solve the number sentence that answers each question below.

GEOGRAPHY CONNECTION

City	Average Yearly Rain (in inches)	City	Average Yearly Rain (in inches)
Chicago, Illinois	33.34	New York, New York	42.82
El Paso, Texas	7.82	Pittsburgh, Pennsylvania	36.30
Los Angeles, California	12.08	Phoenix, Arizona	7.11
Minneapolis, Minnesota	26.36	Richmond, Virginia	44.07
New Orleans, Louisiana	59.74	Washington, D.C.	39.00

1. What is the difference in rainfall between New Orleans and Phoenix? 52.63 inches
2. Is the combined rainfall of Chicago and El Paso greater than the rainfall in New York? no; 33.34 + 7.82 < 42.82
3. What is the difference? 33.4 + 7.82 = 41.16; 42.82 − 41.16 = 1.66
4. The combined rainfall of Phoenix and Minneapolis is nearest to the amount of rainfall in what single city? 7.11 + 26.36 = 33.47; Chicago

106 • *Math Explorations and Applications* Level 3

ASSESSMENT p. 41

UNIT 3 **Mastery Checkpoint 22** Addition and subtraction of decimal numbers (Lesson 106)

Name ____________

The student demonstrates mastery by correctly answering at least 12 of the 15 problems.

Solve. Watch the signs.

1. 4.37 + 5.63 = 10.00
2. 9.3 − 5.5 = 3.8
3. 27.32 + 4.1 = 31.42
4. 8.8 − 6.22 = 2.58
5. 4.73 + 2.62 = 7.35
6. 5.54 + 4.73 = 10.27
7. 3.43 − 2.62 = 0.81
8. 5.05 − 4.5 = 0.55
9. 4.6 + 2.4 = 7.0
10. 6.21 − 5.03 = 1.18
11. 3.7 − 1.85 = 1.85
12. 4.2 + 9.15 = 13.35
13. 9.52 − 8.62 = 0.90
14. 5.72 + 6.28 = 12.00
15. 1.36 + 7.89 = 9.25

Math Explorations and Applications Level 3 • 41

Level 3

◆ **Program Resources** are referenced at point of use.

◆ **Mastery Checkpoint** provides opportunities for teachers to check for student understanding of core skills and concepts.

◆ **Practice, Enrichment,** and **Reteaching** blackline masters and strategies are included for every lesson.

◆ **Assessment Criteria** tie informal assessment to the Lesson Objectives.

◆ **Homework** ideas are always included in Levels 3–6 for added practice and reinforcement.

Assessment tools help students stay on track.

Math Explorations and Applications **aligns teaching and assessment to support learning. With a variety of options, teachers can select appropriate methods to monitor student progress.**

Self-Assessment. *Are You Shiny or Rusty?* activities offer nonthreatening timed tests so that students can see how quickly and accurately they can recall the basic arithmetic facts.

Performance Assessment. Strategies in the Teacher's Guide and the Assessment Book provide opportunities for students to show what they know.

Portfolio Assessment. Suggestions throughout the Teacher's Guide give students an opportunity to demonstrate their mathematical growth.

Informal Assessment

- **Assessment Criteria.** In every lesson teachers are reminded what to look for as they informally assess student responses.
- **Varied Opportunities.** Every Game, Thinking Story, and Act It Out provides an opportunity for teachers to informally assess students' mathematical thinking.
- **Mental Math Exercises.** Daily interactive Mental Math activities offer opportunities for informal assessment and self-assessment.

Formal Assessment

- **Unit Assessment.** Mid-Unit Reviews, Unit Reviews, and Unit Tests provide ready-made formal assessment of students' comprehension.
- **Mastery Checkpoints.** These checkpoints and corresponding evaluations in the Assessment Books indicate times that teachers can check for mastery of specific skills and concepts.
- **Mastery Checkpoint Charts.** Mastery Checkpoints give teachers an easy way to keep track of students' mastery of specific skills.
- **Standardized-Format Tests.** Multiple-choice computation tests provide practice taking standardized tests at the same time they provide one more opportunity to assess students' math skills.

SRA®

MATH

Explorations and Applications

It will change the way students think about math . . . for a lifetime.

***Math Explorations and Applications* is a program with proven results for more than 25 years.**

- The program was developed one grade level at a time, building on valuable field test results to ensure consistency and continuity throughout all grade levels.
- Successfully field-tested in urban, suburban, and rural schools, *Math Explorations and Applications* ensures effectiveness in any teaching situation.
- Teaching strategies throughout the program are based on substantial bodies of research indicating how children learn best.
- Written and updated by a team of distinguished and committed authors, *Math Explorations and Applications* reflects time-tested strategies with proven results.
- We have listened carefully to teachers who use the program. This edition of *Math Explorations and Applications* reflects the many valuable suggestions and comments we have received from talented teachers over the years. We look forward to receiving your comments.

Exceeds
~~Meets~~ **NCTM Standards!**

Authorship

Dr. Stephen S. Willoughby

Mathematics Educator

Stephen S. Willoughby has taught mathematics at all levels, from first grade through graduate courses in schools in Massachusetts, Connecticut, Wisconsin, New York, and Arizona, including the University of Wisconsin and New York University. He is now Professor of Mathematics at the University of Arizona. He received bachelor's and master's degrees from Harvard University and a doctorate from Columbia University.

Dr. Willoughby was President of the National Council of Teachers of Mathematics from 1982 to 1984 and Chairman of the Council of Scientific Society Presidents in 1988. He was a member of the national Board of Advisors for SQUARE ONE TV, chairman of the United States Commission on Mathematics Instruction, and a member of the Education Testing Services Mathematics Advisory Committee for the successor to the National Teacher's Examination, and is now a member of the Education Advisory Panel of New American Schools Development Corporation (NASDC).

Dr. Willoughby has published more than 200 articles and books on mathematics and mathematics education and was senior author of the innovative K–8 mathematics series *Real Math™* published by Open Court.

Dr. Carl Bereiter

Cognitive Psychologist

Carl Bereiter is a professor in the Centre for Applied Cognitive Science, Ontario Institute for Studies in Education, University of Toronto. He holds a Ph.D. in educational psychology from the University of Wisconsin. He has done research and developed educational materials in such diverse areas as preschool education, thinking skills, writing, elementary school mathematics, and science understanding. He is also active in the development of advanced computer-based technology for schools. His scholarly contributions have been recognized by award of a Guggenheim Fellowship, appointments to the Center for Advanced Study in the Behavioral Sciences, election to the National Academy of Education, and an honorary Doctor of Laws from Queens University. His books include *Arithmetic and Mathematics* (1968), *Thinking Games* (1975 with Valerie Anderson), *The Psychology of Written Composition* (1987, with Marlene Scardamalia), and *Surpassing Ourselves: An Inquiry into the Nature and Implications of Expertise* (1993, also with Marlene Scardamalia) and the forthcoming *Education and Mind in the Knowledge Age.*

Dr. Peter Hilton

Mathematician

Peter Hilton is Distinguished Professor of Mathematics Emeritus at the State University of New York (Binghamton) and Distinguished Professor at the University of Central Florida. He holds M.A. and Doctorate of Philosophy degrees from Oxford University and a Ph.D. from Cambridge University. He has an honorary doctorate of humanities from Northern Michigan University, an honorary doctorate of science from the Memorial University of Newfoundland, and an honorary doctorate of science from the Autonomous University of Barcelona. In addition to his activity in research and teaching as a mathematician, he has a continuing interest in mathematics education and has served on many national and international committees and as chairman of the United States Commission on Mathematics Instruction. Dr. Hilton is the author of several important books, his most recent being *Mathematical Reflections*, jointly with Derek Holton and Jean Pedersen, and many research articles on algebraic topology, homological algebra, group theory, and category theory.

Dr. Joseph H. Rubinstein

Biologist and Educator

Joseph H. Rubinstein is Professor of Education and Chairperson of the Department of Education at Coker College, Hartsville, South Carolina. He received B.A., M.S., and Ph.D. degrees in biology from New York University, completing his studies in 1969. His interest in elementary education was kindled by his participation in the late 1960s in an experimental science curriculum development project, the Conceptually Oriented Program in Elementary Science (COPES). During that time he worked in the New York City public schools helping elementary school teachers implement science programs in their classrooms. Dr. Rubinstein served as the Director of Open Court Publishing Company's Mathematics and Science Curriculum Development Center during the development of *Real Math™*, the precursor to *SRA Math Explorations and Applications.* In 1984 he joined the faculty of Coker College, where his principal duties include training prospective teachers to teach mathematics and science.

Reviewers

Dr. Prentice Baptiste
Manhattan, KS

Debney Biggs
Shreveport, LA

Pat Dahl
Vancouver, WA

Karen Hardin
Houston, TX

Susan Humphries
BelAir, MD

Tucky Marchica
Inverness, IL

Dr. Marilyn Neil
Birmingham, AL

Bill Smith
Haddonfield, NJ

Bob Winkler
Overland Park, KS

Game Mat Testers

Grace Brethren Elementary School
Columbus, OH

Huber Ridge Elementary School
Westerville School District
Westerville, OH

St. Paul's Elementary School
Columbus Diocese
Westerville, OH

Tremont Elementary School
Upper Arlington School District
Upper Arlington, OH

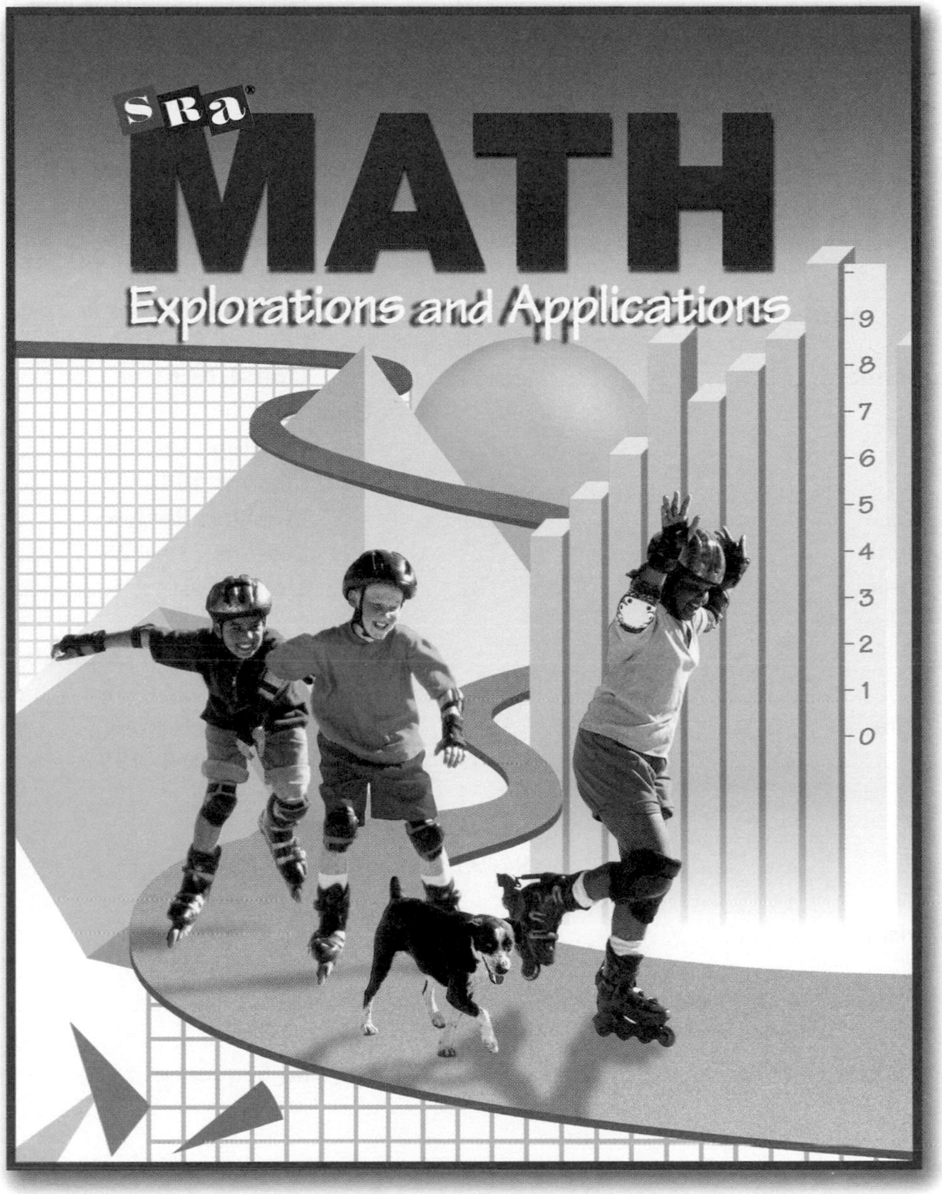

Stephen S. Willoughby
Carl Bereiter
Peter Hilton
Joseph H. Rubinstein
Co-author of Thinking Story® selections **Marlene Scardamalia**

SRA McGraw-Hill
Columbus, Ohio

A Division of The McGraw-Hill Companies

TABLE OF CONTENTS

SRA/McGraw-Hill
A Division of The **McGraw·Hill** *Companies*

1999 imprint
Copyright © 1998 by SRA/McGraw-Hill. All rights reserved. Except as permitted under the United States Copyright Act, no part of this publication may be reproduced or distributed in any form or by any means, or stored in a database or retrieval system, without prior written permission from the publisher.
Printed in the United States of America.

Send all inquiries to:
SRA/McGraw-Hill
250 Old Wilson Bridge Road, Suite 310
Worthington, OH 43085

ISBN 0-02-687864-X

2 3 4 5 6 7 8 9 WEB 02 01 00 99 98

Acknowledgments

Photo Credits
p. T1, (l) ©Jeff Smith/Fotosmith; (r) ©Timothy Fuller; **T3,** ©Aaron Haupt; **T4,** ©Jeff Smith/Fotosmith; **T5,** ©Aaron Haupt; **T6,** ©Jeff Smith/Fotosmith; **T7,** ©Jeff Smith/Fotosmith; **T8,** (l) ©Jeff Smith/Fotosmith; (r) ©Timothy Fuller; **T9,** ©Jeff Smith/Fotosmith; **T10,** ©Jeff Smith/Fotosmith; **T11,** ©Jeff Smith/Fotosmith; **T13,** ©Jeff Smith/Fotosmith; **T14,** ©Timothy Fuller; **T15,** ©Jeff Smith/Fotosmith; **T32, T33, T266B,** ©1997/PhotoDisc.

Cover Credits
Front cover photo, ©Timothy Fuller; **Design and Illustration,** Morgan-Cain & Associates; **Back cover photo,** ©Timothy Fuller and Jeff Smith/Fotosmith.

TEACHING THE PROGRAM

Math Explorations and Applications is based upon the idea of making mathematics real for students. It builds upon what children already know when they enter school and upon what they learn from their experiences outside school. It helps children see that mathematics is useful and important in their own lives, and it makes learning mathematics enjoyable.

Math Explorations and Applications is based upon everyday teaching and learning. In the Teacher's Guide are all the activities that go together to make up the total learning experience. These activities have been tried, criticized, revised, and tried again by hundreds of teachers.

Math Explorations and Applications is based upon sound theory, research, and extensive field testing. It is a program that works.

In every grade the program emphasizes thinking skills, problem-solving strategies, real applications, mental arithmetic, estimation, approximation, measurement, organizing data, geometry, probability, statistics, and algebra. In addition, computational skills are introduced at appropriate levels and are reviewed and maintained in that level and in subsequent levels.

PROGRAM ORGANIZATION

There are three ways that *Math Explorations and Applications* has been carefully organized to introduce and reinforce concepts.

Early Introduction of Concepts

Math Explorations and Applications makes a point of exposing students to core problems and concepts from the beginning. For example, in traditional teaching, students first learn the plus sign and later are introduced to the minus sign. When signs are introduced one at a time, students learn to pay no attention to the sign because it is always the same. Students are trained in this way not to figure out the problem but to follow the pattern.

Similar confusion arises in the traditional teaching of subtraction of multidigit numbers. First, children learn to subtract with numbers that require no regrouping (65 – 32, for example). When they are later introduced to regrouping (62 – 35, for example), they are often confused because they have learned an easy and automatic way to subtract, which turns out to work only sometimes.

In *Math Explorations and Applications*, plus and minus signs are introduced at the same time in Level 1. In Level 2, multidigit subtraction problems that require regrouping, as well as those that do not, are introduced early on. Core mathematical concepts are emphasized in an age-appropriate manner at every level. The early introduction of concepts causes much less trouble and confusion later on because students don't have to unlearn patterns that they have begun to rely on. Furthermore, when students reach middle school and high school, they will already have a firm foundation in core mathematical concepts such as probability, statistics, geometry, and algebra.

Revisiting Concepts

While it is convenient to package teaching into neat, isolated units that deal with a single topic, the learning that goes on in children's minds cannot be so neatly packaged. Children learn, forget, and relearn. They catch a glimmer of an idea, lose it, catch it again, and finally get hold of it firmly enough that it becomes a solid part of understanding. In *Math Explorations and Applications*, concepts like inequalities, missing addends, and base 10 are developed and reviewed continuously over the whole year so that they become part of the child's working knowledge.

Throughout the year concepts and skills are introduced and reappear again and again in subsequent lessons and in Mixed Practice so that students never lose them. For example, basic addition, subtraction, multiplication, and division are a major focus of at least one third of the lessons in Level 3 and are practiced in virtually every Practice and Mixed Practice exercise.

Presenting Concepts in Different Contexts

In Level 4 of *Math Explorations and Applications*, multiplication is introduced and reinforced in more than 50 lessons throughout the entire year in all the following contexts:

- one-digit number multiplication
- two-digit number multiplication
- three-digit number multiplication
- algebra readiness
- area
- commutative property (order of factors)
- decimals
- division
- conversion graphs
- multidigit numbers
- money
- multiplication facts
- multiples of 10
- powers of 10
- problem solving
- repeated addition
- skip counting
- square numbers
- whole numbers

The thoughtful organization at every level of *Math Explorations and Applications* ensures that students are introduced to mathematics concepts and skills in context at appropriate age levels. They encounter these concepts and use these skills again and again throughout the year and in subsequent years in different, age-appropriate contexts.

> ***"There are reasons for almost everything we do in mathematics. Children should be encouraged to discover, or at least see, those reasons. Understanding the reasons will help them remember how to do the mathematics; but more important, it will help them understand that the mathematics is related to their reality and that mathematics can be used to help them understand the real world."***
>
> –Stephen S. Willoughby
> *Mathematics Education for a Changing World*

COMPONENTS CHART

A variety of resources that present math concepts in a way all students can learn!

Components	Levels						
	K	1	2	3	4	5	6
Student Edition	✓	✓	✓	✓	✓	✓	✓
Teacher's Guide	✓	✓	✓	✓	✓	✓	✓
Thinking Story Book		✓	✓	✓			
Game Mat Package	✓	✓	✓	✓	✓	✓	✓
Reteaching Masters		✓	✓	✓	✓	✓	✓
Reteaching Workbook		✓	✓	✓	✓	✓	✓
Reteaching Workbook TE		✓	✓	✓	✓	✓	✓
Practice Masters	✓	✓	✓	✓	✓	✓	✓
Practice Workbook	✓	✓	✓	✓	✓	✓	✓
Practice Workbook TE	✓	✓	✓	✓	✓	✓	✓
Enrichment Masters	✓	✓	✓	✓	✓	✓	✓
Enrichment Workbook	✓	✓	✓	✓	✓	✓	✓
Enrichment Workbook TE	✓	✓	✓	✓	✓	✓	✓
Assessment Masters	✓	✓	✓	✓	✓	✓	✓
Home Connections Masters	✓	✓	✓	✓	✓	✓	✓
Literature Library	✓	✓	✓	✓			
Primary Manipulative Kit	✓	✓	✓				
Primary Overhead Manipulative Kit	✓	✓	✓				
Intermediate Manipulative Kit				✓	✓	✓	✓
Intermediate Overhead Manipulative Kit				✓	✓	✓	✓
Teacher Manipulative Kit	✓	✓	✓	✓	✓	✓	✓
Basic Manipulative Kit	✓	✓	✓	✓	✓	✓	✓
Primary Overhead Calculator	✓	✓	✓	✓			
Intermediate Overhead Calculator					✓	✓	✓
TI-108™ Calculator Package	✓	✓	✓	✓			
Math Explorer™ Calculator Package					✓	✓	✓
Math Explorations and Applications CD-ROM Program		✓	✓	✓	✓	✓	✓
The Cruncher CD-ROM Program and Guide					✓	✓	✓
My Silly CD of Counting CD-ROM	✓						
Professional Development Handbook	✓	✓	✓	✓	✓	✓	✓
Program Video	✓	✓	✓	✓	✓	✓	✓
Teacher Management System	✓	✓	✓	✓	✓	✓	✓

PROGRAM MANAGEMENT

In *Math Explorations and Applications* there are a variety of resources for students and teachers to use to introduce and demonstrate concepts and to practice math skills. These carefully integrated materials each play an important and well-thought-out role in the program as a whole.

TEACHER'S GUIDE

This comprehensive manual gives specific advice for every lesson and lesson component, as well as teaching tips, explanations, and background information.

STUDENT EDITION

The Student Edition provides practice with written problems. It is also used to present games and activities. It is not, however, the main source of concept presentation or skill practice. Student Edition pages supplement the teacher's concept presentation and the practice provided by Mental Math exercises, activities, games, and Thinking Stories.

BASIC MANIPULATIVES

Basic Manipulatives—**Number Cubes, Number Wheels, and Number Strips**—are used throughout *Math Explorations and Applications* in Games and in Mental Math activities that appear in the Teacher's Guide. The Basic Manipulatives allow all students to participate in every Mental Math activity in a nonthreatening way. Mental Math activities provide essential, regular practice in basic math facts. Furthermore, they allow the teacher to informally assess each student's mathematical skill.

The Number Cubes used at Levels 1 and 2 allow students to make any integer from 0 through 100. The students use the cubes to form numbers in games and to show answers during Mental Math exercises. In Levels 3–6, students use Number Wheels for display. Each wheel can be dialed to show any digit from 0 to 9. The wheels allow students to make any integer from 0 through 99,999.

Most Mental Math activities are done in the following three steps. The pace should be lively enough to keep things moving yet not so fast that students have insufficient time to think.

1. "**Find.**" The teacher presents the problem either orally or on the chalkboard. The students find the answer and arrange their Number Cubes or Number Wheel in a position to display it.
2. "**Hide.**" The students hide the answer against their chests. The teacher waits for most of the students to have an answer. Teachers do not need to wait for every student to find and hide an answer, but long enough so that students who are making progress toward a solution have time to finish. Add a "peek-to-be-sure" step to keep all students involved while waiting for the next command.
3. "**Show.**" The students hold up their Number Cubes or Number Wheel so that the teacher can see the response. The teacher quickly checks the responses, shows or tells the correct answer, and quickly moves to the next problem. Only the teacher and the students who got a wrong answer need know about it. Teachers can give these students extra teaching later on.

PRIMARY AND INTERMEDIATE MANIPULATIVE KITS

In the real world, students experience number in many different representations. If in mathematics instruction they are given only one way of representing number—whether with rods, blocks, coins, sticks, or tally marks—they are liable to become dependent upon that one method. In *Math Explorations and Applications* all these ways—and more—of representing number are used.

Whenever appropriate, manipulatives are used to show the connection between the real world and the mathematics. The use of manipulatives is discontinued after a sufficient connection has been made so that the abstract nature of mathematics is not obscured.

LESSON SUPPORT MATERIALS

A variety of extra activities is available to support lesson concepts and skills. Activities in the Practice Workbook provide extra practice in computational skills. Enrichment activities offer extensions, and Reteaching activities help those who have not yet grasped the lesson concept or skill. These activities are keyed to each lesson. Assessment masters provide the Mastery Checkpoints, Mid-Unit Reviews, and Unit Tests.

TECHNOLOGY SUPPORT MATERIALS

- Calculators are suggested for use in appropriate lessons.
- SRA **Cruncher** suggestions are also provided at point of use when a spreadsheet application would be appropriate or would facilitate solving a problem.
- The *Math Explorations and Applications* Software provides extra practice for specific skills in a motivating format.

PACING

Math Explorations and Applications is intended to be taught at a lively pace but not to be rushed through at the expense of achievement. Lessons are generally written to fill a 45-minute time period. Teachers should move quickly from activity to activity. Introductions and lesson closures should be short because these tend to be ineffective and often lose students' attention.

The efficient lesson plans in *Math Explorations and Applications* help teachers gives their students the chance to practice skills, to solve thinking problems, and to do enrichment activities. Here are some tips for using the resources efficiently.

Be prepared. Having necessary materials ready is, of course, important. To help, sections in the Lesson Plans entitled "Looking Ahead" and "Materials" will be useful. This is a good reason to read the lesson in advance.

Watch the clock. The clock can tell a teacher when he or she has concentrated on an activity too long, even before students show signs of restlessness. Teachers should keep an eye on the clock to make sure they don't spend too much time talking or shifting from one activity to another.

Extend lessons to more than one day. Teachers may occasionally find it necessary to spend an extra day on some lessons. This is expected. It is recommended that more than one day be spent on many lessons. The time gained by extending a lesson should go to more teaching and drill on related skills, to related games, or to a review of prerequisite skills.

> *"Whole-class response activities encourage practice, allow students to correct their own errors, and allow the teacher to identify difficulties that individual students are having or that are common to the entire class."*
>
> –Stephen S. Willoughby
> *Mathematics Education for a Changing World*

If you have more than forty-five minutes a day for math. Below are some ideas for extending parts of the lessons.

- Lengthen game periods by five minutes each (more when new games are introduced).
- Repeat whole-group activities when you feel that the students will remain interested.
- Lengthen Mental Math exercises by up to five minutes.
- Lengthen demonstrations and seminars by two or three minutes at most.
- Use the Enrichment masters.

If you have less than forty-five minutes a day for math. Many teachers will be tempted to forgo Games or Thinking Stories in a time crunch, but these elements of *Math Explorations and Applications* are vital for developing mathematical intelligence, without which computational skills have little value. Try these suggestions if there is little time.

- Present the Thinking Stories during reading or some other time outside the regular math period.
- Conduct games outside the regular math period. Set up game-playing sessions every Friday, for example. Be aware, however, that not all games can be transferred to special sessions, because sometimes a game provides practice that will help students complete a particular lesson.
- Complete Mental Math exercises during five-minute periods at the beginning or end of the day or right before or after lunch. These sessions are not always essential to a particular lesson, but they do provide regular drill with Mental Math and basic math facts.

ASSESSMENT

Math Explorations and Applications is unusually rich in opportunities to keep track of–and do something about–individual student progress.

In the Teacher's Guide

Each lesson in the Teacher's Guide provides at least two different assessment suggestions. One is Assessment Criteria, which provides questions teachers can ask themselves as they observe students completing the lesson activities. Additional suggestions include the following:

- Informal assessment (interviews, observation, and oral assessment)
- Formal assessment (Tests, Reviews, Mastery Checkpoints, and Mastery Checkpoint Masters)
- Self-Assessment
- Portfolio and Performance Assessment

In the Student Edition

A formal Mid-Unit Review as well as a Unit Review and a Unit Test are provided in the Student Edition in Levels 1–6. Self-Assessments and timed tests are included throughout the Student Editions for students to evaluate their own performances.

In the Assessment Book

In the Assessment Book, there is a master for each Mastery Checkpoint, and an additional Mid-Unit Review and two Unit Tests, one in standardized (multiple-choice) format. Each unit also provides Performance Assessment activities and Portfolio Assessment suggestions. The Assessment Book includes additional information on the various alternative assessment options that are provided in the program, as well as suggestions for using rubrics to grade these assessments.

Informal Daily Assessment

Use Mental Math, Games, Thinking Stories, and Student Edition pages for day-to-day observation and assessment of how well each student is learning the skills and grasping concepts. Because of their special nature, these activities are an effective and convenient means of monitoring. Games, for example, allow the teacher to watch students practice particular skills under conditions more natural to students than most classroom activities. Mental Math activities allow the teacher to get feedback from each student, to give immediate feedback to each student, and to keep all the students actively involved.

To follow through on daily monitoring, consider the Reteaching strategy or master in each lesson to provide immediate help to students who are having difficulty.

Mastery Checkpoints and Charts

To help teachers formally yet conveniently monitor the progress of each student, there are more than 20 skills identified at each grade level that are important for future progress. These skills are listed on the Mastery Checkpoint Chart in the Assessment Book for each grade level. Each skill is described in detail in the Mastery Checkpoint section of the Teacher's Guide lesson in which teachers can formally assess that skill. These Mastery Checkpoints are an opportunity for teachers to monitor how well students have mastered basic skills and to provide extra help to those who are having trouble. Mastery Checkpoints are placed in the lesson in which most, but not all, of the students are expected to have achieved adequate proficiency in the skill. Teachers should not hold up the class waiting for every student to demonstrate success.

Using the Mastery Checkpoint Chart

- Fill in the names of all the students in the class.
- When a Mastery Checkpoint is encountered in the Teacher's Guide, follow the suggestions for observing and assessing each student's success.
- ✓ Place a check mark in the appropriate column of the Mastery Checkpoint Chart beside the name of each student who demonstrates success on the objective in question.
- **P** Pencil in a *P* in the appropriate column for each student who grasps the concept but still needs further practice to sharpen his or her skill. Assign extra practice to students whose names you marked with a *P*.
- **T** Pencil in a *T* for each student who has not yet grasped the idea and needs further teaching. Give extra teaching or Reteaching to students whose names you marked with a *T*.
- Change Ts to Ps and Ps to check marks when students demonstrate success on the objective. Do not hold up the entire class, however, waiting for all students to demonstrate success. More teaching and practice on a particular skill is always given in a later lesson, usually the following one. At that time teachers can focus on those students who need extra help.

> *"Observation of game-playing activity resembles observation of real-life-out-of-school activities as closely as anything we are likely to see in school. Such observation will often give greater insight into a child's thought patterns than anything else the teacher can do."*
>
> –Stephen S. Willoughby
> *Mathematics Education for a Changing World*

MANIPULATIVE KITS

Component	Game Mat Package (K-6)	Basic (K)	Basic (1-2)	Basic (3-6)	Primary (K-2)	Primary Overhead (K-2)	Intermediate (3-6)	Intermediate Overhead (3-6)	Teacher (K-6)
Angle Ruler							✓		
Attribute Blocks					✓	✓			
Base-10 Blocks				✓	✓	✓	✓		
Beakers									✓
Bills	✓*					✓		✓	
Classifying Counters					✓				
Clock Faces (demonstration or individual)					✓	✓	✓	✓	✓
Coins	✓*					✓		✓	
Counters (opaque or two-sided)	✓				✓	✓	✓	✓	
Cubes (interlocking)					✓		✓		
Decimal Set							✓		
Dual-Dial Scale									✓
Fraction Cubes							✓		
Fraction Tiles					✓	✓		✓	
Funnels							✓		
Geoboard					✓	✓			
Geometric Solids					✓				
Geometric Volume Set							✓		
Math Balance									✓
Metric Grids								✓	
Mirrors					✓		✓		
Number Cubes–0-5 and 5-10 Units	✓	✓	✓	✓					
Number Cubes–0-5 and 5-10 Tens			✓						
Number Line (walk-on)					✓				
Number Strips		✓	✓						
Number Tiles						✓		✓	
Number Wheels				✓					
Pattern Blocks					✓	✓			
Place Markers	✓								
Place Value Pad							✓		
Precision Balance									✓
Protractors							✓		
Shape Set						✓		✓	
Spinners and Dice (blank)						✓	✓	✓	
Stopwatch									✓
Tape Measure					✓		✓		
Thermometer (classroom, demonstration, or individual)					✓	✓	✓	✓	✓
Venn Diagram/Graphing Mat									✓

*not in the Kindergarten package

GAMES AND THINKING STORIES

GAMES

Games do not provide just fun or enrichment in *Math Explorations and Applications;* they are a vital, almost daily part of the program. Games give students a chance to develop their mathematical skills and understandings in situations in which those skills and understandings count. Games provide practice. They give students a means of becoming proficient in the mathematical skills to which they've been introduced. Some games give students a chance to work out important mathematical ideas and problem-solving strategies. Games also give the teacher an opportunity for informal assessment. By observing game-playing sessions, teachers can quickly assess how well individual students have learned the skill being practiced.

Each game involves the use of specific skills, but there is usually also a certain amount of luck involved, so the more able student does not always win. When a lesson plan prescribes a game, it does so because the principal skills involved in that game need attention at that time. Some lesson plans suggest that students play games of their choice. The Game Directory lists principal skills involved in each game to help the teacher select those games that will give each student an appropriate form of practice. Game Mats and Cube Games are the two types of games used in *Math Explorations and Applications*.

GAME MATS

Many of the games in *Math Explorations and Applications* are board games found in the Game Mat package for each grade level. There are five Game Mats in Kindergarten, 13 in Levels 1–3, and 14 in Levels 4–6. In each Game Mat package there are 15 copies of each Game Mat, as well as enough counters, place markers, Number Cubes, and money so that the entire class can play a game at the same time. Also included is A Guide for Using the Game Mats and an overhead transparency of each game for introducing the games to the class. Many of the Game Mats are offered in both a standard and a harder version. A copy of each game can also be found in the back of this Teacher's Guide.

CUBE GAMES

Many games don't require Game Mats. They use Number Cubes or sometimes require no materials at all. These games, presented in the Student Edition in Levels 3–6 and in the Teacher's Guide in Levels K–2, reinforce basic math skills and involve mathematical reasoning.

INTRODUCING GAMES

Here are some tips for making sure that games are played correctly.

- Familiarize yourself with each game by playing it before showing the students how to play it.
- Show, don't just tell, how a game is played. Games should be demonstrated in front of the class when they are first introduced. Overhead Game Mats are provided for this purpose. Verbalize the rules as you demonstrate.
- Make sure each student can see when a game is demonstrated.
- Supervise to see that students get off to the right start after you've introduced a game.
- Let students who know the game rules help those who haven't played it.

ORGANIZING SUCCESSFUL GAME SESSIONS

- Mixing ability levels from time to time, however, keeps some students from having an oppressive sense of their slowness.
- Change groupings from day to day. Students can learn different things by playing with different partners.
- Assign a referee to each group. The referee sees that the rules are followed, reminds players when it is their turn, settles disputes, keeps track of scores, and in some games acts as banker. Associate a sense of honor and responsibility around the role of the referee so that students will be willing to serve as referee.
- Encourage students to play games during free time—in school and at home—as well as during the scheduled game periods.
- Allow students to make up and name their own variations of the games. Whenever students regularly misinterpret a rule, there's a good chance they have discovered a new and, to them, more interesting version of the game. Be alert, however, to avoid versions that reduce the skill-practice value of the game.
- Encourage parents, teacher aides, or older students to participate in game-playing sessions with students.
- Stress enjoyment rather than competition. Emphasize sportsmanship, fair play, and giving each player a turn.
- Teach students to control their excitement and to speak in a low voice.
- Make Game Mats accessible. Store Game Mats so that students can find and return them by themselves.

THINKING STORIES

Thinking Stories are an essential part of *Math Explorations and Applications*. The stories and related thinking problems tap into the child's world of fantasy and humor. They are aimed at developing quantitative intelligence—creativity and common sense in the use of mathematics. The stories allow students to discover the power of their own mathematical common sense and of their innate capacity for reasoning. The stories and problems are filled with surprises, so students cannot apply arithmetic routinely. Instead they must apply mathematical common sense to choose which operation to use, to recognize which data are relevant to the questions asked, to determine whether an answer is absurd, and to decide when calculation isn't necessary.

THINKING STORY CHARACTERS

The various characters in the stories appear in all grade levels. The children in the stories age with each grade level so that they are about the same age as the students reading the stories. All the characters have peculiar thinking patterns that students come to know. Mr. Muddle, for example, is always forgetting things. Ferdie jumps to conclusions, and Mr. Breezy provides too much information. Students are challenged to listen carefully and to try to outthink the characters.

READING THE THINKING STORIES

The Thinking Stories are designed to be read to students. They appear in the Teacher's Guide and in separate Thinking Story books in Levels 1–3. At Levels 4–6 the Thinking Stories appear in three to five or more parts in the student book so that students have an option to read them individually or in groups, depending upon their reading abilities. As the stories unfold, students are asked questions that prompt them to think ahead of the characters—to spot what is wrong with what a character has done or said, to anticipate what is going to happen as a result, or to think of other possibilities that the character hasn't considered.

Following each story is a selection of short problems. Like the story questions, these problems generally require more thinking than computation and have a mixture of difficulty levels.

PACING

Most teachers spend about 15 minutes reading a Thinking Story and discussing the corresponding questions. In many lessons teachers may spend about five minutes on three or four of the questions that follow the story.

The Introduction to the Storybook for Levels 1–3 contains a briefing on the characters and useful hints on presenting stories and problems.

Table of Contents

UNIT 1

Addition and Subtraction

Calculator

Table of Contents

UNIT 2

Multiplication and Division

Calculator (Lessons 35, 46, 47)

Table of Contents

UNIT 3

Algebra Readiness and Geometry

Calculator

Table of Contents

UNIT 4 Multidigit Multiplication

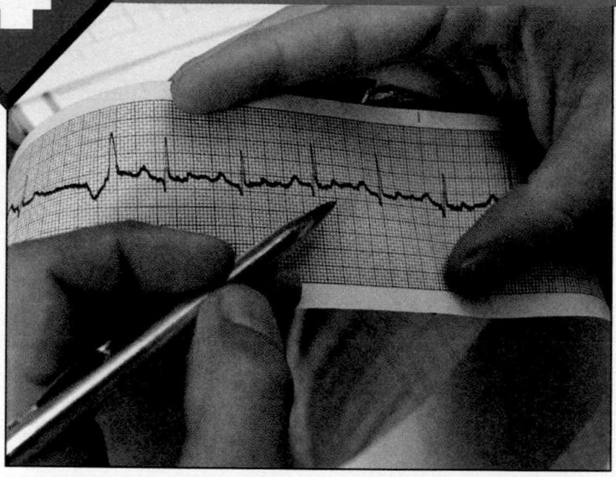

🖩 Calculator

Table of Contents

UNIT 5 Division

🖩 Calculator

Table of Contents

UNIT 6 Fractions and Decimals

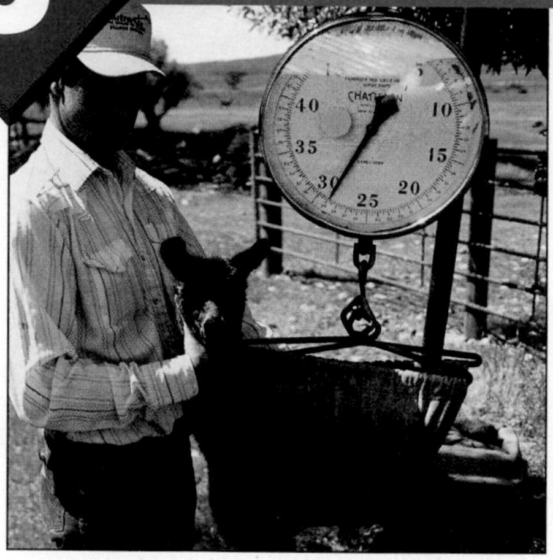

(Calculator icon) Calculator

Dear Student,

You'll find a lot of things in this *Math Explorations and Applications* book. You'll find stories with Mr. Muddle, Ferdie, Portia, Manolita, Marcus, and their friends, whom you may remember from earlier years.

You'll find games that will give you a chance to practice and put to use many of the skills you will be learning.

You'll find stories and examples that will show you how mathematics can help you solve problems and cut down on your work.

You'll be reading and talking about many of the pages with your class. That's because mathematics is something people often learn together and do together.

Of course, this book isn't all fun and games. Learning should be enjoyable, but it also takes time and effort. Most of all, it takes thinking.

We hope you enjoy this book. We hope you learn a lot. And we hope you think a lot.

The Authors of *Math Explorations and Applications*

PACING

HOW TO PACE THE PROGRAM

The lessons in this book are designed to be taught at a lively pace. Students should move quickly from activity to activity. In this way, they will remain alert and interested in what they are learning.

The lively pace is also important because there is much for students to learn at this grade level. Yet, 45 minutes a day is about all that most teachers can devote to mathematics. Therefore, it's important to get as much from those minutes as possible. Here are some tips to help you make the most of your time:

Tips for Making the Most of Your Time

- **Prepare items you'll need for a lesson ahead of time.** See the Lesson Planner sections titled Materials and Program Resources for a complete listing of the items you'll need. The Looking Ahead feature under the Wrap-Up alerts you to any advance preparation needed for an upcoming lesson.
- **Read the lesson plan in advance.** This will save you time and make the lesson run more smoothly.
- **Keep introductions and explanations brief.** You will lose your students' attention if you try to say too much.

HOW TO EXTEND YOUR LESSONS

You might need to spend an extra day teaching some lessons. Lessons that might take an extra day are noted in the individual Lesson Planner and in the Unit Overview Planning Chart—but only you can be the judge. When you decide to let a lesson run two days, try dividing it as follows:

Day 1

- Do all suggested activities, but not the Student Edition pages.
- Use extra time to review the skills students will need for the lesson.
- Modify the Reteaching Stategy/Master and Practice Master for use with the entire class.
- Don't greatly lengthen the demonstration period (K–3).

Day 2

- Review the Mental Math exercises from the preceding day.
- Provide additional teaching and practice on related skills.
- Devote time to a related Cube Game or Game Mat.
- Allow plenty of time for students to do the Student Edition activities.

WHEN YOU HAVE MORE THAN 45 MINUTES FOR MATH

Tips for Making the Best Use of Extra Time

- Lengthen game periods by five minutes each (more when new games are introduced).
- Repeat whole-group activities when you feel that students will remain interested.
- Lengthen Mental Math exercises by up to five minutes each.
- Lengthen demonstrations and activities by two or three minutes at most.
- Use the Reteaching, Practice, and Enrichment Masters. You might also want to use the various Cross-Curricular Connections strategies provided throughout the Teacher's Guide.

WHEN YOU HAVE FEWER THAN 45 MINUTES FOR MATH

Tips for Making the Best Use of Less Time

- Don't eliminate the games or the Thinking Stories. These help develop mathematical intelligence.
- Do the Thinking Story activities outside the regular mathematics period. There might be time the first thing in the morning, right after lunch, or when you have a read-aloud period.
- Conduct games outside the regular mathematics period—every Friday, perhaps— especially if you have another adult or older student to assist you. If a game provides practice that will help students do the Student Edition exercise, play the game during the lesson.
- Conduct Mental Math on basic facts outside the regular mathematics period.
- Reduce a few lesson components by a minute or two.
- Introduce the Problem of the Day at the start of school each morning instead of at the start of the regular mathematics period.

UNIT 1

Addition and Subtraction

UNDERSTANDING NUMBER

OVERVIEW

This unit begins with a review of place value and estimation to give students experiences that develop number sense. Basic facts in addition and subtraction are presented first, followed by the standard algorithm for both operations. Many connections are made to other mathematical and real-world contexts, such as adding to find perimeter, using maps and charts, and thinking intuitively about probability. The unit also introduces fractions, money, and decimals.

Integrated Topics in This Unit Include:

- estimating
- reviewing place value
- reviewing addition and subtraction facts
- reviewing multidigit addition and subtraction
- finding missing addends
- finding perimeter
- using maps and charts
- using relation signs (<, >, and =)
- approximating answers
- introducing the calculator
- reviewing fraction concepts
- relating decimals and money
- adding and subtracting money

FINDING MISSING ADDENDS
APPROXIMATING ANSWERS

"Mathematics can be thought of as a language that must be meaningful if students are to communicate mathematically and apply mathematics productively. Communication plays an important role in helping children construct links between their informal, intuitive notions and the abstract language and symbolism of mathematics; it also plays a key role in helping children make important connections among physical, pictorial, graphic, symbolic, verbal, and mental representations of mathematical ideas."

—NCTM Curriculum and Evaluation Standards for School Mathematics

GAMES

Motivating Mixed Practice

Games provide **basic math skills** practice in cooperative groups. Playing the games also helps students develop **mathematical reasoning.**

Roll a Number	Lesson 2	page 10
Order	Lesson 3	page 13
Roll a 15	Lesson 4	page 15
Don't Go Over 1000	Lesson 12	page 40
Roll a Problem	Lesson 13	page 44
Transaction Game Mat	Lesson 13	page 44
Inequality	Lesson 16	page 55
Fracto 1 and 2 Game Mats	Lesson 20	page 69
Store and Harder Store Game Mats	Lesson 21	page 71
Money Roll	Lesson 22	page 74
Harder Transaction Game Mat	Lesson 23	page 78

THINKING STORY

Integrated Problem Solving

Thinking Stories provide opportunities for students to work in **cooperative groups** and to develop **logical reasoning** while they integrate **reading skills** with mathematics.

Muddle at Bat

Part 1	Lesson 5	pages 18–19
Part 2	Lesson 10	pages 34–35
Part 3	Lesson 14	pages 48–49
Part 4	Lesson 16	pages 56–57
Part 5	Lesson 18	pages 62–63
Part 6	Lesson 24	pages 82–83

Story Summary "Muddle At Bat" focuses on product testing, using Mr. Muddle's test of baseball bats as a model. As the story develops, students evaluate Mr. Muddle's various testing methods and learn to interpret test results. They use their understanding of arithmetic and ratios to decide which baseball bat has the best value.

PROJECT

Making Connections

The Unit 1 Project makes real-world connections. Students work in **cooperative groups** to problem solve and to communicate their findings.

The project presented in the Unit 1 Wrap-Up should be completed in cooperative groups of students trying to determine, without counting, the number of books in the school library. Students should then determine and discuss whether the library has enough books. This project can be worked on during students' free time throughout the unit.

UNIT 1

Addition and Subtraction Lesson Plans

	LESSON	PACING	PRIMARY OBJECTIVES	FEATURE	RESOURCES	NCTM STANDARDS
1	Estimating 4–7	1 day	to review counting, base-10 arithmetic, and estimation	ACT IT OUT	Reteaching Strategy Practice Master 1 Enrichment Master 1	5, 6
2	Place Value 8–11	2 days	to review place value from ones to ten millions	Game	Reteaching Master Practice Master 2 Enrichment Master 2	6
3	Numerical Sequence 12–13	1 day	✓ to evaluate students' abilities to count and write numbers in correct sequence	Game	Reteaching Strategy Practice Master 3 Enrichment Master 3 Assessment Master	6
4	Greatest and Least Numbers 14–15	1 day	to provide practice with place value, numerical sequence, and basic addition facts	Game	Reteaching Strategy Practice Master 4 Enrichment Master 4	6, 7
5	Practicing Addition 16–19	1 day	to review addition facts	Thinking Story	Reteaching Strategy Practice Master 5 Enrichment Master 5	1, 2, 3, 4, 7, 8
6	Practicing Subtraction 20–21	1 day	to review subtraction facts		Reteaching Strategy Practice Master 6 Enrichment Master 6	7, 8
7	Adding and Subtracting 22–23	1 day	✓ to assess students' accuracy and speed with mixed addition and subtraction facts		Reteaching Strategy Practice Master 7 Enrichment Master 7 Assessment Master	2, 4, 8
8	Practicing Addition and Subtraction 24–27	1 day	to review the concept of a function		Reteaching Master Practice Master 8 Enrichment Master 8	1, 2, 3, 4, 8, 13
9	Missing Addends 28–31	1 day	to provide practice finding missing addends		Reteaching Master Practice Master 9 Enrichment Master 9	1, 2, 3, 4, 7
10	Perimeter 32–35	1 day	to provide practice solving problems about perimeter that involve missing dimensions	Thinking Story	Reteaching Strategy Practice Master 10 Enrichment Master 10	1, 2, 3, 4, 8, 9
11	Using Maps and Charts 36–37	1 day	to provide practice in estimating distances on a map and interpreting data on a chart		Reteaching Strategy Practice Master 11 Enrichment Master 11	1, 2, 3, 4, 5, 8, 9
12	Multidigit Addition 38–41	2 days	to provide practice in adding multidigit numbers	Game	Reteaching Master Practice Master 12 Enrichment Master 12	7, 8
13	Multidigit Subtraction 42–45	1 day	to provide practice in subtracting multidigit numbers	Game	Reteaching Master Practice Master 13 Enrichment Master 13	6, 7, 8, 11
14	Multidigit Addition and Subtraction 46–49	1 day	✓ to evaluate students' ability to do multidigit addition and subtraction	Thinking Story	Reteaching Strategy Practice Master 14 Enrichment Master 14 Assessment Master	1, 2, 3, 4, 8
	Mid-Unit Review 50–51				Assessment Master	
15	Applying Addition and Subtraction 52–53	1 day	to provide practice in solving word problems		Reteaching Strategy Practice Master 15 Enrichment Master 15	1, 2, 3, 4, 8

LESSON		PACING	PRIMARY OBJECTIVES	FEATURE	RESOURCES	NCTM STANDARDS
16	**Using Relation Signs . . . 54–57**	1 day	to review the meaning of the relation signs <, >, and =	Game, Thinking Story	Reteaching Strategy Practice Master 16 Enrichment Master 16	1, 2, 3, 4, 6
17	**Addition and Subtraction with Hidden Digits 58–59**	1 day	to provide practice in using approximation techniques to solve problems for which digits of some numbers are unknown		Reteaching Strategy Practice Master 17 Enrichment Master 17	3, 5, 8
18	**Approximation: Applications 60–63**	1 day	✓ to assess mastery of and provide practice in approximating answers to addition and subtraction problems	Thinking Story	Reteaching Strategy Practice Master 18 Enrichment Master 18 Assessment Master	1, 2, 3, 4, 8
19	**Introduction to the Calculator. 64–67**	1 day	to help students recognize that different calculators operate in different ways		Reteaching Strategy Practice Master 19 Enrichment Master 19	6, 8
20	**Estimating with Fractions 68–69**	1 day	to review fractional notation and the use of fractions	Game	Reteaching Master Practice Master 20 Enrichment Master 20	12
21	**Fractions and Money 70–71**	1 day	to provide practice in solving problems involving simple fractions	Game	Reteaching Strategy Practice Master 21 Enrichment Master 21	12
22	**Decimals and Money 72–75**	1 day	to review the use of the decimal point in writing money amounts	Game	Reteaching Master Practice Master 22 Enrichment Master 22	4, 12
23	**Adding and Subtracting Money 76–79**	1 day	to review and provide practice in adding and subtracting money	Game	Reteaching Master Practice Master 23 Enrichment Master 23	1, 2, 3, 4, 12
24	**Using Addition and Subtraction 80–83**	1 day	to provide practice in solving problems that involve money amounts	Thinking Story	Reteaching Strategy Practice Master 24 Enrichment Master 24	1, 2, 3, 4, 5, 12
25	**Making Inferences. 84–85**	1 day	to provide practice in approximating sums and differences		Reteaching Strategy Practice Master 25 Enrichment Master 25	3, 8, 11
26	**Unit 1 Review. 86–89**		to review addition and subtraction		Practice Master 26 Enrichment Master 26	
27	**Unit 1 Practice. 90–93**		to practice addition and subtraction		Practice Master 27 Enrichment Master 27	
	Unit 1 Test 94–95		to review addition and subtraction		Assessment Masters	
	Unit 1 Wrap-Up . . . . 96–97 How Many Books Are in the School Library?			Project		

UNIT CONNECTIONS

INTERVENTION STRATEGIES

In this Teacher's Guide there are specific strategies suggested for students with individual needs. These strategies appear with icons under the headings ESL, Gifted and Talented, Special Needs, Learning Styles, and At Risk, and are provided at the point of use. Following are the icons to look for and the types of strategies that will accompany them:

ESL

English as a Second Language

These strategies, designed for students who do not speak the English language fluently, suggest meaningful ways to present lesson concepts and vocabulary.

GIFTED & TALENTED

Gifted and Talented

These strategies are designed to enrich and extend the lessons and offer further challenges to students who have easily mastered the concepts already presented.

SPECIAL NEEDS

Special Needs

Students who are physically challenged or who have learning disabilities may require alternative ways to complete activities, record answers, use manipulatives, and so on. The strategies labeled with this icon offer appropriate methods of teaching lesson concepts to these students.

LEARNING STYLES

Learning Styles

Each student has his or her individual approach to learning. The strategies labeled with this icon suggest ways to present lesson concepts so that various learning modalities—such as tactile/kinesthetic, visual, and auditory—can be addressed.

AT RISK

At Risk

These strategies highlight the relevancy of the skills presented by making the connection between school and real life. They are directed toward students who appear to be at risk of dropping out of school before graduation.

TECHNOLOGY CONNECTIONS

The following materials, designed to reinforce and extend lesson concepts, are referred to throughout this Teacher's Guide. It might be helpful to either order the software or check it out of the school media center or community library. If your school does not provide Internet access, consider visiting a local library, college, or business specializing in Internet services. Some students may be able to access the Internet at home.

TECHNOLOGY CONNECTION *Look for this* **Technology Connection** *icon.*

- Eisenhower National Clearinghouse: http://www.enc.org; Telnet: enc.org (log in using the word "guest"); or dial (800) 362-4448 (Internet)
- *Hands On Math 2,* from Ventura Educational Systems; Apple, Mac, IBM, for grades 1–8 (software)
- *Math Arcade Games,* from Orange Cherry; Mac; for grades 2–8 (software)
- *Addition and Subtraction Defenders,* from Gamco; Mac, for grades K–6 (software)
- *Math Keys: Unlocking Measure,* from MECC; Mac, IBM, for grades 3–6, available in Spanish (software)
- *Word Problem Square Off,* from Gamco; Mac, for grades 3–4 (software)
- *The Quarter-Mile Fractions,* from Barnum Software; IBM, for grades 4–7 (software)
- *Classroom Market Economy!,* from Per Software, Inc.; Mac, for grades 3–12 (software)

CROSS-CURRICULAR CONNECTIONS

This Teacher's Guide offers specific suggestions on ways to connect the math concepts presented in this unit with other subjects that students are studying. Students can connect math concepts with topics they already know about, and they can find examples of math in other subjects and in real-world situations. These strategies are provided at the point of use.

Look for these icons:

- **Geography**
- **Health**
- **Social Studies**
- **Music**
- **Science**
- **Math**
- **Art**
- **Physical Education**
- **Language Arts**
- **Careers**

LITERATURE CONNECTIONS

The following books are referenced throughout this Teacher's Guide at points where they can be used to introduce, reinforce, or extend specific lesson concepts. You may want to locate these books in your school or community library.

Look for this **Literature Connection** *icon.*

- *Two Ways to Count to Ten: A Liberian Folktale* by Ruby Dee. H. Holt, 1988.
- *One Hundred Hungry Ants* by Elinor J. Pinczes. Houghton Mifflin, 1993.
- *How to Count Sheep Without Falling Asleep* by Ralph Leighton and Carl Feyhman. Prentice Hall, 1976.
- *Domino Addition* by Lynette Long. Charlesbridge Publishing, Inc., 1996.
- *Alexander, Who Used to Be Rich Last Sunday* by Judith Viorst. Atheneum, 1978.
- *How the Second Grade Got $8205.50 to Visit the Statue of Liberty* by Nathan Zimelman. A. Whitman, 1992.
- "Three Mathcateers to the Rescue," *How Do Octopi Eat Pizza Pie? Pizza Math* (pp. 44–57) by Time-Life Inc. Time-Life for Children, 1992.
- *Let's Investigate Quadrilaterals* by Marion Smoothey. Marshall Cavendish, 1993.
- *Rand McNally Children's Atlas of the United States.* Rand McNally, 1992.
- *Pigs Will Be Pigs* by Amy Axelrod. Four Winds Press, 1994.
- "Top Dog," *Math Mini-Mysteries* (pp. 43–44) by Sandra Markle. Atheneum, 1993.
- *Counting Jennie* by Helena Claire Pittman. Carolrhoda Books, 1994.
- "Alice's Adventures in Symbolville," *Alice in Numberland: Fantasy Math* (pp. 48–53) by Time-Life Inc. Time-Life for Children, 1993.
- *Number Puzzles* by Rose Griffiths. Gareth Stevens Inc., 1995.
- *A More or Less Fish Story* by Joanne and David Wylie. Children's Press, 1984.
- *Smart Spending* by Lois Schmitt. Scribner, 1989.

ASSESSMENT OPPORTUNITIES AT-A-GLANCE

LESSON	PORTFOLIO	PERFORMANCE	FORMAL	SELF	INFORMAL	CUMULATIVE REVIEWS	MULTIPLE-CHOICE	MASTERY CHECKPOINTS	ANALYZING ANSWERS
1					✓				
2	✓								
3			✓					✓	✓
4		✓				✓			
5				✓					
6				✓					✓
7			✓	✓				✓	
8	✓								✓
9					✓	✓			✓
10					✓				
11		✓							
12					✓				
13					✓	✓			
14			✓					✓	✓
Mid-Unit Review	✓	✓	✓						
15					✓				
16					✓				
17				✓		✓			
18			✓					✓	✓
19		✓							
20	✓								✓
21					✓	✓			
22	✓								
23		✓							
24		✓							
25					✓	✓			
26	✓	✓	✓						
27						✓			
Unit Test			✓				✓		

ASSESSMENT OPTIONS

PORTFOLIO ASSESSMENT

Throughout this Teacher's Guide are suggestions for activities in which students draw pictures, make graphs, and write about mathematics. Keep students' work to assess growth of understanding as the year progresses.

Lessons 2, 8, Mid-Unit Review, 20, 22, and 26

PERFORMANCE ASSESSMENT

Performance Assessment items focus on evaluating how students think and work as they solve problems. Opportunities for performance assessment can be found throughout the unit. Rubrics and guides for grading can be found in the front of the Assessment Blackline Masters.

Lessons 4, 11, Mid-Unit Review, 19, 23, 24, and 26

FORMAL ASSESSMENT

A Mid-Unit Review, Unit Review, and Unit Test help assess students' understanding of concepts, skills, and problem-solving ability. The *Math Explorations and Applications* CD-ROM Test Generator can create additional unit tests at three ability levels. Also, Mastery Checkpoints are provided periodically throughout the unit.

Lessons 3, 7, 14, Mid-Unit Review, 18, 26, and Unit Test

SELF ASSESSMENT

Throughout the program students are given the opportunity to check their own math skills.

Lessons 5, 6, 7, and 17

INFORMAL ASSESSMENT

A variety of assessment suggestions are provided throughout the unit, including interviews, oral questions or presentations, and debates. Also, each lesson includes Assessment Criteria, a list of questions about each student's progress, understanding, and participation.

Lessons 1, 9, 10, 12, 13, 15, 16, 21, and 25

CUMULATIVE REVIEW

Cumulative Reviews, covering material presented thus far in the year, are provided in the unit for use as either assessment or practice.

Lessons 4, 9, 13, 17, 21, 25, and 27

MULTIPLE-CHOICE TESTS (STANDARDIZED FORMAT)

Each unit provides a Unit Test in standardized format, giving students many opportunities to practice taking tests in this format.

MASTERY CHECKPOINTS

Mastery Checkpoints are provided throughout the unit to assess student proficiency in specific skills. Checkpoints reference appropriate Assessment Blackline Masters and other assessment options. Results of these evaluations can be recorded on the Mastery Checkpoint Chart.

Lessons 3, 7, 14, and 18

ANALYZING ANSWERS

Analyzing Answers items suggest possible sources of student error and offer teaching strategies for addressing difficulties.

Lessons 3, 6, 8, 9, 14, 18, and 20

Look for these icons:

> ***"Assessment is the process of gathering evidence about a student's knowledge of, ability to use, and disposition toward mathematics and of making inferences from that evidence for a variety of purposes."***
>
> *—NCTM Assessment Standards*

MASTERY CHECKPOINTS

WHAT TO EXPECT FROM STUDENTS AS THEY COMPLETE THIS UNIT

❶ NUMERICAL SEQUENCE—LESSON 3

At about this time most students should be able to write well-formed, legible numbers from 0 through 10,000 in correct ascending and descending order, as demonstrated by errors in no more than one sequence on page 12. You can use Assessment Blackline Master page 1 and record the results in the first column of the Mastery Checkpoint Chart.

❷ BASIC ADDITION AND SUBTRACTION FACTS—LESSON 7

At about this time most students should demonstrate mastery of the basic addition and subtraction facts by correctly answering at least 80% of the problems on page 22 in about five minutes. You can also use Assessment Blackline Master page 2. Results of this assessment can be recorded on the Mastery Checkpoint Chart.

❸ MULTIDIGIT ADDITION AND SUBTRACTION—LESSON 14

By this time most students should demonstrate mastery of the multidigit addition and subtraction algorithms by correctly answering at least 80% of the time problems on page 46 or a similar page. You may record the results of this assessment in the appropriate column of the Mastery Checkpoint Chart. You may also wish to assign Assessment Blackline Master page 3 to determine mastery.

❹ APPROXIMATING ANSWERS TO ADDITION AND SUBTRACTION—LESSON 18

By this time most students should be able to approximate answers to addition and subtraction problems. Assess this ability by observing them during the Mental Math drill in Lesson 18. Also, as a regular part of classroom activities, ask students to give an approximate answer when you do a computation problem together. Students who consistently make errors should be checked individually and given extra help. You can record the results of this assessment on the Mastery Checkpoint Chart. You may also wish to assign Assessment Blackline Master page 5 to determine mastery.

UNIT 1

PROGRAM RESOURCES

These additional components of *Math Explorations and Applications* can be purchased separately from SRA/McGraw-Hill.

LESSON	ESSENTIAL MANIPULATIVE KIT	GAME MAT PACKAGE	TEACHER MANIPULATIVE KIT	INTERMEDIATE MANIPULATIVE KIT	INTERMEDIATE OVERHEAD MANIPULATIVE KIT	*THE CRUNCHER* SOFTWARE	*MATH EXPLORATIONS AND APPLICATIONS* CD-ROM
1							Lesson 1
2	Number Cubes						Lesson 2
3	Number Cubes						Lesson 3
4	Number Cubes Number Wheels						Lesson 4
5	Number Wheels	play money		counters	coins, counters		Lesson 5
6	Number Cubes			counters, number line	counters		Lesson 6
7							Lesson 7
8							Lesson 8
9	Number Wheels		balance				Lesson 9
10	Number Wheels						Lesson 10
11							Lesson 11
12	Number Cubes			base-10 blocks, interlocking cubes	base-10 blocks		Lesson 12
13	Number Cubes	Transaction Game, play money		base-10 blocks, interlocking cubes	bills, coins		Lesson 13
14	Number Wheels						Lesson 14
15							Lesson 15
16	Number Cubes						Lesson 16
17							Lesson 17
18							Lesson 18
19			thermometer, number line	base-10 blocks, interlocking cubes	base-10 blocks		Lesson 19
20		Fracto 1 and Fracto 2 Games					Lesson 20
21		Store and Harder Store Games					Lesson 21
22	Number Cubes	play money			bills, coins		Lesson 22
23	Number Cubes	Harder Transaction Game, play money			bills, coins		Lesson 23
24		play money			bills, coins		Lesson 24
25							Lesson 25
26							Lesson 26
27	Number Cubes						Lesson 27

UNIT 1

Student Edition pages 2–3

Addition and Subtraction

INTRODUCING THE UNIT

Using the Student Pages Begin your discussion of the opening unit photo by asking students, "How does a cook or chef use addition and subtraction?" Then read aloud the paragraph on the student page that highlights cooking as a career. This helps make the connection between school and work and encourages students to explore how math is used in the real world.

ACTIVITY Ask students to find a recipe for a food they like. Then have them write the correct amounts for the ingredients they would need if they doubled the recipe.

FYI People have been cooking for thousands of years. Early people did most of their cooking over open fires. Before pottery was invented they broiled meat on spits or boiled it in leather or wooden containers by dropping in hot rocks. By 3000 B.C. Egyptians were baking bread in clay ovens. Later, Romans used iron tripods to cook food. In the Middle Ages, from about A.D. 400 until A.D. 1500, cooking was once again done over open hearths in people's homes. Iron stoves became common in the early 1800s. Since that time the type of fuel that fires stoves and ovens has changed from wood to coal to gas and electricity, but the basic techniques of cooking have remained the same. Stress that once a consistent technology existed, recipes could become more exact, and the experience a cook gained could be written down and reproduced elsewhere. Still, many of the recipes we use today were developed ages ago when conditions were very different. Spices like pepper became popular in the Middle Ages to conceal the taste of food that could not be properly preserved, and yet today a table without a pepper shaker on it seems incomplete. Today in the United States the cuisine of many cultures is familiar, as people from different areas of the world make their home in our country.

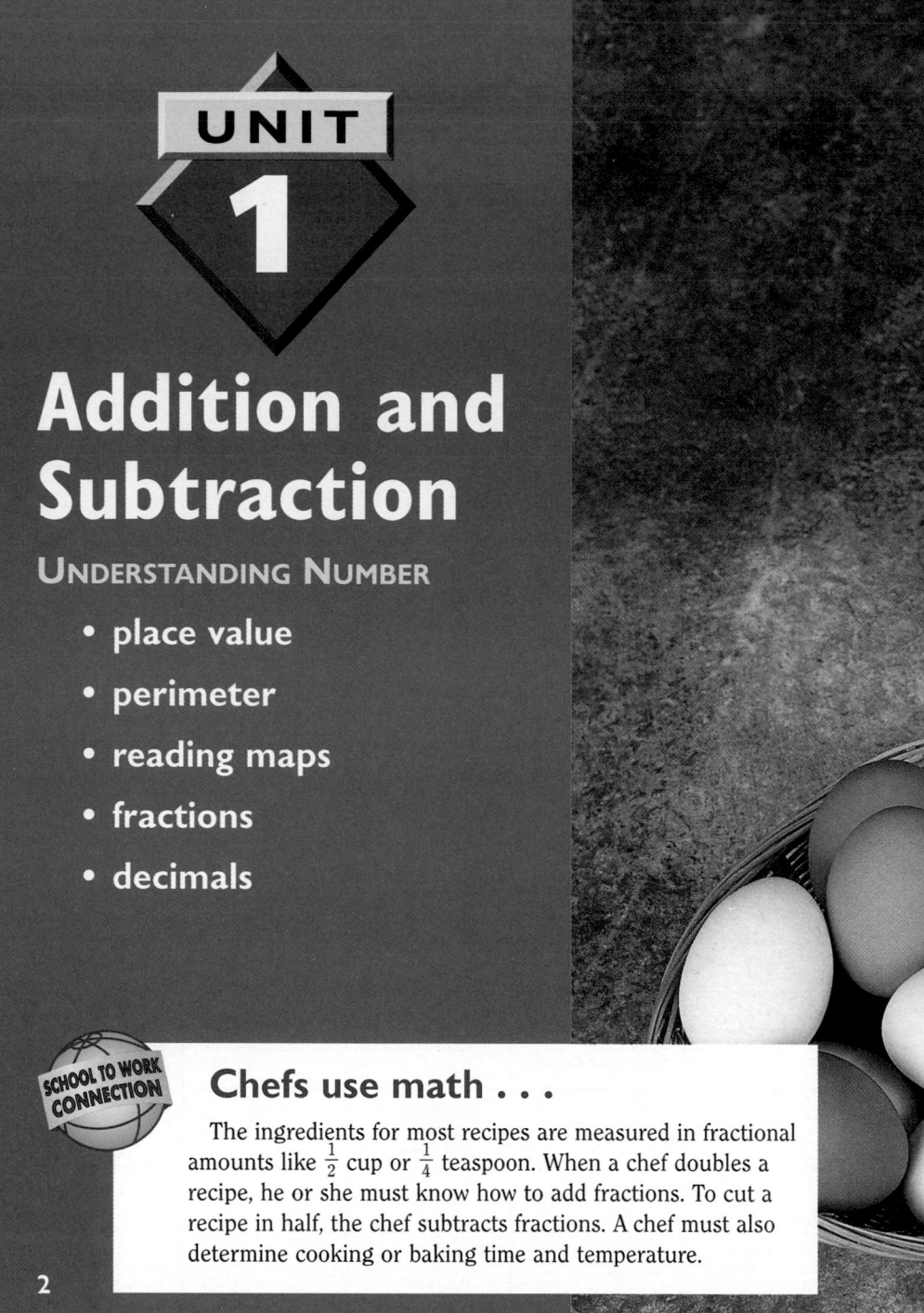

UNIT 1

Addition and Subtraction

UNDERSTANDING NUMBER

- place value
- perimeter
- reading maps
- fractions
- decimals

Chefs use math . . .

The ingredients for most recipes are measured in fractional amounts like $\frac{1}{2}$ cup or $\frac{1}{4}$ teaspoon. When a chef doubles a recipe, he or she must know how to add fractions. To cut a recipe in half, the chef subtracts fractions. A chef must also determine cooking or baking time and temperature.

2

Thinklab™

SRA's Thinklab™ provides a series of creative and logical problem-solving opportunities for individual students. The problems are designed to appeal to different cognitive abilities.

- ▶ Use Problems 1–10 with this unit to reinforce object manipulation (ways and means of dealing with specific data).
- ▶ Use Problems 11–20 with this unit to reinforce perception (extrapolating from and beyond given data).

Enable students to see that careful measurement is essential to following a recipe. Whether a student is interested in a career in cooking or simply in being able to prepare a meal, the ability to add, subtract, multiply, and divide will be tested in making even a simple dish. In some cases, a cook will need to be able to convert one kind of measurement—say metric—into the customary system. At other times it will be necessary to change the proportions of a recipe to serve either more or fewer people. Today people pursuing a career in cooking often go to school for six months or a year to learn the proper techniques. Because cooking is based on how matter behaves under different conditions—heat and cold and in various chemical combinations—an understanding of the fundamentals of science is a great help to being a good cook. Once these things are understood, the artistic side of making food taste its best can come into play.

Home Connections You may want to send home the letter on Home Connections Blackline Masters pages 30–31 the first week of school to introduce families to the *Math Explorations and Applications* program. Then use the letter on pages 32–33 the following week to introduce this unit.

Unit Project This would be a good time to assign the "How Many Books Are in the School Library?" project on pages 96 and 97. Students can begin working on the project in cooperative groups in their free time as they work through the unit. The Unit Project is a good opportunity for students to estimate, analyze data, and initiate a research project.

Cooperate 1

Cooperate 1, published by SRA, provides a series of creative and logical problem-solving opportunities for cooperative groups. The problems are designed to provide practice in problem solving, communication, reasoning, and making connections. *Cooperate 1* presents the following cognitive strategies—perceiving spatial relations, ordering and sequencing, logical deduction, establishing and testing hypotheses, sequential exploration, identifying starting points, attending to detail, organizing information, and screening irrelevant information.

Each Problem Card emphasizes a principal strategy as well as reinforcing other strategies.

- Use Problem Cards 1–2 with this unit to emphasize logical deduction.
- Use Problem Cards 3–4 with this unit to emphasize establishing and testing hypotheses.
- Use Problem Card 5 with this unit to emphasize both ordering and sequencing and attending to detail.

LESSON 1

Student Edition pages 4–7

Estimating

LESSON PLANNER

Objectives

- ▶ to refamiliarize students with numbers
- ▶ to review counting, base-10 arithmetic, and estimation

Context of the Lesson This is the first of four lessons on place value and counting. It reintroduces counting and writing numbers, as well as place value in our base-10 system, from previous grades. Estimation is also included, as it is in many lessons throughout the text.

MANIPULATIVES

jar of small objects, such as marbles or peanuts

Program Resources

Practice Master 1

Enrichment Master 1

For extra practice:
CD-ROM* Lesson 1

1 Warm-Up

5 MINUTES

Problem of the Day Display a **jar of small objects,** such as marbles or peanuts. Have students estimate how many objects are in the jar. Ask them to explain their strategies. Conclude by having a volunteer count the objects. Compare the count with the estimates. (Answers and strategies will vary.)

Problem-Solving Strategies Ask students who have solved the Problem of the Day to share how they solved it and any strategies they used.

MENTAL MATH Count with the class up and down in a number range appropriate to students' abilities. Gradually work toward more difficult ranges. Then provide students with problems such as these.

"What number comes ______?"

a. before 6 (5)
b. after 19 (20)
c. after 30 (31)
d. before 11 (10)
e. before 769 (768)
f. after 999 (1000)
g. before 1001 (1000)
h. after 997 (998)
i. before 1450 (1449)
j. after 1998 (1999)

EXPLORE

LESSON 1

Estimating

ACT IT OUT

A Basket of Apples

The Cortland Apple Orchard gave Jeremy a crate of apples for his school. Help him estimate how many apples there are in the crate. You may want to act out the students taking apples to help solve the problem.

1. Write down your best estimate of how many apples there are in the crate. **Estimates may range from 30 to 5000.**

- ◆ How did you make your estimate?
- ◆ Do you think you have a good chance of being exactly right?

Literature Connection Invite students to read *Two Ways to Count to Ten: A Liberian Folktale* by Ruby Dee.

*available separately

Jeremy's friends helped him carry away the apples.

2 Ten children took ten apples each. How many apples did they take? **100**

There were still lots of apples left.

◆ Now do you know exactly how many apples there were all together?

3 Make a second estimate of how many apples there were.
Reasonable estimates may range from 300 to 2000.

Then ten more children came. They each took ten apples. Then the crate looked like this.

4 So far, 20 children have taken ten apples each. How many apples is that? **200**

5 Make a third estimate of how many apples there were. **A reasonable estimate is approximately 700.**

Unit 1 Lesson 1 • 5

Technology Connection Use the Internet to gain access to Eisenhower National Clearinghouse (ENC). The ENC's address is **http://www.enc.org**; or, if you have Telnet: **enc.org** (log in using the word "guest"); or, dial **(800) 362-4448** from your terminal. These sites provide access to activity guides, reference materials, and other Web sites for teachers and students.

2 Teach

ACT IT OUT **Using the Student Pages** Treat pages 4–5 as a fun activity for the class to work on together. Discuss each set of answers after the students have made estimates. The emphasis should not be on precise answers at this point. Help students who make poor estimates, especially on the first two tries, to realize that they did not yet have enough information to make more precise estimates.

On page 5, before they make their second estimates, be sure that students understand that many more apples remain than have been taken, but that it is not clear how many more. Thus, because they know that 100 apples have been taken, any estimate between 300 and about 2000 could be considered a reasonable estimate of the original number of apples.

After students make their third estimates, have them discuss the strategies they used. At this point, there is a systematic way of making an estimate. There are about 100 apples between each two consecutive hoops of the crate, which means there are six sections of about 100 apples each. If students add that sum to the 100 apples that were on top, they have an estimate of around 700.

Note: All questions marked with a ◆ are discussion questions, intended to be read and discussed with the class. Numbered questions and problems can, as a rule, be done by the students on their own or in groups, although you may wish to discuss some of these with the class.

ESL **Meeting Individual Needs**
Students learning English may have difficulty with the ordinal numbers used in this lesson, such as second, third, and fourth. Pair these students with native English speakers, who can use their fingers to convey the meaning of the ordinal numbers.

◆ **LESSON 1 Estimating**

Teach

Using the Student Pages As students work through the questions on page 6, help them to see that this new information can be used to confirm or refine their earlier estimates to get approximately 700 apples. Point out that even with this additional information they still do not know exactly how many apples are there. However, the information given on page 7 allows students to state the number of apples in the crate with certainty. Help students to see that their estimates improved as they got more information.

SPECIAL NEEDS

Meeting Individual Needs

If any student's numbers are very difficult to read, ask him or her to write those numbers several times as clearly as possible. Students with persistent problems, such as reversal of digits or places, should be brought to the attention of a learning disabilities specialist. If this kind of disability has persisted to this grade level, there could be a more serious underlying problem.

◆ **LESSON 1 Estimating**

ACT IT OUT

More children came and took apples.

6. So far, 30 children have taken ten apples each. How many apples have they taken? **300**

◆ How many apples do you think are left?
The answer should be approximately 400.

7. Make a fourth estimate of how many apples there were.
Estimates should still be approximately 700.

All 30 children came back. They each took another ten apples.

8. Counting both times the children took some apples, how many apples did each child take? **20**

9. How many apples have the 30 children taken all together? **600**

10. Make a fifth estimate of how many apples there were.

Estimates should be approximately 700.

RETEACHING

Reteaching is not needed because this is an introductory lesson that reviews concepts that will be covered more systematically in later lessons.

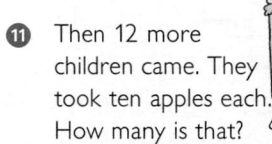

11 Then 12 more children came. They took ten apples each. How many is that? **120**

12 How many apples have been taken all together? **720**

13 How many apples are left? **7**

14 How many apples were there all together? **727**

- Is this an estimate, or are you certain?
- What was your first estimate about how many apples there were?
- What was your second estimate? What was your third estimate?
- What was your fourth estimate? What was your fifth estimate?
- Did your estimates get closer?

MATH JOURNAL

In your Math Journal explain how you made your estimates.

PRACTICE p. 1

LESSON 1 PRACTICE Name____________

A rack in the gym at Richard's school holds tennis balls. It is partially covered so that you cannot count the exact number of balls in the rack. Estimate the total number of balls in the rack.

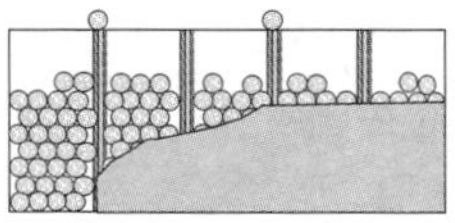

Answers will vary. A reasonable range of answers for the first estimate would be 150–170.

1. Write your best estimate of how many balls there are. ________
2. Richard's friends helped him carry away some balls. Five children took five balls each. How many balls did they take? Make a second estimate of how many balls there were. 25 ________
3. Five more children came. They each took five balls. So far ten children have taken five balls each. How many balls is that? Make a third estimate of how many balls there were. 50 ________
4. More children came and took balls. So far, 15 children have taken five balls each. How many balls have they taken? Make a fourth estimate of how many balls there were. 75 ________
5. All 15 children came back. They each took another five balls. Counting both times the children took some balls, how many balls did each child take? 10
6. How many balls have the 15 children taken all together? 150
7. There are now two balls left in the rack. Make a fifth estimate of how many balls there were all together. 152

Copyright © SRA/McGraw-Hill. Permission is granted to reproduce this page for classroom use.

ENRICHMENT p. 1

LESSON 1 ENRICHMENT Name____________

Keep track of how much food you eat in a week. Choose your favorite protein sources, vegetables, grains, fruits, and dairy products. Enter them on the lines provided. Estimate the number of ounces you eat and enter the amounts in the chart. After a week answer the question below.

Type of Food	Sun.	Mon.	Tue.	Wed.	Thu.	Fri.	Sat.
Protein (such as meat, fish, nuts)							
Vegetables							
Grains (such as bread, pasta, cereal)							
Fruits							
Dairy (such as yogurt, cheese)							

Let's say that for you this is an average week of eating. How much of each food group do you eat in a week, a month, and a year?

Answers will vary.

Copyright © SRA/McGraw-Hill. Permission is granted to reproduce this page for classroom use.

3 Wrap-Up

5 MINUTES

In Closing Summarize the lesson by asking students to share the strategies they used to sharpen their estimates.

ALTERNATIVE ASSESSMENT

Informal Assessment Listen closely as students share their responses and reasoning to informally evaluate their number sense and estimation skills. Students who have difficulty with this lesson should be observed carefully during the next few lessons to see whether the difficulty stems from the nature of this exercise or from a general lack of number sense. More work with base-10 numeration, counting, and order is provided in upcoming lessons.

Assessment Criteria

Did the student . . .

- ✓ contribute to the group discussion?
- ✓ make reasonable estimates based on the information available?
- ✓ adjust estimates to account for new information?
- ✓ communicate the strategies used?

Homework Have students select a container and estimate how many dried beans or other small objects would fill it. Have them fill the container, then count to check their estimates.

LOOKING AHEAD The first game is introduced in Lesson 2. You might wish to play this and other games beforehand with another adult to familiarize yourself with the rules. An optional variation of the "Roll a Number" game in Lesson 2 requires an opaque container, such as a coffee can, and slips of paper with the numbers 0–9 written on them.

GAMES

THE ROLE OF GAMES

Games are an important component of the *Math Explorations and Applications* program. They offer students an opportunity to practice the mathematical skills to which they've been introduced and to develop logical reasoning as they use mathematical strategies. They make learning fun. Games also offer you another way to assess how well your students have learned each skill. There are two types of games presented in this program—Game Mats and Cube Games.

Game Mats

There are five Game Mats in Kindergarten, thirteen in levels 1–3, and fourteen in levels 4–6. In the Game Mat package, you receive 15 copies of each Game Mat, counters, place markers, Number Cubes, and money (not in Kindergarten). In addition, you have *A Guide for Using the Game Mats* and a color transparency for each Game Mat. Each game involves the use of several math skills including mathematical reasoning and probability. Many of the Game Mats are offered in a standard and a harder version.

Cube Games

These games, presented in the Student Edition in levels 3–6 and in the Teacher's Guide for K–2, reinforce basic math skills and involve mathematical reasoning.

TIPS FOR TEACHING GAMES

After reading the rules for each game, which are provided in the lesson where the Cube Game is introduced or on each Game Mat, take the following steps:

- **Play the game yourself.** This will help you identify any difficulties your students might have.
- **Demonstrate how the game is played.** Making sure that everyone can see, say the rules aloud as you play another student or as two or more students play together. For the Game Mats, you may want to use the color overhead transparencies to demonstrate how each game is played.
- **Restate how the game is played.** Ask students to restate the object of the game and rules of the game in their own words to be sure everyone understands how to play.
- **Supervise students' play.** Be sure they get off to the right start.

Tips for Organizing Successful Game Sessions

- **Stress enjoyment rather than competition.** Emphasize sportsmanship, fair play, and taking turns.
- **In general, place students of the same ability together.** This way all students have a more equal chance of winning.
- **Change groupings from day to day.** Students can learn different things by playing with different partners.
- **Be sure students are challenged by a game.** Most Game Mats have a standard and a harder version. Some Cube Games suggest variations to the game.
- **Assign one referee for the day or one for each group.** Students sometimes get so absorbed in their own efforts that they do not follow the rules. A referee can monitor players' moves, keep track of scores, and in some games act as banker.
- **Make Game Mats accessible.** Store mats so that students can find and return them without your help. (You might want to laminate the mats.)

MENTAL MATH EXERCISES

Mental Math exercises offer an easy and practical technique for drilling students' math skills and assessing their performance. With these exercises students usually use either the Number Wheel (Levels 3–6) or Number Cubes (Levels K–6) to display their answers to your oral questions.

NUMBER WHEELS

Number Wheels have five wheels, each of which can be dialed to show any digit from 0 through 9. This allows students to make any integer from 0 through 99,999. To show the number 2047, for example, a student rotates the thousands wheel to show a 2, turns the hundreds wheel to show a 0, and so on. Different colors are used to identify each of the five wheels. On the back of the Number Wheels, the digits 0 through 9 are repeated with the addition of a decimal point.

Tips for Using Number Wheels and Cubes

- **Add a "peek-to-be-sure" step.** This should occur between the "Hide" and "Show" steps of the procedure. It asks students who have already found answers to check them. This keeps them involved as they wait for the "Show" command.
- **Use good judgment to decide when to give the "Show" command.** Give students who are progressing toward a solution time enough to finish, but avoid prolonged waiting because this calls attention to slower students.
- **Encourage your students. Mental Math exercises allow an active exchange between you and your students.** Use this opportunity to give your students plenty of positive reinforcement.

NUMBER CUBES

Number Cubes allow students to make any integer from 0 through 100. In levels 3–6, students use the 0–5 (red) and 5–10 (blue) Number Cubes. To show the number 73, for example, a student should find the 7 face on the 5–10 cube and place that next to the 3 face on the 0–5 cube.

In Levels 1 and 2, each student should be given four cubes—two units cubes, 0–5 (red) and 5–10 (blue), and two tens cubes, 0–5 (yellow) and 5–10 (green). To show the number 43, for example, a student should find the 4 face on the 0–5 tens cube and place that next to the 3 face on the 0–5 units cube.

HOW TO USE WHEELS AND CUBES

1. Present the class with a problem (orally or on the chalkboard) and say "Find."
2. Students determine the answer and dial it on their Number Wheels or position it on their Number Cubes.
3. Say "Hide."
4. Students hide their answers by holding their Wheels or Cubes against their chests.
5. Say "Show," when you see that most students have an answer.
6. Students hold up their Wheels or Cubes so you can see their responses.
7. Check students' responses.
8. Show and/or say the correct answer.
9. Move on to the next problem.

Sometimes the problems in a Mental Math exercise will be complex enough to require paper and pencil. In these cases, have students show their answers to you as you walk around the room.

LESSON 2

Student Edition pages 8–11

Place Value

LESSON PLANNER

Objectives

- ▶ to review place value from ones to ten millions
- ▶ to review base-10 arithmetic

Context of the Lesson This is the second of four lessons on place value and counting. This lesson presents the “Roll a Number” game, which provides practice with place value. More work with base-10 arithmetic and place value is provided in the next two lessons.

MANIPULATIVES

container (opaque) such as a coffee can (optional)

map, globe, or atlas (optional)

paper, ten slips numbered 0–9 (optional)

Program Resources

Number Cubes (0–5 and 5–10)

Reteaching Master

Practice Master 2

Enrichment Master 2

For extra practice:
CD-ROM* Lesson 2

Note: This lesson may take more than one day.

1 Warm-Up

5 MINUTES

Problem of the Day Present this problem orally or on the chalkboard: “I am thinking of a four-digit number. The digits add up to 9. The greatest digit is in the ones place. What is the number?” (Many answers are possible; possibilities include 2034, 1206, and 1035.)

Problem-Solving Strategies Ask students who have solved the Problem of the Day to share how they solved it and any strategies they used.

MENTAL MATH Begin with unison counting. Then challenge students to solve number-before and number-after problems such as these:

“What number comes _____?”

a. before 80 (79)
b. after 99 (100)
c. after 500 (501)
d. before 401 (400)
e. after 1399 (1400)
f. before 4200 (4199)
g. after 9999 (10,000)
h. before 10,000 (9999)
i. before 5999 (5998)
j. after 699 (700)

EXPLORE

LESSON 2

Place Value

Place value lets us read and write numbers of any size using only ten digits. In this lesson you'll explore place value by thinking about groups of tacks.

The Eversharp Company makes and sells tacks.
The tacks are packaged like this:

		Number of Tacks	
		one	1
There are ten tacks on a **strip.**	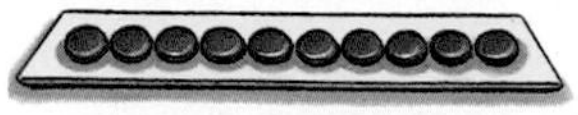	ten	10
There are ten strips on a **card.**	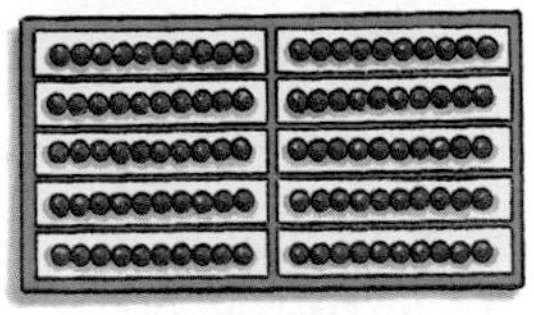	one hundred	100
There are ten cards in a **box.**		one thousand	1,000
There are ten boxes in a **case.**		ten thousand	10,000
There are ten cases in a **shipping carton.**		one hundred thousand	100,000

8 • Addition and Subtraction

Why teach it this way?

Games are an important and carefully integrated part of this mathematics program. Each game provides necessary practice in specific skills. Furthermore, the games help students develop problem-solving skills and intuitive concepts of probability.

Technology Connection Take a look at the software *Hands on Math 2* from Ventura Educational Systems (Apple, Mac, and IBM for grades 1–8) for further practice with place value, base-10 blocks, and addition and subtraction.

*available separately

		Number of Tacks	
There are ten shipping cartons in a **vanload.**		one million	1,000,000
There are ten vanloads in a **truckload.**		ten million	10,000,000

Write the number of tacks. The first one has been done for you. Watch your numbering.

1. 2 shipping cartons and 2 boxes **202,000**
2. 4 cases and 8 cards **40,800**
3. 3 truckloads and 6 cases **30,060,000**
4. 4 shipping cartons, 3 boxes, and 1 strip **403,010**
5. 6 vanloads, 7 cases, and 10 cards **6,071,000**
6. 8 shipping cartons and 4 strips **800,040**
7. 11 cases, 8 cards, and 12 strips **110,920**
8. 1 truckload, 2 boxes, and 8 strips **10,002,080**
9. 3 truckloads, 3 vanloads, and 9 cards **33,000,900**
10. 11 cases and 11 strips **110,110**
11. 1 truckload and 1 box **10,001,000**
12. 3 shipping cartons and 1 case **310,000**
13. 2 cards and 1 strip **210**
14. 4 vanloads and 2 cases **4,020,000**
15. 8 truckloads and 2 cases **80,020,000**

◆ How would you say each number? (For problem 1, you would say "two hundred two thousand.")

❷ Teach

Using the Student Pages Before starting work on pages 8–10, demonstrate the "Roll a Number" game on page 11, which provides practice with place value, so that students may play it as soon as they finish the pages.

Do pages 8–9 as a class activity. Tell students that this is a contrived situation and that they need not remember the number of tacks in each package or vehicle. Have them focus instead on the fact that as you go down the third column, each number is ten times the number above it. As students do problems 1–15 on page 9, encourage them to refer to page 8.

Tell students that we often break up numbers by putting commas after every three digits to make them easier to read. Demonstrate this by writing several numbers on the chalkboard, such as 12,000; 16,798; and 282,392. Explain that while this program does not use a comma in four-digit numbers, some people choose to do so.

If necessary, give students additional problems similar to those on page 9, encouraging them to use page 8 for reference. Be sure to include a few problems that involve regrouping, such as 12 cards and 17 tacks. Include a few problems with numbers only, such as 5 thousands, 6 hundreds, 9 tens, and 3 ones.

Geography Connection Have students use a **map, globe,** or **atlas** to locate Myanmar (formerly Burma) and identify the countries that border it. Then have them use an encyclopedia or almanac to find the current population of those neighboring nations. Students can write the populations in standard form, in expanded form, and in word form. Discuss whether population numbers are accurate.

◆ LESSON 2 Place Value

Teach

Using the Student Pages As students complete page 10, help them make connections between the place value chart, numbers in word form, and numbers in expanded form. As an exercise, have students make a place value pocket chart. Students can insert number cards into it to create multidigit numbers they can read, or form the numbers you or their classmates dictate.

Highlight the position and usefulness of commas in multidigit numbers. Explain that commas can provide clues for reading multidigit numbers. For instance, in the number 123,456,789, the commas are signals to say "million" and "thousand."

GAME Demonstrate and then play the "Roll a Number" game on page 11. It can be played by the whole class or by partners or small groups. This game provides practice with place value and probability.

For most variations of the "Roll a Number" game, ten **slips of paper** numbered 0–9 can be used instead of cubes. This method lends itself well to whole-group participation. The lead player draws slips one at a time from a **coffee can** or other opaque container and calls out each number. The other players write down the numbers on the lines drawn on their papers immediately after each number is called out. Decide beforehand whether slips will be put aside or returned to the container after they are drawn. Each method produces a different strategy for winning.

Some students may want to play a more difficult variation that involves regrouping and a more sophisticated understanding of probability. To play, students roll two cubes (0–5 and 5–10) each time, then write the sum in one of the blanks. After three rolls students regroup and find the values of their numbers. The student with the greatest number wins the round.

PRACTICE

◆ LESSON 2 Place Value

GEOGRAPHY CONNECTION As of mid-1995, the population of Myanmar (formerly Burma) was estimated to be 45,103,809. This lesson will show you how to read that number, and other numbers, by using place value.

MILLIONS			THOUSANDS					
Hundreds	Tens	Ones	Hundreds	Tens	Ones	Hundreds	Tens	Ones
	4	5	1	0	3	8	0	9

Forty-five million, one hundred three thousand, eight hundred nine

The 4 stands for 4 ten millions.	40,000,000
The 5 stands for 5 millions.	5,000,000
The 1 stands for 1 hundred thousand.	100,000
The 0 stands for 0 ten thousands.	0
The 3 stands for 3 thousands.	3,000
The 8 stands for 8 hundreds.	800
The 0 stands for 0 tens.	0
The 9 stands for 9 ones.	9

Write the numbers in standard form. The first one has been done for you.

16. 700 + 30 + 5 **735**
17. 9 + 100 + 2000 **2109**
18. 50 + 5 **55**
19. 900,000 + 6,000 + 500 **906,500**
20. 600 + 20 + 7 **627**
21. 500,000 + 6 + 7,000 **507,006**
22. 1000 + 400 + 8 **1408**
23. 40 + 9 + 90,000 **90,049**
24. 400,000 + 50 + 7 **400,057**
25. 80,000,000 + 300,000 + 9,000 + 200 **80,309,200**
26. 9000 + 10 + 1 **9011**
27. 20 + 700 + 800,000 **800,720**
28. 10,000 + 4,000 + 400 **14,400**
29. 7,000,000 + 300,000 + 60,000 + 900 **7,360,900**
30. 8000 + 10 **8010**
31. 50,000,000 + 30,000 **50,030,000**

10 • Addition and Subtraction

Literature Connection In *One Hundred Hungry Ants* by Elinor J. Pinczes one hundred hungry ants find they can get to a picnic faster if they regroup.

RETEACHING p. 1

LESSON 2 RETEACHING Name________________

Each number in 81,523,419 stands for something different.

Eighty-one million, five hundred twenty-three thousand, four hundred nineteen

The 8 stands for 8 ten millions.	80,000,000
The 1 stands for 1 million.	1,000,000
The 5 stands for 5 hundred thousands.	500,000
The 2 stands for 2 ten thousands.	20,000
The 3 stands for 3 thousands.	3,000
The 4 stands for 4 hundreds.	400
The 1 stands for 1 ten.	10
The 9 stands for 9 ones.	9

What does each number stand for in 63,532,879?

1. The 6 stands for 6 ten millions or 60,000,000.
2. The 3 stands for 3 millions or 3,000,000.
3. The 5 stands for 5 hundred thousands or 500,000.
4. The 3 stands for 3 ten thousands or 30,000.
5. The 2 stands for 2 thousands or 2000.
6. The 8 stands for 8 hundreds or 800.
7. The 7 stands for 7 tens or 70.
8. The 9 stands for 9 ones or 9.

Copyright © SRA/McGraw-Hill. Permission is granted to reproduce this page for classroom use.

Math Explorations and Applications Level 4 • 1

COOPERATIVE LEARNING

GAME

Roll a Number Game

Players: Two or more
Materials: One 0–5 cube (red)
Object: To make the greatest three-digit number
Math Focus: Place value and mathematical reasoning

RULES

1. Draw lines for a three-digit number on your paper, like this:

   _______ _______ _______

2. The first player rolls the cube three times.
3. Each time the cube is rolled, write that number in one of the three blanks you made. After all three rolls, you will have made a three-digit number.
4. The player who makes the greatest three-digit number is the winner of the round.

SAMPLE GAME

Number Rolled:	Amy's Number:	Jack's Number:	Ellen's Number:
First roll 3	3 _ _	_ _ 3	_ 3 _
Second roll 1	3 _ 1	_ 1 3	_ 3 1
Third roll 5	3 5 1	5 1 3	5 3 1

Ellen won this round.

OTHER WAYS TO PLAY THIS GAME

1. The least three-digit number wins.
2. Make a four-digit number. (Roll the cube four times.)
3. The greatest even number wins.
4. Use a 5–10 cube (blue). If a 10 is rolled, roll that cube again.

Unit 1 Lesson 2 • **11**

PRACTICE p. 2

LESSON 2 PRACTICE Name__________

Write the numbers in standard form.

1. 70 + 6 76
2. 300 + 40 + 7 347
3. 900 + 90 + 9 999
4. 2000 + 600 + 4 2604
5. 20,000 + 5000 + 300 25,300
6. 5000 + 60 5060
7. 1 + 80 + 400 481
8. 200,000 + 2000 + 2 202,002
9. 8,000,000 + 400 + 3 8,000,403
10. 7 + 60 + 900 + 7000 7967
11. 100 + 3000 + 60,000 63,100
12. 70,000,000 + 50,000 70,050,000
13. 40 + 9000 + 70,000 79,040
14. 10,000 + 4 10,004
15. 8000 + 800 + 80 + 8 8888
16. 8000 + 700 + 80 + 8 8788
17. 8000 + 800 + 80 + 7 8887
18. 30 + 3000 + 7 3037

2 • *Math Explorations and Applications* Level 4

Copyright © SRA/McGraw-Hill. Permission is granted to reproduce this page for classroom use.

ENRICHMENT p. 2

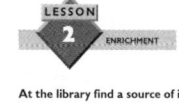

LESSON 2 ENRICHMENT Name__________

At the library find a source of information on the solar system. Then answer the questions below.

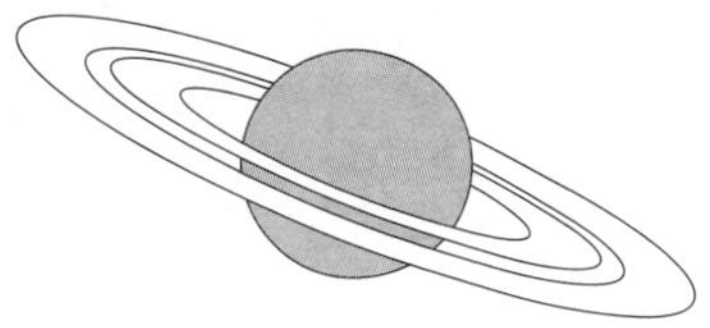

1. What is the distance in millions of kilometers from the sun to each of the planets? All distances are times one million.

Earth	149.6 km	Uranus	2870 km
Pluto	5900 km	Venus	108.2 km
Jupiter	778.3 km	Saturn	1427 km
Neptune	4497 km	Mercury	57.9 km
Mars	227.9 km		

2. Draw a picture of the solar system and label the distances between the sun and the planets.
   See students' work. Order of planets from the sun is Mercury, Venus, Earth, Mars, Jupiter, Saturn, Uranus, Neptune, and Pluto.

2 • *Math Explorations and Applications* Level 4

Copyright © SRA/McGraw-Hill. Permission is granted to reproduce this page for classroom use.

3 Wrap-Up

5 MINUTES

In Closing To summarize the lesson, invite students to explain their strategies for the "Roll a Number" game. Ask them how knowing about place value helps them play the game.

ALTERNATIVE ASSESSMENT

Portfolio Assessment Have students record their understanding of place value by explaining the meaning of the digits in the number 23,405. Have them tell how it differs from the number 2345. Students can place this document in their Math Portfolios as evidence of their ongoing learning.

Assessment Criteria

Did the student . . .

✓ correctly answer at least 75% of the place value problems?

✓ demonstrate understanding of place value as he or she played the game?

✓ identify relationships among the places in the base-10 system?

Homework Have students play the "Roll a Number" game with a family member for reinforcement of place value. A copy of this game can also be found on page 6 of the Home Connections Blackline Masters.

GIFTED & TALENTED

Meeting Individual Needs

Students may enjoy learning the names for numbers greater than millions. To cite some examples, 1000 million is called a *billion*, 1000 billion is called a *trillion*, and the names *quadrillion, quintillion, sextillion, septillion, octillion, nonillion,* and *decillion* follow in the same pattern.

Ask students how long they think it would take to count to 1 million. Record their estimates. Then tell them that if they can count to 150 in a minute, at that rate it would take about 111 hours, or more than four and one-half days, to count to 1 million!

ASSESSMENT

This is the first Mastery Checkpoint at this grade level. Throughout each unit of each grade level, at benchmarks specified on the Mastery Checkpoint Chart, you are able to assess students' progress.

MASTERY CHECKPOINT CHARTS

The Mastery Checkpoint Chart contains a listing of the mastery objectives that are considered important for future progress in mathematics. These benchmarks appear on a chart in the Assessment Blackline Master Book on pages vii-viii. You can determine each student's mastery of specific objectives by his or her performance of the mastery objective in the lesson and/or by using the specific Mastery Checkpoint test provided in the Assessment Blackline Master Book. Those students who are having difficulty with a skill should receive extra help before continuing on in the unit. But an entire class should not be held up until all students learn the skill. Each lesson provides you with either a Reteaching Strategy or a Reteaching Master that will help you present the lesson concept in a slightly different way.

Tips on Using the Mastery Checkpoint Chart

- Fill in the names of all students in your class.
- For each checkpoint on the Mastery Checkpoint Chart, the Teacher's Guide gives opportunities to assess either by observation or by using the Student Edition page(s). Students can also be given the Assessment Blackline Master for that specific Checkpoint.
- Place a check mark (✓) in the appropriate column of the Mastery Checkpoint Chart beside the name of each student who demonstrates success on the objective in question.
- Pencil in a *P* in the appropriate column for each student who, in your judgment, grasps the necessary idea for accomplishing the objective but needs further practice to sharpen his or her skill. Assign extra practice to identified students.
- Pencil in a *T* for each student who has not grasped the necessary idea and therefore needs further teaching. Give extra teaching to identified students.
- Replace *T*s or *P*s with check marks when students demonstrate mastery of a skill.

ASSESSMENT OPPORTUNITIES IN THE PROGRAM

The *Math Explorations and Applications* program offers many opportunities to assess students' skills. Activities that students engage in on a daily basis, such as Mental Math exercises, games, response exercises, Thinking Story discussions, and Student Edition exercises allow you to steadily monitor individual progress.

In the Teacher's Guide

Each lesson in the Teacher's Guide provides at least two different assessment suggestions. One is Assessment Criteria, which gives you questions to ask yourself while you observe students playing a game, completing an activity, participating in a Thinking Story discussion, or working in cooperative groups. The additional suggestions include the following types of assessment:

- informal assessment (interviews, observation, and oral)
- formal assessment (tests, reviews, and checkpoints)
- self assessment
- alternative assessment (portfolio and performance)

In the Student Editions

A formal Mid-Unit Review as well as a Unit Review and a Unit Test are provided in the Student Edition in levels 1–6. The exception is Kindergarten, which has a Mid-Book Review and a Book Test. There are also self-assessments throughout the Student Editions in which students are asked to evaluate their own performance.

In the Assessment Blackline Masters

In the Assessment Blackline Master book there is a page for each Mastery Checkpoint, an additional Mid-Unit Review, and two Unit Tests, one in standardized format. Each unit also provides Performance Assessment activities and Portfolio Assessment suggestions. There is also additional information on the various alternative assessment options that are provided in this program and suggestions for grading these assessments using rubrics.

DAILY MONITORING

The following activities will help you assess your students' progress on a daily basis:

- **Cube Games and Game Mats**
  These allow you to watch students practice specific skills under conditions natural to them.
- **Mental Math Exercises**
  These exercises, which involve Number Wheels and Number Cubes, allow you to see everyone's responses, give immediate feedback, and involve the entire class.
- **Student Edition Exercises**
  These help you determine which skills your students can use on paper and which they need to practice.
- **Thinking Story Sessions**
  These help you determine whether or not your students are able to apply their knowledge of math concepts to everyday common sense problems.

LESSON 3

Student Edition pages 12–13

Numerical Sequence

LESSON PLANNER

Objectives

- ▶ to review counting, the order properties of numbers, place value, and base-10 arithmetic
- ✓ to evaluate students' ability to count and write numbers in correct sequence

Context of the Lesson This is the third of four lessons on place value and counting. This lesson contains a Mastery Checkpoint for numerical sequence. Although counting was reviewed in Lessons 1 and 2, the review in this lesson is more formal.

MANIPULATIVES

calculators* (optional)

Program Resources

Number Cubes (0–5 and 5–10)
Practice Master 3
Enrichment Master 3
Assessment Master
For extra practice:
CD-ROM* Lesson 3

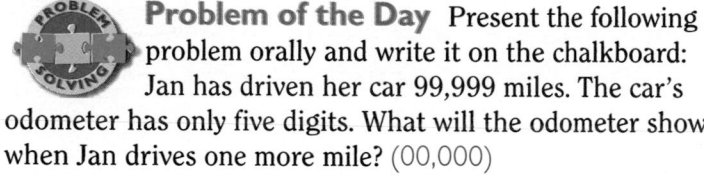

1 Warm-Up

5 MINUTES

Problem of the Day Present the following problem orally and write it on the chalkboard: Jan has driven her car 99,999 miles. The car's odometer has only five digits. What will the odometer show when Jan drives one more mile? (00,000)

Problem-Solving Strategies Ask students who have solved the Problem of the Day to share how they solved it and any strategies they used.

MENTAL MATH Review writing numbers in standard form. Present the following problems orally or write them on the chalkboard:

a. 800 + 40 + 3 = (843)
b. 801 + 40 + 3 = (844)
c. 6000 + 900 + 60 = (6960)
d. 6000 + 901 + 60 = (6961)
e. 500 + 20 + 4 = (524)
f. 502 + 20 + 4 = (526)
g. 3000 + 200 + 60 + 7 = (3267)

MIXED PRACTICE

LESSON 3

Numerical Sequence

Sometimes it's useful to count up. Sometimes it's useful to count down.

Count up. Write the missing numbers.

1. 7, 8, 9, 10, 11, ■, ■, ■, ■, ■, ■, ■, 19 **12, 13, 14, 15, 16, 17, 18**
2. 194, 195, 196, ■, ■, ■, ■, ■, ■, ■, 204 **197, 198, 199, 200, 201, 202, 203**
3. 2987, 2988, 2989, ■, ■, ■, ■, ■, ■, ■, ■, 2998 **2990, 2991, 2992, 2993, 2994, 2995, 2996, 2997**
4. 5098, 5099, ■, ■, ■, 5103 **5100, 5101, 5102**
5. 36,571; 36,572; ■; ■; ■; ■; ■; ■; ■; ■; 36,581 **36,573; 36,574; 36,575; 36,576; 36,577; 36,578; 36,579; 36,580**

Count down. Write the missing numbers.

6. 15, 14, 13, ■, ■, ■, ■, ■, ■, ■, ■, 4 **12, 11, 10, 9, 8, 7, 6, 5**
7. 64, 63, 62, ■, ■, ■, ■, ■, ■, ■, ■, 53 **61, 60, 59, 58, 57, 56, 55, 54**
8. 334, 333, 332, ■, ■, ■, ■, ■, ■, 325 **331, 330, 329, 328, 327, 326**
9. 805, 804, 803, ■, ■, ■, ■, ■, ■, 796 **802, 801, 800, 799, 798, 797**
10. 8403, 8402, 8401, ■, ■, ■, ■, ■, 8395 **8400, 8399, 8398, 8397, 8396**

Count up or down. Write the missing numbers.

11. 13,207; 13,208; 13,209; ■; ■; ■; ■; 13,214 **13,210; 13,211; 13,212; 13,213**
12. 9996; 9997; 9998; ■; ■; ■; ■; 10,003 **9999; 10,000; 10,001; 10,002**
13. 38,004; 38,003; 38,002; ■; ■; ■; 37,998 **38,001; 38,000; 37,999**
14. 146,236; 146,235; 146,234; ■; ■; ■; ■; 146,229 **146,233; 146,232; 146,231; 146,230**
15. 999,997; 999,998; ■; ■; ■; ■; 1,000,003 **999,999; 1,000,000; 1,000,001; 1,000,002**

RETEACHING

Have students use a **calculator*** to find the next or preceding number by adding or subtracting 1. Consider using a mechanical calculator or odometer from a car or bicycle to show students what the gears do when a digit in the tens or hundreds place changes.

PRACTICE p. 3

LESSON 3 PRACTICE Name__________

Count up. Write the missing numbers.

1. 3, 4, 5, 6, 7, 8, 9, 10, 11, 12, 13, 14, 15, 16, 17
2. 284, 285, 286, 287, 288, 289, 290, 291, 292, 293, 294
3. 4667, 4668, 4669, 4670, 4671, 4672, 4673, 4674, 4675
4. 7298, 7299, 7300, 7301, 7302, 7303, 7304, 7305, 7306
5. 62,452; 62,453; 62,454; 62,455; 62,456; 62,457; 62,458

Count down. Write the missing numbers.

6. 18, 17, 16, 15, 14, 13, 12, 11, 10, 9, 8, 7, 6, 5
7. 34, 33, 32, 31, 30, 29, 28, 27, 26, 25, 24, 23, 22
8. 744, 743, 742, 741, 740, 739, 738, 737, 736
9. 504, 503, 502, 501, 500, 499, 498, 497, 496
10. 6603, 6602, 6601, 6600, 6599, 6598, 6597, 6596

Count up or down. Write the missing numbers.

11. 707, 708, 709, 710, 711, 712, 713, 714, 715, 716, 717
12. 418, 417, 416, 415, 414, 413, 412, 411, 410, 409, 408
13. 1014, 1015, 1016, 1017, 1018, 1019, 1020, 1021, 1022
14. 1004, 1003, 1002, 1001, 1000, 999, 998, 997, 996, 995
15. 3097, 3098, 3099, 3100, 3101, 3102, 3103, 3104, 3105

Copyright © SRA/McGraw-Hill. Permission is granted to reproduce this page for classroom use.

Math Explorations and Applications Level 4 • 3

*available separately

COOPERATIVE LEARNING

GAME

Order Game

Players: Two
Materials: Two 0–5 cubes (red), two 5–10 cubes (blue)
Object: To be the first to fill in all the boxes
Math Focus: Place value and mathematical reasoning

RULES

1. Make a game form like the one shown.
2. Roll any three cubes. If you roll a 10, roll that cube again.
3. Combine any two numbers rolled to make a two-digit number. Write your first number in the START box on your game form.
4. On each turn, choose three cubes to roll. Make a two-digit number greater than the last number you made and write it in the next box.
5. If you cannot make a greater two-digit number, or if you choose not to, you lose your turn.
6. The first player to fill in all the boxes on his or her game form is the winner.

ANOTHER WAY TO PLAY THIS GAME

Roll four cubes and make three-digit numbers.

MATH JOURNAL

In your Math Journal explain your strategy for playing this game.

ENRICHMENT p. 3

LESSON 3 ENRICHMENT Name____________

Who was the first president of the United States from Pennsylvania?

To find out, add or subtract each problem. Then write the letter that matches each answer on the blanks. Not all of the letters will be used. The first one is done for you.

1. 9 + 8 = 17 L
2. 6 + 7 = 13 F
3. 9 − 6 = 3 E
4. 10 + 5 = 15 G
5. 7 − 7 = 0 N
6. 4 + 6 = 10 D
7. 12 − 8 = 4 H
8. 10 + 10 = 20 K
9. 13 − 7 = 6 J
10. 0 + 9 = 9 A
11. 5 + 4 + 3 = 12 M
12. 14 − 6 = 8 C
13. 7 + 7 + 7 = 21 T
14. 19 − 10 = 9 A
15. 3 + 5 + 7 = 15 G
16. 18 − 9 = 9 A
17. 7 + 3 + 8 = 18 U
18. 16 − 8 = 8 C
19. 1 + 7 + 6 = 14 S
20. 12 − 5 = 7 B

J	A	M	E	S		B	U	C	H	A	N	A	N
6	9	12	3	14		7	18	8	4	9	0	9	0

Copyright © SRA/McGraw-Hill. Permission is granted to reproduce this page for classroom use.

ASSESSMENT p. 1

UNIT 1

Mastery Checkpoint 1 Numerical sequence (Lesson 3)

Name ____________

The student demonstrates mastery by correctly answering at least 12 of the 15 problems.

Count up. Write the missing numbers.

1. 9, 10, 11, 12, 13, 14, 15, 16, 17, 18, 19, 20
2. 395, 396, 397, 398, 399, 400, 401, 402, 403, 404
3. 1003, 1004, 1005, 1006, 1007, 1008, 1009, 1010, 1011
4. 5553, 5554, 5555, 5556, 5557, 5558, 5559, 5560, 5561
5. 7996, 7997, 7998, 7999, 8000, 8001, 8002, 8003, 8004

Count down. Write the missing numbers.

6. 12, 11, 10, 9, 8, 7, 6, 5, 4, 3, 2, 1
7. 104, 103, 102, 101, 100, 99, 98, 97, 96, 95
8. 444, 443, 442, 441, 440, 439, 438, 437, 436, 435
9. 703, 702, 701, 700, 699, 698, 697, 696, 695, 694
10. 1003, 1002, 1001, 1000, 999, 998, 997, 996, 995

Count up or down. Write the missing numbers.

11. 3205, 3206, 3207, 3208, 3209, 3210, 3211, 3212
12. 8004, 8003, 8002, 8001, 8000, 7999, 7998
13. 5523, 5522, 5521, 5520, 5519, 5518, 5517, 5516
14. 9993; 9994; 9995; 9996; 9997; 9998; 9999; 10,000
15. 6095, 6096, 6097, 6098, 6099, 6100, 6101, 6102

Copyright © SRA/McGraw-Hill. Permission is granted to reproduce this page for classroom use.

❷ Teach

Using the Student Pages Before beginning page 12, demonstrate the "Order" game on page 13 for practice with place value so that students who finish early can play the game immediately.

GAME Introduce the "Order" game by having two students play it at the chalkboard several times. Students can make their own game forms, or you can make forms for them. This game provides practice in place value and probabilistic thinking.

❸ Wrap-Up

5 MINUTES

In Closing Have students explain in their own words how they determine a missing number in a numerical sequence.

ANALYZING ANSWERS Check students' skills by asking them to count up or down from various numbers. It is likely that students who make errors in this kind of exercise but who did well on the oral drills in Lessons 1 and 2 may have been misled by the format of the page.

Mastery Checkpoint 1

At about this time most students should be able to write well-formed, legible numbers from 0 through 10,000 in correct ascending or descending order, as demonstrated by errors in no more than one sequence on page 12. You may wish to record the results in the first column of the Mastery Checkpoint Chart.

Assessment Criteria

Did the student . . .

- ✓ correctly answer at least 80% of the numerical sequences?
- ✓ demonstrate understanding of number order when playing the game?

Homework Have students play the "Order" game with a family member for further practice with place value. A copy of this game can also be found on page 7 of the Home Connections Blackline Masters.

LESSON 4

Student Edition pages 14–15

Greatest and Least Numbers

LESSON PLANNER

Objective

- ▶ to provide practice with place value, numerical sequence, and basic addition facts

Context of the Lesson This is the final lesson of the series that deals with place value and counting. A review of addition facts is provided in Lesson 5.

MANIPULATIVES

none

Program Resources

Number Wheels

Number Cubes (0–5 and 5–10)

Practice Master 4

Enrichment Master 4

For extra practice:
CD-ROM* Lesson 4
Cumulative Review, page 534

1 Warm-Up

5 MINUTES

Problem of the Day Present the following problem to students and write their responses on the chalkboard: Mr. Miller lives on Main Street. He bought three brass numbers so he can display his exact address. He got a 5, a 6, and a 9. What could his address be? (659, 695, 569, 596, 956, or 965 Main Street)

Problem-Solving Strategies Ask students who have solved the Problem of the Day to share how they solved it and any strategies they used.

MENTAL MATH Provide practice with the addition facts in anticipation of the formal review that will begin in Lesson 5.

a. 3 + 3 = (6)	**b.** 3 + 4 = (7)	**c.** 5 + 5 = (10)
d. 5 + 6 = (11)	**e.** 10 + 5 = (15)	**f.** 9 + 3 = (12)
g. 6 + 9 = (15)	**h.** 8 + 5 = (13)	**i.** 7 + 5 = (12)
j. 4 + 9 = (13)	**k.** 7 + 8 = (15)	**l.** 6 + 6 = (12)

***MIXED* PRACTICE**

LESSON 4

Greatest and Least Numbers

Because of place value, the same digits can stand for different numbers. For example, a 7 and a 4 can make 74 or 47. In this lesson you'll use the same digits to make greater and lesser numbers.

You can make different numbers using the digits 5, 2, and 8.

The greatest number you can make is 852.

The least number you can make is 258.

Use a computer or other means to copy and complete the chart.

	Use These Digits	Greatest Number	Least Number
1	4, 7, 1	■ **741**	■ **147**
2	6, 5	■ **65**	■ **56**
3	3, 9	■ **93**	■ **39**
4	6, 7, 1	■ **761**	■ **167**
5	8, 3, 3	■ **833**	■ **338**
6	1, 9, 9	■ **991**	■ **199**
7	6, 9, 1, 2	■ **9621**	■ **1269**
8	7, 5, 7, 5	■ **7755**	■ **5577**
9	1, 6, 2, 2, 4	■ **64,221**	■ **12,246**
10	4, 3, 3, 6, 6	■ **66,433**	■ **33,466**

You can make six different numbers using the digits 1, 2, and 3. Here are the six numbers in order from greatest to least:

321 312 231 213 132 123

Write six different numbers in order from greatest to least.

11. Use the digits 4, 5, and 6. **654, 645, 564, 546, 465, 456**

12. Use the digits 2, 6, and 8. **862, 826, 682, 628, 286, 268**

Literature Connection Invite students to read *How to Count Sheep Without Falling Asleep* by Ralph Leighton and Carl Feyhman. This is a fictional account of how our number system developed, with an emphasis on place value.

RETEACHING

GAME Have students continue to play the "Roll a Number" game or the "Order" game, for place value practice, or have them play the "Rummage Sale" Game Mat from Level 3 for practice with regrouping in preparation for multidigit addition. You might also have students work with Number Wheels for further reinforcement of the relationship between places in the base-10 system.

*available separately

COOPERATIVE LEARNING

GAME

Roll a 15 Game

Players: Two
Materials: Two 0–5 cubes (red), two 5–10 cubes (blue)
Object: To get the sum closer to 15
Math Focus: Addition, subtraction, and mathematical reasoning

RULES

1. Roll the cubes one at a time.
2. Add the numbers as you roll. The sum of all the cubes you roll should be as close to 15 as possible.
3. You may stop after two, three, or four rolls.
4. The player with the sum closer to 15 wins the round.

If you rolled:	The sum would be:
7 and 1 and 4 and 7	19
8 and 5	13
4 and 4 and 8	16
9 and 3 and 3	15
5 and 10	15

ANOTHER WAY TO PLAY THIS GAME

Start at 20 and subtract the numbers rolled. Try to get as close to 5 as possible.

MATH JOURNAL

In your Math Journal describe your strategy for playing this game.

Use the Cumulative Review on page 534 after this lesson.

PRACTICE p. 4

LESSON 4 PRACTICE Name________________

Complete the chart. Use each digit once.

	Use These Digits	Greatest Number	Least Number
1	7, 1, 2	721	127
2	8, 7	87	78
3	4, 9	94	49
4	2, 6, 1	621	126
5	9, 2, 2	922	229
6	4, 5, 5	554	455
7	5, 1, 7, 8	8751	1578
8	8, 4, 8, 4	8844	4488
9	2, 5, 1, 1, 4	54,211	11,245
10	6, 2, 2, 7, 7	77,622	22,677

Write six different numbers in order from greatest to least.

11. Use the digits 6, 7, and 8. 876, 867, 786, 768, 687, 678
12. Use the digits 1, 5, and 7. 751, 715, 571, 517, 175, 157
13. Use the digits 2, 9, and 4. 942, 924, 492, 429, 294, 249
14. Use the digits 2, 6, and 5. 652, 625, 562, 526, 265, 256
15. Use the digits 7, 3, and 6. 763, 736, 673, 637, 376, 367

4 • *Math Explorations and Applications* Level 4

Copyright © SRA/McGraw-Hill. Permission is granted to reproduce this page for classroom use.

ENRICHMENT p. 4

LESSON 4 ENRICHMENT Name________________

Look at the tiles below. Draw the tiles so that they are arranged in a square with no tile in the middle and the total number of dots on each side of the square is 12.

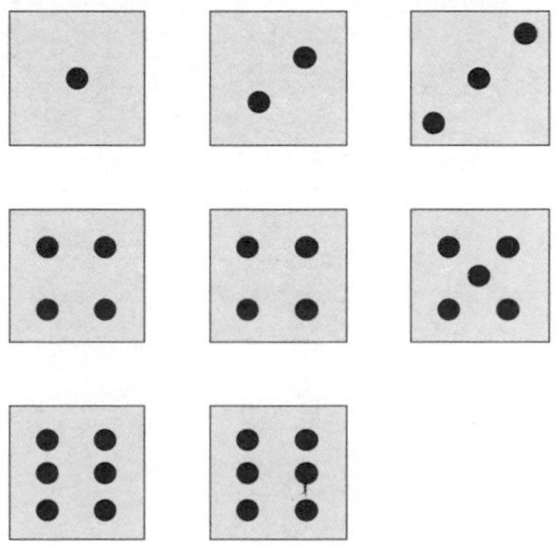

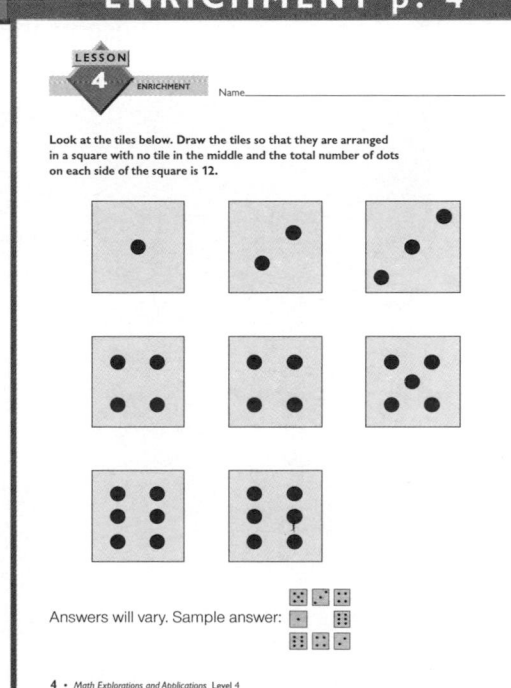

Answers will vary. Sample answer: 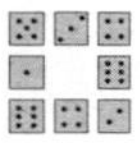

4 • *Math Explorations and Applications* Level 4

Copyright © SRA/McGraw-Hill. Permission is granted to reproduce this page for classroom use.

2 Teach

Using the Student Pages Before starting page 14, you may wish to demonstrate the "Roll a 15" game, which provides practice with addition and subtraction, so that students who finish early may play the game immediately.

With the class, review the example on page 14. Have students complete the rest on their own. Note that in problems 11 and 12 some students may write out all six numbers and then order them, while others may write and order them simultaneously.

GAME Introduce the "Roll a 15" game by playing it with a student at the chalkboard. This game uses addition, subtraction, and probability.

3 Wrap-Up

5 MINUTES

In Closing Ask students what strategy they would use to create the greatest or least possible number using any number of digits.

ALTERNATIVE ASSESSMENT

Performance Assessment Observe as students play the "Roll a Number" or "Order" games. As they play, ask them to explain how they make their strategic decisions. You can also ask students to explain how and when they can tell which player will win a given round. Evaluate students' understanding of place value and numerical sequence.

Assessment Criteria

Did the student . . .

✓ identify the greatest and least number at least 75% of the time?

✓ identify all six possible numbers that can be created from three different digits?

✓ demonstrate proficiency with addition facts while playing the games?

Homework Have students play the "Roll a 15" game (also found on page 9 of the Home Connections Blackline Masters) with a family member for practice with addition and subtraction.

THINKING STORIES

WHAT ARE THINKING STORIES?

Thinking Stories are short stories about common sense mathematical problems, many of which people face every day. Thinking Stories are designed to be read aloud to an entire class. Some Thinking Stories apply lesson concepts, and some introduce or pre-teach an upcoming lesson concept, but the majority of stories simply require students to use their mathematical knowledge and logical reasoning, because real life presents us with a variety of problems at the same time.

The same characters are used in all grade levels. The children in the stories are always the same age as the students at that grade level. Students become familiar with each character and how each one reacts to specific situations.

Tips for Using the Thinking Story Books (Levels 1–3)

- **Read the stories aloud.** Give students time to think about each question, but not so much time that they forget the point of the story.
- **Discuss the problems.** Ask your students how they arrived at their answers. Encourage debate. There are often many ways to solve a problem.
- **Encourage students to think carefully.** Speed should not be emphasized.
- **When possible, let students use Number Cubes.** This will encourage *all* students to respond.
- **Recognize sensible answers.** Even if a student gives an incorrect answer, he or she probably thought carefully about it and should be praised.
- **Encourage students to act out or use manipulatives to solve difficult problems.** This technique may help students organize their thinking.

Levels K–3

In Kindergarten, the Thinking Stories are found in the Teacher's Guide in each lesson. In levels 1–3, the Thinking Stories are presented in both the Teacher's Guide and in a separate book. Interspersed in each story are questions that will prompt your students to think ahead of the story characters. The questions might ask students to identify what is wrong with what a character has done or said, to anticipate what is going to happen as a result, or to think of other possibilities that the character hasn't considered. There are also many additional problems in the separate Thinking Story book (levels 1–3) that can be used at any time.

Levels 4–6

In levels 4–6, the Thinking Stories are presented in the Student Editions. After listening to the story as a class, students can reread the story, either by themselves or in small groups, and discuss the questions at the end.

WHAT ARE THE EXTRA STORY PROBLEMS IN LEVELS 1–3?

In the separate Thinking Story book, there are additional story problems that follow each story. They require students to use the same thinking skills that the story characters used. These problems can be used at any time.

WHAT MAKES THINKING STORIES AND STORY PROBLEMS UNIQUE?

The characters in the stories and problems have peculiarities that your students will come to know. Mr. Muddle, for example, easily forgets things. Ferdie jumps to conclusions without thinking. Mr. Breezy gives more information than is needed and, therefore, makes easy problems seem difficult. Ms. Eng, on the other hand, provides insufficient information to solve the questions and problems she poses. Your students will learn to recognize these peculiarities and avoid them in their own thinking. The stories and problems are filled with so many surprises that your students will be challenged as well as entertained.

WHEN SHOULD I USE THE STORIES AND PROBLEMS?

In Kindergarten, the problems are provided with each individual lesson in the Teacher's Guide. In levels 1–3, the Teacher's Guide will instruct you which of the 20 story selections to use and when to use them. In general, you will be directed to read one story about every five or six lessons. On days when no stories are read, the Teacher's Guide will suggest you read problems—usually three or four—to your students. If it has been a day or two since you read a particular story, you might want to read it again before presenting new story problems. Stories and problems become more difficult as the year progresses.

WHICH THINKING SKILLS ARE STRESSED IN THE STORIES AND PROBLEMS?

Math Skills

- Choosing which operation to use
- Recognizing relevant information
- Recognizing absurd or unreasonable answers
- Deciding when calculation isn't necessary
- Recognizing incorrect answers

Language Arts Skills

- Characterization
- Predicting what will happen in a story
- Making inferences
- Summarizing what has happened in a story
- Listening for details
- Drawing conclusions
- Evaluating information
- Recognizing cause-and-effect relationships
- Forming generalizations

LESSON 5

Student Edition pages 16–19

Practicing Addition

LESSON PLANNER

Objectives

- ▶ to review addition facts
- ▶ to help students develop the broad ability to use mathematical common sense

Context of the Lesson This is the first of a series of six lessons reviewing addition and subtraction facts. A review of subtraction facts begins in Lesson 6. This lesson also contains the first Thinking Story.

MANIPULATIVES

counters*

craft sticks or play coins*

Program Resources

Number Wheels

Practice Master 5

Enrichment Master 5

For career connections:
Careers and Math*

For extra practice:
CD-ROM* Lesson 5

1 Warm-Up

5 MINUTES

Problem of the Day Have groups of students act out this problem to find the solution: Four people meet for the first time. If each person shakes hands with everyone else, how many handshakes will there be? (6)

Problem-Solving Strategies Ask students who have solved the Problem of the Day to share how they solved it and any strategies they used.

MENTAL MATH Have students use their Number Wheels to give the answers to these problems, which involve related addition and subtraction facts. Emphasize speedy recall.

a. 3 + 9 = (12)	**b.** 12 – 9 = (3)
c. 10 + 1 = (11)	**d.** 11 – 1 = (10)
e. 7 + 6 = (13)	**f.** 13 – 6 = (7)
g. 9 + 3 = (12)	**h.** 12 – 3 = (9)
i. 6 + 9 = (15)	**j.** 15 – 9 = (6)
k. 8 + 5 = (13)	**l.** 13 – 5 = (8)

PRACTICE

LESSON 5

Practicing Addition

Keep in shape by practicing your number facts for addition.

SELF ASSESSMENT

Are You Shiny or Rusty?

Very shiny	46 or more right
Shiny	41–45 right
A bit rusty	36–40 right
Rusty	Fewer than 36 right

The letter *n* stands for an unknown number. To solve for *n*, figure out the number that belongs where the *n* is.

Add to solve for *n*.

1. 5 + 3 = *n* **8**	2. 9 + 9 = *n* **18**	3. 4 + 1 = *n* **5**
4. *n* = 6 + 2 **8**	5. 6 + 4 = *n* **10**	6. *n* = 6 + 6 **12**
7. 7 + 1 = *n* **8**	8. *n* = 4 + 6 **10**	9. 10 + 9 = *n* **19**
10. 1 + 7 = *n* **8**	11. 8 + 8 = *n* **16**	12. 0 + 8 = *n* **8**
13. *n* = 5 + 5 **10**	14. 1 + 9 = *n* **10**	15. *n* = 5 + 7 **12**
16. 10 + 10 = *n* **20**	17. 8 + 4 = *n* **12**	18. 4 + 7 = *n* **11**
19. 8 + 7 = *n* **15**	20. 7 + 7 = *n* **14**	21. *n* = 0 + 0 **0**
22. 6 + 5 = *n* **11**	23. 6 + 7 = *n* **13**	24. 3 + 9 = *n* **12**
25. 9 + 2 = *n* **11**	26. 9 + 5 = *n* **14**	27. 3 + 8 = *n* **11**

Why teach it this way?

"Muddle at Bat (Part 1)" is the first part of a six-part Thinking Story in Unit 1. Students may remember many of the characters from earlier grade levels. Each unit contains a four-, five-, or six-part story and story problems that encourage students to apply their mathematical common sense to real or fictitious situations. These stories are a central focus of the program.

*available separately

Add.

28	29	30	31	32	33	34
6 + 5 = **11**	7 + 9 = **16**	2 + 2 = **4**	3 + 7 = **10**	2 + 8 = **10**	1 + 9 = **10**	4 + 8 = **12**

35	36	37	38	39	40	41
3 + 5 + 2 = **10**	0 + 6 + 9 = **15**	8 + 3 + 9 = **20**	6 + 6 + 6 = **18**	7 + 8 + 3 = **18**	4 + 4 + 4 = **12**	1 + 3 + 4 = **8**

Add to solve for *n*.

42. $5 + 3 + 3 + 3 + 4 = n$ **18**
43. $7 + 1 + 3 + 4 + 3 = n$ **18**
44. $4 + 4 + 4 + 4 + 4 = n$ **20**
45. $3 + 3 + 3 + 2 + 2 = n$ **13**
46. $n = 1 + 2 + 3 + 4 + 5$ **15**
47. $n = 5 + 4 + 3 + 2 + 1$ **15**
48. $n = 3 + 3 + 3 + 3 + 3$ **15**
49. $n = 1 + 5 + 2 + 4 + 3$ **15**

Solve.

50. Connie and her brother Dan each have two cats. Their cousin Jim has three cats. How many cats do they have all together? **7**
51. Mary had nine CDs, then she received one CD for her birthday. How many CDs does Mary have now? **10**

FANTASTIC FACT

About 3000 tons of dusty material from space falls on Earth every day.

2 Teach

SELF ASSESSMENT

Using the Student Pages From their work with functions at the third-grade level, students may recall the use of *n* as an unknown. Encourage students to check that their answers make sense. Most students should be "shiny" or "very shiny." Keep track of those who need further practice and be sure they get it in games and other work. Even students with high scores may benefit from some extra practice to increase speed.

COOPERATIVE LEARNING Form cooperative groups to encourage collaborative efforts on the Thinking Story. Encourage all group members to participate in the discussion. Discuss other ways to divide the tasks, such as having one group member serve as reader, another as facilitator, another as recorder, and another as presenter.

To present answers, groups might try one of these methods: one student writes out or makes an oral presentation of the answers for the whole group; each student writes out the agreed-upon answers in his or her own words; or one student writes answers for the group, but other students may write or give oral presentations of their own answers if they disagree.

◆ LESSON 5 Practicing Addition

Teach

Using the Thinking Story "Muddle at Bat" focuses on product testing. By considering absurd methods, students learn that a good product test should provide useful data for intelligent decision making. The first five parts of the story each bring out successively finer points about testing and sampling. In Part 1, Mr. Muddle is hired to test baseball equipment to advise his team which kinds are best. One way to handle Thinking Stories is to divide the class into groups of 4 or 5, with at least one good reader in each group. Let groups read the story and work out the problems together. Alternatively, students can work individually or you can do the story and problems as a class. If students work individually or in groups, bring the whole class together to discuss the story problems.

Answers to Thinking Story Questions:

Although most students will come up with answers like the ones below, accept any reasonable responses.

1. Reasons for disagreeing with Mr. Muddle include: the test is not a good test; only 6 of the 60 doctors had opinions; the doctors chose the bats for bad reasons; doctors do not know anything about bats.
2. Possibilities include length, weight, balance, lack of cracks, strength, and hitting accuracy.
3. Mr. Muddle interviewed 60 doctors, but 54 refused to answer his question. The manager knows that 54 out of 60 is equal to 9 out of 10.

MATH JOURNAL Have students write a brief character sketch of Mr. Muddle in their Math Journals based on what they learn about him in Part 1 of "Muddle at Bat." You might have students associate Mr. Muddle with another fictional character they know from literature, television, films, or cartoons.

◆ LESSON 5 Practicing Addition

THINKING STORY

Muddle at Bat

Part 1

Mr. Muddle was looking for a job again. At last he was hired by a baseball team, the Lakeside Dips. The first day Mr. Muddle came to work wearing a catcher's mask and a fielder's glove. "I'm ready to play any position," he said.

"Position?" grumbled the manager. "We didn't hire you to play ball. We hired you to be a tester."

"What's that?"

"You will test balls, bats, gloves, and so on. We want to know which ones we should buy. For a start, test these three kinds of bats. Find out which kind is best."

Mr. Muddle had been watching TV. He had seen that when people want to find out which things are best, they often ask doctors. So Mr. Muddle took the three bats to all the doctors in town. He asked each doctor which bat he or she thought was best.

When he was finished, Mr. Muddle went back to the manager. This was his report: "Three doctors told me they

Literature Connection Read selections from *Domino Addition* by Lynette Long, which illustrates basic addition through the use of dominoes. Have students write a letter to the author suggesting other common materials she might use to illustrate addition.

RETEACHING

MANIPULATIVES Have students act out addition problems with objects such as **play coins*, craft sticks,** or **counters*.** For example, to solve $7 + 4 = n$, the student counts out seven objects and four objects, then pushes the piles together and counts to see how many objects are in the combined pile.

*available separately

thought the Slugger bat was best. One doctor said the Arrow looked best. Two said they liked the Champ. The other 54 doctors either said they didn't know anything about baseball bats or said they didn't want to be bothered."

"What does that tell you?" the manager asked.

"It tells me the Slugger bat is best, of course," Mr. Muddle said.

The manager snorted. "It tells *me* nine out of ten doctors would rather not be asked," he said.

. . . to be continued

Work in groups. Discuss your answers and how you figured them out. Then compare your answers with those of other groups. **Answers are in margin.**

1. Do you agree with Mr. Muddle that his test shows the Slugger bat is best? Why or why not?
2. What are some good qualities to test a bat for? List as many as you can think of.
3. Why do you think the manager said that nine out of ten doctors would rather not be asked about bats?

3 Wrap-Up (5 MINUTES)

In Closing Have students explain how to solve for n in the addition equation $4 + 5 = n$.

SELF ASSESSMENT Have students list three addition facts that are troublesome to them, or that they recall less quickly than others. Encourage them to think of ways to improve their memory of these facts.

Assessment Criteria

Did the student . . .

✓ explain how to solve for n?

✓ correctly answer at least 80% of the addition facts?

✓ contribute to the Thinking Story discussion?

Homework For further practice with addition facts, have students play the "Roll a 15" game on page 15. A copy of this game can also be found on page 9 in the Home Connections Blackline Masters.

ESL Meeting Individual Needs

Students with limited proficiency in English may have difficulty with the language in the Thinking Stories. You may want to read the Thinking Stories aloud, stopping as necessary to explain or act out words. Use gestures and vocal inflection to help convey the humor and confusion in each situation, or invite small groups of students to act out different sections of the story. Draw sketches or maps as needed.

PRACTICE p. 5

LESSON 5 PRACTICE Name______

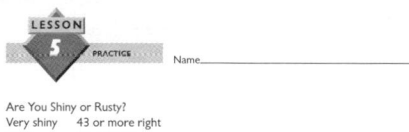

Are You Shiny or Rusty?
Very shiny 43 or more right
Shiny 38–42 right
A bit rusty 33–37 right
Rusty Fewer than 33 right

Add.

1. 7 + 2 = 9	2. 14 = 5 + 9	3. 3 = 2 + 1	4. 6 + 4 = 10
5. 6 = 4 + 2	6. 6 + 6 = 12	7. 8 + 2 = 10	8. 7 + 5 = 12
9. 6 + 4 = 10	10. 8 + 5 = 13	11. 9 = 4 + 5	12. 7 + 3 = 10
13. 6 + 5 = 11	14. 9 + 8 = 17	15. 0 + 4 = 4	16. 8 = 1 + 7
17. 9 + 1 = 10	18. 4 + 8 = 12	19. 4 + 4 = 8	20. 0 + 6 = 6
21. 10 = 7 + 3	22. 9 + 6 = 15	23. 8 + 3 = 11	24. 10 = 5 + 5
25. 2 + 7 = 9	26. 8 + 8 = 16	27. 8 = 3 + 5	28. 5 + 6 = 11
29. 3 + 9 = 12	30. 14 = 7 + 7	31. 9 = 6 + 3	32. 9 + 9 = 18

33. 8 + 4 = 12	34. 9 + 1 = 10	35. 6 + 7 = 13	36. 5 + 5 = 10	37. 2 + 4 = 6	38. 4 + 3 = 7
39. 7 + 6 + 3 = 16	40. 2 + 5 + 6 = 13	41. 4 + 0 + 5 = 9	42. 6 + 6 + 7 = 19	43. 5 + 3 + 8 = 16	44. 3 + 3 + 3 = 9

45. 7 + 2 + 2 + 2 + 3 = 16
46. 2 + 2 + 2 + 2 + 2 = 10
47. 6 + 2 + 4 + 5 + 4 = 21
48. 2 + 3 + 4 + 5 + 6 = 20

Copyright © SRA/McGraw-Hill. Permission is granted to reproduce this page for classroom use.

Math Explorations and Applications Level 4 • 5

ENRICHMENT p. 5

LESSON 5 ENRICHMENT Name______

Conduct a survey among your classmates. What are their favorite foods? Use tally marks to fill in the table.

Food	Tally	Total Number
Meats	Answers will vary.	
Vegetables		
Grains		
Drinks		

If you were planning a dinner for your class, what would you serve? Use the chart to help you plan a menu, then write the menu below.

Answers should include foods from all four groups.

Copyright © SRA/McGraw-Hill. Permission is granted to reproduce this page for classroom use.

Math Explorations and Applications Level 4 • 5

LESSON 6

Student Edition pages 20–21

Practicing Subtraction

LESSON PLANNER

Objective

▶ to review subtraction facts

Context of the Lesson This is the second of six lessons reviewing addition and subtraction facts. A checkpoint for assessing proficiency in both addition and subtraction facts is provided in Lesson 7.

MANIPULATIVES	Program Resources
calculators*	Number Cubes
counters*	Practice Master 6
number line (optional)	Enrichment Master 6
	For extra practice: CD-ROM* Lesson 6

1 Warm-Up

5 MINUTES

Problem of the Day Present this problem and allow students to use **calculators*** to solve it: Jorge wants to subtract 18 from 60 on his calculator, but the key for number 8 will not work. How can he solve this problem on his calculator? (Answers will vary. One way is to subtract 10, then 7, then 1; another is to subtract 10, then 9, and add 1.)

Problem-Solving Strategies Ask students who have solved the Problem of the Day to share how they solved it and any strategies they used.

MENTAL MATH Provide practice with subtraction facts, emphasizing speedy recall.

a. 6 – 1 = (5)	b. 8 – 4 = (4)	c. 7 – 1 = (6)
d. 3 – 3 = (0)	e. 7 – 3 = (4)	f. 10 – 6 = (4)
g. 9 – 4 = (5)	h. 5 – 2 = (3)	i. 7 – 5 = (2)
j. 6 – 4 = (2)	k. 4 – 4 = (0)	l. 8 – 2 = (6)
m. 9 – 5 = (4)	n. 10 – 4 = (6)	o. 10 – 9 = (1)
p. 6 – 2 = (4)	q. 1 – 1 = (0)	r. 9 – 6 = (3)

2 Teach

Using the Student Pages Have students play the subtraction variation of the "Roll a 15" game (page 15). Demonstrate the game before students begin this lesson so they can play it as they finish.

PRACTICE

LESSON 6

Practicing Subtraction

Keep in shape by practicing your number facts for subtraction.

SELF ASSESSMENT

Are You Shiny or Rusty?

Very shiny	64 or more right
Shiny	59–63 right
A bit rusty	54–58 right
Rusty	Fewer than 54 right

Subtract to solve for *n*.

1 $5 - 3 = n$ **2**	2 $10 - 5 = n$ **5**	3 $13 - 6 = n$ **7**
4 $8 - 3 = n$ **5**	5 $n = 9 - 7$ **2**	6 $15 - 6 = n$ **9**
7 $12 - 7 = n$ **5**	8 $16 - 8 = n$ **8**	9 $n = 17 - 8$ **9**
10 $18 - 9 = n$ **9**	11 $n = 16 - 9$ **7**	12 $13 - 9 = n$ **4**
13 $6 - 1 = n$ **5**	14 $20 - 10 = n$ **10**	15 $n = 14 - 6$ **8**
16 $n = 12 - 6$ **6**	17 $14 - 5 = n$ **9**	18 $14 - 7 = n$ **7**
19 $15 - 6 = n$ **9**	20 $6 - 5 = n$ **1**	21 $n = 12 - 9$ **3**
22 $9 - 9 = n$ **0**	23 $7 - 7 = n$ **0**	24 $13 - 7 = n$ **6**
25 $9 - 0 = n$ **9**	26 $n = 13 - 8$ **5**	27 $9 - 8 = n$ **1**
28 $14 - 2 = n$ **12**	29 $11 - 8 = n$ **3**	30 $6 - 3 = n$ **3**
31 $n = 18 - 10$ **8**	32 $n = 11 - 8$ **3**	33 $8 - 0 = n$ **8**
34 $13 - 5 = n$ **8**	35 $15 - 7 = n$ **8**	36 $4 - 3 = n$ **1**

Music Connection Have students make up a rap song or other short musical number to help them learn subtraction facts. They can compose their own melody or create lyrics to an existing song. Invite volunteers to perform their songs for the class.

Literature Connection Students may enjoy reading *Alexander, Who Used to Be Rich Last Sunday* by Judith Viorst, a funny account of how a boy spends his money.

RETEACHING

MANIPULATIVES Provide a **number line** students can use to help them visualize subtraction facts. For instance, to solve 8 – 3, a student would place a finger on 8 and then move it back three numbers to see where it lands. (5)

*available separately

Subtract.

37. 10 − 5 = **5**	38. 6 − 5 = **1**	39. 12 − 7 = **5**	40. 18 − 9 = **9**	41. 20 − 10 = **10**	42. 15 − 2 = **13**
43. 13 − 7 = **6**	44. 16 − 5 = **11**	45. 12 − 9 = **3**	46. 8 − 8 = **0**	47. 10 − 8 = **2**	48. 4 − 2 = **2**
49. 6 − 5 = **1**	50. 14 − 7 = **7**	51. 19 − 10 = **9**	52. 4 − 3 = **1**	53. 17 − 8 = **9**	54. 8 − 7 = **1**
55. 7 − 4 = **3**	56. 9 − 5 = **4**	57. 16 − 7 = **9**	58. 17 − 9 = **8**	59. 10 − 2 = **8**	60. 16 − 8 = **8**
61. 17 − 4 = **13**	62. 10 − 1 = **9**	63. 8 − 0 = **8**	64. 4 − 3 = **1**	65. 6 − 2 = **4**	66. 2 − 2 = **0**

PROBLEM SOLVING

Solve.

67. Ann had ten marbles. She gave six of them to her friend Wendy. How many marbles does Ann have left? **4**

68. Tom received eight presents for his birthday. He unwrapped three of them at his party. How many presents does Tom still have to unwrap? **5**

69. The bicycle shop had 12 new mountain bikes to sell. On Saturday eight of them were sold. How many mountain bikes are left? **4**

FANTASTIC FACT

Skin is the body's largest organ. An average adult human is covered by 14 to 18 square feet of skin, which weighs about 6 pounds.

Unit 1 Lesson 6 • 21

PRACTICE p. 6

LESSON 6 PRACTICE Name____________

Are You Shiny or Rusty?

Very shiny	47 or more right
Shiny	42–46 right
A bit rusty	37–41 right
Rusty	Fewer than 37 right

Subtract.

1. 7 − 2 = 5	2. 4 = 12 − 8	3. 2 − 1 = 1	4. 6 − 4 = 2
5. 2 = 4 − 2	6. 10 − 6 = 4	7. 11 − 4 = 7	8. 7 − 0 = 7
9. 6 − 6 = 0	10. 9 − 2 = 7	11. 3 = 5 − 2	12. 14 − 6 = 8
13. 13 − 5 = 8	14. 9 − 8 = 1	15. 10 − 8 = 2	16. 5 = 6 − 1
17. 9 − 1 = 8	18. 8 − 5 = 3	19. 4 − 4 = 0	20. 6 − 0 = 6
21. 4 = 7 − 3	22. 19 − 9 = 10	23. 8 − 3 = 5	24. 6 = 11 − 5
25. 7 − 5 = 2	26. 17 − 8 = 9	27. 8 = 15 − 7	28. 5 − 5 = 0
29. 15 − 9 = 6	30. 1 = 8 − 7	31. 8 = 16 − 8	32. 6 − 1 = 5

33. 8 − 4 = 4	34. 9 − 1 = 8	35. 10 − 7 = 3	36. 6 − 5 = 1	37. 4 − 4 = 0
38. 7 − 3 = 4	39. 12 − 6 = 6	40. 14 − 5 = 9	41. 9 − 7 = 2	42. 11 − 5 = 6
43. 4 − 3 = 1	44. 9 − 6 = 3	45. 7 − 2 = 5	46. 14 − 4 = 10	47. 8 − 0 = 8
48. 12 − 9 = 3	49. 15 − 6 = 9	50. 9 − 4 = 5	51. 13 − 4 = 9	52. 9 − 9 = 0

Copyright © SRA/McGraw-Hill. Permission is granted to reproduce this page for classroom use.

6 • *Math Explorations and Applications* Level 4

ENRICHMENT p. 6

LESSON 6 ENRICHMENT Name____________

Here is a math trick for you to practice. Try showing it to someone at home.

1. Choose four digits.
2. Arrange the digits to make the greatest and least numbers possible.
3. Subtract the lesser number from the greater number.
4. Rearrange the digits in the answer to make the greatest and least numbers possible.
5. Subtract the lesser number from the greater number.
6. Continue subtracting and rearranging until the answer is 6174.

Now choose four different digits and try the trick again.

How many times did you subtract before you reached 6174?
Answers will vary. Sample answer: for digits 0, 7, 8, 9, four times.

Copyright © SRA/McGraw-Hill. Permission is granted to reproduce this page for classroom use.

6 • *Math Explorations and Applications* Level 4

*available separately

SELF ASSESSMENT

Have students work on pages 20–21 on their own. Most students should be "shiny" or "very shiny." Keep track of those who need further practice, and be sure they receive it in games and other work. Even students with high scores may benefit from some extra practice to improve their speed.

3 Wrap-Up

5 MINUTES

In Closing Have students explain their strategies for remembering difficult subtraction facts.

ANALYZING ANSWERS · MANIPULATIVES

Some students get confused when subtracting descending numbers, as in 6 − 5, and write the next number, 4, rather than the difference between them, which is 1. Others, when subtracting 9 − 0, for example, give the answer as 0, rather than 9. Tell students to be on the lookout for these types of errors when they proofread their work. If necessary have students model the problems with manipulatives such as **counters*.**

SELF ASSESSMENT

Have students write down three subtraction facts that they consider to be difficult to recall. Ask students to think of and write down a plan for recalling these particular facts.

Assessment Criteria

Did the student . . .

- ✓ correctly answer at least 80% of the subtraction problems?
- ✓ finish the pages in a reasonable amount of time?

TECHNOLOGY CONNECTION

Homework Students who are not proficient with all the addition and subtraction facts should continue to practice with flash cards, either with someone who is proficient or using the flash card feature on the CD-ROM.

LESSON 7

Student Edition pages 22–23

Adding and Subtracting

LESSON PLANNER

Objectives

✓ to assess students' accuracy and speed with mixed addition and subtraction facts

▶ to provide practice in using addition to determine distances on a map

Context of the Lesson This is the third of six lessons reviewing addition and subtraction facts. This lesson also contains a Mastery Checkpoint for basic addition and subtraction facts. Work with applications of these facts is provided in Lessons 8–10.

MANIPULATIVES

none

Program Resources

Practice Master 7

Enrichment Master 7

Assessment Master

For extra practice:
CD-ROM* Lesson 7

1 Warm-Up

5 MINUTES

Problem of the Day Present the following problem orally or on the chalkboard and discuss the riddle after students respond: Jenny has two coins that together make 15¢. One of them is not a nickel. What are the two coins? (A dime and a nickel. One is not a nickel, but the other one is!)

Problem-Solving Strategies Ask students who have solved the Problem of the Day to share how they solved it and any strategies they used.

MENTAL MATH Present the following mixed addition and subtraction problems to students. Emphasize speedy recall.

a. 8 + 3 = (11) **b.** 10 – 3 = (7) **c.** 8 – 1 = (7)

d. 10 + 9 = (19) **e.** 13 – 8 = (5) **f.** 11 – 5 = (6)

g. 10 – 9 = (1) **h.** 10 + 4 = (14) **i.** 14 – 7 = (7)

2 Teach

SELF ASSESSMENT

Using the Student Pages Have students complete page 22 as a timed exercise.

LESSON 7

Adding and Subtracting

Try to solve addition and subtraction facts as fast as you can.

SELF ASSESSMENT

Are You Shiny or Rusty?

Very shiny	30 or more right
Shiny	25–29 right
A bit rusty	20–24 right
Rusty	Fewer than 20 right

Add or subtract to solve for *n*. Watch the signs.

1. $6 + 9 = n$ **15**
2. $0 + 0 = n$ **0**
3. $14 - 8 = n$ **6**
4. $12 - 7 = n$ **5**
5. $14 - 5 = n$ **9**
6. $n = 7 + 5$ **12**
7. $19 - 10 = n$ **9**
8. $n = 10 + 10$ **20**
9. $3 + 3 = n$ **6**
10. $6 - 6 = n$ **0**
11. $n = 14 - 9$ **5**
12. $2 + 10 = n$ **12**
13. $6 + 6 = n$ **12**
14. $n = 15 - 7$ **8**
15. $7 + 3 = n$ **10**
16. $16 - 8 = n$ **8**
17. $n = 9 + 5$ **14**
18. $n = 13 - 8$ **5**
19. $7 + 7 = n$ **14**
20. $5 + 5 = n$ **10**
21. $1 + 1 = n$ **2**
22. $n = 2 + 8$ **10**
23. $13 - 5 = n$ **8**
24. $15 - 8 = n$ **7**
25. $n = 15 - 5$ **10**
26. $17 - 10 = n$ **7**
27. $4 + 8 = n$ **12**
28. $8 + 7 = n$ **15**
29. $6 + 7 = n$ **13**
30. $16 - 9 = n$ **7**

Add or subtract.

31. 8 + 5 = **13**
32. 2 + 2 = **4**
33. 15 − 9 = **6**
34. 9 + 9 = **18**
35. 10 + 5 = **15**

RETEACHING

Students who have difficulty answering the map questions may need help with map skills. Have these students work in pairs. Let one student locate the towns in question on the map on page 23 as the other identifies the distances between them. Partners can discuss whether to add or subtract and then whether their answer makes sense.

PRACTICE p. 7

LESSON 7 PRACTICE Name________

Are You Shiny or Rusty?

Very shiny	43 or more right
Shiny	38–42 right
A bit rusty	33–37 right
Rusty	Fewer than 33 right

Add or subtract.

1. 2 + 7 = 9
2. 6 − 4 = 2
3. 7 − 5 = 2
4. 7 − 4 = 3
5. 8 + 8 = 16
6. 7 + 7 = 14
7. 9 − 8 = 1
8. 9 = 3 + 6
9. 4 = 10 − 6
10. 9 + 6 = 15
11. 2 + 0 = 2
12. 0 + 0 = 0
13. 8 = 7 + 1
14. 2 = 5 − 3
15. 1 = 10 − 9
16. 9 + 5 = 14
17. 3 + 7 = 10
18. 9 − 1 = 8
19. 6 − 5 = 1
20. 6 + 7 = 13
21. 4 − 3 = 1
22. 10 + 4 = 14
23. 19 = 10 + 9
24. 5 + 4 = 9
25. 6 + 4 = 10
26. 7 + 5 = 12
27. 3 + 3 = 6
28. 7 − 6 = 1
29. 7 − 3 = 4
30. 5 + 5 = 10
31. 9 − 6 = 3
32. 9 + 9 = 18
33. 10 + 5 = 15
34. 10 − 5 = 5
35. 9 − 7 = 2
36. 10 + 10 = 20
37. 9 + 1 = 10
38. 9 + 7 = 16
39. 8 − 7 = 1
40. 6 − 2 = 4
41. 10 − 3 = 7
42. 8 + 7 = 15
43. 4 + 4 = 8
44. 7 + 2 = 9
45. 2 + 5 = 7
46. 8 − 6 = 2
47. 4 + 7 = 11
48. 10 − 10 = 0

Copyright © SRA/McGraw-Hill. Permission is granted to reproduce this page for classroom use.

*available separately

GEOGRAPHY CONNECTION

You can use your addition and subtraction skills to figure out distances on a map.

Study the map. Then answer the questions.

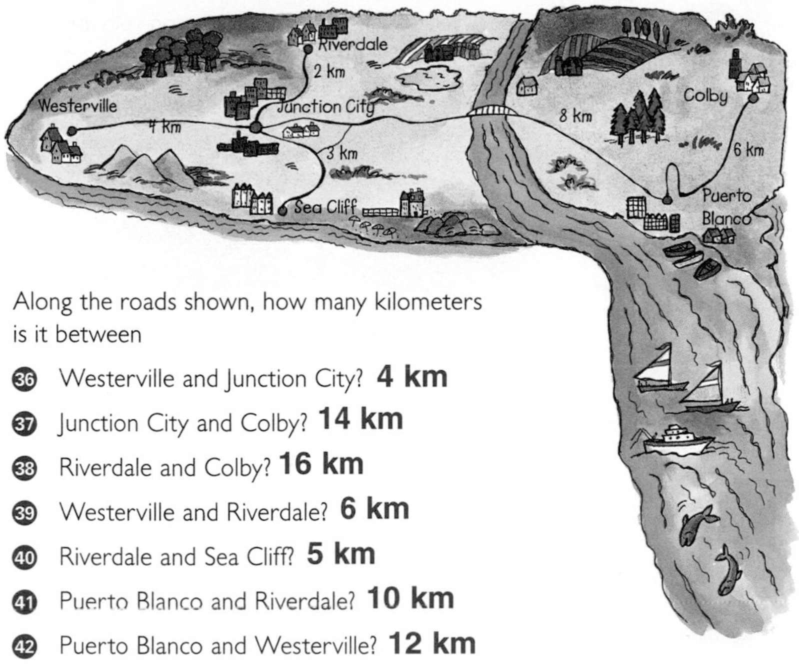

Along the roads shown, how many kilometers is it between

36. Westerville and Junction City? **4 km**
37. Junction City and Colby? **14 km**
38. Riverdale and Colby? **16 km**
39. Westerville and Riverdale? **6 km**
40. Riverdale and Sea Cliff? **5 km**
41. Puerto Blanco and Riverdale? **10 km**
42. Puerto Blanco and Westerville? **12 km**
43. Sea Cliff and Colby? **17 km**
44. Westerville and Sea Cliff? **7 km**
45. Westerville and Colby? **18 km**
46. From Westerville, is it a shorter trip to Puerto Blanco or to Sea Cliff? How much shorter? **Sea Cliff; 5 km**
47. From Colby, is it a longer trip to Sea Cliff or to Riverdale? How much longer? **Sea Cliff; 1 km longer**
48. Which is farther, Junction City to Sea Cliff or Junction City to Riverdale? How much farther? **Junction City to Sea Cliff; 1 km farther**
49. If you drove from Westerville to Sea Cliff to Riverdale, how many kilometers would you drive in all? **12**

Unit 1 Lesson 7 • 23

Before assigning page 23, briefly discuss some local distances in kilometers to be sure students have a real sense of this unit of length. Mention that it takes about 12 minutes to walk 1 kilometer.

Discuss how to decide how far it is from Sea Cliff to Puerto Blanco along the roads shown on the map. The rules require staying on the roads shown. Do one or two more problems with the whole class. Then have students solve the remaining problems on their own. Students should include units of measure in their answers to avoid ambiguity and to check if answers are reasonable.

3 Wrap-Up

5 MINUTES

In Closing Ask students to share the strategies they used to solve a certain fact problem. Also have them explain how they used the map to answer the questions about distances between towns.

Mastery Checkpoint 2

At about this time most of the students should demonstrate mastery of the basic addition and subtraction facts by correctly answering at least 80% of the problems on page 22 in about five minutes. You can also use Assessment Blackline Masters page 2. Results of this assessment can be recorded on the Mastery Checkpoint Chart.

Assessment Criteria

Did the student . . .

- ✓ correctly answer at least 80% of the addition and subtraction facts?
- ✓ demonstrate the ability to read and calculate distances from a map?
- ✓ communicate strategies used to solve the map questions?

REAL-WORLD CONNECTION

Homework Have students measure or estimate the distance in kilometers from their homes to school and to other landmarks or buildings in your community.

ENRICHMENT p. 7

LESSON 7 ENRICHMENT Name__________

COOPERATIVE LEARNING

Players: Two

Materials: Two Number Cubes labeled 0–5

Rules

One player (the game host) chooses a number between 150 and 50. The other player (the counter) rolls the Number Cubes and adds the numbers. If the number on both cubes is 0, roll again. The counter must count backward by the total of the numbers on the cubes, starting from the game host's number. When the counter gets to 0 or the nearest number to 0, that ends the play. For example, the game host chooses 60, the numbers on the cubes total 7, and the counter counts, "60, 53, 46, 39, 32, 25, 18, 11, 4."

If the count is correct, the counter gets one point. Switch roles and play another round. The first player to reach ten points wins.

The game host could check the counter's accuracy by writing down the numbers or by using a calculator to count backward. Enter the number on the calculator and be ready to go as soon as the cubes are rolled.

Here is how to use a calculator to count backward.

1. Enter the starting number.
2. Press the minus key.
3. Enter the counting number.
4. Press the = key.
5. The display shows the correct number.

Now every time you press the = key, the calculator counts backward by the second number you entered.

Copyright © SRA/McGraw-Hill. Permission is granted to reproduce this page for classroom use.

Math Explorations and Applications Level 4 • 7

ASSESSMENT p. 2

UNIT 1

Mastery Checkpoint 2 Basic facts 1 (addition and subtraction facts) (Lesson 7)

Name __________

The student demonstrates mastery by correctly answering at least 40 of the 50 problems.

Add or subtract.

1. 8 = 11 − 3	2. 11 − 5 = 6	3. 15 + 0 = 15	4. 14 − 6 = 8
5. 3 = 12 − 9	6. 6 + 9 = 15	7. 9 = 17 − 8	8. 12 + 8 = 20
9. 7 + 7 = 14	10. 12 = 9 + 3	11. 8 + 8 = 16	12. 9 = 15 − 6
13. 9 + 2 = 11	14. 9 + 5 = 14	15. 16 − 6 = 10	16. 9 − 9 = 0
17. 16 = 7 + 9	18. 5 = 13 − 8	19. 8 = 15 − 7	20. 12 − 6 = 6
21. 9 = 19 − 10	22. 11 + 8 = 19	23. 10 + 10 = 20	24. 6 + 4 = 10
25. 18 − 9 = 9	26. 7 + 6 = 13	27. 11 = 17 − 6	28. 18 = 7 + 11
29. 8 + 4 = 12	30. 13 − 5 = 8	31. 6 + 8 = 14	32. 7 − 4 = 3

Add or subtract.

33. 13 − 6 = 7	34. 3 + 3 = 6	35. 15 − 6 = 9	36. 8 + 8 = 16	37. 10 + 8 = 18	38. 14 − 7 = 7
39. 8 + 9 = 17	40. 14 − 8 = 6	41. 13 − 7 = 6	42. 3 + 7 = 10	43. 7 + 5 = 12	44. 16 − 2 = 14
45. 12 − 4 = 8	46. 9 + 9 = 18	47. 14 − 7 = 7	48. 12 − 3 = 9	49. 5 + 4 = 9	50. 12 + 4 = 16

Copyright © SRA/McGraw-Hill. Permission is granted to reproduce this page for classroom use.

2 • *Math Explorations and Applications* Level 4

LESSON 8

Student Edition pages 24–27

Practicing Addition and Subtraction

LESSON PLANNER

Objectives

- to review the concept of a function
- to provide further practice in addition and subtraction
- to provide practice in solving simple word problems that involve addition and subtraction

Context of the Lesson This is the fourth of six lessons reviewing addition and subtraction facts. Intuitive work with functions has been introduced in previous grades and will be studied in more depth in Unit 3. More word problems involving addition and subtraction facts are included in the next two lessons.

MANIPULATIVES

boxes (optional)

paper, colored (optional)

posterboard (optional)

Program Resources

Reteaching Master

Practice Master 8

Enrichment Master 8

For extra practice:
CD-ROM* Lesson 8

1 Warm-Up 5 MINUTES

Problem of the Day Pose the following problem orally, then have students explain their reasoning: Eleni had some money to go shopping. She spent \$5. On the way home, she found a five-dollar bill. How much money does she have now? (She has the amount she began with. Spending \$5 is like subtracting 5; finding \$5 is like adding 5; so there is no change in the original amount with which she started.)

Problem-Solving Strategies Ask students who have solved the Problem of the Day to share how they solved it and any strategies they used.

MENTAL MATH Present the following mixed addition and subtraction fact problems to students. Emphasize speedy recall.

a. 7 + 7 = (14) **b.** 8 − 7 = (1) **c.** 11 − 9 = (2)

d. 9 + 2 = (11) **e.** 11 − 7 = (4) **f.** 11 − 6 = (5)

g. 9 − 8 = (1) **h.** 6 + 3 = (9) **i.** 3 + 8 = (11)

j. 15 − 5 = (10) **k.** 10 + 6 = (16) **l.** 4 + 8 = (12)

***

LESSON 8

Practicing Addition and Subtraction

ALGEBRA READINESS

Suppose you put a number into this function machine. The machine will add 5 to it. We say that the function rule for this machine is +5.

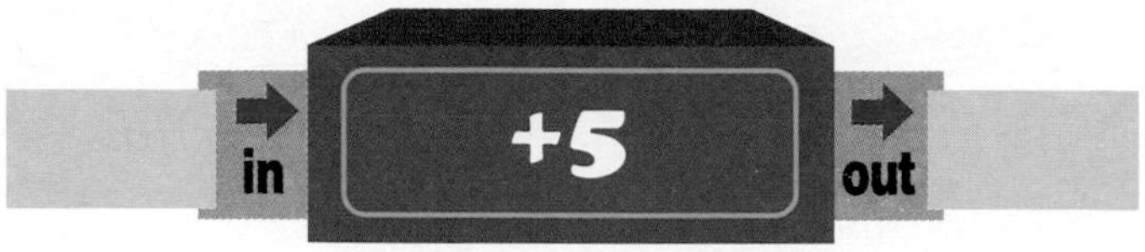

If you put 3 into the machine, 8 will come out.

If you put 5 into the machine, 10 will come out.

Use a computer or other means to draw and complete this chart for a +5 function machine.

+5

In	Out	
3	8	
5	10	
7	■	**12**
9	■	**14**
11	■	**16**
13	■	**18**

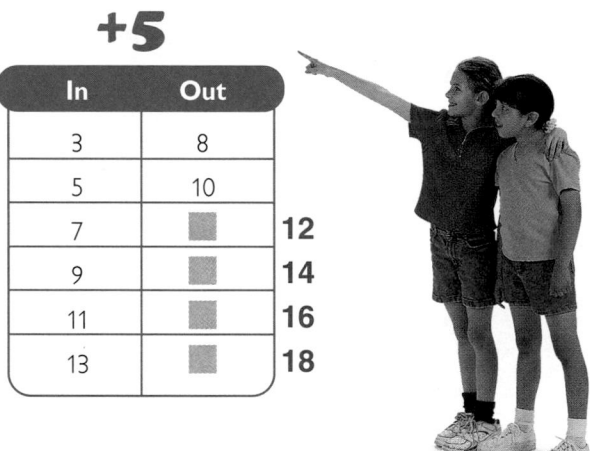

***

Art Connection Invite students to create their own three-dimensional function machines out of old **boxes** or other materials. They can also use **colored paper** or **posterboard** to create eye-catching and original function charts that they can display in the classroom.

Literature Connection For a humorous account of the expenses and profits of a series of class fundraisers, invite students to read *How the Second Grade Got \$8205.50 to Visit the Statue of Liberty* by Nathan Zimelman.

*available separately

ALGEBRA READINESS

Use a computer or other means to draw and complete each chart. Watch the function rule.

❶ **−5**

In	Out
10	5
12	7
14	9
16	**11**
18	**13**
20	**15**

❷ **+2**

In	Out
0	2
1	**3**
2	**4**
3	**5**
4	**6**
5	**7**

❸ **−3**

In	Out
4	**1**
7	**4**
10	**7**
13	**10**
16	**13**
19	**16**

❹ **+10**

In	Out
40	**50**
50	**60**
60	**70**
70	**80**
80	**90**
90	**100**

❺ **+9**

In	Out
1	**10**
2	**11**
3	**12**
4	**13**
5	**14**
6	**15**

❻ **−4**

In	Out
14	**10**
12	**8**
10	**6**
8	**4**
6	**2**
4	**0**

❼ **−10**

In	Out
60	**50**
50	**40**
40	**30**
30	**20**
20	**10**
10	**0**

❽ **+7**

In	Out
2	**9**
3	**10**
5	**12**
6	**13**
8	**15**
9	**16**

❾ **−6**

In	Out
19	**13**
17	**11**
15	**9**
13	**7**
11	**5**
9	**3**

❷ Teach

Using the Student Pages Tell students that the machine illustrated on page 24 always adds 5 to whatever number is inserted. Ask what number the machine would produce if they put in the number 3. (8) What would it produce if the number 5 were put in? (10) Write the numbers in a chart as on page 24. Then have students copy and complete the function charts on page 25. Be sure they understand that the number at the top represents the rule the machine will apply to all numbers in that chart.

Students who are new to *Math Explorations and Applications* may not be familiar with function machines. You may wish to spend some time discussing them before students work on page 25. Note that functions are formally taught in Unit 3.

Technology Connection Invite students to check out the software *Math Arcade Games* from Orange Cherry (Mac, for grades 2–8) for further practice with addition and subtraction.

◆ LESSON 8 Practicing Addition and Subtraction

Teach

COOPERATIVE LEARNING **Using the Student Pages** Do one or two problems on these pages with the class to be sure students know how to solve them. Encourage students to draw pictures or to act out the situations to help them understand the problems. Have students solve the remaining problems on their own or in small groups.

ESL **Meeting Individual Needs**

Some of your students may not read or understand English well enough to solve the word problems on pages 26–27 on their own. You might pair these students with native English speakers who can try to explain or pantomime the situations to them. The goal is to help students experience the mathematics without being held back by language barriers.

◆ LESSON 8 Practicing Addition and Subtraction

In solving problems like these, you may find it helpful to draw pictures or act out the stories. All prices include sales tax.

Lydia has $18. Josh has $13.

10. Does Lydia have enough money to buy a checkers set, a calculator, and a bicycle horn? **no**

11. Suppose Josh buys a checkers set and pays for it with a $10 bill. How much change should he get? **$4**

12. Lydia has already spent $5 today. If she buys a bicycle horn, how much will she have spent today? **$12**

13. Suppose Lydia buys a checkers set and a calculator. How much money will she have left? **$4**

14. Suppose Josh owes his mother $5 and wants to give it to her today. Would he be able to give it to her if he buys
    - **a.** only the bicycle horn? **yes**
    - **b.** only the checkers set? **yes**
    - **c.** only two checkers sets? **no**

26 • Addition and Subtraction

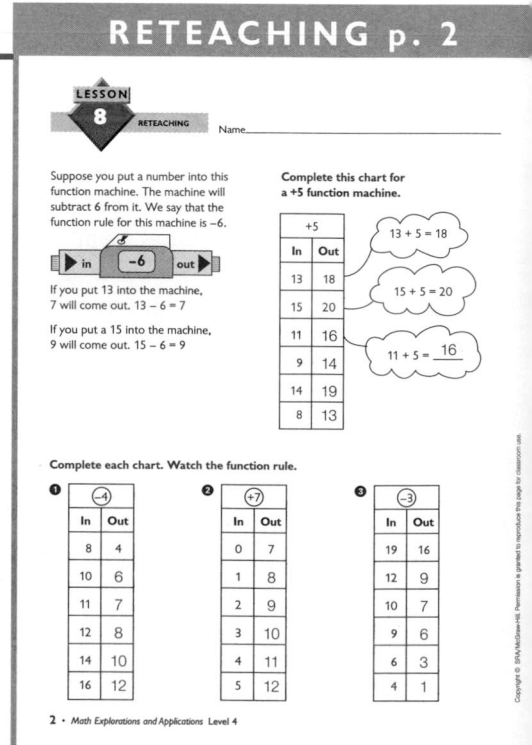

RETEACHING p. 2

LESSON 8 RETEACHING Name__________

Suppose you put a number into this function machine. The machine will subtract 6 from it. We say that the function rule for this machine is −6.

If you put 13 into the machine, 7 will come out. 13 − 6 = 7

If you put a 15 into the machine, 9 will come out. 15 − 6 = 9

Complete this chart for a +5 function machine.

+5	
In	Out
13	18
15	20
11	16
9	14
14	19
8	13

13 + 5 = 18

15 + 5 = 20

11 + 5 = 16

Complete each chart. Watch the function rule.

1.

−4	
In	Out
8	4
10	6
11	7
12	8
14	10
16	12

2.

+7	
In	Out
0	7
1	8
2	9
3	10
4	11
5	12

3.

−3	
In	Out
19	16
12	9
10	7
9	6
6	3
4	1

2 • *Math Explorations and Applications* Level 4

Copyright © SRA/McGraw-Hill. Permission is granted to reproduce this page for classroom use.

Use the information on page 26 to help you answer these questions.

15 Suppose Lydia decides to buy a calculator.

a. How much money will she have left? **$10**

b. If she then wants to buy a basketball, will she have enough money? **no**

16 Suppose the store owner puts the basketballs on sale for $9. How much has the price been lowered? **$4**

17 Suppose Josh buys a calculator and a softball. Will he be on time for the 3:00 softball game? **can't tell**

18 Suppose Lydia buys a basketball and Josh buys a checkers set and a can of tennis balls.

a. Who spent more money? **Lydia**

b. How much more? **$4**

c. Can Josh now buy a bicycle horn? **no**

d. Can Lydia now buy a softball and a can of tennis balls? **no**

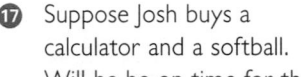

FANTASTIC FACT **To figure the temperature (in degrees Fahrenheit), count the number of times a cricket chirps in 15 seconds and add 37.**

PRACTICE p. 8

LESSON 8 PRACTICE Name__________

ALGEBRA READINESS **Complete each chart. Watch the function rule.**

1 (−3)

In	Out
18	15
15	12
12	9
9	6
6	3
3	0

2 (+4)

In	Out
0	4
1	5
2	6
3	7
4	8
5	9

3 (−8)

In	Out
18	10
16	8
14	6
12	4
10	2
8	0

4 (+6)

In	Out
3	9
5	11
7	13
9	15
11	17
13	19

5 (−10)

In	Out
90	80
80	70
70	60
60	50
50	40
40	30

6 (−2)

In	Out
19	17
16	14
13	11
10	8
7	5
4	2

Copyright © SRA/McGraw-Hill. Permission is granted to reproduce this page for classroom use.

ENRICHMENT p. 8

LESSON 8 ENRICHMENT Name__________

When you get into a cab, the driver has the rates posted next to the fare box: $3.00 base fare; $2.00 per mile; $0.50 for each extra person.

1 Complete the chart for the cost of a cab ride for one person.

Miles	Fare (dollars)
1	5
2	7
3	9
4	11
5	13
10	23
11	25
12	27

2 The trip from the airport to your hotel is 12 miles. How much does the fare box read at the end of the trip? $27

3 The fare from the hotel to the office is $7.00. How far was the trip? 2 miles

4 You take a friend to a restaurant. How much will a cab cost round-trip if the restaurant is 4 miles away? $11.50

5 In the morning you have breakfast at a diner, then call for a cab to the airport. The ride costs $23. How far is it from the diner to the airport? 10 miles

Copyright © SRA/McGraw-Hill. Permission is granted to reproduce this page for classroom use.

3 Wrap-Up 5 MINUTES

In Closing Have students use their own words to describe what a function machine does.

ANALYZING ANSWERS Sometimes students see things in word problems that are not intended, and thus arrive at unexpected yet reasonable and defensible answers. This is natural because word problems, due to the limited information provided, can be ambiguous. Seeing more than is intended in word problems should be encouraged because it fosters critical thinking. Therefore, it is important to support students who think through problems even if they do not arrive at the expected answer.

ALTERNATIVE ASSESSMENT **Portfolio Assessment** Ask students to write a paragraph or two for their Math Portfolios explaining how they go about solving word problems. Encourage them to tell how they know whether to add or subtract and how they verify that their answers fit the information given.

Assessment Criteria

Did the student . . .

✓ explain how a function machine works and apply this understanding to the problems?

✓ correctly answer at least 75% of the function machine problems?

✓ communicate strategies used to solve the word problems?

Homework Have each student construct a function chart and give it to another student to try to complete.

LOOKING AHEAD The next lesson includes the "Numbers on the Back" activity, which is illustrated on page 28. You will need 32 sheets of $8\frac{1}{2} \times 11$-inch paper—two of each labeled with numbers from 0 to 10 and one of each labeled with numbers from 11 to 20. You will also need pins or tape to fasten the sheets onto students' backs.

LESSON 9

Student Edition pages 28–31

Missing Addends

LESSON PLANNER

Objectives

- to provide practice finding missing addends
- to review writing and solving simple equations related to word problems

Context of the Lesson This is the fifth of six lessons reviewing addition and subtraction facts.

MANIPULATIVES

balance* and weights (optional)

index cards (optional)

pins, paper clips, or tape

32 paper "signs" (two for each number 0–10; one for each number 11–20)

Program Resources

Number Wheels

Reteaching Master

Practice Master 9

Enrichment Master 9

For extra practice:

CD-ROM* Lesson 9

Cumulative Review, page 535

1 Warm-Up

5 MINUTES

Problem of the Day Present this problem to the class: Alex, Brett, and Chen have a total of $18. Together, Chen and Alex have as much money as Brett has by herself. Together, Brett and Alex have $6 more than Chen has. How much money does each person have? (Alex has $3, Brett has $9, Chen has $6.)

Problem-Solving Strategies Ask students who have solved the Problem of the Day to share how they solved it and any strategies they used.

MENTAL MATH Provide practice with mixed addition and subtraction facts. Have students use their Number Wheels to show answers quickly.

a. 3 + 1 = (4)	b. 11 – 3 = (8)	c. 14 – 8 = (6)
d. 12 – 8 = (4)	e. 3 + 6 = (9)	f. 4 + 7 = (11)
g. 1 + 6 = (7)	h. 11 – 9 = (2)	i. 11 – 6 = (5)
j. 3 + 8 = (11)	k. 15 – 8 = (7)	l. 13 – 4 = (9)
m. 5 + 8 = (13)	n. 9 + 6 = (15)	o. 13 – 9 = (4)

PRACTICE

LESSON 9

Missing Addends

Jeremy's class is doing the "Numbers on the Back" activity.

What number does Jeremy have on his back?

ALGEBRA READINESS

In each case, write the number that Jeremy has on his back. The first one has been done for you.

	Brittany has:	The sum is:	Jeremy has:
1	9	14	5
2	6	16	■ 10
3	2	8	■ 6
4	7	14	■ 7
5	7	16	■ 9
6	10	11	■ 1
7	3	9	■ 6
8	0	6	■ 6
9	7	15	■ 8
10	8	8	■ 0

Language Arts Connection Have students create their own word problems that involve missing terms. They can write each problem on an **index card** and put the solution on the back. Collect the cards in a class file of word problems. Students can add problems to the file throughout the year. You can use the problem file as a source for homework, classwork, or extra credit work. Alternatively, you can word-process the problems and create a class book.

*available separately

ALGEBRA READINESS

In each problem below, think of the n as a number on your back that you can't see. You can see the other number on a partner's back and the class has told you the sum or difference. If they told you the difference, they also told you whose number was greater.

Solve for *n*.

11 $n + 5 = 7$ **2**	12 $15 - n = 10$ **5**	13 $2 + n = 10$ **8**
14 $2 + n = 7$ **5**	15 $15 - n = 9$ **6**	16 $n + 6 = 15$ **9**
17 $10 - n = 6$ **4**	18 $15 - n = 8$ **7**	19 $10 + n = 20$ **10**
20 $10 - n = 4$ **6**	21 $0 + n = 9$ **9**	22 $n + 6 = 14$ **8**
23 $n - 10 = 6$ **16**	24 $3 + n = 13$ **10**	25 $2 + n = 12$ **10**
26 $7 + n = 10$ **3**	27 $3 + n = 12$ **9**	28 $6 + n = 18$ **12**
29 $8 + n = 10$ **2**	30 $n + 4 = 13$ **9**	31 $0 + n = 8$ **8**
32 $9 + n = 10$ **1**	33 $n + 5 = 13$ **8**	34 $9 + n = 12$ **3**
35 $10 + n = 10$ **0**	36 $n + 6 = 13$ **7**	37 $2 + n = 12$ **10**
38 $8 + n = 17$ **9**	39 $9 + n = 18$ **9**	40 $4 + n = 15$ **11**

Does the missing-term sentence help you solve the problem? Solve for *n*.

41 Abigail has seven horse figures. She would like to have ten horse figures. How many more horse figures does she need?
$7 + n = 10$ **3**

42 Sam plans to take a 10-mile bicycle trip. He has already ridden 4 miles. How far does he still have to go?
$4 + n = 10$ **6 miles**

43 Kumar had 12 crayons. He lost some. He still has eight crayons. How many did he lose?
$12 - n = 8$ **4**

44 Wendy is reading a story that starts on page 1 and ends on page 12. She just finished reading page 8. How many more pages does she have to read?
$8 + n = 12$ **4**

2 Teach

Introducing the "Numbers on the Back" Activity Prepare **number signs** and demonstrate the "Numbers on the Back" activity. Students may remember a similar activity, the "Missing Factor" game, from Level 3. Ask two volunteers to come to the front of the room. Attach a number to each student's back (for example, a 7 to one and a 5 to the other) without letting them see the numbers. Let the two students look at each other's number, but not at their own. Ask the class, "What is the sum of the two numbers?" They answer, "12." Now each player must decide what number is on his or her back. Repeat with two other volunteers. After about five rounds, change the game to subtraction, as follows: Suppose John has the number 9 on his back, and Mary has the number 4 on hers. Ask the class whether John's number can be subtracted from Mary's number. (No, because John's number is greater.) Ask whether Mary's number can be subtracted from John's number. (Yes) Ask for the answer. (5) Now each player must guess his or her own number. Always start a round in the subtraction game by asking all three questions, even when the answer to the first question is yes.

Using the Student Pages After you demonstrate the "Numbers on the Back" activity, have students solve the problems on page 28. These problems imitate the activity. Students should answer "5" for the question on page 28. Then have students complete page 29 on their own.

Literature Connection You may wish to have students read "Three Mathcateers to the Rescue" from *How Do Octopi Eat Pizza Pie? Pizza Math* by Time-Life, Inc. Students can enjoy an adventure while solving riddles.

◆ LESSON 9 Missing Addends

Teach

ALGEBRA READINESS

Using the Student Pages Consider doing all or part of page 30 with the class. Note that the answer to problem 45 assumes that Barbara's family travels from home directly to the beach. The answer to problem 48 assumes that Isaac had no money before earning the $7. Students should go on to page 31 when they finish. Tell students who have difficulty with page 31 to read each problem carefully, or read the problems to them.

LEARNING STYLES

MANIPULATIVES

Meeting Individual Needs

Students who are kinesthetic or visual learners may benefit from using a **double-pan balance*** to reinforce the concept of finding missing terms. Have a student place a different amount of numbered weights on each side of the balance. Then ask another student to decide how many additional numbered weights must be placed for balance and where they belong.

◆ LESSON 9 Missing Addends

ALGEBRA READINESS

Solve.

45 Barbara's family lives 15 kilometers from Sandy Hook Beach. They left home to drive to Sandy Hook Beach. They have already driven 8 kilometers. How much farther is it to the beach? **7 km**

46 Brenda sells hot dogs at the game. She began with $8 in her pocket. Now she has $17. How much money has she taken in so far? **$9**

47 Ricardo's cat had a litter of kittens. He has found homes for two of them. He needs to find homes for the other four. How many kittens were in the litter? **6**

48 Isaac wants to buy a video that costs $16. He has earned $7. How much more money does he need? **$9**

49 Yesterday Mina bought a bag of marbles. She lost nine playing with Tran. Now she has only nine marbles. How many were in the bag? **18**

FANTASTIC FACT

The squid has the largest eyes of any animal yet discovered. Its eyes are the size of dinner plates.

30 • Addition and Subtraction

TECHNOLOGY CONNECTION

Technology Connection

Refer students to the software *Addition and Subtraction Defenders* from Gamco (Mac, grades K–6) for further practice with addition and subtraction facts on 18 skill levels.

RETEACHING p. 3

LESSON 9 RETEACHING Name__________

Subtraction is the opposite of addition. Look at the number sentences.

$5 + 6 = 11$ $7 + 6 = 13$
$11 - 5 = 6$ $13 - 7 = 6$

We can use these facts to help solve number sentences that have one of the numbers missing.

Example 1:

Solve for n. $5 + n = 11$

Solve for n by using subtraction.
$5 + n = 11$
$11 - 5 = n$
$11 - 5 = 6$
So, $n = 6$.

Example 2:

Solve for n. $n - 7 = 8$

Solve for n by using addition.
$n - 7 = 8$
$8 + 7 = n$
$8 + 7 = 15$
So, $n = 15$.

Always check to be sure your answer makes sense.

Solve for n.

1 $4 + n = 10$ $n =$ 6
2 $n - 4 = 7$ $n =$ 11
3 $13 - n = 5$ $n =$ 8
4 $n + 9 = 17$ $n =$ 8
5 $n - 6 = 9$ $n =$ 15
6 $9 + n = 16$ $n =$ 7
7 $n + 5 = 7$ $n =$ 2
8 $15 - n = 8$ $n =$ 7

Use a number sentence to solve each problem.

9 Rick had $18 when he left for the store. He came home with $7. How much did he spend? $11

10 Kylie spent 16 hours in ballet and tap classes. She spent nine hours in ballet classes. How many hours did she spend in tap classes? 7

Copyright © SRA/McGraw-Hill. Permission is granted to reproduce this page for classroom use.

Math Explorations and Applications Level 4 • 3

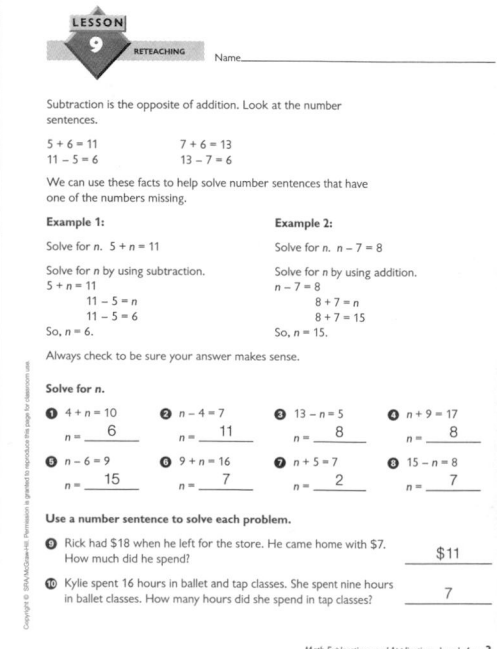

*available separately

Solve these problems.

50. Andy has four cents. He wants nine cents for milk money. How much more money does he need? **5 cents**
51. Jiro gave away two bananas. He has six left. How many bananas did he start with? **8**
52. Last night Trina had five apples, but she ate some. How many does she have now? **can't tell**
53. After his birthday, Karim had 12 model rockets. He broke some and now has nine rockets left. How many rockets did he break? **3**
54. During band Quentin broke three clarinet reeds. Now he has four reeds. How many reeds did he have at the beginning of band? **7**
55. After school Paco ate three cookies from the plate. Now there are five left. How many cookies were on the plate when Paco came home from school? **8**
56. Olga has to do ten math problems. She has done six problems. How many problems are left to do? **4**
57. Every week Ines runs 14 kilometers. She has run 10 kilometers so far this week. How many more kilometers does she need to run this week? **4**
58. Yesterday Vera had five baseball cards, then she won some more. How many does she have now? **can't tell**
59. Chloe picked nine baskets of strawberries. She needs 20 baskets to make some jam. How many more baskets must she pick? **11**

Use the Cumulative Review on page 535 after this lesson.

PRACTICE p. 9

LESSON 9 PRACTICE Name______________

Solve these problems.

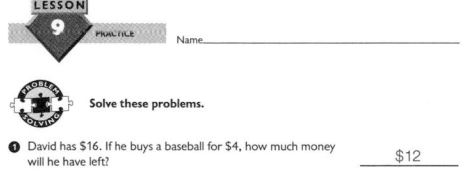

1. David has $16. If he buys a baseball for $4, how much money will he have left? $12
2. Jan bought 12 cookies. She ate some and now has seven cookies left. How many cookies did she eat? 5
3. Alan runs 20 kilometers every week. So far this week he has run 12 kilometers. How many more kilometers does he need to run this week? 8
4. There were nine posters on Emiko's wall, but some fell off. There are seven posters left on the wall. How many fell off? 2
5. Chris gave away five baseball cards. She has seven left. How many cards did she start with? 12
6. Bill had six crayons. He found some more. How many does he have now? can't tell
7. Carlos needs to collect 16 tree leaves for a display. So far he has collected six leaves. How many more leaves does he need? 10
8. Nancy has 10¢. She wants to buy a pencil that costs 15¢. How much more money does she need? 5¢
9. If Luisa had ten peaches and ate three, how many would she have left? 7
10. There were 15 problems on a math quiz. Keith missed two. How many problems did he get right? 13

Copyright © SRA/McGraw-Hill. Permission is granted to reproduce this page for classroom use.

Math Explorations and Applications Level 4 • 9

ENRICHMENT p. 9

LESSON 9 ENRICHMENT Name______________

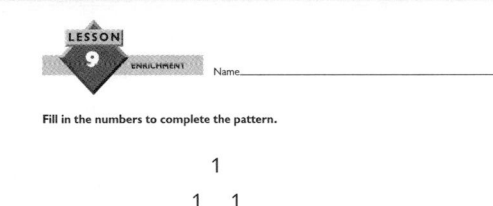

Fill in the numbers to complete the pattern.

1
1 1
1 2 1
1 3 3 1
1 4 6 4 1
1 5 10 10 5 1
1 6 15 20 15 6 1
1 7 21 35 35 21 7 1
1 8 28 56 70 56 28 8 1

Write a sentence that describes the pattern.
Answers will vary. Sample answer: Each number is the sum of the two numbers above: 0 + 1 = 1, 1 + 4 = 5, and so on.

Copyright © SRA/McGraw-Hill. Permission is granted to reproduce this page for classroom use.

Math Explorations and Applications Level 4 • 9

3 Wrap-Up 5 MINUTES

In Closing Have students explain how the "Numbers on the Back" activity relates to the story problems. Ask them how an equation (number sentence) reflects the situation in a story problem.

ANALYZING ANSWERS

Evaluate students who are having difficulty solving simple word problems. If the difficulty is in relating a number sentence to the problem, students may benefit from drawing or acting out the situation. Make sure they check to see if their answers make sense in the context of the problem. If the difficulty is with basic addition and subtraction facts, provide opportunities for further practice.

ALTERNATIVE ASSESSMENT

Informal Assessment Observe students as they do the "Numbers on the Back" activity to see that they grasp the concept of missing terms in addition and subtraction. You might have small groups play the game to provide further practice and create other opportunities for informal assessment.

Evaluate students' abilities to solve word problems by asking them how they knew which operation to use, how they determined the answer, and how they decided whether the answer made sense.

Assessment Criteria

Did the student . . .

- ✓ correctly answer at least 75% of the computation problems?
- ✓ correctly solve at least 75% of the word problems?
- ✓ communicate strategies used to find missing terms?

Homework Assign Practice Master 9 for further practice with finding missing addends.

LOOKING AHEAD Save the materials you used in the "Numbers on the Back" activity. You will need them in Lesson 41 for another activity.

LESSON 10

Student Edition pages 32–35

Perimeter

LESSON PLANNER

Objectives

- ▶ to provide practice using more than two addends by calculating perimeters of various polygons
- ▶ to provide practice solving problems about perimeter that involve missing dimensions
- ▶ to help students develop the broad ability to use mathematical common sense

Context of the Lesson This is the sixth of six lessons reviewing addition and subtraction facts. Work with perimeters will appear throughout Level 4. This lesson also presents Part 2 of "Muddle at Bat," a six-part Thinking Story.

MANIPULATIVES

baseball equipment (optional)

yarn or string (optional)

Program Resources

Number Wheels

Practice Master 10

Enrichment Master 10

For career connections: Careers and Math*

For extra practice: CD-ROM* Lesson 10

1 Warm-Up

5 MINUTES

Problem of the Day Present the following problem: Two numbers have a sum of 13 and a difference of 3. What are the numbers? (8 and 5)

Problem-Solving Strategies Ask students who have solved the Problem of the Day to share how they solved it and any strategies they used.

MENTAL MATH Ask students to solve the following multidigit addition and subtraction problems and use their Number Wheels to show the answer. Within each set of problems, gradually increase the complexity to help students see the relationship between the easier problems and the more difficult ones.

a. 4 + 2 = (6)	**b.** 8 + 1 = (9)
40 + 20 = (60)	80 + 10 = (90)
41 + 20 = (61)	800 + 100 = (900)
41 + 10 = (51)	801 + 100 = (901)

(continued on page 33)

PRACTICE

LESSON 10

Perimeter

The **perimeter** of a figure is the distance around it. To find the perimeter of this square, add 3 + 3 + 3 + 3.

The perimeter is 12 centimeters.

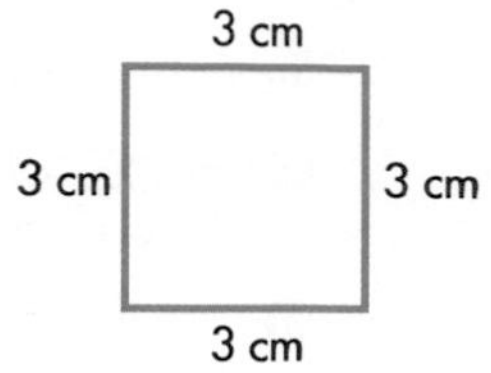

Find the perimeter.

❶

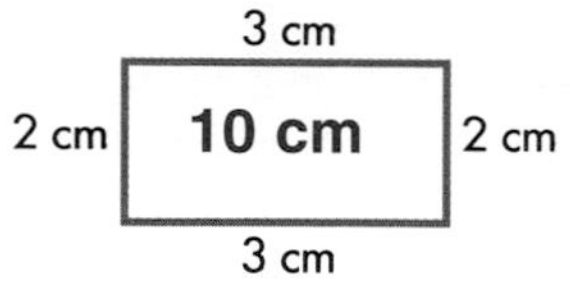

❷

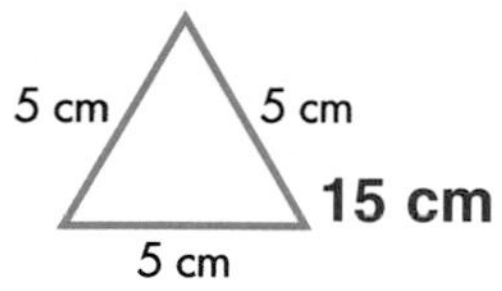

❸

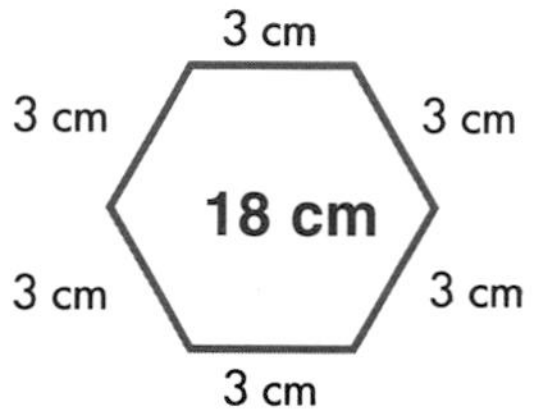

❹

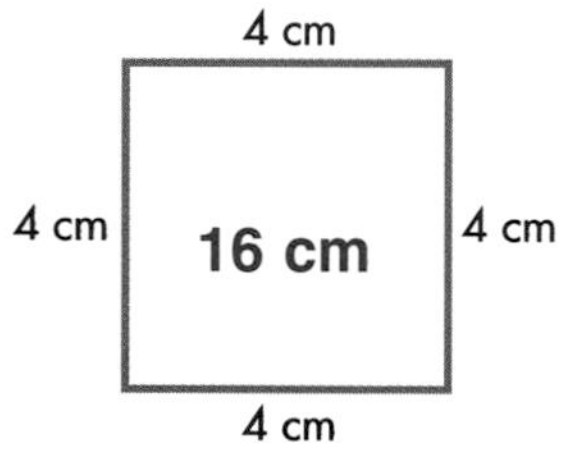

❺

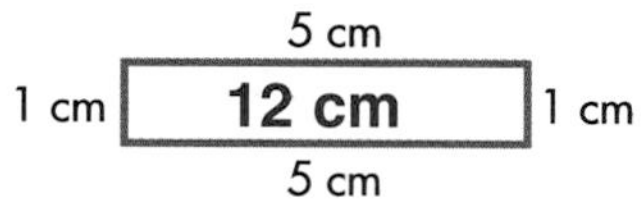

❻

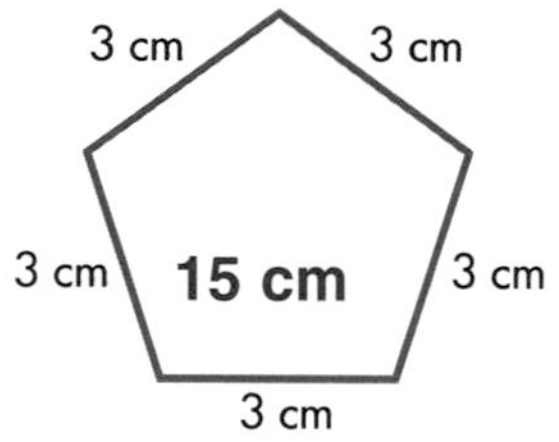

Physical Education Connection Students who are not familiar with baseball may have difficulty discussing Mr. Muddle's tasks for the baseball team. Group these students with others who know the game. You might bring in various kinds of **baseball equipment** to help students identify and better understand the types of equipment.

*available separately

Solve these problems. Drawing diagrams might help.

7. Central Park is shaped like a rectangle. The length of one side of the park is 300 yards. A second side is 150 yards. If Troy runs around the perimeter of the park, how far will he run? **900 yards**

8. One side of Seward Park, which is square-shaped, measures 235 yards. What length of fencing is needed to completely fence in the park? **940 yards**

9. In an equilateral triangle, all three sides are equal. The perimeter of a garden shaped like an equilateral triangle is 24 feet. What is the length of each of the sides? **8 feet**

10. In an isosceles triangle, two sides are equal. The perimeter of an isosceles triangle is 30 inches. One of its sides is 12 inches. What are the lengths of the other sides? **9 inches**

11. On a baseball field, all of the bases lie at the corners of a square. The distance between first and second base is 90 feet.
    a. How far is it around the bases? **360 feet**
    b. About how far does a player run if he or she hits a triple? **270 feet**

12. Go to the library to find out the dimensions of a football field.
    a. What is the length of the field? **120 yards including the end zones, 100 yards not including the end zones**
    b. What is the width of the field? **53 yards**
    c. What is the perimeter of the field? **306 yards**

13. Each side of a square measures 5 centimeters. What is its perimeter? **20 cm**

Mental Math (continued)

c. 8 – 4 = (4)	**d.** 9 – 2 = (7)
80 – 40 = (40)	90 – 20 = (70)
81 – 40 = (41)	900 – 200 = (700)
81 – 50 = (31)	905 – 200 = (705)

2 Teach

Using the Student Pages Define *perimeter* as the distance around a figure. Ask for realistic examples of situations that might require finding perimeter. Examples include determining jogging distance around a field, fencing a garden, and buying framing for a picture. Before students do the problems on page 32, remind them that *cm* is the symbol for centimeter(s). Also encourage them to make diagrams to help them solve the word problems on page 33.

Note: A regulation football field is 100 yards (91.4 meters) long and 53 yards (48.5 meters) wide, with 10 more yards (9.1 meters) for each end zone. When you discuss answers to problem 12 on page 33, determine whether students included the lengths of the two end zones in their calculations.

Technology Connection Try the software *Math Keys: Unlocking Measure* from MECC (Mac, IBM for grades 3–6) for further practice with measurement. Concepts covered include length, height, perimeter, and area.

LEARNING STYLES

Meeting Individual Needs
Musical and artistic learners may have more success finding perimeter if they verbalize the dimensions in a rhythmical way or if they use a crayon or marker to "draw" the perimeter, stating the dimensions as they move around the outside of the object or drawing.

◆ LESSON 10 Perimeter

Teach

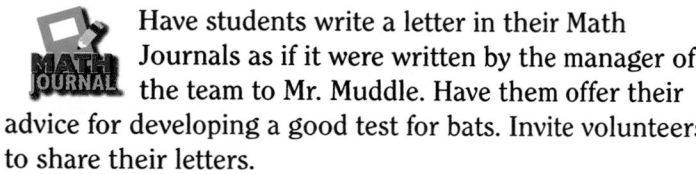

Using the Thinking Story "Muddle at Bat (Part 2)" focuses on what makes a good product performance test. Mr. Muddle attempts to devise a test to evaluate bats for hitting. By considering an absurd test that leads to an unwarranted conclusion, students learn about sampling errors and interpreting test results.

Answers to Thinking Story Questions:

1. Mr. Muddle thinks the Arrow bat is best because he got his only hit with it.
2. It was just an accident. Also, he had more tries with the Arrow bat. It is possible that the Arrow bat is wider or lighter or in some way better suited to Mr. Muddle's batting ability.
3. Having more batters try each kind of bat the same number of times in the same way. It would probably also be helpful to have different pitchers pitching in different styles, because one bat might be better for hitting fast balls, another might be better for hitting curves, and so on.
4. 12 m

MATH JOURNAL Have students write a letter in their Math Journals as if it were written by the manager of the team to Mr. Muddle. Have them offer their advice for developing a good test for bats. Invite volunteers to share their letters.

◆ LESSON 10 Perimeter

THINKING STORY

Muddle at Bat

Part 2

You may want to refer to the first part of the Thinking Story, on pages 18–19.

The manager's face turned red with anger. "I don't care what doctors say about a bat. I want to know how well a bat does what it's supposed to do. How well does it swing? How far can it hit a ball? How strong is it?"

Mr. Muddle first set out to test the bats for hitting. He asked the pitcher to throw to him as he tested the bats. Mr. Muddle swung at ten pitches with the Slugger bat. He missed every time. Then he changed to the Arrow bat. He kept missing with it, too. On the 24th pitch, he managed to hit a ball. The ball went hopping back to the pitcher.

"Nice hit, Mr. Muddle," said the pitcher. "Just ten times farther and you'd have had a home run."

Finally Mr. Muddle tried the Champ bat. He made 17 swings and misses. By then the pitcher was tired of throwing to him and quit. Mr. Muddle reported to the manager. "I'm proud to say that the Arrow bat is far better than any other for getting hits."

. . . to be continued

Literature Connection For further practice with perimeter, read with students selections from *Let's Investigate Quadrilaterals* by Marion Smoothey. Focus on the investigations that involve determining perimeter. You might have students work in pairs or small groups to undertake some of these investigations as class or homework projects.

RETEACHING

Work with students who have trouble finding the perimeter of figures. First make sure that they know the meaning of the abbreviation *cm* (centimeters). Then have students use their fingers to "walk off" the distance around the figure, saying the length of each side as they go.

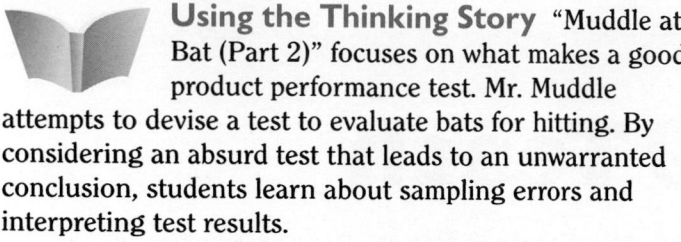

Work in groups. Discuss your answers and how you figured them out. Then compare your answers with those of other groups. **Answers are in margin.**

1. Why did Mr. Muddle say the Arrow bat is best? What do you think?
2. What are some reasons why Mr. Muddle might have hit the ball with the Arrow bat and not with the others?
3. What would be a better way to find out which bat is best for getting hits?
4. For a home run the ball would have to go about 120 meters. If the pitcher is right, how far did Mr. Muddle hit the ball?

PRACTICE p. 10

LESSON 10 PRACTICE

Name________________

Find the perimeter.

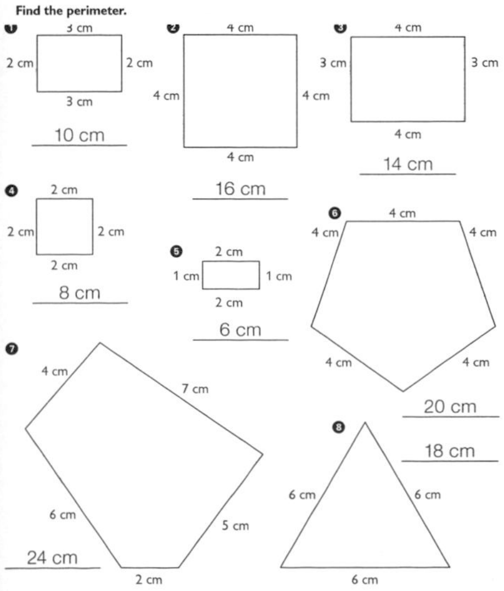

Copyright © SRA/McGraw-Hill. Permission is granted to reproduce this page for classroom use.

ENRICHMENT p. 10

LESSON 10 ENRICHMENT

Name________________

In a magic square all the rows and columns add up to the same number. Use the magic square below to answer the questions.

8	1	6
3	5	7
4	9	2

1. Each row and column of the square add up to what number? 15
2. Add 2 to all the numbers in the square. Write the new numbers in one of the squares below.

10	3	8
5	7	9
6	11	4

7	0	5
2	4	6
3	8	1

3. Is the new square still magic? yes
4. Subtract 3 from all the numbers in the new square. Write the numbers in the blank grid.
5. Is the new square still magic? yes

Copyright © SRA/McGraw-Hill. Permission is granted to reproduce this page for classroom use.

3 Wrap-Up (5 MINUTES)

In Closing Have students determine the perimeter of a classroom book, window, or poster.

ALTERNATIVE ASSESSMENT

Informal Assessment Observe students as they solve the perimeter problems on pages 32–33. Encourage them to verbalize their strategies. During the Thinking Story discussion, invite students to share their responses to Mr. Muddle's approach to the bat-testing situation, as well as to the specific questions on the page.

Assessment Criteria

Did the student . . .

✓ demonstrate an understanding of perimeter?

✓ communicate strategies used to analyze and solve the problems on missing dimensions?

✓ contribute to the Thinking Story discussion?

Homework Have students determine the perimeter of their bed, their pillow, a window, and a table at home. Have them sketch each object and label its dimensions.

GIFTED & TALENTED · MANIPULATIVES

Meeting Individual Needs

Some students may be curious about finding the perimeter of curved objects. Tell them that the term perimeter applies only to the dimensions of polygons. The measure of distance around a circle is called *circumference.* Although this concept is not formally addressed at the fourth-grade level, students might enjoy using **yarn** or **string** to find the distance around the outside of round objects, such as tires, plates, CDs, and so on.

LESSON 11

Student Edition pages 36–37

Using Maps and Charts

LESSON PLANNER

Objectives

- to provide practice in estimating distances on a map by comparing the unknown distances with known distances
- to provide practice in reading and interpreting data on a chart
- to provide practice in using multidigit numbers and approximating differences between numbers

Context of the Lesson This is the first of five lessons on addition and subtraction with multidigit numbers. Work with the algorithm begins in the next lesson. A checkpoint for assessing mastery is included in Lesson 14. Work on applications of multidigit addition and subtraction is provided in Lesson 15.

MANIPULATIVES

yarn or string (optional)

encyclopedia, almanac, or on-line source (optional)

Program Resources

Practice Master 11

Enrichment Master 11

For extra practice: CD-ROM* Lesson 11

1 Warm-Up

5 MINUTES

Problem of the Day Present the following problem on the chalkboard, then have students explain their solution methods: On Sunday, Tim paid $40 for a radio. On Monday, he sold the radio for $45. On Tuesday, he decided to buy it back, but the new owner wanted $50. Tim paid that price, but then he resold the radio on Friday for $55. Did Tim lose or make money? How much? (He made $10.)

Problem-Solving Strategies Ask students who have solved the Problem of the Day to share how they solved it and any strategies they used.

MENTAL MATH Provide practice with mixed addition and subtraction of greater numbers. Have students do the problems as chain calculations, showing intermediate answers so that they have a fresh start on each problem.

a.	50 + 25 = (75)	**b.**	80 − 20 = (60)
	75 + 1000 = (1075)		60 + 100 = (160)
	1075 − 50 = (1025)		160 + 2000 = (2160)
	1025 − 50 = (975)		2160 − 60 = (2100)

PRACTICE

LESSON 11

Using Maps and Charts

You can often tell when answers are wrong, even without calculating the solution.

GEOGRAPHY CONNECTION

Estimate the driving distances, in kilometers, between the following United States cities. For each pair of cities four distances are given in kilometers, but only one is correct. Select the correct distance.

1. New York City to Washington, D.C.
   a. 1974 **(b.)** 375 **c.** 1050 **d.** 35
2. New York City to Atlanta
   a. 503 **b.** 3475 **c.** 1020 **(d.)** 1353
3. Los Angeles to Miami
   (a.) 4323 **b.** 6219 **c.** 3219 **d.** 649
4. Denver to New York City
   a. 1594 **(b.)** 2849 **c.** 4129 **d.** 739
5. Chicago to Dallas
   (a.) 1475 **b.** 2138 **c.** 931 **d.** 4321
6. Chicago to Denver
   a. 976 **(b.)** 1201 **c.** 3011 **d.** 1603
7. Cleveland to Seattle
   a. 4975 **b.** 3232 **(c.)** 3778 **d.** 2178

Geography Connection Have students consult an **encyclopedia, almanac,** or **on-line source** to find out population data for your state and one other state for 1970, 1980, and 1990. Help students select different states so the class can compile a broad range of data. Present the information in a class chart. Challenge students to create and answer questions based on the data.

Literature Connection Have students follow an adventure while solving riddles using the *Rand McNally Children's Atlas of the United States.*

RETEACHING

Students who have difficulty estimating map distances might benefit by using a piece of **yarn** or **string** to mark the distance between any two cities. They can compare that length with other distances on the map.

*available separately

Study the chart. Then answer the questions for the cities listed in the table.

Population Change in Five U.S. Cities

City	1970 Population	1980 Population	1990 Population
Anchorage, Alaska	48,081	174,431	226,338
Cleveland, Ohio	750,879	573,822	505,616
Dallas, Texas	844,401	904,599	1,007,618
New York City, New York	7,895,563	7,071,639	7,322,564
Phoenix, Arizona	584,303	789,704	983,403

8. Name the city or cities that had a smaller population in 1990 than in 1970. **Cleveland, New York City**
9. Name the city or cities that had a greater population in 1990 than in 1970. **Anchorage, Dallas, Phoenix**
10. Name the city with the greatest population in 1970. In 1980. In 1990. **New York City had the greatest population in all three decades.**
11. How many people lived in Dallas in 1980? Do you think your answer is exactly right? **904,599; no**
12. Which city showed the greatest gain in population when you compare 1970 and 1990? **Phoenix**
13. Which city showed the greatest loss in population when you compare 1970 and 1990? **New York City**
14. Did any city lose in population between 1970 and 1980 and gain in population between 1980 and 1990? If so, which city or cities? **yes; New York City**

MATH JOURNAL

Use information in the chart to make up two more problems. Write them in your Math Journal.

2 Teach

Using the Student Pages Work through the first problem on page 36, and others as needed, with the class. Let those who catch on complete the page on their own. Work with the other students on estimating the distances by comparing them with known distances shown on the map. Point out that three of the four choices in each question are clearly wrong.

Have students go through the problems on page 37 on their own, then have them answer the questions together as a class. Point out that in problem 8 students should compare figures for 1970 and 1990, regardless of what happened from 1970 to 1980 and from 1980 to 1990. Also, discuss with students why the answer to the second question in item 11 is "no." Lead students to see that it is not possible to be sure that everyone in such a large group is counted. It takes a long time to count that many people, and the population changes during the count. Some people die, some are born, and some move. Explain that a count of people in a city (a census) is simply a very good estimate.

3 Wrap-Up

5 MINUTES

In Closing Summarize the lesson by asking students to explain how they made their estimates on driving distances and how they compared populations in the chart.

ALTERNATIVE ASSESSMENT

Performance Assessment Have students use an almanac to identify three United States cities with changes in population between 1970 and 1990: one whose population has grown, one whose population has decreased, and one whose change in population is greater than 100,000.

Assessment Criteria

Did the student . . .

✓ correctly answer at least 75% of the problems?

✓ contribute to the discussion about making estimates based on a map?

Homework Have students find out the current population of your community. Have them write several statements that compare the population with the populations given in the chart on page 37. You may also wish to assign Enrichment Master 11.

PRACTICE p. 11

LESSON 11 PRACTICE Name________

Study the chart. Then answer the questions for the zoos listed in the table.

Major Public Zoos in the United States

Zoo	Yearly Attendance	Acres	Number of Animal Species
Baltimore	600,000	180	1200
Brookfield	2,000,000	215	400
Los Angeles	1,400,000	80	440
Philadelphia	1,300,000	42	437
St. Louis	2,700,000	83	699
San Diego	3,000,000	125	800

1. Which zoo has the greatest attendance? San Diego
2. Does the zoo in problem 1 also have the greatest number of species of animals? no
3. Which zoo has the least attendance? Baltimore
4. Does the zoo in problem 3 also have the least number of acres? no
5. Which two zoos have about the same number of acres? Los Angeles, St. Louis
6. Which three zoos have about the same number of species of animals? Brookfield, Los Angeles, Philadelphia
7. Does any one zoo have all three—the least attendance, the least number of acres, and the least number of species of animals? no
8. Does any one zoo have all three—the greatest attendance, the greatest number of acres, and the greatest number of species of animals? no

Copyright © SRA/McGraw-Hill. Permission is granted to reproduce this page for classroom use.

Math Explorations and Applications Level 4 • 11

ENRICHMENT p. 11

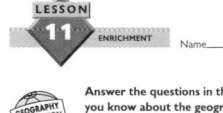

LESSON 11 ENRICHMENT Name________

GEOGRAPHY CONNECTION

Answer the questions in the chart by recalling what you know about the geography of the United States. Then study a map to check your answers. Some of the answers may surprise you.

Question	First Answer	Second Answer
1 Which state is farthest west?	Answers will vary.	Alaska
2 Which state is farthest south?		Hawaii
3 Which state is farthest north?		Alaska
4 Which state is farthest east?		Alaska or Maine
5 Which state has the largest area?		Alaska
6 Which state has the smallest area?		Rhode Island
7 Which state has the longest coastline on the Atlantic Ocean?		Florida
8 Which state has the longest coastline on the Pacific Ocean?		Alaska
9 Which state has the longest coastline on the Gulf of Mexico?		Florida
10 Which state touches the greatest number of other states?		Tennessee

Copyright © SRA/McGraw-Hill. Permission is granted to reproduce this page for classroom use.

Math Explorations and Applications Level 4 • 11

LESSON 12

Student Edition pages 38–41

Multidigit Addition

LESSON PLANNER

Objectives

- ▶ to review the standard algorithm for multidigit addition
- ▶ to provide practice in adding multidigit numbers

Context of the Lesson This is the second of five lessons on multidigit addition and subtraction and is a review of material taught in the second- and third-grade programs. A checkpoint for assessing mastery appears in Lesson 14.

MANIPULATIVES

base-10 materials* (optional)

Program Resources

Number Cubes (0–5 and 5–10)
Reteaching Master
Practice Master 12
Enrichment Master 12
For extra practice:
CD-ROM* Lesson 12

Note: This lesson may take more than one day.

1 Warm-Up

5 MINUTES

Problem of the Day Present the following problem on the chalkboard, and encourage students to find more than one solution: Fill in each box of the puzzle with a digit from 1 to 6. Use each digit only once. When you finish, the sum of the numbers along each side of the triangle must be 10. (Answers may vary; one possible answer is shown.)

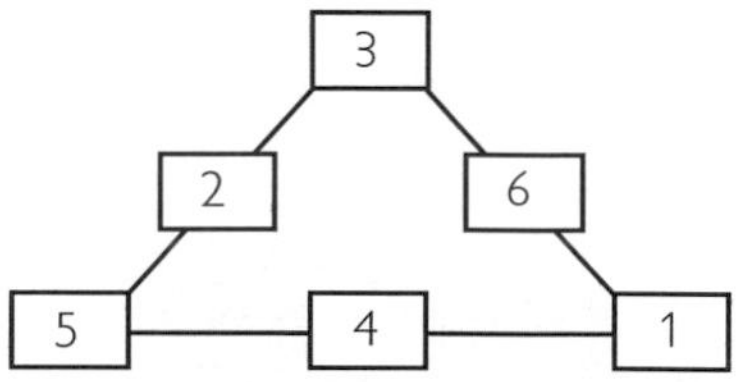

Problem-Solving Strategies Ask students who have solved the Problem of the Day to share how they solved it and any strategies they used.

PRACTICE

LESSON 12

Multidigit Addition

HEALTH CONNECTION

Sean orders a slice of pepperoni pizza and a garden salad with dressing. The salad has 225 calories. The pizza has 389 calories. Add to find the total number of calories in Sean's meal.

Add: 225 + 389 = ?

Here's how:

$$\begin{array}{r} 1 \\ 225 \\ +\ 389 \\ \hline 4 \end{array}$$

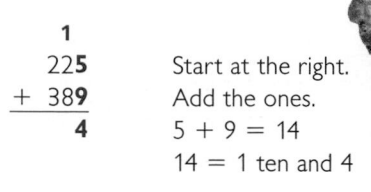

Start at the right.
Add the ones.
5 + 9 = 14
14 = 1 ten and 4

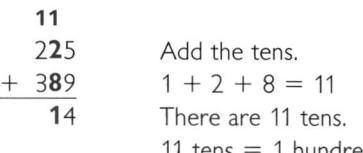

$$\begin{array}{r} 11 \\ 225 \\ +\ 389 \\ \hline 14 \end{array}$$

Add the tens.
1 + 2 + 8 = 11
There are 11 tens.
11 tens = 1 hundred and 1 ten

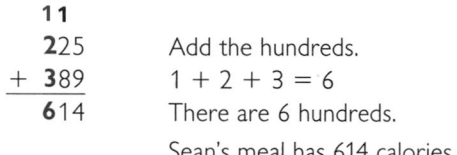

$$\begin{array}{r} 11 \\ 225 \\ +\ 389 \\ \hline 614 \end{array}$$

Add the hundreds.
1 + 2 + 3 = 6
There are 6 hundreds.
Sean's meal has 614 calories.

Remember: **Start at the right. Use the same rules in every column.**

Here are more examples:

$$\begin{array}{r} 1\ 1\quad 1\ 1 \\ 23,475 \\ +\ 48,639 \\ \hline 72,114 \end{array} \qquad \begin{array}{r} 1\quad 1\ \ \\ 4907 \\ +\ \ \ 685 \\ \hline 5592 \end{array}$$

Why teach it this way?

The direction "use shortcuts when you can" appears on almost every page of multidigit arithmetic exercises. Each of these pages contains some items that can be done more easily without the standard algorithm. For example, in problems such as 25 + 25 or 75 + 75, students may know the answer because these numbers are used with money. Mixing in such problems helps students to recognize when a standard algorithm may be less appropriate than some other method.

*available separately

Add. Use shortcuts when you can.

1	2	3	4	5
35	92	25	75	63
+ 42	+ 30	+ 25	+ 75	+ 72
77	**122**	**50**	**150**	**135**

6	7	8	9	10
125	499	562	602	100
+ 237	+ 499	+ 31	+ 718	+ 95
362	**998**	**593**	**1320**	**195**

11	12	13	14
500	5712	15,576	89,341
+ 499	+ 6314	+ 37,659	+ 10,659
999	**12,026**	**53,235**	**100,000**

15	16	17	18
4315	1395	29,324	323,759,902
+ 2690	+ 7239	+ 65,591	+ 474,621,326
7005	**8634**	**94,915**	**798,381,228**

19	20	21	22	23
35	19	31	25	565
63	25	25	25	394
+ 75	36	324	25	237
173	+ 143	+ 567	+ 25	+ 465
	223	**947**	**100**	**1661**

24	25	26	27	28
600	2374	464	621	297
+ 900	+ 1042	+ 280	+ 289	+ 30
1500	**3416**	**744**	**910**	**327**

Literature Connection

Encourage students to select a favorite author. Have them search in the library for the titles of two to four books by that author and the number of pages in each of those books. Have students create word problems using multidigit addition based upon the total number of pages in the different books. Direct students to put these problems in their Math Portfolios.

MENTAL MATH Challenge students with the following problems involving addition and subtraction facts. Present them as missing-term problems for algebraic practice.

a. 1 + (2) = 3	b. 11 − (10) = 1	c. 14 − (6) = 8
d. (12) − 10 = 2	e. 12 − (4) = 8	f. 7 + (2) = 9
g. (15) − 6 = 9	h. 2 + (4) = 6	i. 15 − (2) = 13

2 Teach

Using the Student Pages You might wish to demonstrate the "Don't Go Over 1000" game, which provides practice with multidigit addition, on page 41 first, so students can play it as they finish pages 38–40.

Review the addition algorithm with students by going through the first example on page 38 with the class. Ask questions about what to do at each step and have students answer in unison. You may wish to solve the problems at the bottom of page 38 in the same way.

Briefly go over a few problems on page 39 with students as needed. In all examples emphasize that the same rules apply to all places (ones, tens, hundreds, and so on). Then have students work independently to complete page 39. Point out that in real life, a good estimate (798 or 800 million) would suffice for problems like item 18. Also, calculators or computers are normally used to solve this kind of problem.

COOPERATIVE LEARNING One way to reinforce the addition algorithm is to have students work cooperatively to complete addition problems. Form groups of three or four students. Within a group, each student takes responsibility for one place in a problem. He or she states the steps out loud so that the other group members can verify that they are correct. The next student picks up where the previous student left off to continue finding the solution. Students can alternate places in subsequent problems. Having students verbalize their thinking helps to establish the algorithm firmly in their minds.

◆ LESSON 12 Multidigit Addition

Teach

Using the Student Pages You may wish to demonstrate the "Don't Go Over 1000" game on page 41 with a few students at the chalkboard before beginning page 40, so students can play the game when they finish. This game provides practice with multidigit addition. Students should use approximation techniques to complete page 40. For example, the answer to problem 30 must be greater than 120 but less than 100 + 200, or 300, so choices *b* and *c* are clearly wrong. For each problem have students decide which two answers are clearly wrong and then write in the remaining choice. Work through several items with the class as needed. Then let students complete the page independently. Encourage them to check their work on page 39 to see whether they have given any obviously wrong answers.

GAME Introduce the "Don't Go Over 1000" game on page 41. Have students play in groups of two or three. This game provides practice with multidigit addition, place value, and probabilistic thinking. A copy of this game can also be found on page 10 of the Home Connections Blackline Masters.

SPECIAL NEEDS · MANIPULATIVES

Meeting Individual Needs

If students have the facts memorized but have trouble with the algorithm, focus on the steps. You may wish to use **base-10 materials*** to go over why the algorithm works. Some students will be able to do the algorithm correctly without understanding why it works. They may be better able to understand it after becoming proficient with the steps. Assign the Reteaching Master on page 4 for further practice.

◆ LESSON 12 Multidigit Addition

Without using pencil and paper, you can often tell whether an answer could be right.

Jensen's TV Store

ITEM	COST	
M2117		
Television	$375	62
Tax	26	29
Total	$638	52

In each problem, two of the answers don't make sense, and one is correct. Choose each correct answer. Discuss your methods for finding the answers. Which methods worked best?

29	49 + 49 = ■	(a.) 98	b. 198	c. 518
30	84 + 120 = ■	(a.) 204	b. 34	c. 974
31	36 + 71 = ■	a. 67	(b.) 107	c. 227
32	125 + 237 = ■	a. 1762	b. 222	(c.) 362
33	275 + 129 = ■	a. 104	(b.) 404	c. 804
34	27 + 54 = ■	(a.) 81	b. 31	c. 171
35	48 + 71 = ■	a. 199	b. 319	(c.) 119
36	472 + 376 = ■	a. 1028	b. 628	(c.) 848
37	359 + 982 = ■	a. 1041	(b.) 1341	c. 941
38	412 + 562 = ■	(a.) 974	b. 1274	c. 774
39	73 + 793 = ■	a. 766	b. 1066	(c.) 866
40	1475 + 325 = ■	a. 800	(b.) 1800	c. 2800
41	1379 + 1682 = ■	a. 4061	b. 2061	(c.) 3061
42	2257 + 1279 = ■	(a.) 3536	b. 536	c. 5536
43	4778 + 173 = ■	a. 951	(b.) 4951	c. 4751
44	7253 + 347 = ■	a. 10,600	b. 7000	(c.) 7600

40 • Addition and Subtraction

LITERATURE CONNECTION

Literature Connection Invite students to read *Pigs Will Be Pigs* by Amy Axelrod, in which pigs add up found money to buy a meal.

RETEACHING p. 4

LESSON 12 RETEACHING Name________________

Example: 319 + 482 = ?

Step 1

```
   1
  3 1 9
+ 4 8 2
      1
```

Add the ones.
9 + 2 = 11
11 ones = 1 ten and 1 one
Write the 1 ten above the tens place.

Step 2

```
 1 1
  3 1 9
+ 4 8 2
    0 1
```

Add the tens.
1 + 1 + 8 = 10
10 tens = 1 hundred and 0 tens
Write the 1 hundred above the hundreds place.

Step 3

```
 1 1
  3 1 9
+ 4 8 2
  8 0 1
```

Add the hundreds.
1 + 3 + 4 = 8 hundreds

Add.

1. 500 + 65 = 565	2. 721 + 489 = 1210	3. 28 + 485 = 513	4. 65,265 + 14,876 = 80,141
5. 399 + 499 = 898	6. 300 + 89 = 389	7. 698 + 222 = 920	8. 43,389 + 27,433 = 70,822
9. 1752 + 4638 = 6390	10. 550 + 550 = 1100	11. 569 + 477 = 1046	12. 89,659 + 10,341 = 100,000

4 • *Math Explorations and Applications* Level 4

Copyright © SRA/McGraw-Hill. Permission is granted to reproduce this page for classroom use.

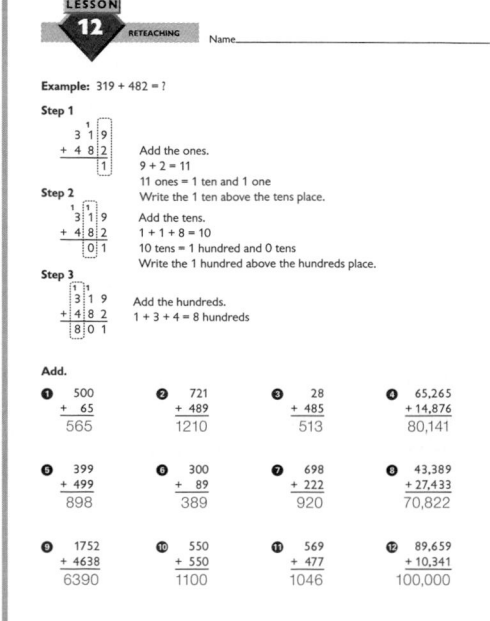

*available separately

COOPERATIVE LEARNING

GAME

Don't Go Over 1000 Game

Players: Two or more
Materials: Two 0–5 cubes (red), two 5–10 cubes (blue)
Object: To get the sum closest to, but not over, 1000
Math Focus: Place value, multidigit addition, and mathematical reasoning

RULES

1. Roll all four cubes. If you roll a 10, roll that cube again.
2. Combine three of the numbers rolled to make a three-digit number.
3. Roll all four cubes again. Make a second three-digit number and add it to your first number.
4. You may stop after your second roll, or you may make another three-digit number and add it to your previous sum.
5. The player whose sum is closest to, but not over, 1000 is the winner.

SAMPLE GAME

Megan rolled:	Megan wrote:	Rosalie rolled:	Rosalie wrote:
5 4 3 6	643	0 5 9 1	519
3 6 7 2	+ 327	3 7 7 1	+ 137
	970		656
Megan stopped.		8 2 3 9	+ 329
			985

Rosalie was the winner.

MATH JOURNAL

If you played this game again, would you play it the same way? Explain why or why not in your Math Journal.

③ Wrap-Up (5 MINUTES)

In Closing Have students verbalize the steps of the addition algorithm using this problem: 654 + 987 = (1641)

ALTERNATIVE ASSESSMENT

Informal Assessment Have students work as partners to role-play teaching multidigit addition. Have one student act as the teacher and the other as a student who does not know the algorithm. Then have them reverse roles. Listen carefully as students explain the algorithm to each other.

Assessment Criteria

Did the student . . .

- ✓ correctly answer at least 75% of the addition problems?
- ✓ demonstrate and communicate effective approximation techniques?
- ✓ evaluate answers for accuracy and sense?

Homework Have students make up worksheets with ten problems that have three-, four-, and five-digit addends. Have them complete their worksheets.

LOOKING AHEAD In preparation for an optional activity in the next lesson, ask students to bring in pennies. You may want to provide pennies for students who do not bring any.

PRACTICE p. 12

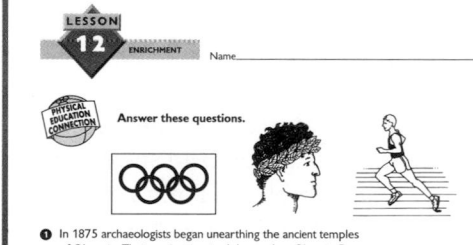

LESSON 12 PRACTICE Name________

Add.

1. 65 + 23 = 88
2. 27 + 31 = 58
3. 45 + 45 = 90
4. 86 + 39 = 125
5. 66 + 66 = 132
6. 48 + 92 = 140
7. 200 + 37 = 237
8. 600 + 287 = 887
9. 548 + 273 = 821
10. 805 + 345 = 1150
11. 3872 + 7954 = 11,826
12. 74,315 + 26,494 = 100,809
13. 2,893,417 + 6,484,385 = 9,377,802
14. 27 + 36 + 45 = 108
15. 216 + 387 + 691 = 1294
16. 305 + 165 + 425 + 95 = 990
17. 903 + 769 + 542 + 281 = 2495
18. 207 + 711 + 491 + 355 = 1764
19. 576 + 143 + 278 + 685 = 1682
20. 473 + 221 + 852 + 315 = 1861
21. 370 + 825 + 564 + 231 = 1990
22. 428 + 917 + 666 + 190 = 2201
23. 783 + 216 + 405 + 504 = 1908
24. 113 + 332 + 810 + 275 = 1530
25. 702 + 636 + 470 + 173 = 1981

12 • *Math Explorations and Applications* Level 4

Copyright © SRA/McGraw-Hill. Permission is granted to reproduce this page for classroom use.

ENRICHMENT p. 12

LESSON 12 ENRICHMENT Name________

PHYSICAL EDUCATION CONNECTION

Answer these questions.

1. In 1875 archaeologists began unearthing the ancient temples of Olympia. Their project inspired the modern Olympic Games. The first Games of modern times were held 21 years later. What year was it? 1896
2. The summer Olympic Games were held in Los Angeles in 1932. Los Angeles hosted the summer Games again 52 years later. What year was it? 1984
3. Paris, France, hosted the summer Games in 1900 and again 24 years later. What year was it? 1924
4. London, England, hosted the summer Games in 1908 and again 40 years later. What year was it? 1948
5. Lake Placid, New York, hosted the winter Games in 1932 and again 48 years later. What year was it? 1980
6. In the 1994 winter Olympic Games, Norway won ten gold medals, 11 silver medals, and five bronze medals. How many medals did Norway win all together? 26
7. In the 1992 summer Olympic Games, Russia won 45 gold medals, 38 silver medals, and 29 bronze medals. How many medals did Russia win all together? 112
8. In the 1992 summer Olympic Games, the United States won 37 gold medals, 34 silver medals, and 37 bronze medals. How many medals did the United States win all together? 108

12 • *Math Explorations and Applications* Level 4

Copyright © SRA/McGraw-Hill. Permission is granted to reproduce this page for classroom use.

LESSON 13

Student Edition pages 42–45

Multidigit Subtraction

LESSON PLANNER

Objectives

- ▶ to review the standard algorithm for multidigit subtraction
- ▶ to provide practice in subtracting multidigit numbers
- ▶ to review place value and intuitive ideas about probability

Context of the Lesson This lesson, the third of five lessons on multidigit addition and subtraction, reviews material taught at the second- and third-grade levels. Multidigit subtraction is reviewed throughout the fourth-grade level. This lesson also presents applications of multidigit addition and subtraction.

MANIPULATIVES

- pennies (optional)
- play money *
- base-10 materials* (optional)

Program Resources

- "Transaction" Game Mat
- Number Cubes
- Reteaching Master
- Practice Master 13
- Enrichment Master 13

For additional math integration:
Math Throughout the Day*

For extra practice:
CD-ROM* Lesson 13
Cumulative Review, page 536

PRACTICE

LESSON 13

Multidigit Subtraction

Trini sold 594 tickets for the spring music festival. She sold 378 adult tickets. The rest were children's tickets. How many children's tickets did Trini sell? You can subtract to find the difference.

Subtract: 594 − 378 = ?

$\begin{array}{r} 594 \\ -\ 378 \\ \hline \end{array}$	Start at the right. Subtract the ones. You can't subtract 8 from 4.
$\begin{array}{r} 5\not{9}\not{4} \\ -\ 378 \\ \hline \end{array}$	Regroup the 9 tens and 4.
$\begin{array}{r} 8\,14 \\ 5\not{9}\not{4} \\ -\ 378 \\ \hline \end{array}$	9 tens and 4 = 8 tens and 14
$\begin{array}{r} 8\,14 \\ 5\not{9}\not{4} \\ -\ 378 \\ \hline 6 \end{array}$	Subtract the ones. 14 − 8 = 6
$\begin{array}{r} 8\,14 \\ 5\not{9}\not{4} \\ -\ 378 \\ \hline 16 \end{array}$	Subtract the tens. 8 − 7 = 1 There is 1 ten.
$\begin{array}{r} 8\,14 \\ 5\not{9}\not{4} \\ -\ 378 \\ \hline 216 \end{array}$	Subtract the hundreds. 5 − 3 = 2 There are 2 hundreds. Trini sold 216 children's tickets.

42 • Addition and Subtraction

1 Warm-Up

5 MINUTES

Problem of the Day Present the following problem, and have students use **play money*** to solve it: Jamaal has three coins worth less than one dollar. If he lost one coin, he would have exactly half as much money as he has now. What coins does Jamaal have? (1 dime and 2 nickels. Losing the dime, Jamaal's total drops from 20¢ to 10¢, which is exactly half.)

Problem-Solving Strategies Ask students who have solved the Problem of the Day to share how they solved it and any strategies they used.

COOPERATIVE LEARNING One way to reinforce the subtraction algorithm is to have students work together to solve subtraction problems. Form groups of three students and ask each student to take responsibility for one part of a problem. He or she states the steps aloud and other group members verify that they are correct. The next student picks up where the previous student left off to continue finding the solution. Students can alternate places in subsequent problems.

*available separately

905
− 466

What do you do in a case like this?
There are no tens to regroup.

8915
~~905~~
− 466

9 hundreds is the same as 90 tens.
Regroup 90 tens and 5.
90 tens and 5 = 89 tens and 15

8915
~~905~~
− 466
439

Now subtract.

Subtract. Use shortcuts when you can.

1. 35 − 23 **12**
2. 65 − 29 **36**
3. 47 − 40 **7**
4. 47 − 39 **8**
5. 93 − 87 **6**
6. 425 − 425 **0**
7. 691 − 25 **666**
8. 201 − 187 **14**
9. 905 − 377 **528**
10. 391 − 280 **111**
11. 276 − 137 **139**
12. 672 − 314 **358**
13. 6542 − 3000 **3542**
14. 1000 − 3 **997**
15. 349,619,721 − 218,700,399 **130,919,322**

Add or subtract. Use shortcuts when you can.

16. 871 − 645 **226**
17. 700 − 200 **500**
18. 901 + 675 **1576**
19. 279 + 813 **1092**
20. 700 + 200 **900**
21. 700 − 199 **501**
22. 307 − 295 **12**
23. 492 − 374 **118**
24. 770 + 199 **969**
25. 700 − 201 **499**
26. 496 − 496 **0**
27. 285 + 139 **424**

Technology Connection Refer students to the software *Word Problem Square Off* from Gamco (Mac, grades 3–4) for further practice with one- and two-step problems, adding and subtracting of up to four digits, and multiplying and dividing through 9 × 9.

MENTAL MATH Provide problems that will prepare students for multidigit subtraction problems with 0s in the minuend. Encourage students to respond quickly.

a. 90 is how many tens? (9)
b. 20 is how many tens? (2)
c. 1000 is how many tens? (100)
d. 800 is how many tens? (80)
e. 5000 is how many tens? (500)
f. 30 is how many tens? (3)
g. 3000 is how many tens? (300)
h. 100 is how many tens? (10)
i. 600 is how many tens? (60)
j. 4000 is how many tens? (400)

❷ Teach

Using the Student Pages Demonstrate the "Roll a Problem" game on page 45, which provides practice with multidigit arithmetic, and the "Transaction" Game Mat, which reinforces the skill of adding and subtracting amounts of money, before beginning the lesson so that students may play as they finish their work on pages 42–44.

Work through the problem on page 42 with the class. Then do several problems with four- or five-digit numbers and with different numbers of digits in the two numbers. Emphasize that the rules are the same for each column. Then work through the problem at the top of page 43. Do at least one more example with the class, using 0 as one or more of the digits in the minuend. Students will find their work cumbersome if they apply the regrouping methods shown on page 42, particularly if there are many 0s, as in:

20,000
−16,785

For this reason, we show a more efficient method of regrouping. Let students do the problems on page 43 individually. When they have finished, they can begin playing the games. Encourage them to play the subtraction variation of the "Roll a Problem" game.

◆ LESSON 13 Multidigit Subtraction

Teach

Using the Student Pages You may wish to have students work in pairs to solve the problems on page 44. Encourage them to write a number sentence or to use manipulatives to help solve each problem. Discuss the problems with the class, and ask volunteers to share their solution strategies.

The "Roll a Problem" game lends itself well to a whole-group activity. This game provides practice with multidigit arithmetic, place value, and mathematical reasoning. Demonstrate by playing it once or twice with you as the leader. Play at the chalkboard while students play at their seats. Make sure students write each number before the cube is rolled again. After several rounds, have students figure out the best possible score. Be sure to demonstrate the subtraction variation. Remind students that answers less than 0 are not allowed. The minuend (top number) must be as great or greater than the subtrahend (bottom number), otherwise a player cannot win a round. Students who have played this game (in previous grades) may find variation 2 more interesting and challenging.

Introducing the "Transaction" Game Mat Demonstrate "Transaction" for the class by playing it with one or two students. The focus of this game is adding and subtracting amounts of money and maintaining a record of money transactions. Have students play in groups of two or three. Complete instructions can be found on the Game Mat. A copy of the "Transaction" Game Mat can also be found on page 607 of this Teacher's Guide.

◆ LESSON 13 Multidigit Subtraction

Answer the following questions.

28. On school days Boris needs at least 20 minutes to eat breakfast, three minutes to brush his teeth, 15 minutes to get dressed, and seven minutes to gather all of the materials he needs. What's the least amount of time it takes Boris to get ready for school? **45 minutes**

29. At the beginning of the school year, Park Elementary had 311 students. During the year, 14 students moved away and 12 new students entered the school. How many students were there at the end of the school year? **309**

30. In 1900 the population of Park City was about 27,800. By 1950 the population was about 36,200. By about how much did the population increase? **8400**

31. Damon and his friends went bowling. In his first game Damon had a score of 131. Halfway through his second game he had a score of 89. How many more points did he need in the second game to beat his previous score? **43**

32. Ronda wants to use her babysitting money to pay for a new bicycle. She kept track of the money she earned for four weeks. She earned $15 the first week, $25 the second week, $20 the third week, and $27 the fourth week. How much more money does she need to make in order to buy a bicycle that costs $120? **$33**

33. Abraham Lincoln was born on February 12, 1809. He became president on March 4, 1861. How old was he when he became president? **52 years old**

FANTASTIC FACT

If the average adult human's blood vessels were attached end-to-end, they would form a tube more than 60,000 miles (97,000 km) long.

44 • Addition and Subtraction

SPECIAL NEEDS

Meeting Individual Needs

If students have the facts memorized but have trouble with the algorithm for multidigit subtraction, focus on the steps. You may wish to use **base-10 materials*** to go over why the algorithm works. However, some students will be able to do the algorithm correctly without understanding why it works, and may be better able to understand it after becoming proficient with the steps. Have these students repeat the steps in unison for specific problems. Continue to provide extra practice for students who still have trouble with the basic facts by assigning the Reteaching Master on page 5.

Real-World Connection

Have students bring in old **pennies** they find and figure out how old each coin is. Lead a discussion by asking questions such as: "Are some of the pennies older than you are?" "Are some of them older than any adults you know?" Bring in spare pennies for students who don't bring any. You might get a large number of pennies and do a frequency distribution graph of the mint years on the chalkboard. This is a graph of years versus number of pennies from each year. Discuss the shape of the graph.

RETEACHING p. 5

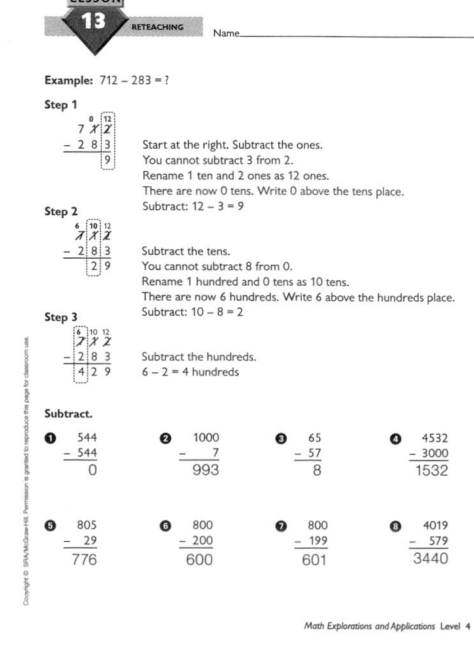

LESSON 13 RETEACHING Name______

Example: 712 – 283 = ?

Step 1

Start at the right. Subtract the ones.
You cannot subtract 3 from 2.
Rename 1 ten and 2 ones as 12 ones.
There are now 0 tens. Write 0 above the tens place.
Subtract: 12 – 3 = 9

Step 2

Subtract the tens.
You cannot subtract 8 from 0.
Rename 1 hundred and 0 tens as 10 tens.
There are now 6 hundreds. Write 6 above the hundreds place.
Subtract: 10 – 8 = 2

Step 3

Subtract the hundreds.
6 – 2 = 4 hundreds

Subtract.

1. 544 – 544 = 0
2. 1000 – 7 = 993
3. 65 – 57 = 8
4. 4532 – 3000 = 1532
5. 805 – 29 = 776
6. 800 – 200 = 600
7. 800 – 199 = 601
8. 4019 – 579 = 3440

Copyright © SRA/McGraw-Hill. Permission is granted to reproduce this page for classroom use.

Math Explorations and Applications Level 4 • 5

*available separately

COOPERATIVE LEARNING

GAME

Roll a Problem Game

Players: Two or more
Materials: One 0–5 cube (red)
Object: To get the greatest sum
Math Focus: Multidigit arithmetic, place value, and mathematical reasoning

RULES

1. Use blanks to outline an addition problem on your paper, like this:

```
   ___ ___
+  ___ ___
-----------
```

2. The first player rolls the cube four times.
3. Each time the cube is rolled, write that number in one of the blanks in your outline.
4. When all the blanks have been filled in, find the sum of the two two-digit numbers.
5. The player with the greatest sum is the winner.

OTHER WAYS TO PLAY THIS GAME

1. Try to get the least sum.
2. Add two three-digit numbers.
3. Add three two-digit numbers.
4. Use a 5–10 cube. If a 10 is rolled, roll again.
5. Subtract. Try to get the least difference, 0 or greater.

MATH JOURNAL

In your Math Journal explain how you played this game.

Use the Cumulative Review on page 536 after this lesson.

PRACTICE p. 13

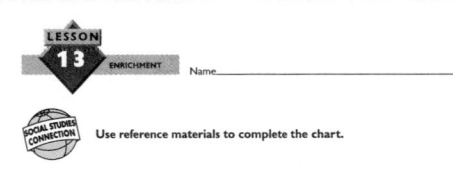

LESSON 13 PRACTICE

Name________________

Subtract.

1. 74 − 23 = 51
2. 88 − 80 = 8
3. 92 − 37 = 55
4. 71 − 69 = 2
5. 44 − 39 = 5
6. 683 − 421 = 262
7. 745 − 227 = 518
8. 304 − 178 = 126
9. 120 − 88 = 32
10. 708 − 224 = 484
11. 900 − 43 = 857
12. 500 − 429 = 71
13. 400 − 172 = 228
14. 800 − 355 = 445
15. 304 − 267 = 37
16. 5000 − 3 = 4997
17. 6453 − 2001 = 4452
18. 1783 − 599 = 1184
19. 4865 − 1037 = 3828
20. 860 − 243 = 617
21. 440 − 284 = 156
22. 807 − 359 = 448
23. 610 − 247 = 363
24. 1700 − 408 = 1292
25. 4,567,983 − 2,743,697 = 1,824,286
26. 641 − 293 = 348
27. 784 − 652 = 132
28. 2976 − 1849 = 1127
29. 2194 − 1999 = 195
30. 2,763,471 − 1,092,343 = 1,671,128

Copyright © SRA/McGraw-Hill. Permission is granted to reproduce this page for classroom use.

ENRICHMENT p. 13

LESSON 13 ENRICHMENT

Name________________

SOCIAL STUDIES CONNECTION

Use reference materials to complete the chart.

Event in American History Answers shown are for the year 1998.	**Year**	**About How Many Years Ago Was This?**
1. Massachusetts requires towns of more than 50 homes to establish primary schools.	1647	351
2. The Declaration of Independence is signed.	1776	222
3. George Washington defeats the British at Yorktown.	1781	217
4. The Constitution of the United States is adopted.	1788	210
5. The United States buys the Louisiana Purchase.	1803	195
6. Francis Scott Key writes "The Star-Spangled Banner."	1814	184
7. General Andrew Jackson wins the battle of New Orleans.	1815	183
8. The great Chicago fire leaves 90,000 people homeless.	1871	127
9. Booker T. Washington starts Tuskegee Institute.	1881	117
10. The Boston Red Sox win the first World Series.	1903	95

Copyright © SRA/McGraw-Hill. Permission is granted to reproduce this page for classroom use.

3 Wrap-Up

5 MINUTES

In Closing Have students verbalize the steps of the subtraction algorithm using this problem: 705 − 368. (337)

ALTERNATIVE ASSESSMENT

Informal Assessment Have students role-play teaching someone to do multidigit subtraction. One student acts as the teacher while you or another student pretends to be unfamiliar with the algorithm. Listen carefully as students explain the algorithm to determine whether they know and apply the steps correctly.

Assessment Criteria

Did the student . . .

- ✓ correctly answer at least 75% of the subtraction problems?
- ✓ apply appropriate multidigit addition and subtraction techniques to solve word problems?
- ✓ evaluate his or her answers for accuracy and reasonableness?

Homework Have students play the subtraction variation of the "Roll a Problem" game for further practice with multidigit subtraction. A copy of this game can also be found on page 11 of the Home Connections Blackline Masters.

ESL

Meeting Individual Needs

Students with limited proficiency in English may have difficulty solving the word problems on page 44. You might pair these students with native English speakers or bilingual students, who can try to act out the problems, simplify the language, or isolate the numbers so that ESL students can work through the arithmetic.

LESSON 14

Student Edition pages 46–49

Multidigit Addition and Subtraction

LESSON PLANNER

Objectives

✓ to evaluate students' ability to do multidigit addition and subtraction

▶ to help students develop the broad ability to use mathematical common sense

Context of the Lesson This is the fourth of five lessons on multidigit addition and subtraction. This lesson has a checkpoint for assessing mastery of the multidigit addition and subtraction algorithms, and more practice is provided in subsequent lessons. This lesson also contains Part 3 of "Muddle at Bat," a six-part Thinking Story.

MANIPULATIVES

globe or other sphere

Program Resources

Number Wheels

Practice Master 14

Enrichment Master 14

Assessment Master

For career connections:
Careers and Math*

For extra practice:
CD-ROM* Lesson 14

1 Warm-Up

5 MINUTES

Problem of the Day Present this problem and tell students that there are six possible answers: Kim counted all the books in the library. She used the total in a riddle for the librarian to solve. Kim says she counted more than 2000, but not as many as 3000, books. She says that all the digits in the total are even, no digit repeats, and there is no 6. What guesses might the librarian give for the number of books Kim counted? (2048, 2084, 2408, 2480, 2804, 2840)

Problem-Solving Strategies Ask students who have solved the Problem of the Day to share how they solved it and any strategies they used.

MIXED PRACTICE

LESSON 14

Multidigit Addition and Subtraction

Add or subtract.

❶ 22 + 31 = **53**	❷ 63 − 41 = **22**	❸ 36 − 21 = **15**	❹ 67 + 22 = **89**	❺ 93 − 36 = **57**
❻ 27 + 49 = **76**	❼ 48 + 35 = **83**	❽ 82 − 57 = **25**	❾ 67 + 74 = **141**	❿ 77 − 68 = **9**
⓫ 34 − 19 = **15**	⓬ 83 + 28 = **111**	⓭ 368 + 121 = **489**	⓮ 529 + 310 = **839**	⓯ 476 − 287 = **189**
⓰ 687 − 321 = **366**	⓱ 568 − 37 = **531**	⓲ 329 + 692 = **1021**	⓳ 474 + 289 = **763**	⓴ 274 + 189 = **463**
㉑ 6725 + 1235 = **7960**	㉒ 7925 + 2136 = **10,061**	㉓ 2748 − 1692 = **1056**	㉔ 1897 − 769 = **1128**	㉕ 28,133 − 14,960 = **13,173**

PROBLEM SOLVING

Solve.

㉖ Clara and Tomás ran for school president. Clara got 743 votes. Tomás got 916 votes.

a. Who won? **Tomás**

b. By how many votes? **173**

c. How many students attend the school? **can't tell**

d. How many people voted? **1659**

FANTASTIC FACT

It would take a car traveling 100 miles per hour more than 29 million years to reach Earth's nearest star, Proxima Centauri.

46 • Addition and Subtraction

Science Connection Explain to students that a planet's orbital path around the sun is not a perfect circle. Scientists have determined each planet's minimum and maximum distance from the sun, the average of which is given in the chart on page 47. Help interested students find out more about the variations in distance from the sun that each planet reaches during its orbit. Students can create a table that presents the minimum and maximum distance of each planet from the sun and then use these data to create addition and subtraction problems for classmates to solve.

*available separately

SCIENCE CONNECTION

Planet	Average Distance from Sun (in millions of miles)	Diameter (in miles)
Mercury	36	3,031
Venus	67	7,519
Earth	93	7,927
Mars	141	4,221
Jupiter	383	88,734
Saturn	887	74,977
Uranus	1,783	32,000
Neptune	2,794	30,450
Pluto	3,666	1,430

Answer the following questions based on the table.

27. How much greater is the diameter of Earth than the diameter of Mars? **3706 miles**

28. What is the difference between the average distance from the sun to Neptune and to Earth? **2701 million miles**

29. Jupiter's greatest distance from the sun is 124 million miles greater than its average distance. What is Jupiter's greatest distance from the sun? **507 million miles**

30. Which two planets have the least difference in diameter? What is the difference between their diameters? **Venus and Earth 408 miles**

31. Which two planets have the greatest difference in diameter? What is the difference between their diameters? **Jupiter and Pluto; 87,304 miles**

32. Suppose Earth and Venus are both at their average distances from the sun. What is the closest they could be to each other? What is the farthest they could be from each other? **26 million miles; 160 million miles**

MENTAL MATH Provide practice in adding and subtracting multiples of 10, 100, 1000, and 10,000. Have students use their Number Wheels to show the answers.

a. 90 + 70 = (160)
b. 150 – 60 = (90)
c. 400 + 800 = (1200)
d. 1400 – 800 = (600)
e. 800 + 800 = (1600)
f. 8000 + 8000 = (16,000)
g. 9000 – 8000 = (1000)
h. 13,000 – 7000 = (6000)
i. 60,000 + 70,000 = (130,000)
j. 40,000 – 35,000 = (5000)
k. 11,000 – 3000 = (8000)
l. 90,000 + 80,000 = (170,000)

2 Teach

MANIPULATIVES **Using the Student Pages** Have students complete the problems on page 46 on their own. You can use their work as an assessment as specified in the Mastery Checkpoint. Before students begin page 47, you may need to clarify the meaning of *diameter* (the length of a line segment that starts at one point on a circle, passes through the center of the circle, and ends at the opposite point on that circle). Use a **globe** or **other sphere** to show what this measurement would mean in terms of the diameter of a planet.

LITERATURE CONNECTION **Literature Connection** You may wish to show students a copy of *Math Mini-Mysteries* by Sandra Markle. Have them use the "Top Dog" data on the numbers of different registered breeds of dogs (pages 43–44) to create addition and subtraction problems for classmates to solve.

Teach

Using the Thinking Story "Muddle at Bat (Part 3)" centers on interpreting the results of a performance test. The students read about a bat test that produces insufficient information to draw a reliable conclusion. This prompts discussion of how to design a better test.

Answers to Thinking Story Questions:

1. It is hard to tell because it is not known how many times Sandy batted with each bat. Even so, 20 hits is not much different than 19.
2. Maybe he batted more times with the Arrow bat. It may be that he was just getting warmed up and was starting to get tired when he used the Champ bat; it was just luck; it was how the pitcher pitched; or the bat was better for him.
3. See question 3 of "Muddle at Bat," Part 2 (page 35). This asks the same question, but students should be able to give fuller answers this time.

MATH JOURNAL In their Math Journals, have students predict what Mr. Muddle is likely to do in the next part of the story. After they read Part 4 of "Muddle at Bat" they can consult their predictions and compare them with the story.

SPECIAL NEEDS

Meeting Individual Needs

Students who have difficulty remembering previous events in the story may need to reread the first two parts of "Muddle at Bat" before they proceed with Part 3. Even those students who remember what happened before may benefit from rereading Parts 1 and 2 to lead into Part 3.

◆ LESSON 14 Multidigit Addition and Subtraction

THINKING STORY

Muddle at Bat

Part 3

You may want to refer to previous parts of this Thinking Story, on pages 18–19 and 34–35.

"You should use one of our regular players," said the manager. "After all, we don't care how good a bat is for you. We want to know how good it is for them."

Mr. Muddle asked Sandy Hare, leading batter for the Dips, to try the bats. First Sandy batted for a while with the Slugger bat. He had 19 hits with it. Then he batted for a while with the Arrow bat and got 20 hits. When he used the Champ bat, he had only 11 hits.

"I am happy to say that I was right," Mr. Muddle told the manager. "The Arrow bat is by far the best for getting hits."

. . . to be continued

RETEACHING

Review the following technique with students who have difficulty remembering partial sums in column addition. First add the ones digits of the first two numbers and write the sum off to the side. If there is a ten in the answer, write a 1 at the top of the tens column, add that column, and then add the answer to the sum at the ones column, and so on.

PRACTICE p. 14

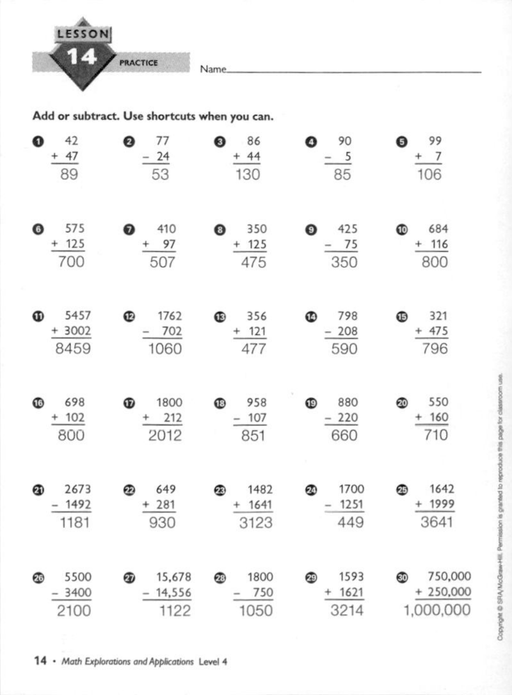

LESSON 14 PRACTICE Name______

Add or subtract. Use shortcuts when you can.

1. 42 + 47 = 89	2. 77 − 24 = 53	3. 86 + 44 = 130	4. 90 − 5 = 85	5. 99 + 7 = 106
6. 575 + 125 = 700	7. 410 + 97 = 507	8. 350 + 125 = 475	9. 425 − 75 = 350	10. 684 + 116 = 800
11. 5457 + 3002 = 8459	12. 1762 − 702 = 1060	13. 356 + 121 = 477	14. 798 − 208 = 590	15. 321 + 475 = 796
16. 698 + 102 = 800	17. 1800 + 212 = 2012	18. 958 − 107 = 851	19. 880 − 220 = 660	20. 550 + 160 = 710
21. 2673 − 1492 = 1181	22. 649 + 281 = 930	23. 1482 + 1641 = 3123	24. 1700 − 1251 = 449	25. 1642 + 1999 = 3641
26. 5500 − 3400 = 2100	27. 15,678 − 14,556 = 1122	28. 1800 − 750 = 1050	29. 1593 + 1621 = 3214	30. 750,000 + 250,000 = 1,000,000

14 • Math Explorations and Applications Level 4

Copyright © SRA/McGraw-Hill. Permission is granted to reproduce this page for classroom use.

Work in groups. Discuss your answers and how you figured them out. Then compare your answers with those of other groups. **Answers are in margin.**

1. Do you agree with Mr. Muddle that the Arrow bat was by far the best? Why or why not?
2. What are some reasons why Sandy Hare might have gotten more hits with the Arrow bat?
3. How would you change the test to make it more fair?

3 Wrap-Up (5 MINUTES)

In Closing Ask students to explain what they think makes a fair test, using their own examples or events in the Thinking Story to explain.

ANALYZING ANSWERS For those students who made procedural errors or who have difficulty regrouping numbers, check whether the difficulty is with the facts or the algorithm. If the trouble is with the algorithm, focus on the steps; if it is with the facts, give extra practice or have students play fact games.

Mastery Checkpoint 3

By this time most students should demonstrate mastery of the multidigit addition and subtraction algorithms by correctly answering at least 80% of the problems on page 46 or a similar page. You may record the results of this assessment in the appropriate column of the Mastery Checkpoint Chart. You may also wish to assign Assessment Blackline Masters page 3 to determine mastery.

Assessment Criteria

Did the student . . .

- ✓ correctly answer at least 80% of the addition and subtraction problems?
- ✓ communicate strategies used to create and solve problems based on given data?
- ✓ contribute to the Thinking Story discussion?
- ✓ demonstrate greater understanding of the importance of conducting a fair test?

Homework Have students play the "Roll a Problem" game on page 45 with a family member for further practice with multidigit arithmetic. A copy of this game can also be found on page 11 of the Home Connections Blackline Masters.

ENRICHMENT p. 14

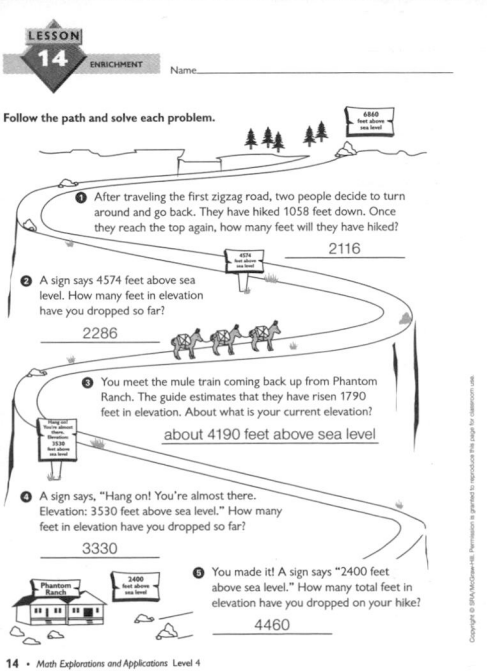

LESSON 14 ENRICHMENT Name________

Follow the path and solve each problem.

6860 feet above sea level

1. After traveling the first zigzag road, two people decide to turn around and go back. They have hiked 1058 feet down. Once they reach the top again, how many feet will they have hiked? 2116

4574 feet above sea level

2. A sign says 4574 feet above sea level. How many feet in elevation have you dropped so far? 2286
3. You meet the mule train coming back up from Phantom Ranch. The guide estimates that they have risen 1790 feet in elevation. About what is your current elevation? about 4190 feet above sea level

Hang on! You're almost there. Elevation: 3530 feet above sea level

4. A sign says, "Hang on! You're almost there. Elevation: 3530 feet above sea level." How many feet in elevation have you dropped so far? 3330

Phantom Ranch

2400 feet above sea level

5. You made it! A sign says "2400 feet above sea level." How many total feet in elevation have you dropped on your hike? 4460

14 • *Math Explorations and Applications* Level 4

Copyright © SRA/McGraw-Hill. Permission is granted to reproduce this page for classroom use.

ASSESSMENT p. 3

UNIT 1 **Mastery Checkpoint 3** Multidigit addition and subtraction (Lesson 14)

Name ________

The student demonstrates mastery by correctly answering at least 28 of the 35 problems.

Add or subtract.

1. 33 + 21 = 54
2. 54 − 23 = 31
3. 47 − 32 = 15
4. 56 + 33 = 89
5. 84 − 26 = 58
6. 38 + 59 = 97
7. 28 + 37 = 65
8. 73 − 46 = 27
9. 76 + 47 = 123
10. 88 − 79 = 9
11. 43 − 18 = 25
12. 73 + 38 = 111
13. 447 + 242 = 689
14. 417 + 520 = 937
15. 598 − 232 = 366
16. 479 − 48 = 431
17. 334 + 798 = 1132
18. 553 − 298 = 255
19. 5697 + 3425 = 9122
20. 3695 − 1234 = 2461
21. 44 + 63 = 107
22. 58 − 34 = 24
23. 56 − 23 = 33
24. 38 + 76 = 114
25. 93 − 68 = 25
26. 57 − 28 = 29
27. 43 − 19 = 24
28. 87 + 12 = 99
29. 74 − 56 = 18
30. 67 + 29 = 96
31. 796 − 489 = 307
32. 387 + 275 = 662
33. 4586 + 2138 = 6724
34. 4821 − 3962 = 859
35. 5736 − 2879 = 2857

Math Explorations and Applications Level 4 • 3

Copyright © SRA/McGraw-Hill. Permission is granted to reproduce this page for classroom use.

UNIT 1

Student Edition pages 50–51

Mid-Unit Review

The Mid-Unit Review pinpoints troublesome skill areas for students, allowing time for additional practice and reteaching before the unit ends. If students did not do well on the Mid-Unit Review and have completed additional practice, you may want to use the Mid-Unit Review provided on Assessment Blackline Masters page 4.

Using the Student Pages Have students complete problems 1–45 on pages 50 and 51 on their own. You might treat this review as a formal assessment of students' skills and have students complete this review as a timed test. See suggestions on page 51.

UNIT 1 ASSESSMENT

Mid-Unit Review

Write the numbers in standard form.

1. 800 + 70 + 4 **874**
2. 90,000,000 + 7 + 5000 **90,005,007**
3. 1000 + 30 + 2 **1032**
4. 10,000 + 400 + 5 **10,405**
5. 30,000 + 2000 + 700 + 50 + 1 **32,751**
6. 5,000,000 + 200,000 + 10,000 + 300 **5,210,300**
7. 3 + 80 + 200 + 600,000 + 9,000,000 **9,600,283**

Count up or down. Write the missing numbers.

8. 397, 398, 399, ■, ■, ■, ■, 404 **400, 401, 402, 403**
9. 903, 902, 901, ■, ■, ■, ■, ■, 895 **900, 899, 898, 897, 896**
10. 8,000,104; 8,000,103; 8,000,102; ■; ■; ■; ■; 8,000,097 **8,000,101; 8,000,100; 8,000,099; 8,000,098**

Write the greatest number and the least number.

11. Use the digits 5, 3, and 8. **853; 358**
12. Use the digits 6, 8, 2, and 1. **8621; 1268**

Write six different numbers in order from greatest to least.

13. Use the digits 2, 8, and 9. **982, 928, 892, 829, 298, 289**
14. Use the digits 1, 4, and 7. **741, 714, 471, 417, 174, 14**

Add or subtract to solve for *n*.

15. $7 + 4 = n$ **11**	16. $17 - 9 = n$ **8**	17. $15 - 8 = n$ **7**
18. $4 + 9 = n$ **13**	19. $8 + 8 = n$ **16**	20. $13 - 6 = n$ **7**
21. $6 + 9 = n$ **15**	22. $8 - 6 = n$ **2**	23. $n = 14 - 8$ **6**
24. $n = 8 + 6$ **14**	25. $n = 4 + 9$ **13**	26. $n = 15 - 9$ **6**
27. $n + 8 = 17$ **9**	28. $13 = n + 6$ **7**	29. $7 + n = 14$ **7**
30. $15 = 9 + n$ **6**	31. $12 = 5 + n$ **7**	32. $8 + n = 16$ **8**

Use a computer or other means to copy and complete each chart. Watch the function rule.

33 **−6**

In	Out
26	■ **20**
18	■ **12**
16	■ **10**
12	■ **6**
7	■ **1**

34 **+8**

In	Out
0	■ **8**
2	■ **10**
5	■ **13**
10	■ **18**
22	■ **30**

Solve these problems.

35 Reba had $13. She bought a belt for $7. How much money does she have left? **$6**

36 David had $15. He bought an artist's pad for $6 and a paint set for $7. Can he afford to buy a $3 paintbrush? **no**

37 Bike horns usually cost $10. They are on sale for $7. How much money would Emma save by buying a horn at the sale price? **$3**

Find the perimeter.

38 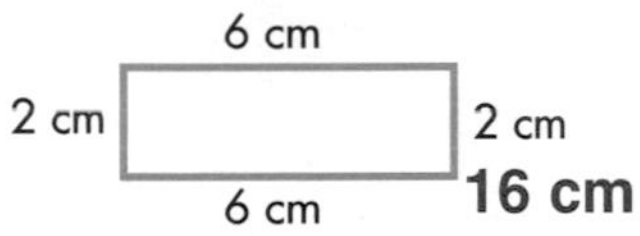

16 cm

39 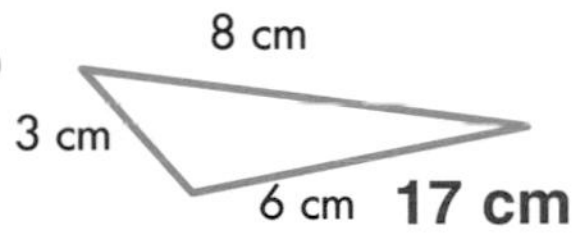

17 cm

In each problem, two of the answers don't make sense, and one is correct. Choose the correct answers.

40 49 + 39 = (a.) 88 b. 188 c. 718

41 1375 + 225 = a. 600 (b.) 1600 c. 2600

42 793 − 627 = (a.) 166 b. 1420 c. 400

43 1614 − 876 = a. 1207 b. 175 (c.) 738

44 66 + 104 = (a.) 170 b. 17 c. 1700

45 2350 − 2245 = a. 50 (b.) 105 c. 507

Unit 1 Mid-Unit Review • 51

ASSESSMENT p. 4

UNIT 1 **Mid-Unit Review** (Use after Lesson 14.)

Name ______

The student demonstrates mastery by correctly answering at least 12 of the 15 problems.

Count up or down. Write the missing numbers.

1 720, 721, 722, 723, 724, 725

2 10,052; 10,053; 10,054; 10,055; 10,056; 10,057

3 9655, 9654, 9653, 9652, 9651, 9650, 9649

Add or subtract to solve for *n*.

4 $n = 6 + 2$ $n =$ 8

5 $8 - 7 = n$ $n =$ 1

6 $7 + n = 10$ $n =$ 3

7 $11 - 8 = n$ $n =$ 3

8 $18 - 9 = n$ $n =$ 9

9 $3 + 8 = n$ $n =$ 11

10 $5 + 9 = n$ $n =$ 14

11 $13 = n + 6$ $n =$ 7

Solve these problems.

12 Kamran picked nine tomatoes in the afternoon. Then she used three in a salad. How many are left? 6

13 A square has sides which are each 5 cm long. How long is the perimeter? 20 cm

14 Fahrman wants to buy a radio-controlled car that costs $53. He has saved $26. How much more does he need to save? $27

15 If the distance from New York City to Shanghai is 14,643 km, how far is a round trip from New York City to Shanghai? 29,286 km

Copyright © SRA/McGraw-Hill. Permission is granted to reproduce this page for classroom use.

4 • *Math Explorations and Applications* Level 4

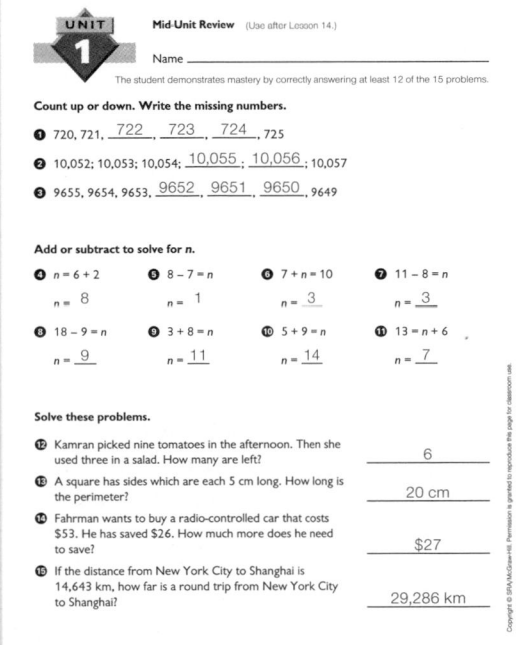

Timed Test Throughout this Teacher's Guide there are suggestions for sets of exercises to be completed as a "timed test." This usually occurs on pages of basic facts where the focus is on speedy recall. It gives each student a chance to improve as the year goes on. Invite students to keep their scores on the pages in their Math Journals or keep the actual pages in their Math Portfolios so that they can track their improvement.

Here are some suggestions for giving timed tests:

- Before students begin, they should number their papers in the same way as the problems in the book.
- Have all students start at the same time.
- Write 0 on the chalkboard as you tell them to start; after one minute erase the 0 and write 1; after two minutes write 2; and so on. Have students write that number at the tops of their papers when they finish the test so they know how long they took to complete the test.
- Grade the papers yourself or have students correct their own papers as you call out the answers. Encourage the students to brainstorm ways to improve their times on future tests.

Home Connections You may want to send home the letter on Home Connections Blackline Masters pages 34–35 to provide additional activities that families can complete together. These activities apply the skills presented in this unit.

ALTERNATIVE ASSESSMENT

Portfolio Assessment As students work through the second half of this unit, the Portfolio Assessment task provided on Assessment Blackline Masters page 93 can be used to evaluate students' ability to add and subtract amounts of money.

ALTERNATIVE ASSESSMENT

Performance Assessment Performance Assessment Task 1, provided on Assessment Blackline Masters pages 67–68, can be used at this time to evaluate students' proficiency with addition and subtraction. You may want to administer this assessment with individual students or in small groups.

Unit Project This would be a good time to assign the "How Many Books Are in the School Library?" project on pages 96 and 97. Students can begin working on the project in cooperative groups in their free time as they work through the unit. The Unit Project is a good opportunity for students to estimate, analyze data, and initiate a research project.

LESSON 15

Student Edition pages 52–53

Applying Addition and Subtraction

LESSON PLANNER

Objectives

- ▶ to provide practice in solving word problems
- ▶ to provide a realistic application of addition

Context of the Lesson This is the fifth of five lessons on multidigit addition and subtraction. Approximating sums and differences will be discussed in Lessons 17 and 18.

MANIPULATIVES

none

Program Resources

Practice Master 15

Enrichment Master 15

For extra practice:
CD-ROM* Lesson 15

1 Warm-Up (5 MINUTES)

Problem of the Day Present the following problem orally or on the chalkboard: Two numbers have a sum of 1300 and a difference of 300. What are the numbers? (800 and 500)

Problem-Solving Strategies Ask students who have solved the Problem of the Day to share how they solved it and any strategies they used.

MENTAL MATH Introduce a new kind of drill. Explain that you will present problems and students will determine whether the answer is more than 40. If it is, they show thumbs up; if it is less than 40, they show thumbs down. For variety, if an answer is exactly 40, have students stand up.

a. 25 + 14 (thumbs down)
b. 34 + 7 (thumbs up)
c. 42 – 3 (thumbs down)
d. 32 + 8 (stand up)
e. 38 – 8 (thumbs down)
f. 21 + 30 (thumbs up)
g. 26 + 34 (thumbs up)
h. 30 – 11 (thumbs down)

PROBLEM SOLVING

LESSON 15

Applying Addition and Subtraction

Answer these questions.

Amalia needs 55¢ for mailing a letter. She has these stamps:

1. Can Amalia make exactly 55¢ in postage stamps? **yes**
2. Which stamps make exactly 55¢? **20¢, 20¢, and three 5¢**
3. How many postage stamps will Amalia have left? **1**
4. What will be the total value of the stamps she has left? **32¢**

These three children are collecting baseball cards. Lia has 742 cards, Peter has 643, and A. J. has 392.

5. How many more cards does A. J. need to have as many as Lia? **350**
6. How many more cards does Peter need to have as many as Lia? **99**
7. Suppose Peter gives A. J. 343 cards. Will A. J. then have as many cards as Lia? **no**
8. Suppose Lia gives A. J. 200 cards. Will A. J. then have as many as Lia? **no; he will have more**
9. **Challenge:** How many cards would Lia have to give to A. J. for the two of them to have the same number? **175**

Why teach it this way?

From time to time suggestions are presented for collecting data about real situations and then doing some appropriate arithmetic. Although the amount of arithmetic may seem less than the time spent collecting data, these activities can be motivating and develop thinking and problem-solving skills.

Literature Connection Invite students to read *Counting Jennie* by Helena Claire Pittman and to make addition and subtraction problems from daily situations like Jennie does.

RETEACHING

Review the following technique with students who have difficulty remembering partial sums in column addition. First add the ones digits of the first two numbers and write the sum off to the side. If there is a 10 in the answer, write a 1 at the top of the tens column, add that column, and then add the answer to the sum at the ones column, and so on.

*available separately

REAL-WORLD CONNECTION

Sasha made a chart to help her find the least expensive supermarket. First she decided which items she wanted. Can you complete the bottom line of Sasha's chart?

Item	Price		
	Super-Duper Supermarket	Hi-Value Supermarket	Best-Buy Supermarket
1 dozen eggs (Grade AA large)	$1.09	$1.05	$1.15
1 quart of apple juice (Top-Core brand)	$1.25	$1.37	$1.29
2 pounds of potatoes	$ 0.88	$ 0.96	$ 0.80
Total	**$3.22**	**$3.38**	**$3.24**

10. Which supermarket is least expensive for the three items listed? **Super-Duper Supermarket**
11. Which supermarket is most expensive? **Hi-Value Supermarket**
12. For each supermarket, write the total amount in cents. **322¢, 338¢, 324¢**
13. Sasha met Mr. Tanaka, who was going shopping. "I have to buy bread, butter, apples, and peanut butter, " said Mr. Tanaka. "Do you know which supermarket will be least expensive?" he asked. Does Sasha know the answer to Mr. Tanaka's question? Why or why not? **no; no prices are given for those items**

◆ Go comparison shopping. Use a computer or pencil and paper to make a chart like the one above. Write the names of the stores you will go to and the items you will check prices for. Then fill in your chart with the prices you find.

❷ Teach

COOPERATIVE LEARNING Using the Student Pages

Encourage students to think about the first four questions on page 52. Ask them to work with a partner to answer the questions. Then ask students to explain how they solved the challenge (question 9). Some may do it by trial and error; others may simply take half of the difference.

Have students work individually on page 53. Discuss the answers as a class. Point out when discussing question 13 that the differences in the total prices for the three items tested are too small to suggest a trend. Students should understand that Sasha does not know the prices for these items in each store. For the comparison-shopping activity, help students determine the prices of items in advance so they can compare totals. If possible, they should decide on brands and quantities. If they cannot find the same brands in different stores, they should look for comparable quantity and quality.

❸ Wrap-Up

5 MINUTES

In Closing Have students explain how they know when to add and when to subtract in word problems.

ALTERNATIVE ASSESSMENT

Informal Assessment Circulate as students complete pages 52 and 53. Invite them to explain what strategies they are using and why, and how they know whether to add or subtract. Keep anecdotal notes if desired.

Assessment Criteria

Did the student . . .

✓ correctly answer at least 75% of the word problems?

✓ use the right operation to fit the situation in each problem?

✓ communicate the problem-solving strategies used?

✓ check that answers seemed reasonable and fit the facts?

PRACTICE p. 15

LESSON 15 PRACTICE Name________

Patty made a chart to help her find the least expensive store. First she decided which brands and products she wanted, then she recorded their prices. Complete the bottom line of Patty's chart.

Item	Price		
	Larry's Mart	More for Less	Best Mart
Shiny Shampoo (travel size)	89¢	78¢	85¢
Bath Powder (travel size)	85¢	95¢	92¢
Best Toothpaste (travel size)	69¢	75¢	72¢
Total	243¢	248¢	249¢

1. Which store is least expensive for the three items listed? Larry's Mart
2. Which store is most expensive? Best Mart
3. For each store write the total amount in dollars and cents. $2.43; $2.48; $2.49
4. Patty met Mrs. O'Leary, who was going shopping. "I have to buy soap, hair conditioner, bath tissue, and paper towels," said Mrs. O'Leary. "Do you know which store will be most expensive?" she asked. Does Patty know the answer to Mrs. O'Leary's question? Why or why not? Answers will vary. Possible answer: Not sure. She only knows the prices of the items in the chart.

Copyright © SRA/McGraw-Hill. Permission is granted to reproduce this page for classroom use.

Math Explorations and Applications Level 4 • 15

ENRICHMENT p. 15

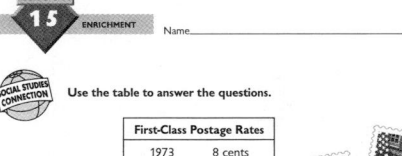

LESSON 15 ENRICHMENT Name________

SOCIAL STUDIES CONNECTION **Use the table to answer the questions.**

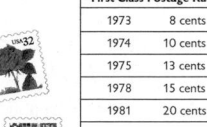

First-Class Postage Rates	
1973	8 cents
1974	10 cents
1975	13 cents
1978	15 cents
1981	20 cents
1985	22 cents
1988	25 cents
1991	29 cents
1995	32 cents

1. In what year was the largest rate increase? 1981
2. What was the rate increase that year? 5 cents
3. What is the difference between the lowest and the highest rate? 24 cents
4. What was the longest amount of time between rate increases? 4 years
5. How many times did that number of years pass between rate increases? 2
6. How many times did the rate increase by 2 cents? 3
7. How many times did the rate increase by 3 cents? 3
8. Congress issued the first postage stamp in 1847. In 1855, Congress required all mail to have stamps. How many years passed from the year the first stamp was issued to the year stamps were required? 8

Copyright © SRA/McGraw-Hill. Permission is granted to reproduce this page for classroom use.

Math Explorations and Applications Level 4 • 15

REAL-WORLD CONNECTION

Homework Have students interview an adult family member or friend about how and when that person does comparison shopping in real life.

LESSON 16

Student Edition pages 54–57

Using Relation Signs

LESSON PLANNER

Objectives

- ▶ to review the meaning of the relation signs <, >, and =
- ▶ to provide practice in using the relation signs to compare numbers, sums, and differences
- ▶ to help students develop the broad ability to use mathematical common sense

Context of the Lesson Inequalities and the use of the three common relation signs have been taught in previous grade levels and will come up in varying contexts throughout the year. This lesson also contains Part 4 of "Muddle at Bat," a six-part Thinking Story.

MANIPULATIVES	Program Resources
none	Number Cubes
	Practice Master 16
	Enrichment Master 16
	For career connections: Careers and Math*
	For extra practice: CD-ROM* Lesson 16

1 Warm-Up 5 MINUTES

Problem of the Day Present this problem: Place the signs +, –, and = between the numbers to make a true number sentence. Keep the numbers in the order in which they are given: 6 5 4 1 8. (6 + 5 – 4 + 1 = 8)

Problem-Solving Strategies Ask students who have solved the Problem of the Day to share how they solved it and any strategies they used.

MENTAL MATH Provide problems in which students show thumbs up for answers greater than 100 or thumbs down for answers less than 100.

a. 100 + 1 (thumbs up)

b. 100 – 1 (thumbs down)

c. 200 – 150 (thumbs down)

d. 300 – 199 (thumbs up)

(continued on page 55)

MIXED PRACTICE

LESSON 16

Using Relation Signs

Do you remember what these signs mean?

< > =

Here are some examples:

25 < 30 means 25 **is less than** 30.

10 > 7 means 10 **is greater than** 7.

4 + 9 = 13 means 4 plus 9 **is equal to** 13.

Copy each statement and replace ● with <, >, or = to make each statement true.

1. 27 ● 19 **>**
2. 11 ● 77 + 66 **<**
3. 39 ● 52 + 49 **<**
4. 36 ● 18 **>**
5. 79 ● 77 + 10 **<**
6. 8 + 9 ● 8 – 2 **>**
7. 19 ● 79 **<**
8. 16 ● 21 + 3 **<**
9. 18 – 9 ● 18 + 3 **<**
10. 4 + 3 ● 3 + 4 **=**
11. 56 ● 40 + 20 **<**
12. 33 – 6 ● 33 – 7 **>**
13. 9 ● 19 + 10 **<**
14. 39 ● 29 + 29 **<**
15. 49 + 3 ● 49 + 5 **<**
16. 100 ● 73 + 10 **>**
17. 63 ● 33 + 23 **>**
18. 77 – 16 ● 74 – 16 **>**
19. 84 ● 73 – 10 **>**
20. 55 ● 55 – 13 **>**
21. 20 – 15 ● 25 – 10 **<**

PROBLEM SOLVING

Solve.

22. Mr. Bannerji has $100. Does he have enough money to pay for
    - **a.** a jacket and a tie? **no**
    - **b.** a pair of pants and a sweater? **yes**
    - **c.** a sweater and three ties? **yes**

Literature Connection With students, read the story "Alice's Adventures in Symbolville" on pages 48–53 of *Alice in Numberland: Fantasy Math* edited by Sara Mark, et al. You might invite volunteers to take turns reading parts of the story, or have students record some of the inequalities used in the story.

*available separately

COOPERATIVE LEARNING

Inequality Game

Players: Two
Materials: Two 0–5 cubes (red), two 5–10 cubes (blue)
Object: To fill in an inequality statement correctly
Math Focus: Identifying inequalities and mathematical reasoning

RULES

1. Make one of these game forms on a sheet of paper:

   ___ < ___ or ___ > ___

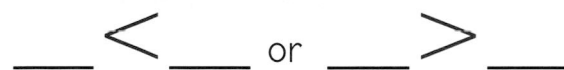

2. Roll all four cubes, make two two-digit numbers, and write their sum on either side of the inequality sign. If you roll a 10, roll that cube again.
3. The other player rolls all four cubes, makes two two-digit numbers, and writes his or her sum in the remaining space.
4. If the inequality statement is true, the other player wins. If the inequality statement is false, you win.
5. Players take turns being first.

MATH JOURNAL

If you played this game again, how would you play it? Would you use the same strategy? Explain your strategy in your Math Journal.

LEARNING STYLES

Meeting Individual Needs

Students who are visual learners may benefit from thinking of the relation sign < as a slanted "L" for "less than." Or you might draw for them a fish whose mouth is made of the inequality sign. This fish tries to eat the greater number. For example:

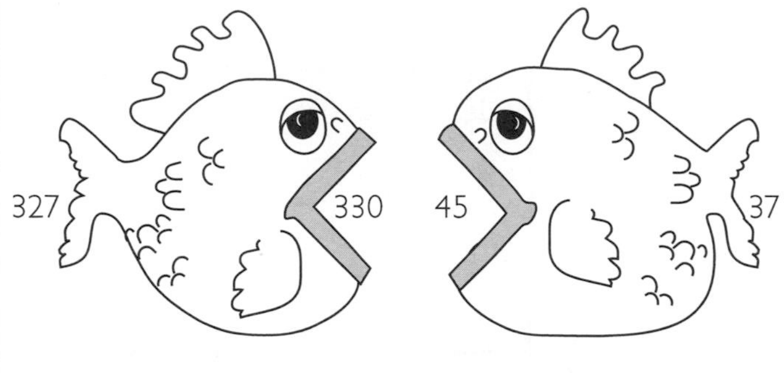

Mental Math (continued)

- **e.** 80 + 7 (thumbs down)
- **f.** 59 + 80 (thumbs up)
- **g.** 59 – 9 (thumbs down)
- **h.** 51 + 29 (thumbs down)
- **i.** 80 + 37 (thumbs up)
- **j.** 90 – 5 (thumbs down)
- **k.** 48 + 68 (thumbs up)
- **l.** 99 – 1 (thumbs down)
- **m.** 88 + 13 (thumbs up)
- **n.** 49 – 19 (thumbs down)
- **o.** 150 – 30 (thumbs up)
- **p.** 190 – 80 (thumbs up)

2 Teach

Using the Student Pages Demonstrate the "Inequality" game on page 55 for practice with relation signs before students begin work on page 54. Those who finish early may play immediately. Remind students that the small ends of the < and > signs always point to the lesser number and the large ends point to the greater number. If the two numbers have the same value, we use the equal sign, =, which is the same at both ends. Solve a few problems on page 54 with the class to show students that they do not need to add or subtract to complete these problems. In problem 12, for example, discuss why 33 – 6 must be greater than 33 – 7 without calculating the differences. If students insist on doing the calculations, let them do so. Assign the remaining problems for students to do individually. When students have finished, allow some time to discuss their methods for finding the answers.

Play the "Inequality" game at the chalkboard with a student. The math focus of this game is recognizing true and false inequality statements and mathematical reasoning. Some students may remember the game from Level 3. Ask students to read the inequalities aloud to provide practice in saying the symbols correctly and in using numbers that make the statement true.

Teach

Using the Thinking Story In "Muddle at Bat (Part 4)" Mr. Muddle devises another bat test, this time using baseball players. This installment of the story centers on the importance of controlling variables when designing a good performance test. By analyzing the results of the test, students develop an intuitive understanding of the importance of sample size and of the concept of ratio in terms of batting average.

Answers to Thinking Story Questions:

1. Sandy Hare got the most hits, but Speck Tackle got the most hits for the number of times he was at bat. Speck got a hit more than half the time; Sandy and Al got hits less than half the time. Some students may be interested in the batting averages: 15 for 40 is .375, 12 for 41 is .293, and 5 for 8 is .625.
2. No, because it is unclear whether the differences are because of the bats, the players, the combination of bats and players, or other factors that might affect hitting and fielding.

MATH JOURNAL Have students summarize in their Math Journals the first four parts of the story, and then rate Mr. Muddle's progress as a product tester.

THINKING STORY

Muddle at Bat

Part 4

You may want to refer to previous parts of this Thinking Story, on pages 18–19, 34–35, and 48–49.

Mr. Muddle thought of a better way to test baseball bats. He tested how well the bats worked in real games. For the next two weeks, Sandy Hare always used the Arrow bat when he played. Al Button, the second-best batter on the team, always used the Slugger bat. And Speck Tackle, a pinch hitter, used the Champ bat. Mr. Muddle went to every game. He kept a record of what happened.

Sandy Hare batted 40 times and got 15 hits with the Arrow bat. Al Button, with his Slugger, batted 41 times and got 12 hits. Speck Tackle, using the Champ bat, batted eight times and got five hits.

. . . to be continued

RETEACHING

Although most students can identify the greater or lesser quantity in a number statement, some write the wrong sign, or read the sign incorrectly, when the lesser number appears first. Have these students point to either the greater or lesser quantity. Then help them determine the correct sign to use to complete the statement. Remind students to read a number sentence from left to right, just as they read sentences with words. They must use the sign they can read from left to right to describe the correct relationship.

Work in groups. Discuss your answers and how you figured them out. Then compare your answers with those of other groups. **Answers are in margin.**

1. Who do you think did the best hitting? Why?
2. Does this test tell you which bat is best for getting hits? Explain.

❸ Wrap-Up (5 MINUTES)

In Closing Ask students to use a relation sign to make the statement 16 + 13 □ 12 + 15 true. (>)

ALTERNATIVE ASSESSMENT

Informal Assessment Have students explain in their own words how they know which relation signs to use in the statements they created playing the "Inequality" game. Then have them read a few of the statements aloud so you can ascertain whether they understand the meaning of the signs.

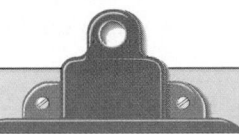

Assessment Criteria

Did the student . . .

- ✓ correctly answer at least 75% of the relation problems?
- ✓ recognize how to evaluate relation statements without doing the calculations?
- ✓ contribute to the Thinking Story discussion?
- ✓ demonstrate an intuitive understanding of batting average?

PRACTICE p. 16

LESSON 16 PRACTICE Name______________________

What is the right sign? Draw <, >, or =.

1. 32 (>) 27	2. 42 (<) 52
3. 84 (<) 88	4. 104 (<) 401
5. 768 (>) 678	6. 6 + 7 (<) 23
7. 12 (<) 11 + 11	8. 105 (>) 100 − 5
9. 58 (<) 62 + 8	10. 84 (>) 70 + 9
11. 100 (<) 100 + 50	12. 200 (<) 127 + 139
13. 67 − 18 (>) 20	14. 72 (<) 70 + 20
15. 38 (<) 41 + 27	16. 66 (>) 66 − 6
17. 70 + 1 (>) 68	18. 16 + 16 (<) 116
19. 2 + 3 (<) 4 + 3	20. 16 + 7 (=) 7 + 16
21. 16 − 7 (<) 16 + 7	22. 50 + 20 (=) 20 + 50
23. 50 + 20 (>) 50 − 20	24. 27 + 6 (>) 17 + 3
25. 48 − 20 (>) 32 − 20	26. 58 + 7 (>) 54 + 4
27. 27 − 4 (>) 21 − 3	28. 86 − 18 (>) 50 − 25
29. 105 − 28 (<) 125 − 18	30. 47 + 39 (=) 39 + 47
31. 64 − 16 (<) 39 + 42	32. 84 − 29 (<) 62 + 10

16 • *Math Explorations and Applications* Level 4

Copyright © SRA/McGraw-Hill. Permission is granted to reproduce this page for classroom use.

ENRICHMENT p. 16

LESSON 16 ENRICHMENT Name______________________

Use the picture to solve each problem. List all possible answers. Write <, >, or = above the problem where the signs are spelled out in each sentence.

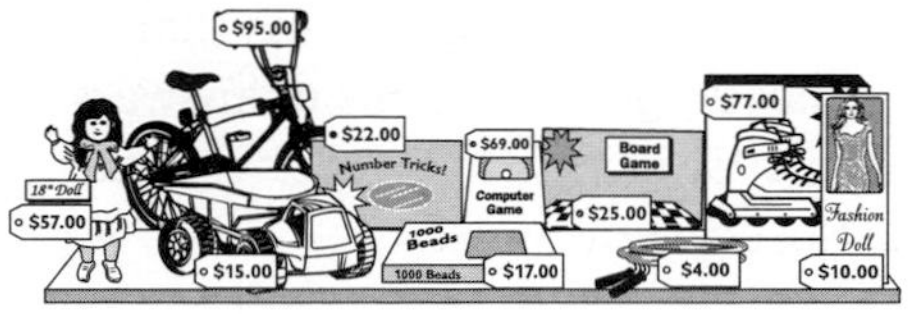

1. Which two toys have a total price less (<) than $15.00?
   fashion doll and jump rope; $10.00 + $4.00 = $14.00
2. If you buy the computer game and one other toy, the total price equals (=) $73.00.
   computer game and jump rope; $69.00 + $4.00 = $73.00
3. If you buy the number tricks and one other toy, the total price is less (<) than $40.00.
   fashion doll, truck, beads, jump rope; $22.00 + $10.00 = $32.00; $22.00 + $15.00 = $37.00; $22.00 + $17.00 = $39.00; $22.00 + $4.00 = $26.00
4. If you buy these two items, the total price is greater (>) than $50.00 but less (<) than $75.00.
   Possible answer: computer game and jump rope, $69.00 + $4.00 = $73.00; 18" doll and fashion doll, $57.00 + $10.00 = $67.00; 18" doll and beads, $57.00 + $17.00 = $74.00

16 • *Math Explorations and Applications* Level 4

Copyright © SRA/McGraw-Hill. Permission is granted to reproduce this page for classroom use.

Homework Have students play the "Inequality" game with a family member for further practice with identifying inequalities. A copy of this game can also be found on page 12 of the Home Connections Blackline Masters.

Student Edition pages 58–59

LESSON 17 Addition and Subtraction with Hidden Digits

LESSON PLANNER

Objective

- ▶ to provide practice in using approximation techniques to solve problems for which digits of some numbers are unknown

Context of the Lesson Approximation techniques have been taught previously, but the paint-spot format used in this lesson is new. This format will continue to be used throughout this and subsequent grade levels. A checkpoint for monitoring individual students' progress with approximation by detecting obviously wrong answers is provided in Lesson 18.

MANIPULATIVES

none

Program Resources

Practice Master 17

Enrichment Master 17

For extra practice:

CD-ROM* Lesson 17

Cumulative Review, page 537

1 Warm-Up 5 MINUTES

Problem of the Day Present the following problem to students and challenge them to find the 15 possible answers: Use only the digits 3, 4, and 5 to make two-digit numbers. Then use those numbers to make as many different true statements as you can with the < sign. (There are many possible answers, for example, 44 < 45 and 34 < 45.)

Problem-Solving Strategies Ask students who have solved the Problem of the Day to share how they solved it and any strategies they used.

MENTAL MATH Have students respond to the following problems by showing whether the answer is obviously wrong (thumbs down) or possibly correct (thumbs up). When finished, you may want to briefly discuss techniques students used to decide whether the answers were reasonable.

a. 700 – 100 = 600 (thumbs up)

b. 550 + 100 = 650 (thumbs up)

(continued on page 59)

LESSON 17 Addition and Subtraction with Hidden Digits

ALGEBRA READINESS

Paint has been spilled on these two pages. One answer is correct in each case. Decide which answer is correct, then discuss methods for solving these problems.

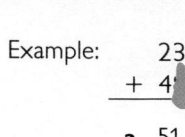

Example: 23 + 4_

a. 51
b. 61
(c.) 71

The sum must be at least 63. It could be as much as 72. So the correct answer must be **c**, 71.

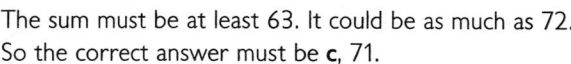

1. 68 + 2_ — **a.** 86 **(b.)** 96 **c.** 106
2. 204 + 7_ — **a.** 99 **(b.)** 279 **c.** 949
3. 53_ + 330 — **a.** 259 **(b.)** 863 **c.** 1059
4. 2_5 + 3_ — **a.** 83 **b.** 492 **(c.)** 613
5. 456 + 31_ — **a.** 143 **(b.)** 769 **c.** 283
6. 670_ + ___ — **a.** 6532 **(b.)** 7413 **c.** 9705
7. 87 – 3_ — **(a.)** 51 **b.** 64 **c.** 92
8. 82 – 3_ — **(a.)** 46 **b.** 56 **c.** 66

Literature Connection For illustrations and questions that encourage predictions of answers, refer students to *Number Puzzles* by Rose Griffiths.

RETEACHING

Suggest that students who experience difficulty solving paint-spot problems use trial and error to eliminate answer choices. Have them try each answer choice to see if it might make sense. Encourage students to verbalize their thinking as they consider each possibility to help them focus their strategies.

Another strategy is to try breaking up the problems into more manageable steps. First tell students that the clues they need are there. Have students tell how many and which digits are covered by the paint. Then have them identify the operation sign. Finally, help them approximate a range of answers to narrow down the choices.

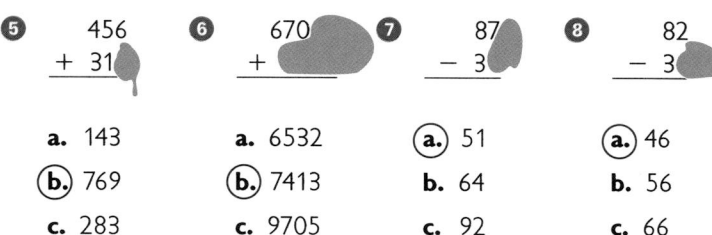

*available separately

9. 100 − 7▢ — a. 15 (b.) 25 c. 35

10. 74▢ − 283 — a. 406 b. 582 (c.) 462

11. 8▢ − 3▢5 — (a.) 482 b. 607 c. 758

12. 30▢ − ▢ — (a.) 206 b. 317 c. 402

13. 812 − 368 — (a.) 4▢ b. 5▢ c. 6▢

14. 7904 − 6▢ — a. 1250 (b.) 725▢ c. 76▢

15. 3406 − 759 — a. ▢757 b. ▢747 (c.) ▢647

16. 207 + 6▢ — a. 367 (b.) 269 c. 142

17. 875 − 10▢ — (a.) 771 b. 975 c. 676

18. 65 − 4▢ — a. 13 (b.) 23 c. 103

19. 273 + 1▢5 — a. 329 b. 128 (c.) 398

20. 46▢ + 21▢ — a. 690 b. 258 (c.) 675

ANTASTIC FACT

The highest mountains on the moon, the lunar Appennines, reach more than 24,600 feet.

se the Cumulative Review on page 537 after this lesson.

Mental Math (continued)

c. 320 + 100 = 420 (thumbs up)

d. 586 + 299 = 596 (thumbs down)

e. 238 + 47 = 285 (thumbs up)

2 Teach

Using the Student Pages Be sure that everyone understands the paint-spot format. Then discuss the example. You may wish to go over a few other problems on pages 58 and 59 to be sure students understand the reasoning they can use to solve them. Encourage students to work in small groups and to discuss what they know for certain about each problem. These are difficult problems, but they provide excellent practice in thinking, approximating, and applying an understanding of our number system.

3 Wrap-Up

In Closing Have students solve the following problem on their own: Ramón can't remember how much money his mother gave him to buy a loaf of bread. He knows he has $2.75 in his pocket, and he also has a receipt that shows "Bread, $1.25." How much did he have to start with? ($4.00)

SELF ASSESSMENT

Have each student write a brief statement that describes the kinds of math reasoning they used to solve paint-spot problems. Invite them to include their reactions to this kind of problem.

PRACTICE p. 17

LESSON 17 PRACTICE Name__________

ALGEBRA READINESS

Choose the correct answer. Discuss your methods.
Methods will vary. Correct answers are given.

1. 76 + 2▢ = b — a. 90 b. 100 c. 110
2. 302 + ▢9 = a — a. 381 b. 481 c. 1011
3. 626 + 5▢0 = c — a. 146 b. 1056 c. 1146
4. 275 + ▢4 = c — a. 99 b. 199 c. 299
5. 41▢ + 1▢ = b — a. 375 b. 425 c. 525
6. 83▢ + 79 = b — a. 809 b. 917 c. 1009
7. 2▢▢ + 424 = b — a. 90 b. 700 c. 900
8. 35▢ + 1▢9 = b — a. 420 b. 530 c. 600
9. 7▢0 + 125 = a — a. 845 b. 948 c. 1045
10. 98 − 3▢ = a — a. 64 b. 72 c. 94
11. 7▢ − 56 = b — a. 9 b. 19 c. 29
12. 746 − 40▢ = c — a. 137 b. 237 c. 337
13. 3▢4 − 122 = a — a. 182 b. 282 c. 420
14. 71▢ − 53▢ = b — a. 95 b. 185 c. 225
15. 2▢▢8 − 809 = c — a. 669 b. 769 c. 1869
16. 4▢5▢ − 739 = b — a. 4911 b. 3919 c. 3809

Copyright © SRA/McGraw-Hill. Permission is granted to reproduce this page for classroom use.

Math Explorations and Applications Level 4 • 17

ENRICHMENT p. 17

LESSON 17 ENRICHMENT Name__________

The numbers 1 2 3 4 5 6 7 8 are arranged consecutively. Put the numbers in the squares so that no consecutive numbers are adjacent vertically, horizontally, or diagonally.

Answers will vary. Possible solution:

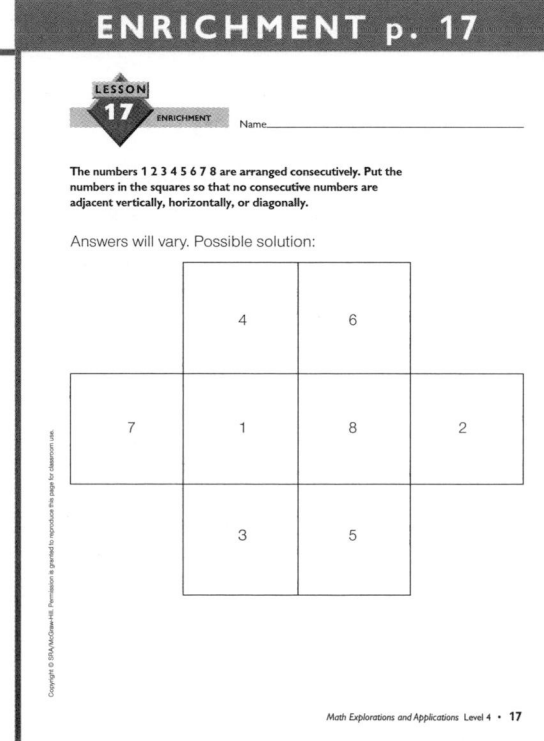

	4	6	
7	1	8	2
	3	5	

Copyright © SRA/McGraw-Hill. Permission is granted to reproduce this page for classroom use.

Math Explorations and Applications Level 4 • 17

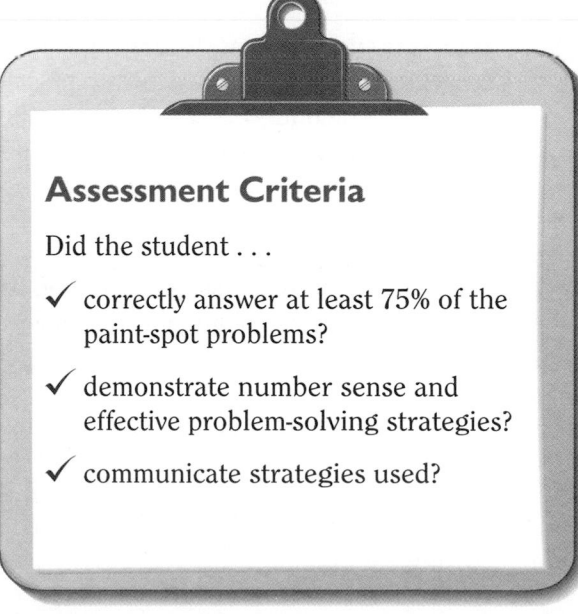

Assessment Criteria

Did the student . . .

✓ correctly answer at least 75% of the paint-spot problems?

✓ demonstrate number sense and effective problem-solving strategies?

✓ communicate strategies used?

Homework Challenge students to use crayons or markers to create four "paint-spot" problems for classmates to solve.

LESSON 18

Student Edition pages 60–63

Approximation: Applications

LESSON PLANNER

Objectives

✓ to assess mastery of and provide practice in approximating answers to addition and subtraction problems

▶ to help students develop the broad ability to use mathematical common sense

Context of the Lesson This is the second of two lessons on approximating with multidigit numbers. It includes a checkpoint for assessing mastery of approximating answers to addition and subtraction problems. More work with approximation is included regularly throughout the year. This lesson also contains Part 5 of "Muddle at Bat," a six-part Thinking Story.

MANIPULATIVES

restaurant menu (optional)

Program Resources

Practice Master 18
Enrichment Master 18
Assessment Master
For career connections: Careers and Math*
For extra practice: CD-ROM* Lesson 18

1 Warm-Up (5 minutes)

Problem of the Day Present this problem: Taco Town is having a sale. During the sale, you can buy one taco for 49¢, two tacos for 79¢, three for $1.09, and so on. If you had $2.50, how many sale tacos could you buy? (7: the first taco costs 49¢, each subsequent taco costs 30¢.)

Problem-Solving Strategies Ask students who have solved the Problem of the Day to share how they solved it and any strategies they used.

MENTAL MATH Give problems with answers and have students show thumbs down for obviously wrong answers and thumbs up for possibly correct ones. Tell students that the answer to a problem will be correct if it is not obviously wrong.

a. 438 + 200 = 338 (thumbs down)

b. 400 + 972 = 672 (thumbs down)

(continued on page 61)

PROBLEM SOLVING

LESSON 18 Approximation: Applications

SOCIAL STUDIES CONNECTION

Sometimes you don't need an exact answer. Select the best answer for each problem. You don't have to do the calculations.

1. George Washington was born in 1732. About how many years ago was that?
   (**a.**) About 270 **b.** About 170 **c.** About 570

2. The zipper was invented in 1891. About how many years ago was that?
   a. About 50 **b.** About 150 (**c.**) About 100

3. Christopher Columbus reached America in 1492. About how many years ago was that?
   (**a.**) About 500 **b.** About 250 **c.** About 100

4. The American Declaration of Independence was signed in 1776. About how many years ago was that?
   a. About 100 (**b.**) About 200 **c.** About 300

5. According to the 1990 census, the population of Houston, Texas, was 1,630,553 and the population of Chicago, Illinois, was 2,783,726. About how many more people lived in Chicago than in Houston?
   a. About 115,000 (**b.**) About 1,150,000 **c.** About 11,500,000

60 • Addition and Subtraction

Why teach it this way?

Keep in mind that students have a natural tendency to seek the security of an "exact" answer, even when a precise answer is inappropriate. This program provides many instances in which estimation or approximation are more appropriate than a precise calculation. Whenever you have the opportunity, provide more of these examples for students.

Science Connection

Have students find out when some famous inventions first appeared, or when famous inventors were born. They can use the information to create their own estimation problems similar to the ones on these pages and give them to classmates to solve.

*available separately

6. In 1994, 66,435,252 passengers flew into or out of Chicago's O'Hare Airport. That same year 54,090,579 passengers flew into or out of Atlanta's Hartsfield Airport. About how many more passengers flew into or out of O'Hare than Hartsfield?

   (a.) 12,300,000 **b.** 1,230,000 **c.** 123,000

7. In 1996 the United States minted $69,858,000 worth of 50-cent pieces (half-dollars). About how many coins is that?

   (a.) 140,000,000 **b.** 13,970,000 **c.** 5,000,000

8. In 1995 the number of kilometers of railroad track in Canada was 56,000; in Mexico it was 19,573. About how many more kilometers of track did Canada have than Mexico?

   a. 3640 (b.) 36,400 **c.** 364

9. The air distance between Boston, Massachusetts, and Seattle, Washington, is 4016 kilometers. The air distance between Boston and Los Angeles, California, is 3131 kilometers. Boston is about how much farther away from Seattle than it is from Los Angeles?

   a. 90 kilometers **b.** 710 kilometers (c.) 900 kilometers

Literature Connection Have students work in groups to read *A More or Less Fish Story* by Joanne and David Wylie, and make up a set of clues that would lead classmates to an approximation. Ask groups to exchange clues.

Mental Math (continued)

c. 864 – 800 = 64 (thumbs up)
d. 521 + 300 = 421 (thumbs down)
e. 328 + 300 = 628 (thumbs up)
f. 500 – 438 = 62 (thumbs up)
g. 500 – 400 = 900 (thumbs down)
h. 600 + 228 = 828 (thumbs up)
i. 926 – 600 = 626 (thumbs down)
j. 580 + 900 = 980 (thumbs down)
k. 320 – 100 = 220 (thumbs up)
l. 1000 – 888 = 300 (thumbs down)

2 Teach

COOPERATIVE LEARNING **Using the Student Pages** Divide the class into small groups and have students act out problems, such as the seventh one, with lesser numbers. For example, if $10 in 50-cent pieces were minted, how many coins would that be? (20) Once students decide which operation is needed, they should be able to solve the problem by approximating.

AT RISK MANIPULATIVES

Meeting Individual Needs
Tell students that being able to approximate reasonable answers or eliminate unreasonable ones from consideration is a useful skill in many real-life situations. For instance, they need not find an exact total in advance to know that they cannot afford a $3.00 sandwich, a $1.50 order of fries, and a $1.00 drink if they have only $4.00 to spend. Have students use a **restaurant menu** to approximate meals they could buy for $4.00, for $6.00, and for $8.00.

◆ LESSON 18 Approximation: Applications

Teach

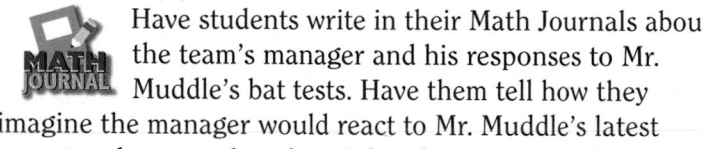

Using the Thinking Story Part 5 of "Muddle at Bat" presents yet another test of bats. This time Mr. Muddle tests ten of each kind of bat, but uses unreliable test methods. Part 5 concludes the discussion of designing a good performance test—one in which interpretation of the results yields useful information.

Answers to Thinking Story Questions:

1. 30
2. Bats of the same brand will not necessarily have exactly the same strength. If only one bat were tested, it might be an especially strong one or a faulty one.
3. If the first rock was a big one, then it is not likely that hitting bats against a still larger rock would make a difference. Although a rock might yield or move when hit, a smaller rock might yield or move more.
4. Mr. Muddle's test is not sensitive enough to tell whether there is a difference among three brands of bats. To find out whether some are stronger, a way would be needed for reproducing the type of impact made on a bat by a pitched ball and of repeating the impact (either at the same level of intensity or at gradually increasing levels of intensity, depending on whether the test was for breaking point or endurance).

MATH JOURNAL Have students write in their Math Journals about the team's manager and his responses to Mr. Muddle's bat tests. Have them tell how they imagine the manager would react to Mr. Muddle's latest report and suggest how he might advise Mr. Muddle.

◆ LESSON 18 Approximation: Applications

THINKING STORY

Muddle at Bat

Part 5

You may want to refer to previous parts of this Thinking Story, on pages 18–19, 34–35, 48–49, and 56–57.

One day when Al Button was batting, his Slugger bat broke. "That proves Slugger bats are no good," he said. "Let's use Arrow bats."

The manager said, "Not so fast. I want a better test." He told Mr. Muddle to take ten of each kind of bat and test how strong they were.

Mr. Muddle carried all the bats off in a wagon. He kept going until he found a big rock. Then he took each bat and hit it against the rock. Not one of the bats broke. "All of the bats are strong," Mr. Muddle told the manager.

"Give them a harder test," said the manager.

Mr. Muddle went back and found a bigger rock. He hit each bat against the rock. Again, none of them broke.

"Give them a harder test yet," said the manager.

RETEACHING

Break down each approximation problem into steps. First have students identify the operation. Then have them identify the key data needed to solve the problem. For instance, problems that ask "How long ago . . . ?" require students to know the current year. Allow students to rewrite the numbers in any way that will facilitate comparing them.

PRACTICE p. 18

LESSON 18 PRACTICE Name__________

SOCIAL STUDIES CONNECTION **Sometimes you don't need an exact answer. Select the best answer for each problem. You don't have to do the calculations.**

1. Jamestown, Virginia, was established in 1607. About how many years ago was that? **a.** About 400 **b.** About 40 **c.** About 140 — a
2. France recognized America's independence in 1778. About how many years ago was that? **a.** About 20 **b.** About 200 **c.** About 50 — b
3. The United States of America negotiated the Louisiana Purchase from France in 1803. About how many years ago was that? **a.** About 100 **b.** About 20 **c.** About 200 — c
4. X rays were discovered by German physicist Wilhelm Roentgen in 1895. About how many years ago was that? **a.** About 100 **b.** About 10 **c.** About 50 — a
5. In 1990 the population of Kansas City, Missouri, was 435,146, and the population of Memphis, Tennessee, was 610,337. About how many more people lived in Memphis than in Kansas City? **a.** About 175,000 **b.** About 1,750,000 **c.** About 17,500 — a
6. In 1990 the population of Dallas, Texas, was 1,006,877, and the population of Indianapolis, Indiana, was 741,952. About how many more people lived in Dallas than in Indianapolis? **a.** About 2500 **b.** About 25,000 **c.** About 250,000 — c
7. The air distance between Chicago, Illinois, and Salt Lake City, Utah, is 1260 miles. The air distance between Chicago and San Francisco, California, is 1858 miles. Chicago is about how much farther from San Francisco than it is from Salt Lake City? **a.** About 60 miles **b.** About 600 miles **c.** About 6 miles — b

Copyright © SRA/McGraw-Hill. Permission is granted to reproduce this page for classroom use.

Mr. Muddle went out again with his wagon full of bats. On the street he stopped to watch a crew tearing down a building. The workers had a crane that swung a huge steel ball back and forth. When the steel ball hit a wall, the wall crashed down. Mr. Muddle put all the bats on the ground. He asked the workers, "Would you try to break these bats with your steel ball?"

"Are you sure you want us to do that?" asked one of the workers.

"Yes," said Mr. Muddle. "I'm giving the bats a test."

The steel ball came crashing down on the bats. Pieces of wood flew into the air.

Later Mr. Muddle reported to the manager. "The bats are all alike. They all passed the easy tests and they all failed the hard test."

. . . to be continued

Work in groups. Discuss your answers and how you figured them out. Then compare your answers with those of other groups. **Answers are in margin.**

1. How many bats did Mr. Muddle test?
2. Why should he have to test so many bats? Why not one of each kind?
3. Was the second test harder than the first? Explain.
4. Is Mr. Muddle right that the bats are all alike? If some are stronger, how could you find out?

❸ Wrap-Up

5 MINUTES

In Closing Discuss with students when it makes sense to approximate and when it makes sense to determine an exact answer.

ANALYZING ANSWERS

Students who consistently make errors in the Mental Math exercise should be checked individually to determine the nature of the difficulty. It may simply be trouble with the format of the exercise. If they can detect obviously wrong sums and differences in problems given in writing or given orally in a one-to-one situation, check off their names on the Mastery Checkpoint Chart. However, if the trouble is with approximating, present problems like the ones in the exercise, but simpler. Ask students to explain why the answer is or is not obviously wrong. For example, 38 + 75 cannot be 353 because each addend is less than 100, so the sum must be less than 200.

Mastery Checkpoint 4

By this time most students should be able to approximate answers to addition and subtraction problems. Assess this ability by observing them during the Mental Math drill. Also, as a regular part of classroom activities, ask students to give an approximate answer when you do a computation problem together. Students who consistently make errors should be checked individually and given extra help. You can record the results of this assessment on the Mastery Checkpoint Chart. You may also wish to assign Assessment Blackline Masters page 5 to determine mastery.

ENRICHMENT p. 18

LESSON 18 ENRICHMENT

Name________________

Ratings for Sleeping Bags					
Model	Polar	Tundra	Arctic	Snuggler	Commodore
Price	$225	$129	$230	$266	$119
Weight	3 pounds, 4 ounces	3 pounds, 1 ounce	2 pounds, 6 ounces	4 pounds, 2 ounces	3 pounds, 8 ounces
Roominess	3	3	3	3	3
Temperature	2	3	4	3	2
Sturdiness	3	3	4	4	3
Overall	2	4	4	3	3
0–very poor 1–poor 2–fair 3–good 4–very good 5–excellent					

The chart above shows some of the performance ratings for five sleeping bags. All the bags are supposed to keep you warm at 20° Fahrenheit. "Temperature" shows how well each bag keeps you warm. "Overall" takes into account all the ratings.

Answer these questions.

1. Which bag is the heaviest? Snuggler
2. Which bag would be easiest to carry for long distances in a backpack? Arctic
3. You don't usually go camping when the temperature is below 20° Fahrenheit. Which bags would be OK for your camping trips? Tundra, Arctic, Snuggler, Commodore, Polar
4. You don't have a lot of money to spend on a bag, and you go camping about once a year. Which bag would be the most sensible choice for you? Why? Answers will vary. Sample answer: Tundra; it is one of the least expensive but still has a good overall rating.

Copyright © SRA/McGraw-Hill. Permission is granted to reproduce this page for classroom use.

18 • *Math Explorations and Applications* Level 4

ASSESSMENT p. 5

UNIT 1

Mastery Checkpoint 4 Detecting obviously wrong answers (Lesson 18)

Name________________

The student demonstrates mastery by correctly answering at least 8 of the 10 problems.

In each problem, two of the answers are clearly wrong and one is correct. Choose the correct answer.

1. 39 + 39 = b   a. 38   b. 78   c. 108
2. 73 + 130 = a   a. 203   b. 103   c. 903
3. 125 − 75 = b   a. 190   b. 50   c. 200
4. 38 − 19 = c   a. 29   b. 49   c. 19
5. 115 + 227 = b   a. 242   b. 342   c. 442
6. 253 − 147 = c   a. 206   b. 176   c. 106
7. 3525 − 314 = b   a. 511   b. 3211   c. 6211

Solve these problems. Ring the correct answer.

8. There are 375 students seated for an assembly. The assembly room holds 500. About how many more students can be seated before the room is full?
   (a.) 100   b. 25   c. 200
9. The first grade wants to add flowers to two planting areas at school. A plant nursery has donated 650 bulbs. They plant 240 in one area. About how many bulbs must they place in the second area?
   a. 150   (b.) 400   c. 600
10. Jeremy has about 158 marbles. His friend Robert had 312 at last count. Between the two of them, about how many marbles do they have?
   a. 400   b. 500   (c.) 470

Copyright © SRA/McGraw-Hill. Permission is granted to reproduce this page for classroom use.

Math Explorations and Applications Level 4 • 5

Assessment Criteria

Did the student . . .

✓ correctly answer at least 80% of the approximation problems?

✓ communicate estimation strategies used?

✓ contribute to the Thinking Story discussion?

Homework Have students devise an appropriate test for Mr. Muddle's bats.

LESSON 19

Student Edition pages 64–67

Introduction to the Calculator

LESSON PLANNER

Objectives

- to help students recognize that different calculators operate in different ways
- to emphasize the importance of entering data into calculators accurately
- to introduce the concept of negative numbers

Context of the Lesson This is the first lesson in Level 4 that focuses on using a calculator as a problem-solving tool.

MANIPULATIVES

base-10 materials (place value blocks*, craft sticks, rubber bands) (optional)

calculators*

number lines, large*

weather thermometer* (optional)

Program Resources

Practice Master 19

Enrichment Master 19

For extra practice: CD-ROM* Lesson 19

1 Warm-Up

5 MINUTES

Problem of the Day Present this problem: Louis is five years older than Kelly. The sum of their ages is the greatest two-digit number that is less than 20. Figure out their ages. (Louis is 12, Kelly is 7.)

Problem-Solving Strategies Ask students who have solved the Problem of the Day to share how they solved it and any strategies they used.

MENTAL MATH Have students practice solving multidigit addition and subtraction problems quickly.

a. 400 + 700 = (1100)

b. 300 – 250 = (50)

c. 9000 + 5000 = (14,000)

d. 6000 + 8000 = (14,000)

e. 1000 – 300 = (700)

f. 14,000 – 4000 = (10,000)

LESSON 19

Introduction to the Calculator

Calculators are useful machines. They can do all sorts of calculations very quickly. However, they only do what somebody tells them to do. Sometimes the calculator may not do what you think it will. You should explore any calculator you plan to use to see if it does what you expect.

The display is the rectangular window that communicates information to you. Once the calculator is turned on you should see "0." on the display. Experiment with the calculator.

Solve the following problems both with your calculator and in your head. Does the calculator get the right answers?

1. 2 + 2 = ? **4**
2. 10 + 10 = ? **20**
3. 2 × 3 = ? **6**
4. 8 ÷ 2 = ? **4**
5. 100 + 100 = ? **200**
6. 5 × 5 = ? **25**
7. 50 × 50 = ? **2500**
8. 500 × 500 = ? **250,000**
9. 5000 × 5000 = ? **25,000,000**
10. 50,000 × 50,000 = ? **2,500,000,000**
11. 500,000 × 500,000 = ? **250,000,000,000**

Did the calculator get the right answer for every problem? Did it do anything strange? What did the answers to questions 10 and 11 look like? Calculator displays have only a small space to show the digits of their answers. Most can show only eight or ten digits.

Why teach it at this time?

Students have used calculators in previous levels of the *Math Explorations and Applications* program. Calculators are reintroduced at this point in Level 4 as a follow-up to the general arithmetic review. Negative numbers are introduced at this time because they may appear on calculators as students experiment.

*available separately

When a calculator tries to show more digits than it can, it may give an error message (maybe an "E" or some other symbol on the display). Directions for your calculator should tell you what it will do and what to do next. Sometimes the calculator will "lock" and stop working until you do something, like press the ON/C key.

12. Using the memory key, find the sum of 5 × 6, 4 × 7, and 3 × 8. Press the CLEAR key between each problem. **82**

Some calculators have a constant function built in so that if you do a problem like 4 + 4 = and then press the = key again it will show 12. Press the = key a third time and it will show 16, and so on. For others you have to press a special key to use the constant feature. See if you can figure out how your calculator does this.

13. Clear the calculator and press 50 – 5 =. Does the display show 45? Continue subtracting 5 repeatedly. What numbers do you get? What happens after you reach 0? What is the number that came right after 0 in this sequence? Is there a negative symbol on the calculator? **yes; 40, 35, 30, 25, 20, 15, 10, 5, 0; you start to get negative numbers; –5; yes**

14. Continue subtracting 5. Look at the number line below. Does the calculator show the numbers you'd expect it to show? **yes**

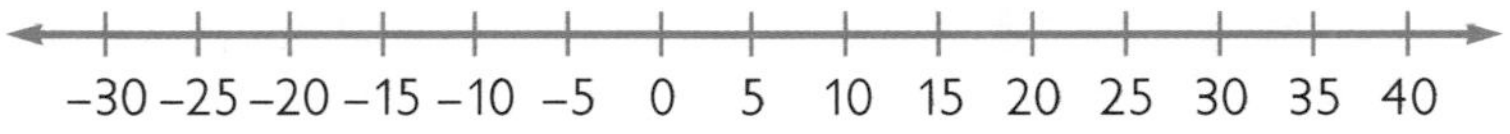

15. If you started at 20 and continually subtracted 4, what are the first three numbers you would expect to appear after 0? Try this on your calculator and see if you get the same numbers. **–4, –8, –12**

MATH JOURNAL

Try different operations with your calculator to find out more about how it works. Write about your findings in your Math Journal.

FANTASTIC FACT

Salt water is, on the average, 3.3 to 3.7% salt. If the salt in all the oceans were combined, it would form a solid mass of salt the size of Africa.

2 Teach

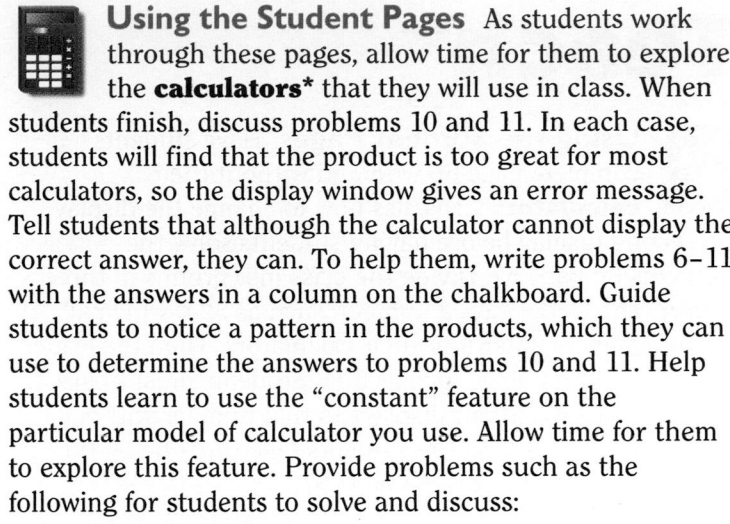

Using the Student Pages As students work through these pages, allow time for them to explore the **calculators*** that they will use in class. When students finish, discuss problems 10 and 11. In each case, students will find that the product is too great for most calculators, so the display window gives an error message. Tell students that although the calculator cannot display the correct answer, they can. To help them, write problems 6–11 with the answers in a column on the chalkboard. Guide students to notice a pattern in the products, which they can use to determine the answers to problems 10 and 11. Help students learn to use the "constant" feature on the particular model of calculator you use. Allow time for them to explore this feature. Provide problems such as the following for students to solve and discuss:

- If you start at 0 and keep adding 3, will you get to 30? To 31? (yes; no)
- If you start at 0 and keep adding 5, will you get to 95? To 5464? (yes; no)
- If you start at 150 and keep subtracting 3, will you get to 1? (no)
- If you start at 0 and keep adding 99, what pattern do you notice in the answers? (The hundreds place increases by 1 and the tens decrease by 1.)

Use the **number line** to discuss the meaning of negative numbers. Help students associate negative numbers with real-world situations, such as degrees below zero on a cold day or an amount of money they owe. Point to the 25 and ask students how to subtract 15 on the number line. (Move three places to the left, ending at 10.) If they subtract 15 again, they move three more spaces left, ending at -5, having crossed the 0 point. Have students read that number as "negative 5." Explain that in certain situations, it is possible to subtract a greater number from a lesser number, which results in a negative number. Use the number line to model some examples, such as 20 minus 50 (–30).

MATH CONNECTION

Math Connection Help students understand the function of the memory keys if they appear on your classroom **calculators***. Memory keys are often labeled M+, M–, and MRC. On most calculators, users press the MRC key once to display anything held in the memory and twice to clear memory. Once the memory is clear, have students press 5 x 6 = M+. This should place the product of 5 and 6 in memory. Most calculators display a small "M" to tell users that there is something in the memory. To find the sum of 30 and 7, students can press MRC + 7 =. When they push MRC the 30 should reappear. Then the calculator will add 7 to it and display 37. Encourage students to experiment with the memory functions. Emphasize that the normal CLEAR key will not clear what is in memory.

*available separately

◆ LESSON 19 Introduction to the Calculator

Teach

Using the Student Pages Have students complete page 66 with and without their **calculators***. Discuss how to change the display to the second display before having students solve the problems on page 67. Divide the class into groups of three or four. The leader says a number, such as 594, which all group members enter into their calculators. Then the leader says a second number, such as 504. Students must figure out how to change their displays to that number without clearing them. After all the students take turns being the leader, have groups work on page 67.

Students who have difficulty changing the display may benefit from using manipulative materials, such as **base-10 blocks*** or **craft sticks** bundled into tens, hundreds, and thousands. Have students use the manipulatives to model the first number and then add or remove materials as needed to get the second number. Then have them repeat their actions on the calculator.

◆ LESSON 19 Introduction to the Calculator

Add and subtract with and without your calculator. See if you get the same answer both ways. Watch your numbering.

16. 2 − 1 − 1 − 1 − 1 **−2**
17. 20 − 10 − 10 − 10 − 10 **−20**
18. 10 − 80 **−70**
19. 80 − 10 **70**
20. 8 − 10 **−2**
21. 100 − 80 **20**
22. −2 + 5 **3**
23. −20 + 50 **30**
24. 1 − 5 **−4**
25. 10 − 50 **−40**
26. 100 − 50 **50**
27. 6 − 6 **0**
28. 8 − 8 **0**
29. 80 − 80 **0**

Add and subtract without using your calculator. Then use your calculator to see whether you get the same answer.

30. 783 + 97 **880**
31. 880 − 97 **783**
32. 783 − 80 **703**
33. 703 + 80 **783**
34. 7 + 5 **12**
35. 70 + 50 **120**
36. 700 + 500 **1200**
37. 7000 + 5000 **12,000**
38. 17 − 8 **9**
39. 170 − 80 **90**
40. 1700 − 800 **900**
41. 7 − 7 **0**
42. 7 − 8 **−1**
43. 70 − 80 **−10**
44. 700 − 800 **−100**
45. 49 + 501 **550**
46. 48 + 52 **100**
47. 480 + 520 **1000**
48. 626 + 24 **650**
49. 509 + 20 **529**
50. 529 − 20 **509**
51. 600 − 298 **302**
52. 6000 − 2980 **3020**
53. 3 − 6 **−3**
54. 30 − 60 **−30**
55. 60 − 30 **30**

Technology Connection

Some computer software has a built-in calculator function. Users enter numbers and operations on a calculator screen with a mouse. Answers appear in the display window and look like they would on a hand-held calculator. If you have access to a computer with this software, allow students to experiment with it to see whether the computer calculator works in the same way as their hand-held **calculators***.

RETEACHING

Students who have difficulty understanding negative numbers may benefit from looking at a weather **thermometer***. Show students that when the temperature is extremely cold, it is referred to as "below zero" and is a negative number. Give students some below-zero temperatures and have them draw what the thermometer would look like.

*available separately

Figure out how to change the first display to the second display. Try to use no more than one step. Watch your numbering.

56	0.	72.	+72	57	−8.	10.	+18
58	783.	83.	−700	59	70.	−20.	−90
60	46.	346.	+300	61	51.	1000.	+949
62	2000.	2010.	+10	63	297.	800.	+503
64	2000.	1998.	−2	65	408.	478.	+70
66	457.	407.	−50	67	−5.	7.	+12
68	7000.	5000.	−2000	69	90.	−40.	−130
70	1600.	900.	−700	71	3333.	3030.	−303
72	1600.	1900.	+300	73	2345.	1234.	−1111
74	900.	0.	−900	75	830.	1100.	+270
76	401.	40.	−361	77	30.	70.	+40
78	539.	509.	−30	79	700.	300.	−400
80	49.	650.	+601	81	−70.	30.	+100

PROBLEM SOLVING

Solve these problems.

82. Winter Elementary School has 400 students. Packard Elementary School has 600 students. How many students do the two schools have all together? **1000**

83. The temperature outside was −20°F in the morning. By late afternoon the temperature was 10°F. By how much did the temperature rise? **30°F**

84. The Cook family's cat had six kittens. Two of the kittens were adopted by neighbors, and the Cooks decided to keep three kittens. How many kittens still need to be adopted? **1**

FANTASTIC FACT

It takes the planet Pluto 247 Earth years to complete an orbit of the sun.

3 Wrap-Up (5 MINUTES)

In Closing Have students explain what a negative number is and give real-life examples of negative numbers.

ALTERNATIVE ASSESSMENT

Performance Assessment Circulate through the classroom as students complete page 67. Notice what they do to change the first display to the second display. Keep records of their actions, comments, and questions.

Assessment Criteria

Did the student . . .

- ✓ demonstrate reasonable proficiency with the calculator?
- ✓ communicate understanding of negative numbers?
- ✓ explain how to solve the display-change problems?

Homework Have students invent a simple game for two players that involves using a **calculator***. They should try out the game with a family member and be prepared to teach classmates.

LEARNING STYLES

Meeting Individual Needs

Note students who consistently use a calculator to solve problems they could easily do mentally. Discuss this with students to see whether they do this because they want to be sure they have a correct answer, have difficulty with mental math, or simply enjoy using a calculator. Help them identify times when it makes sense to use a calculator and times when mental math is more convenient.

PRACTICE p. 19

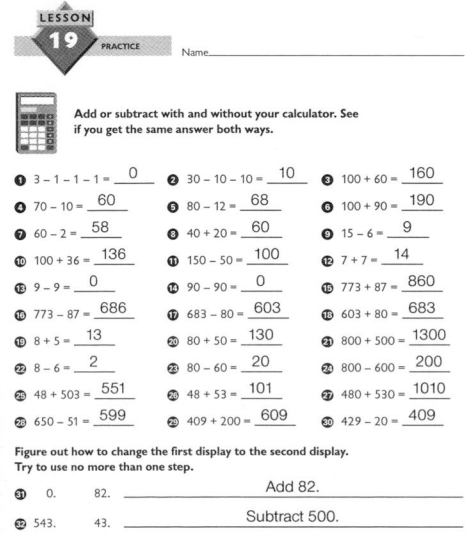

LESSON 19 PRACTICE Name________

Add or subtract with and without your calculator. See if you get the same answer both ways.

1. 3 − 1 − 1 − 1 = 0
2. 30 − 10 − 10 = 10
3. 100 + 60 = 160
4. 70 − 10 = 60
5. 80 − 12 = 68
6. 100 + 90 = 190
7. 60 − 2 = 58
8. 40 + 20 = 60
9. 15 − 6 = 9
10. 100 + 36 = 136
11. 150 − 50 = 100
12. 7 + 7 = 14
13. 9 − 9 = 0
14. 90 − 90 = 0
15. 773 + 87 = 860
16. 773 − 87 = 686
17. 683 − 80 = 603
18. 603 + 80 = 683
19. 8 + 5 = 13
20. 80 + 50 = 130
21. 800 + 500 = 1300
22. 8 − 6 = 2
23. 80 − 60 = 20
24. 800 − 600 = 200
25. 48 + 503 = 551
26. 48 + 53 = 101
27. 480 + 530 = 1010
28. 650 − 51 = 599
29. 409 + 200 = 609
30. 429 − 20 = 409

Figure out how to change the first display to the second display. Try to use no more than one step.

31. 0. 82. Add 82.
32. 543. 43. Subtract 500.
33. 36. 836. Add 800.
34. 800. 0. Subtract 800 or multiply by 0.
35. 5. 100. Add 95 or multiply by 20.

Copyright © SRA/McGraw-Hill. Permission is granted to reproduce this page for classroom use.

Math Explorations and Applications Level 4 • 19

ENRICHMENT p. 19

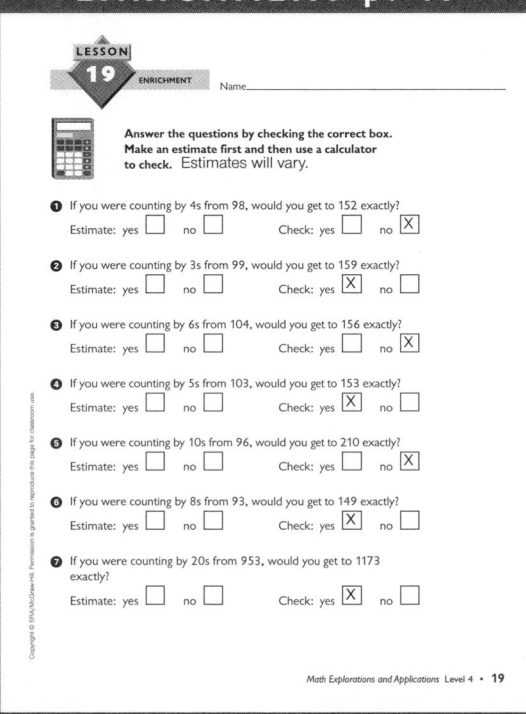

LESSON 19 ENRICHMENT Name________

Answer the questions by checking the correct box. Make an estimate first and then use a calculator to check. Estimates will vary.

1. If you were counting by 4s from 98, would you get to 152 exactly?
   Estimate: yes ☐ no ☐ Check: yes ☐ no ☒
2. If you were counting by 3s from 99, would you get to 159 exactly?
   Estimate: yes ☐ no ☐ Check: yes ☒ no ☐
3. If you were counting by 6s from 104, would you get to 156 exactly?
   Estimate: yes ☐ no ☐ Check: yes ☐ no ☒
4. If you were counting by 5s from 103, would you get to 153 exactly?
   Estimate: yes ☐ no ☐ Check: yes ☒ no ☐
5. If you were counting by 10s from 96, would you get to 210 exactly?
   Estimate: yes ☐ no ☐ Check: yes ☐ no ☒
6. If you were counting by 8s from 93, would you get to 149 exactly?
   Estimate: yes ☐ no ☐ Check: yes ☒ no ☐
7. If you were counting by 20s from 953, would you get to 1173 exactly?
   Estimate: yes ☐ no ☐ Check: yes ☒ no ☐

Copyright © SRA/McGraw-Hill. Permission is granted to reproduce this page for classroom use.

Math Explorations and Applications Level 4 • 19

*available separately

LESSON 20

Student Edition pages 68–69

Estimating with Fractions

LESSON PLANNER

Objectives

- to review fractional notation and the use of fractions
- to provide practice in estimating fractional quantities
- to provide practice in determining whether a given use of fractions makes sense

Context of the Lesson This is the first of five lessons designed to refamiliarize students with the use of fractions and decimals.

MANIPULATIVES

paper

Program Resources

"Fracto 1" and "Fracto 2" Game Mats

Reteaching Master

Practice Master 20

Enrichment Master 20

For additional math integration: Math Throughout the Day*

For extra practice: CD-ROM* Lesson 20

1 Warm-Up (5 MINUTES)

Problem of the Day Have students act out this problem to verify their answers: Suppose you have a piece of **paper**. You fold it in half, then in half again, and then in half one more time. Then you unfold the paper completely. How many sections will you see? (8)

Problem-Solving Strategies Ask students who have solved the Problem of the Day to share how they solved it and any strategies they used.

MENTAL MATH Review fractional notation. Write a fraction on the chalkboard and have students respond in unison with the name of the fraction.

a. $\frac{2}{3}$ (two thirds) **b.** $\frac{1}{6}$ (one sixth)

c. $\frac{1}{5}$ (one fifth) **d.** $\frac{1}{3}$ (one third)

e. $\frac{1}{2}$ (one half) **f.** $\frac{2}{7}$ (two sevenths)

g. $\frac{5}{8}$ (five eighths) **h.** $\frac{3}{4}$ (three fourths)

i. $\frac{6}{7}$ (six sevenths) **j.** $\frac{5}{6}$ (five sixths)

PRACTICE

LESSON 20

Estimating with Fractions

Fractions are often used to describe parts of a whole.

Answer these questions.

1. About how full is the fuel tank?
   a. $\frac{1}{2}$ full **b.** $\frac{1}{3}$ full **(c.)** $\frac{3}{4}$ full

2. About how much of the pie is left?
   (a.) $\frac{1}{6}$ **b.** $\frac{1}{16}$ **c.** $\frac{1}{3}$

3. About how full is the glass?
   a. $\frac{1}{4}$ full **(b.)** $\frac{1}{2}$ full **c.** $\frac{2}{3}$ full

4. About how much of the triangle is colored?
   a. $\frac{1}{2}$ **(b.)** $\frac{2}{3}$ **c.** $\frac{3}{4}$

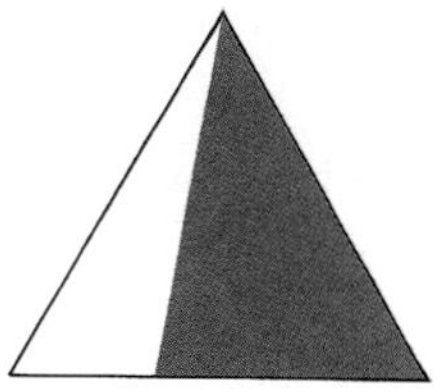

5. About how much of the bookshelf is empty?
   a. $\frac{1}{8}$ **(b.)** $\frac{1}{3}$ **c.** $\frac{1}{2}$

6. The length of the short stick is about what fraction of the length of the long stick?
   (a.) $\frac{1}{8}$ **b.** $\frac{1}{4}$ **c.** $\frac{1}{3}$

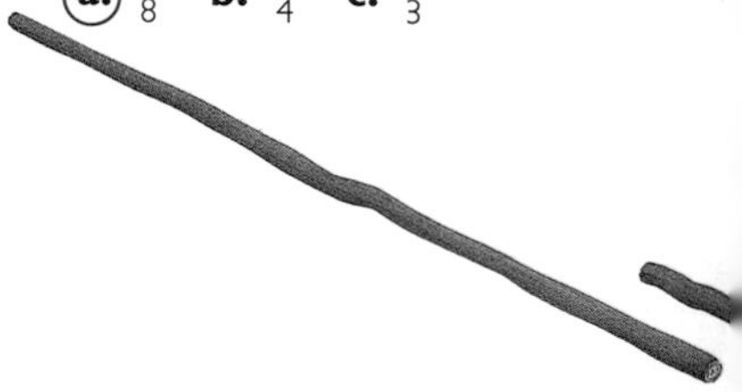

ANALYZING ANSWERS Check on students who have trouble with any exercises in this lesson to determine if the difficulty is with fractional notation. This is indicated when the student correctly answers oral but not written questions involving fractions. Focus on reviewing the meaning of the numerator and denominator.

RETEACHING p. 6

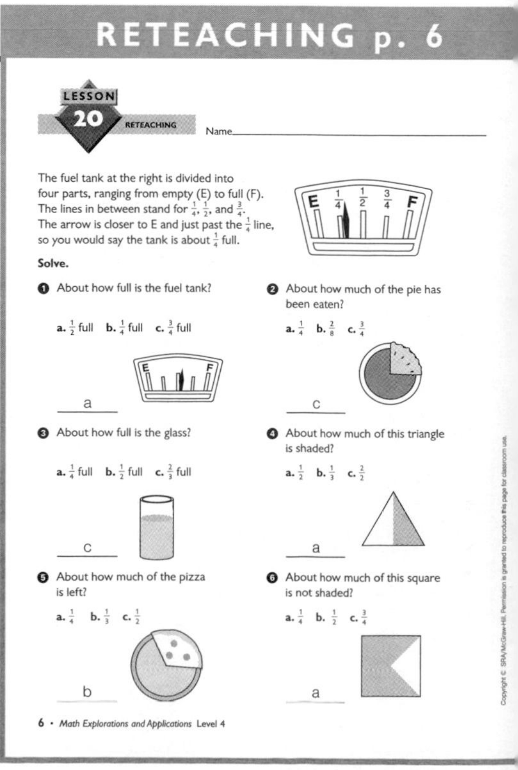

LESSON 20 RETEACHING Name________

The fuel tank at the right is divided into four parts, ranging from empty (E) to full (F). The lines in between stand for $\frac{1}{4}$, $\frac{1}{2}$, and $\frac{3}{4}$. The arrow is closer to E and just past the $\frac{1}{4}$ line, so you would say the tank is about $\frac{1}{4}$ full.

Solve.

1. About how full is the fuel tank?
   a. $\frac{1}{2}$ full **b.** $\frac{1}{4}$ full **c.** $\frac{3}{4}$ full
   a

2. About how much of the pie has been eaten?
   a. $\frac{1}{4}$ **b.** $\frac{2}{8}$ **c.** $\frac{3}{4}$
   c

3. About how full is the glass?
   a. $\frac{1}{4}$ full **b.** $\frac{1}{2}$ full **c.** $\frac{2}{3}$ full
   c

4. About how much of this triangle is shaded?
   a. $\frac{1}{2}$ **b.** $\frac{1}{3}$ **c.** $\frac{2}{2}$
   a

5. About how much of the pizza is left?
   a. $\frac{1}{4}$ **b.** $\frac{1}{3}$ **c.** $\frac{1}{2}$
   b

6. About how much of this square is not shaded?
   a. $\frac{1}{4}$ **b.** $\frac{1}{2}$ **c.** $\frac{3}{4}$
   a

6 • *Math Explorations and Applications* Level 4

Copyright © SRA/McGraw-Hill. Permission is granted to reproduce this page for classroom use.

*available separately

Which statements do not make sense? Write your reasons.

7. In Diana's class, $\frac{1}{2}$ of the students are girls, and $\frac{2}{3}$ are boys. **does not make sense**
8. In Masani's class, $\frac{1}{2}$ of the students are boys, and $\frac{3}{4}$ of the students are wearing sneakers. **makes sense**
9. Eric tossed a coin 12 times. $\frac{1}{2}$ of the tosses turned up heads. $\frac{1}{4}$ of the tosses turned up tails. **does not make sense**
10. Jordan is using a recipe that makes three servings. Only two people will be eating, so Jordan makes $\frac{2}{3}$ of the amount given for each ingredient. **makes sense**
11. There are ten fireplace logs in a bundle. If five logs are burned, $\frac{1}{2}$ of the bundle is left. **makes sense**
12. In $\frac{1}{2}$ of an hour, Dan, Rachel, and Leon planted a small flower garden. If they started at 9:00 A.M., they must have worked until 10:30 A.M. **does not make sense**
13. The bottom half of this bottle holds more juice than the top half.

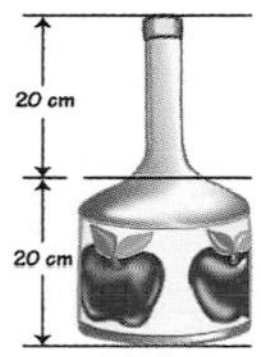

It depends; it makes sense if the "bottom half" refers to half the height of the bottle and not half the volume.

14. A spinner has six parts of the same size.
    a. $\frac{1}{2}$ of the area of the spinner is red. **makes sense**
    b. If you spin the spinner many times, you would land on red about $\frac{1}{2}$ of the time. **makes sense**

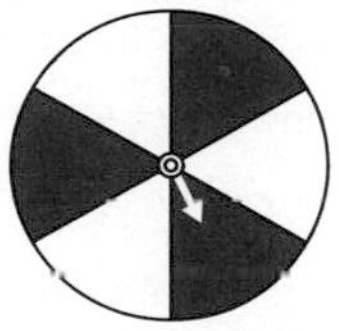

15. Mai ate $\frac{1}{2}$ of her birthday cake on Monday, $\frac{1}{2}$ on Tuesday, and $\frac{1}{2}$ on Wednesday. **does not make sense**

❷ Teach

Using the Student Pages You may wish to first demonstrate the "Fracto" Game Mats, which provide practice with recognizing fractional areas of circles and rectangles, so students can play them as they finish page 69.

Solve one or two of the problems on page 68 with the class and have students complete the page on their own. Ask volunteers to explain to the class why they picked the answers they did. When the whole class has finished page 68, use the same technique for page 69. Some questions will have more than one reasonable answer.

GAME

Introducing the "Fracto" Game Mats These Game Mats provide practice with mental addition of fractions and recognizing fractional areas of circles and rectangles. Demonstrate "Fracto 1" by playing it with a student. Complete directions are on the Game Mat. Encourage students to play "Fracto 2" when they feel they have mastered "Fracto 1." A copy of the "Fracto" Game Mats can also be found on pages 592–593 of this Teacher's Guide.

❸ Wrap-Up

5 MINUTES

In Closing Have students explain why it is impossible to have a "bigger half" of something. (If an object is truly cut in half, then by definition it must have two equal parts.)

ALTERNATIVE ASSESSMENT

Portfolio Assessment Have each student make a list of at least ten ways in which fractions are used in daily life. Have them add their lists to their Math Portfolios.

PRACTICE p. 20

LESSON 20 PRACTICE Name__________

Choose the correct answer.

1. About how much of the square is shaded?
   (a.) $\frac{1}{4}$ b. $\frac{1}{2}$ c. $\frac{2}{3}$

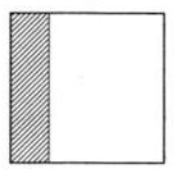

2. About how full is the fuel tank?
   a. $\frac{3}{4}$ (b.) $\frac{1}{4}$ c. $\frac{1}{2}$

3. About how much of the cake is left?
   a. $\frac{1}{2}$ (b.) $\frac{2}{3}$ c. $\frac{1}{5}$

4. The length of the short pipe is about what fraction of the length of the long pipe?
   a. $\frac{1}{4}$ b. $\frac{1}{2}$ (c.) $\frac{2}{3}$

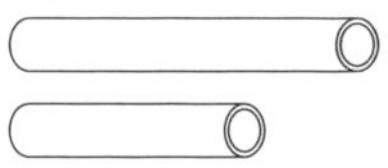

5. About how full is the glass?
   (a.) $\frac{4}{5}$ b. $\frac{2}{5}$ c. $\frac{1}{5}$

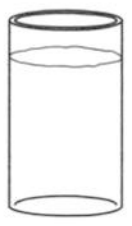

6. About how much of the yard has not been mowed?
   a. $\frac{1}{3}$ b. $\frac{1}{4}$ (c.) $\frac{3}{4}$

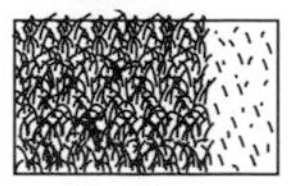

Copyright © SRA/McGraw-Hill. Permission is granted to reproduce this page for classroom use.

20 • *Math Explorations and Applications* Level 4

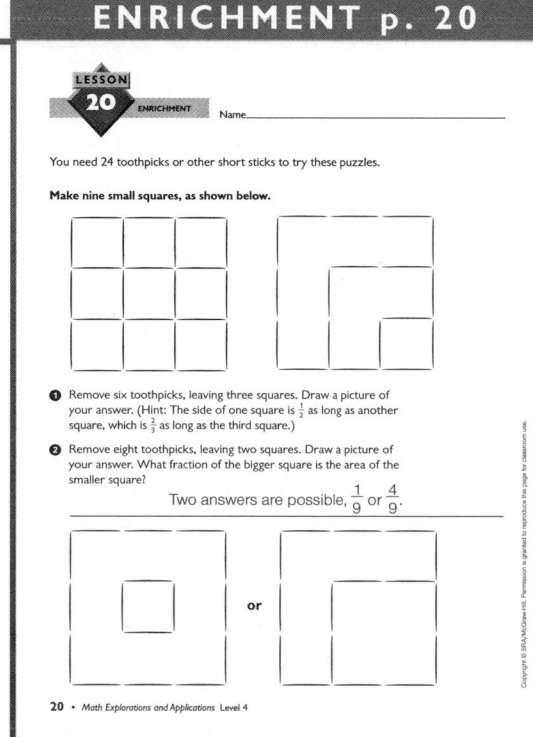

ENRICHMENT p. 20

LESSON 20 ENRICHMENT Name__________

You need 24 toothpicks or other short sticks to try these puzzles.

Make nine small squares, as shown below.

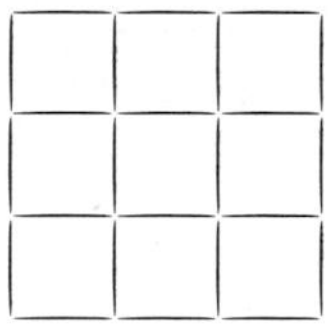

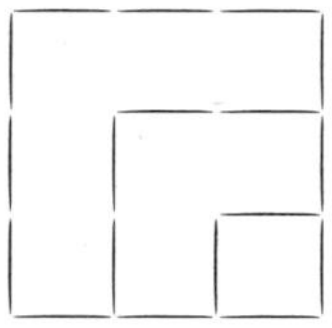

1. Remove six toothpicks, leaving three squares. Draw a picture of your answer. (Hint: The side of one square is $\frac{1}{2}$ as long as another square, which is $\frac{2}{3}$ as long as the third square.)
2. Remove eight toothpicks, leaving two squares. Draw a picture of your answer. What fraction of the bigger square is the area of the smaller square?
   Two answers are possible, $\frac{1}{9}$ or $\frac{4}{9}$.

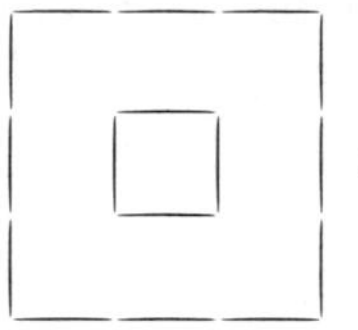

or

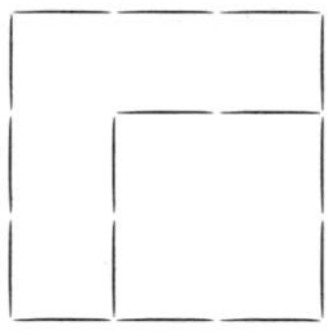

Copyright © SRA/McGraw-Hill. Permission is granted to reproduce this page for classroom use.

20 • *Math Explorations and Applications* Level 4

Assessment Criteria

Did the student . . .

- ✓ demonstrate recall of fraction concepts?
- ✓ contribute to the fraction estimation discussion?
- ✓ communicate his or her thinking about the fraction statements?

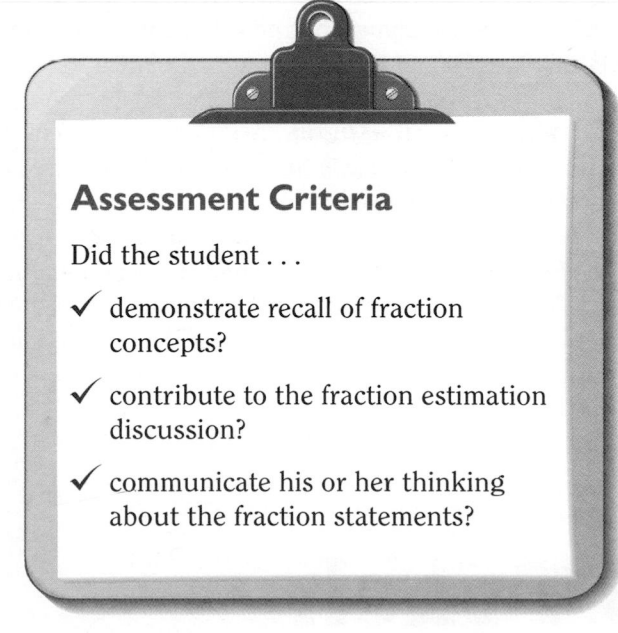

Homework Assign Practice Master 20 for further concept development.

LESSON 21

Student Edition pages 70–71

Fractions and Money

LESSON PLANNER

Objectives

- to provide practice in comparing fractions of a dollar with the number of cents they represent
- to provide practice in solving problems involving simple fractions of numbers
- to provide practice in mental manipulation of common fractions

Context of the Lesson This is the second of five lessons reviewing the use of fractions and decimals.

MANIPULATIVES

none

Program Resources

"Store" and "Harder Store" Game Mats

Practice Master 21

Enrichment Master 21

For additional math integration:
Math Throughout the Day*

For extra practice:
CD-ROM* Lesson 21
Cumulative Review, page 538

1 Warm-Up

5 MINUTES

Problem of the Day Present this problem to students: Rafael has 80¢. He has twice as many nickels as dimes, but no other kinds of coins. What coins does Rafael have? (8 nickels, 4 dimes)

Problem-Solving Strategies Ask students who have solved the Problem of the Day to share how they solved it and any strategies they used.

MENTAL MATH Present these addition problems with common fractions. Have students hold thumbs up if the sum is greater than 1, thumbs down if it is less than 1, or stand if the sum is 1.

a. $\frac{1}{4} + \frac{1}{4}$ (thumbs down) **b.** $\frac{1}{3} + \frac{1}{3}$ (thumbs down)

c. $\frac{3}{4} + \frac{1}{2}$ (thumbs up) **d.** $\frac{1}{5} + \frac{2}{5}$ (thumbs down)

2 Teach

Using the Student Pages Demonstrate the "Store" Game Mat, which provides practice with forming amounts of

LESSON 21

Fractions and Money

You can use the United States' money system to understand fractions.

dollar

one dollar = 100 cents
1 dollar = 100¢

half-dollar

one half-dollar = 50 cents
$\frac{1}{2}$ of 100¢ = 50¢

quarter

one quarter dollar = 25 cents
$\frac{1}{4}$ of 100¢ = 25 cents

dime

one tenth dollar = 10 cents
$\frac{1}{10}$ of 100¢ = 10 cents

Write the amount as a fraction of a dollar. Then write how many cents. The first one has been done for you.

	Coins	Fraction of a Dollar	Cents
1		$\frac{2}{4}$	50¢
2		$\frac{3}{4}$ ■	■ 75¢
3		$\frac{2}{10}$ ■	■ 20¢
4		$\frac{7}{10}$ ■	■ 70¢
5		$\frac{4}{4}$ or 1 ■	■ 100¢

- How many quarters are in one dollar? **4**
- How many quarters are in one half-dollar? **2**
- How many dimes are in one dollar? **10**
- How many dimes are in one half-dollar? **5**
- Which would you rather have, ten dimes or four quarters? **Both sets of coins represent the same amount of money.**

Social Studies Connection Students who are from other countries or who have traveled outside the United States may be familiar with other monetary systems. Invite these students to explain the fractional relationships among coins in other countries. If possible, encourage them to bring in foreign coins they may have at home to show the class. Another option is to mount a display of coins and bills from other countries with their fractional relationships. You might also wish to have students do this activity as a research project, working in small groups.

RETEACHING

Extensive reteaching and practice are not essential at this time because fractions will be covered formally in Unit 6. However, you may wish to take advantage of instances in which fractions arise as part of regular classroom activities, such as telling time.

*available separately

Solve.

6. Dr. Kumi is driving to a town 100 kilometers from her home. She has 40 kilometers left to go. Is she halfway there yet? **yes; she is more than halfway there**

7. A bicycle that usually sells for $100 is on sale for $72. Is that more than $\frac{1}{4}$ off the regular price? **yes**

8. In a class of 16 students, $\frac{3}{4}$ of the students are girls. Are there more boys than girls in the class? **no**

9. Last night DeAnna read the first 27 pages of a 120-page book. Has she read a third of the book yet? **no**

10. Eddie is baking muffins. The recipe calls for 800 grams of flour and two eggs. Because Eddie has only one egg, he can make only $\frac{1}{2}$ the recipe. How much flour will he use? **400 g**

11. Maureen cut her pie into eight equal slices. Seven slices were eaten. Is more than $\frac{1}{4}$ of the pie left? **no**

12. The gas tank on Mr. Lee's car holds 84 liters. He just put in 64 liters of gas to fill the tank. About how full was the tank before filling?

   (a.) About $\frac{1}{4}$ full **b.** About $\frac{1}{2}$ full **c.** About $\frac{3}{4}$ full

13. Tim is saving money to buy a kite that costs $20.00. He has saved $9.57. Has he saved $\frac{1}{2}$ the cost of the kite yet? **no**

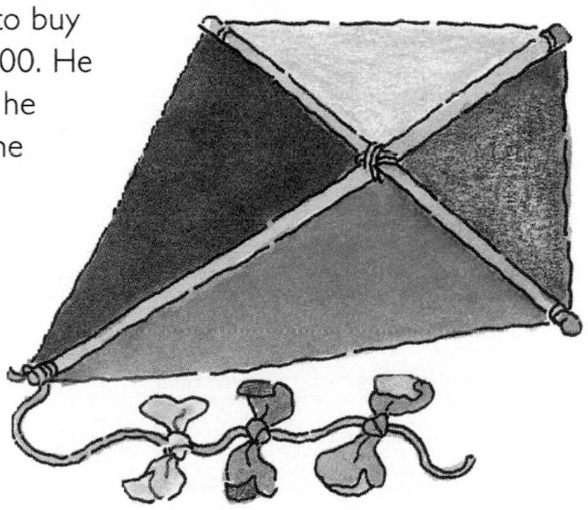

Use the Cumulative Review on page 538 after this lesson.

money, so that students can play the game as they finish their work on pages 70–71.

Briefly review with the class the information about fractions of a dollar given at the top of page 70. Let students solve problems 2–5 on their own. Then do the discussion questions at the bottom of the page with the entire class.

Solve one or two of the problems on page 71 with the class. Then let students solve the remaining problems on their own and discuss them together afterward. If students are having difficulty, do the entire page as a class. Note that an algorithm for finding fractions of numbers will be covered in Unit 6. In the meantime, have students practice using simple fractions of numbers.

Introducing the "Store" and "Harder Store" Game Mats Demonstrate the "Store" and "Harder Store" Game Mats for the class by playing them with students. These Game Mats provide practice with making change. Complete directions are on the Game Mats. A copy of the "Store" Game Mats can also be found on pages 605–606 of this Teacher's Guide.

3 Wrap-Up (5 MINUTES)

In Closing Have students state what fractional part of one dollar each United States coin represents.

Informal Assessment Have students share examples of the use of fractions in their own lives. Listen for how accurately students describe the fractions and how well they express an understanding of the concept of fractions as parts of a whole.

PRACTICE p. 21

LESSON 21 PRACTICE Name__________

Solve these problems.

1. Heather cut her birthday cake into 12 equal pieces. Then eight pieces were eaten. Is more than $\frac{1}{2}$ of the cake left? no
2. At Mark's school, $\frac{3}{4}$ of the teachers are women. Are there more women teachers than men teachers at Mark's school? yes
3. A sweater usually sells for $10. It is on sale for $8. Is that more than $\frac{1}{4}$ off the regular price? no
4. Last week Peter started knitting a scarf that will have 16 identical sections. He has knitted six sections so far. Is the scarf more than $\frac{1}{2}$ finished yet? no
5. A bicycle costs $75. Rosa is saving money to buy it. She has saved $29. Has she saved more than $\frac{1}{3}$ of the cost of the bicycle yet? yes
6. Mr. Wong is driving to the beach, which is 100 kilometers from his house. He has 60 kilometers left to go. Is he more than halfway there? no
7. Brenda is baking cookies. The recipe calls for 1000 grams of sugar and 1800 grams of flour. Because Brenda has only 500 grams of sugar, she can make only $\frac{1}{2}$ of the recipe. How many grams of flour should she use? 900
8. The gas tank of Mrs. Jensen's car holds 40 liters. She just put in 29 liters of gas to fill the tank. About how full was the tank before the gas was added? a

   a. About $\frac{1}{4}$ full **b.** About $\frac{1}{2}$ full **c.** About $\frac{3}{4}$ full

Copyright © SRA/McGraw-Hill. Permission is granted to reproduce this page for classroom use.

Math Explorations and Applications Level 4 • 21

ENRICHMENT p. 21

LESSON 21 ENRICHMENT Name__________

Juana likes the pattern she saw in a book about Native American pottery. Here's a drawing of a section of it. The original pattern is 54 centimeters long.

She wants to use a small version of the design on a cup that she made from clay. The small pattern should fit exactly around the cup, which is 27 centimeters around.

Solve.

1. What fraction of the original pattern length can she use to make the new pattern fit exactly? $\frac{1}{2}$
2. On graph paper, draw the pattern in the new size. See students' work.
3. Now design your own pattern on graph paper. See students' work.
4. Draw a smaller version, one third the length and one third the height of your original pattern. same as answer 3, but $\frac{1}{3}$ size
5. What happens if you make the pattern half as long but leave the height the same?
   Answers will vary. Sample answer: The pattern gets thinner.

Copyright © SRA/McGraw-Hill. Permission is granted to reproduce this page for classroom use.

Math Explorations and Applications Level 4 • 21

Assessment Criteria

Did the student . . .

- ✓ correctly answer at least 75% of the problems?
- ✓ contribute to the discussion?
- ✓ communicate an understanding of fractions and money?

Homework Assign Practice Master 21 or Enrichment Master 21 for further concept development.

LESSON 22

Student Edition pages 72–75

Decimals and Money

LESSON PLANNER

Objectives

- to review the use of the decimal point in writing money amounts
- to assist in comparing money amounts using the relation signs <, >, and =
- to provide problems that involve making change

Context of the Lesson This is the third of five lessons that review fractions and decimals. Work with decimals in this sequence is restricted to money. Students have worked with money and decimals in previous grade levels. The next two lessons give practice adding and subtracting money amounts.

MANIPULATIVES

play money*

Program Resources

Number Cubes
Reteaching Master
Practice Master 22
Enrichment Master 22
For extra practice:
CD-ROM* Lesson 22

1 Warm-Up

5 MINUTES

Problem of the Day Present this problem and list students' responses: Thea has five coins—a penny, a nickel, a dime, a quarter, and a half-dollar. Find all the amounts of money she can make with just two of her coins. (6¢, 11¢, 15¢, 26¢, 30¢, 35¢, 51¢, 55¢, 60¢, 75¢)

Problem-Solving Strategies Ask students who have solved the Problem of the Day to share how they solved it and any strategies they used.

MENTAL MATH Provide practice estimating fraction sums. Students show thumbs up if the sum is greater than 1, thumbs down if the sum is less than 1, or stand up if the sum is equal to 1.

a. $\frac{1}{3} + \frac{1}{4} =$ (thumbs down)
b. $\frac{1}{3} + \frac{2}{3} =$ (stand up)
c. $\frac{1}{6} + \frac{5}{6} =$ (stand up)
d. $\frac{4}{5} + \frac{1}{3} =$ (thumbs up)
e. $\frac{1}{5} + \frac{1}{2} =$ (thumbs down)
f. $\frac{1}{3} + \frac{1}{6} =$ (thumbs down)
g. $\frac{3}{4} + \frac{2}{3} =$ (thumbs up)
h. $\frac{1}{4} + \frac{1}{2} =$ (thumbs down)

MIXED PRACTICE

LESSON 22

Decimals and Money

Another way to understand money is to use decimals.

1 dollar = $1.00

50¢ = $0.50

Write the amount shown in cents, then in dollars and cents. The first one has been done for you.

1		35¢	$0.35
2		■ 57¢	■ $0.57
3		■ 78¢	■ $0.78
4		■ 89¢	■ $0.89
5		■ 130¢	■ $1.30
6		■ 163¢	■ $1.63
7		207¢ ■	$2.07 ■

Why teach it this way?

For decimals less than 1, *Math Explorations and Applications* generally follows the convention of writing a 0 in the ones place. There are three reasons for this:

1. It is the Standard International (SI) convention.
2. It emphasizes the decimal point. For example, it is less likely that 0.7 will be read as 7 than .7 will.
3. Most hand-held calculators display numbers less than 1 with a 0 in the ones place.

You might explain these points to students, particularly if they ask about the 0. However, in cases in which a 0 in the ones place might confuse rather than clarify, as in some problems involving multiplication of decimals, money amounts are shown without the 0. (See the "Store" Game Mat for an example.) Accept correct answers without the 0 as valid.

*available separately

25¢ = $0.25   10¢ = $0.10   5¢ = $0.05   1¢ = $0.01

Write the amount in dollars and cents.

8. 10 cents = ■ **$0.10**
9. 1 dollar and 2 dimes = ■ **$1.20**
10. 2 dimes = ■ **$0.20**
11. 3 dollars and 4 dimes = ■ **$3.40**
12. 4 dimes and 7 cents = ■ **$0.47**
13. 6 dollars and 3 cents = ■ **$6.03**
14. 8 dimes and 6 cents = ■ **$0.86**
15. 1 dollar, 3 dimes, and 6 cents = ■ **$1.36**
16. 8 cents = ■ **$0.08**
17. 3 dollars, 6 dimes, and 2 cents = ■ **$3.62**
18. 5 dollars and 5 cents = ■ **$5.05**
19. 2 dollars, 2 dimes, and 2 cents = ■ **$2.22**
20. 6 dimes and 6 cents = ■ **$0.66**
21. 5 cents = ■ **$0.05**
22. 1 dollar and 1 cent = ■ **$1.01**
23. 1 dollar, 1 dime, and 1 cent = ■ **$1.11**

Copy each statement. Replace ● with <, >, or = to make the statement true.

24. $4.00 ● $3.48 **>**
25. $9.43 ● $19.43 **<**
26. $6.00 ● $5.98 **>**
27. $11.11 ● $1.11 **>**
28. $3.28 ● $3.28 **=**
29. $96 ● $96.00 **=**
30. $2.80 ● $0.28 **>**
31. $0.04 ● $4.04 **<**
32. $0.97 ● $97 **<**
33. $38.95 ● $40 **<**
34. $21.31 ● $35.57 **<**
35. $18.95 ● $18.95 **=**
36. $17.99 ● $18.00 **<**
37. $20.00 ● $20.01 **<**
38. $4.75 ● $3.88 **>**
39. $19.00 ● $20.99 **<**

Unit 1 Lesson 22 • **73**

CULTURAL DIVERSITY

Students who have lived or traveled in other parts of the world may be acquainted with other monetary systems and other ways to write money amounts. Invite them to show how to write money amounts in other countries and, if possible, to display coins or bills from that country.

❷ Teach

PROBLEM SOLVING

Using the Student Pages Demonstrate the "Money Roll" game on page 75 before students begin work on these pages so that they can play when they finish the problems. This game provides practice with decimal and money notation.

MANIPULATIVES

Discuss the money information presented on pages 72 and 73. Call attention to how the decimal point is used in money amounts to separate dollars from cents. Emphasize the need to use 0 as a place holder for decimal money amounts under ten cents. Then have students work on these pages. Use **play money*** to help you.

SPECIAL NEEDS

Meeting Individual Needs

Students who have repeated difficulty writing money amounts in decimal form may benefit from using a simple template, such as the one used in the "Money Roll" game. The template should give the dollar sign, the decimal point, and two places to the left and to the right of the decimal point: $ _ _ . _ _. Students who use this template will eventually become familiar with the correct way to write money amounts in decimal form.

*available separately

◆ LESSON 22 Decimals and Money

Teach

Using the Student Pages Provide **play money*** to help students solve the problems on page 74. You might have them work on the money problems in pairs or small groups. Encourage them to examine their work to make sure they have found the best possible solutions.

Demonstrate the "Money Roll" game by playing it at the chalkboard with a student. This game focuses on using decimal and money notation, place value, and mathematical reasoning. Students may find similarities between this game and the "Roll a Number" game, although strategic differences do exist. Let two other students play as others observe various strategies. Then have students play in pairs. A copy of "Money Roll" can also be found on page 13 of the Home Connections Blackline Masters.

◆ LESSON 22 Decimals and Money

Suppose you work the cash register of a store. You want to give change with the fewest coins. Which coins would you use?

40. A pen costs 57 cents. A customer gives you three quarters. **1 dime, 1 nickel, 3 pennies**
41. A pencil costs 34 cents. A customer gives you four dimes. **1 nickel, 1 penny**
42. A pad costs 80 cents. A customer gives you one dollar. **2 dimes**
43. A calculator costs $4.32. A customer gives you a five-dollar bill. **1 half-dollar, 1 dime, 1 nickel, 3 pennies**
44. An eraser costs 63 cents. A customer gives you three quarters. **1 dime, 2 pennies**
45. A notebook costs $2.69. A customer gives you three dollars. **1 quarter, 1 nickel, 1 penny**
46. A box of envelopes costs $1.25. A customer gives you one dollar and one half-dollar. **1 quarter**

Which of the following are possible? For those that are possible, list the coins. For those that are not possible, write *not possible.*

47. Make 57 cents with five coins. **2 quarters, 1 nickel, 2 pennies**
48. Make 23 cents with four coins. **not possible**
49. Make 57 cents with four coins. **1 half-dollar, 1 nickel, 2 pennies**
50. Make 20 cents with three coins. **1 dime, 2 nickels**
51. Make 89 cents with ten coins. **1 half-dollar, 2 dimes, 3 nickels, 4 pennies**
52. Make 61 cents with three coins. **1 half-dollar, 1 dime, 1 penny**
53. Make 51 cents with four coins. **not possible**
54. Make 51 cents with five coins. **1 quarter, 2 dimes, 1 nickel, 1 penny**

FANTASTIC FACT **An astronaut in a space suit weighs 300 pounds on Earth but only 50 pounds on the moon.**

74 • Addition and Subtraction

Technology Connection Refer students to *The Quarter Mile Fractions* from Barnum Software (IBM, for grades 4–7) for more review of computational skills and introductory fraction skills.

RETEACHING p. 7

LESSON 22 RETEACHING Name______________________

The names and values of money are shown below.

1 dollar = $1.00 | 1 half-dollar 50¢ = $0.50 | 1 quarter 25¢ = $0.25 | 1 dime 10¢ = $0.10 | 1 nickel 5¢ = $0.05 | 1 penny 1¢ = $0.01

Example:
Laura has $2.99. Write the amount of money in dollars and cents.

$2.00 + $0.75 + $0.20 + $0.04 = $2.99

Write the amount in dollars and cents.

1. 3 dimes and 1 nickel = $0.35
2. 1 dollar and 4 nickels = $1.20
3. 2 dollars, 5 dimes, and 5 pennies = $2.55
4. 4 dollars, 2 quarters, and 6 nickels = $4.80

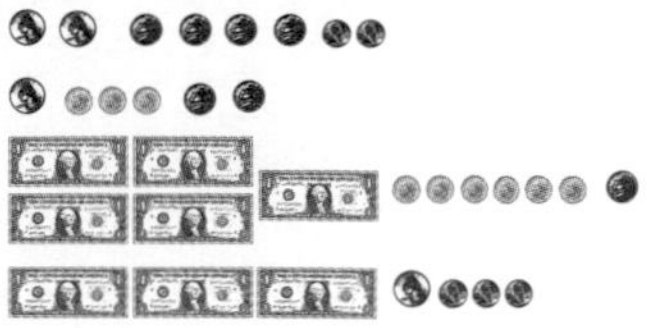

5. = $0.72
6. = $0.65
7. = $5.65
8. = $3.28

Copyright © SRA/McGraw-Hill. Permission is granted to reproduce this page for classroom use.

Math Explorations and Applications Level 4 • 7

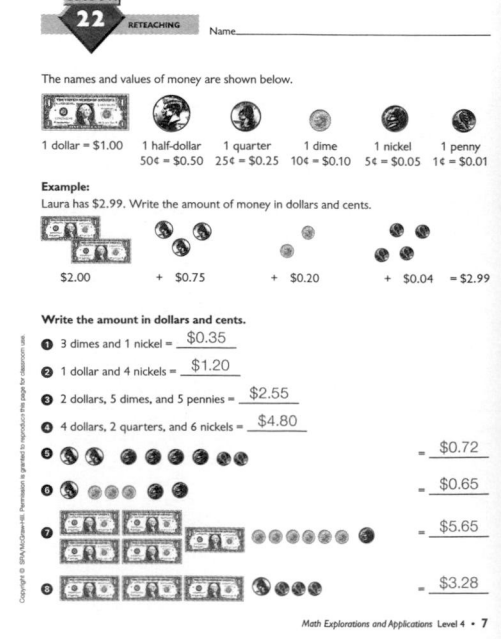

*available separately

COOPERATIVE LEARNING

GAME

Money Roll Game

Players: Two
Materials: One 0–5 cube (red), one 5–10 cube (blue)
Object: To make a number for the greater amount of money
Math Focus: Place value, decimal and money notation, and mathematical reasoning

RULES

1. Use blanks, a decimal point, and a dollar sign to outline an amount of money on your paper, like this:
   $ ___ ___ . ___ ___
2. Players take turns rolling either cube.
3. Each time a cube is rolled, both players write that number in one of the blanks in their outlines. If you roll a 10, roll that cube again.
4. The player who makes the number for the greater amount of money is the winner.

SAMPLE GAME

Number rolled:	Peggy wrote:	Katie wrote:
3	$ ___ ___ . 3 ___	$ ___ ___ . ___ 3
7	$ ___ ___ . 3 7	$ ___ 7 . ___ 3
8	$ 8 ___ . 3 7	$ ___ 7 . 8 3
6	$ 8 6 . 3 7	$ 6 7 . 8 3

Peggy was the winner.

OTHER WAYS TO PLAY THIS GAME

1. Use only a 0–5 cube or a 5–10 cube.
2. Use ten pieces of paper numbered 0–9 instead of cubes.

❸ Wrap-Up 5 MINUTES

In Closing Have students explain the strategies they used in the "Money Roll" game. Also have them identify similarities and differences between money amounts written in cents only and in dollars and cents.

ALTERNATIVE ASSESSMENT

Portfolio Assessment Have students explain how to accurately write money amounts in two different ways. They can base their explanation on writing five cents, fifteen cents, and one dollar and 50 cents. Have students keep these papers in their Math Portfolios.

Assessment Criteria

Did the student . . .

- ✓ correctly count and write money amounts in two different formats?
- ✓ identify a relationship between money amounts using <, >, or =?
- ✓ explain the strategies used to solve change problems?
- ✓ actively participate in the "Money Roll" game?

PRACTICE p. 22

LESSON 22 PRACTICE Name________________

Write the amount in dollars and cents. Watch your numbering.

1. 15 cents $0.15
2. 3 dimes $0.30
3. 5 nickels and 1 dime $0.35
4. 5 dimes and 4 cents $0.54
5. 6 cents $0.06
6. 4 dimes and 7 cents $0.47
7. 7 nickels $0.35
8. 1 quarter and 1 dime $0.35
9. 3 dimes, 2 nickels, and 3 cents $0.43
10. 1 dollar and 2 dimes $1.20
11. 1 dollar and 4 nickels $1.20
12. 2 dollars and 8 dimes $2.80
13. 1 dollar, 2 quarters, and 2 dimes $1.70
14. 1 dollar, 1 dime, and 2 cents $1.12
15. 1 dollar, 1 nickel, and 7 cents $1.12
16. 3 dollars and 3 quarters $3.75
17. 2 dollars and 7 dimes $2.70
18. 5 dollars, 2 dimes, and 2 cents $5.22
19. 4 dollars and 1 cent $4.01
20. 3 dollars, 2 quarters, and 6 cents $3.56

What is the right sign? Draw <, >, or =.

21. $5.00 (>) $4.49
22. $60.40 (>) $6.04
23. $22.22 (>) $2.22
24. $35 (=) $35.00
25. $86.00 (=) $86
26. $0.24 (<) $2.40
27. $0.05 (<) $5.05
28. $42.00 (=) $42
29. $0.97 (<) $97
30. $5.99 (>) $5.19
31. $15 (=) $15.00
32. $0.67 (<) $6.70

Copyright © SRA/McGraw-Hill. Permission is granted to reproduce this page for classroom use.

22 • *Math Explorations and Applications* Level 4

ENRICHMENT p. 22

LESSON 22 ENRICHMENT Name________________

Look at the numbers in the squares. Write a dollar and a cent amount so that the cent amount will give you the least number of coins in your pocket. Then list the coins you are carrying in your pocket for the cent amount. (You might want to use play money to try out the amounts.) Answers will vary. Possible answers are given.

1. [6] [1] [3] [7] $73.16; 1 dime, 1 nickel, 1 penny
2. [5] [8] [9] [2] $98.25; 1 quarter
3. [4] [6] [5] [3] $64.35; 1 quarter, 1 dime
4. [1] [8] [5] [6] $86.15; 1 dime, 1 nickel
5. [2] [7] [9] [3] $93.27; 1 quarter, 2 pennies
6. [4] [5] [1] [8] $84.15; 1 dime, 1 nickel
7. [1] [3] [6] [7] $76.31; 1 quarter, 1 nickel, 1 penny
8. [5] [5] [4] [4] $44.55; 1 half-dollar, 1 nickel
9. [1] [1] [2] [7] $72.11; 1 dime, 1 penny

Copyright © SRA/McGraw-Hill. Permission is granted to reproduce this page for classroom use.

22 • *Math Explorations and Applications* Level 4

Homework Have students count the money in two places where money is kept at home, such as a piggy bank, wallet, change purse, or cookie jar. Have them record each amount in two ways.

LESSON 23

Student Edition pages 76–79

Adding and Subtracting Money

LESSON PLANNER

Objectives

- to review and provide practice in adding and subtracting money amounts
- to assist in applying adding and subtracting money amounts to problems dealing with bank balances

Context of the Lesson This is the fourth of five lessons that review fractions and decimals. Unit 6 provides work on adding and subtracting decimals other than money amounts.

MANIPULATIVES

newspapers or store flyers

play money*

Program Resources

"Harder Transaction" Game Mat

Number Cubes

Reteaching Master

Practice Master 23

Enrichment Master 23

For additional math integration: Math Throughout the Day*

For extra practice: CD-ROM* Lesson 23

1 Warm-Up (5 minutes)

Problem of the Day Present the following problem. Let students use **play money*** to model their solutions: Jacob wants to make exactly one dollar using at least one of each of the five kinds of coins. Which ten coins could he use? (1 half-dollar, 1 quarter, 1 dime, 2 nickels, 5 pennies)

Problem-Solving Strategies Ask students who have solved the Problem of the Day to share how they solved it and any strategies they used.

MENTAL MATH Provide practice with fractions of money amounts. Emphasize speedy response.

a. $\frac{1}{2}$ of a half-dollar (25¢) **b.** $\frac{3}{4}$ of $1.00 (75¢)

c. $\frac{1}{5}$ of 25¢ (5¢) **d.** $\frac{3}{5}$ of $1.00 (60¢)

e. $\frac{1}{4}$ of 60¢ (15¢) **f.** $\frac{3}{4}$ of $10.00 ($7.50)

g. $\frac{1}{4}$ of $100.00 ($25.00) **h.** $\frac{1}{10}$ of $20.00 ($2.00)

MIXED PRACTICE

LESSON 23

Adding and Subtracting Money

Rosa had $1.29. Then she was given a $5 bill for her birthday. When she told Dan, he said, "I can tell you how much money you have all together." Then he added like this: "You had $1.29, and the 5 more you got makes $1.34 in all."

"That can't be," said Rosa. "You should be more careful when you add numbers with decimal points."

◆ Why doesn't Dan's answer make sense?

Then Rosa added like this:

```
  $1.29
+  5.00
  $6.29
```

"I guess that answer makes more sense," said Dan. "But you wrote zeros after the 5."

"That's right, " said Rosa. "But whether I write $5 or $5.00, it's still five dollars."

In each problem, two of the answers are clearly wrong and one is correct. Choose each correct answer.

1	$2.98 + $4.00	**a.** $3.02	(**b.**) $6.98	**c.** $3.38
2	$3.05 − $1.50	(**a.**) $1.55	**b.** $2.90	**c.** $4.55
3	$6.75 + $1.25	**a.** $7.00	**b.** $6.90	(**c.**) $8.00
4	$0.50 + $0.47	**a.** $9.70	**b.** $97.00	(**c.**) $0.97
5	$0.37 − $0.12	**a.** $25.00	(**b.**) $0.25	**c.** $0.49
6	$3.98 + $0.45	(**a.**) $4.43	**b.** $3.43	**c.** $4.75

Technology Connection Refer students to *Classroom Market Economy!* from Per Software, Inc. (Mac, for grades 3–12) to review adding and subtracting with money. In this record-keeping program, students have bank accounts and are paid a weekly salary for doing assigned work.

*available separately

When you add numbers, like 475 and 137, you line them up like this:

475 + 137	You add ones to ones, tens to tens, and so on.

When you add amounts of money, like $4.75 and $1.37, you line up the decimal points.

$4.75 + 1.37	You add cents to cents, dimes to dimes, dollars to dollars, and so on.

When you subtract numbers, like 178 from 342, you line them up like this:

342 − 178	You subtract ones from ones, tens from tens, and so on.

When you subtract amounts of money, like $1.78 from $3.42, you line up the decimal points.

$3.42 − 1.78	You subtract cents from cents, dimes from dimes, dollars from dollars, and so on.

Here are two examples to help you.

A. $65.47 + $39.80
Remember to line up the decimal points:

  $65.47
+ 39.80
$105.27

B. $14.98 + $17
You can write $17 as $17.00 to help you line up the decimal points:

  $14.98
+ 17.00
$31.98

Add or subtract. Use shortcuts when you can.

7. $15 + $3.98 **$18.98**
8. $5.98 + $3.15 **$9.13**
9. $5.37 + $43 **$48.37**
10. $0.25 + $0.75 **$1.00**
11. $2.00 − $1.25 **$0.75**
12. $6.35 − $1.27 **$5.08**
13. $19.99 − $9.99 **$10.00**
14. $11.99 − $0.49 **$11.50**
15. $13.98 − $1.39 **$12.59**
16. $20.00 + $31.98 **$51.98**
17. $16.99 − $2.49 **$14.50**
18. $12.60 − $10.62 **$1.98**
19. $14.65 + $2.55 **$17.20**
20. $2.10 + $6.08 **$8.18**
21. $10.50 − $2.25 **$8.25**

❷ Teach

Using the Student Pages As needed, review the "Money Roll" game introduced in Lesson 22. This game provides practice with decimal and money notation and place value. You might also demonstrate the "Harder Transaction" Game Mat. Students can play these games as soon as they finish their work on pages 76–79. This game focuses on adding and subtracting amounts of money.

Read the story on page 76, and go over the discussion question with the class. Emphasize that $5 and $5.00 are two ways to write the same money amount. Do one or two problems with the class. Highlight the strategy of eliminating the two obviously wrong choices. Then let students do the remaining problems on their own.

Next, go over the examples on page 77 with the class. Remind students to line up the decimal points to do the problems on the bottom of the page. Although they may write whole-dollar amounts of money either way–$10 or $10.00, for example–emphasize that writing an amount such as $43.00 with its two decimal places can be especially helpful in subtraction.

LEARNING STYLES GAME

Meeting Individual Needs

Students who learn best by playing games or working in groups can get extra practice with addition, subtraction, and decimal notation by playing the "Roll a Problem" game, the "Money Roll" game, or the "Transaction" and "Harder Transaction" Game Mats.

◆ LESSON 23 Adding and Subtracting Money

Teach

Using the Student Pages Discuss with the class the information about bank accounts presented on page 78. Do the first one or two problems with students, and have them do the rest independently. Point out that problems 22–27 are separate problems; the new balance students obtain for problem 22 is *not* used in problem 23, and so on. You may want students to work in pairs to solve the problems on page 79. Encourage partners to discuss and verify each other's solutions and strategies. Provide recent copies of local **newspapers** or **store flyers** students can consult to check their estimates for problem 34.

Introducing the "Harder Transaction" Game Mat Briefly demonstrate the "Harder Transaction" game by playing it with one or two students for a few minutes. The focus of this game is adding and subtracting amounts of money, maintaining a record of money transactions, and place value. Complete instructions can be found on the Game Mat. A copy of this game can also be found on page 608 of this Teacher's Guide.

AT RISK Meeting Individual Needs

Help students recognize the importance of the ability to maintain a bank account and to understand basic money transactions. Have them list and estimate the total cost of some of the things they or their family spend money on in a given week. You may also wish to visit one or more local banks to familiarize students with some of the conveniences account holders enjoy and to help them comparison-shop as if they were planning to open their own bank accounts.

◆ LESSON 23 Adding and Subtracting Money

The **balance** in a bank account is how much money you have in the bank. When you take out money, it's called a **withdrawal.** When you put in money, it's called a **deposit.**

Alicia had $62.93 in her bank account. She made a withdrawal of $18.50. What is her balance now?

$62.93	**—old balance**
− 18.50	**—withdrawal**
$44.43	**—new balance**

Damon had $146.50 in his bank account. Then he made a deposit of $25.95. What is his balance now?

$146.50	**—old balance**
+ 25.95	**—deposit**
$172.45	**—new balance**

Liam, Hector, Kizzie, Gloria, Jeb, and Ben also have bank accounts. This chart shows the deposits and withdrawals they made this week. Write the new balance for each person.

		Old Balance	Deposit	Withdrawal	New Balance	
22	Liam	$32.50	$6.50	–	■	**$39.00**
23	Hector	$75.00	–	$20.00	■	**$55.00**
24	Kizzie	$65.98	$11.75	–	■	**$77.73**
25	Gloria	$82.76	$18.07	–	■	**$100.83**
26	Jeb	$107.98	–	$25.25	■	**$82.73**
27	Ben	$40.75	–	$5.00	■	**$35.75**

28. After Ben withdrew $5.00 from his account, as shown in the chart, he made the following withdrawal and deposits. What was his final balance?

Deposit $15.25
Deposit $12.94
Withdrawal $10.00
$53.94

RETEACHING p. 8

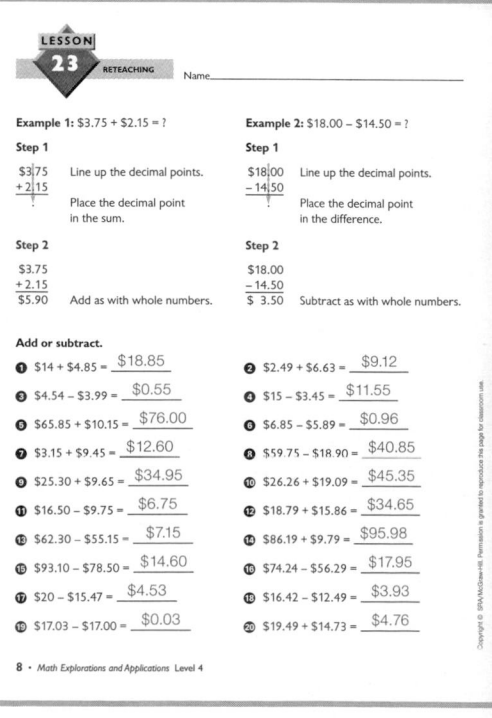

LESSON 23 RETEACHING Name______

Example 1: $3.75 + $2.15 = ?

Step 1

$3.75
+2.15

Line up the decimal points.

Place the decimal point in the sum.

Step 2

$3.75
+2.15
$5.90 Add as with whole numbers.

Example 2: $18.00 – $14.50 = ?

Step 1

$18.00
– 14.50

Line up the decimal points.

Place the decimal point in the difference.

Step 2

$18.00
– 14.50
$ 3.50 Subtract as with whole numbers.

Add or subtract.

1. $14 + $4.85 = $18.85
2. $2.49 + $6.63 = $9.12
3. $4.54 – $3.99 = $0.55
4. $15 – $3.45 = $11.55
5. $65.85 + $10.15 = $76.00
6. $6.85 – $5.89 = $0.96
7. $3.15 + $9.45 = $12.60
8. $59.75 – $18.90 = $40.85
9. $25.30 + $9.65 = $34.95
10. $26.26 + $19.09 = $45.35
11. $16.50 – $9.75 = $6.75
12. $18.79 + $15.86 = $34.65
13. $62.30 – $55.15 = $7.15
14. $86.19 + $9.79 = $95.98
15. $93.10 – $78.50 = $14.60
16. $74.24 – $56.29 = $17.95
17. $20 – $15.47 = $4.53
18. $16.42 – $12.49 = $3.93
19. $17.03 – $17.00 = $0.03
20. $19.49 + $14.73 = $4.76

8 • *Math Explorations and Applications* Level 4

Copyright © SRA/McGraw-Hill. Permission is granted to reproduce this page for classroom use.

Solve these problems.

29 Mark has $4.23. He wants to buy a book that costs $7.50 plus 38 cents tax. How much more money does he need? **$3.65**

30 Sara had $7.48. She bought some things at the store. When she came home she had $5.76. How much did she spend at the store? **$1.72**

31 Maggie's total bill at the supermarket was $25.87. She gave the clerk three ten-dollar bills. How much change should she get? **$4.13**

32 Max wants a CD that costs about $14.00 including tax. He has already saved $9.25. About how much more must he save? **$4.75**

33 Tickets to the museum cost $6.00 for adults and $2.50 for children.

a. On Saturday Mr. and Mrs. Brown took their two children to the museum. Mrs. Brown gave the clerk $20.00. How much change should she get? **$3**

b. On Tuesdays tickets to the museum are half price. How much would the Browns have saved if they had gone to the museum on Tuesday? **$8.50**

REAL-WORLD CONNECTION

34 Estimate. About how much money do these foods cost? After you make your estimate, check the prices in a newspaper advertisement or at a supermarket. **Answers will depend on local supermarket prices.**

1 gallon of milk

1 quart of orange juice

1 dozen large eggs

2 pounds of apples

1 loaf of bread

1 box of your favorite cereal

5 pounds of sugar

3 Wrap-Up (5 MINUTES)

In Closing Ask students why it is important for someone to know the exact amount of money in his or her bank account. Also have them explain the importance of lining up decimal points when adding or subtracting money amounts.

ALTERNATIVE ASSESSMENT

Performance Assessment You may wish to use students' work on page 79 as an assessment of their ability to add and subtract money amounts. If so, have them complete the page independently and make any corrections they wish to make before they submit their work.

Assessment Criteria

Did the student . . .

✓ correctly answer at least 75% of the computation problems and 5 of the 6 word problems?

✓ contribute to the discussion of banking?

✓ communicate strategies used to solve the word problems?

Homework Have students imagine that they have $100 in a bank account. Tell them that they may spend some or all of it any way they wish. Have them look through catalogs, newspaper ads, or store flyers to find at least three items they would like to buy. Have them show their running balance as if they paid for each item separately out of this bank account.

SPECIAL NEEDS · MANIPULATIVES

Meeting Individual Needs

Students who have difficulty adding or subtracting money amounts may benefit from working with **play money***. Help them see why answers do not make sense when the decimal points are not lined up by modeling simple problems such as $1.00 + $10.00.

PRACTICE p. 23

LESSON 23 PRACTICE Name________

In each problem two of the answers are clearly wrong and one is correct. Choose the correct answer.

1	$6.20 + $3.10 = b	**a.** $7.40	**b.** $9.30	**c.** $3.10
2	$0.98 – $0.61 = c	**a.** $1.59	**b.** $1.49	**c.** $0.37
3	$5.40 + $3.60 = c	**a.** $8.00	**b.** $1.80	**c.** $9.00
4	$9.05 – $6.30 = a	**a.** $2.75	**b.** $15.35	**c.** $3.75
5	$0.47 + $0.86 = b	**a.** $2.00	**b.** $1.33	**c.** $1.42
6	$2.75 – $1.50 = b	**a.** $0.75	**b.** $1.25	**c.** $4.25
7	$4.98 + $1.79 = b	**a.** $5.48	**b.** $6.77	**c.** $1.97
8	$0.75 + $3.25 = c	**a.** $5.00	**b.** $2.29	**c.** $4.00
9	$8.15 + $2.15 = b	**a.** $6.00	**b.** $10.30	**c.** $9.25
10	$1.98 + $0.49 = c	**a.** $1.37	**b.** $1.49	**c.** $2.47
11	$8.00 – $6.50 = c	**a.** $2.50	**b.** $14.50	**c.** $1.50
12	$6.98 + $2.39 = a	**a.** $9.37	**b.** $4.02	**c.** $8.56
13	$4.86 – $0.59 = c	**a.** $4.65	**b.** $3.37	**c.** $4.27
14	$7.98 + $3.98 = c	**a.** $4.00	**b.** $10.96	**c.** $11.96
15	$6.25 + $1.75 = a	**a.** $8.00	**b.** $7.50	**c.** $4.25
16	$10.00 – $2.47 = b	**a.** $8.53	**b.** $7.53	**c.** $7.63

PROBLEM SOLVING **Solve these problems.**

17 William has $5.00. He wants to buy a ball that costs $8.15. There is a tax of 41 cents. How much more money must he save? $3.56

18 At the store the bill came to $32.39. Rhonda gave the clerk two 20-dollar bills. How much change should she get? $7.61

Copyright © SRA/McGraw-Hill. Permission is granted to reproduce this page for classroom use.

ENRICHMENT p. 23

LESSON 23 ENRICHMENT Name________

You have made three mistakes in your savings account bank book. Find them. Then make all the necessary corrections.

Date	Description	Credit	Debit	Balance
11/20/97	Deposit	15.00		15.00
12/15/97	Deposit	10.00		25.00
12/20/97	Deposit	12.00		37.00
1/31/98	Deposit	15.75		52.75
2/12/98	Withdrawal		10.00	1. 42.75 41.75
2/27/98	Deposit	10.50		53.25 52.25
3/15/98	Deposit	9.75		63.00 62.00
4/15/98	Withdrawal		15.00	48.00 47.00
4/30/98	Deposit	20.00		68.00 67.00
5/20/98	Deposit	17.00		2. 85.00 74.00
6/4/98	Deposit	10.00		3. 95.00 64.00
7/1/98	Withdrawal		10.00	85.00 54.00

Copyright © SRA/McGraw-Hill. Permission is granted to reproduce this page for classroom use.

*available separately

LESSON 24

Student Edition pages 80–83

Using Addition and Subtraction

LESSON PLANNER

Objectives

- to provide practice in using approximation, addition, and subtraction to solve problems that involve money amounts
- to provide practice using data presented in chart form
- to help students develop the broad ability to use mathematical common sense

Context of the Lesson This is the fifth of five lessons on using fractions and decimals. It also includes "Muddle at Bat (Part 6)," the last part of the Thinking Story.

MANIPULATIVES

play money* (optional)

restaurant menu

Program Resources

Practice Master 24

Enrichment Master 24

For career connections: Careers and Math*

For extra practice: CD-ROM* Lesson 24

1 Warm-Up (5 MINUTES)

Problem of the Day Present this problem: Where Isaac lives, the sales tax is 5¢ for every dollar spent. Isaac has $20. He wants to buy a sweater that costs $18 plus tax. Does he have enough money? If so, how much money will he have left? (Yes; the tax is 90¢, making the total cost of the sweater $18.90; he will have $1.10 left.)

Problem-Solving Strategies Ask students who have solved the Problem of the Day to share how they solved it and any strategies they used.

MENTAL MATH Provide practice in adding and subtracting money amounts based on the arithmetic facts. Emphasize speedy response.

a. $7 + $8 = ($15)	**b.** $17 – $9 = ($8)
c. $10 + $7 = ($17)	**d.** $9 + $7 = ($16)
e. $15 – $6 = ($9)	**f.** $10 – $6 = ($4)
g. $3 + $8 = ($11)	**h.** $12 – $4 = ($8)
i. $7 + $8 = ($15)	**j.** $8 + $8 = ($16)
k. $11 – $3 = ($8)	**l.** $9 – $5 = ($4)

MIXED PRACTICE

LESSON 24

Using Addition and Subtraction

SANDWICHES		SALADS	
Hamburger (100 grams)	75¢	Potato Salad	55¢
Super Burger (200 grams)	$1.50	Lettuce and Tomato	30¢
Turkey Sandwich	90¢	Bean Salad	40¢
Cheese Sandwich	55¢	Cole Slaw	25¢
DRINKS		**DESSERTS**	
Milk	20¢	Pie	65¢
Juice	25¢	Gelatin	40¢
		Ice Cream	50¢

All prices include tax

Donna wants to eat something different for lunch each school day. But she can spend only $2.50 or less on lunch. She wants to buy at least one sandwich, one salad, one dessert, and one drink each day.

Donna has made a chart so that she can plan her lunches for the week. She knows what she will buy on Monday, and she has selected a sandwich for Tuesday. **Answers will vary depending on student choices.**

Help Donna plan her menu for the rest of the week. Use a computer or other means to copy and complete the chart.

	Day	Sandwich	Salad	Dessert	Drink	Total Price
	Monday	Hamburger 75¢	Potato salad 55¢	Pie 65¢	Milk 20¢	$2.15
1	Tuesday	Super Burger $1.50	■	■	■	■
2	Wednesday	■	■	■	■	■
3	Thursday	■	■	■	■	■
4	Friday	■	■	■	■	■

Why teach it at this time?

"Muddle at Bat (Part 6)" involves arithmetic that students have not yet reviewed, but it provides preparation for the work on multiplication in the next unit. While some students may remember multiplication techniques from the third-grade level, do not insist that everyone use multiplication to solve the story problems. Students can use **play money***, repeated addition, or any other reasonable approach.

*available separately

Answer the following questions based on the cafeteria menu. Assume Donna still can spend only $2.50 and always orders one sandwich, one salad, one dessert, and one drink.

5. How much is the least expensive lunch Donna can have? **$1.40**
6. Which menu items can Donna not have on the same day as she has a Super Burger? **any menu item that costs more than $1**
7. What is the most expensive lunch possible with only one drink and one food from each category? **$2.95**
8. How many different combinations of one sandwich and one salad could a student order? **16**
9. Roger is allergic to milk, milk products, and tomatoes, and he does not like hamburgers. Would Roger be able to have a different lunch every day, Monday through Friday? **9 no, unless he eats a lunch that doesn't include one item from each category**
10. Why might a 200-gram Super Burger cost less than twice as much as a 100-gram hamburger? **Two hamburgers could cost more because they include two buns and two servings of toppings.**

Add or subtract.

11. 483 + 169 = **652**	12. 295 + 184 = **479**	13. 1492 − 1285 = **207**	14. 291 − 105 = **186**	15. 764 + 892 = **1656**
16. 2476 + 9321 = **11,797**	17. 8921 − 6430 = **2491**	18. 1847 + 3433 = **5280**	19. 279 − 108 = **171**	20. 1000 + 899 = **1899**
21. 64,258 − 21,796 = **42,462**	22. 74,185 − 23,431 = **50,754**	23. 649 + 291 = **940**	24. 2701 − 905 = **1796**	25. 3842 − 1650 = **2192**

ANTASTIC FACT

It takes five seconds for the sound of thunder to travel 1 mile.

2 Teach

Using the Student Pages Discuss the conditions of the cafeteria problems on page 80. Be sure students can read the items on the menu and notice that tax is included in each posted price. You may want to complete Donna's Tuesday lunch choices with the class. Then let students work individually, in pairs, or in small groups on the rest of the week's menu. When students finish this page, have them go on to solve the problems on page 81. Bring the class together to discuss the solutions. Discuss with students ways that they might solve problem 8.

ESL

Meeting Individual Needs

Students with limited English proficiency may not be familiar with menu vocabulary or with the names of foods that are well-known to many Americans, such as a Reuben sandwich. You may wish to clarify menu categories, such as main dishes, side dishes, and desserts, and explain meal specials that may include several items at one price. You might obtain or prepare illustrated menus to help these students complete the problems successfully.

Health Connection

Using a **menu** from a local restaurant, work with students to choose meals that stay within a budget agreed upon by the group and that are balanced and nutritious. Discuss the major food groups so that students can choose meals that are both tasty and healthful.

◆ LESSON 24 Using Addition and Subtraction

Teach

Using the Thinking Story In the last part of "Muddle at Bat" Mr. Muddle determines the cost of various numbers of bats at different prices. Encourage students to use **play money*** to help them answer question 3 on page 83. After students have determined the answer, discuss what Mr. Muddle gained for the team by taking advantage of each bat company's best sales offer. (He spent $25 less than the cost of buying 20 of the cheapest bats, and he got some of each type of bat. This may help the players by providing them with a choice of bats to best suit their hitting styles.)

Answers to Thinking Story Questions:

1. $500 for 20 Sluggers; $480 for 20 Arrows; $475 for 20 Champs. (Let students use play money to model different ways to buy 20 bats, keeping track of their results.)
2. Champ bats.
3. Mr. Muddle bought 12 Champs for $255 ($330 minus $75). Then he bought four Arrows for $120 and got another Arrow free. Then he bought three Sluggers for $75, making 20 bats for a total of $450.

MATH JOURNAL Have students write about the mathematical concepts that have been useful in evaluating Mr. Muddle's job performance and product tests. Encourage students to write as Mr. Muddle's "math advisor," whose goal is to offer him a clear explanation of these concepts.

◆ LESSON 24 Using Addition and Subtraction

THINKING STORY

Muddle at Bat

Part 6

You may wish to refer to previous parts of this Thinking Story, on pages 18–19, 34–35, 48–49, 56–57, and 62–63.

"Since you can't tell what kind of bat is best," said the manager, "we'll buy the cheapest ones. Find out what the best deal is for buying 20 new bats."

This is what Mr. Muddle found out:

- ◆ Slugger bats cost $25 each.
- ◆ Arrow bats cost $30 each, but if you buy four, you get one extra bat free.
- ◆ Champ bats are two for $55, but if you buy a dozen or more you get a $75 discount. That is, you get $75 back.

Literature Connection Ask students what it means to be an informed consumer. Guide them to recognize that this means knowing how to make wise decisions about spending money. Read *Smart Spending* by Lois Schmitt as a class, or have groups of students read different portions of it and report to the class. Discuss the suggestions and ideas in the book that can help young people to become informed consumers.

RETEACHING

Provide **play money*** students can use to model the cafeteria problems on pages 80–81.

*available separately

Mr. Muddle told his friend Marcus, "I get all mixed up trying to figure out how much 20 bats will cost." Marcus helped him. It was hard work, but together they were able to find the cheapest way to buy 20 bats.

. . . the end

Work in groups. Discuss your answers and how you figured them out. Then compare your answers with those of other groups. **Answers are in margin.**

1. How much will 20 Sluggers cost? 20 Arrows? 20 Champs?
2. What kind of bat is cheapest if you buy 20 of them?
3. You may be surprised to know that Mr. Muddle bought 20 bats for $450. Can you figure out how he did that?

3 Wrap-Up (5 MINUTES)

In Closing Discuss how students can determine a best buy when prices are presented in different units.

ALTERNATIVE ASSESSMENT

Performance Assessment You might use the problems on pages 80 and 81 as a performance assessment of students' ability to solve word problems that involve adding, subtracting, and comparing money amounts given in a table. You may wish to have students complete these problems on their own or have them present detailed explanations of their solution strategies.

Assessment Criteria

Did the student . . .

- ✓ communicate strategies used to approach and solve the word problems?
- ✓ correctly answer at least 75% of the word problems?
- ✓ contribute to the Thinking Story discussion?
- ✓ determine the prices of the different kinds and combinations of bats?

Homework Have students obtain a take-out **menu** from a local restaurant or deli. Set a reasonable price limit, such as $6 for a main course, a side dish, and a beverage, and have students use the prices on the menu to plan a different lunch order for each day of the week.

PRACTICE p. 24

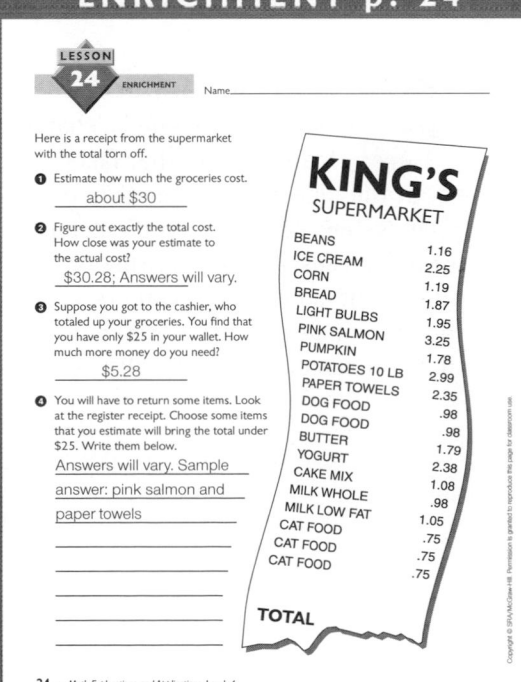

LESSON 24 PRACTICE Name________________

MEDIUM CHEESE PIZZA $6.00		
MEAT TOPPINGS	VEGETABLE TOPPINGS	DRINKS
pepperoni–90¢	mushrooms–45¢	cola–80¢
sausage–85¢	green peppers–40¢	root beer–90¢
hamburger–80¢	olives–50¢	lemon-lime–75¢
ham–75¢	onions–35¢	

A. J. budgets $8.00 per week to spend on a pizza meal. He wants to always get one meat topping, one vegetable topping, and a drink. Help A. J. plan some meals. Answers may vary. Possible answer: sausage, 85¢; onions, 35¢; cola, 80¢; total $8.00.

Complete the chart.

Week	Meat	Vegetable	Drink	Total Price
1. $6.00 +	pepperoni, 90¢	onions, 35¢	lemon-lime, 75¢	$8.00
2.	sausage, 85¢			
3.				
4.				

Use the menu to answer these questions.

1. Assume that A. J. still can spend only $8.00 and that he always orders one pizza with one meat topping, one vegetable topping, and one drink. What is the least expensive meal A. J. could have? pizza with ham and onions and a lemon-lime ($7.85)
2. A. J. gets some extra money for his birthday so he decides to order a medium pizza with everything on it. How much will the pizza cost (without any drink)? $11.00

Copyright © SRA/McGraw-Hill. Permission is granted to reproduce this page for classroom use.

24 • *Math Explorations and Applications* Level 4

ENRICHMENT p. 24

LESSON 24 ENRICHMENT Name________________

Here is a receipt from the supermarket with the total torn off.

1. Estimate how much the groceries cost. about $30
2. Figure out exactly the total cost. How close was your estimate to the actual cost? $30.28; Answers will vary.
3. Suppose you got to the cashier, who totaled up your groceries. You find that you have only $25 in your wallet. How much more money do you need? $5.28
4. You will have to return some items. Look at the register receipt. Choose some items that you estimate will bring the total under $25. Write them below. Answers will vary. Sample answer: pink salmon and paper towels

KING'S
SUPERMARKET

BEANS	1.16
ICE CREAM	2.25
CORN	1.19
BREAD	1.87
LIGHT BULBS	1.95
PINK SALMON	3.25
PUMPKIN	1.78
POTATOES 10 LB	2.99
PAPER TOWELS	2.35
DOG FOOD	.98
DOG FOOD	.98
BUTTER	1.79
YOGURT	2.38
CAKE MIX	1.08
MILK WHOLE	.98
MILK LOW FAT	1.05
CAT FOOD	.75
CAT FOOD	.75
CAT FOOD	.75
TOTAL	

Copyright © SRA/McGraw-Hill. Permission is granted to reproduce this page for classroom use.

24 • *Math Explorations and Applications* Level 4

LESSON 25

Student Edition pages 84–85

Making Inferences

LESSON PLANNER

Objectives

- ▶ to provide practice in approximating sums and differences
- ▶ to provide practice with making inferences from incomplete data in a table

Context of the Lesson This is the last lesson before the unit review.

MANIPULATIVES

posterboard

Program Resources

Practice Master 25

Enrichment Master 25

For extra practice:

CD-ROM* Lesson 25

Cumulative Review, page 539

1 Warm-Up

5 MINUTES

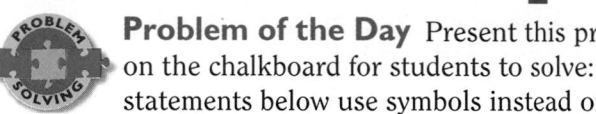

Problem of the Day Present this problem on the chalkboard for students to solve: The statements below use symbols instead of numbers. The symbol x stands for the same number each time it appears. Find a value for x so that both number sentences are true.

$x + x = 4$ $\quad$ $x - x = 0$ $\quad$ ($x = 2$)

Problem-Solving Strategies Ask students who have solved the Problem of the Day to share how they solved it and any strategies they used.

MENTAL MATH Provide practice in adding and subtracting money amounts.

a. \$3.50 + \$2.00 = (\$5.50)
b. \$0.75 + \$0.25 = (\$1.00)
c. \$2.75 – \$0.75 = (\$2.00)
d. \$3.00 – \$2.50 = (\$0.50)
e. \$15.00 + \$10.00 = (\$25.00)
f. \$30.00 + \$31.00 = (\$61.00)
g. \$85.00 – \$70.00 = (\$15.00)
h. \$100.00 – \$25.00 = (\$75.00)
i. \$7.25 – \$6.10 = (\$1.15)
j. \$3.30 – \$2.95 = (\$0.35)
k. \$1.75 + \$1.75 = (\$3.50)
l. \$9.75 + \$10.25 = (\$20.00)

LESSON 25

Making Inferences

Planet	Average Distance from the Sun (in millions of kilometers)
Mercury	58
Venus	108
Earth	299
Mars	456
Jupiter	778
Saturn	1429
Uranus	2863
Neptune	4491
Pluto	5879

SCIENCE CONNECTION

Use the table to choose the best answer.

1. How far is Earth from the sun?
   a. 58 million km (b.) 299 million km c. 778 million km
2. Which of these planets is usually farthest from the sun?
   a. Mars b. Earth (c.) Pluto
3. About how much farther from the sun is Pluto than Uranus?
   a. 1000 million km (b.) 3000 million km c. 5000 million km
4. About how much farther from the sun is Jupiter than Earth?
   (a.) 500 million km b. 700 million km c. 900 million km
5. About how much farther from the sun is Pluto than Mercury?
   a. 1 million km b. 10 million km (c.) 5800 million km
6. About how much farther from the sun is Uranus than Saturn?
   (a.) 1400 million km b. 2800 million km c. 4200 million km
7. About how much farther from the sun is Jupiter than Mars?
   a. 100 million km b. 200 million km (c.) 300 million km

Science Connection Have students make charts that present other facts about the nine known planets in our solar system, such as their diameters, orbital speeds, lengths of orbit, or number of moons. They can present the data on decorative **posterboard** that you can display in the classroom.

RETEACHING

Review estimating sums and differences with lesser numbers, using problems such as those found on page 84.

*available separately

Lynn completed a survey about the birthdays of all the students at Evers School. She recorded the results on a chart. But she lost about half of the chart when her dog chewed it up. Study what is left of Lynn's chart.

Month	Number of Student Birthdays
January	15
February	18
March	13
April	20
May	17
June	16

Give exact answers to these questions.

8. How many students have birthdays in
   a. February? **18** **b.** June? **16**
9. Name a month in which exactly 17 students have birthdays. **May**
10. How many more students have birthdays in February than in January? **3**
11. How many students have birthdays during the first three months of the year? **46**

Make good estimates about the answers to these questions.

12. About how many students have birthdays in
    a. August? **b.** September? **Reasonable estimates range from 13 to 20.**
13. About how many students have birthdays during the second half of the year? **A reasonable estimate is 100.**
14. About how many students do you think there are in Evers School? **A reasonable estimate is 200.**

Use a computer or other means to make a similar chart for your school or class. See how well you can estimate the number of birthdays in the whole year from the number in the first half of the year (January through June).

MATH JOURNAL

Make up some problems that can be answered from the chart. Write them in your Math Journal. Ask a friend to answer them.

Use the Cumulative Review on page 539 after this lesson.

2 Teach

PROBLEM SOLVING

Using the Student Pages Review the table on page 84 with the class to ensure that students understand the information it presents. Remind students that the abbreviation for kilometer is *km*. Explain that students need not compute exact answers to solve the problems on the page, but they should apply approximation skills to choose the best answer. Do one or two problems with the class, then have students finish the page on their own.

Make sure students realize that the chart on page 85 is incomplete. Although they will be able to use the information they can see to answer problems 8–11, they will have to use their number sense to make reasonable estimates for problems 12–14. For problem12, reasonable estimates may fall between 13 and 20.

3 Wrap-Up

5 MINUTES

In Closing Have students explain how they get information from a table and how they make reasonable estimates when information is not available.

ALTERNATIVE ASSESSMENT

Informal Assessment Observe students as they work on these two pages. As you circulate through the class, ask students questions about their reasoning. You might want to keep anecdotal notes for later reference.

Assessment Criteria

Did the student . . .

- ✓ correctly answer at least 75% of the approximation problems?
- ✓ contribute to the discussion?
- ✓ communicate how he or she made inferences from incomplete data?

REAL-WORLD CONNECTION

Homework Have students create charts about their families, their neighborhoods, their homes, or other topics of interest to them. Tell them to present at least four rows of data. Display the charts in the classroom so students can use them to create questions to ask one another.

PRACTICE p. 25

LESSON 25 PRACTICE Name____________

The store manager made a chart of the number of shirts sold during one week at his store. The bottom of the chart was accidentally torn off. Study what is left of his chart.

Day	Number of Shirts Sold
Monday	35
Tuesday	33
Wednesday	30
Thursday	32
Friday	35

Give exact answers to the questions below.

1. How many shirts were sold on
   a. Tuesday? 33
   b. Thursday? 32
2. On which day were exactly 30 shirts sold? Wednesday
3. On which two days were the same number of shirts sold? Monday and Friday
4. How many more shirts were sold on Friday than on Wednesday? 5

Estimate the answers to these questions.

5. About how many shirts will be sold on Saturday? about 32 or 33
6. If the store is closed on Sunday, about how many shirts were sold during the entire week? about 197 or 198
7. The store manager decided to hold a sale and stay open longer on Saturday. He sold at least as many shirts on Saturday as he did on Tuesday and Wednesday combined. About how many shirts did he sell on Saturday? at least 63
8. Make up three questions that can be answered from the chart. Ask a friend to answer your questions. Answers will vary. Sample answers:
   1. How many shirts were sold on Monday? 35
   2. How many shirts were sold on Wednesday? 30
   3. How many shirts were sold on Friday? 35

Copyright © SRA/McGraw-Hill. Permission is granted to reproduce this page for classroom use.

ENRICHMENT p. 25

LESSON 25 ENRICHMENT Name____________

The table below shows the number of people who speak a certain native tongue. A native tongue is the first language someone learns. The table shows the top 20 languages of the world.

Native-Tongue Speakers			
1. Chinese	1000 million	11. French	70 million
2. English	350 million	12. Panjabi	70 million
3. Spanish	250 million	13. Javanese	65 million
4. Hindi	200 million	14. Bihari	65 million
5. Arabic	150 million	15. Italian	60 million
6. Bengali	150 million	16. Korean	60 million
7. Russian	150 million	17. Telugu	55 million
8. Portuguese	135 million	18. Tamil	55 million
9. Japanese	120 million	19. Marathi	50 million
10. German	100 million	20. Vietnamese	50 million

Answer these questions.

1. How many people speak Hindi as a native tongue? 200 million
2. Which language has the most speakers? Chinese
3. How many people speak Korean? 60 million
4. What is the fifteenth largest group of people speaking a language as their native tongue? Italian
5. How many people speak the top five languages? 1950 million

Copyright © SRA/McGraw-Hill. Permission is granted to reproduce this page for classroom use.

LESSON 26

Student Edition pages 86–89

Unit 1 Review

Using the Student Pages Use this Unit 1 Review as a preliminary unit test to indicate areas in which each student is having difficulty or in which the entire class may need help. If students do well on the Unit 1 Review, you may wish to skip directly to the next unit. If not, you may spend a day or so helping students overcome their individual difficulties before they take the Unit Test.

Next to each set of problems is a list of the lessons in the unit covered in those problems. Students can refer to a specific lesson for additional instruction if they need help. You can also use this information to make additional assignments based on the previous lesson concepts.

GAME **Problems 1–4** For students who have trouble deciding what comes next in these numerical sequence problems, give oral practice in counting from given numbers and in telling what number comes between two other numbers. The "Order" game on page 13 may also serve as remediation, if played with a student who is not having trouble with order. This game provides practice with place value and mathematical reasoning. For students who have trouble counting down, first check to make sure that they know what is expected of them. Encourage them to practice by themselves. You might suggest that they use a book for practice by starting at any page in the book and turning the pages backward, trying to say the page numbers before they actually see them.

GAME **Problems 5–13** Students who miss more than one of these addition and subtraction facts problems should be assessed to determine the nature of the difficulty. These students may benefit from working with flash cards or playing the "Roll a 15" game on page 15. This game provides practice with addition, subtraction, and mathematical reasoning.

Problems 14–22 For students who miss more than one of these missing-term problems, check to see whether the difficulty stems from lack of knowledge of the facts, confusion about the format of the problem, or from both. Reteach as necessary.

Problems 23–42 Students who miss more than one of these multidigit addition and subtraction problems should be assessed to see if the difficulty is with the algorithms or basic facts, or simply due to carelessness. Reteach as necessary using an appropriate method.

ASSESSMENT

LESSON 26

Unit 1 Review

Count up or down. Write the missing numbers.

Lesson 3

1. 47, 48, 49, ■, ■, ■, ■, ■, 55 **50, 51, 52, 53, 54**
2. 5494, 5493, 5492, ■, ■, ■, ■, 5487 **5491,5490,5489,5488**
3. 666, 667, 668, ■, ■, ■, ■, ■, 674 **669, 670, 671, 672, 673**
4. 26,549; 26,548; 26,547; ■; ■; ■; ■; 26,542 **26,546; 26,545; 26,544; 26,543**

Add or subtract to solve for *n*.

Lessons 5–7

5. $17 - 7 = n$ **10**
6. $n = 6 + 8$ **14**
7. $15 - 6 = n$ **9**
8. $8 + 9 = n$ **17**
9. $n = 7 + 9$ **16**
10. $14 - 8 = n$ **6**
11. $12 - 6 = n$ **6**
12. $n = 5 + 8$ **13**
13. $7 + 7 = n$ **14**

Solve for *n*.

Lessons 8, 9

14. $8 + n = 12$ **4**
15. $14 = n + 5$ **9**
16. $5 + n = 10$ **5**
17. $n - 7 = 10$ **17**
18. $9 = 17 - n$ **8**
19. $n - 10 = 6$ **16**
20. $n + 6 = 18$ **12**
21. $15 = n + 8$ **7**
22. $18 = 9 + n$ **9**

Add or subtract.

Lessons 12–15

23. 87 − 46 **41**
24. 49 + 73 **122**
25. 492 + 764 **1256**
26. 231 − 108 **123**
27. 792 + 83 **875**
28. 201 − 49 **152**
29. 643 + 27 **670**
30. 896 − 498 **398**
31. 2741 + 893 **3634**
32. 205 − 106 **99**
33. 4812 + 689 **5501**
34. 2974 − 105 **2869**
35. 63,587,304 − 24,069,253 **39,518,051**
36. 30,942,176 + 58,417,926 **89,360,102**
37. 27 + 62 + 48 **137**
38. 95 + 106 + 247 **448**
39. 8921 − 4639 **4282**
40. 4761 + 2984 **7745**
41. 743 − 646 **97**
42. 29,873 − 21,791 **8,082**

Replace ● with <, >, or =.

Lessons 16, 22

43. $4.75 ● $3.89 **>**
44. $5.62 ● $5.62 **=**
45. $2.75 ● $2.57 **>**
46. $21.31 ● $36.57 **<**
47. $18.99 ● $25.47 **<**
48. $17.99 ● $18.00 **<**
49. $25.44 ● $16.43 **>**
50. $28.00 ● $32.50 **<**
51. $2.98 ● $2.98 **=**

Add or subtract.

Lesson 23

52. $3.50 + $4.61 **$8.11**
53. $8.03 − $3.99 **$4.04**
54. $2.49 + $6.98 **$9.47**
55. $5.00 − $3.21 **$1.79**
56. $9.68 + $17.97 **$27.65**
57. $8.43 − $2.73 **$5.70**
58. $16.43 + $10.41 **$26.84**
59. $18.41 − $2.90 **$15.51**
60. $10.00 − $5.50 **$4.50**

Find the perimeter.

Lesson 10

61. **8 cm**

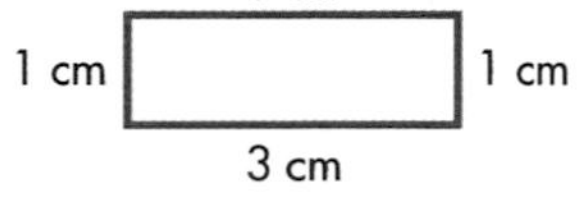

62. **10 cm**

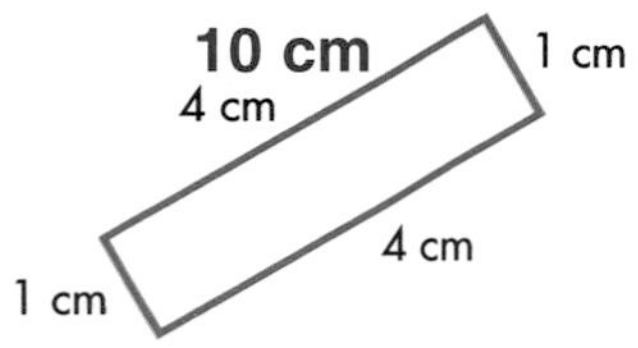

63. **9 cm**

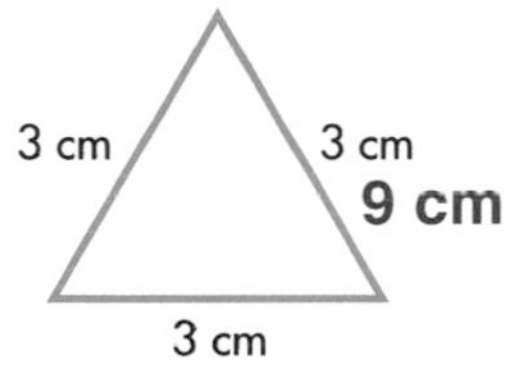

64. **32 cm**

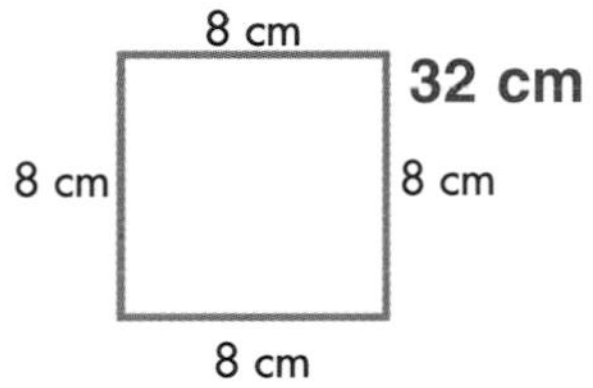

Study the chart. Then give exact answers to these questions.

Lesson 11

65. How many boys ride to school? **80**
66. How many students ride the bus? **100**
67. How many more girls ride to school than walk? **16**
68. How many students ride to school in a car? **41**
69. How many more boys than girls ride in cars? **5**

How We Go to School

	Boys	Girls
Walk	32	45
Bus	57	43
Car	23	18

Problems 43–51 Students who miss more than one of these relation signs problems should be assessed individually to see if the difficulty results from carelessness, not understanding the dollar-and-cent notation, or incorrect use of the relation signs. Reteach using an appropriate strategy. The "Money Roll" game on page 75 provides additional practice with place value and using decimal and money notation.

Problems 52–60 Students who miss more than one of these problems on adding and subtracting amounts of money should be assessed to see if they can add and subtract multidigit whole numbers. Reteach as necessary. If the difficulty is with decimals, emphasize the similarity between these problems and whole-number problems and the importance of lining up the decimal points. The "Transaction" Game Mat provides help with adding and subtracting money and maintaining a record of money transactions.

Problems 61–64 To help students who miss more than one of these perimeter problems, explain that *perimeter* means "distance around." Then suggest that they mark a starting point and add as they trace or "walk" with their fingers around the figure until they get back to the starting point. Do this procedure with real objects, such as pictures or desk surfaces.

Problems 65–69 Students who miss one or more of these chart questions should be assessed to see that they are reading the chart correctly and that they are adding and subtracting accurately. Provide additional practice if necessary.

◆ LESSON 26 Unit 1 Review

Problems 70–73 To help students who miss more than two of these problems on approximating and using a table, first be sure they understand how to read a table. Suggest that the students draw pictures for each problem. Students who know how to solve the problems but have difficulty rounding numbers or approximating sums and differences should work similar problems, including approximation with lesser numbers.

◆ LESSON 26 Unit 1 Review

GEOGRAPHY CONNECTION

Distances from New York, New York

City	Distance (in kilometers)
Alexandria, Egypt	8,034
Bombay, India	13,175
Colón, Panama	3,178
Istanbul, Turkey	8,064
Lisbon, Portugal	4,717
Paris, France	4,830
St. John's, Newfoundland	1,740
Shanghai, China	14,643

Use the table to choose the best answer.

Lessons 11, 14, 18, 25

70. About how much farther is it from Lisbon to New York than from Lisbon to St. John's?
   a. About 1,500 km
   b. About 3,000 km
   (c.) Not enough information

71. About how much farther is it from New York to Istanbul than from New York to Paris?
   a. About 1,500 km
   (b.) About 3,000 km
   c. About 5,000 km

72. About how far is it from Alexandria to New York to Shanghai?
   a. About 16,000 km
   b. About 8,000 km
   (c.) About 22,500 km

73. About how far is it from Bombay to New York to Colón?
   a. About 14,500 km
   (b.) About 16,000 km
   c. About 18,000 km

RETEACHING

Students who have difficulty with this Unit Review should have further opportunity to review and to practice the skills before they proceed on with the next unit. For each set of problems there are specific suggestions for reteaching. These suggestions can be found in the margins.

Lesson 20

74. About how full is the gas tank?

a. Completely full
(b.) $\frac{3}{4}$ full
c. $\frac{1}{2}$ full

75. About how full is the pitcher?

a. $\frac{3}{4}$
b. $\frac{1}{3}$
(c.) $\frac{1}{2}$

76. About what fraction of the spinner is red?

a. About $\frac{1}{3}$
b. About $\frac{1}{2}$
(c.) About $\frac{2}{3}$

PROBLEM SOLVING

Lessons 13, 15, 21

Solve these problems.

77. The car Ms. Simon wants to buy costs about $9000. She has saved about $4500. About how much more money does she need? **$4500**

78. Yesterday Sabina bought a bicycle for $98. Today she bought a basket for it for $13. Jane bought the same kind of bicycle with a basket for $109. Who paid less for her bicycle and basket? **Jane**

79. Ahmed is 11 years old. He is four years older than his brother and six years older than his sister. How old is his brother? **7**

80. Dwayne ran around the track 17 times in one direction and six times in the other direction. How many times did he run around the track? **23**

Problems 74–76 Students who miss more than one of these estimating fractional quantities problems should be assessed to see if they understand fractional notation and if they have a feel for quantities expressed with fractions. More practice with fractions will be provided in Unit 6.

Problems 77–80 Students who miss more than one of these word problems should be assessed to see that they can read the problems with understanding. Encourage students to act out the problems or draw pictures.

ALTERNATIVE ASSESSMENT

Portfolio Assessment If you have not already completed the Portfolio Assessment task provided on Assessment Blackline Masters page 93, it can be used at this time to evaluate students' ability to add and subtract amounts of money.

ALTERNATIVE ASSESSMENT

Performance Assessment Performance Assessment Task 2, provided on Assessment Blackline Masters pages 69–70, can be used at this time to evaluate students' proficiency with estimating. You may want to administer this assessment to individual students or small groups of students.

Unit Project If you have not already assigned the "How Many Books Are in the School Library?" project on pages 96 and 97, you may want to do so at this time. This project is a good opportunity for students to estimate, analyze data, and initiate a research project.

PRACTICE p. 26

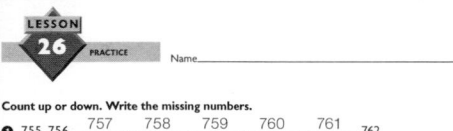

LESSON 26 PRACTICE Name__________

Count up or down. Write the missing numbers.

1. 755, 756, 757, 758, 759, 760, 761, 762
2. 15,628; 15,627; 15,626; 15,625; 15,624; 15,623; 15,622; 15,621; 15,620

Add or subtract to solve for *n*.

3. $15 - 7 = n$ 8
4. $n = 8 + 7$ 15
5. $n = 10 - 6$ 4
6. $16 - 8 = n$ 8
7. $4 + 9 = n$ 13
8. $n = 6 + 5$ 11

Solve for *n*.

9. $8 = 16 - n$ 8
10. $4 + n = 10$ 6
11. $n - 9 = 7$ 16
12. $n + 6 = 14$ 8
13. $18 - n = 9$ 9
14. $17 = 9 + n$ 8

Add or subtract.

15. 53,487,403 − 24,059,357 = 29,428,046
16. 40,972,195 + 68,427,327 = 109,399,522
17. 12,645 − 999 = 11,646

What is the right sign? Draw <, >, or =.

18. $5.21 (>) $5.19
19. $99.88 (<) $99.90
20. $0.44 (<) $4.04

PROBLEM SOLVING **Solve these problems.**

21. Maria swam 16 laps on Monday and seven laps on Tuesday. How many laps did she swim all together? 23
22. How many more laps did Maria swim on Monday than she swam on Tuesday? 9

26 • *Math Explorations and Applications* Level 4

Copyright © SRA/McGraw-Hill. Permission is granted to reproduce this page for classroom use.

ENRICHMENT p. 26

LESSON 26 ENRICHMENT Name__________

Try this puzzle. Use a calculator and reference materials to help you find the answers.

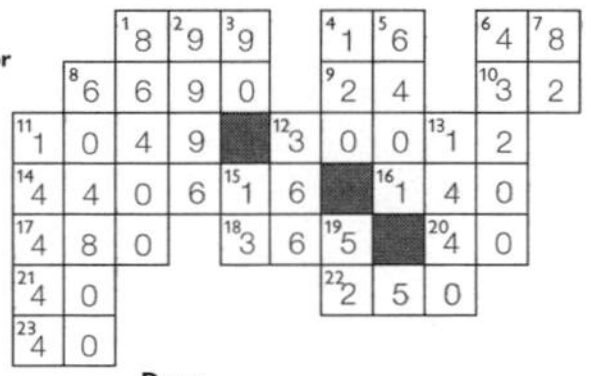

Across

1. 29 × 31, or (30 × 30) – 1
4. Atomic weight of oxygen
6. Number of states in the United States in 1958
8. Number of minutes in 223 half-hours
9. Number of checkers on the board when a checker game starts
10. Number of squares of each color on a checkerboard
11. 660 seconds to 11:00 P.M.
12. Number of eggs in 2501 dozen
14. Number of keys on 5007 pianos
16. 100 minutes past noon
17. Number of hours in 20 days
18. Number of days in the year 1997
20. Number of musicians in 5 octets
21. Number of musicians in 8 quintets
22. Number of quarters needed to make $62.50
23. Number of musicians in 10 quartets

Down

1. Number of seconds in a day
2. (100 × 100) – (2 × 2)
3. Number of degrees in a right angle
4. Number of degrees in an angle of a regular hexagon
5. (80 × 80) + (1 × 1)
6. Number of minutes in April
7. Number of centimeters in 820 millimeters
8. Number of seconds in a week
11. Number of seconds in 4 hours and 44 seconds
12. Number of days in the year 1996
13. Number of minutes in a day
15. Baker's dozen
19. Number of weeks in a year

26 • *Math Explorations and Applications* Level 4

Copyright © SRA/McGraw-Hill. Permission is granted to reproduce this page for classroom use.

LESSON 27

Student Edition pages 90–93

Unit 1 Practice

Using the Student Pages The purpose of these pages is to provide additional practice for those students who demonstrated a need for it on the Unit Review. You may wish to assign only the specific exercises in this Unit Practice in which students need further reinforcement. Listed in the margin beside each instruction line are the lessons covered in the unit so that you or the students can refer to the specific lesson for additional review and instruction.

GAME Students who do not require additional practice on specific concepts may enjoy playing any of the games you have played so far, such as the "Roll a Number" game on page 11. This game provides practice with place value and mathematical reasoning. These students may also help by practicing **flash card** drills and playing appropriate games with students who need additional practice or by actually teaching certain procedures to other students.

You may want to use the Cumulative Review on page 540 after this lesson.

MIXED PRACTICE

LESSON 27

Unit 1 Practice

Lessons 5–9

Add or subtract.

1. $5 + 8 = n$ **13**
2. $n = 4 + 4$ **8**
3. $18 - 8 = n$ **10**
4. $n = 8 + 8$ **16**
5. $n = 5 + 8$ **13**
6. $17 - 8 = n$ **9**
7. $n = 12 - 10$ **2**
8. $8 - 8 = n$ **0**
9. $n = 7 + 9$ **16**
10. $n = 14 - 6$ **8**
11. $8 + 3 = n$ **11**
12. $n = 16 - 9$ **7**
13. $2 + 8 = n$ **10**
14. $n = 12 - 9$ **3**
15. $14 - 9 = n$ **5**
16. $n = 16 - 10$ **6**

ALGEBRA READINESS

Lessons 5–9

Solve for *n*. Watch the signs.

17. $8 + n = 13$ **5**
18. $6 + n = 15$ **9**
19. $10 = 13 - n$ **3**
20. $14 - n = 6$ **8**
21. $15 = 8 + n$ **7**
22. $n - 5 = 10$ **15**
23. $10 = 17 - n$ **7**
24. $14 = n + 9$ **5**
25. $4 + n = 8$ **4**
26. $4 = n - 9$ **13**
27. $8 + n = 14$ **6**
28. $10 = n - 8$ **18**
29. $12 = 6 + n$ **6**
30. $9 = 18 - n$ **9**
31. $8 + n = 8$ **0**
32. $10 = n - 7$ **17**

Lesson 5 **Add.**

33	34	35	36	37	38
7	6	5	3	1	2
9	8	4	5	3	3
6	3	6	8	5	5
+ 5	+ 2	+ 3	+ 1	+ 7	+ 7
27	**19**	**18**	**17**	**16**	**17**

39	40	41	42	43	44
5	8	5	3	7	9
+ 6	+ 9	+ 9	+ 9	+ 6	+ 2
11	**17**	**14**	**12**	**13**	**11**

Lesson 5 **Add. Solve for *n*.**

45. $5 + 7 + 3 = n$ **15**
46. $9 + 7 + 3 = n$ **19**
47. $6 + 7 + 5 = n$ **18**
48. $8 + 6 + 4 = n$ **18**
49. $8 + 3 + 7 + 4 = n$ **22**
50. $3 + 2 + 9 + 4 = n$ **18**
51. $3 + 5 + 2 = n$ **10**
52. $5 + 9 + 8 + 1 = n$ **23**
53. $7 + 4 + 7 + 3 = n$ **21**
54. $2 + 7 + 4 = n$ **13**
55. $4 + 2 + 8 + 1 = n$ **15**
56. $6 + 2 + 1 + 4 = n$ **13**
57. $8 + 1 + 2 = n$ **11**
58. $5 + 4 + 3 + 1 = n$ **13**
59. $7 + 3 + 2 + 4 = n$ **16**

Lesson 12 **Add.**

60. 56 + 97 = **153**
61. 83 + 46 = **129**
62. 186 + 39 = **225**
63. 39 + 208 = **247**
64. 346 + 287 = **633**
65. 470 + 208 = **678**
66. 3408 + 2697 = **6105**
67. 210 + 25 = **235**
68. 789 + 300 = **1089**
69. 3461 + 2879 = **6340**

Lesson 13 **Subtract.**

70. 793 − 200 = **593**
71. 92 − 67 = **25**
72. 607 − 289 = **318**
73. 573 − 381 = **192**
74. 491 − 268 = **223**
75. 60 − 37 = **23**
76. 589 − 280 = **309**
77. 260 − 173 = **87**
78. 3508 − 809 = **2699**
79. 6379 − 370 = **6009**

Lessons 14, 15 **Add or subtract. Watch the signs.**

80. 593 + 248 = **841**
81. 28 + 7 = **35**
82. 43,572 − 1,281 = **42,291**
83. 53,408,761 + 721,508 = **54,130,269**
84. 3,472,694 + 5,309,721 = **8,782,415**
85. 61,204 − 34,561 = **26,643**
86. 793 + 291 = **1084**
87. 804,721 − 712,438 = **92,283**

ALGEBRA READINESS

Lesson 17 **Find the missing digit.**

88. 407 − 229 = 1■8 **7**
89. 602 − 345 = 25■ **7**
90. 321 − 285 = ■6 **3**
91. 775 − 391 = 3■4 **8**
92. 274 − 106 = 16■ **8**
93. 437 − 328 = 1■9 **0**
94. 581 − 437 = 14■ **4**
95. 862 − 392 = 4■0 **7**
96. 349 − 178 = 1■1 **7**
97. 943 − 271 = 6■2 **7**

◆ LESSON 27 Unit 1 Practice

◆ LESSON 27 Unit 1 Practice

Add or subtract. Watch the signs.

Lesson 23

98. $2.30 + 5.40 = **$7.70**
99. $6.81 + 7.93 = **$14.74**
100. $3.75 + 4.25 = **$8.00**
101. $5.25 − 3.75 = **$1.50**
102. $18.75 + 14.50 = **$33.25**
103. $4.73 − 3.98 = **$0.75**
104. $18.75 − 14.50 = **$4.25**
105. $6.00 − 1.75 = **$4.25**

Replace ● in each statement with <, >, or =.

Lessons 16, 22

106. $6.38 ● $4.98 **>**
107. $5.05 ● $5.05 **=**
108. $3.76 ● $4.00 **<**
109. $5.11 ● $5.51 **<**
110. $7.00 ● $6.97 **>**
111. $4.00 ● $4 **=**
112. $5.05 ● $5.50 **<**
113. $8.95 ● $8.59 **>**
114. $23.70 ● $2.37 **>**
115. $2.39 ● $2.93 **<**
116. $7.53 ● $7.00 **>**
117. $9.00 ● $9 **=**

PROBLEM SOLVING

Solve.

Lesson 20

118. After school Miguel, Billy, and Tracy ate six of the twelve brownies Billy's father had baked. About what fraction of the brownies did they eat?

a. About $\frac{1}{4}$ **(b.)** About $\frac{1}{2}$ **c.** About $\frac{3}{4}$

119. The United Fund drive in Seneca has a goal of $50,000. So far, $30,000 has been raised. About what fraction of the goal has been raised so far?

a. About $\frac{1}{5}$ **b.** About $\frac{2}{5}$ **(c.)** About $\frac{3}{5}$

120. Kim put all her comic books in a stack. So did Paco. The height of Kim's stack is about what fraction of the height of Paco's stack?

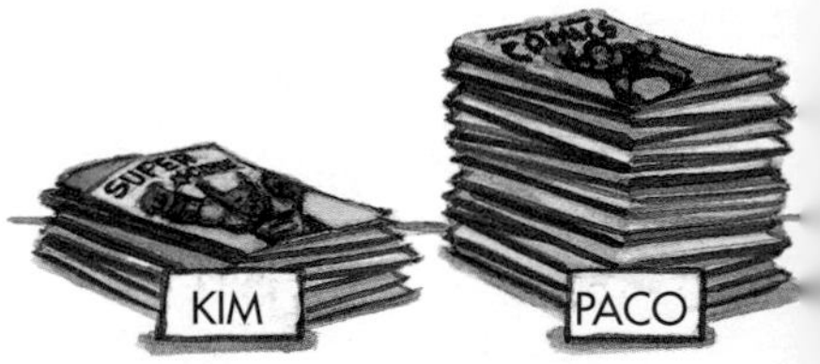

(a.) About $\frac{1}{3}$ **b.** About $\frac{1}{2}$

c. About $\frac{1}{8}$

92 • Addition and Subtraction

RETEACHING

Students who have difficulty with this Unit Practice should have further opportunity to review and to practice the skills before they proceed on with the next unit. Beside each set of problems is a reference to the lesson or lessons from which the problems were taken. You may want to review the individual lessons with students who are having difficulty with them.

Lesson 21 **Write each amount as a fraction of a dollar. Then write it as cents. The first one has been done for you.**

	Coins	Fraction of a Dollar	Cents
121		$\frac{3}{4}$	75¢
122		$\frac{7}{10}$	70¢
123		$\frac{1}{4}$	25¢
124		$\frac{3}{10}$	30¢

Solve these problems.

Lessons 13, 15, 21

125 Franklin wants to swim 20 laps in the pool. If he swims 11, has he swum more than $\frac{1}{2}$ of them? **yes**

126 Hannah has walked six blocks from her house toward her aunt's house. There are 13 blocks between their houses. About what part of the distance has she walked?
a. About $\frac{1}{4}$ **b.** About $\frac{3}{4}$ **(c.)** About $\frac{1}{2}$

127 There are 1000 meters in a kilometer. How many meters are there in 2 kilometers? **2000**

128 There are 1000 grams in a kilogram. How many grams are there in 2 kilograms? **2000**

129 Juan weighs 47 kilograms. His father weighs 76 kilograms. What is the difference in their weights? **29 kg**

130 Jess bought a car for $12,000. He withdrew $7345 from his savings account to pay for it. How much money does Jess still owe for the car? **$4655**

Use the Cumulative Review on page 540 after this lesson.

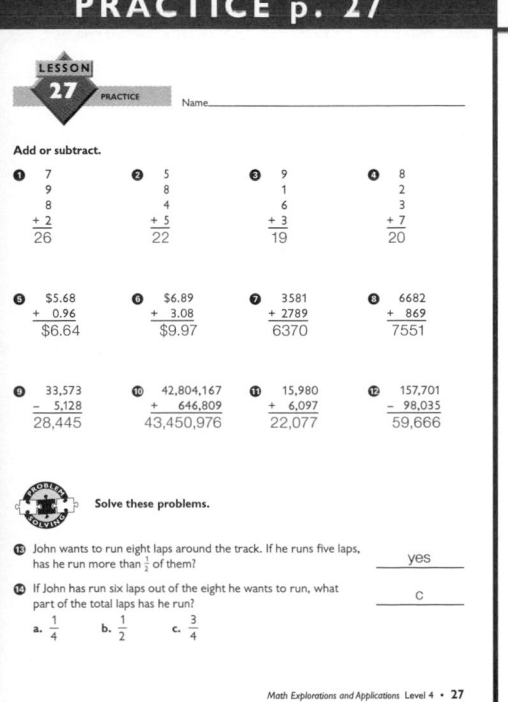

PRACTICE p. 27

LESSON 27 PRACTICE Name__________

Add or subtract.

1. 7 + 9 + 8 + 2 = 26
2. 5 + 8 + 4 + 5 = 22
3. 9 + 1 + 6 + 3 = 19
4. 8 + 2 + 3 + 7 = 20
5. $5.68 + 0.96 = $6.64
6. $6.89 + 3.08 = $9.97
7. 3581 + 2789 = 6370
8. 6682 + 869 = 7551
9. 33,573 − 5,128 = 28,445
10. 42,804,167 + 646,809 = 43,450,976
11. 15,980 + 6,097 = 22,077
12. 157,701 − 98,035 = 59,666

Solve these problems.

13. John wants to run eight laps around the track. If he runs five laps, has he run more than $\frac{1}{2}$ of them? yes
14. If John has run six laps out of the eight he wants to run, what part of the total laps has he run? c

a. $\frac{1}{4}$ **b.** $\frac{1}{2}$ **c.** $\frac{3}{4}$

Math Explorations and Applications Level 4 • **27**

ENRICHMENT p. 27

LESSON 27 ENRICHMENT Name__________

Some years stay the same when you turn them upside down.
Look at this year upside down.

1691

It's still 1691.

Try this puzzle. It has a few "upside-down" years in it.

Across
1. Upside-down year, one year before the bicentennial (200th anniversary) of the famous trip made by Columbus
5. 1 less than 6 across
6. First upside-down year in the 81st century
7. Most recent upside-down year

1 (1)	2 (6)	3 (9)	4 (1)
5 (8)	0	0	7
6 (8)	0	0	8
7 (1)	9	6	1

Down
1. Upside-down year 19 years before 1900
2. Next upside-down year
3. (300 × 30) + (2 × 3)
4. One century before 1 down

Copyright © SRA/McGraw-Hill. Permission is granted to reproduce this page for classroom use.

Math Explorations and Applications Level 4 • **27**

UNIT 1

Student Edition pages 94–95

Unit Test

Using the Student Pages The Unit 1 Test on Student Edition pages 94 and 95 provides an opportunity to formally evaluate your students' proficiency with concepts developed in this unit. It is similar in content and format to the Unit 1 Review. Students who did well on the Unit 1 Review may not need to take this test. Students who did not do well on the Unit 1 Review should be provided with additional practice opportunities, such as the Unit 1 Practice pages, before taking the Unit 1 Test. For further evaluation, you may wish to have these students take the Unit 1 Test in standardized format, provided on Assessment Blackline Masters pages 101–110 or the Unit 1 Test on Assessment Blackline Masters pages 6–9.

UNIT 1 ASSESSMENT

Unit Test

Count up or down. Write the missing numbers.

1. 526, 525, 524, ■, ■, ■, ■, ■, 518 **523, 522, 521, 520, 519**
2. 207, 208, 209, ■, ■, ■, ■, 214 **210, 211, 212, 213**
3. 85, 84, 83, ■, ■, ■, ■, ■, ■, 76 **82, 81, 80, 79, 78, 77**

ALGEBRA READINESS

Add or subtract to solve for *n*. Watch the signs.

4. $n = 8 + 9$ **17**	5. $17 - 9 = n$ **8**	6. $10 = 19 - n$ **9**
7. $n = 13 - 6$ **7**	8. $n = 8 + 6$ **14**	9. $6 + n = 13$ **7**
10. $6 + 9 = n$ **15**	11. $11 - 2 = n$ **9**	12. $n - 14 = 3$ **17**
13. $7 + 8 = n$ **15**	14. $n = 16 - 9$ **7**	15. $5 + n = 18$ **13**
16. $n = 8 - 3$ **5**	17. $n = 9 + 5$ **14**	18. $14 - 5 = n$ **9**
19. $5 + 9 = n$ **14**	20. $3 + 9 = n$ **12**	21. $17 = n + 5$ **12**

Add or subtract.

22. $45 + 38$ = **83**
23. $927 - 359$ = **568**
24. $271 + 899$ = **1170**
25. $4789 + 2228$ = **7017**
26. $4789 - 2228$ = **2561**
27. $12{,}021 - 2{,}867$ = **9154**
28. $36 + 49 + 82$ = **167**
29. $329 + 472 + 605$ = **1406**
30. $405 + 328 + 82$ = **815**
31. $839 + 642 + 100$ = **1581**

Replace ● with <, >, or =.

32. \$6.58 ● \$3.27 **>**	33. \$11.22 ● \$13.08 **<**	34. \$6.39 ● \$6.93 **<**
35. \$5.05 ● \$5.05 **=**	36. \$14.00 ● \$14 **=**	37. \$2.55 ● \$2.45 **>**

Add or subtract.

38. \$7.05 − \$6.88 **\$0.17**	39. \$6.00 − \$2.50 **\$3.50**	40. \$5.95 − \$2.90 **\$3.05**
41. \$86. 41 + \$3.98 **\$90.39**	42. \$122.67 + \$8.05 **\$130.72**	43. \$80.00 + \$4.93 **\$84.93**

94 • Addition and Subtraction

Find the perimeter.

44 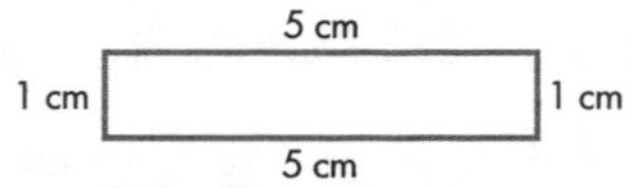

12 cm

45 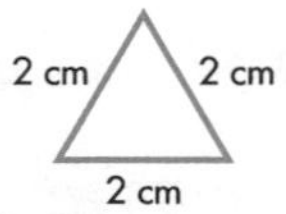

6 cm

46 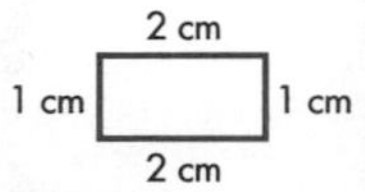

6 m

Solve.

47 About how much of the rectangle is colored?

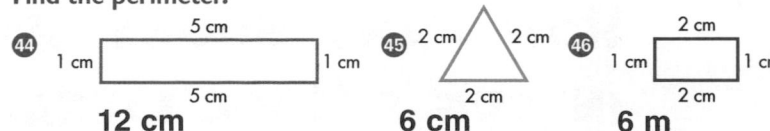

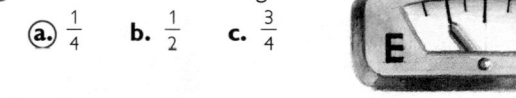

a. $\frac{1}{4}$ b. $\frac{1}{2}$ (c.) $\frac{7}{8}$

48 About how full is the glass?

a. $\frac{1}{2}$ b. $\frac{2}{3}$ (c.) $\frac{1}{4}$

49 About how full is the gas tank?

(a.) $\frac{1}{4}$ b. $\frac{1}{2}$ c. $\frac{3}{4}$

PROBLEM SOLVING

Solve these problems.

50 The talking movie was invented in 1927. The telephone was invented 51 years earlier. In what year was that? **1876**

51 There were 12 people who finished a 10,000-meter race. Charlene finished third. How many people finished behind her? **9**

52 Mark weighs 37 kilograms. Two years ago he weighed 31 kilograms. How much weight did he gain in those two years? **6 kg**

53 Chicago, Illinois, is about 460 kilometers from St. Louis, Missouri. About how far is a round trip between these cities? **920 km**

Theodore Roosevelt was born in 1858. Franklin Roosevelt was born in 1882.

54 Who was older in 1890? **Theodore Roosevelt**

55 How old was Franklin Roosevelt in 1890? **8 years old**

ASSESSMENT p. 6

UNIT 1

Unit 1 Test (Use after Lesson 27.) Page 1 of 4

Name ____________________

The student demonstrates mastery by correctly answering at least 36 of the 45 problems.

Count up or down. Write the missing numbers.

1. 36, 37, 38, 39, 40, 41, 42, 43, 44
2. 6783, 6782, 6781, 6780, 6779, 6778, 6777, 6776
3. 34,691; 34,690; 34,689; 34,688; 34,687; 34,686; 34,685; 34,684
4. 555, 556, 557, 558, 559, 560, 561, 562, 563

Solve for *n*. Watch the signs.

5. $18 - 8 = n$ $n =$ 10
6. $7 + 9 = n$ $n =$ 16
7. $12 + 7 = n$ $n =$ 19
8. $n = 3 + 8$ $n =$ 11
9. $18 - 9 = n$ $n =$ 9
10. $11 - 5 = n$ $n =$ 6
11. $7 + n = 14$ $n =$ 7
12. $n - 10 = 7$ $n =$ 17
13. $n + 9 = 14$ $n =$ 5

Add or subtract.

14. 59,745,439 + 40,435,661 = 100,181,100
15. 74,986,507 − 35,067,446 = 39,919,061
16. 696 + 281 = 977
17. 783 − 429 = 354

Draw <, >, or = to make each statement true.

18. \$3.55 (<) \$4.89
19. \$4.98 (=) \$4.98
20. \$44.33 (>) \$33.44
21. \$19.89 (>) \$18.99
22. \$7.87 (<) \$8.78
23. \$26.88 (=) \$26.88

Copyright © SRA/McGraw-Hill. Permission is granted to reproduce this page for classroom use.

6 • *Math Explorations and Applications* Level 4

UNIT 1

Student Edition pages 96–97

Wrap-Up

PRESENTING THE PROJECT

Project Objective

- to provide an opportunity to make estimates, analyze data, and initiate a research project within the context of the school library

To begin the project, discuss the data on page 96 and allow different arguments. Some students might argue that Mark won the contest because his second estimate was closest. (There were about 4450 books in the library when the second estimate was made.) Others might argue that Todd's estimates were the best because his first estimate was very close, and his second estimate was also reasonable.

Present the "Have Your Own Contest" problem on page 97 and initiate a discussion about how to conduct a fair contest. Use **The Cruncher*** to create a table for help with estimation.

- Should we estimate without visiting the library?
- If not, how much time should we allow in the library before making our estimates?
- How will we determine the winner?

After establishing the contest rules and determining the winner, have students tell or write how they made their estimates.

Next, initiate a discussion about the adequacy of the library and, if appropriate, what students might do to improve it.

- Do students find books with the information they need?
- Is there room for more books?
- Will the Internet or on-line services make the library less important?

If necessary, work with your school's administration and school librarian to help students develop a long-range plan for increasing the number of volumes in the library. Plans might include raising money or receiving book donations.

What Is a Math Project? Math projects in *Math Explorations and Applications* are real-world, problem-solving activities in which students use many different mathematics skills. These mathematics projects are not word problems that focus on one skill area; rather, students must draw from all that they already know about mathematics to complete the projects. They offer students freedom to problem-solve on their own or ask teachers and classmates to help them with the necessary mathematics skills.

UNIT 1 WRAP-UP

PROJECT

COOPERATIVE LEARNING

HOW MANY BOOKS ARE IN THE SCHOOL LIBRARY?

Six students in Mrs. Yonteff's fourth-grade class had a contest. Each student estimated the number of books in the school library. Their first estimates were made without visiting the library. Their second estimates were made after visiting the library for five minutes.That was too short a time to count the books. They recorded their estimates to determine who won the contest.

Here's how they recorded their estimates.

NAME	FIRST ESTIMATE	SECOND ESTIMATE
Mark	152,345	4750
Sara	23,456	5675
Wendy	1265	3896
Todd	5000	5500
Nancy	47,568	3987
Ahmad	10,450	8934

When the contest was over, the class asked Mr. Culyer, the librarian, how many books were in the library. He said that according to his records, the library had more than 4650 books. Most of the time about 200 library books are checked out.

When to Assess the Project

Assessment should occur throughout all stages of a project.

- **Before a project,** assess to find out what students already know and what their interests are.
- **During a project,** assess to check progress and provide assistance.
- **After a project,** assess to find out what students learned and to evaluate the quality of the learning.

What to Assess In the project approach to mathematics students have the opportunity to demonstrate a variety of competencies. Teachers can choose to evaluate students on any or all of the following.

- **Basic skills** include reading, writing, arithmetic and mathematics, speaking, and listening.

*available separately

1. Whose estimate was the highest before visiting the library?
   Mark's
2. Whose estimate was the lowest before visiting the library?
   Wendy's
3. Whose estimate changed the most after visiting the library? By how much? **Mark's; 147,595**
4. Whose estimate changed the least after visiting the library?
   Todd's
5. Who do you think made the most accurate estimates? Write your reasons. **See margin on page 96.**

Have Your Own Contest

Estimate how many books are in your school library.

Decide how to make the contest fair.

◆ Does your school have enough books in the library? How can you find out? If more books are needed, what can you do to help?

- **Thinking skills** include thinking creatively, making decisions, solving problems, and thinking visually.
- **Interpersonal skills** include individual responsibility, self-esteem, ability to work in a group, and self-management.

Refer to page 172 for information on how to assess.

Why Use Projects in Mathematics? Projects give students a reason to learn mathematics. They provide a direct route to mathematics literacy and are a powerful way for students to apply math concepts in real-world situations. As with the problems and projects people face in their daily lives, the problem-solver must decide which skills to use to complete the project. These projects are suggestions only; you and your students may wish to generate and implement your own ideas.

Creating a Project Environment Projects invite students to explore and experiment. When students begin a project, you may want to arrange the classroom furniture to be more conducive to group work. Students will be better able to focus on the project if resources are readily available in the classroom, so you may wish to gather materials ahead of time.

The Teacher's Role During a project, the teacher's role is to serve as a guide rather than an information source by asking questions that encourage students to think about the problem and use their problem-solving skills, and by encouraging students to generate more questions to explore. For these projects you are not expected to know all the answers or be able to solve all the problems, but rather to model good problem-solving and investigative behaviors.

Grouping Projects can be completed by individual students, but students often learn more by working together. Ideally, cooperative group projects mix students of different ability levels so that all students learn from each other and have a chance to succeed.

Successful group work does not just happen. Groups need to establish expectations of the roles and responsibilities of every member. Encourage group members to ensure that everyone makes an overall contribution to the project .

Wrapping Up the Project Bring closure to the project. If the project resulted in a significant improvement for the library, you might want to contact your local newspaper to give students recognition for their efforts.

Assessing the Project Note two groups of students: those whose estimates are significantly off and those who resist estimating and try to count the books to get a precise answer. Pay special attention to both groups of students during activities that involve estimation.

Homework Have students write why they think the library is or is not adequate.

UNIT 2

Multiplication and Division

OPERATIONS

OVERVIEW

This unit begins with multiplication by 0, 1, 2, and 10. Then students use the multiplication table and area models to develop the rest of the basic multiplication facts over several lessons. Students calculate elapsed time, choose appropriate measurement units in both the customary and metric systems, and are introduced to the concept of upper and lower bounds in estimating area. Division is introduced through problem solving and through its relationship to multiplication. Students apply their skills in all four operations to solve problems. They explore the role of parentheses in evaluating expressions with more than one operation.

Integrated Topics in This Unit Include:

- multiplying by 0, 1, 2, and 10
- reviewing multiplication facts
- applying multiplication
- calculating elapsed time
- choosing appropriate measurement units
- determining upper and lower bounds to estimate area
- finding missing factors
- relating multiplication and division
- dividing with and without remainders
- applying division
- finding common multiples
- using parentheses and introducing order of operations
- choosing the correct operation to solve a problem

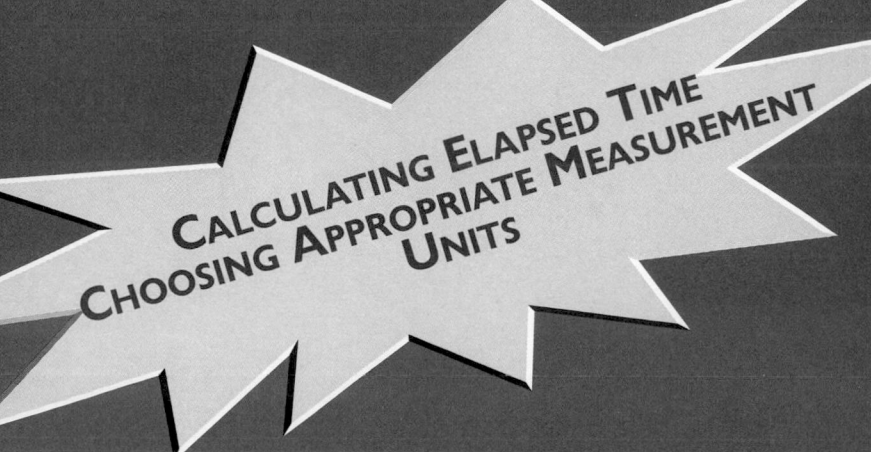

CALCULATING ELAPSED TIME
CHOOSING APPROPRIATE MEASUREMENT UNITS

> *"Strong evidence suggests that conceptual approaches to computation instruction result in good achievement, good retention, and a reduction in the amount of time children need to master computational skills. Furthermore, many of the errors children typically make are less prevalent."*
>
> *—NCTM Curriculum and Evaluation Standards for School Mathematics*

GAMES

Motivating Mixed Practice

Games provide **basic math skills** practice in **cooperative groups.** Playing the games also helps students develop **mathematical reasoning.**

Multiple Crossing Game Mat	Lesson 29	page 105
Multiplication Table and Harder Multiplication Table Game Mats	Lesson 30	page 107
Shopping and Harder Shopping Game Mats	Lesson 31	page 109
Add the Products Game	Lesson 32	page 111
Minutes and Harder Minutes Game Mats	Lesson 35	page 122
Customary Unit Game Mat	Lesson 36	page 125
Metric Unit Game Mat	Lesson 37	page 127
Multigo Game Mats	Lesson 41	page 140
Cubo Game	Lesson 48	page 162

THINKING STORY

Integrated Problem Solving

Thinking Stories provide opportunities for students to work in **cooperative groups** and develop **logical reasoning** while they integrate **reading skills** with mathematics.

Money Matters

Part 1	Lesson 33	pages 114–115
Part 2	Lesson 40	pages 134–135
Part 3	Lesson 43	pages 146–147
Part 4	Lesson 45	pages 152–153

Story Summary "Money Matters" focuses on counting, adding, and subtracting money by using examples of raising money, shopping, and combining bills of varying worth. Students refine their understanding of accumulating money and their knowledge of how to break a sum into various bills and coins.

PROJECT

Making Connections

The Unit 2 Project makes real-world connections. Students work in **cooperative groups** to problem solve and to communicate their findings.

The project presented in the Unit 2 Wrap-Up asks students to work with a multiplication table to discover patterns. They should then explain these patterns to a friend. This project can be undertaken throughout the unit during students' free time.

UNIT 2

MULTIPLICATION AND DIVISION LESSON PLANS

	LESSON	PACING	PRIMARY OBJECTIVES	FEATURE	RESOURCES	NCTM STANDARDS
28	Multiplying by 0, 1, 2, and 10 ... 100–103	1 day	to review basic rules for multiplying by 0, 1, 2, and 10		Reteaching Strategy Practice Master 28 Enrichment Master 28	7
29	Multiplying by 5 and 9 ... 104–105	1 day	to review the multiples of 5 and 9	Game	Reteaching Strategy Practice Master 29 Enrichment Master 29	6, 7, 8
30	Reviewing Multiplication Facts ... 106–107	1 day	to provide a means of self-assessment for multiplication facts	Game	Reteaching Strategy Practice Master 30 Enrichment Master 30	8
31	Using Multiplication: Area of a Square ... 108–109	1 day	to provide a context for the "square" multiplication facts	Game	Reteaching Strategy Practice Master 31 Enrichment Master 31	7, 8, 9
32	Multiplying by 3, 4, 6, and 8 ... 110–111	1 day	to review the multiplication facts for 3, 4, 6, and 8	Game	Reteaching Strategy Practice Master 32 Enrichment Master 32	8
33	Multiplication Facts ... 112–115	1 day	✓ to assess students' proficiency in speedy and accurate recall of the multiplication facts	Thinking Story	Reteaching Strategy Practice Master 33 Enrichment Master 33 Assessment Master	1, 2, 3, 4, 8
34	Using Multiplication ... 116–119	1 day	to provide practice in solving word problems		Reteaching Strategy Practice Master 34 Enrichment Master 34	1, 2, 3, 4, 9, 11
35	Calculating Elapsed Time ... 120–123	1 day	to provide practice solving problems that involve elapsed time	Game	Reteaching Master Practice Master 35 Enrichment Master 35	1, 2, 3, 4, 6, 8
36	Choosing Appropriate Customary Units ... 124–125	1 day	to review and provide practice using customary units of measure for length, weight, and liquid volume	Game	Reteaching Master Practice Master 36 Enrichment Master 36	10
37	Choosing Appropriate Metric Units ... 126–127	1 day	to review the names of and relationships among metric units of length, weight, and volume	Game	Reteaching Master Practice Master 37 Enrichment Master 37	10
38	Practice with Linear Measurement ... 128–129	1 day	to review metric units of length, weight, and volume		Reteaching Strategy Practice Master 38 Enrichment Master 38	10
39	Area: Upper and Lower Bounds ... 130–131	1 day	to introduce the concept of establishing upper and lower bounds to estimate area		Reteaching Strategy Practice Master 39 Enrichment Master 39	5, 7, 8, 9, 10
40	Multiplication Practice ... 132–135	1 day	✓ to assess participation in Thinking Story discussions	Thinking Story	Reteaching Strategy Practice Master 40 Enrichment Master 40 Assessment Master	1, 2, 3, 4, 8
	Mid-Unit Review ... 136–137				Assessment Masters	

	LESSON	PACING	PRIMARY OBJECTIVES	FEATURE	RESOURCES	NCTM STANDARDS
41	**Finding Missing Factors** **138–141**	1 day	to review missing-factor problems	Game	Reteaching Strategy Practice Master 41 Enrichment Master 41	1, 2, 3, 4,
42	**Multiplication and Division** **142–143**	1 day	to show the inverse relationship between multiplication and division		Reteaching Master Practice Master 42 Enrichment Master 42	7
43	**Keeping Sharp** **144–147**	1 day	to provide practice with basic arithmetic facts for all four operations	Thinking Story	Reteaching Strategy Practice Master 43 Enrichment Master 43	1, 2, 3, 4, 8
44	**Division with Remainders** **148–149**	1 day	to introduce division with remainders		Reteaching Master Practice Master 44 Enrichment Master 44	1, 2, 3, 4, 7, 8
45	**Division Review** **150–153**	1 day	✓ to asses students' proficiency in division facts	Thinking Story	Reteaching Strategy Practice Master 45 Enrichment Master 45 Assessment Master	1, 2, 3, 4, 8
46	**Common Multiples** **154–155**	1 day	to introduce the concept of least common multiple		Reteaching Strategy Practice Master 46 Enrichment Master 46	6, 13
47	**Parentheses** **156–159**	1 day	to introduce students to the use of parentheses and order of operations	ACT IT OUT	Reteaching Master Practice Master 47 Enrichment Master 47	7
48	**Applying Math** **160–163**	1 day	✓ to assess students' ability to choose the correct operation to solve a given word problem	Game	Reteaching Strategy Practice Master 48 Enrichment Master 48 Assessment Master	1, 2, 3, 4, 8
49	**Unit 2 Review** **164–165**		to review multiplication and division		Practice Master 49 Enrichment Master 49	
50	**Unit 2 Practice** **166–169**		to practice multiplication and division		Practice Master 50 Enrichment Master 50	
	Unit 2 Test **170–171**		to review multiplication and division		Assessment Masters	
	Unit 2 Wrap-Up ..... **172–173** Exploring the Multiplication Table			**Project**		

UNIT CONNECTIONS

INTERVENTION STRATEGIES

In this Teacher's Guide there are specific strategies suggested for students with individual needs. These strategies appear with icons under the headings ESL, Gifted and Talented, Special Needs, Learning Styles, and At Risk, and are provided at the point of use. Following are the icons to look for and the types of strategies that will accompany them:

ESL

English as a Second Language

These strategies, designed for students who do not speak the English language fluently, suggest meaningful ways to present lesson concepts and vocabulary.

GIFTED & TALENTED

Gifted and Talented

These strategies are designed to enrich and extend the lessons and offer further challenges to students who have easily mastered the concepts already presented.

SPECIAL NEEDS

Special Needs

Students who are physically challenged or who have learning disabilities may require alternative ways to complete activities, record answers, use manipulatives, and so on. The strategies labeled with this icon offer appropriate methods of teaching lesson concepts to these students.

LEARNING STYLES

Learning Styles

Each student has his or her individual approach to learning. The strategies labeled with this icon suggest ways to present lesson concepts so that various learning modalities—such as tactile/kinesthetic, visual, and auditory—can be addressed.

AT RISK

At Risk

These strategies highlight the relevancy of the skills presented by making the connection between school and real life. They are directed toward students who appear to be at risk of dropping out of school before graduation.

TECHNOLOGY CONNECTIONS

The following materials, designed to reinforce and extend lesson concepts, are referred to throughout this Teacher's Guide. It might be helpful to either order the software or check it out of the school media center or community library.

TECHNOLOGY CONNECTION

Look for this **Technology Connection** *icon.*

- *Whole Numbers: Multiplication and Division,* from Gamco; Apple, IBM, for grades 3–10 (software)
- *Interactive Math Journey,* from The Learning Company; Mac, for grades 1–4 (software)
- *Target Math,* from Critical Thinking Software & Books; Apple, Mac, IBM, for grades 3–12 (software)
- *Math Computation I,* from EPC; Mac, for grades 1–5, available in Spanish (software)

CROSS-CURRICULAR CONNECTIONS

This Teacher's Guide offers specific suggestions on ways to connect the math concepts presented in this unit with other subjects that students are studying. Students can connect math concepts with topics they already know about, and they can find examples of math in other subjects and in real-world situations. These strategies are provided at the point of use.

Look for these icons:

Geography	Health
Social Studies	Music
Science	Math
Art	Physical Education
Language Arts	Careers

LITERATURE CONNECTIONS

The following books are referenced throughout this Teacher's Guide at points where they can be used to introduce, reinforce, or extend specific lesson concepts. You may want to locate these books in your school or community library.

Look for this **Literature Connection** *icon.*

- *Each Orange Had 8 Slices* by Paul Giganti, Jr. Greenwillow Books, 1992.
- *Six-Dinner Sid* by Inga Moore. Simon & Schuster Books for Young Readers, 1991.
- *Sea Squares* by Joy Hulme. Hyperion, 1991.
- *Math-A-Magic Number Tricks for Magicians* by Laurence B. White, Jr. A. Whitman, 1990.
- *From One to One Hundred* by Terri Sloat. Dutton Children's Books, 1991.
- *Counting on Frank* by Rod Clement. G. Stevens Children's Books, 1991.
- *Stone Fox* by John Reynolds Gardiner. HarperCollins, 1980.
- *The Math Whiz* by Betsy Duffey. Viking, 1990.
- *Mathematical Games for One or Two* by Mannis Charosh. T. Crowell, 1972.
- *The Greatest Guessing Game* by Robert Froman. Crowell, 1978.
- *The Rajah's Rice* adapted by David Barry. Scientific American Books for Young Readers, 1994.
- *Arithmetic* by Carl Sandburg. Scientific American Books for Young Readers, 1994.

ASSESSMENT OPPORTUNITIES AT-A-GLANCE

LESSON	PORTFOLIO	PERFORMANCE	FORMAL	SELF	INFORMAL	CUMULATIVE REVIEWS	MULTIPLE-CHOICE	MASTERY CHECKPOINTS	ANALYZING ANSWERS
28					✓				
29	✓								
30				✓					
31	✓								
32					✓	✓			
33			✓	✓				✓	
34					✓				
35		✓							
36					✓				
37	✓					✓			
38		✓							
39					✓				
40			✓	✓				✓	✓
Mid-Unit Review	✓	✓	✓						
41				✓					
42	✓					✓			
43					✓				
44					✓				
45			✓					✓	✓
46					✓				
47					✓	✓			
48			✓					✓	
49	✓	✓	✓						
50						✓			
Unit Test			✓				✓		

ASSESSMENT OPTIONS

PORTFOLIO ASSESSMENT

Throughout this Teacher's Guide are suggestions for activities in which students draw pictures, make graphs, and write about mathematics. Keep students' work to assess growth of understanding as the year progresses.

Lessons 29, 31, 37, Mid-Unit Review, 42, and 49

PERFORMANCE ASSESSMENT

Performance Assessment items focus on evaluating how students think and work as they solve problems. Opportunities for performance assessment can be found throughout the unit. Rubrics and guides for grading can be found in the front of the Assessment Blackline Masters.

Lessons 35, 38, Mid-Unit Review, and 49

FORMAL ASSESSMENT

A Mid-Unit Review, Unit Review, and Unit Test help assess students' understanding of concepts, skills, and problem-solving ability. The *Math Explorations and Applications* CD-ROM Test Generator can create additional unit tests at three ability levels. Also, Mastery Checkpoints are provided periodically throughout the unit.

Lessons 33, 40, Mid-Unit Review, 45, 48, 49, and Unit Test

SELF ASSESSMENT

Throughout the program students are given the opportunity to check their own math skills.

Lessons 30, 33, 40, and 41

INFORMAL ASSESSMENT

A variety of assessment suggestions are provided throughout the unit, including interviews, oral questions or presentations, and debates. Also, each lesson includes Assessment Criteria, a list of questions about each student's progress, understanding, and participation.

Lessons 28, 32, 34, 36, 39, 43, 44, 46, and 47

CUMULATIVE REVIEW

Cumulative Reviews, covering material presented thus far in the year, are provided in the unit for use as either assessment or practice.

Lessons 32, 37, 42, 47, and 50

MULTIPLE-CHOICE TESTS (STANDARDIZED FORMAT)

Each unit provides a Unit Test in standardized format, giving students many opportunities to practice taking tests in this format.

MASTERY CHECKPOINTS

Mastery Checkpoints are provided throughout the unit to assess student proficiency in specific skills. Checkpoints reference appropriate Assessment Blackline Masters and other assessment options. Results of these evaluations can be recorded on the Mastery Checkpoint Chart.

Lessons 33, 40, 45, and 48

ANALYZING ANSWERS

Analyzing Answers items suggest possible sources of student error and offer teaching strategies for addressing difficulties.

Lessons 40 and 45

Look for these icons:

ALTERNATIVE ASSESSMENT ANALYZING ANSWERS SELF ASSESSMENT

> ***"In order to develop mathematical power in all students, assessment needs to support the continued mathematics learning of each student."***
>
> *—NCTM Assessment Standards*

MASTERY CHECKPOINTS

WHAT TO EXPECT FROM STUDENTS AS THEY COMPLETE THIS UNIT

❺ MULTIPLICATION FACTS THROUGH 10 × 10—LESSON 33

At about this time most students should demonstrate mastery of multiplication facts through 10 × 10 by correctly answering at least 80% of the problems on pages 112–113 or a similar page. Most students should finish in ten minutes or less. Confirm students' mastery individually or during Mental Math drills so that you can tell whether they have memorized the multiplication facts or are getting answers by skip counting or by repeated addition. Provide extra help for students who fall short of the desired level of mastery. Record the results of the assessment on the Mastery Checkpoint Chart. You may also use Assessment Blackline Masters pages 10–11 to determine mastery.

❻ THINKING STORY PARTICIPATION—LESSON 40

At this time you may want to begin formally assessing students' participation in Thinking Story discussions. The manner in which you assess participation will depend on how you conduct Thinking Story sessions. If students work in groups, observe them during group work. Otherwise, observe students as they work independently and spot check their answers to the story questions. Observe how each student participates in whole-class discussions. You may want to invite students who do not participate in group discussions to talk to you individually. Continue this kind of assessment in subsequent Thinking Story lessons. You may want to assign Assessment Blackline Masters page 13 to determine mastery. Record the results on the Mastery Checkpoint Chart.

❼ DIVISION—LESSON 45

By this time most students should demonstrate understanding of division and begin to be proficient in the division facts, including division facts with remainders. Students should correctly answer at least 80% of the problems on page 150. You may wish to assign Assessment Blackline Masters page 14 to determine mastery. Record the results of this assessment on the Mastery Checkpoint Chart.

❽ CORRECT OPERATION—LESSON 48

At this time most students should be able to demonstrate understanding of when to add, subtract, multiply, or divide in a particular situation, and understanding of when no operation is necessary, by using the correct operation in at least 12 of the 15 word problems on pages 160–161 and in three of the four problems on page 162, or similar pages. Or, you may wish to assign Assessment Blackline Masters page 15 to determine mastery and record the results of this assessment on the Mastery Checkpoint Chart.

UNIT 2

PROGRAM RESOURCES

THESE ADDITIONAL COMPONENTS OF *MATH EXPLORATIONS AND APPLICATIONS* CAN BE PURCHASED SEPARATELY FROM SRA/MCGRAW-HILL.

LESSON	BASIC MANIPULATIVE KIT	GAME MAT PACKAGE	TEACHER MANIPULATIVE KIT	INTERMEDIATE MANIPULATIVE KIT	INTERMEDIATE OVERHEAD MANIPULATIVE KIT	*THE CRUNCHER* SOFTWARE	*MATH EXPLORATIONS AND APPLICATIONS* CD-ROM
28							Lesson 28
29		Multiple Crossing Game					Lesson 29
30		Multiplication Table and Harder Multiplication Table Games					Lesson 30
31		Shopping and Harder Shopping Games					Lesson 31
32	Number Cubes						Lesson 32
33	Number Wheels			counters	counters		Lesson 33
34	Number Wheels	play money		base-10 blocks, counters	bills, coins, counters		Lesson 34
35	Number Wheels	Minutes and Harder Minutes Games	clock	clock faces	clock faces		Lesson 35
36		Customary Unit Game	tape measure				Lesson 36
37		Metric Unit Game	tape measure, scale, beakers				Lesson 37
38	Number Wheels			angle ruler			Lesson 38
39				angle ruler			Lesson 39
40							Lesson 40
41		Multigo 1 and Multigo 2 Games					Lesson 41
42							Lesson 42
43	Number Wheels						Lesson 43
44		play money			bills, coins		Lesson 44
45				base-10 blocks, counters	base-10 blocks, counters		Lesson 45
46							Lesson 46
47							Lesson 47
48	Number Cubes						Lesson 48
49	Number Cubes						Lesson 49
50	Number Cubes						Lesson 50

UNIT 2

Student Edition pages 98–99

Multiplication and Division

INTRODUCING THE UNIT

Using the Student Pages Begin your discussion of the opening unit photo by asking students, "Have you ever thought about the math skills track coaches and athletes must have?" Then read aloud the paragraph on the student page that highlights a career as a coach. This helps make the connection between school and work and encourages students to explore how math is used in the real world.

MANIPULATIVES

ACTIVITY Challenge students to time themselves in running a half mile using a **stopwatch***. Ask them to calculate, based on the time they come up with, how long it would take them to run a mile or two miles. Suggest that for their calculations they imagine they would run the longer distances at the same rate as the shorter race.

SCHOOL TO WORK CONNECTION

FYI Organized track and field events were being held in Greece as early as 1400 B.C. Known as the Olympic Games, these events were intended to honor the gods. Contestants were expected to do their best without any financial reward. At first there was only one event–a running race of about 200 yards. But by 708 B.C. a new event called the pentathlon became popular. The pentathlon combined five different sports–wrestling, sprinting, hurling the discus and the javelin, and long jumping. These skills were considered to be important in warfare, but the Greeks also felt that cultivating the health and strength of the body was important to being a whole and educated person. The last of the ancient Olympic Games was held in A.D. 394, at which point they were halted because the original motive of the games, to honor the gods, had faded in favor of winning monetary prizes. The games were revived in 1896 by a Frenchman named Coubertin, who believed that international amateur sports could help promote world peace. In the second modern Olympics in 1900, women competed for the first time.

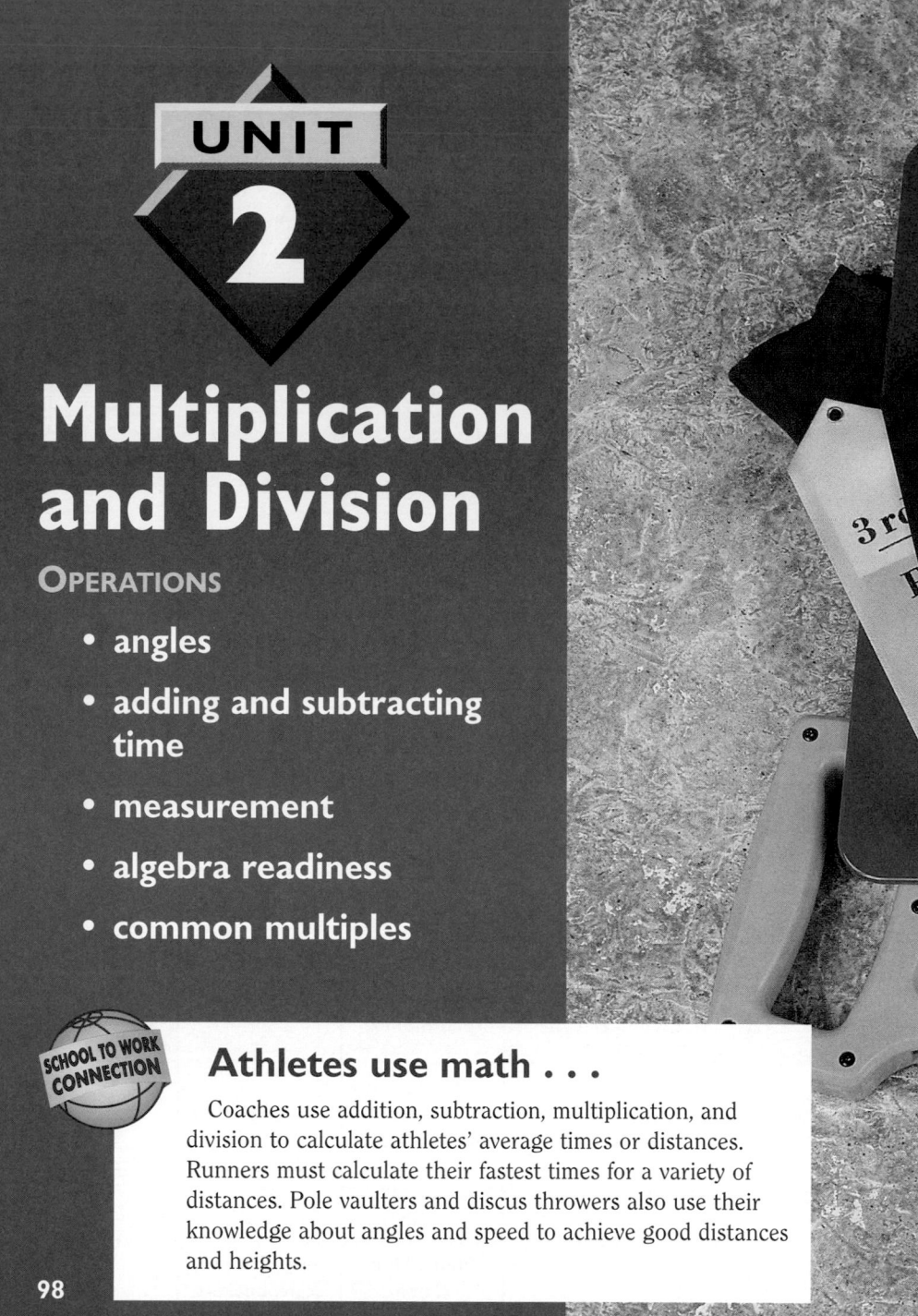

UNIT 2

Multiplication and Division

OPERATIONS

- angles
- adding and subtracting time
- measurement
- algebra readiness
- common multiples

SCHOOL TO WORK CONNECTION

Athletes use math . . .

Coaches use addition, subtraction, multiplication, and division to calculate athletes' average times or distances. Runners must calculate their fastest times for a variety of distances. Pole vaulters and discus throwers also use their knowledge about angles and speed to achieve good distances and heights.

98

PROBLEM SOLVING

Thinklab™

SRA's *Thinklab*™ provides a series of creative and logical problem-solving opportunities for individual students. The problems are designed to appeal to different cognitive abilities.

- Use Problems 21–30 with this unit to reinforce creative insight (developing abstract relationships from given data).
- Use Problems 31–40 with this unit to reinforce perceiving image patterns (analysis of pattern and structure).

*available separately

In the track and field of today, modern training methods rely heavily on mathematics. Runners must know their abilities with an almost scientific exactitude in order to pace themselves. Also, because timekeeping has been revolutionized by technological developments, winning can often mean a matter of hundredths or thousandths of a second. Precision in technique is more closely tied to the clock than ever before. A competitor must be able to calculate without the aid of a watch just how well he or she is doing at a particular moment in time. In many events it is not enough for athletes to know if they are ahead of or behind their opponents. Athletes often are working against their own best times, on a schedule decided by themselves and their coaches. Students wishing to pursue a career in athletic coaching should know that math is an important part of all sports, whether it is in the analysis of statistics or in the timing of a given performance.

Home Connections You may want to send home the Home Connections Blackline Masters letter on pages 36–37 to introduce this unit.

Unit Project This would be a good time to assign the "Exploring the Multiplication Table" project on pages 172 and 173. Students can begin working on the project in cooperative groups in their free time as they work through the unit. The Unit Project is a good opportunity for students to explore and find patterns on the multiplication table and to use one of the patterns in solving a difficult problem.

Cooperate 1

Cooperate 1, published by SRA, provides a series of creative and logical problem-solving opportunities for cooperative groups. The problems are designed to provide practice in problem solving, communication, reasoning, and making connections. *Cooperate 1* presents the following cognitive strategies–perceiving spatial relations, ordering and sequencing, logical deduction, establishing and testing hypotheses, sequential exploration, identifying starting points, attending to detail, organizing information, and screening irrelevant information.

Each Problem Card emphasizes a principal strategy as well as reinforcing other strategies.

- ▶ Use Problem Card 6 with this unit to emphasize both ordering and sequencing and attending to detail.
- ▶ Use Problem Cards 7–8 with this unit to emphasize ordering and sequencing.
- ▶ Use Problem Cards 9–10 with this unit to emphasize sequential exploration.

LESSON 28

Student Edition pages 100–103

Multiplying by 0, 1, 2, and 10

LESSON PLANNER

Objectives

- to review the concept of multiplication by whole numbers as repeated addition
- to review the concept of multiplication as commutative
- to review basic rules for multiplying by 0, 1, 2, and 10

Context of the Lesson This is the first of seven lessons that review the multiplication facts. A checkpoint for assessing speedy recall is provided in Lesson 33.

MANIPULATIVES

flash cards (optional)

multiplication table

Program Resources

Practice Master 28

Enrichment Master 28

For extra practice:
CD-ROM* Lesson 28

1 Warm-Up

5 MINUTES

Problem of the Day Present the following number sequence on the chalkboard: 590, 1085, 1580, 2075, 2570. . . . Ask students to figure out the pattern, then provide the next four numbers. (The numbers in the series are found by adding 495, and the next four are 3065, 3560, 4055, 4550.)

Problem-Solving Strategies Ask students who have solved the Problem of the Day to share how they solved it and any strategies they used.

MENTAL MATH Students can practice skip counting by 10s, then 2s, then 5s. Extend the level of difficulty as appropriate for your students. If students are proficient at this, prepare them for upcoming lessons by extending the skip counting to 3s, then 4s, 6s, 7s, 8s, and 9s. Do not expect proficiency in skip counting by more difficult numbers; this ability is not essential at this time.

PRACTICE

LESSON 28

Multiplying by 0, 1, 2, and 10

George knows his birthday is exactly eight weeks from today. He wants to know how many days that is. He starts counting on the calendar, "1, 2, 3, 4, 5, 6, 7, 8, 9, . . ."

"I know a better way," Sharon says. "Add 7 and 7 and 7, and so on until you've added eight 7s."

$7 + 7 + 7 + 7 + 7 + 7 + 7 + 7 = ?$

- Do you know a quicker way? **multiply 8×7**
- Do you remember what 8 × 7 is? **56**

SEPTEMBER
SUNDAY
MONDAY
TUESDAY
WEDNESDAY
THURSDAY
FRIDAY
SATURDAY

Solve these problems.

There are seven days in a week.

1. How many days are there in eight weeks? $8 \times 7 = n$ **56**
2. How many days are there in seven weeks? $7 \times 7 = n$ **49**
3. How many days are there in six weeks? $6 \times 7 = n$ **42**
4. How many days are there in five weeks? $5 \times 7 = n$ **35**
5. How many days are there in nine weeks? $9 \times 7 = n$ **63**

100 • Multiplication and Division

Language Arts Connection Have students make up a rhyme or a riddle based on a multiplication fact that they have trouble remembering. Students can share their rhymes or try out their riddles on classmates.

*available separately

Remember, to find the area of a rectangle, multiply the length by the width.

What is the area of the rectangle?

Area = 3 × 5 square centimeters

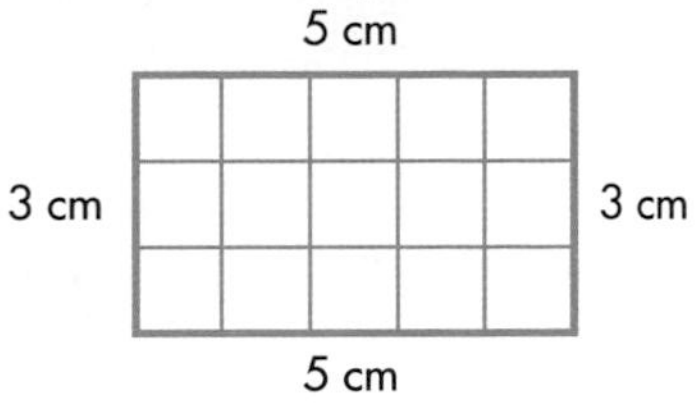

Let's turn the rectangle on its side.

Area = 5 × 3 square centimeters

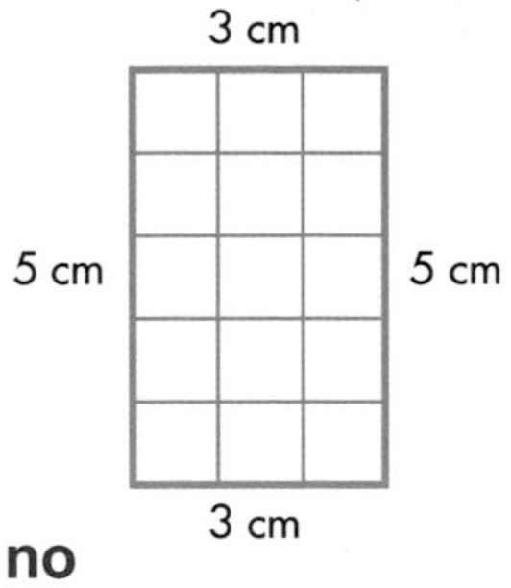

- Did the area of the rectangle change? **no**
- Does 3 × 5 = 5 × 3? **yes**
- What is 3 × 5? **15**
- What is 5 × 3? **15**

Rule: The order in which two numbers are multiplied makes no difference to the answer.

Multiply. Compare the problems in each pair.

6. 2 × 5 = *n* **10**; 5 × 2 = *n*
7. 1 × 8 = *n* **8**; 8 × 1 = *n*
8. 10 × 4 = *n* **40**; 4 × 10 = *n*
9. 5 × 5 = *n* **25**; 5 × 5 = *n*
10. 9 × 0 = *n* **0**; 0 × 9 = *n*
11. 3 × 4 = *n* **12**; 4 × 3 = *n*
12. 3 × 9 = *n* **27**; 9 × 3 = *n*
13. 5 × 8 = *n* **40**; 8 × 5 = *n*
14. 6 × 9 = *n* **54**; 9 × 6 = *n*
15. 7 × 9 = *n* **63**; 9 × 7 = *n*
16. 6 × 4 = *n* **24**; 4 × 6 = *n*
17. 4 × 8 = *n* **32**; 8 × 4 = *n*
18. 2 × 4 = *n* **8**; 4 × 2 = *n*
19. 3 × 5 = *n* **15**; 5 × 3 = *n*
20. 9 × 1 = *n* **9**; 1 × 9 = *n*
21. 4 × 2 = *n* **8**; 2 × 4 = *n*

Literature Connection

For illustrations that introduce the concept of multiplication, refer students to *Each Orange Had 8 Slices* by Paul Giganti, Jr.

2 Teach

Using the Student Pages Complete page 100 with the class. When you get to the second discussion question, point out that the three most commonly forgotten multiplication facts are 7 x 8 = 56, 7 x 6 = 42, and 6 x 8 = 48. Knowing that these facts are difficult for many people might encourage students to remember them. You might wish to quiz students on these facts from time to time.

Page 101 focuses on the idea of the commutative property of multiplication. Knowing the word *commutative* is not as important as understanding that the order of the factors in multiplication does not affect the product. By comparing the rectangles on the page, students should recognize that 3 x 5 is the same as 5 x 3. Help students to understand that a similar rotation and comparison can be done with a rectangle of any size. Have students solve problems 6–21 on their own. Then check answers as a class.

◆ LESSON 28 Multiplying by 0, 1, 2, and 10

Teach

Using the Student Pages Do page 102 with the class. Be sure slower students are participating and understanding. Review the following rules with students. Then have them complete page 103 independently.

1. Multiplying a number by 0 gives 0.
2. Multiplying a number by 1 gives the same number.
3. Multiplying a number by 2 is the same as doubling the number or adding the number to itself.
4. Multiplying a number by 10 can be achieved by writing a 0 after the number.

LEARNING STYLES

Meeting Individual Needs

The goal of all work with multiplication facts is speedy recall. Students can succeed in memorizing the facts in different ways. Musical learners may sing the tables to a familiar tune or simply recite the products in a rhythmical way. Visual learners may benefit from seeing the facts on **flash cards** or on tables. Kinesthetic learners may need to write the facts to help recall them. Artistic learners may create mnemonics for difficult facts by relating them to colors, patterns, or designs. Encourage students to develop creative and effective strategies to increase speedy recall, and invite them to share their ideas with the class.

◆ LESSON 28 Multiplying by 0, 1, 2, and 10

Solve these problems.

There are seven days in a week.

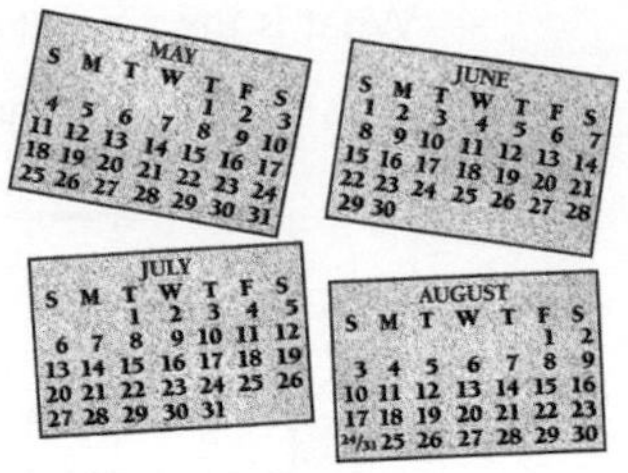

22. How many days are there in two weeks?
 $2 \times 7 = n$ **14**
23. How many days are there in one week?
 $1 \times 7 = n$ **7**
24. How many days are there in zero weeks?
 $0 \times 7 = n$ **0**
25. How many days are there in ten weeks?
 $10 \times 7 = n$ **70**

There are five fingers on a hand.

26. How many fingers are there on two hands?
 $2 \times 5 = n$ **10**
27. How many fingers are there on one hand?
 $1 \times 5 = n$ **5**
28. How many fingers are there on zero hands?
 $0 \times 5 = n$ **0**
29. How many fingers are there on ten hands?
 $10 \times 5 = n$ **50**

MATH JOURNAL

In your Math Journal state a rule and give an example for:

- **Multiplying by 2.** **Multiplying a number by 2 is the same as doubling it or adding it to itself. $2 \times 6 = 12$**
- **Multiplying by 1.** **Multiplying a number by 1 doesn't change the number. $1 \times 8 = 8$**
- **Multiplying by 0.** **Multiplying a number by 0 gives 0. $0 \times 9 = 0$**
- **Multiplying by 10.** **To multiply a number by 10, put a 0 to the right of the number. $10 \times 4 = 40$**

Multiply. Watch your numbering.

30. $6 \times 10 = n$ **60**
32. $9 \times 10 = n$ **90**
34. $7 \times 10 = n$ **70**
31. $10 \times 6 = n$ **60**
33. $10 \times 9 = n$ **90**
35. $10 \times 7 = n$ **70**

102 • Multiplication and Division

Technology Connection Try the software *Whole Numbers: Multiplication and Division* from Gamco (Apple and IBM versions available), which provides further practice with multiplication, addition, and subtraction.

RETEACHING

For some students, memorizing multiplication facts can be an arduous task. Help students at risk by breaking this goal into smaller tasks. For example, help them see that because of the commutative property of multiplication, there are fewer discrete facts for them to memorize than they may think. Provide repeated but brief drills to help students memorize related facts, such as 2s and 4s or 5s and 10s. Allow students to consult a facts table while they are learning.

Multiply to solve for *n*.

36 $0 \times 5 = n$ **0**	37 $4 \times 10 = n$ **40**	38 $6 \times 2 = n$ **12**
39 $5 \times 0 = n$ **0**	40 $2 \times 9 = n$ **18**	41 $10 \times 2 = n$ **20**
42 $8 \times 1 = n$ **8**	43 $9 \times 2 = n$ **18**	44 $1 \times 9 = n$ **9**
45 $1 \times 8 = n$ **8**	46 $1 \times 10 = n$ **10**	47 $7 \times 0 = n$ **0**
48 $2 \times 7 = n$ **14**	49 $10 \times 0 = n$ **0**	50 $0 \times 8 = n$ **0**
51 $2 \times 10 = n$ **20**	52 $5 \times 10 = n$ **50**	53 $8 \times 10 = n$ **80**
54 $10 \times 4 = n$ **40**	55 $2 \times 8 = n$ **16**	56 $7 \times 2 = n$ **14**

Multiply.

57 7×1 = **7**	58 6×2 = **12**	59 7×10 = **70**	60 10×8 = **80**	61 4×10 = **40**
62 10×2 = **20**	63 8×0 = **0**	64 5×2 = **10**	65 2×8 = **16**	66 2×7 = **14**
67 1×8 = **8**	68 0×1 = **0**	69 2×10 = **20**	70 2×9 = **18**	71 10×5 = **50**
72 4×1 = **4**	73 9×1 = **9**	74 7×2 = **14**	75 10×0 = **0**	76 8×2 = **16**

For many people, two of the hardest multiplication facts to remember are $7 \times 8 = 56$ and $7 \times 6 = 42$. Try to remember them!

77 8×7 = **56**	78 7×6 = **42**	79 7×8 = **56**	80 6×7 = **42**

3 Wrap-Up (5 MINUTES)

In Closing Challenge volunteers to state the rules for multiplying by 0, 1, 2, and 10.

ALTERNATIVE ASSESSMENT

Informal Assessment Identify students who may need extra help or additional practice with the basic facts so that you can help them later if necessary.

Assessment Criteria

Did the student . . .

- ✓ correctly answer at least 75% of the computation problems?
- ✓ contribute to the discussion of multiplication rules?
- ✓ communicate strategies used to multiply by 0, 1, 2, and 10?

Homework Have students make a practice sheet of any multiplication facts they are unable to recall quickly. Or, you might provide copies of an incomplete **multiplication table** that students can fill in.

PRACTICE p. 28

LESSON 28 PRACTICE Name__________

Multiply. Compare the problems in each pair.

1 $2 \times 7 = n$ 14	2 $1 \times 9 = n$ 9	3 $5 \times 6 = n$ 30
$7 \times 2 = n$ 14	$9 \times 1 = n$ 9	$6 \times 5 = n$ 30
4 $8 \times 0 = n$ 0	5 $3 \times 6 = n$ 18	6 $9 \times 4 = n$ 36
$0 \times 8 = n$ 0	$6 \times 3 = n$ 18	$4 \times 9 = n$ 36

Multiply to solve for *n*.

7 $0 \times 4 = n$ 0	8 $5 \times 10 = n$ 50	9 $5 \times 2 = n$ 10
10 $4 \times 0 = n$ 0	11 $2 \times 7 = n$ 14	12 $10 \times 3 = n$ 30
13 $7 \times 1 = n$ 7	14 $2 \times 9 = n$ 18	15 $5 \times 4 = n$ 20
16 $1 \times 7 = n$ 7	17 $8 \times 1 = n$ 8	18 $6 \times 0 = n$ 0
19 $2 \times 8 = n$ 16	20 $1 \times 10 = n$ 10	21 $10 \times 2 = n$ 20

Multiply.

22 6×1 = 6	23 8×2 = 16	24 6×5 = 30	25 0×9 = 0	26 9×6 = 54
27 1×6 = 6	28 2×8 = 16	29 5×6 = 30	30 9×0 = 0	31 6×3 = 18
32 5×7 = 35	33 7×2 = 14	34 7×0 = 0	35 6×6 = 36	36 5×3 = 15

28 • *Math Explorations and Applications* Level 4

Copyright © SRA/McGraw-Hill. Permission is granted to reproduce this page for classroom use.

ENRICHMENT p. 28

LESSON 28 ENRICHMENT Name__________

Show two different ways to divide each set of items into groups with the same number of items in each group. Write the multiplication number sentence that tells how you grouped the items. Sample answers:

1
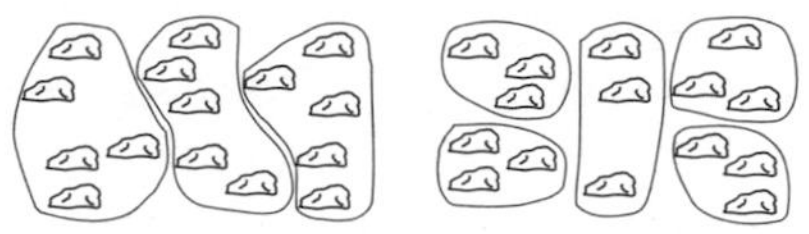

$3 \times 5 = 15$ $5 \times 3 = 15$

2
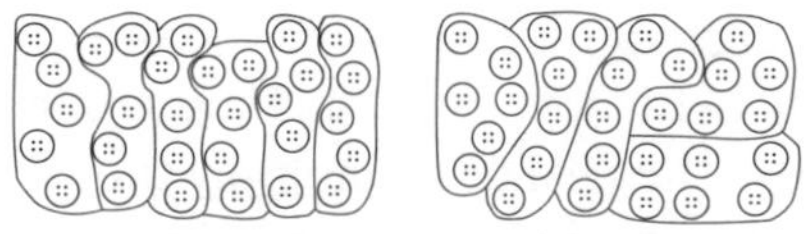

$6 \times 5 = 30$ or 3×10 $5 \times 6 = 30$ or 10×3

3

$4 \times 5 = 20$ $5 \times 4 = 20$

28 • *Math Explorations and Applications* Level 4

Copyright © SRA/McGraw-Hill. Permission is granted to reproduce this page for classroom use.

LESSON 29

Student Edition pages 104–105

Multiplying by 5 and 9

LESSON PLANNER

Objectives

- ▶ to review the use of the multiplication table
- ▶ to review the multiples of 5 and 9
- ▶ to introduce the "adding digits" check for multiples of 9

Context of the Lesson This is the second of seven lessons on the multiplication facts.

MANIPULATIVES

calculators* (optional)

beanbags (optional)

Program Resources

"Multiple Crossing" Game Mat

Practice Master 29

Enrichment Master 29

For additional math integration: Math Throughout the Day*

For extra practice: CD-ROM* Lesson 29

1 Warm-Up

5 MINUTES

Problem of the Day Present the following problem on the chalkboard, allowing students to use **calculators*** if they wish: What is 5 x 7 x 10 x 4 x 1 x 2 x 0? (0, because anything multiplied by 0 is 0)

Problem-Solving Strategies Ask students who have solved the Problem of the Day to share how they solved it and any strategies they used.

MENTAL MATH Review the following multiplication facts with 0, 1, 2, and 10 as factors. Have students recite the entire fact as they give each product.

a. 0 x 1 = (0)	**b.** 2 x 5 = (10)	**c.** 2 x 9 = (18)
d. 1 x 2 = (2)	**e.** 5 x 1 = (5)	**f.** 9 x 2 = (18)
g. 1 x 5 = (5)	**h.** 5 x 2 = (10)	**i.** 0 x 2 = (0)

2 Teach

Using the Student Pages You may wish to demonstrate the "Multiple Crossing" Game Mat first, which provides practice with multiplication facts, so that students who finish early can begin to play immediately.

PRACTICE

LESSON 29

Multiplying by 5 and 9

7 × 8 = ?

The multiplication table is a short way to list the multiplication facts. To find 7 × 8, look in the row marked 7 and the column marked 8.

x	0	1	2	3	4	5	6	7	8	9	10
0	0	0	0	0	0	0	0	0	0	0	0
1	0	1	2	3	4	5	6	7	8	9	10
2	0	2	4	6	8	10	12	14	16	18	20
3	0	3	6	9	12	15	18	21	24	27	30
4	0	4	8	12	16	20	24	28	32	36	40
5	0	5	10	15	20	25	30	35	40	45	50
6	0	6	12	18	24	30	36	42	48	54	60
7	0	7	14	21	28	35	42	49	56	63	70
8	0	8	16	24	32	40	48	56	64	72	80
9	0	9	18	27	36	45	54	63	72	81	90
10	0	10	20	30	40	50	60	70	80	90	100

◆ What number do you find there? **56**

◆ Did you expect to find that number? **yes**

Use the table to find these facts.

1. 8 × 7 = *n* **56**
2. 7 × 6 = *n* **42**
3. 7 × 7 = *n* **49**
4. 8 × 8 = *n* **64**

Compare the columns marked 5 and 10 on the multiplication table.

x	0	1	2	3	4	5	6	7	8	9	10
0	0	0	0	0	0	0	0	0	0	0	0
1	0	1	2	3	4	5	6	7	8	9	10
2	0	2	4	6	8	10	12	14	16	18	20
3	0	3	6	9	12	15	18	21	24	27	30
4	0	4	8	12	16	20	24	28	32	36	40
5	0	5	10	15	20	25	30	35	40	45	50
6	0	6	12	18	24	30	36	42	48	54	60
7	0	7	14	21	28	35	42	49	56	63	70
8	0	8	16	24	32	40	48	56	64	72	80
9	0	9	18	27	36	45	54	63	72	81	90
10	0	10	20	30	40	50	60	70	80	90	100

◆ What is 4 × 10? **40**
What is 4 × 5? **20**

◆ What is 6 × 10? **60**
What is 6 × 5? **30**

◆ What is 8 × 10? **80** What is 8 × 5? **40**

To multiply 8 × 10, you can write 8 with a 0 after it. To multiply 8 × 5, you can write $\frac{1}{2}$ of 8 (which is 4) with a 0 after it. This is because 5 is $\frac{1}{2}$ of 10.

Try to solve these problems without looking at the multiplication table.

5. 2 × 5 = *n* **10**
6. 4 × 5 = *n* **20**
7. 6 × 5 = *n* **30**
8. 8 × 5 = *n* **40**
9. 10 × 5 = *n* **50**
10. 5 × 6 = *n* **30**
11. 5 × 8 = *n* **40**
12. 5 × 10 = *n* **50**

Physical Education Connection Create a game in which students toss **beanbags** at a target to create factors they multiply. Draw a target with chalk on the playground, or lay out concentric circles with rope on a grassy field. Number each section, like a dartboard, and provide beanbags that students can toss. Have students toss the beanbags, multiply the numbers, and keep a running total of the products. Encourage students to create additional rules and ways to determine a winner.

RETEACHING

Reteaching may be postponed until the next lesson, when students assess how well they have learned the facts reviewed so far. You may want to assign Enrichment Master 29 to students.

*available separately

To solve 7 × 5 isn't so easy. But here's a way: You know that 6 × 5 is 30. Now add one more 5 to make 7 × 5. That's 30 and 5 more, which is 35.

Try to solve these problems without looking at the multiplication table.

13. 3 × 5 = n **15**
14. 5 × 5 = n **25**
15. 7 × 5 = n **35**
16. 9 × 5 = n **45**
17. 5 × 7 = n **35**
18. 5 × 1 = n **5**
19. 5 × 9 = n **45**
20. 5 × 3 = n **15**

On the multiplication table, compare the 9 and 10 columns.

◆ What is 7 × 10? **70** What is 7 × 9? **63**
Is it 70 − 7? **yes**

◆ What is 8 × 10? **80** What is 8 × 9? **72**
Is it 80 − 8? **yes**

To find 7 × 9, you can find 7 × 10 and then subtract 7.

To find 8 × 9, you can find 8 × 10 and then subtract 8.

◆ What can you do to find 6 × 9? **Subtract 6 from 6 × 10**

×	0	1	2	3	4	5	6	7	8	9	10
0	0	0	0	0	0	0	0	0	0	0	0
1	0	1	2	3	4	5	6	7	8	9	10
2	0	2	4	6	8	10	12	14	16	18	20
3	0	3	6	9	12	15	18	21	24	27	30
4	0	4	8	12	16	20	24	28	32	36	40
5	0	5	10	15	20	25	30	35	40	45	50
6	0	6	12	18	24	30	36	42	48	54	60
7	0	7	14	21	28	35	42	49	56	63	70
8	0	8	16	24	32	40	48	56	64	72	80
9	0	9	18	27	36	45	54	63	72	81	90
10	0	10	20	30	40	50	60	70	80	90	100

Now try these. Solve for *n*.

21. 9 × 8 = n **72**
22. 9 × 7 = n **63**
23. 7 × 9 = n **63**
24. 5 × 9 = n **45**
25. 4 × 9 = n **36**
26. 9 × 9 = n **81**
27. 9 × 6 = n **54**
28. 3 × 9 = n **27**
29. 9 × 2 = n **18**
30. 6 × 9 = n **54**
31. 8 × 9 = n **72**
32. 9 × 1 = n **9**

◆ What happens when you add the digits in the answer to 9 × 8?

9 × 8 = 72

7 + 2 = 9 The sum of the digits is 9.

33. Add the digits in each answer for problems 21 through 32.
For each problem the sum is 9.

PRACTICE p. 29

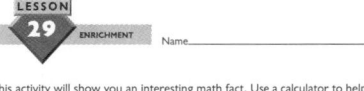

LESSON 29 PRACTICE Name__________

Use the multiplication table to find these facts.

1. 7 × 8 = 56
2. 8 × 8 = 64
3. 8 × 6 = 48
4. 4 × 8 = 32

×	0	1	2	3	4	5	6	7	8	9	10
0	0	0	0	0	0	0	0	0	0	0	0
1	0	1	2	3	4	5	6	7	8	9	10
2	0	2	4	6	8	10	12	14	16	18	20
3	0	3	6	9	12	15	18	21	24	27	30
4	0	4	8	12	16	20	24	28	32	36	40
5	0	5	10	15	20	25	30	35	40	45	50
6	0	6	12	18	24	30	36	42	48	54	60
7	0	7	14	21	28	35	42	49	56	63	70
8	0	8	16	24	32	40	48	56	64	72	80
9	0	9	18	27	36	45	54	63	72	81	90
10	0	10	20	30	40	50	60	70	80	90	100

Use the multiplication table to compare columns marked 9 and 4.

5. What is 4 × 9? 36
6. What is 4 × 4? 16
7. What is 6 × 9? 54
8. What is 6 × 4? 24
9. What is 9 × 9? 81
10. What is 8 × 4? 32

Solve for *n*.

11. 8 × 9 = n 72
12. 7 × 9 = n 63
13. 6 × 6 = n 36
14. 7 × 5 = n 35
15. 9 × 2 = n 18
16. 2 × 5 = n 10
17. 8 × 3 = n 24
18. 5 × 5 = n 25
19. 3 × 7 = n 21
20. 10 × 4 = n 40
21. 9 × 4 = n 36
22. 5 × 7 = n 35
23. 8 × 4 = n 32
24. 8 × 10 = n 80
25. 9 × 5 = n 45
26. 6 × 4 = n 24
27. 7 × 4 = n 28
28. 10 × 7 = n 70

Copyright © SRA/McGraw-Hill. Permission is granted to reproduce this page for classroom use.

ENRICHMENT p. 29

LESSON 29 ENRICHMENT Name__________

This activity will show you an interesting math fact. Use a calculator to help you.

1. Multiply 111 by 9. 999
2. Add the digits from problem 1. Add the digits in the sum you get until you have only one digit. 9
3. Multiply 27 by 5. 135
4. Add the digits from problem 3 until you have only one digit. 9

The answer in problems 2 and 4 is 9. Whenever you multiply a number by 9, or a multiple of 9, the digits in the product add up to 9.

5. Try it again by multiplying 45 by 21, then adding the digits of the product.
945; sums to 9

Are these numbers multiples of 9?

6. 214,250 no
7. 2,181,816 yes
8. 419,895 yes
9. 2,268,941 no
10. 93,462,255 yes

Copyright © SRA/McGraw-Hill. Permission is granted to reproduce this page for classroom use.

Go over both pages with the students. Ask them to find various products on the multiplication table. As you start work with the 5 and 10 columns, review the even multiples of 10. Show the relationship between even multiples of 5 and of 10. For an odd multiple of 5, show that the product can be found by adding 5 to the next-lower even multiple. Point out that all multiples of 5 end in 0 or 5; odd multiples end in 5, and even multiples end in 0.

After everyone has finished problem 33, ask the class how to recognize a multiple of 9. (The sum of the digits is 9.) Emphasize that this rule works only for multiples of 9, and only for multiples through 10 x 9. For greater multiples the sum of the digits may not be 9, but it will always be a multiple of 9.

GAME **Introducing the "Multiple Crossing" Game Mat** Demonstrate the "Multiple Crossing" Game Mat by playing it with some students as others watch. This Game Mat emphasizes practice with multiplication facts and probability. Complete directions can be found on the Game Mat. A copy of "Multiple Crossing" can also be found on page 598.

3 Wrap-Up

5 MINUTES

In Closing Have students explain how to identify multiples of 9.

ALTERNATIVE ASSESSMENT

Portfolio Assessment Have students write down which multiplication facts are still giving them trouble, along with ideas about how they could remember these facts. Have students place this information in their Math Portfolios.

Assessment Criteria

Did the student . . .

✓ correctly answer at least 75% of the multiplication problems?

✓ contribute to the discussion?

✓ demonstrate increased proficiency with the multiplication facts?

Homework Assign Practice Master 29 or Enrichment Master 29 for further concept development.

LOOKING AHEAD For the next lesson, you will need to draw a blank multiplication table on the chalkboard or on a transparency.

LESSON 30

Student Edition pages 106–107

Reviewing Multiplication Facts

LESSON PLANNER

Objective

- ▶ to provide a means of self-assessment for multiplication facts

Context of the Lesson This is the third of seven lessons that review multiplication facts.

MANIPULATIVES

flash cards (optional)

multiplication table

slips of paper (optional)

boxes (optional)

Program Resources

"Multiplication Table" and "Harder Multiplication Table" Game Mats

Practice Master 30

Enrichment Master 30

For additional math integration: Math Throughout the Day*

For extra practice: CD-ROM* Lesson 30

1 Warm-Up

5 MINUTES

Problem of the Day Present the following problem on the chalkboard: Find a pair of numbers whose product is twice their sum. (There is more than one answer: 3 x 6 = 18 and 3 + 6 = 9; 4 x 4 = 16 and 4 + 4 = 8)

Problem-Solving Strategies Ask students who have solved the Problem of the Day to share how they solved it and any strategies they used.

MENTAL MATH Provide practice with multiplication facts, concentrating on the 0, 1, 2, 5, 9, and 10 facts. Begin to emphasize speedy recall.

a. 2 x 1 = (2)	**b.** 0 x 1 = (0)	**c.** 2 x 9 = (18)
d. 5 x 1 = (5)	**e.** 10 x 9 = (90)	**f.** 2 x 5 = (10)
g. 1 x 5 = (5)	**h.** 9 x 2 = (18)	**i.** 10 x 5 = (50)
j. 0 x 9 = (0)	**k.** 5 x 2 = (10)	**l.** 9 x 5 = (45)
m. 0 x 2 = (0)	**n.** 5 x 10 = (50)	**o.** 10 x 1 = (10)
p. 10 x 2 = (20)	**q.** 9 x 10 = (90)	**r.** 5 x 9 = (45)

LESSON 30

Reviewing Multiplication Facts

You may be surprised to find out how many of the multiplication facts you already know.

- ◆ Use a computer or other means to draw and complete this multiplication table.

×	0	1	2	3	4	5	6	7	8	9	10
0	0	0									
1		1									
2		2	4	6		10	12	14			
3				9	12	15		21			
4								28	32		
5									40		
6								42	48		
7								49			
8							48	56			
9							54				
10							60	70			

How many multiplication facts do you know?

- ◆ Do you know the 0, 1, 2, and 10 multiplication facts? If you do, cross off the 0, 1, 2, and 10 columns and the 0, 1, 2, and 10 rows.
- ◆ Do you know the 5 and 9 multiplication facts? If you do, cross off the 5 and 9 rows and columns. **If students answered yes to these questions, all but 24 facts will be crossed off.**

If you do not know these multiplication facts, practice them!

Do you remember these? Solve for *n*.

❶ 7 × 8 = *n* **56** ❷ 8 × 7 = *n* **56** ❸ 6 × 7 = *n* **42** ❹ 7 × 6 = *n* **42**

There are 121 facts listed in the multiplication table.

- ◆ How many do you know?
- ◆ How many are left to learn?

COOPERATIVE LEARNING **Help a classmate learn the multiplication facts. Ask each other several multiplication facts. You may use the multiplication table to help you.**

Literature Connection A roaming cat gets six of everything in *Six-Dinner Sid* by Inga Moore.

RETEACHING

Have students who are still having trouble with multiplication facts write the difficult problems individually on **slips of paper** with the answers on the back. Then have students put their slips in individual **boxes** and draw slips at random. When they get one right, they can take that problem out of their box. Continue until the box is empty.

Have students work in pairs or small groups with **flash cards** and games. Continue such practice for the rest of this unit and throughout the next so that when multidigit multiplication is covered in Unit 4, all students will be ready.

*available separately

Keep in shape by practicing your multiplication facts.

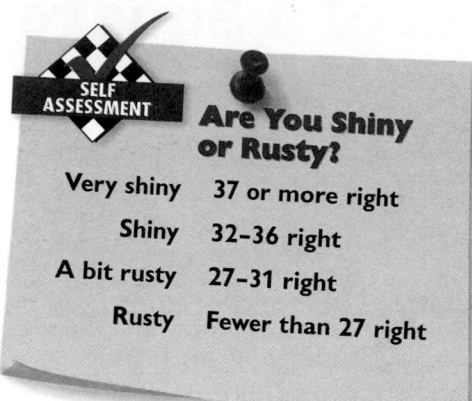

SELF ASSESSMENT

Are You Shiny or Rusty?

Very shiny	37 or more right
Shiny	32–36 right
A bit rusty	27–31 right
Rusty	Fewer than 27 right

Multiply to solve for *n*.

5 $5 \times 8 = n$ **40**	6 $0 \times 8 = n$ **0**	7 $5 \times 4 = n$ **20**	8 $1 \times 5 = n$ **5**
9 $4 \times 9 = n$ **36**	10 $1 \times 8 = n$ **8**	11 $7 \times 5 = n$ **35**	12 $5 \times 3 = n$ **15**
13 $7 \times 8 = n$ **56**	14 $2 \times 8 = n$ **16**	15 $2 \times 5 = n$ **10**	16 $5 \times 9 = n$ **45**
17 $6 \times 7 = n$ **42**	18 $7 \times 2 = n$ **14**	19 $9 \times 5 = n$ **45**	20 $9 \times 2 = n$ **18**
21 $10 \times 6 = n$ **60**	22 $2 \times 9 = n$ **18**	23 $0 \times 9 = n$ **0**	24 $9 \times 3 = n$ **27**
25 $7 \times 0 = n$ **0**	26 $8 \times 7 = n$ **56**	27 $9 \times 9 = n$ **81**	28 $9 \times 4 = n$ **36**
29 $8 \times 9 = n$ **72**	30 $7 \times 6 = n$ **42**	31 $3 \times 9 = n$ **27**	32 $9 \times 8 = n$ **72**
33 $6 \times 9 = n$ **54**	34 $5 \times 6 = n$ **30**	35 $2 \times 2 = n$ **4**	36 $10 \times 7 = n$ **70**

Multiply.

37 9×6 = **54**	38 9×7 = **63**	39 2×6 = **12**	40 5×2 = **10**	41 2×0 = **0**
42 5×7 = **35**	43 5×10 = **50**	44 10×5 = **50**	45 0×10 = **0**	46 5×6 = **30**

❷ Teach

Using the Student Pages Introduce the "Multiplication Table" and "Harder Multiplication Table" Game Mats first, so that students can play as they finish pages 106–107. These provide practice with multiplication facts. Then do page 106 as a class, filling in a blank **multiplication table** on the chalkboard or on a transparency. Practice the facts for 0, 1, 2, and 10. Cross off facts the whole class knows, including their commuted forms. If possible, leave the table on the chalkboard or overhead projector so that in subsequent lessons, you can cross off additional rows and columns as proficiency is demonstrated. Have students complete page 107 independently. Most students should be "shiny" or "very shiny."

GAME

Introducing the "Multiplication Table" and "Harder Multiplication Table" Game Mats Demonstrate these games, which provide practice with multiplication facts. As students finish the easier version, they can move on to the harder one. Complete instructions can be found on each Game Mat. A copy of these Game Mats can also be found on pages 599–600 of this Teacher's Guide.

❸ Wrap-Up

5 MINUTES

In Closing Brainstorm a list of ways to learn multiplication facts that students have not yet mastered.

SELF ASSESSMENT

Encourage students to keep records of their scores in the "Are You Shiny or Rusty?" exercise so that in subsequent assessments of multiplication facts they can compete against themselves. Students who get all the facts correct should seek to increase their speed of recall.

Assessment Criteria

Did the student . . .

- ✓ correctly answer at least 80% of the multiplication facts ?
- ✓ contribute to the discussion about ways to learn the multiplication facts?
- ✓ demonstrate increased proficiency with the multiplication facts?

Homework Assign Practice Master 30 for reviewing multiplication facts.

PRACTICE p. 30

LESSON 30 PRACTICE Name__________

Complete this multiplication table.

×	0	1	2	3	4	5	6	7	8	9	10
0	0	0	0	0	0	0	0	0	0	0	0
1	0	1	2	3	4	5	6	7	8	9	10
2	0	2	4	6	8	10	12	14	16	18	20
3	0	3	6	9	12	15	18	21	24	27	30
4	0	4	8	12	16	20	24	28	32	36	40
5	0	5	10	15	20	25	30	35	40	45	50
6	0	6	12	18	24	30	36	42	48	54	60
7	0	7	14	21	28	35	42	49	56	63	70
8	0	8	16	24	32	40	48	56	64	72	80
9	0	9	18	27	36	45	54	63	72	81	90
10	0	10	20	30	40	50	60	70	80	90	100

Solve for *n*.

1 $5 \times 0 = n$ 0	2 $6 \times 6 = n$ 36	3 $7 \times 5 = n$ 35
4 $4 \times 3 = n$ 12	5 $5 \times 9 = n$ 45	6 $8 \times 4 = n$ 32
7 $3 \times 7 = n$ 21	8 $5 \times 8 = n$ 40	9 $9 \times 3 = n$ 27
10 $8 \times 6 = n$ 48	11 $2 \times 8 = n$ 16	12 $8 \times 3 = n$ 24

30 • *Math Explorations and Applications* Level 4

Copyright © SRA/McGraw-Hill. Permission is granted to reproduce this page for classroom use.

ENRICHMENT p. 30

LESSON 30 ENRICHMENT Name__________

Solve the problems. Then decode the message.

1 $9 \times 5 =$ 45 A	2 $2 \times 5 =$ 10 K	3 $5 \times 7 =$ 35 R
4 $4 \times 3 =$ 12 B	5 $8 \times 5 =$ 40 L	6 $6 \times 9 =$ 54 S
7 $7 \times 1 =$ 7 C	8 $9 \times 4 =$ 36 M	9 $9 \times 8 =$ 72 T
10 $6 \times 3 =$ 18 D	11 $6 \times 6 =$ 36 M	12 $6 \times 5 =$ 30 U
13 $5 \times 5 =$ 25 E	14 $3 \times 8 =$ 24 G	15 $8 \times 6 =$ 48 V
16 $8 \times 8 =$ 64 F	17 $4 \times 5 =$ 20 N	18 $4 \times 2 =$ 8 W
19 $4 \times 6 =$ 24 G	20 $2 \times 2 =$ 4 O	21 $3 \times 0 =$ 0 X
22 $7 \times 7 =$ 49 H	23 $9 \times 3 =$ 27 P	24 $7 \times 8 =$ 56 Y
25 $5 \times 3 =$ 15 I	26 $7 \times 6 =$ 42 Q	27 $9 \times 9 =$ 81 Z

Why doesn't the O(4) C(7) E(25) A(45) N(20) S(54) A(45) Y(56) G(24) O(4) O(4) D(18) - B(12) Y(56) E(25)?

I(15) T(72) P(27) R(35) E(25) F(64) E(25) R(35) S(54) T(72) O(4) W(8) A(45) V(48) E(25).

30 • *Math Explorations and Applications* Level 4

Copyright © SRA/McGraw-Hill. Permission is granted to reproduce this page for classroom use.

LESSON 31

Student Edition pages 108–109

Using Multiplication: Area of a Square

LESSON PLANNER

Objectives

- to provide a context for the "square" multiplication facts
- to introduce students to special instances of the Pythagorean theorem
- to provide practice in finding areas of triangles by counting squares

Context of the Lesson This is the fourth of seven lessons that review multiplication facts. Work with area is expanded in Unit 4. Right angles are covered again in Lesson 68.

MANIPULATIVES

crayons or markers (red, green, and blue)
flash cards (optional)
graph paper

Program Resources

"Shopping" and "Harder Shopping" Game Mats
Practice Master 31
Enrichment Master 31
For additional math integration: Math Throughout the Day*
For extra practice: CD-ROM* Lesson 31

1 Warm-Up

5 MINUTES

Problem of the Day Present the following problem on the chalkboard: A vending machine sells apples for 30¢ each. The machine cannot take pennies, and it will not give change. Name all the combinations of coins you could use to pay for an apple. (1 quarter, 1 nickel; 2 dimes, 2 nickels; 1 dime, 4 nickels; 3 dimes; 6 nickels)

Problem-Solving Strategies Ask students who have solved the Problem of the Day to share how they solved it and any strategies they used.

MENTAL MATH Continue to provide practice with the multiplication facts, including "square" facts. Emphasize speedy recall.

a. 0 x 0 = (0)	**b.** 0 x 1 = (0)	**c.** 10 x 10 = (100)
d. 2 x 9 = (18)	**e.** 9 x 2 = (18)	**f.** 2 x 5 = (10)
g. 9 x 9 = (81)	**h.** 5 x 5 = (25)	**i.** 0 x 2 = (0)

EXPLORE

LESSON 31

Using Multiplication: Area of a Square

A **right angle** looks like this: 

These are right angles: These are not right angles:

- Can you find some right angles in your classroom? **Examples: corner of chalkboard, corner of page or of textbook, etc.**
- Can you find some angles in your classroom that are not right angles? **Examples: alphabet letters such as A, M, N, etc.**

A triangle that has a right angle is called a **right triangle.**

These are right triangles: These are not right triangles:

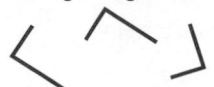

SOCIAL STUDIES CONNECTION

The ancient Greeks found something very interesting about right triangles. They found it by looking at squares on the sides of the triangles. Look at this triangle and the three squares. See if you find anything interesting.

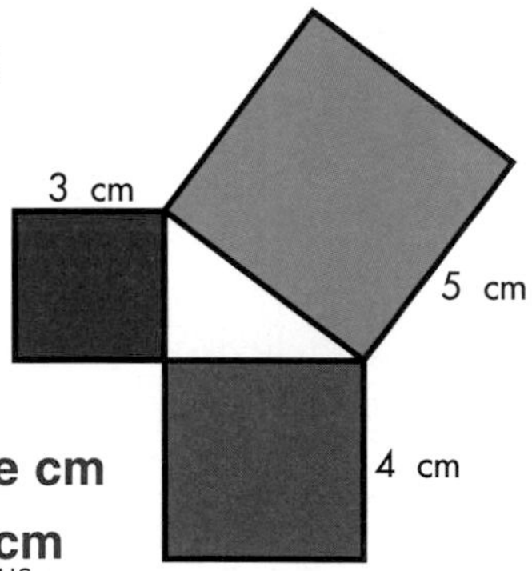

Remember, to find the area of a square, multiply the length of a side by itself.
A = side × side

Solve these problems.

1. What is the area of the red square? **9 square cm**
2. What is the area of the blue square? **16 square cm**
3. What is the area of the red square plus the area of the blue square? **25 square cm**
4. What is the area of the green square? **25 square cm**

LITERATURE CONNECTION

Literature Connection Share the book *Sea Squares* by Joy Hulme with the class. This book presents square numbers from 1 to 10 through vivid illustrations of various sea creatures. Encourage groups of students to create their own books of square numbers based on themes that interest them.

RETEACHING

Students who have trouble remembering the "square" facts should do additional drills with **flash cards,** paper and pencil, the **CD-ROM lesson*,** or manipulatives.

*available separately

Each small box is 1 square centimeter.

- Does the triangle have a right angle? **yes**
- What is the area of the red square? **4 square cm**
- What is the area of the blue square? **4 square cm**
- What is the area of the green square? (Hint: Count the square centimeters. Pair the half squares to make whole squares.) **8 square cm**
- What is the area of the red square plus the area of the blue square? **8 square cm**

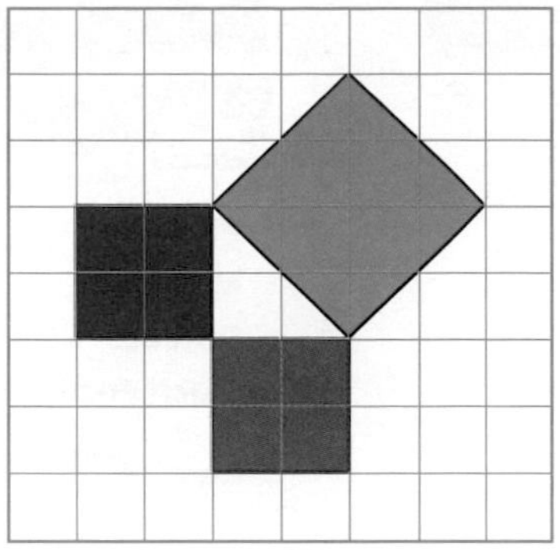

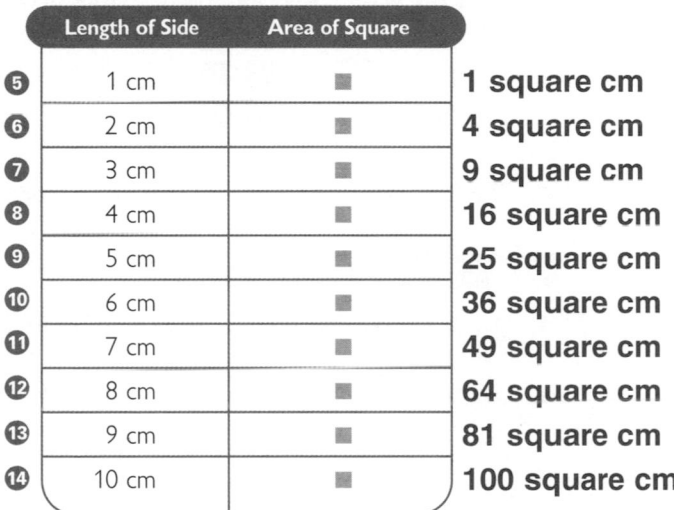

Using graph paper, try this experiment yourself. Complete the chart.

	Length of Side	Area of Square	
5	1 cm	■	**1 square cm**
6	2 cm	■	**4 square cm**
7	3 cm	■	**9 square cm**
8	4 cm	■	**16 square cm**
9	5 cm	■	**25 square cm**
10	6 cm	■	**36 square cm**
11	7 cm	■	**49 square cm**
12	8 cm	■	**64 square cm**
13	9 cm	■	**81 square cm**
14	10 cm	■	**100 square cm**

❷ Teach

Using the Student Pages Begin by demonstrating the "Shopping" Game Mat, which reinforces the multiplication facts, so that students can play the game as they finish pages 108–109. Then do page 108 as a whole-group activity. Go on to the discussion questions at the top of page 109. The emphasis should be on learning the squares of numbers and on exposing students to this relationship involving right triangles. Mastery is not expected. Then have students work on the problems on page 109 in groups, using **graph paper.**

GAME **Introducing the "Shopping" and "Harder Shopping" Game Mats** Demonstrate the "Shopping" Game Mat by playing with three students. This Game Mat involves practice with multiplication facts and making change. Once students have mastered the game, you may wish to have them play the "Harder Shopping" Game Mat. Complete instructions for playing can be found on each Game Mat. A copy of "Shopping" can also be found on pages 601–602.

❸ Wrap-Up 5 MINUTES

In Closing Have students summarize what the ancient Greeks discovered about right triangles and explain what a "square" number is.

ALTERNATIVE ASSESSMENT **Portfolio Assessment** Have students write an explanation of how to find the area of a square and make a drawing or diagram to support their writing for their Math Portfolios.

Assessment Criteria

Did the student . . .

- ✓ correctly identify right angles and right triangles?
- ✓ contribute to the discussion of the Pythagorean theorem?
- ✓ correctly complete the charts about area of squares?

Homework Have students use **graph paper** to try the triangle activity on the Practice Master on page 31 with a right triangle with sides of 6, 8, and 10 centimeters.

PRACTICE p. 31

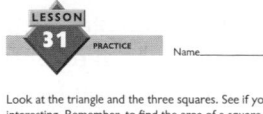

LESSON 31 PRACTICE Name________________

Look at the triangle and the three squares. See if you find anything interesting. Remember, to find the area of a square, multiply the length of a side by itself.

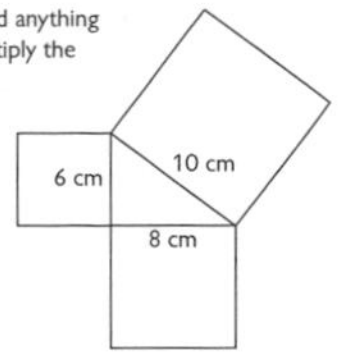

Answer these questions.

1. What is the area of the square with sides of 6 cm? 36 sq cm
2. What is the area of the square with sides of 8 cm? 64 sq cm
3. What is the area of the square with sides of 6 cm plus the area of the square with sides of 8 cm? 100 sq cm
4. What is the area of the square with sides of 10 cm? 100 sq cm
5. What kind of triangle is this? right triangle
6. Do all of the squares have right angles? yes

To find the area of a square, multiply the length of a side by itself.

Complete the charts below.

	Length of Side	Area of Square
7	10 cm	100 sq cm
8	9 cm	81 sq cm
9	8 cm	64 sq cm
10	7 cm	49 sq cm
11	6 cm	36 sq cm

	Length of Side	Area of Square
12	5 cm	25 sq cm
13	4 cm	16 sq cm
14	3 cm	9 sq cm
15	2 cm	4 sq cm
16	1 cm	1 sq cm

Copyright © SRA/McGraw-Hill. Permission is granted to reproduce this page for classroom use.

ENRICHMENT p. 31

LESSON 31 ENRICHMENT Name________________

***A*, *B*, and *C* are squares. Copy and cut out *A* and *B*, cutting along all the solid lines. Rearrange the pieces to show that the Pythagorean theorem, $a^2 + b^2 = c^2$, is true. (Hint: Square *A* is central.)**

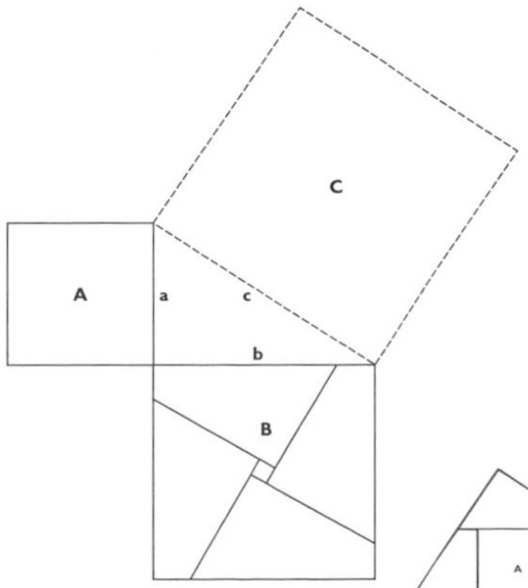

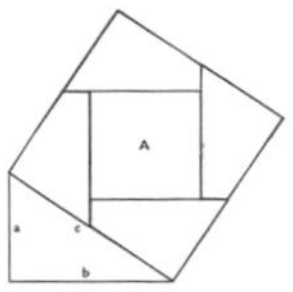

Copyright © SRA/McGraw-Hill. Permission is granted to reproduce this page for classroom use.

LESSON 32

Student Edition pages 110–111

Multiplying by 3, 4, 6, and 8

LESSON PLANNER

Objectives

- to review the multiplication facts for 3, 4, 6, and 8
- to review addition of two-digit numbers

Context of the Lesson This is the fifth in a series of seven lessons that review multiplication facts. A checkpoint for assessing mastery is provided in the next lesson. By the end of this lesson students will have reviewed all the facts through 10 x 10.

MANIPULATIVES

none

Program Resources

Number Cubes (0–5 and 5–10)

Practice Master 32

Enrichment Master 32

For extra practice:

CD-ROM* Lesson 32

Cumulative Review, page 541

1 Warm-Up (5 MINUTES)

Problem of the Day Present the following problem on the chalkboard and discuss students' strategies for solving it: Video Vault sells blank videotapes in bargain packs. Customers can buy tapes in ten-packs or six-packs at great prices. Mr. Biagi bought 72 blank tapes for his school by buying exactly ten bargain packs. How many ten-packs and six-packs did he buy? (three ten-packs and seven six-packs)

Problem-Solving Strategies Ask students who have solved the Problem of the Day to share how they solved it and any strategies they used.

MENTAL MATH Provide practice with all the multiplication facts through 10 x 10. Emphasize speedy recall.

a. 9 x 8 = (72)	**b.** 9 x 4 = (36)
c. 2 x 6 = (12)	**d.** 1 x 8 = (8)
e. 8 x 9 = (72)	**f.** 3 x 6 = (18)
g. 8 x 5 = (40)	**h.** 2 x 7 = (14)
i. 6 x 9 = (54)	**j.** 7 x 10 = (70)
k. 3 x 5 = (15)	**l.** 7 x 3 = (21)
m. 3 x 4 = (12)	**n.** 5 x 3 = (15)
o. 4 x 2 = (8)	**p.** 6 x 1 = (6)
q. 4 x 3 = (12)	**r.** 5 x 4 = (20)

MIXED PRACTICE

LESSON 32

GAME

Multiplying by 3, 4, 6, and 8

COOPERATIVE LEARNING

Add the Products Game

Players:	Two or more
Materials:	Two 0–5 cubes
Object:	To score a total of 50 or more
Math Focus:	Multiplication and addition

RULES

1. Take turns rolling both cubes.
2. On each turn, find the product of the two numbers you roll.
3. Add the product to your last score.

If your score was:	And you rolled:	Your new score would be:
12	3 2	18
36	4 0	36
25	5 1	30

4. The first player whose score totals 50 or more is the winner.

OTHER WAYS TO PLAY THIS GAME

1. Use one 0–5 cube and one 5–10 cube. Try to score a total of 150 or more.
2. Use two 5–10 cubes. Try to score a total of 450 or more.

Literature Connection Invite students to use multiplication to solve the tricks in *Math-A-Magic Number Tricks for Magicians* by Laurence B. White, Jr.

RETEACHING

Use any of the games or strategies introduced so far in this unit to provide extra practice with multiplication facts.

*available separately

You can use the multiplication facts you know to figure out many other facts.

Multiples of 3 can be found by counting by 3s from a product you know.

Example: $3 \times 7 = n$ Let's say you know that $2 \times 7 = 14$.
Then $3 \times 7 = 14 + 7 = 21$.

Multiples of 6 can be found by doubling multiples of 3, because 6 is twice 3.

Example: $6 \times 7 = n$ Let's say you know that $3 \times 7 = 21$.
Then 6×7 is twice 3×7.
So $6 \times 7 = 21 + 21 = 42$.

Multiples of 4 can be found by doubling multiples of 2.

Example: $4 \times 7 = n$ Let's say you know that $2 \times 7 = 14$.
Then 4×7 is twice 2×7.
So $4 \times 7 = 14 + 14 = 28$.

Multiples of 8 can be found by doubling multiples of 4.

Example: $8 \times 9 = n$ Let's say you know that $4 \times 9 = 36$.
Then 8×9 is twice 4×9.
So $8 \times 9 = 36 + 36 = 72$.

Multiply. Solve for *n*.

1 $4 \times 3 = n$ 12	2 $4 \times 6 = n$ 24	3 $6 \times 4 = n$ 24	4 $8 \times 4 = n$ 32
5 $3 \times 6 = n$ 18	6 $6 \times 6 = n$ 36	7 $9 \times 4 = n$ 36	8 $6 \times 8 = n$ 48
9 $7 \times 3 = n$ 21	10 $7 \times 6 = n$ 42	11 $8 \times 7 = n$ 56	12 $9 \times 8 = n$ 72
13 $8 \times 3 = n$ 24	14 $8 \times 6 = n$ 48	15 $4 \times 7 = n$ 28	16 $8 \times 0 = n$ 0
17 $9 \times 3 = n$ 27	18 $9 \times 6 = n$ 54	19 $4 \times 5 = n$ 20	20 $5 \times 8 = n$ 40
21 $3 \times 9 = n$ 27	22 $5 \times 6 = n$ 30	23 $8 \times 8 = n$ 64	24 $10 \times 8 = n$ 80

Use the Cumulative Review on page 541 after this lesson.

PRACTICE p. 32

LESSON 32 PRACTICE Name__________

Solve for *n*.

1 $2 \times 3 = n$ 6	2 $5 \times 6 = n$ 30	3 $8 \times 5 = n$ 40
4 $4 \times 5 = n$ 20	5 $2 \times 8 = n$ 16	6 $0 \times 7 = n$ 0
7 $6 \times 8 = n$ 48	8 $n = 3 \times 8$ 24	9 $5 \times 1 = n$ 5
10 $7 \times 1 = n$ 7	11 $n = 9 \times 2$ 18	12 $3 \times 7 = n$ 21
13 $0 \times 10 = n$ 0	14 $n = 7 \times 6$ 42	15 $8 \times 8 = n$ 64
16 $5 \times 7 = n$ 35	17 $n = 6 \times 9$ 54	18 $n = 16 \times 3$ 48
19 $n = 8 \times 4$ 32	20 $n = 4 \times 4$ 16	21 $n = 5 \times 5$ 25
22 $n = 3 \times 5$ 15	23 $n = 7 \times 8$ 56	24 $9 \times 6 = n$ 54
25 $8 \times 7 = n$ 56	26 $6 \times 7 = n$ 42	27 $4 \times 8 = n$ 32
28 $n = 5 \times 9$ 45	29 $n = 3 \times 9$ 27	30 $6 \times 2 = n$ 12

Multiply.

31 $10 \times 8 = 80$	32 $9 \times 9 = 81$	33 $7 \times 7 = 49$	34 $8 \times 1 = 8$	35 $9 \times 6 = 54$	36 $7 \times 9 = 63$
37 $7 \times 4 = 28$	38 $4 \times 5 = 20$	39 $4 \times 9 = 36$	40 $9 \times 3 = 27$	41 $9 \times 2 = 18$	42 $5 \times 2 = 10$
43 $10 \times 0 = 0$	44 $2 \times 5 = 10$	45 $9 \times 7 = 63$	46 $9 \times 8 = 72$	47 $5 \times 8 = 40$	48 $3 \times 3 = 9$

32 • *Math Explorations and Applications* Level 4

Copyright © SRA/McGraw-Hill. Permission is granted to reproduce this page for classroom use.

ENRICHMENT p. 32

LESSON 32 ENRICHMENT Name__________

Miwa and Kate's parents decided to let them have a party with 15 of their friends. They have $150.00 to spend for their party. Go to a grocery store and fill in the chart for Miwa and Kate. Then answer the questions below. Use a calculator if necessary.

Our Party							
	Number of Items	Cost per Unit	Total Cost		Number of Items	Cost per Unit	Total Cost
Food				**Decorations**			
hamburgers				crepe paper			
pizza				balloons			
buns							
hot dogs				**Paper Goods**			
				plates			
Drinks				napkins			
fruit juice				cups			
soft drinks				utensils			

Answer these questions.

1. How did you find the total cost? Number of items × unit cost
2. After finding the total cost, which food items should Miwa and Kate buy? Answers will vary.
3. If Miwa and Kate have to cut their expenses, what should they cut?

32 • *Math Explorations and Applications* Level 4

Copyright © SRA/McGraw-Hill. Permission is granted to reproduce this page for classroom use.

2 Teach

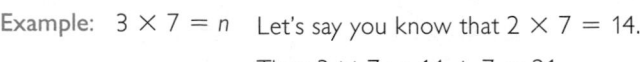

GAME **Using the Student Pages** Have the class play the "Add the Products" game, which provides practice with multiplication and addition. Demonstrate the game and its variations by playing it with students at the chalkboard. Allow time for students to play the basic game and both variations.

Then go over the examples on page 111 with the class. Have students solve problems 1–24 independently.

3 Wrap-Up

5 MINUTES

In Closing Have students share the strategies they used to solve the problems on page 111.

ALTERNATIVE ASSESSMENT **Informal Assessment** Observe students as they play the game and as they complete the exercises. You may wish to keep notes on students who need work on the multiplication facts so that you can assess which students need reteaching.

Assessment Criteria

Did the student . . .

- ✓ actively participate in the game?
- ✓ demonstrate increasing proficiency with the multiplication facts?
- ✓ contribute to the discussion of using known products to find other products?
- ✓ correctly answer at least 80% of the multiplication facts?

Homework Have students play the "Add the Products" game with a family member for further practice with multiplication and addition. A copy of this game can also be found on page 14 of the Home Connections Blackline Masters.

LESSON 33

Student Edition pages 112–115

Multiplication Facts

LESSON PLANNER

Objectives

✓ to assess students' proficiency in speedy and accurate recall of multiplication facts

▶ to help students develop the broad ability to use mathematical common sense

Context of the Lesson This is the sixth of seven lessons on multiplication facts. Practice with these facts is provided throughout the rest of the unit and in later lessons throughout Level 4. This lesson also contains a Mastery Checkpoint for recall of multiplication facts as well as Part 1 of "Money Matters," a four-part Thinking Story.

MANIPULATIVES

counters* (optional)

flash cards (optional)

Program Resources

Number Wheels

Practice Master 33

Enrichment Master 33

Assessment Master

For career connections: Careers and Math*

For extra practice: CD-ROM* Lesson 33

1 Warm-Up (5 MINUTES)

Problem of the Day Present this brain teaser to the class: Two parents and two children have 30 $1 bills. They share the money equally. There is no money left over. How do they do it? (One answer: the group is a grandmother, her son, and his daughter. This is only three people because the man is a parent and the grandmother's child. So each person gets $10.)

Problem-Solving Strategies Ask students who have solved the Problem of the Day to share how they solved it and any strategies they used.

MENTAL MATH Provide practice with basic multiplication facts. Emphasize speedy recall. Have students use their Number Wheels to show the answers.

a. 4 x 4 = (16)	b. 3 x 3 = (9)
c. 4 x 5 = (20)	d. 3 x 8 = (24)
e. 3 x 2 = (6)	f. 2 x 8 = (16)
g. 4 x 7 = (28)	h. 3 x 7 = (21)
i. 2 x 4 = (8)	j. 6 x 7 = (42)

MIXED PRACTICE

LESSON 33

Multiplication Facts

You have now reviewed all of the multiplication facts. Try to solve the problems quickly while still getting the right answers.

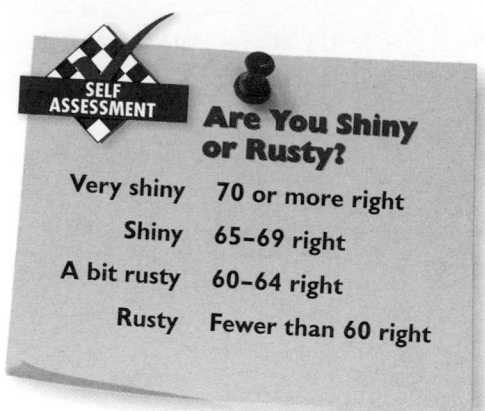

SELF ASSESSMENT

Are You Shiny or Rusty?

Very shiny	70 or more right
Shiny	65–69 right
A bit rusty	60–64 right
Rusty	Fewer than 60 right

Multiply to solve for *n*.

1. $5 \times 3 = n$ **15**	2. $n = 4 \times 3$ **12**	3. $8 \times 5 = n$ **40**
4. $n = 4 \times 5$ **20**	5. $3 \times 1 = n$ **3**	6. $n = 7 \times 0$ **0**
7. $8 \times 2 = n$ **16**	8. $n = 2 \times 8$ **16**	9. $3 \times 7 = n$ **21**
10. $5 \times 10 = n$ **50**	11. $7 \times 8 = n$ **56**	12. $5 \times 7 = n$ **35**
13. $n = 2 \times 7$ **14**	14. $5 \times 0 = n$ **0**	15. $n = 3 \times 6$ **18**
16. $7 \times 1 = n$ **7**	17. $n = 6 \times 5$ **30**	18. $10 \times 1 = n$ **10**
19. $0 \times 8 = n$ **0**	20. $4 \times 6 = n$ **24**	21. $7 \times 6 = n$ **42**
22. $n = 2 \times 5$ **10**	23. $6 \times 7 = n$ **42**	24. $n = 6 \times 10$ **60**
25. $4 \times 4 = n$ **16**	26. $n = 9 \times 2$ **18**	27. $9 \times 5 = n$ **45**
28. $10 \times 7 = n$ **70**	29. $1 \times 8 = n$ **8**	30. $8 \times 8 = n$ **64**
31. $3 \times 4 = n$ **12**	32. $n = 2 \times 7$ **14**	33. $6 \times 4 = n$ **24**
34. $7 \times 3 = n$ **21**	35. $n = 9 \times 3$ **27**	36. $n = 10 \times 2$ **20**

COOPERATIVE LEARNING Encourage students to help each other learn multiplication facts. They may have developed their own unique tricks or mnemonic devices that they could share with classmates. They might prepare their own **flash cards** for facts with which they are having trouble. Partners can quiz each other with the individualized cards until those facts have been learned.

*available separately

Multiply.

37. 5×5 **25**	38. 9×8 **72**	39. 7×8 **56**	40. 9×6 **54**	41. 9×9 **81**	42. 5×1 **5**
43. 8×9 **72**	44. 5×9 **45**	45. 6×7 **42**	46. 7×7 **49**	47. 6×6 **36**	48. 3×8 **24**
49. 6×8 **48**	50. 5×4 **20**	51. 7×8 **56**	52. 3×8 **24**	53. 6×4 **24**	54. 10×1 **10**

55. 6×1 **6**	56. 0×6 **0**	57. 9×7 **63**	58. 6×9 **54**
59. 3×3 **9**	60. 9×4 **36**	61. 3×9 **27**	62. 7×6 **42**
63. 5×6 **30**	64. 2×7 **14**	65. 6×8 **48**	66. 2×0 **0**
67. 7×5 **35**	68. 4×7 **28**	69. 8×3 **24**	70. 3×9 **27**
71. 5×8 **40**	72. 5×3 **15**	73. 8×4 **32**	74. 3×1 **3**

Solve.

75. Tom gets five baseball cards in every pack of gum that he buys. How many cards will he get in three packs? **15**

On your paper, draw a ring around the problems that took you a long time and the ones you got wrong. Make flash cards for these facts and practice them.

MATH JOURNAL

In your Math Journal make a list of real-life examples of when you use multiplication.

2 Teach

SELF ASSESSMENT

Using the Student Pages Explain to students that they will complete the exercises on these pages as a timed test. Make sure they understand that one must be able to say or write multiplication facts quickly and accurately in order to concentrate on more difficult aspects of a problem. Before students start writing answers, have them number their papers from 1–75. Refer them to the assessment key at the top of page 112. When you return students' papers, have them check their answers and correct any errors they may have made.

LEARNING STYLES

Meeting Individual Needs

Students who are musical or rhythmic learners may find it easier to memorize the multiplication facts by setting them to a familiar melody or rhythmic pattern. Encourage students to help each other develop memorization aids, or consult the school's music teacher for suggestions.

LITERATURE CONNECTION

Literature Connection You may wish to have students look at *From One to One Hundred* by Terri Sloat and use multiplication to determine how many objects they are asked to find in each illustration.

> *Knowing the addition, subtraction, multiplication, and division facts "by heart" (or by mind) is at least as important as it ever was, and many other lower-order skills are still essential so that we can concentrate on the higher-order skills.*
>
> —Stephen S. Willoughby, *Mathematics Education for a Changing World*

Teach

Using the Thinking Story "Money Matters (Part 1)," the first of the four-part Thinking Story in Unit 2, centers on the finances of putting on a show. Part 1 explores the value and pricing of tickets.

Answers to Thinking Story Questions:

1. $10.
2. Perhaps none of the ten people who paid 1¢ to see the show would have been willing to pay $1 to see it.
3. The important point is that the value of the ticket is not in the ticket itself, but in what it gives permission to do. So the question is not whether the pieces of paper were worth $1 each, but whether seeing the show was worth $1.
4. They were all sitting on a door at that time.

MATH JOURNAL Have students respond in their Math Journals to Willy's decision about ticket prices. Ask them to write a brief dialogue or skit for a discussion that they might have with Willy or his friends regarding this issue. Volunteers may enjoy acting out the dialogues or skits for classmates.

THINKING STORY

Money Matters

Part 1

Portia and Marcus had the idea of starting a club. Manolita, Ferdie, and Willy joined it. They needed a clubhouse. Mr. Breezy said they could use a shed in his backyard, but they would have to get a new door for it.

"How much will a door cost?" Portia asked.

"You should be able to get a used door for about $10," said Mr. Breezy.

Where would they get $10? "Let's put on a show," said Ferdie. "We'll make people pay money to see it."

Everyone thought that was a good idea. The children found funny clothes to wear. They made a stage by laying an old door on top of some boxes. They cut up pieces of paper and made ten $1 tickets.

Ten people came to the show. Portia sang. Marcus told jokes. Manolita did magic tricks. Ferdie danced. And Willy sold tickets. Everyone liked the show. When it was over, the children rushed to Willy's ticket booth.

"I sold every ticket," Willy said proudly.

"How much money do we have?" the others asked.

"Ten cents," said Willy.

RETEACHING

MANIPULATIVES Students who are not yet proficient with all their multiplication facts should continue to practice. Have students work in pairs to model addition and multiplication facts with **counters***. For example, have one student model the equation 4 × 2 = 8 while another models 2 + 2 + 2 + 2 = 8. Guide students to understand that the models look the same because multiplication is repeated addition.

PRACTICE p. 33

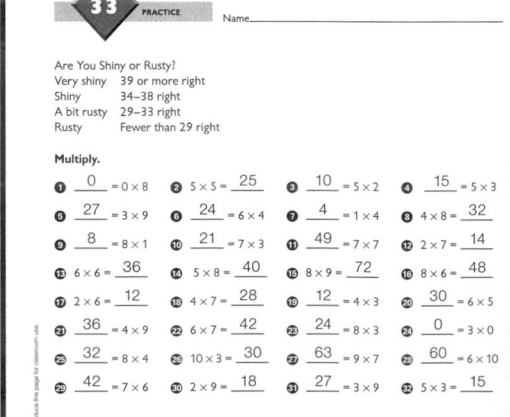

LESSON 33 PRACTICE Name____________

Are You Shiny or Rusty?

Very shiny	39 or more right
Shiny	34–38 right
A bit rusty	29–33 right
Rusty	Fewer than 29 right

Multiply.

1. 0 = 0 × 8	2. 5 × 5 = 25	3. 10 = 5 × 2	4. 15 = 5 × 3
5. 27 = 3 × 9	6. 24 = 6 × 4	7. 4 = 1 × 4	8. 4 × 8 = 32
9. 8 = 8 × 1	10. 21 = 7 × 3	11. 49 = 7 × 7	12. 2 × 7 = 14
13. 6 × 6 = 36	14. 5 × 8 = 40	15. 8 × 9 = 72	16. 8 × 6 = 48
17. 2 × 6 = 12	18. 4 × 7 = 28	19. 12 = 4 × 3	20. 30 = 6 × 5
21. 36 = 4 × 9	22. 6 × 7 = 42	23. 24 = 8 × 3	24. 0 = 3 × 0
25. 32 = 8 × 4	26. 10 × 3 = 30	27. 63 = 9 × 7	28. 60 = 6 × 10
29. 42 = 7 × 6	30. 2 × 9 = 18	31. 27 = 3 × 9	32. 5 × 3 = 15

Multiply.

33. 5 × 4 = 20	34. 3 × 2 = 6	35. 7 × 0 = 0	36. 8 × 8 = 64	37. 8 × 6 = 48	38. 4 × 9 = 36
39. 7 × 1 = 7	40. 9 × 6 = 54	41. 4 × 4 = 16	42. 6 × 3 = 18	43. 7 × 6 = 42	44. 5 × 3 = 15

Copyright © SRA/McGraw-Hill. Permission is granted to reproduce this page for classroom use.

*available separately

"Just a minute," said Marcus. "We made ten $1 tickets. You said you sold all of them."

"That's right," said Willy. "I sold them for a penny apiece. Here's the money."

"A penny apiece!" they all shouted. "Tickets were supposed to be a dollar apiece!"

"Nobody told me that," Willy said. "I charged what I thought they were worth. I didn't think a little piece of paper was worth a dollar. I figured each ticket cost us about a penny. So that's what I charged."

The children all sat down sadly on their stage. "Now we'll never get a door," Ferdie moaned.

"Yes, we will," said Marcus.

Work in groups. Discuss your answers and how you figured them out. Then compare your answers with those of other groups. **Answers are in margin.**

1. How much money would the children have made if Willy had sold all the tickets for the amount planned?
2. Perhaps they wouldn't have made any money at all if Willy had asked as much as he was supposed to for the tickets. How could that be?
3. Do you agree with Willy that it wouldn't be fair to sell tickets for a dollar when they cost only about a penny to make? Why or why not?
4. How could Marcus be so sure they will get a door?

3 Wrap-Up (5 MINUTES)

In Closing Discuss with students some advantages and disadvantages of working with a group of people to raise money for a common goal.

Mastery Checkpoint 5

At about this time most students should demonstrate mastery of multiplication facts through 10 x 10 by correctly answering at least 80% of the problems on pages 112–113. Most students should finish in 15 minutes or less. Confirm students' mastery individually or during Mental Math drills so you can tell whether they have memorized the multiplication facts or are getting answers by skip counting or by repeated addition. Record the results of the assessment on the Mastery Checkpoint Chart. You may also use Assessment Blackline Masters page 10 to determine mastery.

Assessment Criteria

Did the student . . .

✓ explain how to solve for *n*?

✓ correctly answer at least 80% of the multiplication facts?

✓ contribute to the Thinking Story discussion?

Homework Have students play the "Add the Products" game on page 110 with a family member for further practice with addition and multiplication. A copy of this game can also be found on page 14 of the Home Connections Blackline Masters.

ENRICHMENT p. 33

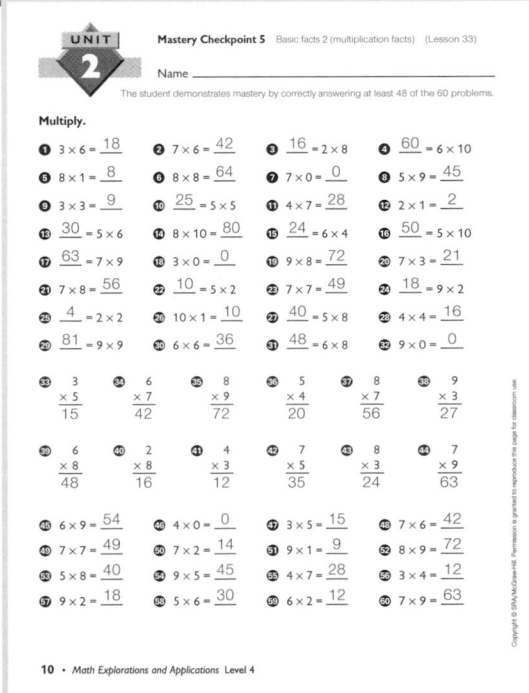

LESSON 33 ENRICHMENT Name________________

Follow the rule under each computer to find the two products. Write both products on the right side of the computer. Add the products to find a sum. The sums hold the keys to the riddle. The first one has been done for you.

What do you call a fish who drives underwater?

1. 8, 9; ×4: 32 + 36 = 68 U
2. 7, 5; ×6: 42 + 30 = 72 C
3. 9, 3; ×3: 27 + 9 = 36 I
4. 6, 5; ×9: 54 + 45 = 99 V
5. 8, 5; ×5: 40 + 25 = 65 R
6. 4, 1; ×7: 28 + 7 = 35 B
7. 7, 3; ×4: 28 + 12 = 40 S
8. 10, 6; ×2: 20 + 12 = 32 E
9. 8, 9; ×8: 64 + 72 = 136 D

A S(40) C(72) U(68) B(35) A D(136) R(65) I(36) V(99) E(32) R(65)

Copyright © SRA/McGraw-Hill. Permission is granted to reproduce this page for classroom use.

Math Explorations and Applications Level 4 • **33**

ASSESSMENT p. 10

UNIT 2 **Mastery Checkpoint 5** Basic facts 2 (multiplication facts) (Lesson 33)

Name________________

The student demonstrates mastery by correctly answering at least 48 of the 60 problems.

Multiply.

1. 3 × 6 = 18	2. 7 × 6 = 42	3. 16 = 2 × 8	4. 60 = 6 × 10
5. 8 × 1 = 8	6. 8 × 8 = 64	7. 7 × 0 = 0	8. 5 × 9 = 45
9. 3 × 3 = 9	10. 25 = 5 × 5	11. 4 × 7 = 28	12. 2 × 1 = 2
13. 30 = 5 × 6	14. 8 × 10 = 80	15. 24 = 6 × 4	16. 50 = 5 × 10
17. 63 = 7 × 9	18. 3 × 0 = 0	19. 9 × 8 = 72	20. 7 × 3 = 21
21. 7 × 8 = 56	22. 10 = 5 × 2	23. 7 × 7 = 49	24. 18 = 9 × 2
25. 4 = 2 × 2	26. 10 × 1 = 10	27. 40 = 5 × 8	28. 4 × 4 = 16
29. 81 = 9 × 9	30. 6 × 6 = 36	31. 48 = 6 × 8	32. 9 × 0 = 0

33. 3 × 5 = 15	34. 6 × 7 = 42	35. 8 × 9 = 72	36. 5 × 4 = 20	37. 8 × 7 = 56	38. 9 × 3 = 27
39. 6 × 8 = 48	40. 2 × 8 = 16	41. 4 × 3 = 12	42. 7 × 5 = 35	43. 8 × 3 = 24	44. 7 × 9 = 63

45. 6 × 9 = 54	46. 4 × 0 = 0	47. 3 × 5 = 15	48. 7 × 6 = 42
49. 7 × 7 = 49	50. 7 × 2 = 14	51. 9 × 1 = 9	52. 8 × 9 = 72
53. 5 × 8 = 40	54. 9 × 5 = 45	55. 4 × 7 = 28	56. 3 × 4 = 12
57. 9 × 2 = 18	58. 5 × 6 = 30	59. 6 × 2 = 12	60. 7 × 9 = 63

Copyright © SRA/McGraw-Hill. Permission is granted to reproduce this page for classroom use.

10 • *Math Explorations and Applications* Level 4

LESSON 34

Student Edition pages 116–119

Using Multiplication

LESSON PLANNER

Objectives

- ▶ to provide practice in solving word problems
- ▶ to provide practice in making and using charts
- ▶ to review how to find the area of a rectangle and prepare students for work on upper and lower bounds of area

Context of the Lesson This is the seventh of seven lessons on multiplication facts. Functions like those on page 118 were used in the Level 3 program and in Lesson 8 of this program. They will be covered in depth in Unit 3.

MANIPULATIVES

calculator*
counters*
play money*
tape player and audio cassette (optional)
graph paper or centimeter cubes*

Program Resources

Number Wheels
Practice Master 34
Enrichment Master 34
For extra practice: CD-ROM* Lesson 34

1 Warm-Up

5 MINUTES

Problem of the Day Present the following problem on the chalkboard: Figure out two ways to describe the pattern. Then find the next three numbers. 90, 81, 72, 63, 54, . . . (The pattern is in descending multiples of 9; or, as the tens digit decreases by 1, the ones digit increases by 1; the next three numbers are 45, 36, and 27.)

Problem-Solving Strategies Ask students who have solved the Problem of the Day to share how they solved it and any strategies they used.

MENTAL MATH Provide practice with multiplication facts. Students can use Number Wheels to show the products.

a. 5 × 6 = (30) **b.** 6 × 2 = (12)
c. 9 × 3 = (27) **d.** 8 × 8 = (64)
e. 6 × 8 = (48) **f.** 4 × 10 = (40)

(continued on page 117)

PROBLEM SOLVING

LESSON 34

Using Multiplication

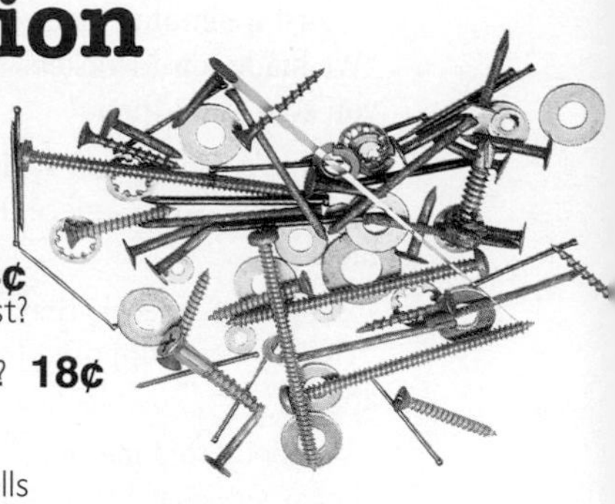

Elena works in a hardware store. Washers cost 2¢ each.

Answer these questions.

1. How much do seven washers cost? **14¢**
2. How much do nine washers cost? **18¢**
3. Elena made a chart so she won't have to multiply each time she sells washers. Her chart looks like this:

Washer Chart (×2)

Number of washers	1	2	3	4	5	6	7	8	9	10
Amount (in cents)	2	4	**6**	**8**	**10**	**12**	**14**	**16**	**18**	**20**

Use a computer or other means to draw the chart.

4. Nails also cost 2¢ each. Elena decides to make a nail chart. What will it look like? Do you think she should make the chart? **It will look exactly like the chart for washers; no**
5. Small springs cost 7¢ each. Make a chart for springs like Elena's chart for washers. **Chart should look like washers chart but with multiples of 7 for "Amount in cents."**
6. Lag bolts cost 7¢ each. Either make a chart for lag bolts or write what you could use instead. **You could use the chart for the small springs.**
7. Sets of hooks and eyes cost 9¢ each. Make a hook-and-eye chart. **Chart should look like washers chart but with multiples of 9 for "Amount in cents."**
8. Make a chart for sandpaper that costs 10¢ a sheet. **Chart should look like washers chart but with multiples of 10 for "Amount in cents."**

Why teach it at this time?

Comparing the areas of squares will help prepare students for the work on upper and lower bounds, which appears in Lesson 39.

*available separately

Jiro works at a shop that sells stickers. Most stickers cost 20¢, 30¢, 40¢, and so on up to $1.00. On Saturday the store is having a half-price sale, so Jiro decided to make a half-price chart.

Use a computer or other means to draw and complete Jiro's chart. Use play money to help if you need it.

Sticker Chart

Price (in cents)	20	30	40	50	60	70	80	90	100
Half-Price (in cents)	10	**15**	**20**	25	**30**	**35**	**40**	**45**	**50**

Use Jiro's chart to answer the following questions.

9 On half-price day,

a. How much would you pay for one sticker regularly priced at 40¢ each? **20¢**

b. How much would you pay for two stickers regularly priced at 40¢ each? **40¢**

c. How much would you pay for one sticker that usually costs 50¢ each? **25¢**

d. How much would you pay for two stickers that usually cost 50¢ each? **50¢**

10 How much would you pay for both a 20¢ sticker and a 40¢ sticker at the regular price? **60¢**

11 How much would you pay for a 20¢ sticker and a 40¢ sticker at half-price? **30¢**

12 How much would you save all together on the stickers in question 11 at the half-price sale? **30¢**

13 How much would you pay all together for three 30¢-stickers and two 60¢-stickers at the regular price? At half price? **$2.10; $1.05**

Mental Math (continued)

g. 6 x 3 = (18) **h.** 8 x 7 = (56)

i. 9 x 6 = (54) **j.** 4 x 8 = (32)

k. 6 x 5 = (30) **l.** 6 x 6 = (36)

m. 5 x 7 = (35) **n.** 6 x 10 = (60)

o. 8 x 10 = (80) **p.** 6 x 4 = (24)

q. 4 x 9 = (36) **r.** 9 x 7 = (63)

2 Teach

Using the Student Pages Once students understand how to use the price chart on page 116, let them work independently to solve the problems on pages 116 and 117. If necessary, students can model the problems with manipulative objects, such as **counters*** or crayons to represent the washers, or **play money*** to represent the stickers.

SPECIAL NEEDS

Meeting Individual Needs

If students have trouble reading word problems, either read the problems aloud or pair good readers with less capable ones. Alternatively, you might record the problems on an **audiocassette** so that students can listen to the tape and solve the problems independently.

Technology Connection Refer students to the software *Interactive Math Journey* from The Learning Company (Mac, for Grades 1–4) for practice with basic computation (addition, subtraction, and multiplication), pattern recognition, fractions, measurement, place value, early geometry, and symmetry.

*available separately

◆ LESSON 34 Using Multiplication

Teach

Using the Student Pages If necessary, remind students of the function table format they used in Lesson 8 (pages 24–27). Most students should be able to work with the function tables on page 118. Point out the similarity of these charts to the price charts on pages 116 and 117, then have students complete the charts on their own. Do page 119 as a whole-group activity, or assign it to individuals or pairs. Discuss the problems when students finish.

LEARNING STYLES — MANIPULATIVES

Meeting Individual Needs Artistic and kinesthetic or hands-on learners may benefit from using centimeter **graph paper** or **centimeter cubes*** to compare the areas of the squares on page 119. They can model each square in actual size and use their models to answer the comparison questions.

> *We can remember—always—that at the heart of problem solving is the most basic and human skill of all—thinking.*
>
> —Stephen S. Willoughby, *Teaching Mathematics: What Is Basic?*

◆ LESSON 34 Using Multiplication

Use a computer or other means to draw and complete the charts. Complete them by finding what numbers the machines will send out.

14 ×5

In	Out
1	5
2	10
3	15
4	20
5	25

15 ×3

In	Out
8	24
7	21
6	18
5	15
4	12

16 ×7

In	Out
0	0
2	14
4	28
6	42
8	56

17 ×2

In	Out
0	0
2	4
4	8
6	12
8	16

18 ×6

In	Out
8	48
7	42
6	36
5	30
4	24

19 ×8

In	Out
8	64
4	32
2	16
1	8
0	0

20 ×4

In	Out
0	0
2	8
4	16
6	24
8	32

21 ×10

In	Out
3	30
9	90
6	60
4	40
2	20

22 ×9

In	Out
9	81
8	72
7	63
6	54
5	45

118 • Multiplication and Division

Literature Connection Share *Counting on Frank* by Rod Clement with the class. Have students use multiplication to calculate answers to the unusual problems the book presents.

RETEACHING

Help students who have trouble completing function tables by emphasizing that the price charts for washers and stickers are like function tables turned sideways. You might also ask students to act out putting numbers into a function machine. Have one student act as the function machine with a particular rule (for example, +2). One at a time, each student gives the function-machine student a number (on an **index card**). The function-machine student performs the function on this number (using mental math, the chalkboard, or a **calculator***) and hands back the answer (on an **index card**).

*available separately

Remember, to find the area of a rectangle, multiply the length by the width. $A = l \times w$

What is the area of each rectangle?

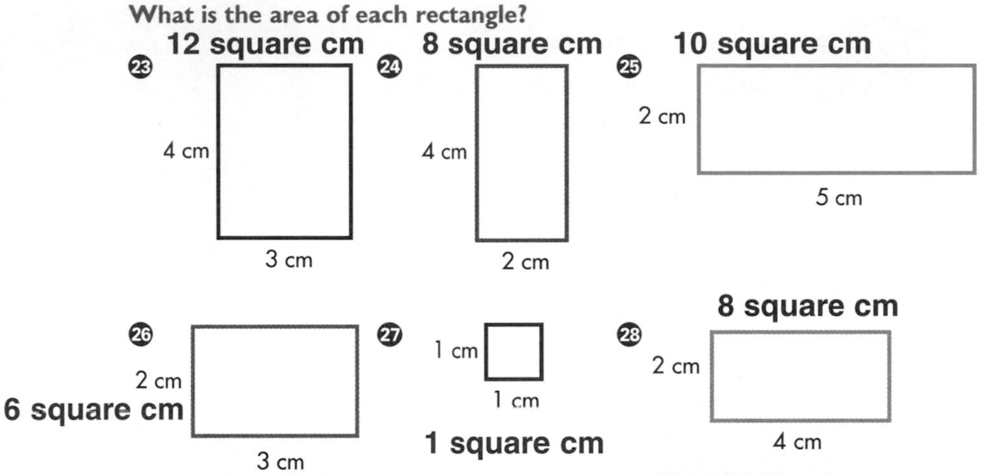

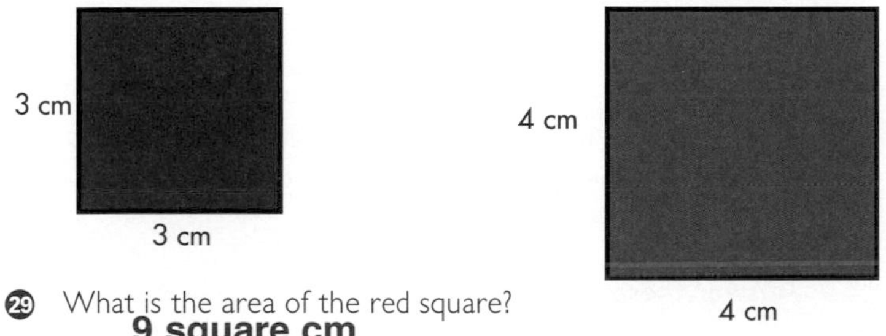

29 What is the area of the red square? **9 square cm**

30 What is the area of the blue square? **16 square cm**

Each side of the green square is between 3 and 4 centimeters long.

31 Can the area of the green square be less than 9 square centimeters? **no**

32 Can the area of the green square be more than 16 square centimeters? **no**

Trace the green square. Compare its area with the areas of the red and blue squares.

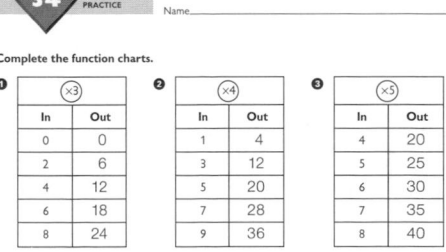

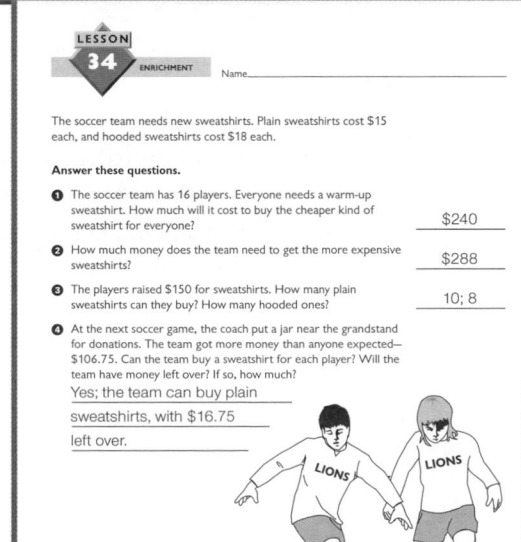

PRACTICE p. 34

LESSON 34 PRACTICE Name__________

Complete the function charts.

1 (×3)

In	Out
0	0
2	6
4	12
6	18
8	24

2 (×4)

In	Out
1	4
3	12
5	20
7	28
9	36

3 (×5)

In	Out
4	20
5	25
6	30
7	35
8	40

Save-More is having a half-price sale on pens. The manager asks you to make a half-price chart. This has been started for you.

Complete the chart. Use play money for help if you need it.

4

Price (in cents)	60	70	80	90	100
Half-price (in cents)	30	35	40	45	50

PROBLEM SOLVING **Use the chart above to solve these problems.**

5 How much will you pay for a pen that normally costs $1.00? 50¢

6 How much will you pay for two pens that are regularly priced at 70¢ each? 70¢

7 How much will you save when you buy a pen at half price that was regularly priced at 90¢? 45¢

Copyright © SRA/McGraw-Hill. Permission is granted to reproduce this page for classroom use.

ENRICHMENT p. 34

LESSON 34 ENRICHMENT Name__________

The soccer team needs new sweatshirts. Plain sweatshirts cost $15 each, and hooded sweatshirts cost $18 each.

Answer these questions.

1 The soccer team has 16 players. Everyone needs a warm-up sweatshirt. How much will it cost to buy the cheaper kind of sweatshirt for everyone? $240

2 How much money does the team need to get the more expensive sweatshirts? $288

3 The players raised $150 for sweatshirts. How many plain sweatshirts can they buy? How many hooded ones? 10; 8

4 At the next soccer game, the coach put a jar near the grandstand for donations. The team got more money than anyone expected—$106.75. Can the team buy a sweatshirt for each player? Will the team have money left over? If so, how much?
Yes; the team can buy plain sweatshirts, with $16.75 left over.

Copyright © SRA/McGraw-Hill. Permission is granted to reproduce this page for classroom use.

❸ Wrap-Up (5 MINUTES)

In Closing Have students describe how to compare the sizes of the three colored squares on page 119.

ALTERNATIVE ASSESSMENT **Informal Assessment** Observe students as they work on the various problems in this lesson. Encourage them to verbalize their reasoning and explain how they use a price chart and a function table. Listen carefully as students present their logic for solving problems 31 and 32 on page 119 so you can determine how best to present the topic of upper and lower bounds in Lesson 39.

Assessment Criteria

Did the student . . .

- ✓ communicate strategies used to complete and use price charts?
- ✓ accurately complete the function tables?
- ✓ correctly answer at least 75% of the computation problems on pages 116–117?
- ✓ contribute to the discussion of comparing the area of squares?

Homework Have students make a chart for sales tax on whole dollar amounts from $1 to $10 based on the sales tax rate in your area. If your area does not charge sales tax, use any reasonable number, such as 6¢ for each dollar spent.

LESSON 35

Student Edition pages 120–123

Calculating Elapsed Time

LESSON PLANNER

Objectives

- to provide practice solving problems that involve elapsed time
- to provide practice calculating elapsed time that requires regrouping units of time
- to provide practice adding and subtracting with negative numbers

Context of the Lesson This is the first of four lessons on measurement. This is the only lesson that deals with calculating elapsed time.

MANIPULATIVES

calculators*

calendars

clocks, analog with movable hands*, and digital

number line showing negative numbers

Program Resources

"Minutes" and "Harder Minutes" Game Mats

Number Wheels

Reteaching Master

Practice Master 35

Enrichment Master 35

For additional math integration: Math Throughout the Day*

For extra practice: CD-ROM* Lesson 35

1 Warm-Up

5 MINUTES

Problem of the Day Present this problem to students: Tino has a digital clock in his room. One night he could not sleep. As he tossed and turned, he would see the image of his clock in a mirror. Twice between 9:00 P.M. and midnight, the numbers in the mirror looked just the same as the digits on the clock. At what times did this happen? (10:01 P.M., 11:11 P.M.)

Problem-Solving Strategies Ask students who have solved the Problem of the Day to share how they solved it and any strategies they used.

PROBLEM SOLVING

LESSON 35

Calculating Elapsed Time

PHYSICAL EDUCATION CONNECTION

How long is a basketball game?

National Basketball Association (NBA) rules call for the following times.

Regulation Time

- The four quarters are each 12 minutes long.
- The break between the first and second quarters is $1\frac{1}{2}$ minutes.
- The half-time break is ten minutes.
- The break between the third and fourth quarters is $1\frac{1}{2}$ minutes.
- Time-outs can be called for various reasons.

Overtime

- If a game is tied, an overtime period of five minutes is allowed. The five-minute overtime periods continue until there is a winner.

Answer these questions.

How long will a basketball game last if

1. There are no time-outs and no overtime? **61 minutes, or 1 hour and 1 minute**
2. There are eight minutes of time-outs and two overtime periods? **79 minutes, or 1 hour and 19 minutes**
3. There are 17 minutes of time-outs and no overtime? **78 minutes, or 1 hour and 18 minutes**

FANTASTIC FACT **Not all whales sing, but humpback whales are known for their beautiful songs. Humpbacks can sing for half an hour at a time and can be heard underwater for hundreds of miles.**

120 • Multiplication and Division

ESL **Meeting Individual Needs**

Students with limited English proficiency may have difficulty reading and understanding this lesson. You may want to have these students work with native English speakers, who can help explain and clarify terms.

*available separately

7 Each game will last 73 minutes, so the total time will be 73 + 30 + 73 = 176 minutes, or 2 hours and 56 minutes. The second game will end at 9:56 P.M.

Times for high school basketball games are different.

- The four quarters are each eight minutes long.
- There is a one-minute break between the first and second quarters and between the third and fourth quarters.
- There is a ten-minute halftime break between the second and third quarters.
- There are three-minute overtime periods.
- Time-outs can be called for various reasons.

Answer these questions.

How long will a high school basketball game last if

4. There are no time-outs and no overtime? **44 minutes**

5. There are three overtime periods and ten minutes of time-outs? **63 minutes, or 1 hour and 3 minutes**

6. There are 21 minutes of time-outs and no overtime? **65 minutes, or 1 hour and 5 minutes**

Linton High School wants to schedule two basketball games for the same evening. There will be a girls' game and a boys' game. Suppose there are two overtime periods, 23 minutes of time-outs per game, and a 30-minute break between games.

7. What time will the second game end if the first game starts at 7 P.M.?

8. Suppose the principal wants the second game to end by 9 P.M. About what time should the first game start? Explain your reasoning. **If the first game starts at about 6 P.M., the second game should be over by 9 P.M.**

MATH JOURNAL

In your Math Journal write a paragraph describing real-life situations in which calculating elapsed time is important.

MENTAL MATH Provide practice with equivalent measures of time. Students can show their responses with Number Wheels.

a. 1 week = _____ days (7)
b. 1 day = _____ hours (24)
c. 1 hour = _____ minutes (60)
d. 1 minute = _____ seconds (60)
e. 3 weeks = _____ days (21)
f. 2 days = _____ hours (48)
g. 5 hours = _____ minutes (300)
h. 10 minutes = _____ seconds (600)

2 Teach

Using the Student Pages Demonstrate the "Minutes" and "Harder Minutes" Game Mats before beginning the lesson so that students may play them as they finish their work. These games provide practice with telling time. Tell students that *elapsed time* means how much time has gone by. Present some simple problems that involve elapsed time, such as how much time passes between the start of the school day and the start of math class, or how much time goes by during lunch. Then discuss the following problem: If it takes about 45 minutes to get to the sports arena, about how long does it take to get to *and* from the arena? Help students understand that they can answer by saying 90 minutes or, because 60 minutes = one hour, they can regroup and say one hour 30 minutes. Have students do these pages independently or in small groups. Then discuss answers as a class.

LEARNING STYLES · MANIPULATIVES

Meeting Individual Needs
Students who are visual or kinesthetic learners may benefit from using a **clock*** with movable hands to visualize time as it passes and to model the elapsed time in the basketball game.

*available separately

◆ LESSON 35 Calculating Elapsed Time

Teach

Using the Student Pages Provide analog **clocks*** with movable hands, digital clocks, and **calendars** to help students solve the problems on page 122. Emphasize that all answers should be stated in their simplest form. For example, the answer "four weeks ten days" is technically correct, but since seven days = one week, students should regroup and state the answer as "five weeks three days." Have students work in pairs to solve the problems on page 122.

Tell students that they may use **calculators*** to do the chain computations on page 123. However, encourage them to look for shortcuts and to recognize problems that may be easier to do mentally. For example, in problem 21, it may be faster for students to count by 2s from 5 to reach the answer of 11 than to enter so many digits and symbols into the calculator. Some students may want to use a **number line** that shows negative numbers.

Introducing the "Minutes" and "Harder Minutes" Game Mats Demonstrate the "Minutes" and "Harder Minutes" Game Mats by playing each with several students. "Minutes" provides practice with telling time to five-minute intervals, and "Harder Minutes" provides practice with telling time to the minute. A copy of the "Minutes" Game Mat can also be found on pages 594–595 of this Teacher's Guide.

CULTURAL DIVERSITY Some students may be unfamiliar with the game of basketball or with the terminology used in this lesson. Invite students who understand the game to clarify for classmates the object, the rules, and the major aspects of play. If possible, arrange for students to see a live game or a video of a game.

◆ LESSON 35 Calculating Elapsed Time

Solve these problems. Simplify each answer. You may use a calculator.

9. 1 week 4 days + 3 weeks 6 days = ■ **5 weeks 3 days**
10. 13 weeks 5 days + 12 weeks 4 days = ■ **26 weeks 2 days**
11. 2 hours 50 minutes + 3 hours 40 minutes = ■ **6 hours 30 minutes**
12. 2 weeks 5 days − 1 week 4 days = ■ **1 week 1 day**
13. 5 weeks 2 days − 2 weeks 5 days = ■ **2 weeks 4 days**
14. 3 days 12 hours + 2 days 14 hours = ■ **6 days 2 hours**
15. 3 weeks 5 days 13 hours 47 minutes + 5 weeks 8 days 21 hours 7 minutes = ■ **10 weeks 10 hours 54 minutes**
16. 23 weeks 6 days 9 hours 32 minutes + 17 weeks 5 days 12 hours 48 minutes = ■ **41 weeks 4 days 22 hours 20 minutes**
17. 23 weeks 6 days 9 hours 32 minutes − 17 weeks 5 days 12 hours 48 minutes = ■ **6 weeks 20 hours 44 minutes**
18. 16 weeks 4 days 8 hours − 11 weeks 5 days 7 hours 31 minutes = ■ **4 weeks 6 days 29 minutes**
19. 4 days 40 minutes − 2 hours 35 minutes = ■ **3 days 22 hours 5 minutes**
20. 6 days 17 hours + 1 week 7 hours = ■ **2 weeks**

FANTASTIC FACT **Halley's Comet was first observed 2200 years ago.**

122 • Multiplication and Division

Physical Education Connection Work with the gym teacher to arrange for students to observe or play a game of basketball. It may be necessary to revise the rules to suit the ability level of the group. If it is inconvenient or inappropriate for students to play an actual game, you can run skill drills on some of the fundamentals of the game, such as dribbling, shooting, and passing.

RETEACHING p. 9

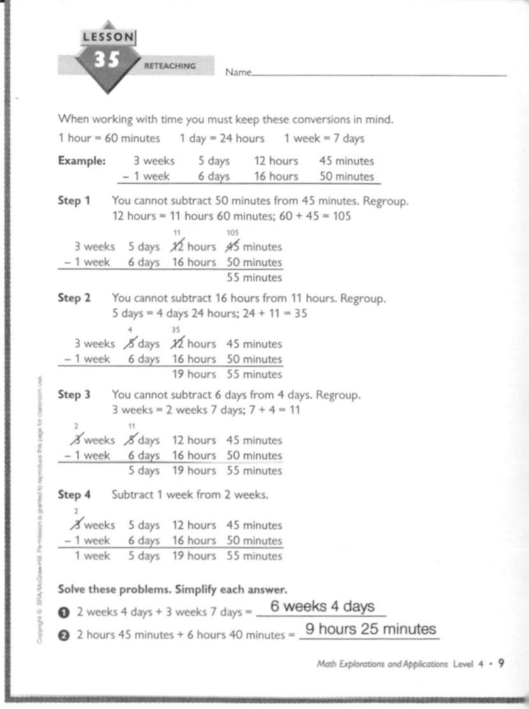
LESSON 35 RETEACHING Name________________

When working with time you must keep these conversions in mind.

1 hour = 60 minutes 1 day = 24 hours 1 week = 7 days

Example:

3 weeks	5 days	12 hours	45 minutes
− 1 week	6 days	16 hours	50 minutes

Step 1 You cannot subtract 50 minutes from 45 minutes. Regroup. 12 hours = 11 hours 60 minutes; 60 + 45 = 105

3 weeks	5 days	~~12~~ 11 hours	~~45~~ 105 minutes
− 1 week	6 days	16 hours	50 minutes
			55 minutes

Step 2 You cannot subtract 16 hours from 11 hours. Regroup. 5 days = 4 days 24 hours; 24 + 11 = 35

3 weeks	~~5~~ 4 days	~~12~~ 35 hours	45 minutes
− 1 week	6 days	16 hours	50 minutes
		19 hours	55 minutes

Step 3 You cannot subtract 6 days from 4 days. Regroup. 3 weeks = 2 weeks 7 days; 7 + 4 = 11

~~3~~ 2 weeks	~~5~~ 11 days	12 hours	45 minutes
− 1 week	6 days	16 hours	50 minutes
	5 days	19 hours	55 minutes

Step 4 Subtract 1 week from 2 weeks.

~~3~~ 2 weeks	5 days	12 hours	45 minutes
− 1 week	6 days	16 hours	50 minutes
1 week	5 days	19 hours	55 minutes

Solve these problems. Simplify each answer.

1. 2 weeks 4 days + 3 weeks 7 days = 6 weeks 4 days
2. 2 hours 45 minutes + 6 hours 40 minutes = 9 hours 25 minutes

Copyright © SRA/McGraw-Hill. Permission is granted to reproduce this page for classroom use.

Math Explorations and Applications Level 4 • 9

*available separately

Add or subtract. Use a calculator if you wish.

21. 5 + 2 + 2 + 2 **11**
22. 11 − 2 − 2 − 2 **5**
23. 1091 + 3 + 3 + 3 **1100**
24. 2000 − 3 − 3 − 3 **1991**
25. 5 − 2 − 2 − 2 **−1**
26. −1 − 2 − 2 − 2 **−7**
27. −7 + 2 + 2 + 2 **−1**
28. −1 + 2 + 2 + 2 **5**
29. 50 − 60 **−10**
30. 300 − 500 **−200**
31. −20 + 90 **70**
32. −500 − 100 **−600**
33. −80 + 30 **−50**
34. 6 − 3 − 3 − 3 **−3**
35. 400 − 900 **−500**
36. −80 − 20 **−100**
37. 10 − 20 − 20 **−30**
38. 10 − 20 − 20 − 20 **−50**
39. −4 − 2 − 2 − 2 − 2 **−12**
40. −3 + 3 + 3 + 3 **6**
41. −8 − 4 − 7 − 2 − 0 **−21**
42. −4 + 9 − 6 + 2 − 2 **−1**
43. 110 − 40 − 60 + 2 **12**
44. −18 + 12 − 7 − 4 + 2 **−15**

PROBLEM SOLVING

Solve the following problems.

45. Christine has two weeks and one day of school until summer vacation. Her cousin Jenny, who lives in Florida, has one week and two days left until vacation. How many days will Jenny be out of school while Christine is in school? **6 days**
46. It took Russ three days and 14 hours to finish the cross country race. It took Gary 2 days and 19 hours to finish. How many hours faster was Gary? **19 hours**
47. Jean's family took a trip to the beach. They drove for one hour and 40 minutes. Angie's family went to the mountains. They drove for two hours and 35 minutes. How much longer was Angie's trip? **55 minutes**

PRACTICE p. 35

LESSON 35 PRACTICE Name____________

PHYSICAL EDUCATION CONNECTION

High school basketball rules call for the following times.

Regulation Time

The four quarters are each eight minutes long.
The break between the first and second quarters and between the third and fourth quarters is one minute.
The break between the second and third quarters is ten minutes.
The clock can be stopped for various reasons, which adds to the length of a game.

Overtime

If a game is tied, three minutes of overtime are allowed. There is a one-minute break between overtime periods if needed.

Answer these questions.

How long will a basketball game last if time

1. is not stopped and there is no overtime? 44 minutes
2. is stopped for ten minutes and there is one overtime? 58 minutes
3. is stopped for 25 minutes but there is no overtime? 69 minutes, or 1 hour 9 minutes
4. is stopped for 30 minutes and there are two overtimes? 82 minutes, or 1 hour 22 minutes
5. is stopped for $10\frac{1}{2}$ minutes and there are two overtimes? $62\frac{1}{2}$ minutes, or 1 hour $2\frac{1}{2}$ minutes
6. is stopped for $22\frac{1}{2}$ minutes and there are three overtimes? $78\frac{1}{2}$ minutes, or 1 hour $18\frac{1}{2}$ minutes

Copyright © SRA/McGraw-Hill. Permission is granted to reproduce this page for classroom use.

ENRICHMENT p. 35

LESSON 35 ENRICHMENT Name____________

REAL-WORLD CONNECTION

Fill in the chart below to plan a one-week vacation to a place you would like to visit. Then answer the questions.

Our Trip to ________					
	Unit Total	Total Cost		Unit Total	Total Cost
Driving Time			**Hotels**		
miles					
miles per hour					
length of drive					
Food Expenses			**Entertainment**		
number of family members					
$5.00 per meal					

1. How far away is your destination? Answers will vary.
2. How many people will go? ______
3. Estimate how much it will cost for your family to eat three meals per day on your trip. ______
4. Make a plan to save money on meals. Accept all reasonable plans. Students might suggest that they choose a hotel that offers free breakfast. They might decide to buy food at a grocery store and eat breakfast in the hotel room. They might make their own lunches and decide to eat out only one meal per day.

Copyright © SRA/McGraw-Hill. Permission is granted to reproduce this page for classroom use.

3 Wrap-Up (5 MINUTES)

In Closing Have students explain how to add 3 hours and 50 minutes + 4 hours and 45 minutes and how to present the answer in its simplest form. (8 hrs 35 min)

ALTERNATIVE ASSESSMENT

Performance Assessment You may wish to use pages 120–122 as an assessment of students' ability to work with elapsed time. Observe them as they solve the elapsed-time problems. Note students who consistently give answers in minutes rather than in hours and minutes, who fail to simplify answers in general, or who simplify answers incorrectly. These students may benefit from extra work converting between units of time.

Assessment Criteria

Did the student . . .

- ✓ contribute to the discussion of elapsed time?
- ✓ communicate strategies used to solve problems that involve elapsed time?
- ✓ accurately simplify answers to the most convenient unit of time?
- ✓ demonstrate understanding of adding and subtracting with negative numbers?

Homework Assign Practice Master 35 for further practice with calculating elapsed time.

LESSON 36

Student Edition pages 124–125

Choosing Appropriate Customary Units

LESSON PLANNER

Objective

- to review and provide practice using customary units of measure for length, weight, and liquid volume

Context of the Lesson This is the second of four lessons on measurement. This lesson reviews customary units of measure.

MANIPULATIVES

customary tools for measuring length*

objects to be measured for length

Program Resources

"Customary Unit" Game Mat

Reteaching Master

Practice Master 36

Enrichment Master 36

For additional math integration: Math Throughout the Day*

For extra practice: CD-ROM* Lesson 36

1 Warm-Up 5 MINUTES

Problem of the Day Present this problem to students: There are six people in the Ying family. By tradition, on Chinese New Year each member of the family gives a good-luck orange to every other member of the family. How many oranges does the family need to honor this tradition? (Each person needs five oranges to be able to give one to every other person in the family. So, 6 x 5 = 30.)

Problem-Solving Strategies Ask students who have solved the Problem of the Day to share how they solved it and any strategies they used.

MENTAL MATH / MANIPULATIVES: Provide practice in estimating measures of length. Have students give their estimates in customary units of measure and then, after each estimate, use **measuring tools** to check for accuracy. (Estimates should improve after each object is measured.)

a. length of a pencil

b. length of a notebook

c. length of an umbrella

d. height of a lamp

LESSON 36

Choosing Appropriate Customary Units

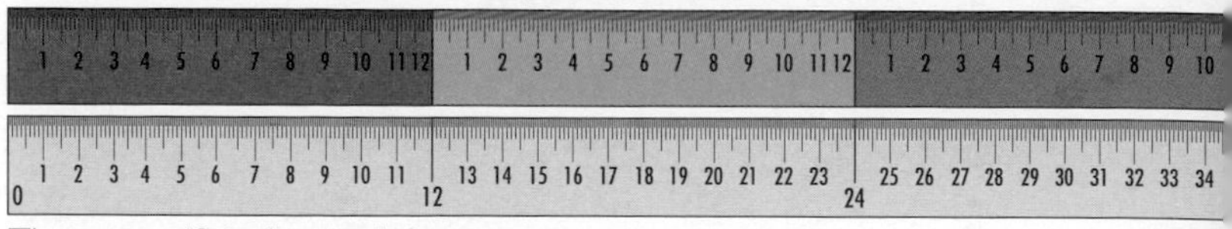

There are 12 inches in 1 foot.
There are 3 feet in 1 yard.
There are 1760 yards, or 5280 feet, in 1 mile.

Remember:

There are 16 ounces in 1 pound.
There are 2000 pounds in 1 ton.

Remember:

There are 8 fluid ounces in 1 cup.
There are 2 cups in 1 pint.
There are 2 pints in 1 quart.
There are 4 quarts in 1 gallon.

Why teach it this way?

Whenever you teach measurement, it is best to have students estimate first, then measure to check their estimates. Estimating requires active mental involvement, which helps students retain what they learn and sharpens their estimating skills, while measuring alone generally poses little mental difficulty.

RETEACHING p. 10

LESSON 36 RETEACHING Name________________

You can use the charts below to decide if a measurement makes sense.

An inch is smaller than a foot. A foot is smaller than a yard. A yard is smaller than a mile.	An ounce is smaller than a pound. A pound is smaller than a ton.	A fluid ounce is smaller than a cup. A cup is smaller than a pint. A quart is smaller than a gallon.
12 inches = 1 foot 3 feet = 1 yard 1760 yards = 1 mile	16 ounces = 1 pound 2000 pounds = 1 ton	8 fluid ounces = 1 cup 2 cups = 1 pint 2 pints = 1 quart 4 quarts = 1 gallon

For each problem the unit of measure in one of the statements makes more sense than the other. Complete the sentence. Choose the unit that makes more sense. If you think both make sense, explain why.

1. The car weighs about **64,000 ounces** or **2 tons.** 2 tons
2. My house is **2 miles** or **3520 yards** from the library. 2 miles
3. The watering can holds **8 quarts** or **2 gallons** of water. both make sense
4. The bag of potatoes weighs **10 pounds** or **160 ounces.** 10 pounds
5. Kathleen added **2 cups** or **16 ounces** of broth to the soup. 2 cups

10 • *Math Explorations and Applications* Level 4

Copyright © SRA/McGraw-Hill. Permission is granted to reproduce this page for classroom use.

*available separately

For each problem the measure in one of the statements makes more sense than the other. Choose the one that makes more sense. It may be hard to decide which one makes more sense. If you think that both make sense, explain why.

1. I'm going to buy **64 fluid ounces** or **[2 quarts]** of milk.
2. Hakim is about $1\frac{3}{4}$ **yards** or **[5 feet, 3 inches]** tall.
3. I want to buy **[10 pounds]** or **160 ounces** of potatoes.
4. The package contains **[4 ounces]** or **[$\frac{1}{4}$ pound]** of jellybeans. **Both are standard measures for packages of candy.**
5. The library is about **[2 miles]** or **3520 yards** from the hospital.
6. The truck weighs about **8000 pounds** or **[4 tons.]**
7. The bottle of perfume holds about **[2 ounces]** or $\frac{1}{8}$ **pint.**
8. Allie's desk at school is about **[3 feet]** or **[1 yard]** wide. **Both are standard measures and easy to visualize.**
9. The car's gasoline tank holds about **[13 gallons]** or **52 quarts** of gas.
10. I need **[4 quarts]** or **[1 gallon]** of apple juice. **Beverages are sold in both quart and gallon containers.**
11. The classroom is about **[40 feet]** or **480 inches** long.
12. The box contains **[$15\frac{1}{2}$ ounces]** or **[almost a pound]** of cereal. **Both are acceptable because the box is probably labeled with ounces, but pounds are a familiar measure.**
13. The barrel holds **[54 gallons]** or **216 quarts** of oil.
14. The step is about **[11 inches]** or **[1 foot]** high.
15. My older brother weighs about **[160 pounds]** or **2560 ounces.**

14 **Both are standard measures and easy to visualize.**

REAL-WORLD CONNECTION

First estimate. Then measure to check. **Answers will vary.**

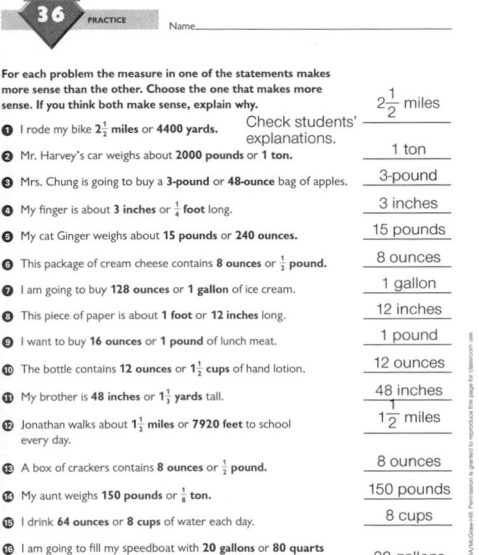

- Name three places that are about 1 mile from your school.
- Find three items that come in 1-pint packages.
- Name three items that might weigh about 1 pound.
- Name three items that come in packages of 1 cup.

PRACTICE p. 36

LESSON 36 PRACTICE Name______________

For each problem the measure in one of the statements makes more sense than the other. Choose the one that makes more sense. If you think both make sense, explain why.

1. I rode my bike $2\frac{1}{2}$ **miles** or **4400 yards.** Check students' explanations.	$2\frac{1}{2}$ miles
2. Mr. Harvey's car weighs about **2000 pounds** or **1 ton.**	1 ton
3. Mrs. Chung is going to buy a **3-pound** or **48-ounce** bag of apples.	3-pound
4. My finger is about **3 inches** or $\frac{1}{4}$ **foot** long.	3 inches
5. My cat Ginger weighs about **15 pounds** or **240 ounces.**	15 pounds
6. This package of cream cheese contains **8 ounces** or $\frac{1}{2}$ **pound.**	8 ounces
7. I am going to buy **128 ounces** or **1 gallon** of ice cream.	1 gallon
8. This piece of paper is about **1 foot** or **12 inches** long.	12 inches
9. I want to buy **16 ounces** or **1 pound** of lunch meat.	1 pound
10. The bottle contains **12 ounces** or $1\frac{1}{2}$ **cups** of hand lotion.	12 ounces
11. My brother is **48 inches** or $1\frac{1}{3}$ **yards** tall.	48 inches
12. Jonathan walks about $1\frac{1}{2}$ **miles** or **7920 feet** to school every day.	$1\frac{1}{2}$ miles
13. A box of crackers contains **8 ounces** or $\frac{1}{2}$ **pound.**	8 ounces
14. My aunt weighs **150 pounds** or $\frac{1}{8}$ **ton.**	150 pounds
15. I drink **64 ounces** or **8 cups** of water each day.	8 cups
16. I am going to fill my speedboat with **20 gallons** or **80 quarts** of gasoline.	20 gallons
17. My foot is about $\frac{3}{4}$ **foot** or **9 inches** long.	9 inches

Copyright © SRA/McGraw-Hill. Permission is granted to reproduce this page for classroom use.

36 • *Math Explorations and Applications* Level 4

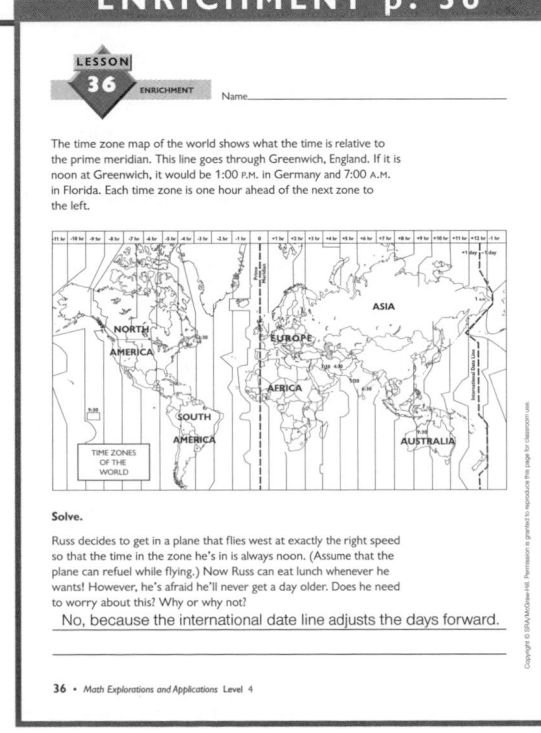

ENRICHMENT p. 36

LESSON 36 ENRICHMENT Name______________

The time zone map of the world shows what the time is relative to the prime meridian. This line goes through Greenwich, England. If it is noon at Greenwich, it would be 1:00 P.M. in Germany and 7:00 A.M. in Florida. Each time zone is one hour ahead of the next zone to the left.

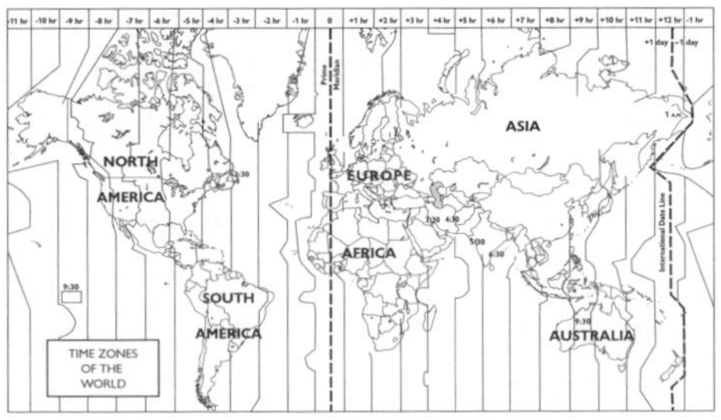

Solve.

Russ decides to get in a plane that flies west at exactly the right speed so that the time in the zone he's in is always noon. (Assume that the plane can refuel while flying.) Now Russ can eat lunch whenever he wants! However, he's afraid he'll never get a day older. Does he need to worry about this? Why or why not?

No, because the international date line adjusts the days forward.

Copyright © SRA/McGraw-Hill. Permission is granted to reproduce this page for classroom use.

36 • *Math Explorations and Applications* Level 4

2 Teach

Using the Student Pages You may want to demonstrate the "Customary Unit" Game Mat for practice with customary units so that students who finish their work early can play.

Have students work in pairs or small groups on these pages. You may consider doing these pages as a class activity in which individual students answer questions and give reasons for their answers.

GAME

Introducing the "Customary Unit" Game Mat The "Customary Unit" Game Mat provides practice with choosing customary units of measure. Complete instructions are on the Game Mat. A copy can also be found on page 588 of this Teacher's Guide.

3 Wrap-Up

5 MINUTES

In Closing Discuss strategies students use to make and refine estimates of measures.

ALTERNATIVE ASSESSMENT

Informal Assessment Listen carefully to the reasons students offer for choosing a particular measure. Note students whose estimates are far off, especially during Mental Math exercises. Challenge students whose estimates are generally accurate by selecting more complex measures to estimate or by having them estimate using less common units of measure.

Assessment Criteria

Did the student . . .

- ✓ contribute to the discussion of estimates and actual measures in customary units?
- ✓ communicate strategies used to make and refine estimates of measure?
- ✓ provide justifiable reasons for his or her choice of units of measure?

Homework Assign Practice Master 36 for further reinforcement of the skill of choosing appropriate customary units of measure.

LESSON 37

Student Edition pages 126–127

Choosing Appropriate Metric Units

LESSON PLANNER

Objective

- ▶ to review the names of and relationships among metric units of length, weight, and volume

Context of the Lesson This lesson focuses on the names of and relationships among metric units of measure and is the third lesson in a series on measurement.

MANIPULATIVES

containers calibrated in metric units of volume*

tools for measuring metric length and weight

objects for measuring length

Program Resources

"Metric Unit" Game Mat

Reteaching Master

Practice Master 37

Enrichment Master 37

For additional math integration: Math Throughout the Day*

For extra practice: CD-ROM* Lesson 37 Cumulative Review, page 542

1 Warm-Up

5 MINUTES

Problem of the Day Present this problem on the chalkboard. Have students use scrap paper to solve it and tell them there are several solutions: Put five Xs in the grid so that no row, column, or diagonal is completely filled. (One solution is shown.)

	×	×
×	×	
		×

Problem-Solving Strategies Ask students who have solved the Problem of the Day to share how they solved it and any strategies they used.

MENTAL MATH

Provide practice in estimating measures of length. Have students give their estimates in metric units of measure and then, after each estimate, use **measuring tools** to check for accuracy. (Estimates should improve after each object is measured.)

a. length of a pencil
b. length of a notebook
c. length of an umbrella
d. height of a lamp

MIXED PRACTICE

LESSON 37

Choosing Appropriate Metric Units

People in most other countries and some businesses in this country use the metric system of measures. One way to remember the relationships among units in the metric system is to think about the system of money we use. This chart shows the relationships.

Units of Length	Units of Weight	Units of Volume	United States Currency	Number in Basic Unit
millimeter	milligram	milliliter	mill	1000
centimeter	centigram	centiliter	cent	100
decimeter	decigram	deciliter	dime	10
meter*	gram	liter*	dollar*	1
dekameter	dekagram	dekaliter	10 dollars	0.1
hectometer	hectogram	hectoliter	100 dollars	0.01
kilometer	kilogram*	kiloliter	1000 dollars	0.001

The chart shows that just as there are 100 cents in 1 dollar, there are 100 centimeters in 1 meter. An asterisk marks the basic units.

Use the chart to answer these questions.

1. How many cents are in $1? **100**
2. How many centimeters are in 1 meter? **100**
3. How many dollars are in $1000? **1000**
4. How many grams are in 1 kilogram? **1000**
5. How many milliliters are in 1 liter? **1000**
6. How many mills are in $1? **1000**

CULTURAL DIVERSITY

Students who come from nations that use the metric system may not find it useful to refer to the relationship to United States currency given in the metric system chart on page 126. Rather, they may use their knowledge of the metric system to better understand American money. These students may be more proficient at estimating in metric units of measure than in customary units. To help all students benefit from each other's skills, form cooperative groups that include students from different backgrounds.

RETEACHING p. 11

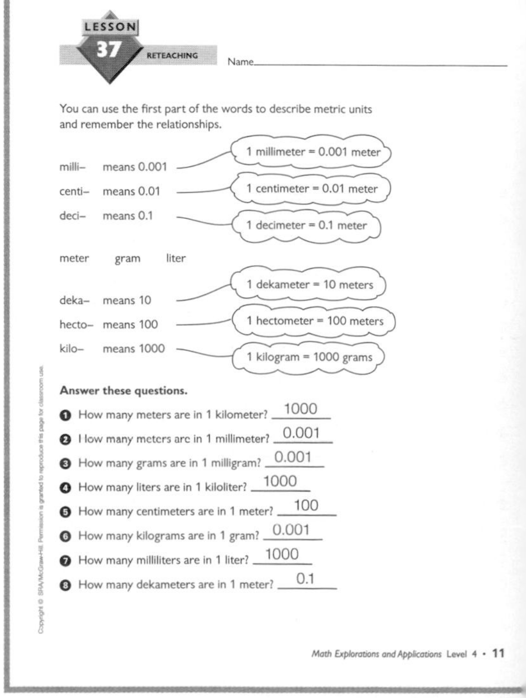

LESSON 37 RETEACHING Name________

You can use the first part of the words to describe metric units and remember the relationships.

milli– means 0.001 — 1 millimeter = 0.001 meter
centi– means 0.01 — 1 centimeter = 0.01 meter
deci– means 0.1 — 1 decimeter = 0.1 meter

meter gram liter

deka– means 10 — 1 dekameter = 10 meters
hecto– means 100 — 1 hectometer = 100 meters
kilo– means 1000 — 1 kilogram = 1000 grams

Answer these questions.

1. How many meters are in 1 kilometer? 1000
2. How many meters are in 1 millimeter? 0.001
3. How many grams are in 1 milligram? 0.001
4. How many liters are in 1 kiloliter? 1000
5. How many centimeters are in 1 meter? 100
6. How many kilograms are in 1 gram? 0.001
7. How many milliliters are in 1 liter? 1000
8. How many dekameters are in 1 meter? 0.1

Copyright © SRA/McGraw-Hill. Permission is granted to reproduce this page for classroom use.

Math Explorations and Applications Level 4 • 11

*available separately

Prepare three questions that can be answered by studying the chart. Exchange questions with a friend. Can you answer all the questions with the chart in front of you? Can you do it without the chart?

Use a dictionary to help answer these questions.

7. What does the prefix *milli-* mean? **thousandth**
8. What does the prefix *centi-* mean? **hundredth**
9. What does the prefix *kilo-* mean? **thousand**
10. Define the following words. How does each word relate to the metric system?
    - **a.** millisecond **one thousandth of a second**
    - **b.** century **one hundred years**
    - **c.** kilowatt **one thousand watts**

    The prefixes for these words are also used in the metric system.

REAL-WORLD CONNECTION

Visit a supermarket or study supermarket advertisements in the newspaper.

11. List five products that are labeled in metric units of volume. **Examples: bottled beverages, liquid soaps**
12. List five products that are labeled in metric units of weight. **Examples: spices, cereal, sugar**

First estimate. Then measure to check.

- Find three items that measure 1 centimeter. **Examples: staple, bean, fingernail**
- Find three items that weigh about 1 gram. **Examples: small paper clip, postage stamp, rubber band**
- Find three items that are measured in liters. **Examples: soda, bottled water, liquid detergent**
- Find three items that are measured in kilograms. **Examples: sugar, soil, sand**

Discuss the reasons why some products are packaged in whole units, such as 1 kilogram or 1 liter, while other products are packaged in an unusual number of units, such as 452 grams or 240 milliliters. **Products that are easily divided into small amounts are packaged as whole units; products not easily divided into small amounts are often packaged in unusual number units.**

Use the Cumulative Review on page 542 after this lesson.

❷ Teach

COOPERATIVE LEARNING **Using the Student Pages** You may want to demonstrate the "Metric Unit" Game Mat, which focuses on using metric units of measure, so that students who finish work on these pages early can play.

Have students work in pairs or small groups to solve the problems on pages 126 and 127 and have **measuring tools** available. You may consider doing these pages as a class activity. Emphasize the relationship between metric units and corresponding units of American money. Note that supermarket products that come in "round" quantities such as 500 grams are measured in metric units when packed. Items packed in "odd" numbers of metric units were probably measured in customary units, which were then converted to metric units.

GAME **Introducing the "Metric Unit" Game Mat** This Game Mat provides practice with using the metric system to measure. Complete directions are on the Game Mat and on page 589 of this Guide.

❸ Wrap-Up

5 MINUTES

In Closing Have students explain the patterns they observe among metric units of measure.

ALTERNATIVE ASSESSMENT **Portfolio Assessment** Have students write a brief essay that explains their understanding of the relationships among units of the metric system. Students can add these essays to their Math Portfolios as evidence of ongoing learning.

Assessment Criteria

Did the student . . .

- ✓ contribute to the discussion of the names of and relationships among metric measures?
- ✓ communicate understanding of a pattern among metric units of measure?
- ✓ participate in the supermarket investigation?

Homework Assign Practice Master 37 for further practice measuring with metric units.

PRACTICE p. 37

LESSON 37 PRACTICE Name__________

Units of Length	Units of Weight	Units of Volume	United States Currency	Number in Basic Unit
millimeter	milligram	milliliter	mill	1000
centimeter	centigram	centiliter	cent	100
decimeter	decigram	deciliter	dime	10
meter*	gram	liter*	dollar*	1
dekameter	dekagram	dekaliter	10 dollars	0.1
hectometer	hectogram	hectoliter	100 dollars	0.01
kilometer	kilogram*	kiloliter	1000 dollars	0.001

*Basic units

Use the chart to answer these questions.

1. How many milligrams are in 1 gram? 1000
2. How many deciliters are in 1 liter? 10
3. How many dimes are in $10? 100
4. How many grams are in 1 hectogram? 100
5. How many hectometers are in 1 kilometer? 10
6. How many cents are in $100? 10,000
7. How many centiliters are in 1 liter? 100
8. How many mills are in 1 dime? 100
9. How many dimes are in $100? 1000
10. Find three items that are measured in kilometers. Check students'
11. Find three items that are measured in milligrams. answers.

Copyright © SRA/McGraw-Hill. Permission is granted to reproduce this page for classroom use.

Math Explorations and Applications Level 4 • 37

ENRICHMENT p. 37

LESSON 37 ENRICHMENT Name__________

Use the chart. Estimate the length of each item. Use millimeters, centimeters, and meters. Then find each item at home and take an accurate measurement. How close were your estimates?

Measurements of Things at Home		
	Estimate	Actual
the thickness of an envelope	Answers	will vary.
the width of a bathroom door		
the height of your bedroom door		
the length of the largest piece of furniture		
the width of your refrigerator		
the height of your favorite chair		
the length of a dresser		
the width of your bedroom window		
the height of your front door		
the thickness of your mattress		
the width of your stove		
the thickness of two stacked pennies		
the thickness of two stacked nickels		
the length of your bedroom		
the width of your bedroom		
the height of a gallon of milk		
the length of your kitchen sink		
the width of a cereal bowl		
the height of a crayon box		
the thickness of your toothbrush handle		

Copyright © SRA/McGraw-Hill. Permission is granted to reproduce this page for classroom use.

Math Explorations and Applications Level 4 • 37

LESSON 38

Student Edition pages 128–129

Practice with Linear Measurement

LESSON PLANNER

Objectives

- to review metric units of length, weight, and volume
- to provide an opportunity to build and use a simple scale

Context of the Lesson This is the last of four lessons on measurement. Both customary and metric units of measure are covered.

MANIPULATIVES

index cards
marbles or other small objects to use as weights
paper clips
paper cups
rubber bands
rulers*
tape

Program Resources

Number Wheels
Practice Master 38
Enrichment Master 38
For extra practice: CD-ROM* Lesson 38

1 Warm-Up (5 MINUTES)

Problem of the Day Provide students with **index cards** 3 inches high and 5 inches wide. Ask: Using an index card as your only tool, how can you draw a line that you know is 1 inch long? (One possible solution: Draw a 5-in. line segment using the card's width. Then use its height to mark off 3 in. to erase. Then fold the remaining 2-in. segment in half. Each half is 1 in. long. Erase a half.)

Problem-Solving Strategies Ask students who have solved the Problem of the Day to share how they solved it and any strategies they used.

MENTAL MATH Provide practice with multiplication facts. Emphasize speedy recall and have students use their Number Wheels to respond.

a. 10 x 6 = (60) **b.** 2 x 7 = (14)
c. 9 x 3 = (27) **d.** 8 x 8 = (64)
e. 0 x 2 = (0) **f.** 4 x 6 = (24)
g. 7 x 6 = (42) **h.** 9 x 8 = (72)

MIXED PRACTICE

LESSON 38

Practice with Linear Measurement

Although it's good to know about patterns in the metric system, you don't have to be able to measure in all of those units. Several units in the chart on page 126 are in common use. Those units are also described below.

Length

Centimeter: An unsharpened pencil is about 19 centimeters long.
Meter: Most classroom doors are about 1 meter wide.
Kilometer: You can walk 1 kilometer in about 12 minutes.

Weight

Gram: A United States nickel weighs about 5 grams.
Kilogram: This book weighs about 1.4 kilograms.

Volume

Liter: Four average-sized glasses hold about 1 liter.
Milliliter: A raindrop is about 1 milliliter of water.

Choose the measure that makes more sense. It may be hard to decide which measure makes more sense. If you think that both make sense, explain why.

1. Yesterday I ran about [**3 kilometers**] or **3000 centimeters.**
2. The box contains [**500 grams**] or **5000 milligrams** of cereal.
3. The glass holds $\frac{1}{5}$ **liter** or [**200 milliliters**] of juice.
4. A square garden measures about [**4 meters**] or **400 centimeters** on each side.
5. I bought **0.457 kilograms** or [**457 grams**] of potatoes.

Why teach it at this time?

The hands-on opportunity to build and use a scale is appropriate to this sequence of lessons on measurement.

Science Connection Encourage students to design and construct other scales. Guide them to consult various science or reference books for ideas, instructions, and illustrations. For example, they might use springs instead of rubber bands, or they might make a double-pan balance. A helpful teacher resource for projects and activities is *Science Is . . .* by Susan V. Bosak.

RETEACHING

Students who are inactive during the scale construction may need greater assistance to conceptualize or build the rubber-band scale. Provide adequate individualized help until these students can move ahead on their own.

*available separately

SCIENCE CONNECTION

Build a rubber band scale like the one in the picture. Perform the following experiment.

6. Measure the length of the rubber band.
7. Place one or two marbles or other weights in the paper cup. Measure the length of the rubber band again.
8. Add another weight. Measure the length of the rubber band. Keep adding weights, one or two at a time. Measure the rubber band after each addition.
9. How does the weight of the objects affect the length of the rubber band?
10. Keep your results in a chart like the one shown.

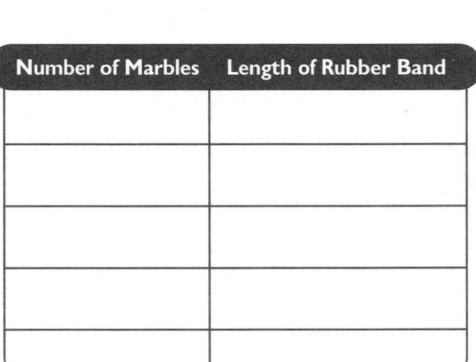

Number of Marbles	Length of Rubber Band

As more weight is added, the length of the rubber band increases.

Now find something that you think weighs more than two marbles, but less than the most marbles you used.

How many marble units does that object weigh?

What other objects can you weigh with your scale?

Try to make a scale that will weigh heavier objects.

Can you modify your scale so you can weigh objects in standard units?

PRACTICE p. 38

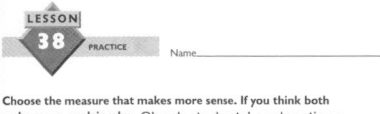

LESSON 38 PRACTICE Name________

Choose the measure that makes more sense. If you think both make sense, explain why. Check students' explanations.

1. I bought **1 kilogram** or **1000 grams** of grapes. 1 kilogram
2. This bag of pretzels weighs **750 grams** or **75,000 milligrams.** 750 grams
3. I rode my bike **2.4 kilometers** or **2400 meters.** 2.4 kilometers
4. My arm is about **60 centimeters** or **0.6 meters** long. 60 centimeters
5. My dog Sam weighs about **16 kilograms** or **16,000 grams.** 16 kilograms
6. This bottle of juice holds about **2 liters** or **0.02 kiloliters.** 2 liters
7. I am going to buy a turkey that weighs **8 kilograms** or **8000 grams.** 8 kilograms
8. My library card is about **6 centimeters** or **0.06 meters** long. 6 centimeters
9. The bottle holds **1 liter** or **1000 milliliters** of water. 1 liter
10. My baby sister is **50 centimeters** or **$\frac{1}{2}$ meter tall.** 50 centimeters
11. My father drives about **30 kilometers** or **3000 meters** to work every day. 30 kilometers
12. A bag of sugar weighs about **2.2 kilograms** or **2200 grams.** 2.2 kilograms
13. Each morning I drink a glass that holds **$\frac{1}{4}$ liter** or **250 milliliters** of grapefruit juice. 250 milliliters
14. My bed is about **2 meters** or **2000 centimeters** wide. 2 meters
15. Mr. Bruce is going to buy about **$\frac{1}{2}$ kilogram** or **500 grams** of peanuts. 500 grams
16. This quarter weighs about **8 grams** or **8000 milligrams.** 8 grams

ENRICHMENT p. 38

LESSON 38 ENRICHMENT Name________

These two charts show how to convert customary units to metric units.

Linear Measures				
inches	×	25.4	=	millimeters
inches	×	2.54	=	centimeters
feet	×	30.48	=	centimeters
feet	×	0.305	=	meters
yards	×	91.44	=	centimeters
miles	×	1.61	=	kilometers

Weight Measures				
ounces	×	28.35	=	grams
pounds	×	453.59	=	grams
pounds	×	0.454	=	kilograms
tons	×	0.91	=	metric tons

Imagine the new rules for sports events that would use the metric system. Use the conversion charts to answer the questions.

1. What race will replace the mile run? 1.61 km
2. How much would a 16-pound shot put weigh? 7.26 kg
3. If you can pole-vault 18 feet, how high is that in meters? 5.49 m
4. A featherweight boxer cannot weigh more than 119 pounds for a match. How many kilograms could he weigh? 54 kg
5. What should the Indianapolis 500 be called? (Hint: The Indianapolis 500 is the name of a long auto race.) Indianapolis 805
6. If the size of a baseball diamond changes from 30 yards to 30 meters, will the number of home runs go up or down? down

2 Teach

COOPERATIVE LEARNING **Using the Student Pages** Go over the measurement benchmarks presented on page 128. If possible, display sample objects used to describe each measurement. Discuss answers to the questions on page 128 as a class.

MANIPULATIVES Have students work in cooperative groups to build rubber-band scales like the one on page 129. You may need to demonstrate how to attach the **rubber band** to the **paper cup** and how best to measure the length of the rubber band after adding weight to the cup. Students can use metric or customary units. The key mathematical idea in this activity is the functional relationship between the length of the rubber band and the weight in the cup. In algebraic terms, students should find that the length of the rubber band, y, increases by z for each **marble** added to the cup.

3 Wrap-Up

5 MINUTES

In Closing Have groups display their rubber-band scales and describe the mathematical relationships discovered.

ALTERNATIVE ASSESSMENT **Performance Assessment** Observe students as they work in groups to construct their scales, gather data on the functional relationship between weights in the cup and length of the rubber band, and present their findings to the class. Encourage them to explain their construction methods and verbalize the functional relationship they find.

Assessment Criteria

Did the student . . .

- ✓ contribute to the discussion of metric units of measure?
- ✓ communicate strategies used to choose the better measure?
- ✓ actively participate in the construction of the scale?
- ✓ gather, present, and interpret data using the scale?

Homework Have students use household objects to construct another type of scale or to modify the rubber-band scale to make it work more effectively.

LESSON 39

Student Edition pages 130–131

Area: Upper and Lower Bounds

LESSON PLANNER

Objectives

- to provide practice with multiplication facts
- to apply multiplication to solve problems
- to introduce the concept of establishing upper and lower bounds to estimate area
- to provide practice in measuring length using a centimeter ruler

Context of the Lesson This lesson provides practice with applications of multiplication. The next lesson provides a third self-assessment of mastery of multiplication facts.

MANIPULATIVES

centimeter rulers*

graph paper (optional)

Program Resources

Practice Master 39

Enrichment Master 39

For extra practice: CD-ROM* Lesson 39

1 Warm-Up

5 MINUTES

Problem of the Day Present the following problem on the chalkboard and encourage students to draw a picture or use a pattern to solve it: A painter's easel adjusts to ten different heights. Each level is 3 inches from the one before. The fourth level from the bottom is 27 inches high. How high is the highest level? (45 inches)

Problem-Solving Strategies Ask students who have solved the Problem of the Day to share how they solved it and any strategies they used.

MENTAL MATH Provide practice with problems involving approximation. Have students respond by showing thumbs up for answers greater than 200, thumbs down for answers less than 200, and by standing up for answers that are exactly 200.

a. 100 + 200 (thumbs up) **b.** 40 + 50 (thumbs down)

c. 250 – 100 (thumbs down) **d.** 4 × 50 (stand up)

e. 300 + 50 (thumbs up) **f.** 220 – 30 (thumbs down)

g. 400 – 100 (thumbs up) **h.** 80 + 130 (thumbs up)

PROBLEM SOLVING

LESSON 39

Area: Upper and Lower Bounds

Amir is thinking of a rectangle. He says, "It is at least 4 centimeters long, but no more than 5 centimeters long. It is at least 1 centimeter wide, but no more than 2 centimeters wide."

Amir can't be thinking of this rectangle, because it is less than 4 cm long.

He can't be thinking of this rectangle, because it is more than 2 cm wide.

He might be thinking of this rectangle.

Which of these rectangles could be the one Amir is thinking of?

Write *yes* or *no* for each one. Use a centimeter ruler to measure. Watch your numbering.

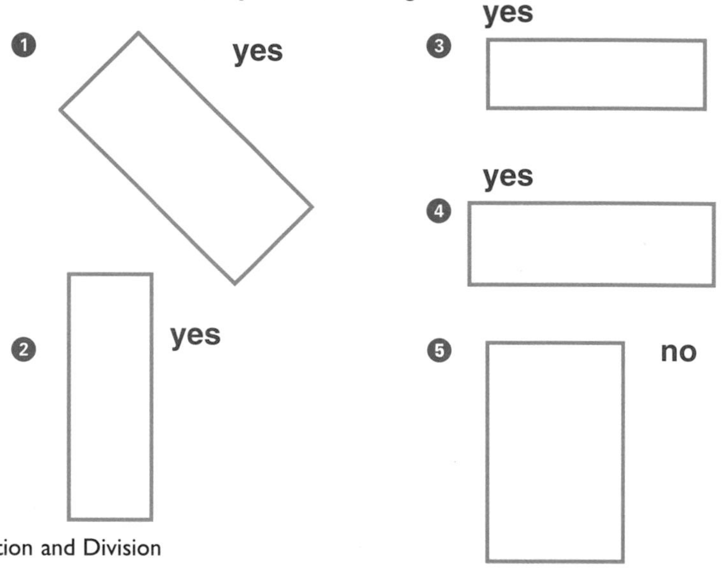

RETEACHING

Continue to provide extra practice with the multiplication facts for students who need it through Mental Math exercises, games, and other activities.

*available separately

Solve these problems.

Onawa and Simon had an argument about whose garden was bigger. They decided to measure. Onawa's garden is at least 9 meters long, but no more than 10 meters long. It is at least 6 meters wide, but no more than 7 meters wide. **6 m** ☐

6. Draw a picture of the smallest garden Onawa might have. **9 m**
7. What is the smallest area Onawa's garden could be? **54 sq. m**
8. Draw a picture of the largest garden Onawa might have. **7 m** ☐
9. What is the largest area Onawa's garden could be? **70 sq. m** **10m**

Simon's garden is at least 8 meters long, but no more than 9 meters long. It is at least 7 meters wide, but no more than 8 meters wide. **7 m** ☐

10. Draw a picture of the smallest garden Simon might have. **8 m**
11. What is the smallest area Simon's garden could be? **56 sq. m**
12. Draw a picture of the largest garden Simon might have. **8 m** ☐
13. What is the largest area Simon's garden could be? **72 sq. m** **9 m**
14. Can you tell whose garden has the greater area, Onawa's or Simon's? **can't tell from given information because ranges overlap**

Complete this chart about other people's gardens.

	Garden Owner	Length (meters)		Width (meters)		Area (square meters)	
		At Least	No More Than	At Least	No More Than	At Least	No More Than
15	Anita	9	10	4	5	36	■ **50**
16	Larry	7	8	7	8	■ **49**	■ **64**
17	Celia	8	9	5	6	■ **40**	■ **54**
18	Jesse	6	7	5	6	■ **30**	■ **42**

❷ Teach

Using the Student Pages Do page 130 as a whole-class activity. If necessary, refer to the work done with area in Lesson 34. Have **centimeter rulers*** available.

On page 131, solve problems 6–14 with the class. Draw pictures on the chalkboard, or ask students to draw them on the chalkboard, to help students visualize the problems. Also encourage students to draw pictures as they solve problems 15–18 on their own.

❸ Wrap-Up

5 MINUTES

In Closing Ask students to explain how drawing diagrams can help them solve problems.

ALTERNATIVE ASSESSMENT

Informal Assessment Observe students as they complete the problems on these pages. Check that they use the ruler correctly, draw pictures that fit the data, and multiply correctly to find the range of areas.

Assessment Criteria

Did the student . . .

- ✓ use the ruler properly?
- ✓ contribute to the discussion about approximating area?
- ✓ draw pictures that represent the information given?
- ✓ complete the chart accurately?

Homework Have students design their own problem modeled on the opening problem on page 130.

SPECIAL NEEDS

Meeting Individual Needs

Students who have difficulties drawing may have trouble completing this lesson. These students may benefit from using **graph paper** to draw the rectangles that represent the gardens.

PRACTICE p. 39

LESSON 39 PRACTICE Name____

Daniel is thinking of a rectangle. He says, "It is at least 3 centimeters long but no more than 4 centimeters long. It is at least 1 centimeter wide, but no more than 2 centimeters wide."

Which of these rectangles can be the one Daniel is thinking of? Write yes or no for each one. Use a centimeter ruler to measure.

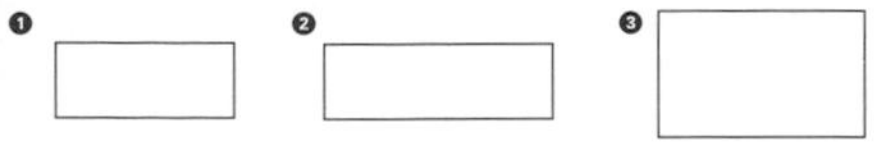

1. yes
2. no
3. no

Complete this chart about children's play areas. Draw diagrams to help you.

	Play area	Length (meters)		Width (meters)		Area (square meters)	
		At least	No more than	At least	No more than	At least	No more than
4	Lon's	8	9	7	8	56	72
5	Carrie's	7	8	5	6	35	48
6	William's	6	7	5	6	30	42
7	Mary's	5	6	8	9	40	54
8	Jesse's	8	9	5	7	40	63

Copyright © SRA/McGraw-Hill. Permission is granted to reproduce this page for classroom use.

Math Explorations and Applications Level 4 • 39

ENRICHMENT p. 39

LESSON 39 ENRICHMENT Name____

With the Chinese puzzle called a tangram you can build shapes with seven pieces of a square.

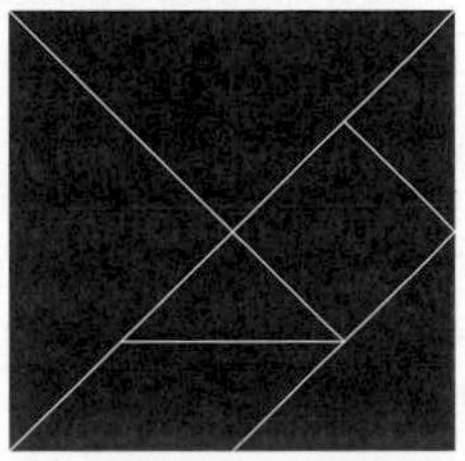

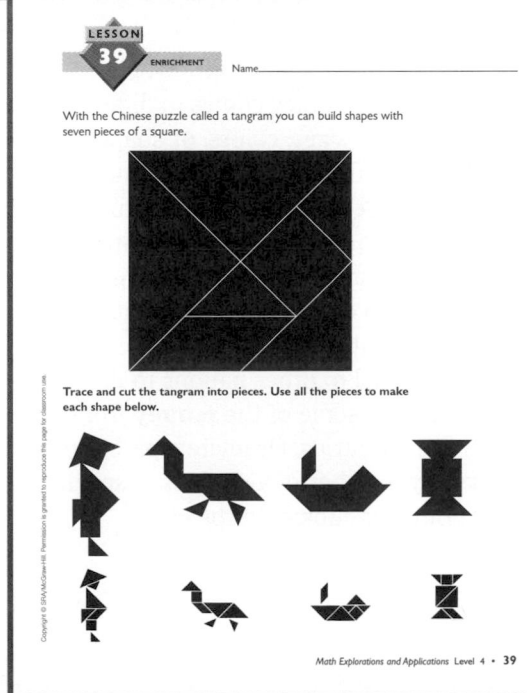

Trace and cut the tangram into pieces. Use all the pieces to make each shape below.

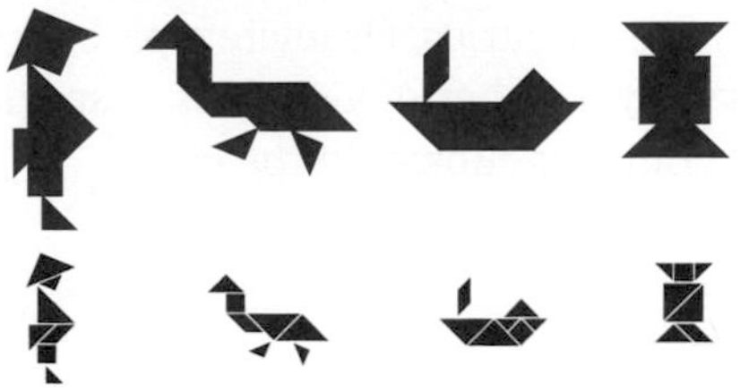

Copyright © SRA/McGraw-Hill. Permission is granted to reproduce this page for classroom use.

Math Explorations and Applications Level 4 • 39

*available separately

LESSON 40

Student Edition pages 132–135

Multiplication Practice

LESSON PLANNER

Objectives

- ▶ to provide further practice with multiplication facts
- ✓ to assess participation in Thinking Story discussions
- ▶ to help students develop the broad ability to use mathematical common sense

Context of the Lesson This lesson provides one of many opportunities in this program for students to assess their progress in performing different mathematical operations. It contains a Mastery Checkpoint to assess participation in Thinking Story discussions. It also includes Part 2 of "Money Matters," a four-part Thinking Story.

MANIPULATIVES

flash cards (optional)

money from other countries (optional)

Program Resources

Practice Master 40

Enrichment Master 40

Assessment Master

For career connections: Careers and Math*

For extra practice: CD-ROM* Lesson 40

1 Warm-Up

5 MINUTES

Problem of the Day Suggest that students draw a picture to solve this problem: The lunch room in Cindy's school has eight square tables. Each table can seat two people on a side. For a special meeting, the principal asks the janitor to push all the tables together into one rectangular table. How many people can sit at the tables in this arrangement? How many can sit at the tables when they are separated? (36; 64)

Problem-Solving Strategies Ask students who have solved the Problem of the Day to share how they solved it and any strategies they used.

MENTAL MATH Present problems involving approximation. Students show thumbs up to indicate possibly correct answers and thumbs down to indicate obviously wrong answers.

a. 5 x 100 = 500 (thumbs up)

b. 96 + 50 = 46 (thumbs down)

(continued on page 133)

***MIXED* PRACTICE**

LESSON 40

Multiplication Practice

These pages will give you a chance to check how well you are doing in remembering multiplication facts quickly.

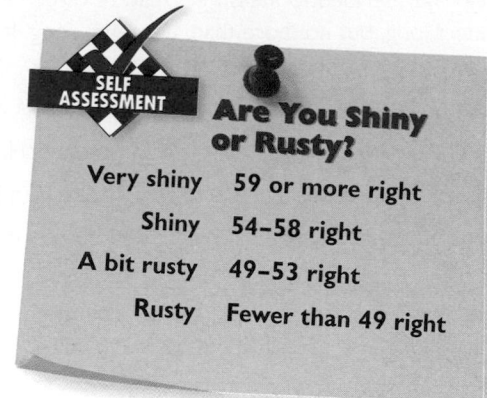

SELF ASSESSMENT

Are You Shiny or Rusty?

Very shiny	59 or more right
Shiny	54–58 right
A bit rusty	49–53 right
Rusty	Fewer than 49 right

Multiply to solve for *n*.

1. $6 \times 10 = n$ **60**	2. $6 \times 6 = n$ **36**	3. $8 \times 7 = n$ **56**
4. $4 \times 3 = n$ **12**	5. $2 \times 7 = n$ **14**	6. $2 \times 4 = n$ **8**
7. $6 \times 0 = n$ **0**	8. $4 \times 6 = n$ **24**	9. $7 \times 1 = n$ **7**
10. $3 \times 5 = n$ **15**	11. $10 \times 10 = n$ **100**	12. $3 \times 9 = n$ **27**
13. $6 \times 9 = n$ **54**	14. $6 \times 8 = n$ **48**	15. $3 \times 3 = n$ **9**
16. $2 \times 2 = n$ **4**	17. $7 \times 7 = n$ **49**	18. $8 \times 9 = n$ **72**
19. $5 \times 7 = n$ **35**	20. $2 \times 8 = n$ **16**	21. $9 \times 9 = n$ **81**
22. $3 \times 6 = n$ **18**	23. $5 \times 2 = n$ **10**	24. $0 \times 3 = n$ **0**
25. $9 \times 8 = n$ **72**	26. $7 \times 6 = n$ **42**	27. $5 \times 9 = n$ **45**
28. $5 \times 6 = n$ **30**	29. $7 \times 9 = n$ **63**	30. $9 \times 2 = n$ **18**
31. $2 \times 4 = n$ **8**	32. $6 \times 9 = n$ **54**	33. $10 \times 0 = n$ **0**
34. $8 \times 1 = n$ **8**	35. $9 \times 3 = n$ **27**	36. $7 \times 3 = n$ **21**

CULTURAL DIVERSITY In many cultures, paper money comes in different sizes, colors, or shapes that highlight the different denominations. Also, some money systems include coins for amounts that are multiples of the basic monetary unit, analogous to having $5 or $10 in United States coins. Invite students who have lived in or traveled to other nations to describe or display some of the **money** from these countries. Or invite a parent or family member of a student to speak about this subject to the class.

Social Studies Connection Some Americans believe the penny has so little value that it should be taken out of circulation. Other people strongly disagree with this and believe that, although a penny has little monetary value, its historical value is important, as is the ability to make exact change. Have students discuss this issue. Encourage individuals to share their opinions. You might hold a debate in which sides present reasoned arguments for and against this point.

*available separately

Multiply.

37. $5 \times 0 =$ **0**
38. $4 \times 4 =$ **16**
39. $2 \times 3 =$ **6**
40. $4 \times 2 =$ **8**
41. $1 \times 8 =$ **8**
42. $6 \times 7 =$ **42**
43. $10 \times 2 =$ **20**
44. $7 \times 8 =$ **56**
45. $0 \times 9 =$ **0**
46. $9 \times 7 =$ **63**
47. $8 \times 6 =$ **48**
48. $2 \times 6 =$ **12**
49. $8 \times 8 =$ **64**
50. $7 \times 5 =$ **35**
51. $5 \times 8 =$ **40**
52. $4 \times 9 =$ **36**
53. $5 \times 5 =$ **25**
54. $6 \times 5 =$ **30**
55. $3 \times 7 =$ **21**
56. $5 \times 4 =$ **20**
57. $6 \times 9 =$ **54**
58. $7 \times 4 =$ **28**
59. $2 \times 9 =$ **18**
60. $10 \times 0 =$ **0**
61. $3 \times 8 =$ **24**

PROBLEM SOLVING

Solve.

62. Jim bought two pencil erasers. Each eraser cost 7¢. How much money did Jim spend on erasers? **14¢**
63. What is the area of a square garden that measures 8 feet on each side? **64 square feet**
64. Gretchen bought three packs of markers. Each pack contained eight markers. How many markers did she buy all together? **24**

Literature Connection With the class, read the story (or excerpts of) *Stone Fox* by John Reynolds Gardiner. Have students use multiplication to determine the size of the potato crop if the farm were two, five, or ten acres.

Mental Math (continued)

c. 380 – 80 = 400 (thumbs down)
d. 52 – 41 = 11 (thumbs up)
e. 101 + 24 = 125 (thumbs up)
f. 460 – 220 = 200 (thumbs down)
g. 330 + 70 = 400 (thumbs up)
h. 896 – 196 = 700 (thumbs up)
i. 2 x 50 = 52 (thumbs down)
j. 57 – 16 = 24 (thumbs down)

2 Teach

SELF ASSESSMENT

Using the Student Pages Have students number their papers from 1–64. Do these pages as a timed test. The goal is for students to improve their speed and accuracy since their previous effort at a timed test of multiplication facts. They can compare their times and scores here with their times and scores for pages 112 and 113 in Lesson 33. Note that there are fewer problems on pages 132–133.

> *. . . if we want students to be really good at a particular skill, or if we want them to really remember and understand a concept, we must arrange for them to practice.*
>
> —Stephen S. Willoughby, *Mathematics Education for a Changing World*

◆ LESSON 40 Multiplication Practice

Teach

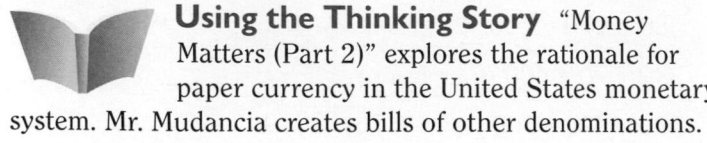

Using the Thinking Story "Money Matters (Part 2)" explores the rationale for paper currency in the United States monetary system. Mr. Mudancia creates bills of other denominations.

Answers to Thinking Story Questions:

1. He glued or pasted a $1 bill and a $5 bill together.
2. His $7 bill was made of three bills glued together—a $5 bill and a $1 bill on the outside, and another $1 bill sandwiched between them.
3. There are many more than five combinations that make $20. Among the possible arrangements of bills are 10-10, 5-5-5-5, 10-5-5, 5-10-5, 2-2-2-2-2-10, and 1-1-10-5-2-1.
4. He could make a $7 bill out of a $5 bill and a $2 bill.
5. About the only reason for having so many denominations of bills is that it might cut down on making change. There are many reasons against it: additional costs of printing money, greater chance of confusing bills, and more difficulty in counting money. $99 bills would not be practical because there are few times that people would use them and they would be hard to count.

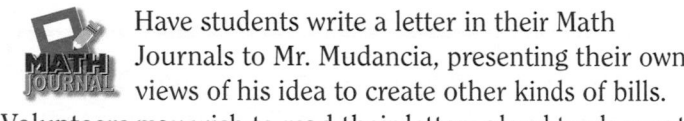

Have students write a letter in their Math Journals to Mr. Mudancia, presenting their own views of his idea to create other kinds of bills. Volunteers may wish to read their letters aloud to classmates.

◆ LESSON 40 Multiplication Practice

THINKING STORY

Money Matters

Part 2

Mr. Mudancia wondered why there were $1 bills, $2 bills, $5 bills, and $10 bills, but not $3, $4, $6, $7, $8, and $9 bills. "I think I could change that a little," he said.

The next day he went to a bookstore to buy a book that cost $6. "Here's a $6 bill," he said to the clerk.

"Something is wrong with this bill," said the clerk. "It's thicker and stiffer than it should be. It says $5 on one side and $1 on the other. This is a fake bill! Police! Police!"

"Calm down," said Mr. Mudancia. "You wanted $6 and I gave you $6. I don't know what you're so worried about. By the way, I think I'll take this magazine, too. How much is it?"

"It's $1."

"Then give me back my $6 bill and I'll give you $7," said Mr. Mudancia.

The clerk was glad to give Mr. Mudancia back his $6 bill. But the clerk was not glad when Mr. Mudancia said, "Here's a $7 bill instead."

RETEACHING

Continue to give practice on multiplication facts using **flash cards,** oral or computer drills, games, or other methods or materials that students enjoy.

PRACTICE p. 40

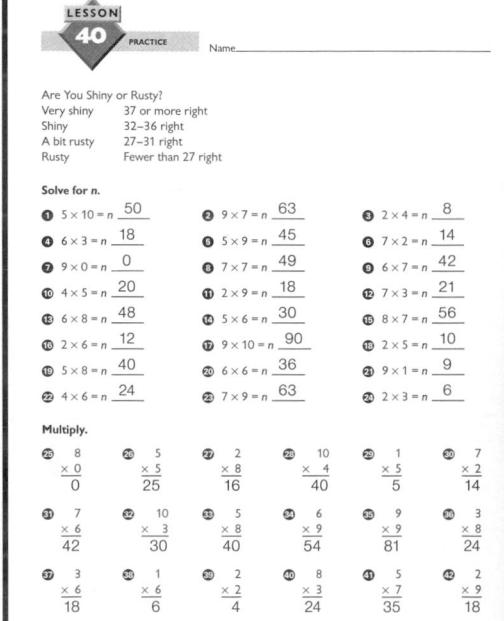

LESSON 40 PRACTICE   Name__________

Are You Shiny or Rusty?

Very shiny	37 or more right
Shiny	32–36 right
A bit rusty	27–31 right
Rusty	Fewer than 27 right

Solve for *n*.

1. $5 \times 10 = n$ 50	2. $9 \times 7 = n$ 63	3. $2 \times 4 = n$ 8
4. $6 \times 3 = n$ 18	5. $5 \times 9 = n$ 45	6. $7 \times 2 = n$ 14
7. $9 \times 0 = n$ 0	8. $7 \times 7 = n$ 49	9. $6 \times 7 = n$ 42
10. $4 \times 5 = n$ 20	11. $2 \times 9 = n$ 18	12. $7 \times 3 = n$ 21
13. $6 \times 8 = n$ 48	14. $5 \times 6 = n$ 30	15. $8 \times 7 = n$ 56
16. $2 \times 6 = n$ 12	17. $9 \times 10 = n$ 90	18. $2 \times 5 = n$ 10
19. $5 \times 8 = n$ 40	20. $6 \times 6 = n$ 36	21. $9 \times 1 = n$ 9
22. $4 \times 6 = n$ 24	23. $7 \times 9 = n$ 63	24. $2 \times 3 = n$ 6

Multiply.

25. $8 \times 0 = 0$	26. $5 \times 5 = 25$	27. $2 \times 8 = 16$	28. $10 \times 4 = 40$	29. $1 \times 5 = 5$	30. $7 \times 2 = 14$
31. $7 \times 6 = 42$	32. $10 \times 3 = 30$	33. $5 \times 8 = 40$	34. $6 \times 9 = 54$	35. $9 \times 9 = 81$	36. $3 \times 8 = 24$
37. $3 \times 6 = 18$	38. $1 \times 6 = 6$	39. $2 \times 2 = 4$	40. $8 \times 3 = 24$	41. $5 \times 7 = 35$	42. $2 \times 9 = 18$

40 • *Math Explorations and Applications* Level 4

Copyright © SRA/McGraw-Hill. Permission is granted to reproduce this page for classroom use.

"This bill is worse then the other one," said the clerk. "It's even thicker and stiffer. And it still says $5 on one side and $1 on the other side. You can't tell me this makes $7!"

"Not everything shows," said Mr. Mudancia.

Work in groups. Discuss your answers and how you figured them out. Then compare your answers with those of other groups. **Answers are in margin.**

1. How did Mr. Mudancia make his $6 bill?
2. Why was his $6 bill thinner than his $7 bill?
3. **Challenge:** What are five different ways that Mr. Mudancia could make a $20 bill?
4. **Detective question:** How could Mr. Mudancia make a $7 bill that was no thicker than the $6 bill he made?
5. Do you think it would be a good idea to have $3, $4, $6, $7, $8, and $9 bills in addition to the bills we already have? Why or why not? What about $99 bills?

3 Wrap-Up (5 MINUTES)

In Closing Discuss with students the advantages of the familiar denominations in the current United States money system.

ANALYZING ANSWERS By now, all students should participate in Thinking Story discussions, be familiar with the routine, and anticipate the types of questions to be asked. If some students are not participating see if the difficulty is with reading. If so, read the story and questions to them, or play the story on audiotape and have them read along. If the difficulty is in interacting effectively with others, try different groupings or have students work alone.

Mastery Checkpoint 6

At this time you may want to begin formally assessing students' participation in Thinking Story discussions based upon the manner in which you conduct them. Observe students as they work in groups or as they work independently. Spot-check their answers to the story questions. Observe student participation in whole-class discussions. Invite students who do not participate in group discussions to talk with you individually. Continue this kind of assessment in subsequent Thinking Story lessons. Record the results on the Mastery Checkpoint Chart.

Assessment Criteria

Did the student . . .

- ✓ explain how to solve for *n*?
- ✓ correctly answer at least 80% of the multiplication problems?
- ✓ contribute to the Thinking Story discussion?

Homework Have students find six different ways Mr. Mudancia could make $75 if he had access to $1 bills, $2 bills, $5 bills, $10 bills, and $20 bills.

LOOKING AHEAD The next lesson requires materials previously used in Lesson 9: two sets of cards or sheets of paper with the numbers from 0 to 10 and tape, pins, or paper clips.

ENRICHMENT p. 40

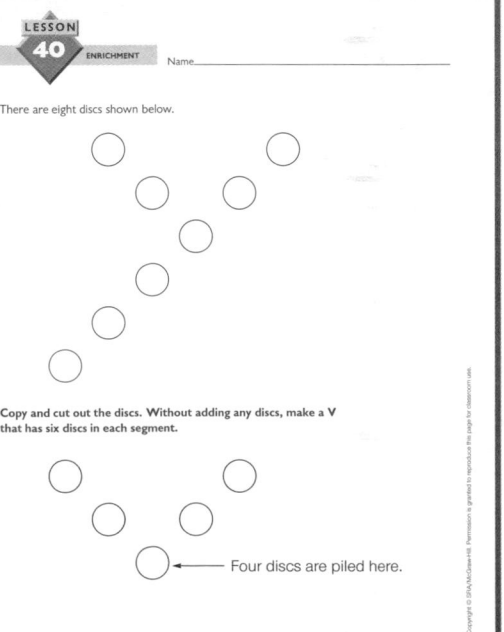

LESSON 40 ENRICHMENT Name____________________

There are eight discs shown below.

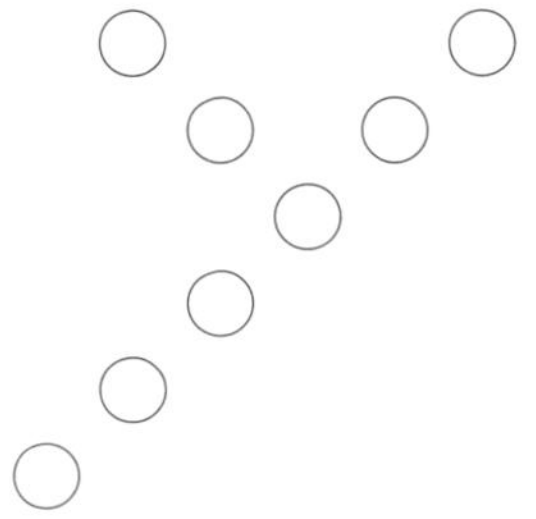

Copy and cut out the discs. Without adding any discs, make a V that has six discs in each segment.

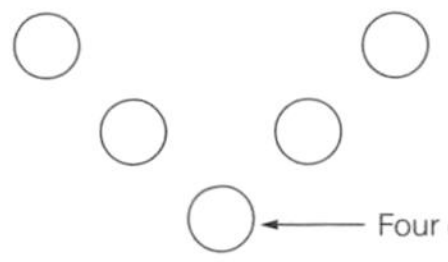

ASSESSMENT p. 13

UNIT 2 Mastery Checkpoint 6 Thinking Story participation (Lesson 40)

Name____________________

How many ways can you make $20 using only standard bills? Use the chart below to record your results.

$1 bills	$5 bills	$10 bills	$20 bills
0	4	0	0
0	2	1	0
0	0	2	0
0	0	0	1
5	3	0	0
5	1	1	0
10	2	0	0
10	0	1	0
20	0	0	0

Coaching Techniques
If students are having trouble finding a solution to the problem, you may find it useful to ask questions such as:

- What are you trying to find out?
- What information do you have to work with?
- What is one possible solution?
- How can you record this solution?
- Is there more than one solution?
- How can you organize your ideas to keep track of what you have tried?
- How will you know when you have found all the possibilities?
- How will you explain your solution strategy to the class?

UNIT 2

Student Edition pages 136–137

Mid-Unit Review

The Mid-Unit Review pinpoints troublesome skill areas for students, allowing time for additional practice and reteaching before the unit ends. If students did not do well on the Mid-Unit Review and have completed additional practice, you may want to use the Mid-Unit Review provided on Assessment Blackline Masters pages 11–12.

Using the Student Pages Have students complete problems 1–40 on pages 136 and 137 on their own. You might treat this review as a formal assessment of students' skills and have students complete this review as a timed test. See suggestions on page 51.

UNIT 2

ASSESSMENT

Mid-Unit Review

Multiply to solve for *n*.

1. $6 \times 0 = n$ **0**
2. $4 \times 6 = n$ **24**
3. $0 \times 3 = n$ **0**
4. $1 \times 8 = n$ **8**
5. $5 \times 5 = n$ **25**
6. $4 \times 4 = n$ **16**
7. $6 \times 9 = n$ **54**
8. $3 \times 5 = n$ **15**
9. $4 \times 8 = n$ **32**
10. $7 \times 2 = n$ **14**
11. $3 \times 7 = n$ **21**
12. $8 \times 5 = n$ **40**

Solve.

13. How many fingers are there on four hands? **20**
14. How many days are there in ten weeks? **70**
15. How many feet are there on six dogs? **24**

Multiply.

16. 7×8 **56**
17. 7×6 **42**
18. 8×9 **72**
19. 9×6 **54**
20. 7×9 **63**
21. 2×6 **12**
22. 8×8 **64**
23. 6×3 **18**
24. 7×7 **49**

Complete the chart.

	Length of Side	Area of Square	
25	2 cm	■	**4 square cm**
26	4 cm	■	**16 square cm**
27	6 cm	■	**36 square cm**
28	8 cm	■	**64 square cm**
29	10 cm	■	**100 square cm**

Which is the right triangle?

30. **C**

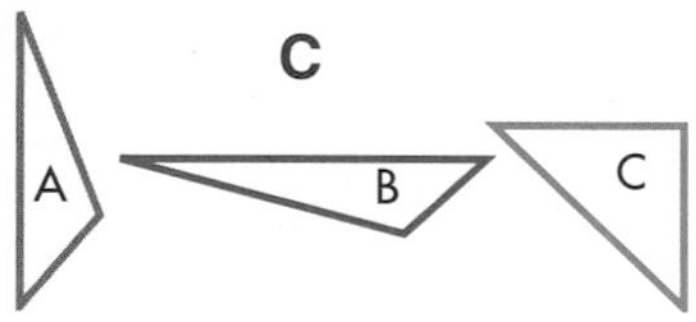

31. **B**

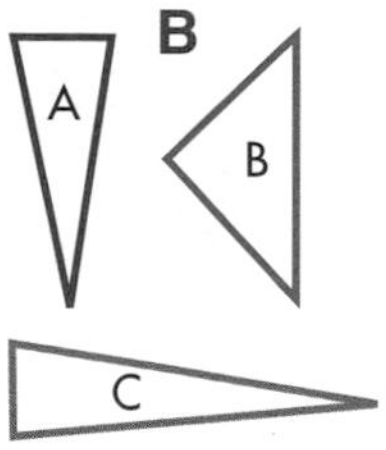

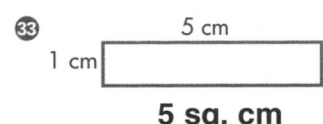

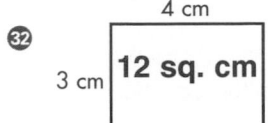

What is the area of each rectangle?

32. 4 cm × 3 cm — **12 sq. cm**

33. 5 cm × 1 cm — **5 sq. cm**

Copy and complete the price chart.

Buttons at 7¢ Each

Number of buttons	1	2	3	4	5	6	7	8	9	10
34. Price (in cents)	7	**14**	**21**	**28**	**35**	**42**	**49**	**56**	**63**	**70**

Choose the measure that makes more sense.

35. The classroom is about **35 feet** or **30 yards** wide. (**35 feet**)
36. A can of soda holds about **30 liters** or **355 milliliters.** (**355 milliliters**)
37. A nickel weighs about **5 grams** or **5 milligrams.** (**5 grams**)
38. A loaf of bread weighs about **10 ounces** or **1 pound.** (**1 pound**)

Copy and complete the function charts.

39. ×9

In	Out
0	**0**
3	**27**
4	**36**
7	**63**
8	**72**
9	**81**

40. ×4

In	Out
10	**40**
8	**32**
6	**24**
3	**12**
1	**4**
0	**0**

ASSESSMENT p. 11

UNIT 2 **Mid-Unit Review** (Use after Lesson 34.) Page 1 of 2

Name ______

The student demonstrates mastery by correctly answering at least 23 of the 30 problems.

Multiply. Solve for n.

1. $2 \times 3 = n$ — $n =$ 6
2. $9 \times 7 = n$ — $n =$ 63
3. $3 \times 8 = n$ — $n =$ 24
4. $5 \times 2 = n$ — $n =$ 10
5. $6 \times 7 = n$ — $n =$ 42
6. $4 \times 8 = n$ — $n =$ 32
7. $5 \times 7 = n$ — $n =$ 35
8. $8 \times 8 = n$ — $n =$ 64
9. $7 \times 3 = n$ — $n =$ 21
10. $6 \times 9 = n$ — $n =$ 54
11. $7 \times 4 = n$ — $n =$ 28
12. $4 \times 6 = n$ — $n =$ 24
13. $8 \times 9 = n$ — $n =$ 72
14. $3 \times 5 = n$ — $n =$ 15
15. $8 \times 2 = n$ — $n =$ 16
16. $9 \times 0 = n$ — $n =$ 0
17. $7 \times 3 = n$ — $n =$ 21
18. $6 \times 6 = n$ — $n =$ 36
19. $4 \times 7 = n$ — $n =$ 28
20. $3 \times 4 = n$ — $n =$ 12

Find the area.

21. 36 sq. ft. (6 ft. × 6 ft.)
22. 40 sq. ft. (8 ft. × 5 ft.)

23. Complete the chart of cookie prices.

Cookies	for one	for two	for three	for four
regular price	20¢	40¢	60¢	80¢
half price	10¢	20¢	30¢	40¢

Copyright © SRA/McGraw-Hill. Permission is granted to reproduce this page for classroom use.

Home Connections You may want to send home the Home Connections Blackline Masters letter on pages 38–39 to provide additional activities that families can complete together. These activities apply the skills presented in this unit.

ALTERNATIVE ASSESSMENT

Portfolio Assessment As students work through the second half of this unit, the Portfolio Assessment task provided on Assessment Blackline Masters page 94 can be used to evaluate students' proficiency with simple division and units of volume.

ALTERNATIVE ASSESSMENT

Performance Assessment Performance Assessment Task 1, provided on Assessment Blackline Masters pages 71–72, can be used at this time to evaluate students' proficiency with estimating lengths. You may want to administer this assessment to individual students or small groups of students.

Unit Project This would be a good time to assign the "Exploring the Multiplication Table" project on pages 172 and 173. Students can begin working on the project in cooperative groups in their free time as they work through the unit. The Unit Project is a good opportunity for students to explore and find number patterns on the multiplication table and to use one of the patterns in solving a difficult problem.

LESSON 41

Student Edition pages 138–141

Finding Missing Factors

LESSON PLANNER

Objectives

- to review missing-factor problems
- to provide practice in using missing factors to solve problems

Context of the Lesson This is the first of five lessons on missing factors and division. Missing-factor exercises and word problems are presented to emphasize the inverse relationship between multiplication and division.

MANIPULATIVES

index cards or sheets of paper

masking tape, pins, or paper clips

Program Resources

"Multigo 1" and "Multigo 2" Game Mats

Practice Master 41

Enrichment Master 41

For additional math integration: Math Throughout the Day*

For extra practice: CD-ROM* Lesson 41

1 Warm-Up 5 MINUTES

Problem of the Day Present this problem on the chalkboard and allow students to use scrap paper to solve it: The following figure represents an unfolded Number Cube with no numbers. Where would you put the numbers 0 to 5 on the cube so that, if you folded the figure back into a cube, the product of every pair of opposite faces would be 6 or less? (One possible answer is shown in the figure.)

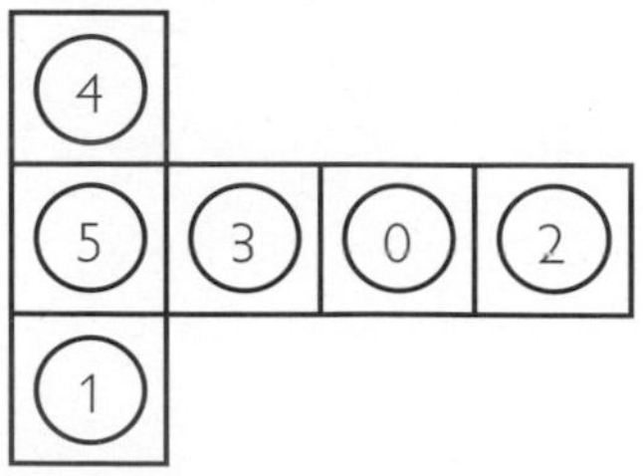

Problem-Solving Strategies Ask students who have solved the Problem of the Day to share how they solved it and any strategies they used.

PRACTICE

LESSON 41

Finding Missing Factors

ALGEBRA READINESS

Taneesha's class is doing the "Missing Factor" activity.

$3 \times n = 15$

What number does Taneesha have on her back? **5**

In each case, write the number that Taneesha has on her back.

	Pak Has This Number	The Product Is	Taneesha Has This Number	
1	3	24	8	
2	6	18	■	3
3	9	45	■	5
4	5	50	■	10
5	4	36	■	9
6	7	49	■	7
7	2	18	■	9
8	10	10	■	1
9	1	8	■	8
10	0	0	■	any numbe

Look at problem 10 again. Can you tell which number Taneesha has? What numbers might she have?

Literature Connection Read *The Math Whiz* by Betsy Duffey, or excerpts from it, with the class. In the story, Marty finds math problems in his daily life. Encourage students to create original math problems based on their daily lives. Suggest that they create missing-addend and missing-factor problems.

*available separately

Solve the following problems.

11. A machine at Dough-Boyz Donuts cuts holes in the middle of nine doughnuts every minute. How many minutes will it take the machine to cut holes in 90 doughnuts? **10** — $n \times 9 = 90$

12. Jorge made eight trips around the park on his bike. He rode a total of 24 kilometers. How long is each trip around the park? **3 km** — $8 \times n = 24$

13. Gina earns $5 each time she mows her aunt's lawn. How many times will she have to mow the lawn to earn the $35 she needs for a new tennis racquet? **7** — $n \times 5 = 35$

14. Grant had $15 when he went to the ball game. He had $6 when he got home. How much did he spend? **$9** — $15 - n = 6$

15. Each day, Katy listens to her radio for four hours. A battery will power the radio for about 36 hours of listening. About how many days can Katy listen to her radio before the battery goes dead? **about 9 days** — $4 \times n = 36$

16. Jared baked 24 cookies. He takes three cookies in his lunch every day. For how many days will he have cookies in his lunch? **8** — $3 \times n = 24$

17. Tim works 15 hours a week at the pizza shop. If he works the same amount of time each of three days during the week, how many hours must he work each day? **5** — $3 \times n = 15$

Technology Connection Refer students to the software *Target Math* from Critical Thinking Software & Books (Apple, Mac, IBM, for grades 3–12) for practice with completing unknown number sentences, mental math skills, logical thinking, deductive reasoning, and probability.

MENTAL MATH Provide practice of multiplication facts. Encourage quick recall.

a.	8 x 3 = (24)	**b.**	7 x 1 = (7)
c.	10 x 8 = (80)	**d.**	7 x 6 = (42)
e.	4 x 3 = (12)	**f.**	8 x 2 = (16)
g.	5 x 6 = (30)	**h.**	6 x 4 = (24)
i.	7 x 2 = (14)	**j.**	7 x 8 = (56)
k.	2 x 4 = (8)	**l.**	8 x 4 = (32)
m.	10 x 6 = (60)	**n.**	6 x 8 = (48)
o.	5 x 4 = (20)	**p.**	7 x 9 = (63)
q.	10 x 4 = (40)	**r.**	8 x 6 = (48)
s.	3 x 7 = (21)	**t.**	4 x 7 = (28)

2 Teach

Using the Student Pages

Demonstrate "Multigo 1" and "Multigo 2" Game Mats, which focus on solving missing term problems. Students may play these games once they have completed the lessons. Before assigning the problems on page 138, do the "Missing Factor" activity with the class. Students may remember it from the Level 3 program or the similar "Numbers on the Back" activity they did with missing addends in Lesson 9. Ask two students to come to the front of the room. Attach a number (on an **index card** or **paper**) to each one's back without letting them see. Then allow the players to look at each other's number but *not* at their own. Ask the class, "What is the product of the two numbers?" After the class responds, each student must determine the number on his or her back. Repeat with two more volunteers. On the third or fourth round, put a 0 on one student's back and any other number on the other student's back. After the round, discuss what happened. Emphasize that when the product is 0, there is no way to be certain what the other factor is.

After doing the "Missing Factor" activity with the class, have students complete page 138 on their own. The problems relate to the activity. Students can go on to page 139 when they finish. Encourage them to read the problems carefully to verify that the equations represent the stories.

◆ LESSON 41 Finding Missing Factors

Teach

Using the Student Pages Have students work independently on page 140. Then have students work in cooperative groups to solve the problems on page 141. Encourage them to discuss their ideas and strategies together and verify that their solutions make sense.

Introducing the "Multigo 1" and "Multigo 2" Game Mats Demonstrate the "Multigo 1" and "Multigo 2" Game Mats by playing them with some students at the front of the class. The games provide practice with solving missing-factor problems related to multiplication facts and mathematical reasoning. A copy of the Game Mats can also be found on pages 596–597 of this Teacher's Guide.

ESL

Meeting Individual Needs

Students with limited English proficiency may have difficulty with the word problems in this lesson. You may need to read the problems to them or simplify the language so they can focus on the mathematics. Use gestures or illustrations to clarify unfamiliar words.

◆ LESSON 41 Finding Missing Factors

Solve.

18. Each day, Craig knits 10 centimeters on the scarf he's making. He wants the scarf to be 1 meter (100 centimeters) long. How many days will it take Craig to make his scarf? **10**

19. Every day, Tanya uses four slices of bread for her lunch sandwiches. A loaf of bread has 28 slices. How many days can Tanya make sandwiches from one loaf of bread? **7**

20. Marcia is inviting 28 friends to her birthday party.

    a. She has four days to write all the invitations. If she writes six invitations each day, will she finish in time? **no**

    b. If she writes seven each day, will she finish in time? **yes**

    c. If she writes eight each day, will she finish in time? **yes**

Solve for *n*.

21. $9 \times n = 27$ **3**	22. $n \times 10 = 60$ **6**	23. $6 \times n = 30$ **5**
24. $3 \times n = 0$ **0**	25. $72 = 9 \times n$ **8**	26. $n \times 6 = 54$ **9**
27. $20 = n \times 10$ **2**	28. $48 = 8 \times n$ **6**	29. $7 \times n = 42$ **6**
30. $6 \times n = 48$ **8**	31. $n \times 8 = 72$ **9**	32. $3 \times n = 27$ **9**
33. $32 = n \times 8$ **4**	34. $5 \times n = 35$ **7**	35. $45 = n \times 5$ **9**
36. $5 \times n = 25$ **5**	37. $6 \times n = 36$ **6**	38. $81 = n \times 9$ **9**
39. $14 = n \times 2$ **7**	40. $n \times 8 = 32$ **4**	41. $64 = n \times 8$ **8**

RETEACHING

No extra teaching is required at this time. However, note students who have difficulty with the missing-factor problems so that you can anticipate difficulties they may have in subsequent division lessons. You may want to assign Enrichment Master 41 for this lesson.

Solve.

42 Raulito has $87 in his bank account. He wants to deposit enough money to bring his balance to exactly $100. How much money should he deposit? **$13**

43 Manuel has already driven 87 miles of a 100-mile trip. How many more miles must he drive? **13 miles**

44 Juanita needs 100 coupons to collect a prize. She already has 87 coupons. How many more coupons does she need? **13**

Do you notice anything about the first three problems on this page? Notice that the mathematics in these problems is the same, only the situations are different. **They can all be solved using the equation $100 - 87 = n$.**

COOPERATIVE LEARNING **Work in groups. Make up other problems that are similar to problems 42, 43, and 44.**

Solve these problems.

45 Richard needs 45 hats for a party. Hats come five to a package. How many packages of hats does he need? **9**

46 Ed had $150 in his bank account. He wrote a check, but he forgot to write down the amount. He called the bank and found out that he has $126 in his account. For what amount was the check written? **$24**

47 Mary wrote a check for $24. That brought the balance in her checking account to $126. What was her balance before she wrote the check? **$150**

48 John had a balance of $250 in his checking account. He wrote one check for $20. Then he wrote another check, but he forgot to record the amount. How much money is in his bank account now? **can't tell**

49 Nina's class just finished Lesson 38 in their geography book. The book has 112 lessons. How many more lessons must the class complete to finish the book? **74**

PRACTICE p. 41

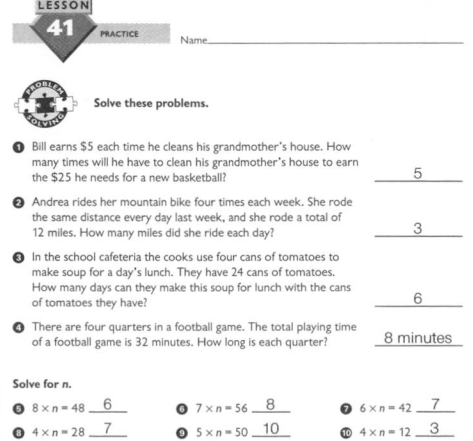

LESSON 41 PRACTICE Name______

Solve these problems.

1. Bill earns $5 each time he cleans his grandmother's house. How many times will he have to clean his grandmother's house to earn the $25 he needs for a new basketball? 5
2. Andrea rides her mountain bike four times each week. She rode the same distance every day last week, and she rode a total of 12 miles. How many miles did she ride each day? 3
3. In the school cafeteria the cooks use four cans of tomatoes to make soup for a day's lunch. They have 24 cans of tomatoes. How many days can they make this soup for lunch with the cans of tomatoes they have? 6
4. There are four quarters in a football game. The total playing time of a football game is 32 minutes. How long is each quarter? 8 minutes

Solve for *n*.

5 $8 \times n = 48$ 6	6 $7 \times n = 56$ 8	7 $6 \times n = 42$ 7
8 $4 \times n = 28$ 7	9 $5 \times n = 50$ 10	10 $4 \times n = 12$ 3
11 $7 \times n = 42$ 6	12 $6 \times n = 54$ 9	13 $8 \times n = 48$ 6
14 $54 = n \times 9$ 6	15 $n \times 4 = 24$ 6	16 $7 \times n = 35$ 5
17 $7 \times n = 63$ 9	18 $8 \times n = 32$ 4	19 $9 \times n = 36$ 4
20 $64 = 8 \times n$ 8	21 $n \times 6 = 18$ 3	22 $9 \times n = 45$ 5
23 $5 \times n = 25$ 5	24 $10 \times n = 80$ 8	25 $n \times 3 = 9$ 3
26 $27 = 9 \times n$ 3	27 $5 \times n = 35$ 7	28 $6 \times n = 54$ 9
29 $1 \times n = 10$ 10	30 $n \times 8 = 72$ 9	31 $n \times 5 = 45$ 9

Copyright © SRA/McGraw-Hill. Permission is granted to reproduce this page for classroom use.

Math Explorations and Applications Level 4 • 41

ENRICHMENT p. 41

LESSON 41 ENRICHMENT Name______

Sarah is going to her family's cabin in the Sierra Mountains for the weekend. She has to bring along her dog, her cat, and a bag of cat food for the cat.

The road ends before it reaches Sarah's cabin, and she must ride a chairlift to get to it. Sarah can carry only one thing on the chairlift at a time. She can carry either one of the animals or the cat food. She is worried that if she leaves them alone, the dog will eat the cat or the cat will eat the cat food.

What will Sarah have to do in order to move her animals and cat food using the chairlift?

First, Sarah takes the cat to the cabin, leaving behind the dog and the cat food. Then she returns for the dog. She takes the dog to the cabin and leaves it there. She then returns to the road—taking the cat with her. She leaves the cat at the roadside and takes the cat food to the cabin. She leaves the cat food and the dog at the cabin, then returns to the roadside to pick up the cat.

Copyright © SRA/McGraw-Hill. Permission is granted to reproduce this page for classroom use.

Math Explorations and Applications Level 4 • 41

3 Wrap-Up (5 MINUTES)

In Closing Ask students why the "Missing Factor" activity can not work with a 0 as one of the factors. (The other factor could be any number, since $n \times 0 = 0$.)

SELF ASSESSMENT Have students write a statement about how they use missing factors to solve problems. Ask them to discuss the relationship between multiplication and division (or between addition and subtraction) and to explain how they know when to use this approach. Have them note aspects of missing factors that they find confusing as well as those they have mastered.

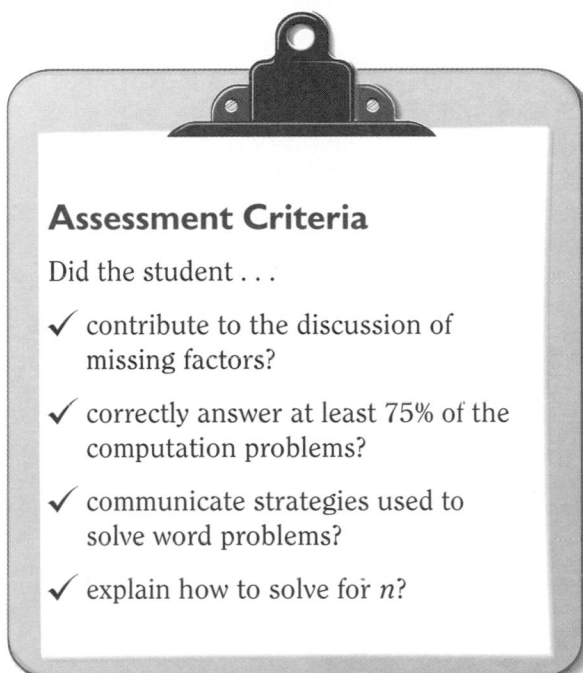

Assessment Criteria

Did the student . . .

- ✓ contribute to the discussion of missing factors?
- ✓ correctly answer at least 75% of the computation problems?
- ✓ communicate strategies used to solve word problems?
- ✓ explain how to solve for *n*?

Homework Assign Practice Master 41 for further practice with finding missing factors.

LESSON 42

Student Edition pages 142–143

Multiplication and Division

LESSON PLANNER

Objectives

- ▶ to provide practice in solving word problems that require missing-factor equations or division
- ▶ to show the inverse relationship between multiplication and division

Context of the Lesson This is the second of five lessons on division. Progress with division facts will be assessed in Lesson 45.

MANIPULATIVES

none

Program Resources

Reteaching Master

Practice Master 42

Enrichment Master 42

For extra practice:
CD-ROM* Lesson 42
Cumulative Review, page 543

1 Warm-Up (5 MINUTES)

Problem of the Day Present the following problem orally or on the chalkboard: Gretchen knows a great deal about spiders and beetles. She knows that spiders have eight legs and beetles have six legs. At an exhibit of rare spiders and beetles, Gretchen counted 34 legs. How many spiders and how many beetles did Gretchen see? (three beetles, two spiders)

Problem-Solving Strategies Ask students who have solved the Problem of the Day to share how they solved it and any strategies they used.

MENTAL MATH Practice multiplication through regular and missing-factor problems, which will prepare students for algebra. Present pairs of related problems so that students see the relationship between them.

a. 7 x 10 = (70)
7 x n = 70 (n = 10)

b. 5 x 4 = (20)
n x 4 = 20 (n = 5)

c. 7 x 6 = (42)
n x 6 = 42 (n = 7)

d. 9 x 9 = (81)
n x 9 = 81 (n = 9)

PROBLEM SOLVING

LESSON 42

Multiplication and Division

Multiplication and division are related. When you solved missing-term problems that involved multiplication, you were getting ready for division.

Use multiplication facts to solve these division problems.

1. Keith earns $4 each hour at his job. Today he earned $20. How many hours did he work today? **5**
2. María has to work only two hours to earn $20. How much does she earn each hour? **$10**
3. Eight children want to share 24 cookies equally. How many cookies should each child get? **3**
4. When the Crickets and the Ravens play football, they can score only by getting touchdowns and kicking extra points. Frankie is the extra-point kicker for the Crickets team. She never misses, so each time they get a touchdown, the Crickets get 7 points. As of halftime, they had scored 42 points. How many touchdowns did they get? **6**
5. Paul kicks extra points for the Ravens football team. He had a bad day and missed every kick, so each touchdown earned only 6 points. How many touchdowns did the Ravens need to score 42 points? **7**
6. In the game between the Crickets and the Ravens, the final score was 56 to 54.
   a. Which team won? **Crickets**
   b. How many touchdowns did the winning team score? **8**
   c. How many touchdowns did the losing team score? **9**

Why teach it this way?

In Unit 5, exercises such as 12 ÷ 3 and 19 ÷ 7 are occasionally shown in the following format:

3)12   7)19

Inform students that the symbol ÷ and the corresponding arrangement of divisor, dividend, and quotient will be helpful later on when they do more complicated division problems.

RETEACHING p. 12

LESSON 42 RETEACHING Name__________

You know that the symbol ÷ means "divided by." The symbol) also means "divided by," but we will divide the number inside this symbol by the number outside the symbol.

For example, 8)64 is the same as 64 ÷ 8.

We read this as "64 divided by 8." This means we are dividing 64 by 8.

Fill in the blanks.

1. 7)56 = 56 ÷ 7
2. 6)36 = 36 ÷ 6

Division is the opposite of multiplication. You can use multiplication to help you divide. For example, 8 × 7 = 56, so 56 ÷ 7 = 8.

3. 5 × 4 = 20, so 20 ÷ 4 = 5
4. 7 × 6 = 42, so 42 ÷ 6 = 7
5. 6 × 6 = 36, so 36 ÷ 6 = 6
6. 3 × 8 = 24, so 24 ÷ 8 = 3

Divide.

7. 9 ÷ 9 = n 1
8. 30 ÷ 5 = n 6
9. 28 ÷ 7 = n 4
10. 0 ÷ 5 = n 0
11. 40 ÷ 8 = n 5
12. 18 ÷ 3 = n 6
13. 27 ÷ 9 = n 3
14. n = 49 ÷ 7 7
15. n = 7 ÷ 1 7
16. 9)18 2
17. 2)8 4
18. 6)42 7
19. 9)63 7
20. 10)50 5
21. 2)12 6
22. 7)35 5
23. 3)15 5
24. 10)100 10
25. 6)48 6

12 • *Math Explorations and Applications* Level 4

Copyright © SRA/McGraw-Hill. Permission is granted to reproduce this page for classroom use.

*available separately

Division undoes multiplication, just as subtraction undoes addition.

- ◆ $8 + 6 = 14$, so $14 - 6 = ?$ **8**
- ◆ $8 \times 6 = 48$, so $48 \div 6 = ?$ **8**
- ◆ $56 = 7 \times 8$, so $56 \div 8 = ?$ **7**
- ◆ $49 = 7 \times 7$, so $? = 49 \div 7$ **7**

Divide. Solve for *n*.

7 $10 \div 10 = n$ **1**	8 $72 \div 9 = n$ **8**	9 $63 \div 7 = n$ **9**
10 $20 \div 5 = n$ **4**	11 $35 \div 7 = n$ **5**	12 $n = 56 \div 8$ **7**
13 $n = 5 \div 1$ **5**	14 $72 \div 8 = n$ **9**	15 $64 \div 8 = n$ **8**
16 $n = 14 \div 7$ **2**	17 $60 \div 6 = n$ **10**	18 $80 \div 10 = n$ **8**
19 $42 \div 7 = n$ **6**	20 $n = 30 \div 5$ **6**	21 $n = 100 \div 10$ **10**
22 $40 \div 8 = n$ **5**	23 $45 \div 9 = n$ **5**	24 $81 \div 9 = n$ **9**
25 $16 \div 2 = n$ **8**	26 $n = 30 \div 10$ **3**	27 $64 \div 8 = n$ **8**

You know that the ÷ sign means "divided by."

Another way to show division is to use this symbol: $\overline{)\quad}$.

Example: $7\overline{)56}$

This means that we are going to divide 56 by 7. Write the answer as shown:

$\begin{array}{r} \mathbf{8} \\ 7\overline{)56} \end{array}$

Divide.

28 $5\overline{)50}$ **10**	29 $7\overline{)63}$ **9**	30 $10\overline{)90}$ **9**	31 $5\overline{)30}$ **6**	32 $8\overline{)16}$ **2**
33 $3\overline{)21}$ **7**	34 $5\overline{)40}$ **8**	35 $1\overline{)2}$ **2**	36 $5\overline{)25}$ **5**	37 $3\overline{)6}$ **2**
38 $9\overline{)18}$ **2**	39 $7\overline{)42}$ **6**	40 $6\overline{)54}$ **9**	41 $4\overline{)28}$ **7**	42 $9\overline{)81}$ **9**

Use the Cumulative Review on page 543 after this lesson.

❷ Teach

Using the Student Pages Before students work on page 142, go over one or two problems with them. Encourage students to draw or act out the situation and to check whether their answers make sense. Remind them to use the inverse operation to check their answers.

Problem 6 may be difficult at first for many students. Suggest that they make up a scoreboard on which they record each touchdown and extra point (either six or seven points). Because 56 does not have a factor of 6 but does have a factor of 7, the Crickets must have won by scoring eight seven-point touchdowns, and the Ravens must have lost by scoring nine six-point touchdowns.

Discuss the first four problems at the top of page 143. Then have students try, as a group, to solve problems such as $18 \div 3 = n$ ($n = 6$). Have students complete the rest of the page on their own.

❸ Wrap-Up

5 MINUTES

In Closing Ask students to draw and identify the two symbols used to represent division and to correctly read problems that use those symbols.

ALTERNATIVE ASSESSMENT

Portfolio Assessment Have students write a brief piece explaining why multiplication and division are related operations. Encourage them to include examples and drawings to support their explanations. Have students date this piece and keep it in their Math Portfolios as a record of ongoing learning.

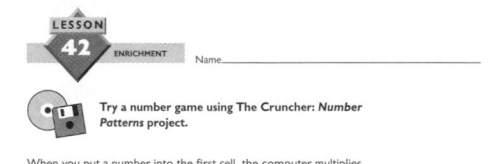

Assessment Criteria

Did the student . . .

- ✓ explain the relationship between multiplication and division?
- ✓ communicate strategies used to solve word problems?
- ✓ correctly answer at least 75% of the division facts?
- ✓ demonstrate understanding and correct usage of both division signs?

Homework Have students create and solve three word problems that involve division.

PRACTICE p. 42

LESSON 42 PRACTICE Name________

Divide.

1 $20 \div 4 =$ 5	2 $27 \div 3 =$ 9	3 $28 \div 4 =$ 7
4 $16 \div 8 =$ 2	5 $36 \div 6 =$ 6	6 $72 \div 9 =$ 8
7 $9 \div 1 =$ 9	8 $42 \div 7 =$ 6	9 $40 \div 4 =$ 10
10 $24 \div 6 =$ 4	11 $27 \div 9 =$ 3	12 $30 \div 3 =$ 10
13 $30 \div 10 =$ 3	14 $56 \div 8 =$ 7	15 $25 \div 5 =$ 5

Divide.

16 $1\overline{)10}$ 10	17 $4\overline{)28}$ 7	18 $7\overline{)21}$ 3	19 $6\overline{)30}$ 5
20 $7\overline{)35}$ 5	21 $2\overline{)18}$ 9	22 $8\overline{)24}$ 3	23 $4\overline{)40}$ 10
24 $3\overline{)21}$ 7	25 $6\overline{)36}$ 6	26 $9\overline{)18}$ 2	27 $6\overline{)42}$ 7

PROBLEM SOLVING **Solve these problems.**

28 Beth earns \$6 for each hour of work. She made \$48 today. How many hours did she work today? 8

29 When Beth works overtime, she only has to work 4 hours to make \$36. How much does she earn each hour working overtime? \$9

30 On a game show each correct answer is worth ten points. Team A scores 90 points and Team B scores 70 points. How many correct answers did each team have? A–9; B–7

Copyright © SRA/McGraw-Hill. Permission is granted to reproduce this page for classroom use.

ENRICHMENT p. 42

LESSON 42 ENRICHMENT Name________

Try a number game using The Cruncher: *Number Patterns* project.

When you put a number into the first cell, the computer multiplies the number by 3, adds 3, divides by 3, and subtracts 1 to end up with the original number. Try several different numbers. Does it always work?

Choose a number		x
Multiply the number by 3		$x \times 3$ or $3x$
Add 3 to the total		$3x + 3$
Divide the total by 3		$(3x + 3) \div 3$
Subtract 1 from the total		$(3x - 3) \div 3 - 1$
Is it the original number?		yes

Use the number 4 instead of 3 and see if the game still works. See what happens if you use the numbers 5, 6, 7, 8, 9, and 10.

The formula works no matter what number is used.

MATH JOURNAL **In your Math Journal explain why this happens.**

Now change the formulas and create your own number game. Try it out! Does it always work? Ask a friend to try it.

Copyright © SRA/McGraw-Hill. Permission is granted to reproduce this page for classroom use.

LESSON 43

Student Edition pages 144–147

Keeping Sharp

LESSON PLANNER

Objectives

- ▶ to provide practice with basic arithmetic facts for all four operations
- ▶ to provide practice adding and subtracting multidigit numbers
- ▶ to help students develop the broad ability to use mathematical common sense

Context of the Lesson This is the third of five lessons involving work with division. This lesson also contains Part 3 of "Money Matters," a four-part Thinking Story.

MANIPULATIVES

real half-dollars, quarters, dimes, nickels, and pennies (optional)

Program Resources

Number Wheels

Practice Master 43

Enrichment Master 43

For career connections:
Careers and Math*

For extra practice:
CD-ROM* Lesson 43

1 Warm-Up

5 MINUTES

Problem of the Day Present this problem to the class: The Great Gizmo performed four juggling shows last Sunday. The first show had 40 people in the audience. For every show after that, Gizmo sold twice as many tickets as for the show before. After the fourth show, how many people had seen the Great Gizmo juggle? (600)

Problem-Solving Strategies Ask students who have solved the Problem of the Day to share how they solved it and any strategies they used.

MENTAL MATH Present a combination of multiplication facts, missing-term, and missing-factor problems. Have students use their Number Wheels to quickly show the answers.

a. $n \times 2 = 8$ ($n = 4$) **b.** $n \times 5 = 40$ ($n = 8$)

c. $2 \times 6 =$ (12) **d.** $n \times 6 = 24$ ($n = 4$)

(continued on page 145)

MIXED PRACTICE

LESSON 43

Keeping Sharp

Keep in shape by practicing adding, subtracting, multiplying, and dividing. Pay attention to the signs.

ALGEBRA READINESS

Add or subtract. Solve for *n*.

1. $8 + 7 = n$ **15**	2. $12 = 3 + n$ **9**	3. $10 = 20 - n$ **10**
4. $16 - 7 = n$ **9**	5. $14 = 7 + n$ **7**	6. $18 - n = 9$ **9**
7. $10 - 10 = n$ **0**	8. $n = 12 - 7$ **5**	9. $16 - 0 = n$ **16**
10. $9 + 8 = n$ **17**	11. $8 = n + 3$ **5**	12. $10 + n = 18$ **8**
13. $4 + n = 7$ **3**	14. $6 + 4 = n$ **10**	15. $17 - n = 10$ **7**
16. $18 = n + 9$ **9**	17. $3 + n = 15$ **12**	18. $12 = 10 + n$ **2**
19. $n - 6 = 2$ **8**	20. $17 - 8 = n$ **9**	21. $5 - 5 = n$ **0**

Add or subtract. Use shortcuts when you can.

22. 25 + 37 = **62**	23. 92 − 35 = **57**	24. 671 − 234 = **437**	25. 1000 − 500 = **500**
26. 76 + 28 = **104**	27. 197 + 803 = **1000**	28. 8216 − 3216 = **5000**	29. 1711 − 1699 = **12**
30. 7345 − 28 = **7317**	31. 250 + 150 = **400**	32. 800 − 750 = **50**	33. 800 − 799 = **1**
34. 25 + 25 + 25 + 25 = **100**	35. 10 + 17 + 3 = **30**	36. 15 + 17 + 18 + 2 = **52**	37. 2 + 9 + 11 + 10 = **32**

Real-World Connection United States coins not only come in different sizes, they have different edge details that help vision-impaired people recognize them. Have students examine real **pennies, nickels, dimes, quarters,** and **half-dollars** to identify features that can be distinguished.

*available separately

Multiply or divide. Solve for *n*.

38 $9 \times 4 = n$ **36**	39 $28 \div 4 = n$ **7**	40 $9 \div n = 3$ **3**
41 $64 \div 8 = n$ **8**	42 $27 \div 3 = n$ **9**	43 $42 = n \times 7$ **6**
44 $8 \times 7 = n$ **56**	45 $10 \times 9 = n$ **90**	46 $36 = 4 \times n$ **9**
47 $18 \div 9 = n$ **2**	48 $8 \times n = 56$ **7**	49 $100 = n \times 10$ **10**
50 $81 \div 9 = n$ **9**	51 $n \times 8 = 32$ **4**	52 $24 \div n = 6$ **4**
53 $63 \div n = 9$ **7**	54 $n \times 8 = 40$ **5**	55 $24 \div n = 4$ **6**
56 $5 = 45 \div n$ **9**	57 $9 \times n = 63$ **7**	58 $n \times 3 = 21$ **7**
59 $42 \div 6 = n$ **7**	60 $9 \times n = 90$ **10**	61 $54 \div n = 9$ **6**
62 $25 \div 5 = n$ **5**	63 $18 \div 6 = n$ **3**	64 $27 \div n = 3$ **9**
65 $10 \times n = 40$ **4**	66 $8 \times n = 0$ **0**	67 $n = 4 \times 9$ **36**
68 $14 \div n = 7$ **2**	69 $7 \times n = 21$ **3**	70 $10 = 5 \times n$ **2**
71 $54 = 9 \times n$ **6**	72 $32 = 8 \times n$ **4**	73 $56 = n \times 8$ **7**
74 $14 = 2 \times n$ **7**	75 $20 = n \times 4$ **5**	76 $8 \times 2 = n$ **16**

Solve these problems.

77 Tad paid 72¢ for eight erasers at the school bookstore. How much did each eraser cost? **9¢**

78 Myers Office Store charges 10¢ per page for copies. Mary needs to copy five pages of her report, and she has 40¢. Does she have enough money to copy her whole report? **No, she needs 10¢ more.**

79 David paid 80¢ for two writing tablets. How much did each tablet cost? **40¢**

Unit 2 Lesson 43 • **145**

Technology Connection Refer students to the software *Math Computation I* from EPC (Mac, for grades 1-5) for further practice with a range of skills from simple addition up to multidigit division. This software is also available in Spanish.

Mental Math (continued)

e. $10 \times 10 = (100)$	**f.** $10 \times 8 = (80)$
g. $5 \times n = 25$ $(n = 5)$	**h.** $n \times 5 = 5$ $(n = 1)$
i. $6 \times n = 18$ $(n = 3)$	**j.** $n \times 1 = 3$ $(n = 3)$
k. $7 - n = 3$ $(n = 4)$	**l.** $4 \times n = 28$ $(n = 7)$
m. $18 + n = 27$ $(n = 9)$	**n.** $n - 4 = 16$ $(n = 20)$

2 Teach

Using the Student Pages Have students work independently on the problems. Remind them to pay attention to the operation required and to use shortcuts when possible.

ESL

Meeting Individual Needs Students with limited English proficiency may have difficulty matching the names of coins to their monetary values. Have these students work with a partner who is fluent in English to practice using the words *penny, nickel, dime,* and *quarter* in simple word problems. Have real **coins** available for students' reference. Students can ask each other questions such as "How many dimes equal 50 cents?" and "How many pennies are equal to a quarter minus a nickel?"

◆ LESSON 43 Keeping Sharp

Teach

Using the Thinking Story In "Money Matters (Part 3)" students compute and estimate or measure to understand that "amount of money" can mean more than the number of coins. Students use a bar graph to help solve the problems.

Answers to Thinking Story Questions:

1. Marcus's stack of quarters should be 4 centimeters high. Willy's stack of dimes should be almost as high as Marcus's stack of quarters. Portia's stack of nickels should be twice as high (8 cm) as Marcus's stack of quarters, and Ferdie's stack of pennies should be four times as high (16 cm) as Marcus's quarters.

2. Students may need a few real coins to help answer this question. Marcus has the most money, Willy has the next-highest amount, Portia the next, and Ferdie the least.

MATH JOURNAL Have students write in their Math Journals an explanation of how two people can have the same number of coins, yet have different amounts of money. Ask them to give a specific example to support their reasoning.

THINKING STORY

◆ LESSON 43 Keeping Sharp

Money Matters

Part 3

Marcus, Portia, Willy, and Ferdie were all collecting coins. One day they got together to see who had the most money.

Marcus had a stack of quarters that was 4 centimeters high.

Willy had a stack of dimes. It was about as high as Marcus's stack.

Portia had a stack of nickels. Her stack was about twice as high as Marcus's stack.

Ferdie had a stack of pennies. His stack was four times as high as Marcus's stack.

Ferdie was excited. "I have the most because my stack is the highest."

"I have the most because quarters are worth the most," said Marcus.

"I have the most because dimes are so thin," said Willy. "If you count my dimes and Marcus's quarters, you'll find that I have more coins than he does."

Portia said, "I think I have the most. Don't forget that my stack is very high and I have nickels."

Literature Connection Students can practice their mathematical skills by playing some of the games in *Mathematical Games for One or Two* by Mannis Charosh.

RETEACHING

Specific reteaching on the new material in this lesson is not essential. Suggest that students complete Enrichment Master 43, which accompanies this lesson.

Work in groups. Discuss your answers and how you figured them out. Then compare your answers with those of other groups. **Answers are in margin.**

1. Copy and complete the bar graph to show the heights of the four stacks of money.

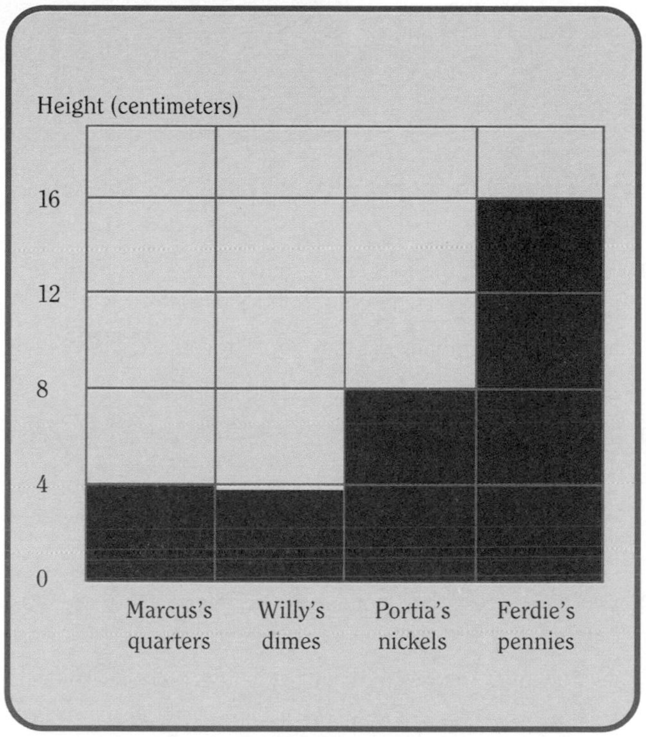

2. **Super detective questions:** Who has the greatest amount of money? The second greatest amount of money? The third greatest amount? Who has the least amount?

PRACTICE p. 43

LESSON 43 PRACTICE Name________

ALGEBRA READINESS

Solve for n. Watch the signs.

1. $8 + 5 = n$ 13
2. $10 = 3 + n$ 7
3. $10 = 15 - n$ 5
4. $14 - 7 = n$ 7
5. $14 = 6 + n$ 8
6. $16 - n = 9$ 7
7. $8 - 8 = n$ 0
8. $n = 11 - 7$ 4
9. $10 - 0 = n$ 10
10. $9 + 9 = n$ 18
11. $11 = n + 3$ 8
12. $9 + n = 17$ 8

Add or subtract. Use shortcuts when you can.

13. 45 + 67 = 112
14. 1500 − 500 = 1000
15. 7215 − 3215 = 4000
16. 450 + 250 = 700
17. 450 − 260 = 190
18. 92 − 38 = 54
19. 77 + 29 = 106
20. 2710 − 2699 = 11
21. 600 − 550 = 50
22. 850 + 59 = 909
23. 581 − 244 = 337
24. 297 + 603 = 900
25. 6424 − 28 = 6396
26. 700 − 699 = 1
27. 554 + 265 = 819

Solve for n. Watch the signs.

28. $9 \times 3 = n$ 27
29. $28 \div 7 = n$ 4
30. $12 \div n = 3$ 4
31. $56 \div 8 = n$ 7
32. $15 \div 3 = n$ 5
33. $49 = n \times 7$ 7
34. $8 \times 8 = n$ 64
35. $10 \times 8 = n$ 80
36. $32 = 4 \times n$ 8
37. $18 \div 2 = n$ 9
38. $8 \times n = 40$ 5
39. $10 \times n = 100$ 10

Copyright © SRA/McGraw-Hill. Permission is granted to reproduce this page for classroom use.

Math Explorations and Applications Level 4 • 43

ENRICHMENT p. 43

LESSON 43 ENRICHMENT Name________

Figure out the next number in each series. Then write a rule that explains the series.

1. 0, 2, 4, 6, 8 — Rule is +2.
2. 1, 5, 9, 13, 17 — Rule is +4.
3. 0, 3, 6, 9, 12 — Rule is +3.
4. 1, 2, 4, 7, 11, 16 — Rule is + 1, + 2, + 3, ...
5. 1, 3, 7, 13, 21, 31 — Rule is + 2, + 4, + 6, ...
6. 1, 2, 4, 8, 16, 32 — Rule is × 2.
7. 1, 2, 6, 24, 120, 720 — Rule is × 2, × 3, × 4, ...
8. 512, 256, 128, 64, 32, 16, 8, 4, 2, 1 — Rule is $\div 2$ or $\times \frac{1}{2}$.
9. 1, $\frac{1}{2}$, $\frac{1}{4}$, $\frac{1}{8}$, $\frac{1}{16}$ — Rule is $\div 2$ or $\times \frac{1}{2}$.
10. 1, 10, 100, 1000, 10,000 — Rule is × 10.

Here is a hard series. The rule that explains it has nothing to do with the value of the numbers. In what order are these numbers?

11. 8, 5, 4, 9, 1, 7, 6, 10, 3, 2
The numbers 1–10 are in alphabetical order according to their spellings.

If you need help, ask your teacher for a hint.

MATH JOURNAL **Make up your own series. Write it in your Math Journal. See if your classmates can figure out the rule you used.**

Copyright © SRA/McGraw-Hill. Permission is granted to reproduce this page for classroom use.

Math Explorations and Applications Level 4 • 43

3 Wrap-Up (5 MINUTES)

In Closing Ask students what conclusions they drew about the amount of money each child has in the Thinking Story.

ALTERNATIVE ASSESSMENT

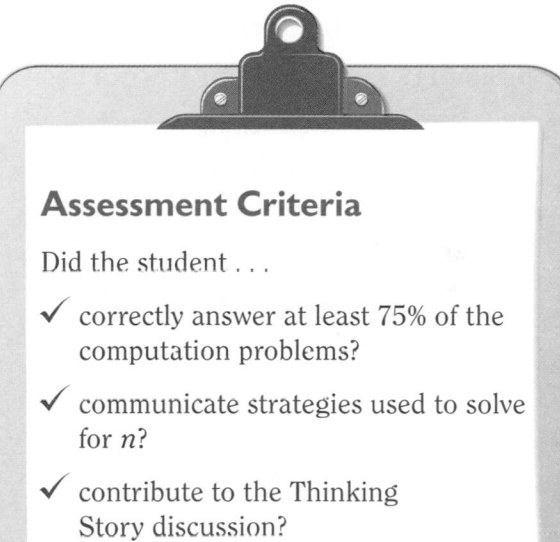

Informal Assessment You may wish to use the exercises on pages 144–145 to informally assess students' mastery of number facts in all four operations and of adding and subtracting multidigit numbers. To do so, record how long it takes students to complete the pages and how accurately they perform.

Assessment Criteria

Did the student . . .

- ✓ correctly answer at least 75% of the computation problems?
- ✓ communicate strategies used to solve for n?
- ✓ contribute to the Thinking Story discussion?

Homework Assign Practice Master 43 to reinforce the skill of solving problems using different operations.

GIFTED & TALENTED · MANIPULATIVES

Meeting Individual Needs

Have students imagine making a straight row of one kind of **coin** by placing the coins edge to edge on a flat surface. Have them assume that the row extends up to, but not beyond, one meter. Ask them to decide whether they would rather have a meter of nickels, of dimes, or of quarters and to share their problem-solving strategies when they present their answers.

LESSON 44

Student Edition pages 148–149

Division with Remainders

LESSON PLANNER

Objectives

- ▶ to provide practice in solving word problems that require division and other operations
- ▶ to introduce division with remainders

Context of the Lesson This is the fourth of five lessons on division. A checkpoint for monitoring individual progress in division facts, including remainders, is provided in the next lesson.

MANIPULATIVES	Program Resources
play money*	Reteaching Master
	Practice Master 44
	Enrichment Master 44
	For extra practice: CD-ROM* Lesson 44

1 Warm-Up

5 MINUTES

Problem of the Day Present the following problem orally or on the chalkboard: The sports program at Camp Hideaway has 24 campers. Find all the ways that 24 campers can form equal-sized teams for various events on Field Day with more than one camper or less than 24 campers. (There are six ways: 2 teams of 12, 3 teams of 8, 4 teams of 6, 6 teams of 4, 8 teams of 3, and 12 teams of 2).

Problem-Solving Strategies Ask students who have solved the Problem of the Day to share how they solved it and any strategies they used.

MENTAL MATH Provide practice with problems that involve inverse operations and that prepare students for algebra. Mix in missing-term problems.

a. $8 + 6 = (14)$
$14 - 8 = (6)$
$n + 6 = 14$ $(n = 8)$

b. $5 \times 8 = (40)$
$40 \div 5 = (8)$
$n \times 8 = 40$ $(n = 5)$

c. $21 \div 7 = (3)$
$3 \times 7 = (21)$
$n \times 7 = 21$ $(n = 3)$

d. $13 - 4 = (9)$
$4 + 9 = (13)$
$n + 4 = 13$ $(n = 9)$

PROBLEM SOLVING

LESSON 44

Division with Remainders

Sasha, Tina, Nikia, and Liza hunted for treasure on the beach. When they found valuable things, they sold them. Sometimes they found money. At the end of each week they divided all their money equally.

Use play money to act out what they did. Answer these questions.

1. The first week, the girls found some shells and coral. They sold these for \$27. They also found \$5 in cash.
   a. How much money did they get all together? **\$32**
   b. How much money should each girl get? **\$8**
2. The second week, they found more shells and an old coin. They sold these for \$31. They also found \$5 in cash.
   a. How much money did they get all together? **\$36**
   b. How much money should each of them get? **\$9**
3. The third week, they found some driftwood and three old bottles. They sold these for \$23. They also found \$7 in cash.
   a. How much money did they get all together? **\$30**
   b. How much money should each of them get?

There are several good answers to the last question. Each person can get \$7, leaving \$2. They can put the \$2 in the fund for next week. Or they can divide it equally. Each person would get an extra 50 cents. Or they could spend the \$2 on something they all could use, such as a water bottle or beach bag.

148 • Multiplication and Division

Literature Connection Ask each student how many chapters are in a book he or she is currently reading or studying and how many pages are in the book. Then ask students how many pages a chapter would have if each chapter has the same number of pages. (Answers will vary, but most answers will probably include a remainder.)

RETEACHING p. 13

LESSON 44 RETEACHING Name____________________

Joshua has 64 science fiction videotapes to put on eight shelves. To make the display look good, he wants to put the same number of videos on each shelf. How many videos will he place on each shelf?

$8\overline{)64}$ = 8 $8 \times 8 = 64$

Joshua had 72 videos to stack on exactly eight shelves in the comedy section of the video store. Then a customer returned one more comedy video. How many videos will Joshua put on each shelf?

When Joshua divides up the videos he has nine videos on each shelf, but he still has the one video left over, or remaining. We can write:

$8\overline{)73}$ = 9 R1

When we read this answer, we say "9 remainder 1."

Divide. Watch for remainders.

1. $2\overline{)15}$ 7 R1	2. $8\overline{)47}$ 5 R7	3. $4\overline{)33}$ 8 R1	4. $8\overline{)45}$ 5 R5	5. $6\overline{)37}$ 6 R1
6. $3\overline{)20}$ 6 R2	7. $5\overline{)36}$ 7 R1	8. $9\overline{)47}$ 5 R2	9. $5\overline{)30}$ 6	10. $9\overline{)45}$ 5
11. $4\overline{)27}$ 6 R3	12. $6\overline{)44}$ 7 R2	13. $8\overline{)26}$ 3 R2	14. $2\overline{)19}$ 9 R1	15. $3\overline{)23}$ 7 R2
16. $9\overline{)72}$ 8	17. $10\overline{)91}$ 9 R1	18. $7\overline{)50}$ 7 R1	19. $10\overline{)75}$ 7 R5	20. $7\overline{)42}$ 6

Copyright © SRA/McGraw-Hill. Permission is granted to reproduce this page for classroom use.

Math Explorations and Applications Level 4 • 13

*available separately

Seven children want to divide 56 cents equally. How much will each child get?

$7\overline{)56}$ **8**

Seven children want to divide 57 cents equally. How much will each child get?

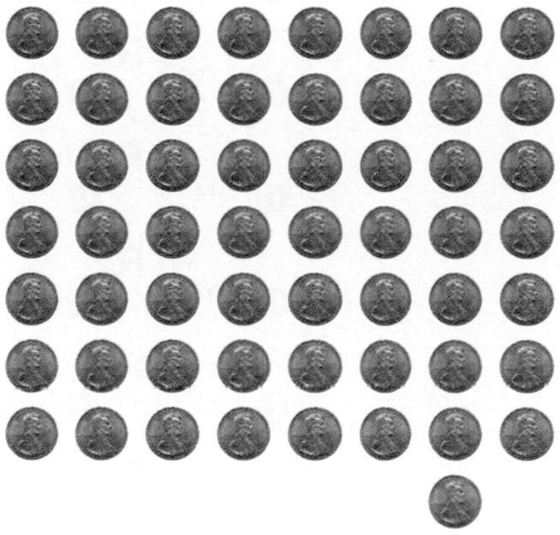

$7\overline{)57}$

After each child gets 8 cents, there is still 1 cent left over. Sometimes we wish to divide a whole number of things equally but cannot do so without something left over, or remaining. We can write:

$7\overline{)57}$ **8 R1**

When we read this answer, we say, "8 remainder 1."

Six children want to divide 40 cents equally. How much will each child get? How much will be left over?

$6\overline{)40}$ **6 R4**

$6 \times 6 = 36 \qquad 40 - 36 = 4$

Each child gets 6 cents, and there are 4 cents remaining.

Divide. Watch for remainders.

4. $8\overline{)48}$ **6**
5. $8\overline{)51}$ **6 R3**
6. $9\overline{)54}$ **6**
7. $9\overline{)58}$ **6 R4**
8. $5\overline{)37}$ **7 R2**
9. $7\overline{)43}$ **6 R1**
10. $3\overline{)26}$ **8 R2**
11. $10\overline{)46}$ **4 R6**
12. $3\overline{)29}$ **9 R2**
13. $6\overline{)36}$ **6**
14. $5\overline{)47}$ **9 R2**
15. $4\overline{)38}$ **9 R2**
16. $6\overline{)63}$ **10 R3**
17. $8\overline{)34}$ **4 R2**
18. $10\overline{)85}$ **8 R5**
19. $2\overline{)15}$ **7 R1**
20. $9\overline{)47}$ **5 R2**
21. $5\overline{)45}$ **9**
22. $7\overline{)54}$ **7 R5**
23. $4\overline{)26}$ **6 R2**

Unit 2 Lesson 44 • **149**

PRACTICE p. 44

LESSON 44 PRACTICE Name________________

Four boys decided to collect aluminum cans, plastic, and paper from the neighborhood. When they collected these recyclable items, they took them to the recycling center. Sometimes they found money along the way. At the end of each week they divided all their money equally.

Use play money to act out these problems and answer the questions.

1. The first week they got $28 for their items at the recycling center. They also found $4 in cash.
   a. How much money did they get all together? $32
   b. How much money should each boy get? $8
2. The second week they got $30 at the recycling center. They also found $6 in cash.
   a. How much money did they get all together? $36
   b. How much money should each boy get? $9
3. The third week they got $25 at the recycling center. They also found $5 in cash.
   a. How much money did they get all together? $30
   b. If they only have one-dollar bills, how many one-dollar bills should each boy get? 7
   c. How many one-dollar bills are left over? 2

Divide. Watch for remainders.

4. $5\overline{)30}$ 6
5. $7\overline{)20}$ 2 R6
6. $4\overline{)21}$ 5 R1
7. $8\overline{)56}$ 7
8. $6\overline{)28}$ 4 R4

Copyright © SRA/McGraw-Hill. Permission is granted to reproduce this page for classroom use.

ENRICHMENT p. 44

LESSON 44 ENRICHMENT Name________________

Imagine you are planning a party for your class at a restaurant.

Many restaurants have copies of their menus that you can take home. Collect some menus to help you decide where you will have your party and what you will eat.

Then use The Cruncher: *Party Planner* project to help you figure out how much you need to order, what the total cost will be, and what the cost will be per person.

Change the number of people. Invite another class. How does what you order and the cost per person change when the number of people you invite changes?

Answers may include the ideas that the party gets more expensive as more people are invited or that there may be a discount for large groups.

Copyright © SRA/McGraw-Hill. Permission is granted to reproduce this page for classroom use.

*available separately

2 Teach

Using the Student Pages Discuss the paragraph at the top of page 148 to be sure students understand the situation it describes. You might have students use **play money*** to act out the problems. Alert them to think carefully about problem 3 and to be ready to discuss their ideas. After students have completed problems 1–3, discuss the paragraph at the bottom of the page, which describes possible solutions to problem 3. This provides a lead-in to page 149.

Before assigning page 149, talk about remainders and the convention of writing them. Solve the first three problems with the class. Then have students complete the page on their own.

3 Wrap-Up

5 MINUTES

In Closing To summarize the lesson, have students explain why 25 pennies cannot be divided evenly among six students. Encourage them to brainstorm a real-life solution to this problem.

Informal Assessment Circulate as students work through this lesson. Observe how they solve division problems. Encourage students to use manipulatives or draw pictures to model problems with remainders. Have them explain their procedures and answers. You may wish to keep anecdotal notes on individual progress to this point.

Assessment Criteria

Did the student . . .

✓ correctly answer at least 75% of the computation problems?

✓ contribute to the discussion of the word problems?

✓ demonstrate an understanding of division with remainders?

Homework Have students work with a family member on division with remainders. Students should draw pictures or use beans, coins, or other small objects to model division problems and then record the results.

LESSON 45

Student Edition pages 150–153

Division Review

LESSON PLANNER

Objectives

✓ to assess students' proficiency with division facts

▶ to provide practice solving word problems that involve division and remainders

▶ to help students develop the broad ability to use mathematical common sense

Context of the Lesson This is the last of five lessons on division. This lesson includes a Mastery Checkpoint for assessing proficiency with division facts and also contains the last installment of "Money Matters," a four-part Thinking Story.

MANIPULATIVES

- base-10 blocks*
- counters*
- flash cards (optional)
- multiplication table (optional)

Program Resources

- Practice Master 45
- Enrichment Master 45
- Assessment Master
- For career connections: Careers and Math*
- For extra practice: CD-ROM* Lesson 45

1 Warm-Up (5 MINUTES)

Problem of the Day Present this problem to the class: Stacy brings two quarters to the sticker store. She likes stars, priced at five for 25¢; rainbows, at four for 36¢; cats, at three for 24¢; pandas, at three for 30¢; and hearts, at 25¢ each. Does Stacy have enough money to buy one of each kind of sticker she likes? If so, does she get back change? If not, how much more money does she need? (One of each sticker costs 57¢, so she would need 7¢ more to buy one of each.)

Problem-Solving Strategies Ask students who have solved the Problem of the Day to share how they solved it and any strategies they used.

MENTAL MATH Provide basic division exercises, some of which have remainders. Students show thumbs up if there is a remainder and thumbs down if there is no remainder.

a. 24 ÷ 8 (thumbs down)

b. 47 ÷ 7 (thumbs up)

(continued on page 151)

PRACTICE

LESSON 45

Division Review

Remember to think about the multiplication facts you know to help you divide.

Divide. Watch for remainders.

1. $4\overline{)30}$ **7 R2**
2. $7\overline{)29}$ **4 R1**
3. $8\overline{)43}$ **5 R3**
4. $5\overline{)38}$ **7 R3**
5. $4\overline{)36}$ **9**
6. $6\overline{)20}$ **3 R2**
7. $5\overline{)22}$ **4 R2**
8. $2\overline{)15}$ **7 R1**
9. $9\overline{)73}$ **8 R1**
10. $10\overline{)26}$ **2 R6**
11. $4\overline{)19}$ **4 R3**
12. $8\overline{)39}$ **4 R7**
13. $5\overline{)17}$ **3 R2**
14. $5\overline{)25}$ **5**
15. $6\overline{)50}$ **8 R2**
16. $9\overline{)56}$ **6 R2**
17. $7\overline{)56}$ **8**
18. $3\overline{)16}$ **5 R1**
19. $2\overline{)12}$ **6**
20. $1\overline{)8}$ **8**
21. $5\overline{)28}$ **5 R3**
22. $6\overline{)34}$ **5 R4**
23. $10\overline{)41}$ **4 R1**
24. $8\overline{)12}$ **1 R4**
25. $7\overline{)51}$ **7 R2**
26. $2\overline{)19}$ **9 R1**
27. $9\overline{)17}$ **1 R8**
28. $6\overline{)55}$ **9 R1**
29. $7\overline{)42}$ **6**
30. $3\overline{)23}$ **7 R2**

Solve these problems.

Mr. Zalesky has a lot of pennies to give away. He tells his neighbors that he will give nine cents to each child who comes to his house on Saturday morning, until he runs out of pennies.

31. Suppose Mr. Zalesky has 78 cents.
    a. How many children will get nine cents? **8**
    b. How many cents will be left? **6**
32. Suppose Mr. Zalesky has 83 cents.
    a. How many children will get nine cents? **9**
    b. How many cents will be left? **2**
33. Suppose he has 63 cents.
    a. How many children will get nine cents? **7**
    b. How many cents will be left? **0**

COOPERATIVE LEARNING / MANIPULATIVES You may wish to have students work on the word problems in small groups. Provide manipulative materials, such as **counters*** or **base-10 blocks***. One student can be the official reader, another the recorder, another the modeler, and another the checker. Encourage group members to discuss solution methods together and to exchange roles for subsequent problems.

*available separately

Solve these problems.

Ed needs 46 noisemakers for a party. At Paul's Party Store noisemakers come five to a box. A box costs $2.00.

34 How many boxes must Ed buy? **10**

35 If Ed buys nine boxes, how many noisemakers will he have? **45**

36 Will he have enough noisemakers? **no**

37 If Ed buys ten boxes, will he have enough noisemakers? **yes**

38 How many will he have? **50**

39 How much money will Ed spend? **$20.00**

COOPERATIVE LEARNING **Work in cooperative groups for these problems. Be sure to explain how you get your answers.**

At Party Palace Ed can buy the same kind of noisemakers in packages of ten to a box. Each box costs $3.00.

40 How many boxes must Ed buy? **5**

41 How much money will he have to spend? **$15.00**

42 At which store should Ed buy the noisemakers? **Party Palace**

43 How much money would Ed save at the less expensive store? **$5.00**

A baseball game has nine innings. The Sluggers were behind 12 to 5 at the end of the sixth inning.

44 How many more runs do the Sluggers need to win the game if the other team doesn't score again? **8**

45 About how many runs per inning is that? **3**

Suppose the Sluggers got one run in the seventh inning and the other team scored two runs.

46 Now how many more runs do the Sluggers need to win? **9**

47 About how many runs per inning is that? **5**

Mental Math (continued)

c. 26 ÷ 3 (thumbs up)

d. 64 ÷ 8 (thumbs down)

e. 84 ÷ 9 (thumbs up)

f. 36 ÷ 6 (thumbs down)

g. 61 ÷ 5 (thumbs up)

h. 56 ÷ 6 (thumbs up)

i. 63 ÷ 9 (thumbs down)

j. 14 ÷ 5 (thumbs up)

k. 72 ÷ 8 (thumbs down)

l. 39 ÷ 8 (thumbs up)

2 Teach

Using the Student Pages Have students work on page 150 independently. Problems 1–30 provide an opportunity for assessing proficiency with division facts and remainders. The problems on page 151 apply division concepts to realistic situations. Have students work in pairs or small groups to solve the problems. Provide manipulative materials such as **base-10 blocks*** and **counters*** for students who wish to use them. Bring the class together to share answers and discuss solution strategies.

Literature Connection With the class, read *The Greatest Guessing Game* by Robert Froman. Discuss with students how the author explains the division process by comparing it to a guessing game.

*available separately

◆ LESSON 45 Division Review

Teach

Using the Thinking Story "Money Matters (Part 4)" centers on using the process of elimination to solve a problem. Mr. Muddle tries to figure out which items he forgot to pay for during a shopping trip.

Answers to Thinking Story Questions:

1. 20 cents
2. If he forgot to pay only for the mousetrap, he would have had $1 left. If he forgot to pay only for the nails he would have had 80¢ left. If he forgot to pay only for the eggs, he would have had $1.60 left—which is what he did have. That's why Loretta thought that Mr. Muddle forgot to pay for the eggs.
3. He would owe $1.40 for the nails and the mousetrap together.
4. Perhaps Loretta overlooked the possibility that Mr. Muddle might have bought two items from one person.

MATH JOURNAL Have students write a letter in their Math Journals to Mr. Muddle, explaining how they figured out his confusion about the money he had left over after shopping. Have them consider ways he could avoid this confusion in the future.

SPECIAL NEEDS

Meeting Individual Needs

Some students have difficulty with division because they do not know their multiplication facts. In order to reinforce the meaning of division and the inverse relationship between multiplication and division and to allow students to make progress with division, you might let them refer to a **multiplication table** as they solve the problems in this lesson.

◆ LESSON 45 Division Review

THINKING STORY

Money Matters

Part 4

Mr. Muddle is very honest, but sometimes he forgets to pay for things. One day he had $3.00 when he went out shopping. He bought a carton of eggs, some nails, and a mousetrap. When he got home, he had $1.60 left.

"I think I forgot to pay someone," he said. "Let's see. The eggs were marked $1.40. The mousetrap was marked 80¢. And the bag of nails was marked 60¢."

Mr. Muddle told Loretta the Letter Carrier about his problem. She said, "If you forgot to pay for something, then it must be the eggs."

"I'm amazed that you can tell what I forgot, just by looking at the eggs," said Mr. Muddle. But he took Loretta's word for it and went to pay the grocer $1.40.

"What's this for?" asked the grocer. "I know that you paid for those eggs. I remember I talked to you in the checkout line."

"This is very confusing," said Mr. Muddle. As he walked along the street, he counted his money again.

RETEACHING

Encourage students who are still having trouble recalling division facts to work in pairs to help each other. They may use **flash cards** of division problems or make up problems to solve orally.

PRACTICE p. 45

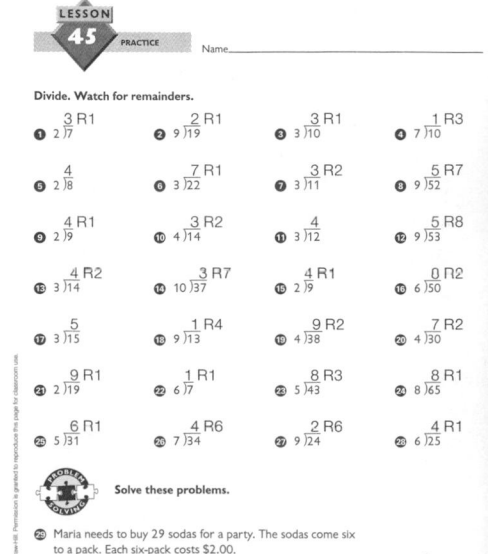

LESSON 45 PRACTICE Name____________

Divide. Watch for remainders.

❶ 2)7 **3 R1**	❷ 9)19 **2 R1**	❸ 3)10 **3 R1**	❹ 7)10 **1 R3**
❺ 2)8 **4**	❻ 3)22 **7 R1**	❼ 3)11 **3 R2**	❽ 9)52 **5 R7**
❾ 2)9 **4 R1**	❿ 4)14 **3 R2**	⓫ 3)12 **4**	⓬ 9)53 **5 R8**
⓭ 3)14 **4 R2**	⓮ 10)37 **3 R7**	⓯ 2)9 **4 R1**	⓰ 6)50 **8 R2**
⓱ 3)15 **5**	⓲ 9)13 **1 R4**	⓳ 4)38 **9 R2**	⓴ 4)30 **7 R2**
21 2)19 **9 R1**	22 6)7 **1 R1**	23 5)43 **8 R3**	24 8)65 **8 R1**
25 5)31 **6 R1**	26 7)34 **4 R6**	27 9)24 **2 R6**	28 6)25 **4 R1**

PROBLEM SOLVING **Solve these problems.**

29 Maria needs to buy 29 sodas for a party. The sodas come six to a pack. Each six-pack costs $2.00.

a. How many six-packs must Maria buy? 5

b. If Maria buys five six-packs, how many sodas will she have? 30

c. How much will it cost for Maria to buy enough sodas? $10

Copyright © SRA/McGraw-Hill. Permission is granted to reproduce this page for classroom use.

"What's the matter, Mr. Muddle?" asked a woman. She was watching him from the door of her hardware shop. "Are you worrying about the $1.40 you owe me?"

Work in groups. Discuss your answers and how you figured them out. Then compare your answers with those of other groups. **Answers are in margin.**

1. If Mr. Muddle had paid for everything, how much money would he have left?
2. Why would Loretta the Letter Carrier think Mr. Muddle had forgotten to pay for the eggs? Why didn't she guess the nails or the mousetrap?
3. How could Mr. Muddle owe the woman at the hardware shop $1.40?
4. Why did Loretta give Mr. Muddle the wrong answer to his problem?

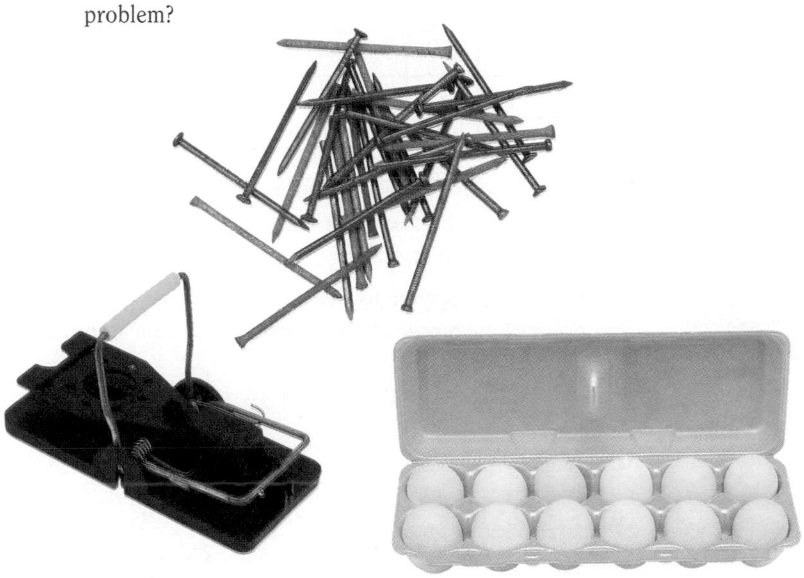

3 Wrap-Up

5 MINUTES

In Closing Have students explain how they figured out the answers to the problems in "Money Matters (Part 4)."

ANALYZING ANSWERS

Check students who are having difficulty solving problems involving division with remainders. If the difficulty is with the facts, provide extra practice. If the trouble stems from the division algorithm, or if students consistently forget to give the remainder or give an incorrect remainder, encourage them to use multiplication to check their answers. Help students practice the steps of the algorithm and remind them that the remainder should always be less than the divisor.

Mastery Checkpoint 7

By this time most students should demonstrate an understanding of division and begin to be proficient with division facts, including division facts with remainders. Students should correctly answer at least 80% of the problems on page 150. You may wish to assign Assessment Blackline Masters page 14 to determine mastery. Record the results of this assessment on the Mastery Checkpoint Chart.

Assessment Criteria

Did the student . . .

- ✓ correctly answer at least 80% of the computation problems?
- ✓ communicate strategies used to solve the word problems?
- ✓ contribute to the Thinking Story discussion?

Homework Assign Practice Master 45 or Enrichment Master 45 for further reinforcement of skills involving division.

ENRICHMENT p. 45

LESSON 45 ENRICHMENT Name__________

Make up a problem for each of the following equations. Then solve the problems. The first one has been done for you.
Answers will vary. Possible answers given.

1. $36 \div 4 = n$ Answer: 9 apples each
Henry has 36 apples. If he shares them with three friends, how many will each person get?
2. $35 \div 7 = n$ Answer: 5 weeks
Ana worked for 35 days. How many weeks did she work?
3. $n = 48 - 29$ Answer: 19 cards
Damien had 48 baseball cards in his collection. He sold 29 of them. How many did he have left?
4. $n = 56 \div 8$ Answer: 7 birds
Debra saw the same number of birds in her backyard each day. In eight days Debra saw a total of 56 birds. How many birds did she see each day?
5. $n = 49 \div 9$ Answer: 5 marbles with 4 left over
Nine friends want to play with 49 marbles. How many will each person get?
6. $n = 38 + 27$ Answer: $65
Anil is saving money. The first month he saved $38. The second month he saved $27. How much does he have now?

Copyright © SRA/McGraw-Hill. Permission is granted to reproduce this page for classroom use.

Math Explorations and Applications Level 4 • **45**

ASSESSMENT p. 14

UNIT 2

Mastery Checkpoint 7 Basic facts 3 (division facts, including remainders)
(Lesson 45)
Name __________
The student demonstrates mastery by correctly answering at least 16 of the 20 problems.

Divide.

1. 3)19 — 6 R1	2. 5)29 — 5 R4	3. 3)24 — 8	4. 4)22 — 5 R2
5. 8)40 — 5	6. 6)50 — 8 R2	7. 6)39 — 6 R3	8. 7)28 — 4
9. 2)12 — 6	10. 5)31 — 6 R1	11. 4)36 — 9	12. 6)26 — 4 R2
13. 8)38 — 4 R6	14. 7)21 — 3	15. 8)25 — 3 R1	16. 5)32 — 6 R2

Solve these problems.

17. June has 26 postcards. She wants to send three postcards to each of eight friends. How many postcards will she have left? 2
18. Jim has 50 pennies. He wants to divide them evenly among six friends. How many pennies will he have left? 2
19. Joe wants to give an equal number of stickers to each of his four friends. If he has 31 stickers, how many will each friend get? How many will he have left? 7; 3
20. Kim has 26 photos she took at the class play. Four photos will fit on each page of her photo album. How many pages will the 26 photos completely fill up? 6

Copyright © SRA/McGraw-Hill. Permission is granted to reproduce this page for classroom use.

14 • *Math Explorations and Applications* Level 4

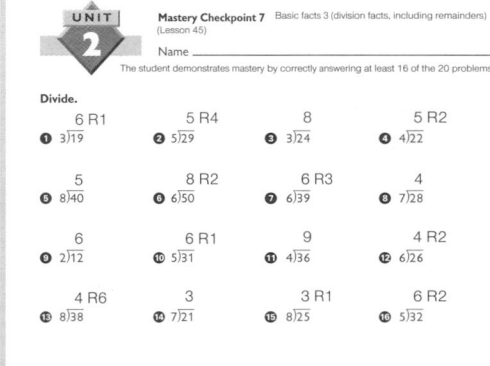

LESSON 46

Student Edition pages 154–155

Common Multiples

LESSON PLANNER

Objectives

- to explore number patterns
- to introduce the concept of least common multiple

Context of the Lesson This lesson extends the idea of multiplication facts by having students examine common multiples. It prepares students for finding the least common denominator when dealing with fractions in Unit 6.

MANIPULATIVES

calculators*

Program Resources

Practice Master 46

Enrichment Master 46

For extra practice:
CD-ROM* Lesson 46

1 Warm-Up

5 MINUTES

Problem of the Day Present the following problem on the chalkboard: Use the digits 1 to 8 to create an eight-digit number. The number must follow two rules. First, no two digits may appear in counting order. Second, the digits in each set between the commas must form a pattern of lesser to greater. (There are several possible answers. One possible answer is 17,358,246.)

Problem-Solving Strategies Ask students who have solved the Problem of the Day to share how they solved it and any strategies they used.

MENTAL MATH Provide practice in skip counting by 2s, 3s, 4s, 5s, 6s, 7s, 8s, 9s, and 10s. Begin with the easier numbers (2, 5, 10) and progress to harder numbers (3, 4, 6, 7, 8, 9).

2 Teach

Using the Student Pages Make sure students understand the mathematical meanings of the terms *factor, product,* and *multiple*. Have them use each term in a sentence or example to demonstrate their understanding. For example, "If I multiply the factors 3 and 4, the product is 12." Read the top of page 154 with the class and discuss how to find a common multiple.

EXPLORE

LESSON 46

Common Multiples

In the multiplication fact 3 × 6 = 18, 3 and 6 are **factors** of 18. Factors are numbers you multiply to get the **product**.

A **multiple** of a number is some whole number multiplied by that number. Multiples of 3 are 3, 6, 9, 12, 15, 18, and so on. Multiples of 6 are 6, 12, 18, 24, 30, and so on.

You can call 18 a **common multiple** of 3 and 6 because it is a multiple of both numbers.

You can use a table to find multiples and common multiples. Here are parts of tables with multiples of 2 and of 5:

	×0	×1	×2	×3	×4	×5
Multiples of 2	0	2	4	6	8	10

	×0	×1	×2	×3	×4	×5
Multiples of 5	0	5	10	15	20	25

Look for a common multiple of 2 and 5. Do you see it? You can extend the tables to find other common multiples. Use a calculator to help you.

COOPERATIVE LEARNING **Work with a partner to find the first three common multiples of each pair of numbers. Watch your numbering.**

1. 3 and 7 **21, 42, 63**
2. 5 and 9 **45, 90, 135**
3. 5 and 4 **20, 40, 60**
4. 2 and 3 **6, 12, 18**
5. 9 and 8 **72, 144, 216**
6. 8 and 5 **40, 80, 120**
7. 6 and 10 **30, 60, 90**
8. 2 and 8 **8, 16, 24**
9. 9 and 12 **36, 72, 108**
10. 5 and 10 **10, 20, 30**
11. 6 and 9 **18, 36, 54**
12. 8 and 12 **24, 48, 72**

154 • Multiplication and Division

ESL MANIPULATIVES

Meeting Individual Needs
Students with limited English proficiency may have difficulty with the vocabulary in this lesson. Help them by demonstrating the task with **manipulatives,** using tables to organize multiples, and circling the common multiples.

RETEACHING

Suggest that students write the multiples of each factor in a table like those on page 154. Then have them circle all the common multiples they see. If there are none, students should extend the tables. Point out that in some cases the least common multiple is one of the factors itself. For example, the least common multiple of 3 and 6 is 6.

*available separately

Answer the following questions.

13. What seems to be true of the first common multiple of each of the pairs listed in exercises 1–6? What seems to be true of the second common multiple of all of the pairs? **The first common multiple is the product of the original pair of numbers. The second common multiple is two times the first one.**

14. In what way are the first common multiples for exercises 7–12 different from those for exercises 1–6? **They are not the product of the original pair of numbers; they are all less than the product.**

15. Look at exercises 1–6. We call a number that divides exactly into another number a **factor** of that number. Is there any whole number greater than 1 that divides evenly into both

    a. 3 and 7? **no** b. 5 and 9? **no**
    c. 5 and 4? **no** d. 2 and 3? **no**
    e. 9 and 8? **no** f. 8 and 5? **no**

16. Look at exercises 7–12. What is the largest whole number that divides evenly into both 6 and 10? [Notice that (6 × 10) ÷ 2 = 30.] What is the largest whole number that divides evenly into both

    a. 2 and 8? **2** b. 9 and 12? **3**
    c. 5 and 10? **5** d. 6 and 9? **3**
    e. 8 and 12? **4**

17. Try to find an interesting pattern for exercises 7–12. **The product of the original pair of numbers divided by the greatest common factor equals the least common multiple.**

18. Think of other pairs of numbers. Predict what their first common multiple will be. Work with a partner to check your prediction. **Check students' answers.**

FANTASTIC FACT

To match the acceleration of an attacking rattlesnake, you would have to drive a car from 0 miles per hour to 60 miles per hour in half a second.

PRACTICE p. 46

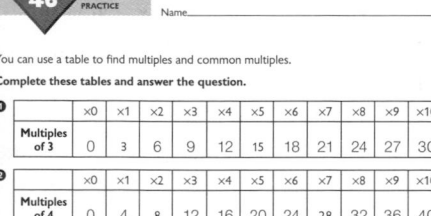

LESSON 46 PRACTICE Name____________

You can use a table to find multiples and common multiples.

Complete these tables and answer the question.

1.

	×0	×1	×2	×3	×4	×5	×6	×7	×8	×9	×10
Multiples of 3	0	3	6	9	12	15	18	21	24	27	30

2.

	×0	×1	×2	×3	×4	×5	×6	×7	×8	×9	×10
Multiples of 4	0	4	8	12	16	20	24	28	32	36	40

3. What are the common multiples of 3 and 4? 12, 24

Find the first three common multiples of each pair of numbers.

4. 4 and 10 20, 40, 60
5. 3 and 5 15, 30, 45
6. 8 and 10 40, 80, 120
7. 2 and 7 14, 28, 42
8. 6 and 8 24, 48, 72
9. 5 and 8 40, 80, 120
10. 4 and 12 12, 24, 36
11. 3 and 9 9, 18, 27
12. 7 and 14 14, 28, 42
13. 7 and 9 63, 126, 189
14. 5 and 6 30, 60, 90
15. 3 and 12 12, 24, 36

Answer these questions.

16. In which problems is there a whole number greater than 1 that divides evenly into both numbers?
problems 4, 6, 8, 10, 11, 12, and 15

17. If there is a common factor for the pair of numbers, how is the first multiple different?
The first common multiple is not the product of the two numbers.

46 • *Math Explorations and Applications* Level 4

Copyright © SRA/McGraw-Hill. Permission is granted to reproduce this page for classroom use.

ENRICHMENT p. 46

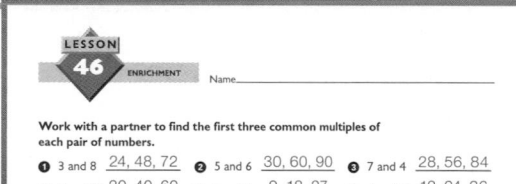

LESSON 46 ENRICHMENT Name____________

Work with a partner to find the first three common multiples of each pair of numbers.

1. 3 and 8 24, 48, 72
2. 5 and 6 30, 60, 90
3. 7 and 4 28, 56, 84
4. 4 and 10 20, 40, 60
5. 9 and 3 9, 18, 27
6. 4 and 12 12, 24, 36

Answer the following questions.

7. What seems to be true of the first common multiple of each of the pairs listed in problems 1–3? Of the second common multiple of all the pairs?
It is the numbers multiplied by each other. It is the first common multiple increased by the same number.

8. In what way are the first common multiples for problems 4–6 different from those for problems 1–3?
The first common multiple is not the numbers multiplied by each other.

9. Look at problems 1–3. Is there any whole number greater than 1 that divides both 3 and 8? 5 and 6? 7 and 4? no; no; no

10. Look at problems 4–6. What is the greatest whole number that divides both 4 and 10? Notice that (4 × 10) ÷ 2 = 20. What is the greatest whole number that divides both 9 and 3? 4 and 12? 2; 3; 4

11. Try to find an interesting pattern for problems 4–6.
The pattern is the same as for problems 1–3 except that it starts with a number that is less than the numbers multiplied by each number. It is that number divided by the greatest whole number that divides both numbers.

46 • *Math Explorations and Applications* Level 4

Copyright © SRA/McGraw-Hill. Permission is granted to reproduce this page for classroom use.

*available separately

Demonstrate how students can find the multiples of a given factor using the constant feature on a **calculator***. First remind students that multiplication is the same as repeated addition. Then show them how to use this concept to find the multiples of 7 on a calculator with the constant feature. Have them enter 7 + 7 = (14), then continue to press = to see the subsequent multiples appear in the display. Have students work in pairs to complete page 154.

Have students complete page 155 in pairs or small groups, or do this page as a whole-class activity.

3 Wrap-Up

5 MINUTES

In Closing Have students explain the meaning of *common multiple* and give an example using the numbers 4 and 6.

ALTERNATIVE ASSESSMENT

Informal Assessment Observe students as they work through the problems in this lesson. Encourage them to verbalize the meanings of the key terms in the lesson: *factor, product, multiple,* and *common multiple.*

Assessment Criteria

Did the student . . .

✓ demonstrate understanding of the concept of common multiples?

✓ contribute to the discussion?

✓ demonstrate the ability to use a calculator as a computational tool?

Homework Have students find the first three common multiples of 2 and 7, of 3 and 5, and of 4 and 10. (14, 15, 20)

MUSIC CONNECTION

Music Connection Have students make up songs that involve skip counting. For example, you might tell students about the popular cheer "Two, four, six, eight, who do we appreciate?"

LESSON 47

Student Edition pages 156–159

Parentheses

LESSON PLANNER

Objectives

- ▶ to introduce students to the use of parentheses and order of operations
- ▶ to demonstrate that not all calculators give the same answer to the same problem when order of operation is involved

Context of the Lesson The use of parentheses and order of operations rules are new topics. Mastery of the use of parentheses is not expected at the fourth-grade level.

MANIPULATIVES

calculators*, preferably several models to reflect different built-in procedures for calculating order of operations

Program Resources

Reteaching Master

Practice Master 47

Enrichment Master 47

For extra practice:
CD-ROM* Lesson 47
Cumulative Review, page 544

1 Warm-Up (5 MINUTES)

Problem of the Day Present this problem to the class: Hari bought lemons at 15¢ each and oranges at 25¢ each. He spent more than $2.00 in all, and spent the same amount of money on each kind of fruit. Figure out the least amount of money Hari could have spent and how many of each fruit he got. ($3.00: $1.50 for 10 lemons and $1.50 for 6 oranges)

Problem-Solving Strategies Ask students who have solved the Problem of the Day to share how they solved it and any strategies they used.

MENTAL MATH Provide practice in division. Have students show thumbs up when there is a remainder and thumbs down when there is no remainder.

a. 35 ÷ 7 (thumbs down)

b. 20 ÷ 3 (thumbs up)

c. 46 ÷ 9 (thumbs up)

(continued on page 157)

EXPLORE

LESSON 47

Parentheses

ACT IT OUT

A Medical Problem

Act out and discuss this story.

Brenda and her friends like to visit Celine, the dog trainer.

"May we help feed your dogs?" the children asked.

"Yes," said Celine. "But first I have to mix some medicine in their food. All the dogs have sore throats from barking so much. You can help me figure out how much medicine to mix in. How much is $4 \times 3 + 2$?"

"It's 14," said Brenda, Jamal, and Cindy.

"It's 20," said Elise and Aaron.

The children argued about which answer was right, but they couldn't decide. Finally Cindy said, "Why don't you tell us the whole problem?"

"It doesn't seem like a very hard problem," Celine said. "I have to give four spoonfuls of medicine to each dog. I have three black dogs and two brown dogs. That is $4 \times 3 + 2$, right?"

"Now we know what the right answer is," they all said.

◆ How could Brenda, Jamal, and Cindy have gotten the answer 14?
They multiplied 4 by 3, then added 2.

Why teach it this way?

People sometimes use mathematical conventions such as "perform multiplication first" or "read from left to right." In general, *Math Explorations and Applications* follows the rule of reading from left to right. Parentheses are introduced now to indicate order of operations that depart from the left-to-right convention.

*available separately

- How could Elise and Aaron have gotten 20? **They added 3 and 2, then multiplied by 4.**
- Which is the right answer to Celine's problem? Why? **20; because she wants to give four spoonfuls of medicine to each of five dogs**
- Can you think of a way to ask the question about the numbers 4, 3, and 2 so that people would know which way to answer it? **Answers will vary, but students should indicate a way to specify the order of operations.**

Here is a way to write the problem that means add 3 and 2, then multiply by 4:

$$4 \times (3 + 2)$$

Here is a way to write the problem that means multiply 4 × 3, then add 2:

$$(4 \times 3) + 2$$

Rule: Do the operations inside the parentheses first.

$4 \times (3 + 2) = 4 \times 5 = 20$

$(4 \times 3) + 2 = 12 + 2 = 14$

$6 + (5 \times 2) = 6 + 10 = 16$

$(6 - 3) \times 6 + 1 = 3 \times 6 + 1 = 18 + 1 = 19$

$(6 + 5) + (3 - 2) + (7 + 9) + (8 + 2) =$
$11 + 1 + 16 + 10 = 38$

$(4 \times 7) + (4 \times 3) = 28 + 12 = 40$

$(8 + 4) + 5 = 12 + 5 = 17$

$18 \div (6 + 3) = 18 \div 9 = 2$

$4 \times (4 - 0) = 4 \times 4 = 16$

Mental Math (continued)

d. 50 ÷ 7 (thumbs up)

e. 30 ÷ 6 (thumbs down)

f. 31 ÷ 8 (thumbs up)

g. 42 ÷ 6 (thumbs down)

h. 19 ÷ 4 (thumbs up)

i. 29 ÷ 6 (thumbs up)

j. 49 ÷ 7 (thumbs down)

k. 65 ÷ 8 (thumbs up)

l. 81 ÷ 9 (thumbs down)

2 Teach

ACT IT OUT

Using the Student Pages You can approach "A Medical Problem" the same way you would any Act It Out. Have students work in groups to read, act out, and discuss the story, and to write their answers in preparation for a class discussion. Be sure students recognize that 4 × 3 + 2 is ambiguous without a specified order of operations. Also be sure they understand how parentheses clarify the order. Go over examples with the class, helping students see how the parentheses rule works in each case.

LITERATURE CONNECTION

Literature Connection Read *The Rajah's Rice,* adapted by David Barry, to the class. In this folktale, a clever girl asks for a reward that sounds too small to have much value, until she asks that the rice be doubled again and again. Have students use parentheses to express the equations in the story.

MUSIC CONNECTION

Music Connection Most students can sing memorable advertising jingles or "tag tunes" by which consumers remember a product. Encourage students to create an original jingle or song to help them remember the general rules for order of operations. They can set words to a tune they know, make up the words and the melody, or perform the jingle as a rap.

◆ LESSON 47 Parentheses

Teach

Using the Student Pages Discuss with the class all or some of the examples a–h at the top of page 158. You might encourage students to refer to these examples as they solve for *n* in problems 1–16. Have students do the problems individually. Go over problems 17 and 18 near the bottom of the page, which are examples to guide students in solving the remaining problems on the page.

Work through the presentation on page 159 with the class. Help students recognize the distinctions among the three possible rules. Explain that people design **calculators*** to perform calculations in a particular order of operations. Therefore, if two people do the same chain equation on different calculators, they may get different answers even if they enter the same data in the same order. You might have students work in pairs to do problems 31–44. Then bring the class together to discuss the results.

◆ LESSON 47 Parentheses

We do operations inside the parentheses first.

Examples:

a. $40 \div (5 + 3) = 40 \div 8 = 5$ b. $(40 \div 5) + 3 = 8 + 3 = 11$

c. $12 - (8 - 3) = 12 - 5 = 7$ d. $(12 - 8) - 3 = 4 - 3 = 1$

e. $7 \times (5 + 4) = 7 \times 9 = 63$ f. $(7 \times 5) + 4 = 35 + 4 = 39$

g. $32 \div (8 \div 2) = 32 \div 4 = 8$ h. $(32 \div 8) \div 2 = 4 \div 2 = 2$

Solve for *n*. Watch the parentheses. Watch the signs.

1. $24 \div (6 \div 2) = n$ **8**
2. $(24 \div 6) \div 2 = n$ **2**
3. $28 - (8 \div 4) = n$ **26**
4. $(28 - 8) \div 4 = n$ **5**
5. $7 \times (4 + 6) = n$ **70**
6. $(7 \times 4) + 6 = n$ **34**
7. $16 + (7 + 5) = n$ **28**
8. $(16 + 7) + 5 = n$ **28**
9. $16 - (7 - 5) = n$ **14**
10. $(16 - 7) - 5 = n$ **4**
11. $(2 \times 3) \times 3 = n$ **18**
12. $2 \times (3 \times 3) = n$ **18**
13. $(18 \div 6) \div 3 = n$ **1**
14. $18 \div (6 \div 3) = n$ **9**
15. $(25 - 12) - (20 - 7) = n$ **0**
16. $4 \times (6 - 6) = n$ **0**

For each problem below, see how many different answers you can get by putting parentheses in different places. The first two have been done for you.

17. $5 + 4 \times 3 = n$

    $(5 + 4) \times 3 = 27$

    $5 + (4 \times 3) = 17$

    There are two answers.

18. $2 \times 10 \div 2 = n$

    $(2 \times 10) \div 2 = 10$

    $2 \times (10 \div 2) = 10$

    There is one answer.

19. $17 - 10 + 1 = n$ **6, 8**
20. $2 \times 3 + 4 = n$ **14, 10**
21. $4 \times 6 \div 3 = n$ **8**
22. $16 + 3 \times 2 = n$ **38, 22**
23. $16 \div 4 \times 2 = n$ **8, 2**
24. $16 - 4 \times 2 = n$ **24, 8**
25. $2 \times 3 \times 4 = n$ **24**
26. $12 - 2 \times 6 = n$ **60, 0**
27. $12 - 2 \times 3 = n$ **30, 6**
28. $8 + 12 \div 2 = n$ **10, 14**
29. $18 \div 6 \times 3 = n$ **9, 1**
30. $8 \times 3 \div 3 = n$ **8**

COOPERATIVE LEARNING For page 159, you might have students work in groups of three, so that each student can try all three approaches to the order of operations. On each problem, students can switch tasks and apply a different rule so that everyone uses all three rules.

RETEACHING p. 14

LESSON 47 RETEACHING Name______________________

Sometimes we can get more than one answer to a problem because we do the problem in a different order.

For example, $2 \times 3 + 2$ will yield two different answers if we do not have rules about the order in which we solve problems. If we multiply first, we have $2 \times 3 = 6$, then $6 + 2 = 8$.

This could be written $(2 \times 3) + 2$.

To solve problems with parentheses, follow these steps:

1. Circle the problem in parentheses.
2. Solve the problem inside the parentheses.
3. Rewrite the whole problem using the answer you found to replace the problem in parentheses.
4. Solve the problem.

Solve for *n* using the above steps.

1. $2 \times (4 + 4) = n$ $n =$ 16
2. $42 \div (3 + 3) = n$ $n =$ 7
3. $(6 + 4) - 5 - 3 = n$ $n =$ 2
4. $(2 \times 4) + 4 = n$ $n =$ 12
5. $(8 - 6) \times 6 = n$ $n =$ 12
6. $16 + (15 \div 5) = n$ $n =$ 19
7. $3 \times (10 \div 5) = n$ $n =$ 6
8. $(20 - 10) - (5 - 3) = n$ $n =$ 8
9. $15 + (7 \times 3) = n$ $n =$ 36
10. $(2 \times 10) \div 4 = n$ $n =$ 5
11. $20 - (10 - 5) - 3 = n$ $n =$ 12
12. $(3 \times 8) - (10 - 5) = n$ $n =$ 19
13. $(3 \times 10) \div 5 = n$ $n =$ 6
14. $20 - 10 - (5 - 3) = n$ $n =$ 8
15. $(12 - 4) \div 2 = n$ $n =$ 4
16. $(6 + 5) \times (3 - 1) = n$ $n =$ 22

14 • *Math Explorations and Applications* Level 4

Copyright © SRA/McGraw-Hill. Permission is granted to reproduce this page for classroom use.

*available separately

Using parentheses always makes it clear which operation to do first. However, some long math problems use lots of parentheses. So, people sometimes use other methods to solve them.

The rule used by many people is to simply do the operations from left to right.

$3 + 7 \times 6 - 5 + 4 = 10 \times 6 - 5 + 4 = 60 - 5 + 4 = 55 + 4 = 59$

A second rule that is sometimes used is to do all of the multiplications and divisions first, and then do the additions and subtractions.

$3 + 7 \times 6 - 5 + 4 = 3 + 42 - 5 + 4 = 45 - 1 = 44$

A third possible rule would be to do all of the additions and subtractions first, and then do the multiplications and divisions.

$3 + 7 \times 6 - 5 + 4 = 10 \times 5 = 50$

Try the problem above with several different people and with several different calculators.

Are the answers different? Which method was used?

Use a calculator if necessary to solve the following problems using each of the three rules. You might discover that two or three of your answers are the same. Sometimes none of your answers will match. Try to predict which answers will be the same before doing the problems (it may save you some work).

Solve.

31. $8 + 7 \times 6 - 4 = ?$ **86, 46, 30**
32. $20 - 3 \times 4 + 6 + 2 \times 8 = ?$ **608, 30, 1632**
33. $2 \times 3 \times 4 + 8 = ?$ **32, 32, 72**
34. $2 \times 3 \times 4 + 8 \times 5 = ?$ **160, 64, 360**
35. $2 + 3 + 4 \times 8 = ?$ **72, 37, 72**
36. $2 + 3 + 4 \times 8 + 2 = ?$ **74, 39, 88**
37. $3 \times 4 + 7 = ?$ **19, 19, 33**
38. $3 + 4 \times 7 = ?$ **49, 31, 49**
39. $2 \times 3 \times 4 \times 5 = ?$ **120, 120, 120**
40. $2 + 3 + 4 + 5 = ?$ **14, 14, 14**
41. $2 \times 3 + 4 \times 5 = ?$ **50, 26, 70**
42. $2 + 3 \times 4 + 5 = ?$ **25, 19, 45**
43. $2 \times 3 \times 4 + 5 = ?$ **29, 29, 54**
44. $2 + 3 + 4 \times 5 = ?$ **45, 25, 45**

Use the Cumulative Review on page 544 after this lesson.

PRACTICE p. 47

LESSON 47 PRACTICE Name____________

Solve for *n*. Watch the parentheses. Watch the signs.

1. $32 \div (8 \div 2) = n$ 8
2. $16 - (6 - 5) = n$ 15
3. $(18 - 5) + 5 = n$ 18
4. $(32 \div 8) \div 2 = n$ 2
5. $(16 - 6) - 5 = n$ 5
6. $18 - (5 + 5) = n$ 8
7. $28 - (4 \div 4) = n$ 27
8. $(3 \times 2) \times 3 = n$ 18
9. $(48 \div 8) \div 2 = n$ 3
10. $(28 - 4) \div 4 = n$ 6
11. $3 \times (2 \times 3) = n$ 18
12. $48 \div (8 \div 2) = n$ 12
13. $4 \times (3 + 6) = n$ 36
14. $(36 \div 6) \div 3 = n$ 2
15. $(4 \times 3) \times 2 = n$ 24
16. $(4 \times 5) + 6 = n$ 26
17. $36 \div (6 \div 3) = n$ 18
18. $4 \times (3 \times 2) = n$ 24
19. $16 + (6 + 5) = n$ 27
20. $(24 - 12) - 8 = n$ 4
21. $24 - (12 - 8) = n$ 20
22. $(16 + 6) + 5 = n$ 27
23. $6 \times (5 - 5) = n$ 0
24. $(6 \times 5) - 5 = n$ 25

For each problem below show how many different answers you can get by putting parentheses in different places.

25. $18 - 10 + 2 = n$ 2
26. $3 \times 3 + 4 = n$ 2
27. $5 \times 6 \div 3 = n$ 1
28. $16 + 4 \times 2 = n$ 2
29. $16 \div 4 \times 4 = n$ 2
30. $16 - 3 \times 2 = n$ 2
31. $3 \times 3 \times 4 = n$ 1
32. $12 - 6 \div 3 = n$ 2
33. $12 + 2 + 3 = n$ 1
34. $6 + 8 + 6 = n$ 1
35. $18 - 6 + 6 = n$ 2
36. $14 \times 2 + 1 = n$ 2
37. $24 \div 3 \div 1 = n$ 1
38. $24 \div 6 \times 2 = n$ 2
39. $24 \div 6 \div 2 = n$ 2

Use a calculator to solve each of the following in three different ways.

40. $3 \times 4 \times 5 \times 6 = n$ 360, 360, 360
41. $3 + 4 + 5 + 6 = n$ 18, 18, 18
42. $3 \times 4 + 5 \times 6 = n$ 102, 42, 162
43. $3 + 4 \times 5 + 6 = n$ 41, 29, 77
44. $3 \times 4 \times 5 + 6 = n$ 66, 66, 132
45. $3 + 4 + 5 \times 6 = n$ 72, 37, 72

Copyright © SRA/McGraw-Hill. Permission is granted to reproduce this page for classroom use.

Math Explorations and Applications Level 4 • **47**

ENRICHMENT p. 47

LESSON 47 ENRICHMENT Name____________

1 2 3 4 5 = ?

If we have a number sentence in which the digits on the left side are in sequence, let's call it a number chain. For example, 12 + 34 − 5 = 41 is a number chain. We can combine the digits on the left and then add, subtract, multiply, divide, or use parentheses, as long as the digits remain in the same order.

COOPERATIVE LEARNING **Work in a small group or with a partner. Make a number chain for each number from 0 through 9, using the digits 1–5. Put your solutions in the chart. A number chain for 0 has been done for you.**

12 − (3 + 4 + 5)	= 0
(1 + 2) × 3 ÷ (4 + 5)	= 1
(1 + 2 + 3 + 4) ÷ 5	= 2
12 ÷ 3 + 4 − 5	= 3
12 × 3 ÷ 4 − 5	= 4
12 ÷ 3 − 4 + 5	= 5
12 + 3 − 4 − 5	= 6
1 + 2 + 3 − 4 + 5	= 7
12 × 3 + 4 ÷ 5	= 8
1 + 2 − 3 + 4 + 5	= 9

Solutions shown are examples only. (Unless otherwise indicated by parentheses, operations are to be done in order from left to right.)

Copyright © SRA/McGraw-Hill. Permission is granted to reproduce this page for classroom use.

Math Explorations and Applications Level 4 • **47**

❸ Wrap-Up (5 MINUTES)

In Closing Have students state the rule about operations inside parentheses.

ALTERNATIVE ASSESSMENT

Informal Assessment Observe and listen as students work through this lesson. Although mastery of this material is not expected at this level, encourage students to share their observations and verbalize their understanding of order of operations.

Assessment Criteria

Did the student . . .

- ✓ contribute to the discussion of the story?
- ✓ communicate strategies used to determine order of operations?
- ✓ explain how to solve for *n*?
- ✓ participate in exploring alternative answers based on varying the order of operations?

Homework Have students create three word problems in which the solutions require the use of parentheses. Have them exchange and solve each other's problems.

LESSON 48

Student Edition pages 160–163

Applying Math

LESSON PLANNER

Objectives

▶ to provide practice in whole-number arithmetic with the four basic operations

✓ to assess students' ability to choose the correct operation to solve a given word problem

Context of the Lesson This, the last lesson of this unit, contains a Mastery Checkpoint for assessing the ability to choose correct arithmetic applications. Students have previously been given practice with mixed word problems and will continue to work with them throughout the program. The next lesson begins the end-of-unit sequence of review, practice, and testing.

MANIPULATIVES

drawing materials (optional)

Program Resources

Number Cubes
Practice Master 48
Enrichment Master 48
Assessment Master
For extra practice:
CD-ROM* Lesson 48

1 Warm-Up

5 MINUTES

Problem of the Day Present the following problem. Explain to students that there is more than one solution: Fill in each box with a digit from 0 through 9 to form a correct addition problem. You must use all ten digits exactly once each.

□□□ + □□□ = □□□□

(one solution: 439 + 587 = 1026)

Problem-Solving Strategies Ask students who have solved the Problem of the Day to share how they solved it and any strategies they used.

MENTAL MATH Provide practice with facts in all four basic operations. Emphasize quick recall, which will be helpful when students play the game introduced in this lesson.

a. 5 + 4 = (9) **b.** 12 – 6 = (6)

c. 6 + 10 = (16) **d.** 81 ÷ 9 = (9)

(continued on page 161)

MIXED PRACTICE

LESSON 48

Applying Math

In this lesson you can apply the skills you've learned to solve different kinds of problems. Use any problem-solving methods that work for you.

PROBLEM SOLVING

Solve.

1. Mike received $24.75 on his birthday. Three days later he got a birthday card with $5 in it. How much money did Mike receive all together for his birthday? **$29.75**
2. The Circle K Ranch is 5 kilometers wide. What is the area of the ranch? **can't tell**
3. Melissa has 35 customers on her paper route. She began her route with 35 papers and now has ten left. How many more papers does she have to deliver? **10**
4. Jeff has a room shaped like a rectangle. It is 4 meters long and 3 meters wide. What is the area of the floor in Jeff's room? **12 square m**
5. Last spring the ecology club planted 108 tree seedlings. Of those, 19 seedlings didn't survive the winter. How many trees made it through the winter? **89**
6. Leilani can ride 1 kilometer on her bike in about four minutes. About how long will it take her to ride to Echo Lake, a distance of 8 kilometers? **about 32 minutes**
7. Paul has 249 stamps in his stamp collection. Jack has 157 stamps. How many stamps do the boys have all together? **406**
8. Billy's rectangular tree house is 4 feet long and 2 feet wide. What is the perimeter of the tree house? **12 feet**

160 • Multiplication and Division

COOPERATIVE LEARNING **MANIPULATIVES** You might consider having students who are proficient with word problems work with those who need help. Encourage peer tutors to help their partners use **manipulatives,** draw pictures, or act out the problems. Effective peer tutors can assist with reading or ask leading questions to help their partners figure out how to solve the problems. Peer tutors can also take turns asking verification questions, such as "Does the answer make sense?" "Does it fit the situation?" or "Does it answer the question asked?"

*available separately

9 In 1980 the population of the state of Arizona was 2,716,546. In 1990 the population was 3,665,228. About how many people moved to or were born in Arizona between 1980 and 1990? **can't tell**

10 Dan has $17.93 and his brother has $14.59. They want to buy their mother a birthday gift. Do they have enough money to buy a sweater that costs $33.00? **no**

11 Leroy wants to put new carpeting in his room. He measured the floor and found that it is a square with sides 4 meters long. He can buy a rectangular piece of carpet that is 8 meters long and 3 meters wide. If he cut up the carpet, would he have enough to cover his floor completely? **yes**

12 The balance in Anya's bank account was $217.86. She withdrew $74.98 to buy in-line skates. What is the balance in her account now? **$142.88**

13 Mr. Chang bought eight cans of juice for a party. Each can serves seven people. How many people can he serve with the juice he bought? **56**

14 Amanda has invited 26 people to a party. She wants to give each person a party hat. Hats come in packages of ten. How many packages does she need to buy? **3**

15 Manuel saved $27 to spend on video games while on vacation. He wants to spend the same amount each of the three weeks of his vacation. How much should he spend each week? **$9**

Mental Math (continued)

e. 7 × 9 = (63)
f. 4 − 4 = (0)
g. 54 ÷ 9 = (6)
h. 8 × 10 = (80)
i. 5 + 8 = (13)
j. 14 ÷ 7 = (2)
k. 4 − 1 = (3)
l. 15 − 10 = (5)
m. 18 ÷ 3 = (6)
n. 6 × 5 = (30)
o. 4 + 6 = (10)
p. 28 ÷ 4 = (7)
q. 4 × 9 = (36)
r. 24 ÷ 3 = (8)

2 Teach

Using the Student Pages Demonstrate "Cubo" so students can play it when they finish the problems on pages 160–162. This game focuses on using mental math with all four operations. Have students work independently on pages 160–161. However, if any students have trouble with reading, you may read the problems to them or to the group. In problem 6, allow for multiple answers since most people could not maintain the same pace for 8 km. As students finish, they can go on to the problems on page 162.

Art Connection Students who enjoy drawing might take one of the word problems in this lesson and convert it into a comic strip or illustration using **drawing materials.** Or they can create an original word problem similar to the ones in this lesson and present it in comic strip form. The cartoon characters can give the necessary information in speech balloons. Compile the completed comic strips in a book, or display them on a bulletin board.

Literature Connection Read the poem "Arithmetic" by Carl Sandburg to the class. Discuss the facets of arithmetic the poem describes.

◆ LESSON 48 Applying Math

Teach

Using the Student Pages Have students work independently on these problems. Again, if any students have trouble with reading, read the problems to them or to the group. Be sure students understand that they must choose the correct operation to fit the situation and solve the problem.

GAME The focus of "Cubo" is to provide practice using mental math with all four arithmetic operations. Play the game with the class two or three times as follows: Roll four Number Cubes and write the numbers on the chalkboard. Have students describe different ways to get 21 or some number close to but greater or less than 21. Write their responses on the chalkboard. Use parentheses when applicable, but point out that students can play the game without them as long as they always perform operations from left to right.

◆ LESSON 48 Applying Math

Read each problem carefully. Think about which operations to use.

Solve.

16. The Nila family and the Lee family walked to the science museum. The Nilas bought four tickets. The Lees bought five tickets. Tickets cost $3 each. How much did the two families spend all together? **$27**

17. The Freeman family drove to the science museum. They bought five tickets. Parking costs $4. Tickets cost $3 each. How much did the Freemans spend in all? **$19**

18. The science museum raised the price of tickets to $4, but also offers a new group plan. A group of up to ten people can buy one group ticket for $5, plus $3 for each person in the group.

    a. How much would a group of four people pay using the group plan? Would they save money compared to buying their tickets separately? **$17; no**

    b. How much would a group of five people pay using the group plan? Would they save money compared to buying their tickets separately? **$20; no, it would cost the same amount.**

    c. How much would a group of ten people pay using the group plan? Would they save money compared to buying their tickets separately? **$35; yes**

19. Mr. and Mrs. Kuhn and their two children ate lunch in the Cosmic Cafeteria at the science museum. They shared a $3 jumbo order of Far-Out French Fries, and each person ordered a Martian Meatball Platter for $5. How much did they spend on lunch all together? **$23**

FANTASTIC FACT **Neptune's largest moon, Triton, is thought to be one of the coldest bodies in the solar system, with a surface temperature of about −455°C.**

162 • Multiplication and Division

RETEACHING

GAME Students who can choose the correct operation but answer incorrectly may need extra practice with the skill that is weak. For example, students who have difficulty with basic facts may benefit from playing "Cubo."

PRACTICE p. 48

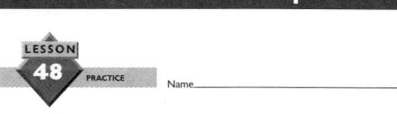

LESSON 48 PRACTICE Name______________________

Solve these problems.

1. Ray had $8.00 and then spent some of it. He now has $5.75. How much money did he spend? $2.25
2. Jake has collected 736 aluminum cans for recycling. The recycling center pays 1¢ per can. How much money will Jake get? $7.36 or 736¢
3. Gillian is building a kite. She needs two pieces of balsa that are each 31 centimeters long and one piece that is 37 centimeters long. How much balsa does she need all together? 99 cm
4. Miss Hawk's garden is 8 meters long and 6 meters wide. What is its area? 48 sq m
5. Pedro has invited 17 people to a party. He wants to serve each of them one can of cola. How many cartons of cola should he buy if there are six cans of cola in each carton? 3
6. Robert had $281.60 in the bank. He withdrew $110.50 to buy a bicycle. How much does he have left in the bank? $171.10
7. If 40 baseball cards are to be divided equally among five children, how many cards should each child get? 8
8. The Abbot family and the Graham family visit a Civil War battlefield. Tickets cost $5 each. The Abbots buy six tickets and the Grahams buy four tickets. How much do the two families spend all together? $50
9. The Abbots go again on a weekday when the tickets are only $3 each for the six of them. They also pay $2 to park. How much do the Abbots spend in all on this day? $20

48 • *Math Explorations and Applications* Level 4

Copyright © SRA/McGraw-Hill. Permission is granted to reproduce this page for classroom use.

GAME

COOPERATIVE LEARNING

Cubo Game

Players: Two or more
Materials: Two 0–5 cubes, two 5–10 cubes
Object: To score as close to 21 as possible
Math Focus: Mental math with all four operations

RULES

1. Roll all four cubes on each turn.
2. Use any combination of the four operations (addition, subtraction, multiplication, and division) on the numbers rolled. Use the number on each cube only once. If two cubes have the same number, you must use both.

If you rolled:	You could make these numbers:	By doing these operations, for example:
3	19	6 − 3 = 3; 3 × 6 = 18; 18 + 1 = 19
6	23	3 × 6 = 18; 18 + 6 = 24; 24 − 1 = 23
6	21	6 − 1 = 5; 5 × 3 = 15; 15 + 6 = 21
1	21	6 − 3 = 3; 6 + 1 = 7; 3 × 7 = 21

3. The player who scores 21 or closest to it is the winner of the round.

ANOTHER WAY TO PLAY THIS GAME

Make the goal a number other than 21.

MATH JOURNAL

In your Math Journal explain your strategy for playing this game.

ENRICHMENT p. 48

LESSON 48 ENRICHMENT Name__________

Try some number tricks using **The Cruncher: *Magic Square*** project. In the 4 x 4 magic square, put each of the numbers 1–16 into one of the cells. The sums of the rows and columns will appear. Use all of the numbers, and use each number only once. Try to get all of the sums to appear as 34.

Record your solution in one of the grids below, then clear the Magic Square and try again. See how many different ways you can solve the square.

One possible answer is:

1	16	15	2
11	3	7	13
12	9	8	5
10	6	4	14

Copyright © SRA/McGraw-Hill. Permission is granted to reproduce this page for classroom use.

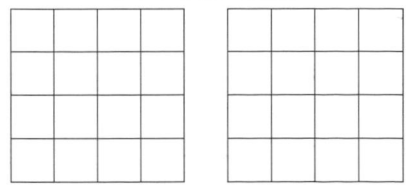

48 • *Math Explorations and Applications* Level 4

ASSESSMENT p. 15

UNIT 2 **Mastery Checkpoint 8** Arithmetic applications (Lesson 48)

Name __________

The student demonstrates mastery by correctly answering at least 8 of the 10 problems.

Solve these problems.

1. The first airplane flew in 1903. The first human-made satellite was launched into space in 1957. How many years after the first airplane flight was the satellite put into space? 54
2. Bert is 152 centimeters tall. His sister is 129 centimeters tall. How much older is Bert than his sister? can't tell
3. Claudio's room is shaped like a rectangle. It is 5 meters long and 4 meters wide. What is the area of the floor in Claudio's room? $20\ m^2$
4. There were 15 bowling teams in a contest. Molly's team came in sixth. How many teams finished behind her team? 9
5. Jamie uses two slices of bread to make a sandwich. He bought a loaf that has 18 slices of bread. How many sandwiches can he make? 9
6. Jana invited seven friends to her house. Each friend wanted two glasses of milk. A carton of milk fills six glasses. How many cartons of milk were needed? 3
7. Jean has to write ten letters. She wants to write the same number of letters each day for the next 5 days. How many letters will she write each day? 2
8. It takes Lincoln five minutes to ride 2 kilometers on his bike. How big is Lincoln's bike? can't tell
9. Naomi had \$57.89 in her bank account. She deposited \$13. How much money is in her account? \$70.89
10. Postcards cost 8¢ each. How much do seven postcards cost all together? 56¢

Copyright © SRA/McGraw-Hill. Permission is granted to reproduce this page for classroom use.

Math Explorations and Applications Level 4 • 15

3 Wrap-Up

5 MINUTES

In Closing Have students explain how they know which operation to use when they solve a word problem.

Mastery Checkpoint 8

At this time most students should be able to understand when to add, subtract, multiply, and divide, or know whether no operation is necessary in a particular situation. They should demonstrate this by using the correct operation in at least 12 of the 15 word problems on pages 160–161 and in three of the four problems on page 162 or similar pages. Or you may wish to assign Assessment Blackline Masters page 15 to determine mastery and record the results of this assessment on the Mastery Checkpoint Chart.

Assessment Criteria

Did the student . . .

- ✓ choose the correct operation at least 80% of the time?
- ✓ correctly solve 75% of the word problems?
- ✓ communicate strategies used to determine the correct operation?
- ✓ actively participate in playing the "Cubo" game?

Homework Have students play "Cubo" with a family member for further practice with mental math using the four operations. A copy of this game can also be found on page 15 of the Home Connections Blackline Masters.

LESSON 49

Student Edition pages 164–165

Unit 2 Review

Using the Student Pages Use this Unit 2 Review as a preliminary Unit Test to indicate areas in which each student is having difficulty or in which the entire class may need help. If students do well on the Unit 2 Review, you may wish to skip directly to the next unit. If not, you may spend a day or so helping students overcome their individual difficulties before they take the Unit Test.

Next to each set of problems is a list of the lessons in the unit covered in those problems. Students can refer to a specific lesson for additional instruction if they need help. You can also use this information to make additional assignments based on the previous lesson concepts.

Problems 1–8 Students who miss more than two of these multiplication facts problems may benefit from flash card practice, oral drill, and appropriate games. The "Add the Products" game on page 110 provides practice with multiplication and addition. The "Shopping" Game Mat reinforces the skills of multiplying by factors up to 9 and making change. The "Multiple Crossing" Game Mat allows for practice with factors up to 10 and mathematical reasoning. Learning the multiplication facts should be a high priority for students at this point. Emphasize speed and accuracy. Make it the responsibility of the whole class to see that everyone is proficient with these facts.

Problems 9–23 Work with students who need extra teaching by focusing on the inverse relationship of multiplication and division. You might provide extra teaching by using objects such as **craft sticks, crayons,** and so on.

Problems 24–33 For students who miss any of these problems, check to see if they are really unsure of the facts by asking for several other facts. These students should be started on a systematic program of remedial work, including flash card drill, special tutoring, and games. Students who respond very slowly or count on their fingers should be helped as well, even if they correctly solve all ten of the problems.

ASSESSMENT

LESSON 49

Unit 2 Review

Lessons 28–30, 32

Multiply.

1. 9 × 6 **54**
2. 8 × 7 **56**
3. 7 × 5 **35**
4. 9 × 3 **27**
5. 3 × 6 **18**
6. 5 × 8 **40**
7. 9 × 8 **72**
8. 4 × 5 **20**

Lesson 44

Divide. Watch for remainders.

9. $9\overline{)18}$ **2**
10. $6\overline{)59}$ **9 R5**
11. $4\overline{)36}$ **9**
12. $7\overline{)21}$ **3**
13. $9\overline{)63}$ **7**
14. $7\overline{)56}$ **8**
15. $4\overline{)37}$ **9 R1**
16. $3\overline{)26}$ **8 R2**
17. $4\overline{)32}$ **8**
18. $10\overline{)51}$ **5 R1**
19. $2\overline{)10}$ **5**
20. $9\overline{)27}$ **3**
21. $7\overline{)49}$ **7**
22. $3\overline{)15}$ **5**
23. $6\overline{)19}$ **3 R1**

Lesson 43

Add or subtract to solve.

24. 7 + 5 = **12**
25. 12 − 9 = **3**
26. 6 + 3 = **9**
27. 6 − 3 = **3**
28. 8 − 5 = **3**
29. 15 − 5 = **10**
30. 8 + 7 = **15**
31. 7 + 6 = **13**
32. 9 − 5 = **4**
33. 3 + 7 = **10**

Solve for *n*. Watch the signs.

34. $n - 4 = 12$ **16**
35. $n = 36 + 25$ **61**
36. $9 \times n = 27$ **3**
37. $n = 14 - 13$ **1**
38. $7 + n = 23$ **16**
39. $32 = n \times 8$ **4**

Lesson 41

Add or subtract.

Lesson 43

40. 73 + 96 = **169**
41. 97 − 38 = **59**
42. 24 + 56 = **80**
43. 89 + 46 = **135**
44. 605 − 416 = **189**
45. 860 + 320 = **1180**
46. 197 − 45 = **152**
47. 4973 − 2984 = **1989**

RETEACHING

Students who have difficulty with this Unit Review should have further opportunity to review and to practice the skills before they proceed on with the next unit. For each set of problems there are specific suggestions for reteaching. These suggestions can be found in the margins.

Lessons 28, 34, 41, 44, 45, 48

Solve these problems.

48. Erica bought eight pencils. They cost 9¢ each. She gave the storekeeper 75¢. How much change should she get? **3¢**

49. The Conlan family had a rectangular swimming pool built.
    a. What would the area of the pool be if it was 8 meters long and 6 meters wide? **48 square m**
    b. Is the area of this pool larger or smaller than the area of a pool that is 7 meters long and 7 meters wide? **smaller**

50. About what is the length of a string that is made by tying two 9-meter strings together? **a little less than 18 m**

51. A kite string is about 65 meters long. Another string that is about 75 meters long is tied to it. About how long is the combined string? **a little less than 140 m**

52. William paid 48¢ for six carrots. How much did each carrot cost? **8¢**

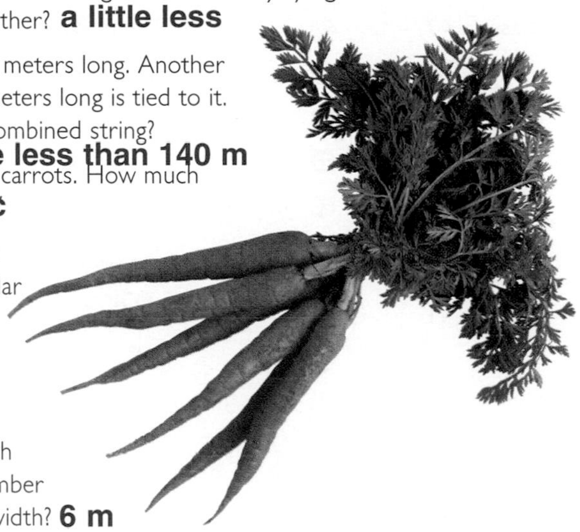

53. Mrs. Sandina knows that the area of her rectangular rug is between 50 and 60 square meters and that the length of the rug is 9 meters. She also knows that the width of the rug is a whole number of meters. What is the width? **6 m**

54. Teresa has 47 stickers to give to five children.
    a. How many stickers will each child get? **9**
    b. How many stickers will be left over? **2**

55. Vance has 47 pears. He wants to give an equal number of pears to each of four children. But he also wants to keep at least ten pears for himself.
    a. How many should he give to each child? **9**
    b. How many should he keep for himself? **11**

PRACTICE p. 49

LESSON 49 PRACTICE Name__________

Multiply.

1. 9 × 5 = 45
2. 8 × 8 = 64
3. 7 × 6 = 42
4. 9 × 4 = 36
5. 4 × 6 = 24
6. 5 × 7 = 35
7. 7 × 8 = 56
8. 8 × 5 = 40

Divide. Don't forget remainders.

9. 9)19 — 2 R1
10. 4)38 — 9 R2
11. 7)60 — 8 R4
12. 3)25 — 8 R1
13. 10 ÷ 5 = 2
14. 54 ÷ 9 = 6
15. 28 ÷ 7 = 4
16. 24 ÷ 3 = 8
17. 3)23 — 7 R2
18. 9)82 — 9 R1
19. 7)50 — 7 R1
20. 6)42 — 7

Solve. Watch the signs.

21. 8 + 5 = 13
22. 12 − 8 = 4
23. 7 + 3 = 10
24. 248 − 163 = 85
25. 408 + 682 = 1090

Solve for *n*. Watch the signs.

26. $n - 6 = 12$ 18
27. $n + 8 = 14$ 6
28. $5 = 20 \div n$ 4
29. $10 - n = 4$ 6
30. $7 + n = 15$ 8
31. $36 \div n = 6$ 6

Solve these problems.

32. Bill has 45 stickers to give to six friends.
    a. How many stickers will each friend get? 7
    b. How many stickers will be left over? 3

Copyright © SRA/McGraw-Hill. Permission is granted to reproduce this page for classroom use.

Math Explorations and Applications Level 4 • 49

ENRICHMENT p. 49

LESSON 49 ENRICHMENT Name__________

Select a typical page in a storybook. Which letter do you think is used most often? Find out. Use tally marks to record the number of times each letter is used on the page.

Letter	Tallies	Total	Letter	Tallies	Total
A			N		
B			O		
C			P		
D			Q		
E			R		
F			S		
G			T		
H			U		
I			V		
J			W		
K			X		
L			Y		
M			Z		

1. Which letter was used most often? Answers will vary.
   Next most often? ________ Least often? ________
2. Compare your results with those of your classmates. Discuss: Are your answers the same? Different? How much different? Why?
3. Do you think the most common letters are the same in every language? Find foreign-language books and repeat this survey with a page from each.

Copyright © SRA/McGraw-Hill. Permission is granted to reproduce this page for classroom use.

Math Explorations and Applications Level 4 • 49

Problems 34–39 Check students who miss more than one of these mixed arithmetic problems and missing-term problems to see whether the trouble is with the facts or the format. Reteach as necessary, using the reteaching strategies from the appropriate lessons.

Problems 40–47 Students who miss more than one of these multidigit addition and subtraction problems should be assessed to see if the difficulty is with the algorithms, basic facts, or carelessness. Reteach as necessary, and urge students who routinely make careless errors to check their work.

Problems 48–55 To help students who need extra teaching with these word problems, first be sure they can read the problems and understand them. Invite students to act out the problems or draw pictures, or allow students to work together.

ALTERNATIVE ASSESSMENT

Portfolio Assessment If you have not already completed the Portfolio Assessment task provided on Assessment Blackline Masters page 94, it can be used at this time to evaluate students' proficiency with simple division and units of volume.

ALTERNATIVE ASSESSMENT

Performance Assessment Performance Assessment Task 2, provided on Assessment Blackline Masters pages 73–74, can be used at this time to evaluate students' proficiency with multiplication and division facts. You may want to administer this assessment to individual students or small groups of students.

Unit Project If you have not already assigned the "Exploring the Multiplication Table" project on pages 172 and 173, you may want to do so at this time. This project is a good opportunity for students to explore and find number patterns on the multiplication table. Students use one of the patterns to solve a difficult problem.

LESSON 50

Student Edition pages 166–169

Unit 2 Practice

Using the Student Pages The purpose of these pages is to provide additional practice for those students who demonstrated a need for it on the Unit Review. You may wish to assign only the specific exercises in this Unit Practice in which students need further reinforcement. Listed in the margin beside each instruction line are the lessons covered in the unit so that you or the students can refer to the specific lesson for additional review and instruction.

GAME Students who do not require additional practice on specific concepts may enjoy playing any of the games you have played so far, such as the "Add the Products" game on page 110. This game provides practice with multiplication facts and multidigit addition. These students may also help by practicing flash card drills and playing appropriate games with students who need remedial practice or by actually teaching certain procedures to other students.

You may want to use the Cumulative Review on page 545 after this lesson.

MIXED **PRACTICE**

LESSON 50

Unit 2 Practice

Solve for *n*.

Lessons 28–30, 32, 41

1. $2 \times 10 = n$ **20**
2. $4 \times n = 28$ **7**
3. $6 \times 8 = n$ **48**
4. $n = 8 \times 9$ **72**
5. $5 \times 9 = n$ **45**
6. $n = 5 \times 5$ **25**
7. $5 \times 9 = n$ **45**
8. $64 = 8 \times n$ **8**
9. $1 \times n = 7$ **7**
10. $n \times 7 = 35$ **5**
11. $9 \times n = 54$ **6**
12. $6 \times 5 = n$ **30**
13. $24 = 4 \times n$ **6**
14. $80 = n \times 10$ **8**
15. $3 \times n = 18$ **6**

Solve for *n*. Watch the parentheses. Watch the signs.

Lesson 47

16. $4 \times (3 + 5) = n$ **32**
17. $17 - (9 - 5) = n$ **13**
18. $n = (3 \times 5) + (3 \times 4)$ **27**
19. $n = (4 + 8) - 3$ **9**
20. $6 + (5 \times 2) = n$ **16**
21. $6 \times (8 - 5) = n$ **18**
22. $(17 - 9) - 5 = n$ **3**
23. $8 \times (2 + 7) = n$ **72**
24. $n = 4 \times (3 - 1)$ **8**
25. $n = 5 + (3 \times 4)$ **17**

Solve for *n*. Watch the signs.

Lesson 41

26. $n = 24 - 8$ **16**
27. $n \div 3 = 7$ **21**
28. $n \times 7 = 63$ **9**
29. $7 \times n = 56$ **8**
30. $56 - n = 18$ **38**
31. $n = 82 - 39$ **43**
32. $8 + 3 = n$ **11**
33. $15 + 6 = n$ **21**
34. $n + 18 = 97$ **79**

Divide to solve for *n*.

Lesson 42

35. $15 \div 3 = n$ **5**
36. $n = 35 \div 7$ **5**
37. $24 \div 8 = n$ **3**
38. $n = 27 \div 9$ **3**
39. $n = 72 \div 9$ **8**
40. $n = 54 \div 9$ **6**
41. $30 \div 10 = n$ **3**
42. $49 \div 7 = n$ **7**
43. $42 \div 6 = n$ **7**

Divide. Watch for remainders.

Lesson 44

44. 7)49 **7**
45. 7)39 **5 R4**
46. 8)72 **9**
47. 5)40 **8**
48. 6)18 **3**
49. 7)50 **7 R1**
50. 5)36 **7 R1**
51. 6)24 **4**
52. 3)24 **8**
53. 8)68 **8 R4**

Solve. Watch the signs.

esson 43

54	55	56	57	58
89	64	19	2379	6497
+ 17	− 23	+ 85	+ 1893	− 2999
106	**41**	**104**	**4272**	**3498**

Solve these problems.

essons 31, 1, 42, 44, 5

59. Andrew bought three pencils for 9¢ each at the department store. How much did they cost all together? **27¢**
60. Julia sells apples at a fruit stand. Today she sold seven apples for 8¢ each. How much money did she take in? **56¢**
61. Jenny needs ten hair ribbons to match each of her outfits. If there are four ribbons in a pack, how many packs must Jenny buy? **3**
62. Oko wants to buy two erasers that cost 35¢ each. How much change should he get for three quarters? **5¢**

Niran wants to buy 35 marbles. They come in bags of ten.

63. How many bags should he buy? **4**
64. How many extra marbles will he have? **5**

A cotton shirt costs $22. Ties cost $8.

65. How much do two cotton shirts cost? **$44**
66. How much do two shirts and four ties cost? **$76**

Patricia's patio is square. It measures 6 meters on each side.

67. What is the area of the patio? **36 square m**
68. What is the perimeter of the patio? **24 m**

There are three rows of bunkbeds in Mr. Garvey's cabin. Each row has nine bunkbeds.

69. How many bunkbeds are there in the cabin? **27**
70. If each bunkbed has a top bed and a bottom bed, how many people can sleep in the cabin? **54**

◆ LESSON 50 Unit 2 Practice

◆ LESSON 50 Unit 2 Practice

PHYSICAL EDUCATION CONNECTION

Use the information in these charts to make up questions. Exchange questions with a friend and solve them.

For example:

- Which stadium has the most seats? **Anaheim Stadium**
- In which stadium is it easiest to hit a home run? Why? **Fenway Park; it has the shortest distances to left and right field, where most home runs are hit**
- How many more seats are there in Cinergy Field than in Wrigley Field? **14,187**

American League Stadiums

Team	Stadium	Home-Run Distances (feet) Left Field	Center Field	Right Field	Seating Capacity
Baltimore Orioles	Oriole Park at Camden Yards	333	400	318	48,262
Boston Red Sox	Fenway Park	310	390	302	34,218
California Angels	Anaheim Stadium	333	404	333	64,593
Chicago White Sox	New Comiskey Park	347	400	347	44,321
Cleveland Indians	Jacobs Field	325	405	325	43,345
Detroit Tigers	Tiger Stadium	340	440	325	52,416
Kansas City Royals	Kauffman Stadium	320	410	320	40,625
Milwaukee Brewers	Milwaukee County Stadium	315	402	315	53,192
Minnesota Twins	Hubert H. Humphrey Metrodome	343	408	327	55,883
New York Yankees	Yankee Stadium	318	408	314	57,545
Oakland A's	Oakland-Alameda County Coliseum	330	400	330	48,219
Seattle Mariners	Kingdome	331	405	312	59,166
Texas Rangers	Ballpark at Arlington	334	400	325	49,178
Toronto Blue Jays	Sky Dome	328	400	328	50,516

168 • Multiplication and Division

RETEACHING

Students who have difficulty with this Unit Practice should have further opportunity to review and to practice the skills before they proceed on with the next unit. Beside each set of problems is a reference to the lesson or lessons from which the problems were taken. You may want to review the individual lessons with students who are having difficulty with them.

National League Stadiums

Team	Stadium	Home-Run Distances (feet) Left Field	Center Field	Right Field	Seating Capacity
Atlanta Braves	Turner Field	335	400	330	49,831
Chicago Cubs	Wrigley Field	355	400	353	38,765
Cincinnati Reds	Cinergy Field	330	404	330	52,952
Colorado Rockies	Coors Field	347	415	350	50,200
Florida Marlins	Pro Player Stadium	330	404	385	47,662
Houston Astros	Astrodome	325	400	325	54,816
Los Angeles Dodgers	Dodger Stadium	330	395	330	56,000
Montreal Expos	Le Stade Olympique/Olympic Stadium	325	404	325	43,739
New York Mets	Shea Stadium	338	410	338	55,601
Philadelphia Phillies	Veterans Stadium	330	408	330	62,382
Pittsburgh Pirates	Three Rivers Stadium	335	400	335	47,971
St. Louis Cardinals	Busch Memorial Stadium	330	402	330	57,672
San Diego Padres	Jack Murphy Stadium	327	405	330	59,022
San Francisco Giants	3 Com Park	335	400	328	63,000

Use the Cumulative Review on page 545 after this lesson.

PRACTICE p. 50

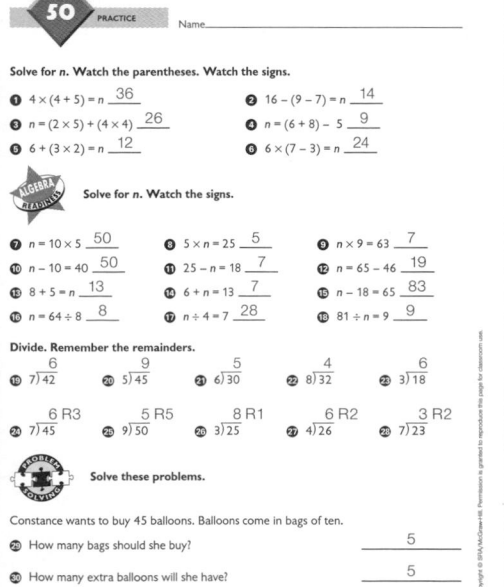

LESSON 50 PRACTICE Name________________

Solve for *n*. Watch the parentheses. Watch the signs.

1. $4 \times (4 + 5) = n$ 36
2. $16 - (9 - 7) = n$ 14
3. $n = (2 \times 5) + (4 \times 4)$ 26
4. $n = (6 + 8) - 5$ 9
5. $6 + (3 \times 2) = n$ 12
6. $6 \times (7 - 3) = n$ 24

ALGEBRA READINESS **Solve for *n*. Watch the signs.**

7. $n = 10 \times 5$ 50
8. $5 \times n = 25$ 5
9. $n \times 9 = 63$ 7
10. $n - 10 = 40$ 50
11. $25 - n = 18$ 7
12. $n = 65 - 46$ 19
13. $8 + 5 = n$ 13
14. $6 + n = 13$ 7
15. $n - 18 = 65$ 83
16. $n = 64 \div 8$ 8
17. $n \div 4 = 7$ 28
18. $81 \div n = 9$ 9

Divide. Remember the remainders.

19. 7)42 6
20. 5)45 9
21. 6)30 5
22. 8)32 4
23. 3)18 6
24. 7)45 6 R3
25. 9)50 5 R5
26. 3)25 8 R1
27. 4)26 6 R2
28. 7)23 3 R2

PROBLEM SOLVING **Solve these problems.**

Constance wants to buy 45 balloons. Balloons come in bags of ten.

29. How many bags should she buy? 5
30. How many extra balloons will she have? 5

Copyright © SRA/McGraw-Hill. Permission is granted to reproduce this page for classroom use.

50 • *Math Explorations and Applications* Level 4

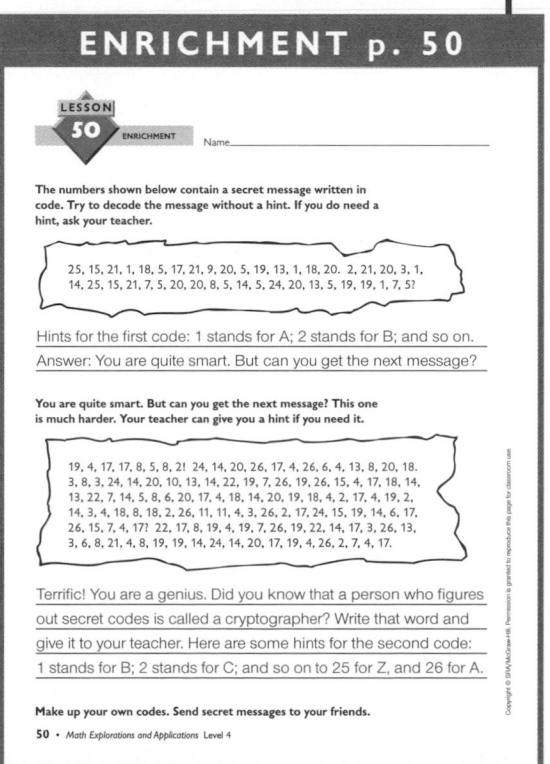

ENRICHMENT p. 50

LESSON 50 ENRICHMENT Name________________

The numbers shown below contain a secret message written in code. Try to decode the message without a hint. If you do need a hint, ask your teacher.

25, 15, 21, 1, 18, 5, 17, 21, 9, 20, 5, 19, 13, 1, 18, 20. 2, 21, 20, 3, 1, 14, 25, 15, 21, 7, 5, 20, 20, 8, 5, 14, 5, 24, 20, 13, 5, 19, 19, 1, 7, 5?

Hints for the first code: 1 stands for A; 2 stands for B; and so on.
Answer: You are quite smart. But can you get the next message?

You are quite smart. But can you get the next message? This one is much harder. Your teacher can give you a hint if you need it.

19, 4, 17, 17, 8, 5, 8, 2! 24, 14, 20, 26, 17, 4, 26, 6, 4, 13, 8, 20, 18. 3, 8, 3, 24, 14, 20, 10, 13, 14, 22, 19, 7, 26, 19, 26, 15, 4, 17, 18, 14, 13, 22, 7, 14, 5, 8, 6, 20, 17, 4, 18, 14, 20, 19, 18, 4, 2, 17, 4, 19, 2, 14, 3, 4, 18, 8, 18, 2, 26, 11, 11, 4, 3, 26, 2, 17, 24, 15, 19, 14, 6, 17, 26, 15, 7, 4, 17? 22, 17, 8, 19, 4, 19, 7, 26, 19, 22, 14, 17, 3, 26, 13, 3, 6, 8, 21, 4, 8, 19, 19, 14, 24, 14, 20, 17, 19, 4, 26, 2, 7, 4, 17.

Terrific! You are a genius. Did you know that a person who figures out secret codes is called a cryptographer? Write that word and give it to your teacher. Here are some hints for the second code: 1 stands for B; 2 stands for C; and so on to 25 for Z, and 26 for A.

Make up your own codes. Send secret messages to your friends.

Copyright © SRA/McGraw-Hill. Permission is granted to reproduce this page for classroom use.

50 • *Math Explorations and Applications* Level 4

UNIT 2

Student Edition pages 170–171

Unit Test

Using the Student Pages The Unit 2 Test on Student Edition pages 170 and 171 provides an opportunity to formally evaluate your students' proficiency with concepts developed in this unit. It is similar in content and format to the Unit 2 Review. Students who did well on the Unit 2 Review may not need to take this test. Students who did not do well on the Unit 2 Review should be provided with additional practice opportunities, such as the Unit 2 Practice pages, before taking the Unit 2 Test. For further evaluation, you may wish to have these students take the Unit 2 Test in standardized format, provided on Assessment Blackline Masters pages 111–120 or the Unit 2 Test on Assessment Blackline Masters pages 16–19.

UNIT 2

ASSESSMENT

Unit Test

Multiply.

1. 9×9 **81**	2. 6×5 **30**	3. 0×9 **0**	4. 8×9 **72**
5. 8×0 **0**	6. 7×3 **21**	7. 9×3 **27**	8. 7×5 **35**

Divide. Don't forget remainders.

9. $5\overline{)40}$ **8**	10. $7\overline{)42}$ **6**	11. $2\overline{)15}$ **7 R1**	12. $6\overline{)24}$ **4**	13. $9\overline{)38}$ **4 R2**
14. $5\overline{)38}$ **7 R3**	15. $6\overline{)39}$ **6 R3**	16. $8\overline{)65}$ **8 R1**	17. $4\overline{)32}$ **8**	18. $8\overline{)17}$ **2 R1**

Solve for *n*.

19. $24 \div (6 \div 2) = n$ **8**	20. $4 \times (6 - 6) = n$ **0**
21. $(16 - 7) - 5 = n$ **4**	22. $(18 \div 6) \div 3 = n$ **1**
23. $2 \times (3 \times 3) = n$ **18**	24. $(16 + 7) + 5 = n$ **28**
25. $(7 \times 4) + 6 = n$ **34**	26. $(7 \times 5) + 4 = n$ **39**

Solve for *n*. Watch the signs.

27. $16 \div 4 = n$ **4**	28. $8 \times 7 = n$ **56**	29. $42 \div 7 = n$ **6**
30. $n \times 7 = 28$ **4**	31. $n \times 8 = 24$ **3**	32. $13 + 28 = n$ **41**
33. $n = 49 \div 7$ **7**	34. $42 - n = 6$ **36**	35. $18 + n = 20$ **2**
36. $3 \times n = 27$ **9**	37. $n + 8 = 17$ **9**	38. $81 \div n = 9$ **9**

Solve. Watch the signs.

39. $54 - 36$ = **18**	40. $83 + 17$ = **100**	41. $207 - 68$ = **139**	42. $118 + 125$ = **243**	43. $297 - 199$ = **98**
44. $39 + 38$ = **77**	45. $465 - 190$ = **275**	46. $7300 - 480$ = **6820**	47. $4802 + 2169$ = **6971**	48. $34{,}621 - 29{,}291$ = **5330**

170 • Multiplication and Division

Find the area.

49 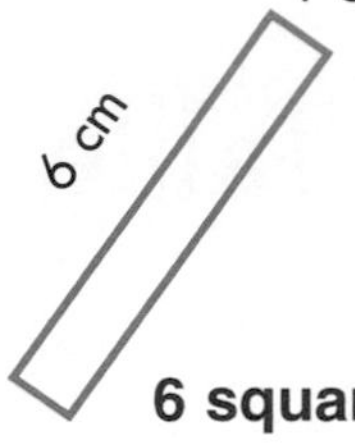

6 square cm

50 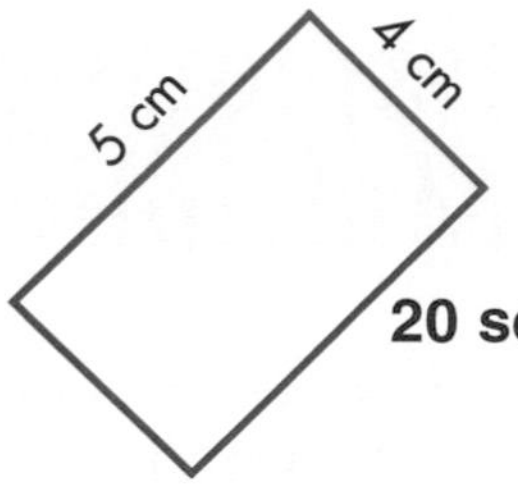

20 square cm

51 

4 square cm

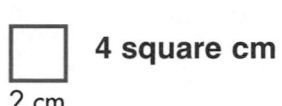

52 **72 square cm**
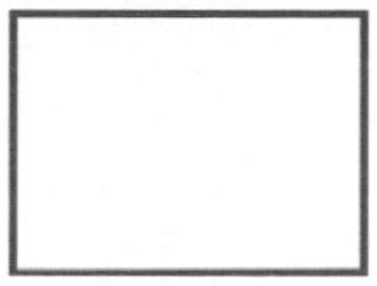

Solve.

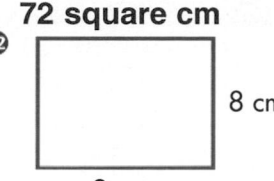

53 There are 12 eggs in a carton. How many eggs are in seven cartons? **84**

54 The refund on a soda bottle is 5¢. How many bottles did Jim return to the grocery store if he received 60¢? **12**

55 Team caps cost $6 each. How much do four team caps cost? **$24**

56 Jill has 20 sweatshirts. She can fit five in each box. How many boxes will she need? **4**

57 Renato planted nine seeds. Three of them sprouted. How many didn't sprout? **6**

58 The top of Adiva's table is 2 meters wide and 3 meters long. What is the area of the tabletop? **6 square m**

59 Kareem needs 30 hamburger buns for a picnic. They come in packages of eight. How many packages should he buy? **4**

60 Katherine's classroom has five groups of desks. Each group has six desks. How many desks are there in the classroom? **30**

ASSESSMENT p. 16

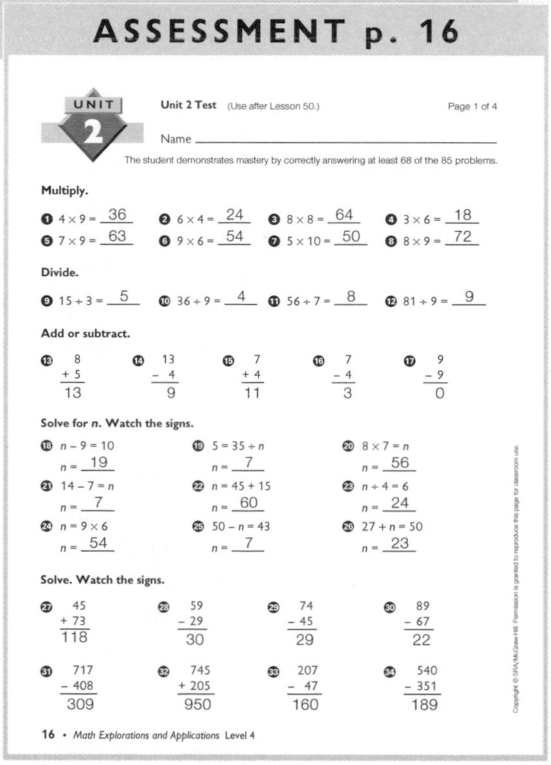

UNIT 2

Unit 2 Test (Use after Lesson 50.) Page 1 of 4

Name ____________________

The student demonstrates mastery by correctly answering at least 68 of the 85 problems.

Multiply.

1 $4 \times 9 =$ 36 2 $6 \times 4 =$ 24 3 $8 \times 8 =$ 64 4 $3 \times 6 =$ 18
5 $7 \times 9 =$ 63 6 $9 \times 6 =$ 54 7 $5 \times 10 =$ 50 8 $8 \times 9 =$ 72

Divide.

9 $15 \div 3 =$ 5 10 $36 \div 9 =$ 4 11 $56 \div 7 =$ 8 12 $81 \div 9 =$ 9

Add or subtract.

13 $8 + 5 =$ 13 14 $13 - 4 =$ 9 15 $7 + 4 =$ 11 16 $7 - 4 =$ 3 17 $9 - 9 =$ 0

Solve for *n*. Watch the signs.

18 $n - 9 = 10$, $n =$ 19 19 $5 = 35 \div n$, $n =$ 7 20 $8 \times 7 = n$, $n =$ 56
21 $14 - 7 = n$, $n =$ 7 22 $n = 45 + 15$, $n =$ 60 23 $n \div 4 = 6$, $n =$ 24
24 $n = 9 \times 6$, $n =$ 54 25 $50 - n = 43$, $n =$ 7 26 $27 + n = 50$, $n =$ 23

Solve. Watch the signs.

27 $45 + 73 =$ 118 28 $59 - 29 =$ 30 29 $74 - 45 =$ 29 30 $89 - 67 =$ 22
31 $717 - 408 =$ 309 32 $745 + 205 =$ 950 33 $207 - 47 =$ 160 34 $540 - 351 =$ 189

Copyright © SRA/McGraw-Hill. Permission is granted to reproduce this page for classroom use.

UNIT 2

Student Edition pages 172–173

Wrap-Up

PRESENTING THE PROJECT

Project Objectives

- to explore and find number patterns on the multiplication table
- to use patterns on a multiplication table to guide students in solving a difficult problem
- to find the sum of all the numbers on a multiplication table

To begin the project, solve the first one or two problems on page 172 with the class. Then have the students work in cooperative groups to finish the problems on the page and make up their own "find the pattern" problems.

Solve the three problems on page 173 with the class. Then challenge the class to find out if the pattern is true for all "squares": Is the product of two numbers that are diagonally opposite always equal to the product of the other two numbers that are diagonally opposite? Allow students to work in cooperative groups to see if they can find a counterexample. The students should see that this is a pattern and that it is always true.

How to Assess Record and use information in ways that you determine will be helpful to you and your students. Below are some ideas for routine forms of assessment.

- **Observations** can take the form of watching, listening, discussing, and questioning.
- **Checklists** can help you focus on specific aspects of your students' learning and behavior.
- **Interviews** can provide valuable insights into students' thoughts about a project.
- **Group assessment** can focus on how well all members of the group fulfill their roles.
- **Student self assessment** provides an opportunity to understand your students' perception of their own strengths, problems, and work habits.
- **Portfolio assessment** can be accomplished by collecting samples of students' work.

UNIT 2 WRAP-UP

PROJECT

Exploring the Multiplication Table

A multiplication table has more in it than just factors and products. It also has patterns.

	0	1	2	3	4	5	6	7	8	9	10
0	0	0	0	0	0	0	0	0	0	0	0
1	0	1	2	3	4	5	6	7	8	9	10
2	0	2	4	6	8	10	12	14	16	18	20
3	0	3	6	9	12	15	18	21	24	27	30
4	0	4	8	12	16	20	24	28	32	36	40
5	0	5	10	15	20	25	30	35	40	45	50
6	0	6	12	18	24	30	36	42	48	54	60
7	0	7	14	21	28	35	42	49	56	63	70
8	0	8	16	24	32	40	48	56	64	72	80
9	0	9	18	27	36	45	54	63	72	81	90
10	0	10	20	30	40	50	60	70	80	90	100

Use the multiplication table to find these patterns. Then write the patterns and extend them.

0, 2, 4, 6, 8, 10, **12**, **14**, **16**, **18**, 20 **22, 24, 26**

6, 12, 18, **24**, 30, 36, **42**, 48, 54, 60 **66, 72, 78**

0, 1, 4, 9, 16, **25**, 36, **49**, **64**, 81, 100 **121, 144, 169**

0, 2, 6, 12, 20, **30**, 42, **56**, 72, 90 **110, 132, 156**

Find other patterns in your multiplication table. Explain your patterns to a friend.

172 • Multiplication and Division

COOPERATIVE LEARNING **Minds on Math** SRA's *Minds on Math* is a series of units covering Problem Solving, Data Collection, Number Sense, Measurement, Money, and Geometry and Spatial Relations. Each unit provides a series of open-ended projects for individuals or small groups. These projects develop problem-solving and critical-thinking skills, utilize real-world materials, emphasize language, and integrate cross-curricular connections. Use projects from *All About Number,* which describes practical applications of operations, number patterns, and probability.

Now look at this part of your multiplication table.

1	2	3	4
2	4	6	8
3	6	9	12
4	8	12	16

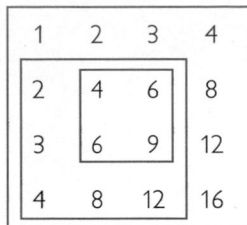

1. How much is 4 × 9? How much is 6 × 6? **36; 36**
2. How much is 4 × 6? How much is 2 × 12? **24; 24**
3. How much is 4 × 4? How much is 1 × 16? **16; 16**

Do these patterns work for all squares in the multiplication table? **yes**

Challenge: Without adding all of the numbers, can you find the sum of all of the numbers in the multiplication table? **3025 (55 × 55)**

First hint: What is the sum of these numbers?

1 + 2 + 3 + 4 + 5 + 6 + 7 + 8 + 9 + 10

Second hint: What is the sum of these numbers? You don't have to add them to find the sum.

2 + 4 + 6 + 8 + 10 + 12 + 14 + 16 + 18 + 20

Third hint: What is the sum of these numbers? You don't have to add them to find the sum.

10 + 20 + 30 + 40 + 50 + 60 + 70 + 80 + 90 + 100

If you need more hints, ask your teacher or work with a friend.

Why teach it at this time?

This project could be introduced at any time. The opportunity to explore the multiplication table extends and supports the main topic in this unit, which is reviewing the multiplication facts.

What Is a Math Project? If this is the first time you have used math projects in your classroom, you may want to refer to pages 96–97 in this Teacher's Guide for more detailed information about effectively implementing and assessing projects.

Challenge Problem Although students may need considerable time and help with this problem, they should feel a sense of accomplishment with its solution. First, go over the first hint with the class. Although students may simply add the numbers, take the opportunity to show them this shortcut. Show that the sum of the numbers:

1 + 2 + 3 + 4 + 5 + 6 + 7 + 8 + 9 + 10

can be thought of as:

1 + 10, 2 + 9, 3 + 8, 4 + 7, 5 + 6, or five groups of 11, or 55.

Spend time on this until all students see a solution.

Another way of looking at the shortcut is to think:

10 + 0, 9 + 1, 8 + 2, 7 + 3, 6 + 4, and 5 left over, or five groups of 10 plus 5, or 55.

If students need a second hint, help them see that the sum of:

2 + 4 + 6 + 8 + 10 + 12 + 14 + 16 + 18 + 20 is 55 + 55, or 110.

Once students realize that the sum of each row on the multiplication table is 55 more than the preceding row, they are well on their way to solving the problem.

The sum is (1 × 55) + (2 × 55) + (3 × 55) + (4 × 55) + (5 × 55) + (6 × 55) + (7 × 55) + (8 × 55) + (9 × 55) + (10 × 55). But because the sum of the whole numbers from 1 to 10 is 55, the answer is 55 × 55, or 3025. If students seem unsure of the validity of the shortcut solution, consider having them work in teams to add the numbers with a calculator.

Homework The thinking that will go into the solution of the challenge problem may be done outside of class.

Wrapping Up the Project Create and display a large multiplication table on a bulletin board with a place where students can post newly discovered patterns.

Assessing the Project Note those students who seem to enjoy the kind of problem solving involved in this unit. Continue to find opportunities to challenge those students using the Enrichment Masters.

UNIT 3

Algebra Readiness and Geometry

SPATIAL SENSE

OVERVIEW

This unit begins by teaching students how to plot points on a coordinate grid. Then students review functions and inverse operations and relate functions to ordered pairs. Students also explore composite functions and graphs of functions. They relate data analysis to graphing by interpreting graphs and choosing the best graph for a given set of data. In this unit students also work on developing geometry concepts such as identifying lines, rays, angles, and perpendicular and parallel lines; congruence; similarity; rotation, reflection, and translations; solid figures; and lines of symmetry. Finally, students explore the area and perimeter of similar figures.

Integrated Topics in This Unit Include:

- locating points on a coordinate grid
- reviewing concepts of functions
- relating ordered pairs and functions
- choosing appropriate scales for the axes of a graph
- introducing composite functions
- finding the inverse of a composite function
- graphing composite functions
- interpreting and selecting appropriate graphical formats
- reviewing points, lines, angles, rays, and right angles
- identifying parallel and perpendicular lines
- introducing congruence and similarity
- exploring rotations, reflections, and translations related to congruence
- finding lines of symmetry

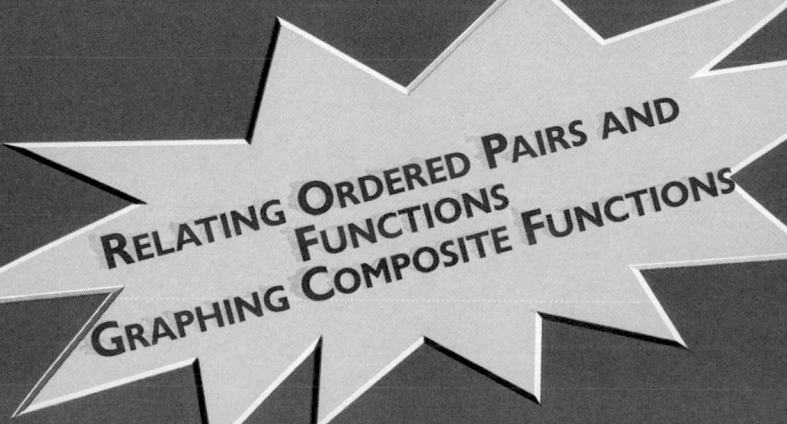

RELATING ORDERED PAIRS AND FUNCTIONS
GRAPHING COMPOSITE FUNCTIONS

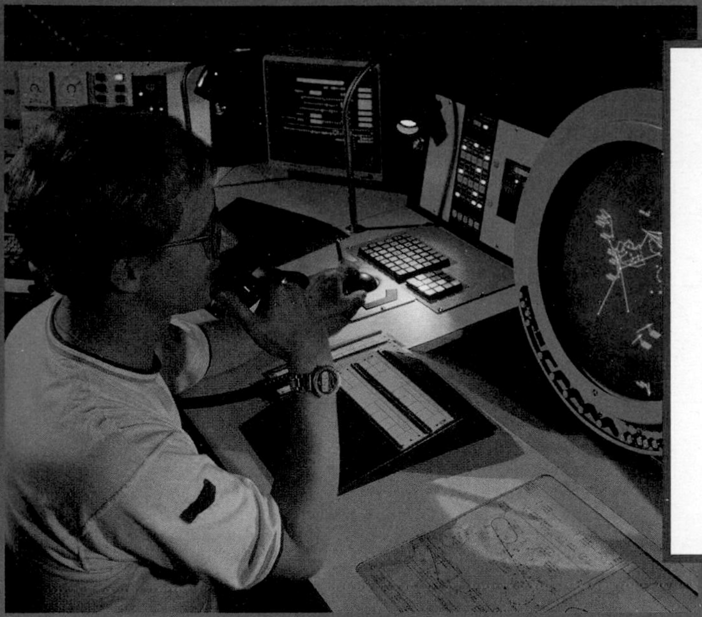

"From the earliest grades, the curriculum should give students opportunities to focus on regularities in events, shapes, designs, and sets of numbers. Children should begin to see that regularity is the essence of mathematics. The idea of a functional relationship can be intuitively developed through observations of regularity and work with generalizable patterns."

—NCTM Curriculum and Evaluation Standards for School Mathematics

GAMES

Motivating Mixed Practice

Games provide **basic math skills** practice in cooperative groups. Playing the games also helps students develop **mathematical reasoning.**

Animal Data Game Mat	Lesson 51	page 177
Baseball Game Mat	Lesson 52	page 179
Snake Game Mat	Lesson 53	page 182
Cubo	Lesson 54	page 184
Baseball Game Mat	Lesson 55	page 190
Snake Game Mat	Lesson 56	page 193
Function	Lesson 57	page 195
Cubo Challenge	Lesson 77	page 261

THINKING STORY

Integrated Problem Solving

Thinking Stories provide opportunities for students to work in **cooperative groups** and to develop **logical reasoning** while they integrate **reading skills** with mathematics.

The Lost Island of Addonia

Part 1	Lesson 55	pages 190–191
Part 2	Lesson 57	pages 196–197
Part 3	Lesson 61	pages 212–213
Part 4	Lesson 63	pages 218–219

Story Summary "The Lost Island of Addonia" focuses on addition as it tells the story of three children stranded on an island where coded numbers are used. The children must decipher the island code in order to map the distance to the library or buy a specific number of hamburgers. Students use their addition skills to crack this code, and they practice quick figuring as they decode the islanders' answers to simple geometry questions.

PROJECT

Making Connections

The Unit 3 Project makes real-world connections. Students work in **cooperative groups** to problem solve and to communicate their findings.

The project presented in the Unit 3 Wrap-Up asks students, either in small groups or individually, to start a stamp collection that features mathematics. Then students design their own stamps and display them along with those of their classmates. This project can be worked on during students' free time throughout the unit.

UNIT 3

Algebra Readiness and Geometry Lesson Plans

	LESSON	PACING	PRIMARY OBJECTIVES	FEATURE	RESOURCES	NCTM STANDARDS
51	Coordinate Grids 176–177	1 day	to teach the convention for graphing ordered pairs of numbers	Game	Reteaching Strategy Practice Master 51 Enrichment Master 51	9, 13
52	Coordinates.......... 178–179	1 day	to provide practice in locating a point with given coordinates	Game	Reteaching Master Practice Master 52 Enrichment Master 52	9, 13
53	Determining Function Rules 180–183	1 day	to review the concept of functions	Game	Reteaching Master Practice Master 53 Enrichment Master 53	8, 13
54	Inverse Functions 184–187	1 day	to review inverse operations	Game	Reteaching Master Practice Master 54 Enrichment Master 54	7, 13
55	Ordered Pairs 188–191	1 day	to show the relationship between functions and ordered pairs of numbers	Game Thinking Story	Reteaching Strategy Practice Master 55 Enrichment Master 55	1, 2, 3, 4, 9, 13
56	Function Rules and Ordered Pairs........ 192–193	1 day	✓ to assess students' understanding of functions and inverse relationships	Game	Reteaching Master Practice Master 56 Enrichment Master 56 Assessment Masters	8, 9, 13
57	Keeping in Shape 194–197	1 day	to reinforce the concept of functions and to practice arithmetic and approximation	Game Thinking Story	Reteaching Strategy Practice Master 57 Enrichment Master 57	1, 2, 3, 4, 5, 13
58	Graphing Ordered Pairs........ 198–199	1 day	to demonstrate the relationships among a function, a set of ordered pairs, and a graph		Reteaching Master Practice Master 58 Enrichment Master 58	4, 9, 13
59	Identifying Scale 200–203	1 day	to identify scales and graph sets of ordered pairs		Reteaching Strategy Practice Master 59 Enrichment Master 59	9
	Mid-Unit Review 204–205				Assessment Masters	
60	Composite Function Rules 206–209	1 day	to introduce composite functions		Reteaching Master Practice Master 60 Enrichment Master 60	1, 2, 3, 4, 13
61	Using Inverse Operations with Composite Functions............. 210–213	1 day	to show how to find the inverse of a composite function	Thinking Story	Reteaching Strategy Practice Master 61 Enrichment Master 61	1, 2, 3, 4, 7, 13
62	Graphing Composite Functions 214–215	1 day	✓ to assess mastery of graphing functions		Reteaching Master Practice Master 62 Enrichment Master 62 Assessment Master	1, 2, 3, 4, 9, 13
63	Keeping Sharp: Facts, Computations, and Fractions 216–219	1 day	to review arithmetic facts, computations, and fractions	Thinking Story	Reteaching Strategy Practice Master 63 Enrichment Master 63	1, 2, 3, 4, 8
64	Graphing Functions 220–221	1 day	to provide practice in graphing functions and in identifying functions from completed graphs		Reteaching Strategy Practice Master 64 Enrichment Master 64	9, 13

	LESSON	PACING	PRIMARY OBJECTIVES	FEATURE	RESOURCES	NCTM STANDARDS
65	**Working with Graphs** **222–225**	1 day	to provide applications for organizing and analyzing data		Reteaching Master Practice Master 65 Enrichment Master 65	11
66	**Choosing an Appropriate Graph** **226–227**	1 day	to give practice interpreting graphical data		Reteaching Strategy Practice Master 66 Enrichment Master 66	2, 4, 11
67	**Revisiting Number Facts** **228–229**	1 day	✓ to assess mastery of the basic arithmetic facts		Reteaching Strategy Practice Master 67 Enrichment Master 67 Assessment Master	1, 2, 3, 4, 8
68	**Lines and Angles** **230–233**	1 day	to allow students to explore relationships among points, lines, and angles		Reteaching Strategy Practice Master 68 Enrichment Master 68	9
69	**Perpendicular and Parallel Lines** **234–237**	1 day	to teach or review recognizing parallel and perpendicular lines		Reteaching Strategy Practice Master 69 Enrichment Master 69	2, 9
70	**Congruence and Similarity** **238–239**	1 day	to introduce the geometric concepts of congruence and similarity		Reteaching Master Practice Master 70 Enrichment Master 70	9
71	**Rotation, Reflection, and Translation** **240–241**	1 day	to have students explore congruency by translation, rotation, and reflection		Reteaching Strategy Practice Master 71 Enrichment Master 71	4, 9
72	**Identifying Solid Figures** **242–245**	1 day	to introduce the names and properties of solid figures: prism, cylinder, sphere, and pyramid		Reteaching Strategy Practice Master 72 Enrichment Master 72	9
73	**Lines of Symmetry** ... **246–249**	2 days	to provide experience in finding lines of symmetry		Reteaching Strategy Practice Master 73 Enrichment Master 73	9, 12
74	**Area and Perimeter: Practice** **250–251**	1 day	to demonstrate the ratio of perimeters and the ratio of areas		Reteaching Strategy Practice Master 74 Enrichment Master 74	9, 10
75	**Unit 3 Review** **252–253**		to review algebra readiness and geometry		Practice Master 75 Enrichment Master 75	
76	**Unit 3 Practice** **254–257**		to practice algebra readiness and geometry		Practice Master 76 Enrichment Master 76	
77	**More Unit 3 Practice 258–261**		to practice algebra readiness and geometry	**Game**	Practice Master 77 Enrichment Master 77	
	Unit 3 Test **262–263**		to review algebra readiness and geometry		Assessment Masters	
	Unit 3 Wrap-Up ..... **264–265** Mathematics and Postage Stamps			**Project**		

UNIT CONNECTIONS

INTERVENTION STRATEGIES

In this Teacher's Guide there are specific strategies suggested for students with individual needs. These strategies appear with icons under the headings ESL, Gifted and Talented, Special Needs, Learning Styles, and At Risk, and are provided at the point of use. Following are the icons to look for and the types of strategies that accompany them:

English as a Second Language
These strategies, designed for students who do not speak the English language fluently, suggest meaningful ways to present the lesson concepts and vocabulary.

Gifted and Talented
These strategies are designed to enrich and extend the lessons and offer further challenges to students who have easily mastered the concepts already presented.

Special Needs
Students who are physically challenged or who have learning disabilities may require alternative ways to complete activities, record answers, use manipulatives, and so on. The strategies labeled with this icon offer appropriate methods of teaching lesson concepts to these students.

Learning Styles
Each student has his or her individual approach to learning. The strategies labeled with this icon suggest ways to present lesson concepts so that various learning modalities–such as tactile/kinesthetic, visual, and auditory–can be addressed.

At Risk
These strategies highlight the relevancy of the skills presented by making the connection between school and real life. They are directed toward students who appear to be at risk of dropping out of school before graduation.

TECHNOLOGY CONNECTIONS

The following materials, designed to reinforce and extend lesson concepts, are referred to throughout this Teacher's Guide. It might be helpful to either order the software and reference book or check them out of the school media center or community library.

Look for this **Technology Connection** *icon.*

- *Pondering Problems,* from Micrograms; Mac, IBM, for grades 2-5 (software)
- *Intermediate Math,* from Queue; Mac, IBM, for grades 3-9 (software)
- *Kids Internet Yellow Pages,* from Osborne; McGraw-Hill (reference book)
- *Graphers,* from Sunburst Communications; Mac, for grades K-4 (software)
- *Math Football,* from Gamco; Mac, IBM, for grades 4-12 (software)
- *The King's Rule,* from Sunburst Communications; Mac, IBM, for grades 4-8 (software)
- *The Math Majors,* from Nordic Software; Mac, for grades K-6 (software)
- *Turtle Math,* from LCSI; Mac, for grades 3-6 (software)
- *Quadrominoes,* from Sunburst Communications; Mac, for grades 4-8 (software)
- *Kid CAD,* from Davidson; IBM, for grades 1-6 (software)

CROSS-CURRICULAR CONNECTIONS

This Teacher's Guide offers specific suggestions on ways to connect the math concepts presented in this unit with other subjects that students are studying. Students can connect math concepts with topics they already know about, and they can find examples of math in other subjects and in real-world situations. These strategies are provided at the point of use.

Look for these icons:

GEOGRAPHY CONNECTION Geography	HEALTH CONNECTION Health
SOCIAL STUDIES CONNECTION Social Studies	MUSIC CONNECTION Music
SCIENCE CONNECTION Science	MATH CONNECTION Math
ART CONNECTION Art	PHYSICAL EDUCATION CONNECTION Physical Education
LANGUAGE ARTS CONNECTION Language Arts	SCHOOL TO WORK CONNECTION Careers

LITERATURE CONNECTIONS

The following books are referenced throughout this Teacher's Guide at points where they can be used to introduce, reinforce, or extend specific lesson concepts. You may want to locate these books in your school or community library.

LITERATURE CONNECTION *Look for this* **Literature Connection** *icon.*

- *Charts and Graphs* by Caroline Arnold. F. Watts, 1984.
- *A Game of Functions* by Robert Froman. Crowell, 1974.
- *Sideways Arithmetic from Wayside School* by Louis Sachar. Scholastic, 1989.
- *The Case of the Unnatural: Mathnet Casebook* by David D. Connell and Jim Thurman. Scientific American Books for Young Readers, 1993.
- "More or Less," *Family Math* (p. 209) by Jean Kerr Stenmark, Virginia Thompson, and Ruth Cossey. Lawrence Hall of Science, University of California, 1986.
- *Help Is on the Way for Charts and Graphs* by Marilyn Berry. Children's Press, 1985.
- *The Magic School Bus Inside a Beehive* by Joanna Cole. Scholastic, 1996.
- *Perplexing Puzzles and Tantalizing Teasers* by Martin Gardner. Dover Publications, 1969, 1988.
- *666 Jellybeans! All That?* by Malcolm E. Weiss. Crowell, 1976.
- *Round Trip* by Ann Jonas. Greenwillow Books, 1983.
- *Rechenka's Eggs* by Patricia Polacco. Philomel Books, 1988.

ASSESSMENT OPPORTUNITIES AT-A-GLANCE

LESSON	ALTERNATIVE ASSESSMENT PORTFOLIO	ALTERNATIVE ASSESSMENT PERFORMANCE	FORMAL	SELF ASSESSMENT SELF	ALTERNATIVE ASSESSMENT INFORMAL	CUMULATIVE REVIEWS	MULTIPLE-CHOICE	MASTERY CHECKPOINTS	ANALYZING ANSWERS
51					✓				
52					✓				✓
53				✓					
54					✓	✓			
55					✓				
56			✓					✓	
57				✓					
58					✓				
59		✓				✓			
Mid-Unit Review	✓	✓	✓						
60		✓							
61					✓				
62			✓					✓	
63	✓					✓			
64					✓				
65					✓				
66									
67			✓	✓				✓	
68					✓	✓			
69	✓								
70		✓							
71					✓				
72	✓								
73					✓	✓			
74					✓				
75	✓	✓	✓						
76									
77						✓			
Unit Test			✓				✓		

ASSESSMENT OPTIONS

PORTFOLIO ASSESSMENT

Throughout this Teacher's Guide are suggestions for activities in which students draw pictures, make graphs, and write about mathematics. Keep students' work to assess growth of understanding as the year progresses.

Mid-Unit Review, Lessons 63, 69, 72, and 75

PERFORMANCE ASSESSMENT

Performance Assessment items focus on evaluating how students think and work as they solve problems. Opportunities for performance assessment can be found throughout the unit. Rubrics and guides for grading can be found in the front of the Assessment Blackline Masters.

Lessons 59, Mid-Unit Review, 60, 70, and 75

FORMAL ASSESSMENT

A Mid-Unit Review, Unit Review, and Unit Test help assess students' understanding of concepts, skills, and problem-solving ability. The *Math Explorations and Applications* CD-ROM Test Generator can create additional unit tests at three ability levels. Also, Mastery Checkpoints are provided periodically throughout the unit.

Lessons 56, Mid-Unit Review, 62, 67, 75, and Unit Test

SELF ASSESSMENT

Throughout the program students are given the opportunity to check their own math skills.

Lessons 53, 57, and 67

INFORMAL ASSESSMENT

A variety of assessment suggestions are provided throughout the unit, including interviews, oral questions or presentations, and debates. Also, each lesson includes Assessment Criteria, a list of questions about each student's progress, understanding, and participation.

Lessons 51, 52, 54, 55, 58, 61, 64, 65, 68, 71, 73, and 74

CUMULATIVE REVIEW

Cumulative Reviews, covering material presented thus far in the year, are provided in the unit for use as either assessment or practice.

Lessons 54, 59, 63, 68, 73, and 77

MULTIPLE-CHOICE TESTS (STANDARDIZED FORMAT)

Each unit provides a Unit Test in standardized format, giving students many opportunities to practice taking tests in this format.

MASTERY CHECKPOINTS

Mastery Checkpoints are provided throughout the unit to assess student proficiency in specific skills. Checkpoints reference appropriate Assessment Masters and other assessment options. Results of these evaluations can be recorded on the Mastery Checkpoint Chart.

Lessons 56, 62, and 67

ANALYZING ANSWERS

Analyzing Answers items suggest possible sources of student error and offer teaching strategies for addressing difficulties.

Lesson 52

Look for these icons:

ALTERNATIVE ASSESSMENT | ANALYZING ANSWERS | SELF ASSESSMENT

> *"Observing, questioning, and listening are the primary sources of evidence for assessment that is continual, recursive, and integrated with instruction."*
>
> *—NCTM Assessment Standards*

MASTERY CHECKPOINTS

WHAT TO EXPECT FROM STUDENTS AS THEY COMPLETE THIS UNIT

❾ FUNCTIONS AND INVERSE RELATIONSHIPS—LESSON 56

By this time students should understand inverse operations. Given a function rule, students should be able to find *x* or *y*. Assess this ability using pages 192–193, on which students should correctly answer 80% of the problems, or by using Assessment Blackline Masters pages 20–21. You may record the results of the assessment on the Mastery Checkpoint Chart.

❿ GRAPHING FUNCTIONS—LESSON 62

By this time most students should be able to plot points on a graph, choose appropriate scales for the *x*- and *y*-axes, and demonstrate some understanding of the graph of a function by correctly answering 80% of the problems on pages 214–215 or on Assessment Blackline Masters pages 24–26.

⓫ BASIC ARITHMETIC FACTS—LESSON 67

By this time most students should demonstrate mastery of the basic facts by correctly answering at least 80% of the problems on page 228 in a reasonable amount of time. You may use Assessment Blackline Masters page 27 and record the results of this assessment on the Mastery Checkpoint Chart.

UNIT 3

PROGRAM RESOURCES

THESE ADDITIONAL COMPONENTS OF *MATH EXPLORATIONS AND APPLICATIONS* CAN BE PURCHASED SEPARATELY FROM SRA/MCGRAW-HILL.

LESSON	ESSENTIAL MANIPULATIVE KIT	GAME MAT PACKAGE	TEACHER MANIPULATIVE KIT	INTERMEDIATE MANIPULATIVE KIT	INTERMEDIATE OVERHEAD MANIPULATIVE KIT	*THE CRUNCHER* SOFTWARE	*MATH EXPLORATIONS AND APPLICATIONS* CD-ROM
51		Animal Data game	graphing mat				Lesson 51
52		Baseball game		angle rulers			Lesson 52
53		Snake game					Lesson 53
54	Number Cubes						Lesson 54
55	Number Cubes	Baseball game					Lesson 55
56		Snake game					Lesson 56
57	Number Cubes		beakers	counters	counters		Lesson 57
58				angle rulers			Lesson 58
59			scale	angle rulers			Lesson 59
60				angle rulers			Lesson 60
61	Number Wheels						Lesson 61
62	Number Wheels						Lesson 62
63	Number Wheels			base-10 blocks	base-10 blocks		Lesson 63
64				angle rulers			Lesson 64
65							Lesson 65
66	Number Wheels			angle rulers			Lesson 66
67							Lesson 67
68							Lesson 68
69				angle rulers			Lesson 69
70	Number Wheels						Lesson 70
71	Number Wheels						Lesson 71
72			clock geometric set	clock faces	clock faces		Lesson 72
73			clock	clock faces angle rulers	clock faces		Lesson 73
74							Lesson 74
75							Lesson 75
76							Lesson 76
77	Number Cubes						Lesson 77

UNIT 3

Student Edition pages 174–175

Algebra Readiness and Geometry

INTRODUCING THE UNIT

Using the Student Pages Begin your discussion of the opening unit photo by asking students, "How do pilots use geometry to help them fly planes? How do air traffic controllers use geometry?" Then read aloud the paragraph on the student page that highlights the careers of a pilot and an air traffic controller. These two jobs are very dependent upon one another. This helps make the connection between school and work and encourages students to explore how math is used in the real world.

ACTIVITY Ask students to use **graph paper** to make a grid of their neighborhood as it would look from an airplane. Have them find the coordinates of their own home on this grid.

FYI The first pilots, in the early years of our century, were happy just to get into the air. Finding out where they were would not become a problem until sustained flights became possible. One of the first flights conducted out of sight of any landmark was the crossing of the English channel by a Frenchman named Blériot in 1910. Blériot had to guess where he was based on such things as wind direction and the position of the sun. He could also use a clock and a basic notion of his speed to know how far he should have traveled by a certain time. These two principles, time and rate of motion, would become the basis of the modern navigation systems used on airplanes today. The direction-finding system on a 747 jumbo jet is actually a computer that takes into account everything from fuel consumption to headwinds to the weight of cargo in order to calculate exactly where the plane should be at a given moment. Satellites further complete the picture, sending updates on a plane's position at regular intervals. This system is so sophisticated that a modern jet can travel by computer on trips of thousands of miles.

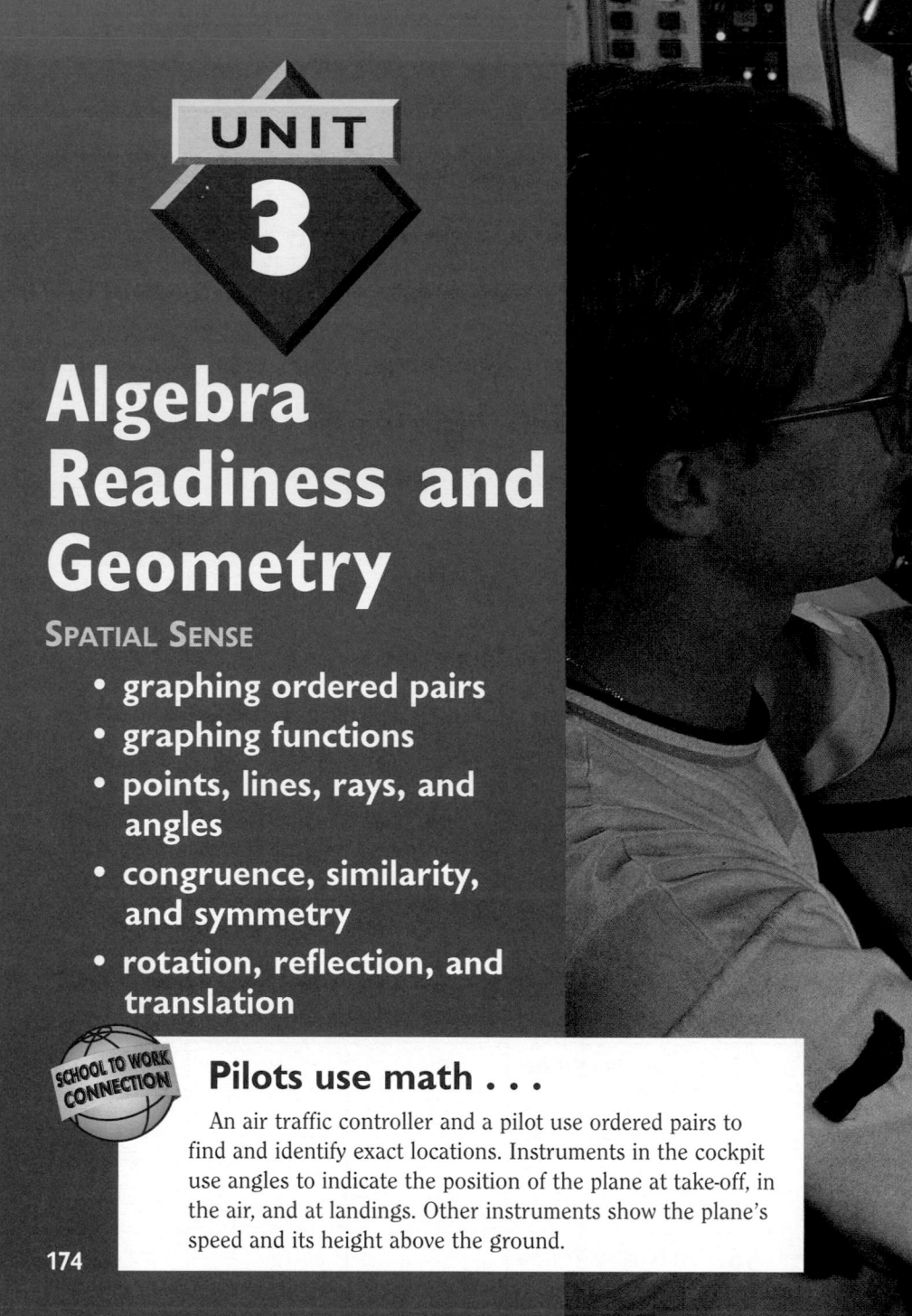

UNIT 3

Algebra Readiness and Geometry

SPATIAL SENSE

- graphing ordered pairs
- graphing functions
- points, lines, rays, and angles
- congruence, similarity, and symmetry
- rotation, reflection, and translation

Pilots use math . . .

An air traffic controller and a pilot use ordered pairs to find and identify exact locations. Instruments in the cockpit use angles to indicate the position of the plane at take-off, in the air, and at landings. Other instruments show the plane's speed and its height above the ground.

174

Thinklab™

SRA's Thinklab™ provides a series of creative and logical problem-solving opportunities for individual students. The problems are designed to appeal to different cognitive abilities.

- Use Problems 41–50 with this unit to reinforce object manipulation (ways and means of dealing with specific data).
- Use Problems 51–60 with this unit to reinforce perception (extrapolating from and beyond given data).

While a modern jet can fly virtually "by wire"—meaning by computer—the roles of the pilot and air traffic controllers remain critical. Just as it is important to know how to calculate without mechanical help in order to estimate correct change, so a pilot must know in his or her own head just how accurate information provided by technology really is. There is no substitute for a thinking person in the cockpit of a plane. And as planes travel between destinations and in the crowded airspace near airports, air traffic controllers must accurately interpret data provided by their equipment. Their ability to make quick decisions based on these data helps them guarantee that planes flying at high speeds and varying altitudes remain safe distances from each other. Especially at night or in bad weather, when visibility is limited, air traffic controllers and pilots must be skilled at interpreting the information that their instruments provide.

Home Connections You may want to send home the Home Connections Blackline Masters letter on pages 40–41 to introduce this unit.

Unit Project This would be a good time to assign the "Mathematics and Postage Stamps" project on pages 264 and 265. Students can begin working on the project in cooperative groups in their free time as they work through the unit. The Unit Project is a good opportunity for students to explore the hobby of stamp collecting, which relates to geography, history, mathematics, and art.

Cooperate 1

Cooperate 1, published by SRA, provides a series of creative and logical problem-solving opportunities for cooperative groups. The problems are designed to provide practice in problem solving, communication, reasoning, and making connections. *Cooperate 1* presents the following cognitive strategies—perceiving spatial relations, ordering and sequencing, logical deduction, establishing and testing hypotheses, sequential exploration, identifying starting points, attending to detail, organizing information, and screening irrelevant information.

Each Problem Card emphasizes a principal strategy as well as reinforcing other strategies.

- Use Problem Cards 11–14 with this unit to emphasize logical deduction.
- Use Problem Card 15 with this unit to emphasize perceiving spatial relations.

Student Edition pages 176–177

LESSON 51 Coordinate Grids

LESSON PLANNER

Objective

- to teach the convention for graphing ordered pairs of numbers

Context of the Lesson This is the first of 13 lessons on graphing and functions. In the *Math Explorations and Applications* program students begin working with functions and graphing in Level 1, but they do little graphing of points and lines before Level 3. Work with functions begins in the third lesson of this sequence (Lesson 53). Checkpoints for monitoring individual students' progress in understanding functions and graphing are provided in Lessons 56 and 62.

MANIPULATIVES

graphing mat* (optional)

Program Resources

"Animal Data" Game Mat
Practice Master 51
Enrichment Master 51
For additional math integration:
Math Throughout the Day*
For extra practice:
CD-ROM* Lesson 51

1 Warm-Up 5 MINUTES

Problem of the Day Present this problem orally or on the chalkboard: Find three *different* ways to extend this number pattern: 3, 6, 10, . . . (Possible answers: adding 1 more each time [15, 21, 28, . . .]; alternately adding 3 and 4 [13, 17, 20, . . .]; doubling and alternately subtracting 0 and 2 [20, 38, 76, . . .].)

Problem-Solving Strategies Ask students who have solved the Problem of the Day to share how they solved it and any strategies they used.

MENTAL MATH Introduce a new type of exercise in which you say that you have a certain amount of money and want to purchase certain items. Students determine whether you have enough money (thumbs up) or not (thumbs down).

Is $10 enough money to buy:

a. a scarf for $4.97 + a hat for $5.60? (thumbs down)
b. shoes for $9.50 + a tie for $2.05? (thumbs down)
c. a scarf for $4.97 + a tie for $2.05? (thumbs up)
d. a hat for $5.60 + shoelaces for $0.69? (thumbs up)
e. shoes for $9.50 + shoelaces for $1.10? (thumbs down)

EXPLORE

LESSON 51 Coordinate Grids

GEOGRAPHY CONNECTION

Graph City is laid out with numbered streets running north and south, and numbered avenues running east and west.

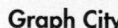

Graph City

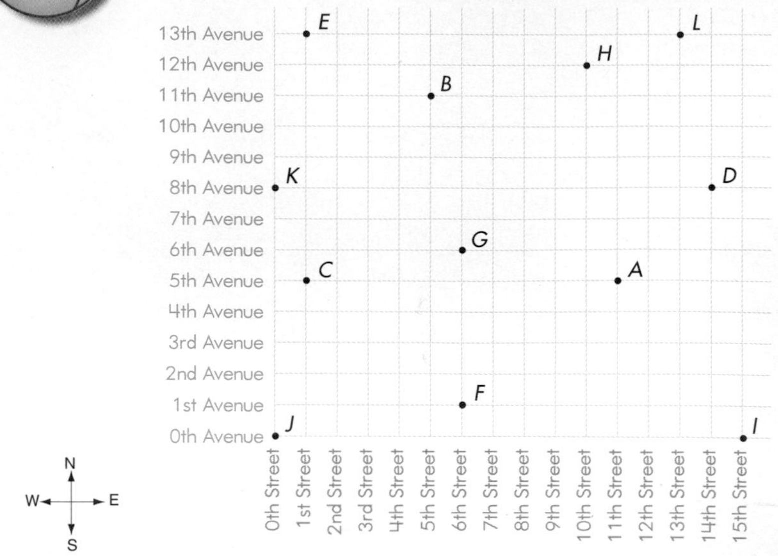

Look at the map of Graph City.

If you went to the corner of 11th Street and 5th Avenue, where would you be? The point is labeled *A*.

- Where is point *B*? **5th Street and 11th Avenue**
- Suppose a friend in Graph City asked you to meet her at the corner of 11th and 5th. Where would you go? **The directions are ambiguous; they could refer to point *A* or point *B*.**
- If your friend didn't go to the same place you went, where do you think she might be? **point *A* or point *B*, wherever you are not**
- What would you do about it? **Students could suggest that they would stay put and hope their friend would realize the misunderstanding and find them, or suggest that they would walk to the "other" 11th and 5th.**

SPECIAL NEEDS

Meeting Individual Needs

Some students may have difficulty remembering which coordinate to give first when naming an ordered pair. Have these students recite the phrase "Over, then up," to help them remember.

RETEACHING

MANIPULATIVES No reteaching strategy is suggested at this time. The next lesson and many others in this unit provide practice with ordered pairs and graphs. You may want to use the **graphing mat*** for further practice with locating coordinates. Have students complete the Enrichment Master on page 51.

*available separately

Suppose the people of Graph City agree to always give the street name first and the avenue name second. Answer these questions.

1. Where is the corner of 11th and 5th? **Point *A***
2. Where is the corner of 5th and 11th? **Point *B***
3. How many blocks would you have to walk to get from 11th and 5th to 5th and 11th? (Do not cut across blocks.) **12**
4. Is there more than one way to get from 11th and 5th to 5th and 11th by walking only 12 blocks? See how many ways you can find. **yes**
5. Suppose you don't cut across blocks and you don't walk in a wrong direction on purpose.
   a. Do all ways of getting from 11th and 5th to 5th and 11th require walking exactly 12 blocks? **yes**
   b. What must you do to make the path longer? **walk in the wrong direction part of the time**
6. How many blocks would you have to walk to get from 8th and 8th to 8th and 8th? **0**
7. How many blocks would you have to walk to get from 4th and 7th to 6th and 3rd? **6**

Give the location of these points on the map of Graph City. Always give the street name first and the avenue name second. The first one has been done for you.

8. *A* **11th and 5th**
9. *E* **1st and 13th**
10. *I* **15th and 0th**
11. *B* **5th and 11th**
12. *F* **6th and 1st**
13. *J* **0th and 0th**
14. *C* **1st and 5th**
15. *G* **6th and 6th**
16. *K* **0th and 8th**
17. *D* **14th and 8th**
18. *H* **10th and 12th**
19. *L* **13th and 13th**

FANTASTIC FACT

The footprints left on the moon by the *Apollo* astronauts will last about 10 million years.

❷ Teach

Using the Student Pages You may wish to teach the "Animal Data" Game Mat, for practice with graphing data, before you begin work on page 176 so that students can play when they finish the problems. Discuss page 176 with the class. Explain that the people of Graph City agree on a convention of giving the street first, then the avenue. This convention is equivalent to the usual convention in graphing of giving the x (or horizontal) coordinate first.

Discuss the first seven questions on page 177. In problem 4, it is unlikely that students will find all the 12-block paths from A to B (there are 924), but they should recognize that there are many. Then have students do problems 9–19 independently.

GAME

Introducing the "Animal Data" Game Mat Demonstrate the "Animal Data" Game Mat with a few students at the front of the class. This Game Mat provides practice with collecting and displaying data on a graph and using compass directions. Complete directions for playing are on the Game Mat. A copy of this Game Mat can also be found on page 583 of this Teacher's Guide.

❸ Wrap-Up

5 MINUTES

In Closing Ask students to explain the rule for naming ordered pairs of numbers.

ALTERNATIVE ASSESSMENT

Informal Assessment Observe students as they complete the lesson. Ask them to explain their thinking as they work.

Assessment Criteria

Did the student . . .

✓ correctly locate and identify points on the coordinate graph?

✓ communicate the convention for naming ordered pairs of numbers?

Homework Have students use the map of Graph City to create two new problems about the points. Invite them to add three landmarks at other points on the map and name those points.

PRACTICE p. 51

LESSON 51 PRACTICE Name__________

Square City

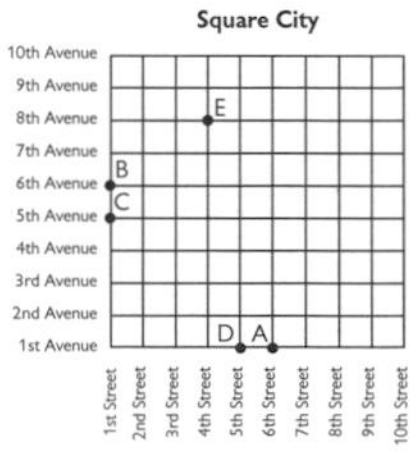

Suppose the people of Square City agree to always give the street name first and the avenue name second.

1. Where is the corner of 6th and 1st? A
2. Where is the corner of 1st and 6th? B
3. How many blocks would you have to walk to get from 6th and 1st to 1st and 6th? (You must not cut across blocks.) ten
4. Is there more than one way to get from 6th and 1st to 1st and 6th by walking only ten blocks? yes

Give the location of these points on the map of Square City. Remember to give the street name first and the avenue name second.

5. C 1st and 5th
6. D 5th and 1st
7. E 4th and 8th

Copyright © SRA/McGraw-Hill. Permission is granted to reproduce this page for classroom use.

Math Explorations and Applications Level 4 • 51

ENRICHMENT p. 51

LESSON 51 ENRICHMENT Name__________

Mr. Quinn has spent the day sightseeing. He is tired and wants to find the shortest route possible back to his hotel.

Here is a map showing Mr. Quinn's location and the location of his hotel. He can only walk east or south on the streets shown by the black grid lines.

How many paths are there to his hotel? 6

Which path is the shortest? There is no shortest path.

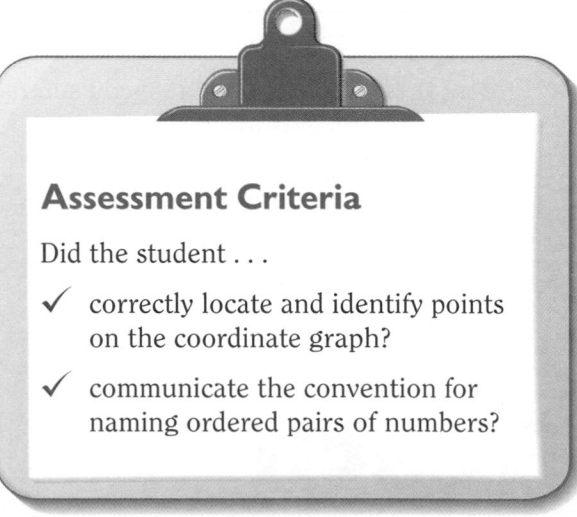

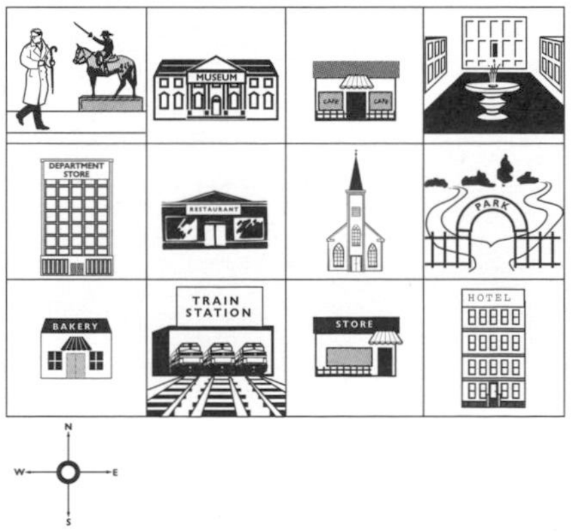

Copyright © SRA/McGraw-Hill. Permission is granted to reproduce this page for classroom use.

Math Explorations and Applications Level 4 • 51

LESSON 52

Student Edition pages 178–179

Coordinates

LESSON PLANNER

Objectives

- ▶ to provide practice in locating a point with given coordinates
- ▶ to provide practice in determining the coordinates of a given point

Context of the Lesson This is the second of 13 lessons on graphing and functions.

MANIPULATIVES

rulers* or straightedges

Program Resources

"Baseball" Game Mat
Reteaching Master
Practice Master 52
Enrichment Master 52
For additional math integration: Math Throughout the Day*
For extra practice: CD-ROM* Lesson 52

1 Warm-Up

5 MINUTES

Problem of the Day Challenge students to solve this problem: A small bunny and a large hare hop up 30 steps. The bunny hops up every other step. The hare hops up every fifth step. On which steps do both land? (Both land on steps 10, 20, and 30.)

Problem-Solving Strategies Ask students who have solved the Problem of the Day to share how they solved it and any strategies they used.

MENTAL MATH Present these multidigit addition and subtraction problems for students to solve mentally.

a. 379 – 279 = (100) **b.** 825 – 600 = (225)
c. 450 + 350 = (800) **d.** 567 + 99 = (666)
e. 240 + 240 = (480) **f.** 727 – 101 = (626)
g. 25 + 75 + 650 = (750) **h.** 960 – 810 = (150)

2 Teach

Using the Student Pages You may wish to introduce the "Baseball" Game Mat before beginning your discussion of page 178 so that students can play when they finish page 179. This game provides practice with locating coordinates.

MIXED PRACTICE

LESSON 52

Coordinates

ALGEBRA READINESS

Places on a graph can be located quickly by pairs of numbers called coordinates. In this lesson you'll learn how to find and name coordinates of locations in Graph City.

You may remember that the people in Graph City say "11th and 5th" as a short way to say "the corner of 11th Street and 5th Avenue."

Here's an even shorter way: (11, 5)

You can use this way for the graph on page 179. For example, to tell where point *B* is, you can write (3, 8).

◆ How would you tell where point *E* is?

The two numbers that tell the location of a point on a graph are called the **coordinates** of that point.

The coordinates of point *B* are (3, 8).
The coordinates of point *E* are (13, 2).

The "sideways" coordinate is given first. The "up-and-down" coordinate is given second.

Answer these questions.

1. What are the coordinates of point *D*? **(14, 10)**
2. What are the coordinates of point *M*? **(8, 3)**
3. What are the coordinates of point *A*? **(6, 6)**
4. What are the coordinates of point *X*? **(2, 5)**
5. What are the coordinates of point *Z*? **(12, 8)**

Solve these riddles by writing the correct letter for each of the coordinates. Use the graph on page 179.

6. What did the acorn say when it grew up?

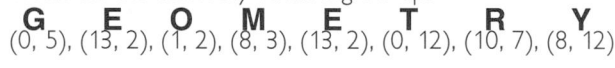

G E O M E T R Y
(0, 5), (13, 2), (1, 2), (8, 3), (13, 2), (0, 12), (10, 7), (8, 12)

or

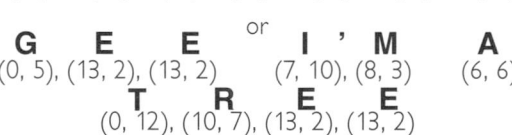

G E E I ' M A
(0, 5), (13, 2), (13, 2) (7, 10), (8, 3) (6, 6)
T R E E
(0, 12), (10, 7), (13, 2), (13, 2)

178 • Algebra Readiness and Geometry

Literature Connection Invite students to read *Charts and Graphs* by Caroline Arnold for an explanation of basic graphs.

RETEACHING p. 15

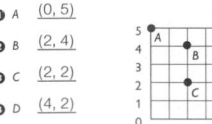

LESSON 52 RETEACHING Name________________

You may remember that the people in Graph City always give the street name first, and then the avenue. They had to have a rule so that they did not mix up the addresses. This is true for points on a graph as well.

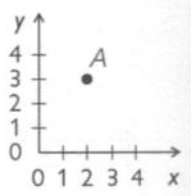

The two numbers that tell the location of a point on a graph are called the **coordinates** of that point. The coordinates of point *A* are 2 spaces over on the *x*-axis and 3 spaces up on the *y*-axis. The location of point *A* would be written as (2, 3).

Remember: The "sideways" coordinate is always given first. The "up and down" coordinate is given second.

The "sideways" line is known as the **x-axis.**

The "up-and-down" line is known as the **y-axis.**

Another way to state the rule is that the *x*-coordinate is given first, and the *y*-coordinate is given second (*x*, *y*).

On this graph the *x*-coordinate is 2, and the *y*-coordinate is 3.

Use the graph below. Name the location of each point given.

1. *A* (0, 5)
2. *B* (2, 4)
3. *C* (2, 2)
4. *D* (4, 2)
5. *E* (5, 0)

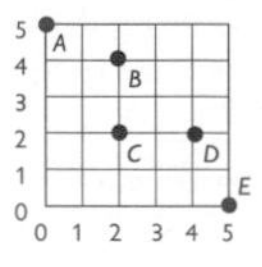

Copyright © SRA/McGraw-Hill. Permission is granted to reproduce this page for classroom use.

Math Explorations and Applications Level 4 • 15

*available separately

7. Which president of the United States would you have gone to if your clothes needed mending?
T A Y L O R
(0, 12), (6, 6), (8, 12), (11, 12), (1, 2), (10, 7)

8. Which two presidents of the United States had the same names as cars?
F O R D
(2, 1), (1, 2), (10, 7), (14, 10) and
L I N C O L N
(11, 12), (7, 10), (13, 5), (5, 13), (1, 2), (11, 12), (13, 5)

9. What kind of sand is found at the bottom of the Pacific Ocean?
W E T S A N D
(5, 2), (13, 2), (0, 12) (3, 10), (6, 6), (13, 5), (14, 10)

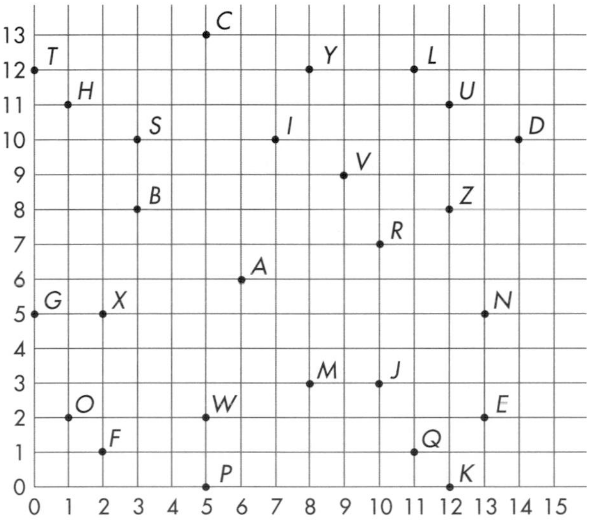

Make up your own riddles or questions and write them in your Math Journal. Ask a friend to solve them.

MATH JOURNAL

You might introduce and begin to use the terms *x-coordinate* and *y-coordinate*. However, the terms *sideways* and *up and down* or *horizontal* and *vertical* are still acceptable. Do problem 1 with the class. Then skip to problem 6 and decode the riddle. Then go on to page 179. Encourage students to make up some coded riddles of their own.

GAME MANIPULATIVES

Introducing the "Baseball" Game Mat Demonstrate the "Baseball" Game Mat by playing a half or full inning with the class. Students will need **rulers***. This Game Mat provides practice with locating coordinates on a graph and probabilistic thinking. Complete directions for playing are on the Game Mat. A copy of "Baseball" can also be found on page 585 of this Teacher's Guide.

3 Wrap-Up

5 MINUTES

In Closing Have students tell how to locate an ordered pair on a graph.

ANALYZING ANSWERS

Check for patterns in students' errors. Students who reverse the order of the coordinates can benefit from using their fingers to locate points. Have them always move first sideways along the *x*-axis, then up to where that line intersects the line that begins on the *y*-axis.

ALTERNATIVE ASSESSMENT

Informal Assessment Challenge students to name the ordered pair for any point on the graph on page 179 and to locate any point for which you name the ordered pair.

Assessment Criteria

Did the student . . .

- ✓ correctly identify points on the graph?
- ✓ correctly give the coordinates for points on the graph?
- ✓ solve the riddles by decoding the words?
- ✓ correctly answer at least 75% of the questions?

Homework Assign Practice Master 52 to reinforce the skill of graphing.

PRACTICE p. 52

LESSON 52 PRACTICE Name______

Use the code graph to translate ordered pairs to letters and answer the riddle.

What did one math book say to the other?

I'VE GOT
(1, 1) (12, 10) (4, 2) (4, 10) (12, 8) (8, 9)

PROBLEMS.
(10, 2) (5, 8) (12, 8) (8, 1) (14, 9) (4, 2) (14, 3) (12, 5)

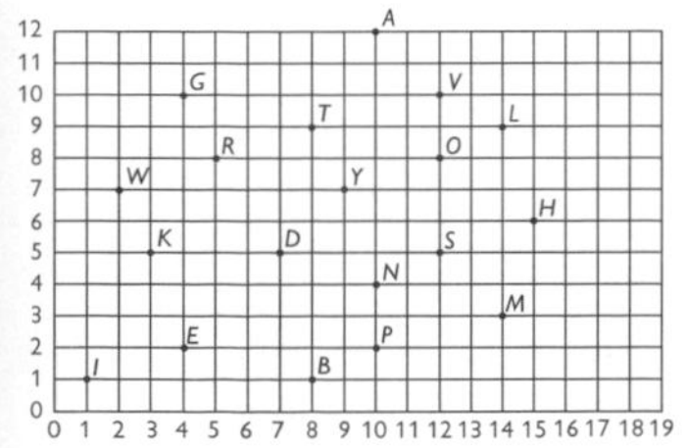

52 • *Math Explorations and Applications* Level 4

ENRICHMENT p. 52

LESSON 52 ENRICHMENT Name______

Use the grid below to write the letters for each coordinate to spell the names of some animals you might see at the zoo.

1. (1, 1) (9, 11) (12, 4) (1, 7) (4, 2) (2, 5) (5, 8) SEA LION
2. (15, 1) (2, 5) (1, 7) (12, 4) (13, 3) (9, 1) (9, 11) (12, 4) (13, 3) POLAR BEAR
3. (1, 1) (4, 2) (9, 1) (9, 11) (13, 3) (4, 2) (12, 4) (5, 8) (11, 8) (4, 2) (7, 6) (9, 11) (13, 3) SIBERIAN TIGER
4. (14, 7) (3, 12) (5, 8) (14, 12) (9, 11) (8, 4) MONKEY
5. (15, 1) (12, 4) (5, 8) (11, 8) (7, 10) (9, 11) (13, 3) PANTHER
6. (1, 1) (9, 11) (12, 4) (1, 7) SEAL
7. (14, 12) (2, 5) (12, 4) (1, 7) (12, 4) KOALA

The names of five other animals can be made from letters on the grid. Can you find them? Write the name of each animal, then write the coordinates for each letter to spell the name. Can you find even more than five?

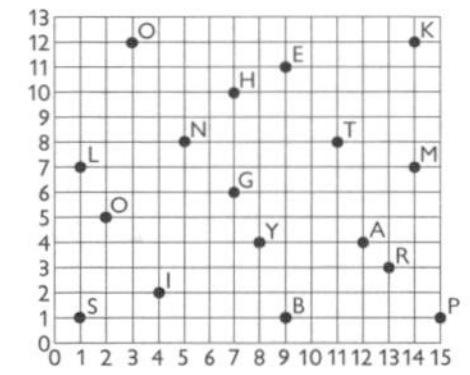

Other animals:
SNAKE (1, 1) (5, 8) (12, 4) (14, 12) (9, 11)
ANTEATER (12, 4) (5, 8) (11, 8) (9, 11) (12, 4) (11, 8) (9, 11) (13, 3)
RAM (13, 3) (12, 4) (14, 7)
ELEPHANT (9,11) (1, 7) (9, 11) (15, 1) (7, 10) (12, 4) (5, 8) (11, 8)
APE (12, 4) (15, 1) (9, 11)

52 • *Math Explorations and Applications* Level 4

*available separately

LESSON 53

Student Edition pages 180–183

Determining Function Rules

LESSON PLANNER

Objectives

- ▶ to review the concept of functions
- ▶ to provide practice with basic arithmetic facts

Context of the Lesson This is the third of 13 lessons on graphing and functions. Work with functions began at the first-grade level. In Level 3, students worked with pictures of function machines and with the arrow notation that this lesson reviews. Unit 1 presented some work with functions.

MANIPULATIVES

none

Program Resources

"Snake" Game Mat
Reteaching Master
Practice Master 53
Enrichment Master 53
For additional math integration:
Math Throughout the Day*
For extra practice:
CD-ROM* Lesson 53

1 Warm-Up

5 MINUTES

Problem of the Day Present the following problem. Explain to students that there is more than one answer: Onawa bought two magnets. One magnet cost 18¢ more than the other. Both prices were two-digit numbers she could divide evenly by 3 but not by 6. How much did each magnet cost? (one possible answer: 15¢ and 33¢)

Problem-Solving Strategies Ask students who have solved the Problem of the Day to share how they solved it and any strategies they used.

MENTAL MATH Provide practice with basic addition, subtraction, multiplication, and division facts. Include some missing-term problems.

a.	$n + 3 = 4$ ($n = 1$)	**b.**	$14 - n = 9$ ($n = 5$)
c.	$13 - 7 =$ (6)	**d.**	$7 \times 4 =$ (28)
e.	$80 \div n = 8$ ($n = 10$)	**f.**	$30 \div n = 5$ ($n = 6$)
g.	$6 \times n = 42$ ($n = 7$)	**h.**	$21 \div 7 =$ (3)
i.	$7 + 8 =$ (15)	**j.**	$n - 4 = 7$ ($n = 11$)
k.	$n \times 9 = 18$ ($n = 2$)	**l.**	$42 \div 6 =$ (7)
m.	$3 \times n = 12$ ($n = 4$)	**n.**	$n - 2 = 10$ ($n = 12$)

LESSON 53

Determining Function Rules

ALGEBRA READINESS

You've worked with function machines with known rules. In this lesson you'll review how to figure out unknown function rules.

This function machine does something to numbers that are put into it. If you put in a 7, a 12 will come out. We will write that like this:

7 —(?)→ 12

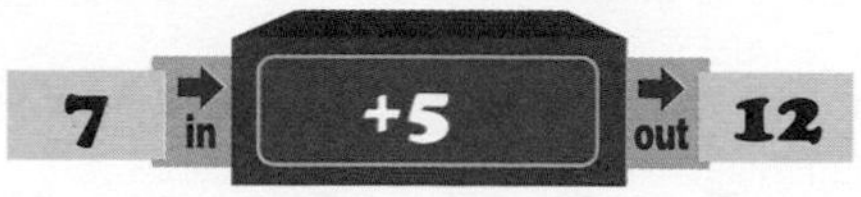

Arrows can be curved or straight. They can go in any direction, but they must point from the number going in to the number coming out.

If we put in 10, 15 will come out.

10 —(?)→ 15

This set of arrow operations shows what happens when we put in 0, 4, 9, and 25.

0 —(?)→ 5

4 —(?)→ 9

9 —(?)→ 14

25 —(?)→ 30

- ◆ What do you think will come out if you put in 100? **105**
- ◆ What do you think the function machine is doing? **adding 5**

The function rule for this machine is **add 5.** We will write the **add 5** function like this:

—(+5)→

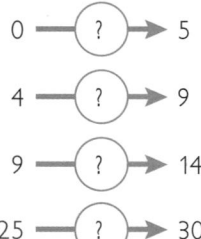

Why teach it this way?

Reviewing and extending the topic of functions in this unit helps students learn one of the most common and useful ideas in mathematics and gives them a significant amount of practice in written and mental arithmetic.

*available separately

Find a function rule for each set of arrow operations.

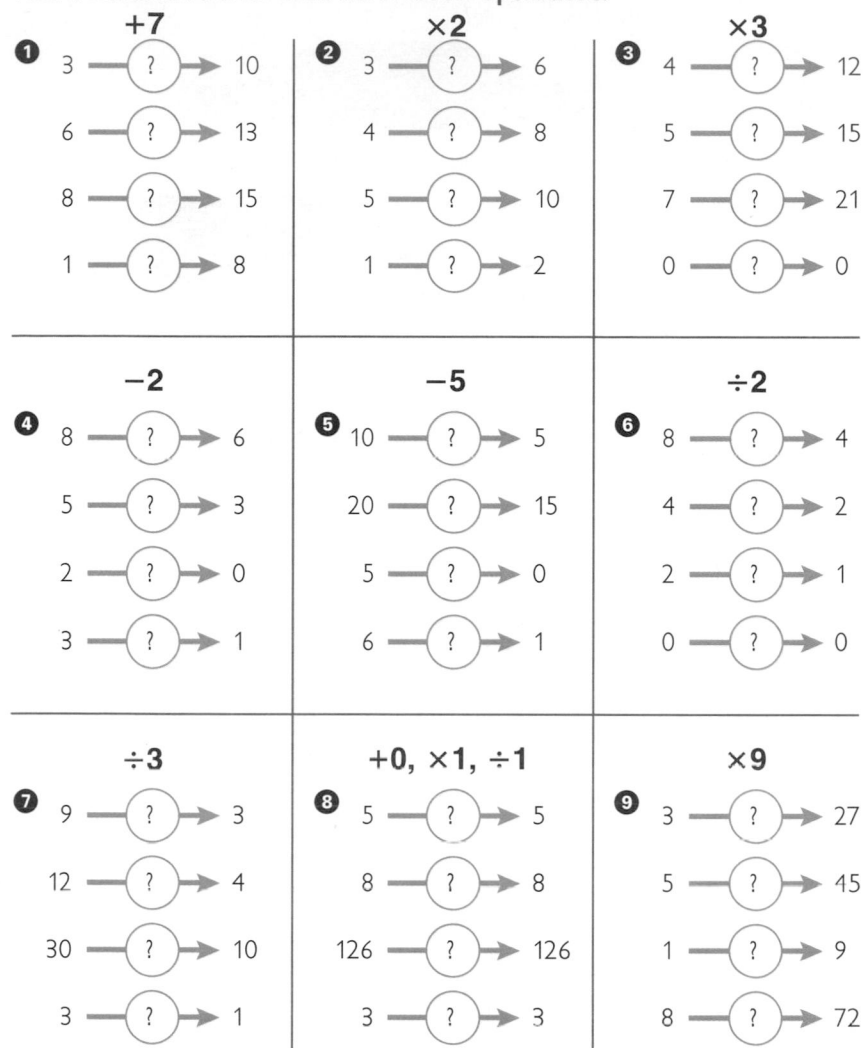

1 +7
- 3 → ? → 10
- 6 → ? → 13
- 8 → ? → 15
- 1 → ? → 8

2 ×2
- 3 → ? → 6
- 4 → ? → 8
- 5 → ? → 10
- 1 → ? → 2

3 ×3
- 4 → ? → 12
- 5 → ? → 15
- 7 → ? → 21
- 0 → ? → 0

4 −2
- 8 → ? → 6
- 5 → ? → 3
- 2 → ? → 0
- 3 → ? → 1

5 −5
- 10 → ? → 5
- 20 → ? → 15
- 5 → ? → 0
- 6 → ? → 1

6 ÷2
- 8 → ? → 4
- 4 → ? → 2
- 2 → ? → 1
- 0 → ? → 0

7 ÷3
- 9 → ? → 3
- 12 → ? → 4
- 30 → ? → 10
- 3 → ? → 1

8 +0, ×1, ÷1
- 5 → ? → 5
- 8 → ? → 8
- 126 → ? → 126
- 3 → ? → 3

9 ×9
- 3 → ? → 27
- 5 → ? → 45
- 1 → ? → 9
- 8 → ? → 72

2 Teach

Using the Student Pages You may wish to demonstrate the "Snake" Game Mat before beginning work on pages 180–183 so that students who finish early can play. This game provides practice with solving missing-term problems.

Complete page 180 with the entire class. Students may be familiar with function machines and arrow notation from work in previous grades. To review, emphasize that arrow notation is a short form of function-machine notation: as you go from the end of the arrow to its point, you perform the operation indicated in the circle. Explain to students that the arrow can go in any direction. Point out that all arrow operations within a set belong to the same function machine. You may find that some students can think of many different functions that produce the results given on page 180. However, the intent of this lesson is to find simple arithmetic function rules, such as add 2, divide by 3, and so on.

Introduce page 181 by doing problem 1 with the class. Then let students complete the page independently. Discuss answers with the whole class. Even a rule such as "give back the same number that went in" makes sense, although it lacks a mathematical description.

Literature Connection Read excerpts from *A Game of Functions* by Robert Froman to familiarize students with situations that involve the concept of functions in everyday life.

◆ LESSON 53 Determining Function Rules

Teach

ALGEBRA READINESS

Using the Student Pages Go over page 182 with students. Help them recognize that although they might think they know a particular function rule, it is not a rule unless it works in all cases.

Have students work in pairs on the problems on page 182. Encourage partners to discuss their ideas to ensure that they find two different function rules for each problem. Have students go on to work independently on page 183.

GAME

Introducing the "Snake" Game Mats Demonstrate the game by playing it for a few minutes in front of the class. This game provides practice with solving missing-term problems, mental arithmetic, and mathematical reasoning. Emphasize that "Snake" allows only addition and subtraction rules. "Harder Snake," which will be introduced in Lesson 120, allows only multiplication and division rules. Complete directions are on the Game Mat. A copy of these Game Mats can be found on pages 603–604 of this Teacher's Guide.

SPECIAL NEEDS

Meeting Individual Needs

Students who are impulsive workers, have organizational problems, or have weak short-term memory may forget that a function rule must work in every case. Model for them a step-by-step process for finding function rules. For example, to solve problem 6 on page 181, you might say:

1. What can you do to 8 to get 4? (Subtract 4 or divide by 2.)
2. What can you do to 4 to get 2? (Subtract 2 or divide by 2.)
3. Now remember, a function machine must do the same thing to each number. So what do you think the rule might be? (Divide by 2.)
4. You may be right, but the only way to be sure is to try your rule on all the remaining examples to check that it always works.

◆ LESSON 53 Determining Function Rules

Suppose you put 4 into a function machine and 20 comes out. What is the function rule?

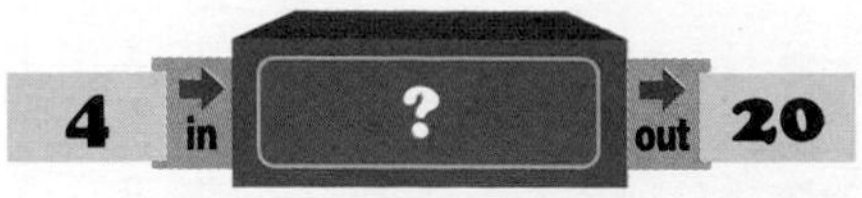

- ◆ Could the function rule be ×5? **yes**
- ◆ If the function rule was ×5 and 6 went into the machine, what would come out? **30**

Let's see what happens when 5 goes into the function machine.

- ◆ With this information do you think the function rule could be ×5? **no; if so, 25 would come out**
- ◆ Can you find a function rule that works with both examples? What is that rule? **yes; +16**

When you try to figure out function rules, it is important to use at least two examples and be sure that the rule fits both of them.

For each of the following, write two possible function rules.

10. 4 —(?)→ 8 **×2, +4**
11. 30 —(?)→ 15 **÷2, −15**
12. 10 —(?)→ 20 **×2, +10**
13. 125 —(?)→ 500 **×4, +375**
14. 3 —(?)→ 21 **×7, +18**
15. 50 —(?)→ 10 **÷5, −40**
16. 15 —(?)→ 30 **×2, +15**
17. 1 —(?)→ 1 **+0, −0, ×1, ÷1**

Challenge: Can you find three rules for problem 17?

182 • Algebra Readiness and Geometry

TECHNOLOGY CONNECTION

Technology Connection For practice with choosing the correct operation, studying data, and problem-solving, refer students to the software *Pondering Problems* from Micrograms (Mac, IBM, for grades 2–5).

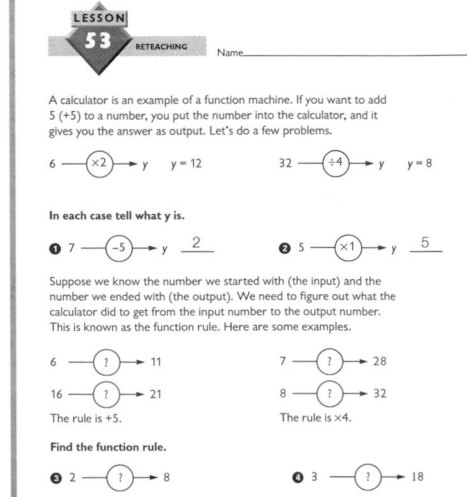

RETEACHING p. 16

LESSON 53 RETEACHING Name__________

A calculator is an example of a function machine. If you want to add 5 (+5) to a number, you put the number into the calculator, and it gives you the answer as output. Let's do a few problems.

6 —(×2)→ y y = 12 32 —(÷4)→ y y = 8

In each case tell what y is.

1. 7 —(−5)→ y 2
2. 5 —(×1)→ y 5

Suppose we know the number we started with (the input) and the number we ended with (the output). We need to figure out what the calculator did to get from the input number to the output number. This is known as the function rule. Here are some examples.

6 —(?)→ 11
16 —(?)→ 21
The rule is +5.

7 —(?)→ 28
8 —(?)→ 32
The rule is ×4.

Find the function rule.

3. 2 —(?)→ 8; 3 —(?)→ 9; 4 —(?)→ 10; 5 —(?)→ 11. The rule is +6.
4. 3 —(?)→ 18; 7 —(?)→ 42; 9 —(?)→ 54; 12 —(?)→ 72. The rule is ×6.

16 • *Math Explorations and Applications* Level 4

Copyright © SRA/McGraw-Hill. Permission is granted to reproduce this page for classroom use.

The rule for a certain function machine is +4. If you put the number 7 into the machine, what number will come out?

Here's another way to ask the same question:

7 —(+4)→ y What is y? **11**

In each case, tell what y is.

18. 7 —(+4)→ y **11**
19. 5 —(+0)→ y **5**
20. 8 —(+4)→ y **12**
21. 5 —(−0)→ y **5**
22. 16 —(+4)→ y **20**
23. 5 —(×1)→ y **5**
24. 7 —(×4)→ y **28**
25. 5 —(÷1)→ y **5**
26. y ←(×4)— 8 **2**
27. y ←(×0)— 5 **0**
28. 6 —(×4)→ y **24**
29. 7 —(×8)→ y **56**
30. 16 —(−4)→ y **12**
31. 27 —(+8)→ y **35**
32. y ←(−4)— 12 **8**
33. 53 —(−12)→ y **41**
34. 16 —(÷4)→ y **4**
35. y ←(×0)— 7 **0**
36. 8 —(÷4)→ y **2**
37. 41 —(×0)→ y **0**
38. 20 —(÷5)→ y **4**
39. 8 —(×2)→ y **16**
40. 43 —(−8)→ y **35**
41. y ←(+7)— 17 **24**

3 Wrap-Up

5 MINUTES

In Closing Have students tell what the *y* stands for in the function machine problems on page 183.

SELF ASSESSMENT

Have students write a brief statement that explains how they figure out function rules and how they verify that they are correct.

Assessment Criteria

Did the student . . .

- ✓ contribute to the discussion of arrow operations?
- ✓ communicate strategies used to determine and verify function rules?
- ✓ explain how to solve for *y?*
- ✓ correctly name at least 75% of the function rules?

Homework Have students write five function-machine problems, like those on page 181 or 183, to exchange with classmates.

> *Thinking is the basic skill in mathematics.*
>
> —Stephen S. Willoughby, *Teaching Mathematics: What Is Basic?*

PRACTICE p. 53

LESSON 53 PRACTICE Name__________

Find a function rule for each set of arrow operations.

1. −4	2. ×5	3. ÷2
10 —(?)→ 6	6 —(?)→ 30	20 —(?)→ 10
12 —(?)→ 8	2 —(?)→ 10	16 —(?)→ 8
14 —(?)→ 10	4 —(?)→ 20	12 —(?)→ 6
4 —(?)→ 0	5 —(?)→ 25	10 —(?)→ 5
4. +6	**5. ×2**	**6. ×1, +0, ÷1, −0**
11 —(?)→ 17	0 —(?)→ 0	6 —(?)→ 6
8 —(?)→ 14	2 —(?)→ 4	4 —(?)→ 4
6 —(?)→ 12	6 —(?)→ 12	0 —(?)→ 0
24 —(?)→ 30	8 —(?)→ 16	50 —(?)→ 50

In each case, tell what y is.

7. 14 —(+6)→ y y = 20
8. 27 —(−6)→ y y = 21
9. 10 —(÷2)→ y y = 5
10. 11 —(×6)→ y y = 66
11. 16 —(÷4)→ y y = 4
12. 16 —(÷2)→ y y = 8
13. 9 —(+8)→ y y = 17
14. 7 —(×5)→ y y = 35

Copyright © SRA/McGraw-Hill. Permission is granted to reproduce this page for classroom use.

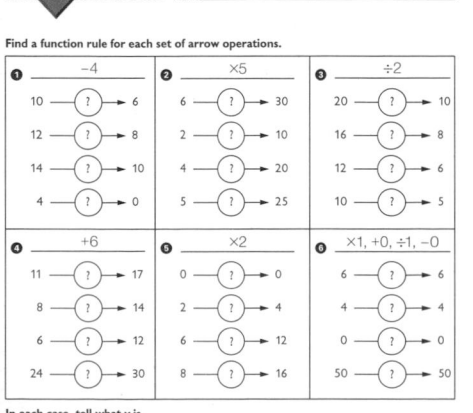

ENRICHMENT p. 53

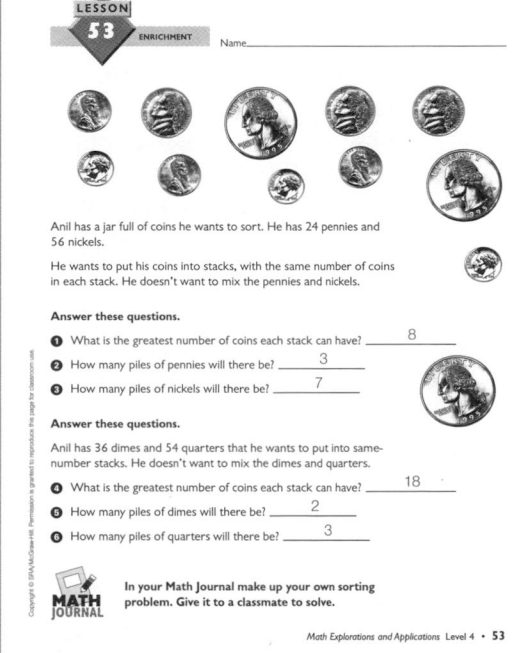

LESSON 53 ENRICHMENT Name__________

Anil has a jar full of coins he wants to sort. He has 24 pennies and 56 nickels.

He wants to put his coins into stacks, with the same number of coins in each stack. He doesn't want to mix the pennies and nickels.

Answer these questions.

1. What is the greatest number of coins each stack can have? 8
2. How many piles of pennies will there be? 3
3. How many piles of nickels will there be? 7

Answer these questions.

Anil has 36 dimes and 54 quarters that he wants to put into same-number stacks. He doesn't want to mix the dimes and quarters.

4. What is the greatest number of coins each stack can have? 18
5. How many piles of dimes will there be? 2
6. How many piles of quarters will there be? 3

MATH JOURNAL **In your Math Journal make up your own sorting problem. Give it to a classmate to solve.**

Copyright © SRA/McGraw-Hill. Permission is granted to reproduce this page for classroom use.

LESSON 54

Student Edition pages 184–187

Inverse Functions

LESSON PLANNER

Objective

▶ to review inverse operations

Context of the Lesson This is the fourth of 13 lessons on graphing and functions. Finding the input by using the inverse operation was taught at the third-grade level and is reviewed here. It will be used throughout Unit 3 and will be developed further in Lessons 61 and 62.

MANIPULATIVES

box or container (optional)

slips of paper, numbered (optional)

Program Resources

Number Cubes

Reteaching Master

Practice Master 54

Enrichment Master 54

For extra practice: CD-ROM* Lesson 54

Cumulative Review, page 546

1 Warm-Up

5 MINUTES

Problem of the Day If you wish, display a calendar students can consult to solve the following problem: Suppose the day after tomorrow is Saturday the 21st. What day was it two days before yesterday? (Monday the 16th)

Problem-Solving Strategies Ask students who have solved the Problem of the Day to share how they solved it and any strategies they used.

MENTAL MATH Play "Cubo" (page 163) with the class. Have students try to make all the numbers from 21 to 0. Extend or change the range of numbers as students become more proficient at the game. A copy of "Cubo" can also be found on page 15 of the Home Connections Blackline Masters.

MIXED PRACTICE

LESSON 54

Inverse Functions

If you know the function rule and the number coming out of a function machine, you can find out the number put into the machine.

For example, if the rule is ×10 and 30 comes out, you know that 3 went in. That's because 3 × 10 = 30.

The rule for a certain function machine is +4. If the number that comes out is 10, what number was put into the machine?

Here's another way to ask the same question:

x —(+4)→ 10 What is x? **6**

In each case, tell what x is.

ALGEBRA READINESS

1. x —(+4)→ 10 **6**
2. x —(−4)→ 4 **8**
3. x —(+4)→ 15 **11**
4. x —(÷2)→ 1 **2**
5. x —(+4)→ 20 **16**
6. x —(÷2)→ 5 **10**
7. x —(−4)→ 10 **14**
8. x —(÷2)→ 6 **12**
9. x —(−4)→ 15 **19**
10. x —(÷2)→ 10 **20**
11. x —(−4)→ 20 **24**
12. x —(÷2)→ 9 **18**
13. x —(×2)→ 14 **7**
14. x —(+9)→ 14 **5**
15. x —(×2)→ 20 **10**
16. x —(−9)→ 14 **23**
17. x —(×2)→ 2 **1**
18. x —(×2)→ 0 **0**
19. x —(×5)→ 10 **2**
20. x —(÷3)→ 3 **9**
21. x —(−8)→ 4 **12**
22. x —(+7)→ 12 **5**

184 • Algebra Readiness and Geometry

Literature Connection Present one of the challenging brain teasers from *Sideways Arithmetic from Wayside School* by Louis Sachar for students to solve. Or let them browse through the book to select brain teasers that appeal to them. Students can work on the solution on their own or in small groups. Allow time for discussion of solution methods.

*available separately

Look at these function machines.

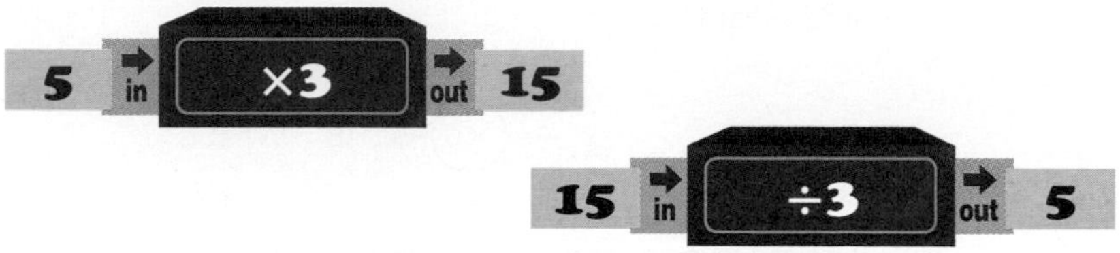

If you put 5 into the first machine, you get out 15. The second machine does the opposite. If you put in 15, you get out 5.

5 —(×3)→ 15   15 —(÷3)→ 5

Because these machines do opposite things, we say that
—(×3)→ is the inverse of —(÷3)→
and —(÷3)→ is the inverse of —(×3)→.
Try to see why —(+5)→ is the inverse of —(−5)→
and —(−5)→ is the inverse of —(+5)→.

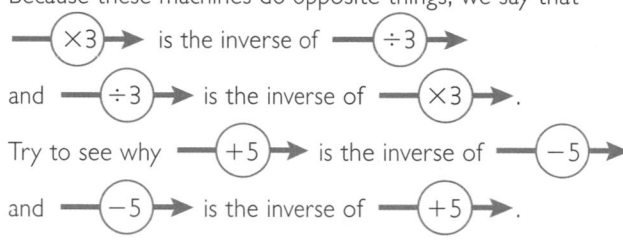

Write the inverse arrow operation.

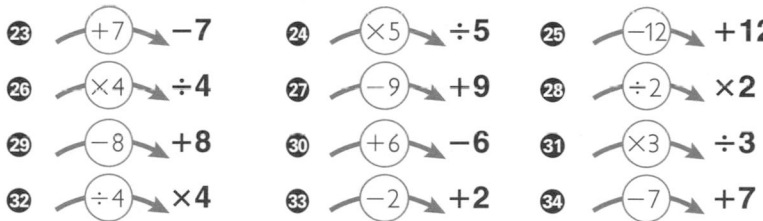

23 (+7) **−7** 24 (×5) **÷5** 25 (−12) **+12**

26 (×4) **÷4** 27 (−9) **+9** 28 (÷2) **×2**

29 (−8) **+8** 30 (+6) **−6** 31 (×3) **÷3**

32 (÷4) **×4** 33 (−2) **+2** 34 (−7) **+7**

35 Suppose a function machine followed this rule:

x —(×3)→ y

What number could you put in to get out 21? **7**

2 Teach

Using the Student Pages Discuss the material at the top of page 184. Then have students try problems 1–22 on their own. Ask them what number they think went into the function machine and why. Allow time for students to discuss and share their solution methods.

Discuss the function machines at the top of page 185. Point out that they perform opposite functions. Explain that *inverse* means opposite. Although the concept is more important than the word, it is convenient to have a term students can associate with functions and operations. If students feel more comfortable with the word *opposite,* let them use it. Emphasize that adding 3 and subtracting 3 are inverses, as are ×3 and ÷3, and so on. When students seem to understand, have them finish this page. Help students get accustomed to drawing a backwards arrow to make a loop when they seek the inverse of a function. Seeing a function "undone" by its inverse can aid them in solving problems that require figuring out what number went into the machine.

Technology Connection Refer students to the software *Intermediate Math* from Queue (Mac, IBM, for grades 3–9) for further practice with order of operations, metrics, decimals and percents, addition with carrying, subtraction, multidigit multiplication, fractions, long division, and word problems.

◆ LESSON 54 Inverse Functions

Teach

ALGEBRA READINESS

Using the Student Pages Have students complete these pages independently. Note that for problem 50 on page 186, any value of *x* will work.

SPECIAL NEEDS

Meeting Individual Needs

Students who do not grasp the concept of functions may need additional time to discuss it. Explain that a function is like a machine that processes numbers. If you put a number in, the machine always does the same thing to it. For example, if the machine's rule is to add 4, any number that goes in will come out 4 greater than it went in. Ask questions such as, "If you know 10 came out, what number must have gone in? How can you know that you are right?"

◆ LESSON 54 Inverse Functions

Inverse arrow operations can help you find what number went into a machine.

Example: x —(×6)→ 18 What is x?

Use the inverse arrow operations.

x —(×6)→ 18
←(÷6)—

We know that $18 \div 6 = 3$.
So the value of x is 3.

Use inverse arrow operations, if they help you, to find the value of *x*.

36. x —(+7)→ 8 **1**
37. x —(+86)→ 100 **14**
38. x —(+17)→ 19 **2**
39. x —(×2)→ 100 **50**
40. x —(−3)→ 10 **13**
41. x —(÷10)→ 4 **40**
42. x —(×5)→ 25 **5**
43. x —(×8)→ 8 **1**
44. x —(×10)→ 90 **9**
45. x —(×10)→ 100 **10**
46. x —(÷4)→ 8 **32**
47. x —(+99)→ 100 **1**
48. x —(−15)→ 0 **15**
49. x —(+0)→ 0 **0**
50. x —(×0)→ 0 **any number**
51. x —(−8)→ 11 **19**
52. x —(÷7)→ 2 **14**
53. x —(×5)→ 35 **7**

Can x have more than one value? Can you solve problem 50?

RETEACHING p. 17

LESSON 54 RETEACHING Name________________

Now that we know the function rule and the output, we need to know the input. The rule is +2 and the number that comes out is 10. What number was put into the machine? Here's another way to ask the same question.

x —(+2)→ 10 What is x?

Let's look at the calculator again to find the answer. We know that if we put in 10 and follow the function rule −2, we will get out 8.

10 —(−2)→ 8

Let's take the function machine and do the opposite. This time we put in 8, follow the function rule +2, and we will get out 10.

8 —(+2)→ 10

You can see that −2 is the inverse of +2. You know that addition is the opposite, or inverse, of subtraction. You can use this to find out what number goes into the machine.

x —(+2)→ 10 By using the inverse arrow operation:

10 —(−2)→ 8 $10 - 2 = 8$, so $8 + 2 = 10$, $x = 8$

Also remember that multiplication is the opposite, or inverse, of division.

In each case tell what *x* is.

1. x —(+6)→ 8 2
2. x —(+45)→ 100 55
3. x —(+10)→ 19 9
4. x —(×2)→ 16 8
5. x —(−5)→ 15 20
6. x —(÷10)→ 6 60

Copyright © SRA/McGraw-Hill. Permission is granted to reproduce this page for classroom use.

Math Explorations and Applications Level 4 • 17

Find *x* or *y*.

54. 3 —(×4)→ *y* **12**
55. *x* —(+7)→ 13 **6**
56. *x* —(+6)→ 13 **7**
57. *x* —(+14)→ 20 **6**
58. 5 —(−3)→ *y* **2**
59. 21 —(÷7)→ *y* **3**
60. *x* —(÷3)→ 7 **21**
61. 19 —(+2)→ *y* **21**
62. 12 —(÷6)→ *y* **2**
63. 17 —(+3)→ *y* **20**
64. *x* —(÷5)→ 3 **15**
65. 18 —(÷3)→ *y* **6**
66. *x* —(−12)→ 3 **15**
67. 1 —(×0)→ *y* **0**
68. 5 —(+10)→ *y* **15**
69. 14 —(−7)→ *y* **7**
70. 5 —(×3)→ *y* **15**
71. *x* —(+8)→ 12 **4**
72. *x* —(×1)→ 15 **15**
73. *x* —(÷5)→ 4 **20**

Find a function rule for each set of arrow operations.

74. 2 —(?)→ 4 4 —(?)→ 6 6 —(?)→ 8 **+2**
75. 8 —(?)→ 2 12 —(?)→ 3 20 —(?)→ 5 **÷4**
76. 6 —(?)→ 12 3 —(?)→ 9 15 —(?)→ 21 **+6**
77. 12 —(?)→ 4 15 —(?)→ 7 9 —(?)→ 1 **−8**
78. 4 —(?)→ 28 2 —(?)→ 14 10 —(?)→ 70 **×7**
79. 10 —(?)→ 5 14 —(?)→ 7 6 —(?)→ 3 **÷2**
80. 10 —(?)→ 13 4 —(?)→ 7 0 —(?)→ 3 **+3**
81. 0 —(?)→ 5 3 —(?)→ 8 9 —(?)→ 14 **+5**

Use the Cumulative Review on page 546 after this lesson.

PRACTICE p. 54

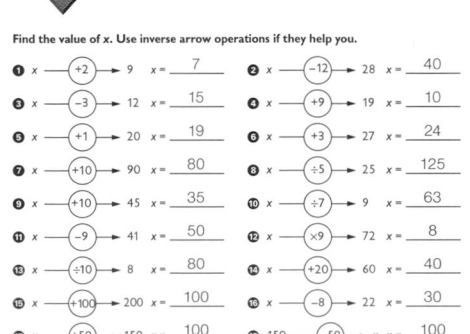

LESSON 54 PRACTICE Name________________

Find the value of *x*. Use inverse arrow operations if they help you.

1. *x* —(+2)→ 9 *x* = 7
2. *x* —(−12)→ 28 *x* = 40
3. *x* —(−3)→ 12 *x* = 15
4. *x* —(+9)→ 19 *x* = 10
5. *x* —(+1)→ 20 *x* = 19
6. *x* —(+3)→ 27 *x* = 24
7. *x* —(+10)→ 90 *x* = 80
8. *x* —(÷5)→ 25 *x* = 125
9. *x* —(+10)→ 45 *x* = 35
10. *x* —(÷7)→ 9 *x* = 63
11. *x* —(−9)→ 41 *x* = 50
12. *x* —(×9)→ 72 *x* = 8
13. *x* —(÷10)→ 8 *x* = 80
14. *x* —(+20)→ 60 *x* = 40
15. *x* —(+100)→ 200 *x* = 100
16. *x* —(−8)→ 22 *x* = 30
17. *x* —(+50)→ 150 *x* = 100
18. 150 —(−50)→ *x* *x* = 100
19. *x* —(÷5)→ 17 *x* = 85
20. 17 —(×5)→ *x* *x* = 85
21. *x* —(×8)→ 64 *x* = 8
22. 64 —(÷8)→ *x* *x* = 8
23. *x* —(−0)→ 21 *x* = 21
24. 21 —(+0)→ *x* *x* = 21
25. *x* —(+30)→ 75 *x* = 45
26. 75 —(−30)→ *x* *x* = 45
27. *x* —(÷6)→ 6 *x* = 36
28. 6 —(×6)→ *x* *x* = 36
29. *x* —(+25)→ 75 *x* = 50
30. 75 —(−25)→ *x* *x* = 50

54 • *Math Explorations and Applications* Level 4

Copyright © SRA/McGraw-Hill. Permission is granted to reproduce this page for classroom use.

ENRICHMENT p. 54

LESSON 54 ENRICHMENT Name________________

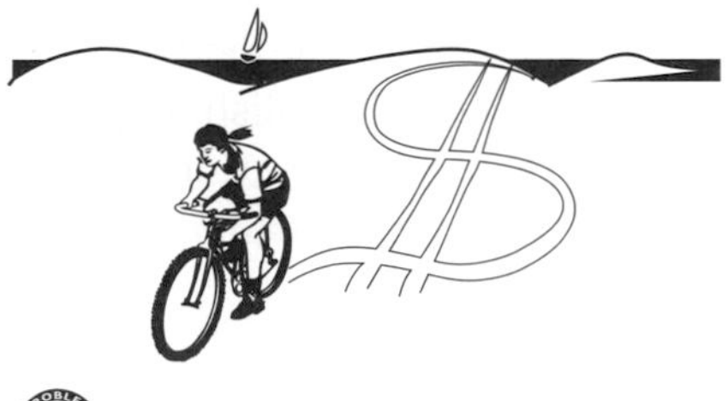

Solve these problems.

Sandy was spending a summer day riding her bike at the beach. She rode in a pattern to make a big S, her initial, in the sand.

Her uncle said, "With your bike, make two lines across your S to make a dollar sign."

1. Into how many segments did Sandy cut the S by riding across it twice? 7

"Now," her uncle said, "make a total of 25 strokes across the S to cut it into even more parts. I'll give you a penny for each part."

2. Will Sandy get $1.00 from her uncle? no
3. Into how many segments did Sandy cut the S by riding across it 25 times? 76

54 • *Math Explorations and Applications* Level 4

Copyright © SRA/McGraw-Hill. Permission is granted to reproduce this page for classroom use.

3 Wrap-Up (5 MINUTES)

In Closing Ask students what the word *inverse* means in mathematics. (An answer such as "opposite" is acceptable.)

ALTERNATIVE ASSESSMENT

Informal Assessment Observe students as they work through the function problems in this lesson. Most students should be able to apply inverse operations to find missing values. Prompt them as necessary by asking them what operation to use. Encourage them to use mental math when they can. Evaluate students who are having trouble by checking whether the difficulty stems from errors in basic facts or from lack of understanding of the function concept.

Assessment Criteria

Did the student . . .

- ✓ demonstrate understanding of the arrow operation notation?
- ✓ contribute to the discussion of inverse operations?
- ✓ communicate strategies used to solve for *x* or *y*?
- ✓ correctly answer at least 75% of the problems?

Homework Have students create four inverse arrow problems—one for each operation—for classmates to solve.

LEARNING STYLES · MANIPULATIVES

Meeting Individual Needs

Kinesthetic and concrete learners may benefit from using a **box** or **container** and numbered **slips of paper** to simulate a function machine. Interpersonal learners can think of a function machine as being very fair—it always applies its rule the same way to any number that goes in.

LESSON 55

Student Edition pages 188–191

Ordered Pairs

LESSON PLANNER

Objectives

- to demonstrate the relationship between functions and ordered pairs of numbers
- to help students develop the broad ability to use mathematical common sense

Context of the Lesson This lesson, the fifth of 13 lessons on graphing and functions, relates functions and ordered pairs to prepare students for relating functions to graphing. This lesson also contains Part 1 of "The Lost Island of Addonia," a four-part Thinking Story.

MANIPULATIVES

none

Program Resources

"Baseball" Game Mat

Number Cubes

Practice Master 55

Enrichment Master 55

For career connections:
Careers and Math*

For additional math integration:
Math Throughout the Day*

For extra practice:
CD-ROM* Lesson 55

1 Warm-Up (5 MINUTES)

Problem of the Day Present this problem to students: Mr. Watson makes three-legged and four-legged stools. Yesterday he used 24 legs. How many of each type of stool did he make? (He made four three-legged stools and three four-legged stools.)

Problem-Solving Strategies Ask students who have solved the Problem of the Day to share how they solved it and any strategies they used.

MENTAL MATH Play "Cubo" (page 163) with the class to practice basic facts. Have students work out combinations of operations mentally and then discuss their solutions. A copy of "Cubo" can also be found on page 15 of the Home Connections Blackline Masters.

EXPLORE

LESSON 55

Ordered Pairs

Look at this function machine.

It works according to this rule: $x \xrightarrow{+5} y$

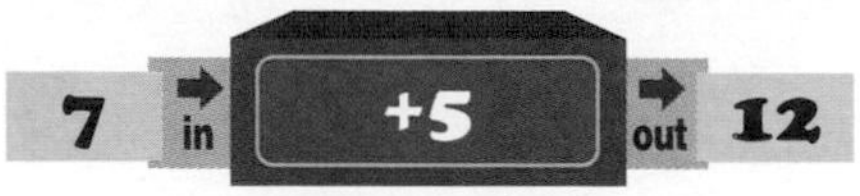

If you put in 7, then 12 comes out.

Let's write that pair of numbers like this: (7, 12)

The first number in the pair (7) is the one that went in. The second number in the pair (12) is the one that came out.

A pair of numbers written this way, (7, 12), is called an **ordered pair.** We call it that because the order is important to show which number is which.

We can list other ordered pairs for the +5 function machine.

If we put in 3, then 8 comes out: (3, 8)

If we put in 9, then 14 comes out: (9, 14)

And so on.

In this way, we can say that a function machine produces ordered pairs of numbers.

ALGEBRA READINESS

Copy each list of ordered pairs, but replace the *x* or *y* with the correct number.

1. $x \xrightarrow{+5} y$ (7, 12), (12, y), (15, y), (0, y), (x, 7) **17; 20; 5; 2**
2. $x \xrightarrow{\div 4} y$ (8, 2), (x, 4), (x, 3), (x, 7), (x, 9) **16; 12; 28; 36**
3. $x \xrightarrow{-3} y$ (9, 6), (7, y), (x, 7), (12, y), (x, 1) **4; 10; 9; 4**
4. $x \xrightarrow{+8} y$ (5, 13), (4, y), (x, 11), (x, 15), (6, y) **12; 3; 7; 14**
5. $x \xrightarrow{\times 5} y$ (1, 5), (3, y), (x, 10), (0, y), (8, y) **15; 2; 0; 40**

188 • Algebra Readiness and Geometry

COOPERATIVE LEARNING You may wish to have students work in pairs to complete the riddles on page 189. After pairs finish, have them each make up their own riddles to exchange with their partners.

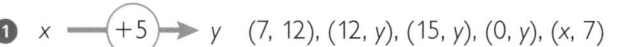

*available separately

6 x —(−9)→ y (11, y), (20, y), (25, y), (x, 0), (x, 8), (x, 9)
2; 11; 16; 9; 17, 18

7 x —(×3)→ y (2, y), (4, y), (8, y), (10, y), (x, 6), (x, 15)
6; 12; 24; 30; 2; 5

8 x —(÷2)→ y (6, y), (18, y), (12, y), (6, y), (x, 7), (x, 1)
3; 9; 6; 3; 14; 2

9 x —(×0)→ y (7, y), (12, y), (50, y), (2589, y), (x, 0)
0; 0; 0; 0; any number

◆ Suppose problem 9 included the ordered pair (x, 7). What would your answer be? **impossible; no number multiplied by 0 is 7**

Here's a secret code to help you solve the riddles below.

A	B	C	D	E	F	G	H	I	J	K	L	M
26	25	24	23	22	21	20	19	18	17	16	15	14

N	O	P	Q	R	S	T	U	V	W	X	Y	Z
13	12	11	10	9	8	7	6	5	4	3	2	1

Use function rules to help solve the riddles. Find the value of *x* or *y* in each ordered pair. Then use the code to find what letter each value stands for.

10 What's a noisy group of people?

Use this function rule: x —(+3)→ y **26, 15, 12, 6, 23, 24, 9, 12, 4, 23**
A LOUD CROWD

(23, y) (12, y), (x, 15), (3, y), (20, y) (21, y), (6, y), (9, y), (x, 7), (x, 26)

11 What's another name for a police chief?

Use this function rule: x —(−5)→ y **26, 7, 12, 11, 24, 12, 11**
A TOP COP

(31, y) (12, y), (17, y), (x, 6) (x, 19), (x, 7), (16, y)

FANTASTIC FACT **Sound travels about five times faster through water than through air.**

❷ Teach

ALGEBRA READINESS **Using the Student Pages** Demonstrate the "Baseball" Game Mat before students begin work on these pages so that those who finish early can play immediately. This game provides practice with locating coordinates on a graph. Go over page 188 with the class. Remind students that they recently worked with ordered pairs (coordinates of points). Make sure they understand the format of problems 1–9 on pages 188–189 by doing the first one as a class. This format differs slightly from the function-machine charts students have used previously and highlights the concept of ordered pairs. Next, show students how to use the code to solve the riddles. Emphasize that they use only the unknown value in each ordered pair to find the answer. Then have them finish the page on their own. Afterward, talk about the discussion question on page 189 with the whole class.

> ***. . . in the early grades, we should try to teach so that most children will become very efficient at simple operations and can spend their time and thought on more advanced ideas.***
>
> —Stephen S. Willoughby,
> *Mathematics Education for a Changing World*

LITERATURE CONNECTION **Literature Connection** Have students read *The Case of the Unnatural: Mathnet Casebook* by David D. Connell and Jim Thurman. Have groups of students figure out the answers to the "Guess My Rule" game in the story and to the activities section at the end of the book.

◆ LESSON 55 Ordered Pairs

Teach

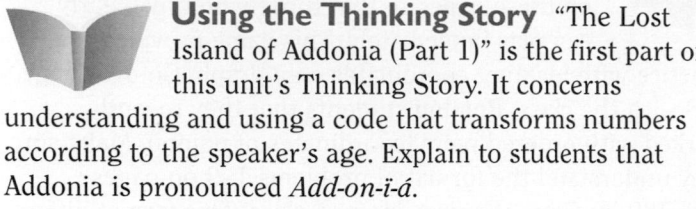

Using the Thinking Story "The Lost Island of Addonia (Part 1)" is the first part of this unit's Thinking Story. It concerns understanding and using a code that transforms numbers according to the speaker's age. Explain to students that Addonia is pronounced *Add-on-ī-á*.

Answers to Thinking Story Questions:

1. Answers will vary according to the ages of students in the class. Each student should add 6 to his or her age. Thus a student who is nine years old would say 15.
2. 20¢
3. 5
4. 83 years old
5. Three kilometers; the old man said it was 86 kilometers, and students figured out that he is 83 years old.

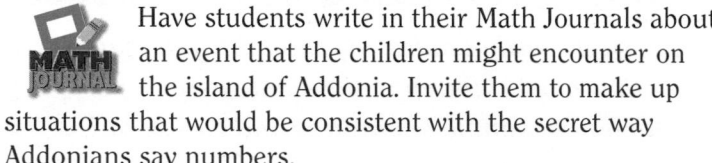

Have students write in their Math Journals about an event that the children might encounter on the island of Addonia. Invite them to make up situations that would be consistent with the secret way Addonians say numbers.

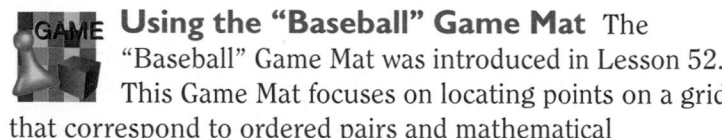

Using the "Baseball" Game Mat The "Baseball" Game Mat was introduced in Lesson 52. This Game Mat focuses on locating points on a grid that correspond to ordered pairs and mathematical reasoning. Play a "half-inning" with several volunteers in front of the class. Make sure students understand how to determine the number of bases for each hit. Ask them to keep careful records of each team's run and outs. A copy of this Game Mat can also be found on page 585 of this Teacher's Guide.

◆ LESSON 55 Ordered Pairs

THINKING STORY

The Lost Island of Addonia

Part 1

After their ship sank, Ferdie, Portia, Manolita, and Marcus spent three days on a raft. Then their raft drifted to the shore of a green island. A woman and a little girl came down to meet them.

"Welcome to Addonia," said the woman.

"Thank you," said Portia. "How far is it to the nearest library? I haven't had anything to read for three days."

"The library is 10 kilometers from here," said the girl.

"That's right," said the woman. "It's 43 kilometers from here."

"Wait a minute," said Marcus. "Something's crazy here." An old man was sitting on a rock near them. Marcus asked him, "Who is telling the truth about how far the library is?"

"They both are," said the old man. "The library is exactly 86 kilometers from here." When he saw how puzzled the children looked, the old man smiled.

"I guess you don't know how we do things here in Addonia," he said. "We have a secret way of saying numbers. It protects us from spies. But you children don't look like spies. I'll tell you the secret. Whenever we say a number, we always add our age to it."

RETEACHING

To help students who are having difficulty with the ordered-pair concept simulate a function machine and keep track of ordered pairs that go through it.

"You mean," said Manolita, "that if it was 2 o'clock, I'd have to say it was 11 o'clock, because I'm nine years old?"

"That's right," said the old man. "And I would say it's 85 o'clock."

. . . to be continued

Work in groups. Discuss your answers and how you figured them out. Then compare your answers with those of other groups. Answers are in margin.

1. If you wanted to talk about six things in Addonia, what number would you say instead?
2. If a ten-year-old wanted 10 cents, what would he or she have to ask for?
3. A 12-year-old in Addonia said, "There are 17 people in my family." How many are there really?
4. **Detective question:** How old is the old man?
5. **Super detective question:** How far is it to the library?

3 Wrap-Up

5 MINUTES

In Closing Have students give today's date, the year, the time, and so on, as if they were in Addonia.

ALTERNATIVE ASSESSMENT

Informal Assessment Observe students as they work through the problems on pages 188–189. Ask them to explain their reasoning and tell how they solved the riddles.

Assessment Criteria

Did the student . . .

- ✓ explain how to use a function rule to create ordered pairs?
- ✓ use the code to solve the riddles?
- ✓ contribute to the Thinking Story discussion?

Homework Have students write a short story about their family, neighborhood, or any other favorite topic. Tell them to include at least four numbers given in the Addonian code. Invite volunteers to share their stories with classmates.

PRACTICE p. 55

LESSON 55 PRACTICE Name________

Copy each list of ordered pairs but replace the *x* or *y* with the correct number.

1. $x \to (-4) \to y$ (10, 6), (7, y), (x, 12), (10, y), (x, 0) 3; 16; 6; 4
2. $x \to (\times 3) \to y$ (3, y), (x, 12), (0, y), (x, 3), (x, 15) 9; 4; 0; 1; 5
3. $x \to (+1) \to y$ (0, y), (x, 2), (2, y), (x, 4), (20, y) 1; 1; 3; 3; 21

Use function rules to answer the questions. Find the value of *x* or *y* in each ordered pair. Then use the code to find what letter each number represents.

X	O	L	M	R	S	T	H	I	E	W	Y	N
1	2	3	4	5	6	7	8	9	10	11	12	13

B	U	D	G	J	V	A	K	Z	C	P	Q	F
14	15	16	17	18	19	20	21	22	23	24	25	26

4. What is the largest member of the cat family?
   Use this function rule: $x \to (+5) \to y$

S	I	B	E	R	I	A	N
(1, y)	(4, y)	(9, y)	(5, y)	(0, y)	(4, y)	(15, y)	(8, y)

T	I	G	E	R
(2, y)	(4, y)	(12, y)	(5, y)	(0, y)

Copyright © SRA/McGraw-Hill. Permission is granted to reproduce this page for classroom use.

Math Explorations and Applications Level 4 • 55

ENRICHMENT p. 55

LESSON 55 ENRICHMENT Name________

Here are three different views of the same block.

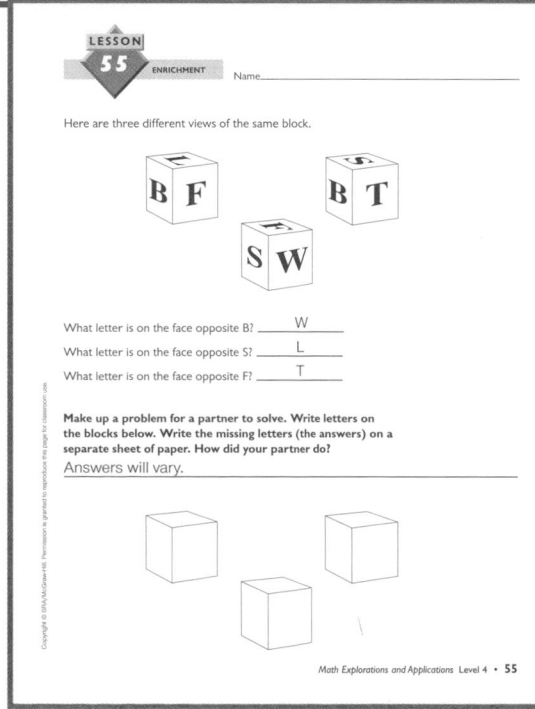

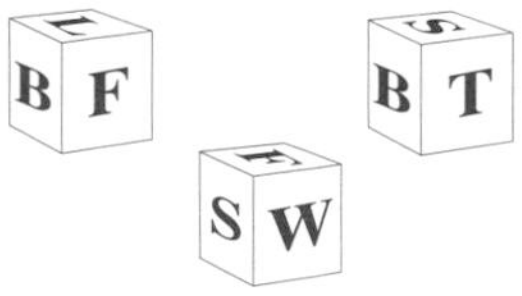

What letter is on the face opposite B? W

What letter is on the face opposite S? L

What letter is on the face opposite F? T

Make up a problem for a partner to solve. Write letters on the blocks below. Write the missing letters (the answers) on a separate sheet of paper. How did your partner do?

Answers will vary.

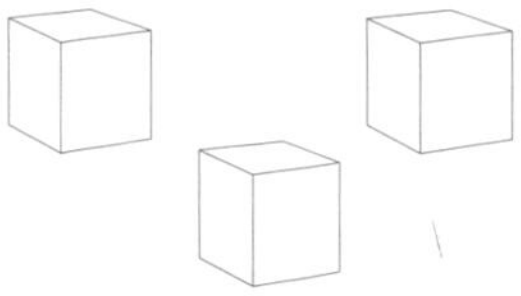

Copyright © SRA/McGraw-Hill. Permission is granted to reproduce this page for classroom use.

Math Explorations and Applications Level 4 • 55

ESL

Meeting Individual Needs

Students with limited proficiency in English may not know all the words involved in the riddles or in their answers. For example, they may not know the word *cop* is slang for *police officer*. If necessary, read the answers aloud to students to accentuate the rhyme in the word pairs. Discuss the meaning of the words or show students pictures to help them understand the meaning of the riddle.

LESSON 56

Student Edition pages 192–193

Function Rules and Ordered Pairs

LESSON PLANNER

Objectives

- ▶ to demonstrate the relationships among functions, ordered pairs, and a table of ordered pairs
- ▶ to provide further arithmetic practice
- ✓ to assess students' understanding of functions and inverse relationships

Context of the Lesson This lesson, the sixth of 13 lessons on functions and graphing, helps prepare students for graphing the ordered pairs that are produced by a function, which they begin doing in Lesson 58. A Mastery Checkpoint for functions and inverse relationships is provided in this lesson.

MANIPULATIVES

none

Program Resources

"Snake" Game Mat
Reteaching Master
Practice Master 56
Enrichment Master 56
Assessment Master
For additional math integration: Math Throughout the Day*
For extra practice: CD-ROM* Lesson 56

1 Warm-Up (5 MINUTES)

Problem of the Day Present this problem orally or on the chalkboard. Melissa dropped her math book and it fell open to an even-numbered page facing an odd-numbered page. The sum of the two pages was 115. What were the pages numbered? (57 and 58)

Problem-Solving Strategies Ask students who have solved the Problem of the Day to share how they solved it and any strategies they used.

MENTAL MATH Provide mixed practice by giving problems and asking "Is the answer more than 500?" If it is, students show thumbs up. If the answer is less than 500, they show thumbs down. If the answer is exactly 500, students stand up.

a. 650 − 90 (thumbs up) **b.** 2000 ÷ 4 (stand up)
c. 50 × 50 (thumbs up) **d.** 390 + 240 (thumbs up)
e. 99 × 12 (thumbs up) **f.** 80 × 8 (thumbs up)

MIXED PRACTICE

LESSON 56

Function Rules and Ordered Pairs

In this lesson you will do more work with function rules.

ALGEBRA READINESS

Find the values of *x* in the ordered pairs.

1. x —(+5)→ y: (x, 5), (x, 7), (x, 15), (x, 205), (x, 73) — **0, 2, 10, 200, 68**
2. x —(−5)→ y: (x, 5), (x, 25), (x, 30), (x, 35), (x, 45) — **10, 30, 35, 40, 50**
3. x —(÷8)→ y: (x, 1), (x, 3), (x, 8), (x, 9), (x, 10) — **8, 24, 64, 72, 80**

This is a completed function machine chart.

x —(×6)→ y

x	y
3	18
8	48
2	12
0	0
1	6

The chart shows some things about the function

x —(×6)→ y

The chart shows that when $x = 3$, $y = 18$; when $x = 8$, $y = 48$; and so on.

Use a computer or other means to draw these charts. Solve for *x* or *y*.

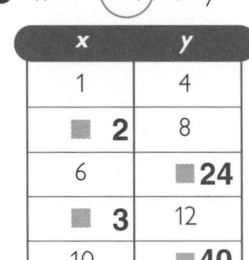

4. x —(×4)→ y

x	y
1	4
■ **2**	8
6	■ **24**
■ **3**	12
10	■ **40**

5. x —(+3)→ y

x	y
■ **4**	7
2	■ **5**
5	■ **8**
■ **22**	25
6	■ **9**

6. x —(×8)→ y

x	y
0	■ **0**
■ **3**	24
2	■ **16**
1	8
■ **4**	32

RETEACHING p. 18

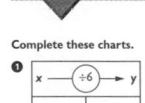

LESSON 56 RETEACHING Name______________________

To find a function rule, see what must be done to *x* to get *y*. Sometimes more than one rule could apply, so try all possibilities to find which one is correct. Remember that inverse operations can help you find values in ordered pairs.

Example:

x —(?)→ y

x	y
6	12
12	18
?	20

To get from 6 to 12 you could multiply by 2.

6 —(×2)→ 12 Does this work with 12 and 18?
12 —(×2)→ 18 No. 12 × 2 = 24, so try again.

You could also add 6 to 6 to get to 12.

6 —(+6)→ 12 Does this work with 12 and 18?
12 —(+6)→ 18 Yes. The rule is +6.
x —(+6)→ 20 Use the inverse. 20 − 6 = 14, 14 + 6 = 20. Now fill in the blank.

Complete these charts.

1. x —(−3)→ y

x	y
18	15
23	20
33	30
6	3

2. x —(+4)→ y

x	y
4	8
31	35
41	45
0	4

3. x —(÷10)→ y

x	y
100	10
200	20
300	30
400	40

Copyright © SRA/McGraw-Hill. Permission is granted to reproduce this page for classroom use.

PRACTICE p. 56

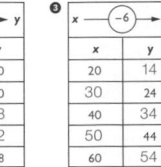

LESSON 56 PRACTICE Name______________________

Complete these charts.

1. x —(÷6)→ y

x	y
36	6
30	5
24	4
18	3
6	1

2. x —(×4)→ y

x	y
5	20
0	0
2	8
8	32
7	28

3. x —(−6)→ y

x	y
20	14
30	24
40	34
50	44
60	54

Find the function rules before you complete these charts.

4. +10 — x —(?)→ y

x	y
5	15
10	20
15	25
50	60
100	110

5. −8 — x —(?)→ y

x	y
12	4
11	3
10	2
9	1
8	0

6. +0, −0, ×1, or ÷1 — x —(?)→ y

x	y
2	2
5	5
0	0
100	100
50	50

Copyright © SRA/McGraw-Hill. Permission is granted to reproduce this page for classroom use.

*available separately

7 $x \rightarrow (+7) \rightarrow y$

x	y
8	■ **15**
30	■ **37**
■ **20**	27
6	■ **13**
100 ■	107

8 $x \rightarrow (\times 6) \rightarrow y$

x	y
3	■ **18**
■ **9**	54
10	■ **60**
■ **8**	48
7	■ **42**

9 $x \rightarrow (-3) \rightarrow y$

x	y
■ **8**	5
■ **13**	10
■ **12**	9
24	■ **21**
3	■ **0**

10 $x \rightarrow (\times 7) \rightarrow y$

x	y
7	■ **49**
0	■ **0**
10	■ **70**
■ **2**	14
■ **3**	21

11 $x \rightarrow (-4) \rightarrow y$

x	y
■ **19**	15
■ **25**	21
■ **76**	72
■ **7**	3
■ **23**	19

12 $x \rightarrow (+6) \rightarrow y$

x	y
■ **19**	25
■ **29**	35
■ **39**	45
■ **49**	55
■ **59**	65

Find the function rules before you complete these charts.

13 $x \rightarrow (?) \rightarrow y$ **×1, ÷1, +0, −0**

x	y
100	■ **100**
3	3
2	■ **2**
7	■ **7**
25	25

14 $x \rightarrow (?) \rightarrow y$ **×3**

x	y
3	9
20	60
5	15
■ **9**	27
■ **10**	30

15 $x \rightarrow (?) \rightarrow y$ **×0**

x	y
6	0
20	■ **0**
5	0
31	■ **0**
12	■ **0**

❷ Teach

Using the Student Pages Demonstrate the "Snake" Game Mat before students begin page 192 so they can play as they finish their work. This game provides practice with solving missing-term problems. Have students do pages 192–193 independently. For problem 15, expect the answer ×0; however, "subtract the number that went in" can be considered correct.

GAME **Using the "Snake" Game Mat** Demonstrate and then have students play the "Snake" game. This game involves solving missing-term problems, mental arithmetic, and mathematical reasoning. A copy of this game can also be found on page 603 of this Guide.

❸ Wrap-Up

5 MINUTES

In Closing Summarize the lesson by asking students to explain the meaning of *inverse*.

Mastery Checkpoint 9

By this time students should understand inverse operations. Given a function rule, students should be able to find *x* or *y*. This ability may be assessed using pages 192–193, on which students correctly answer at least 80% of the problems, or by using Assessment Blackline Masters pages 20–21. You may record the results of the assessment on the Mastery Checkpoint Chart.

Assessment Criteria

Did the student . . .

- ✓ contribute to the discussion of inverse operations?
- ✓ accurately complete the function charts?
- ✓ explain how to find the missing values of *x* or *y*?
- ✓ correctly answer at least 80% of the computation problems?

Homework Have students create a function chart for a classmate to solve.

ENRICHMENT p. 56

LESSON 56 ENRICHMENT Name____________________

Find the pattern for each set of ordered pairs. Add two more ordered pairs to each list. Then write a possible function rule for each set.

1. (4, 16), (1, 4), (8, 32), (9, 36), (6 , 24), (10 , 40)
Function rule: $x \times 4 = y$
2. (0, 0), (12, 4), (30, 10), (15, 5), (18 , 6), (45 , 15)
Function rule: $x \div 3 = y$
3. (10, 12), (5, 7), (8, 10), (0, 2), (22 , 24), (19 , 21)
Function rule: $x + 2 = y$
4. (10, 0), (15, 5), (12, 2), (31, 21), (50 , 40), (17 , 7)
Function rule: $x - 10 = y$
5. (24, 2), (60, 5), (144, 12), (96, 8), (36 , 3), (72 , 6)
Function rule: $x \div 12 = y$
6. (88, 34), (75, 21), (65, 11), (93, 39), (74 , 20), (66 , 12)
Function rule: $x - 54 = y$
7. (5, 116), (112, 223), (36, 147), (64, 175), (1 , 112), (50 , 161)
Function rule: $x + 111 = y$
8. (4, 60), (15, 225), (2, 30), (6, 90), (1 , 15), (10 , 150)
Function rule: $x \times 15 = y$

Copyright © SRA/McGraw-Hill. Permission is granted to reproduce this page for classroom use.

ASSESSMENT p. 20

UNIT 3 **Mastery Checkpoint 9** Functions and inverses (Lesson 56) Page 1 of 2

Name ____________________

The student demonstrates mastery by correctly answering at least 16 of the 20 problems.

Use inverse operations to find the values of *x* in the ordered pairs. (The first one has been done for you.)

1. $x \rightarrow (-4) \rightarrow y$ (x, 0) 4 (x, 7) 11 (x, 19) 23 (x, 56) 60 (x, 97) 101
2. $x \rightarrow (\div 7) \rightarrow y$ (x, 3) 21 (x, 7) 49 (x, 8) 56 (x, 9) 63 (x, 5) 35
3. $x \rightarrow (\times 3) \rightarrow y$ (x, 27) 9 (x, 18) 6 (x, 21) 7 (x, 15) 5 (x, 9) 3

Complete these charts.

4. $x \rightarrow (+6) \rightarrow y$

x	y
4	10
6	12
8	14
15	21
48	54

5. $x \rightarrow (\times 5) \rightarrow y$

x	y
1	5
3	15
7	35
9	45
0	0

6. $x \rightarrow (\div 4) \rightarrow y$

x	y
0	0
4	1
36	9
16	4
28	7

7. $x \rightarrow (-7) \rightarrow y$

x	y
14	7
16	9
8	1
12	5
13	6

8. $x \rightarrow (\div 6) \rightarrow y$

x	y
42	7
54	9
30	5
24	4
12	2

9. $x \rightarrow (-5) \rightarrow y$

x	y
12	7
15	10
13	8
10	5
11	6

10. $x \rightarrow (\div 9) \rightarrow y$

x	y
18	2
36	4
45	5
63	7
81	9

11. $x \rightarrow (+8) \rightarrow y$

x	y
5	13
7	15
4	12
6	14
9	17

Copyright © SRA/McGraw-Hill. Permission is granted to reproduce this page for classroom use.

LESSON **57**

Student Edition pages 194–197

Keeping in Shape

LESSON PLANNER

Objectives

- ▶ to reinforce the concept of functions
- ▶ to provide practice in arithmetic and approximation and in detecting obviously wrong answers to computations
- ▶ to help students develop the broad ability to use mathematical common sense

Context of the Lesson This lesson, the seventh of 13 lessons on graphing and functions, also contains Part 2 of "The Lost Island of Addonia," a four-part Thinking Story.

MANIPULATIVES

beakers*

counters* (optional)

objects for measuring volume

Program Resources

Number Cubes

Practice Master 57

Enrichment Master 57

For career connections: Careers and Math*

For extra practice: CD-ROM* Lesson 57

1 Warm-Up

5 MINUTES

Problem of the Day Present this problem to students: Granny gave $10 to her five grandchildren. She said, "I want you to divide the money so that my oldest grandchild gets 25¢ more than my next-oldest grandchild, who should get 25¢ more than my next-oldest grandchild, and so on." If the five grandchildren follow Granny's instructions, how much money will the youngest grandchild get? ($1.50)

Problem-Solving Strategies Ask students who have solved the Problem of the Day to share how they solved it and any strategies they used.

MENTAL MATH / MANIPULATIVES

Provide practice with estimating customary measures of volume. Present an object to the class and have students estimate its volume. After each estimate, have a volunteer use a **beaker*** to measure the object to verify the estimate. (Estimates should improve after each object is measured.)

a. a spoon **b.** a coffee mug

c. a milk carton **d.** a vase

MIXED **PRACTICE**

LESSON **57**

Keeping in Shape

COOPERATIVE LEARNING

GAME

Function Game

Players:	Two or more
Materials:	Two 0–5 cubes, two 5–10 cubes
Object:	To score closest to 100 without going over
Math Focus	Mental math (with all four operations) and mathematical reasoning

RULES

1. Make a blank function machine chart like this:
2. The first player rolls all four cubes to get the values of *x*. Write all four values of *x* in your chart.
3. Select a function and write it in the blank circle at the top of your chart.
4. Using your function rule, find the values of *y*.
5. Find the sum of all the values of *y*.
6. The player with the sum closest to, but not over, 100 wins the round.

x → (?) → *y*

x	*y*

SAMPLE GAME

Mario's Chart: *x* → (×4) → *y*

x	*y*
5	20
4	16
6	24
8	32
Sum	92

Anna's Chart: *x* → (+18) → *y*

x	*y*
5	23
4	22
6	24
8	26
Sum	95

JoAnn's Chart: *x* → (+20) → *y*

x	*y*
5	25
4	24
6	26
8	28
Sum	103

Anna was the winner of this round.

194 • Algebra Readiness and Geometry

Literature Connection Teach students to play the "More or Less" game from page 209 of *Family Math* by Jean Kerr Stenmark, Virginia Thompson, and Ruth Cossey. In this game, players add or subtract a designated number from the numbers 1–100. Students can play in pairs or in small groups.

*available separately

It's a good idea to keep practicing your math skills. In this lesson, you'll use your mental math skills and estimating skills. Watch the signs.

In each problem, two of the answers are clearly wrong and one is correct. Choose the correct answer.

1	409 + 618	a. 2197	b. 517
		(c.) 1027 (circled)	
2	597 − 522	a. 1119	b. 175
		(c.) 75 (circled)	
3	756 − 318	(a.) 438 (circled)	b. 1074
		c. 108	
4	543 − 178	(a.) 365 (circled)	b. 165
		c. 665	
5	4195 − 3167	a. 128	(b.) 1028 (circled)
		c. 7278	
6	1618 + 9322	a. 20,940	b. 8030
		(c.) 10,940 (circled)	
7	522 + 973	a. 2595	(b.) 1495 (circled)
		c. 1005	
8	241 − 75	(a.) 166 (circled)	b. 316
		c. 66	
9	5376 + 3261	(a.) 8637 (circled)	b. 837
		c. 12,637	
10	233 + 167	(a.) 400 (circled)	b. 690
		c. 190	
11	4603 − 4346	a. 8257	b. 1257
		(c.) 257 (circled)	
12	537 + 386	a. 1023	b. 623
		(c.) 923 (circled)	
13	180 + 436	a. 416	(b.) 616 (circled)
		c. 896	
14	2102 − 1569	(a.) 533 (circled)	b. 3683
		c. 293	

❷ Teach

Using the Student Pages Demonstrate the "Function" game by playing it with the class two or three times. This game provides practice with mental arithmetic and mathematical reasoning. On the chalkboard, draw a blank function-machine chart like the one on page 194. Have each student draw a similar one on a sheet of paper. Go over the sample games on the student page to check that students understand the object of the game. Students may use paper and pencil to calculate the sum, but they should use mental math to find the values of y.

When students finish playing the game, have them complete page 195 independently. Remind them that they should solve these problems by approximating to eliminate the two answers that are clearly wrong. As students finish, they can play the "Function" game in pairs or small groups.

ESL **Meeting Individual Needs**

For students with limited proficiency in English, it may be useful to relate the mathematical use of the word *function* to its more general definition. Work with these students to distinguish function machines from real machines or functional items. For example, washing machines, ovens, and showers all have functions that students can name. Encourage them to use their imaginations and suggest machines with new functions.

Technology Connection Students can look through *Kids Internet Yellow Pages* from Osborne, McGraw-Hill, an internet reference book that lists student-appropriate sites on hundreds of subjects.

◆ LESSON 57 Keeping in Shape

Teach

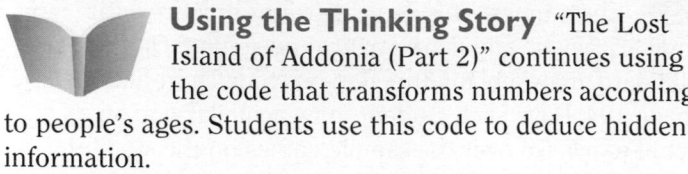

Using the Thinking Story "The Lost Island of Addonia (Part 2)" continues using the code that transforms numbers according to people's ages. Students use this code to deduce hidden information.

Answers to Thinking Story Questions:

1. The cook could tell that Ferdie was more than four years old. So in Addonia, Ferdie would be asking for fewer than 0 hamburgers!
2. 22 years old. Students can figure this out from the fact that the cook made four hamburgers and said, "You only ordered 26," or from the fact that he said "twenty-third" when he meant "first."
3. "First you say one thing and second (or next) you say something else."
4. The cook must have thought Ferdie was eight years old, because when Ferdie asked for 12 hamburgers the cook made four.

MATH JOURNAL Have students write in their Math Journals the number of hamburgers Ferdie should have ordered if he wanted 12 of them, using Addonian rules for saying numbers. Have students suggest how the cook could make ordering easier.

LEARNING STYLES · MANIPULATIVES

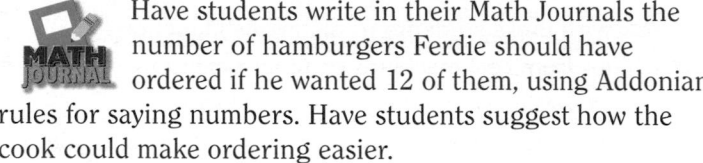

Meeting Individual Needs
Students who are concrete learners or who interpret things very literally may need help understanding and applying the Addonian code to numbers. You might have these students use **counters*** to model Addonian numbers, or have them use their own ages as a benchmark for figuring out other numbers in this Thinking Story.

◆ LESSON 57 Keeping in Shape

THINKING STORY

The Lost Island of Addonia

Part 2

You may want to refer to the first part of this Thinking Story on pages 190–191.

On the way to the library, the children passed a hamburger stand. "Let's get some food," said Ferdie. "It's true we haven't had anything to read for three days. But we haven't had anything to eat, either."

"We'd like four hamburgers, please," Ferdie told the cook.

"I'm not sure I can make so few hamburgers," said the cook.

"He's right," Marcus said. "One hamburger each isn't very much when we're so hungry. Let's get three each."

"All right," said Ferdie. "Please make us 12 hamburgers."

"I think I know how many that is," said the cook. He made them four hamburgers.

"Where are the others?" Ferdie asked.

"You ordered only 26, didn't you?" the cook asked.

"I give up," said Ferdie. "There's no way to get what you want in this country."

RETEACHING

No particular reteaching or practice is suggested at this time. Encourage students to complete Enrichment Master 57 for this lesson.

*available separately

"Let me try," said Manolita. She said to the cook, "You see how many hamburgers you made for us? Please make that many again and then make that many again."

"I wish you children would make up your minds," said the cook. "Twenty-third you say 23 things and 24th you say something else."

. . . to be continued

Work in groups. Discuss your answers and how you figured them out. Then compare your answers with those of other groups. **Answers are in margin.**

1. Why couldn't the cook make the four hamburgers Ferdie asked for?
2. How old was the cook?
3. How would you say the last thing that the cook said? Say it our way, not the Addonian way.
4. **Detective question:** How old did the cook think Ferdie was?

❸ Wrap-Up 5 MINUTES

In Closing Ask students to explain the strategies they used to play the "Function" game.

SELF ASSESSMENT Have students write a brief statement that explains what they have learned about functions up to this point in the unit. Encourage them to describe ideas that they understand clearly as well as those with which they have difficulty.

Assessment Criteria

Did the student . . .

- ✓ communicate strategies used to play the "Function" game?
- ✓ use approximation to choose the correct answer?
- ✓ explain how to eliminate answers that are clearly wrong?
- ✓ contribute to the Thinking Story discussion?

PRACTICE p. 57

LESSON 57 PRACTICE Name______________________

In each problem two of the answers are clearly wrong and one is correct. Choose the correct answer.

1. 309 + 617 — a. 2016 b. 326 (c.) 926
2. 597 − 498 — a. 1095 b. 199 (c.) 99
3. 402 − 142 — a. 360 b. 544 (c.) 260
4. 745 − 337 — (a.) 408 b. 1008 c. 112
5. 643 − 278 — (a.) 365 b. 165 c. 835
6. 850 + 759 — a. 91 (b.) 1609 c. 1509
7. 3295 − 2167 — a. 128 (b.) 1128 c. 5128
8. 1647 + 9353 — a. 20,000 b. 8000 (c.) 11,000
9. 6439 − 5161 — (a.) 1278 b. 1338 c. 11,600
10. 525 + 985 — a. 460 (b.) 1510 c. 4510
11. 243 − 77 — (a.) 166 b. 316 c. 66
12. 685 + 85 — a. 600 (b.) 770 c. 785
13. 5467 + 3261 — (a.) 8728 b. 828 c. 1728
14. 433 + 267 — (a.) 700 b. 890 c. 290
15. 433 − 253 — (a.) 180 b. 220 c. 686
16. 5603 − 5346 — a. 8257 b. 1257 (c.) 257
17. 526 + 397 — a. 1523 b. 223 (c.) 923
18. 805 + 805 — a. 805 b. 0 (c.) 1610
19. 260 + 437 — a. 297 (b.) 697 c. 237
20. 3103 − 2568 — (a.) 535 b. 5035 c. 135
21. 4130 − 255 — a. 3975 (b.) 3875 c. 4125
22. 466 + 466 — (a.) 932 b. 822 c. 0
23. 2206 − 1150 — a. 1156 (b.) 1056 c. 3356
24. 5485 + 3741 — a. 1744 b. 8125 (c.) 9226

Copyright © SRA/McGraw-Hill. Permission is granted to reproduce this page for classroom use.

Math Explorations and Applications Level 4 • **57**

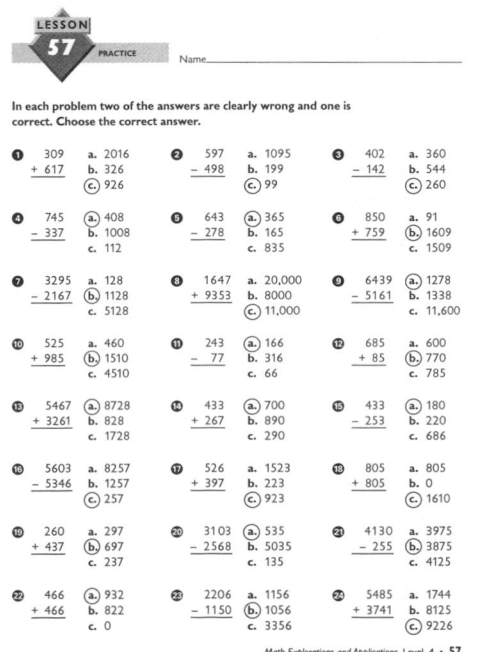

ENRICHMENT p. 57

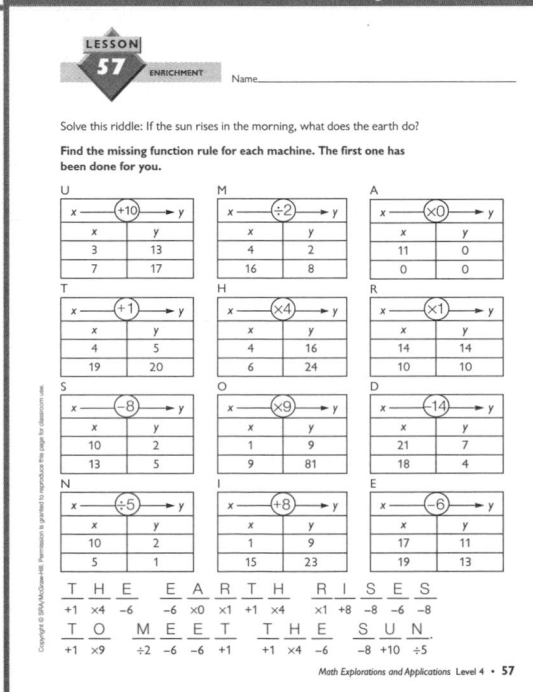

LESSON 57 ENRICHMENT Name______________________

Solve this riddle: If the sun rises in the morning, what does the earth do?

Find the missing function rule for each machine. The first one has been done for you.

U: x → (+10) → y

x	y
3	13
7	17

M: x → (÷2) → y

x	y
4	2
16	8

A: x → (×0) → y

x	y
11	0
0	0

T: x → (+1) → y

x	y
4	5
19	20

H: x → (×4) → y

x	y
4	16
6	24

R: x → (×1) → y

x	y
14	14
10	10

S: x → (−8) → y

x	y
10	2
13	5

O: x → (×9) → y

x	y
1	9
9	81

D: x → (−14) → y

x	y
21	7
18	4

N: x → (÷5) → y

x	y
10	2
5	1

I: x → (+8) → y

x	y
1	9
15	23

E: x → (−6) → y

x	y
17	11
19	13

T H E   E A R T H   R I S E S
+1 ×4 −6   −6 ×0 ×1 +1 ×4   ×1 +8 −8 −6 −8

T O   M E E T   T H E   S U N.
+1 ×9   ÷2 −6 −6 +1   +1 ×4 −6   −8 +10 ÷5

Copyright © SRA/McGraw-Hill. Permission is granted to reproduce this page for classroom use.

Math Explorations and Applications Level 4 • **57**

Homework Have students play the "Function" game with a family member for further practice with mental arithmetic. A copy of this game can also be found on page 16 of the Home Connections Blackline Masters.

LOOKING AHEAD You will need graph paper for the next lesson and many subsequent lessons in this unit. We suggest paper with 0.5-centimeter squares for most work. However, for the first few graphing sessions, you may prefer paper with 1-centimeter squares.

LESSON 58

Student Edition pages 198–199

Graphing Ordered Pairs

LESSON PLANNER

Objectives

- to demonstrate the relationships among a function, a set of ordered pairs, and a graph
- to teach how to graph points that correspond to ordered pairs

Context of the Lesson This is the eighth of 13 lessons on functions and graphing. Informal work with graphing functions was included in Level 3 as students graphed multiples of numbers.

MANIPULATIVES

graph paper with at least 0.5-cm squares

rulers* or straightedges

Program Resources

Reteaching Master

Practice Master 58

Enrichment Master 58

For extra practice:
CD-ROM* Lesson 58

1 Warm-Up (5 MINUTES)

Problem of the Day Present this problem orally or on the chalkboard, and have students explain how they solved it: A book has 150 pages. How many 8s are used in the page numbers throughout the book? (25)

Problem-Solving Strategies Ask students who have solved the Problem of the Day to share how they solved it and any strategies they used.

MENTAL MATH Tell students about a machine that multiplies by 2 and then subtracts 2 from whatever number is put into it. Ask them what number would come out if they put in the following numbers. This exercise provides practice with algebraic equations.

a. 4 (6)	**b.** 2 (2)	**c.** 3 (4)
d. 8 (14)	**e.** 7 (12)	**f.** 6 (10)
g. 5 (8)	**h.** 10 (18)	**i.** 9 (16)

MIXED PRACTICE

LESSON 58

Graphing Ordered Pairs

ALGEBRA READINESS

Once you have used a function rule to find ordered pairs, you can display them on a graph.

1. Copy the list of ordered pairs, but replace each x or y with the correct number.

   $x \xrightarrow{+2} y$ (0, y), (7, y), (10, y), (x, 3), (x, 5), (x, 10)

   2, 9, 12, 1, 3, 8

2. You may want to use graphing software to make a graph. Use the ordered pairs you found in problem 1 as coordinates of points on your graph.

   Remember that the first (or x) number tells how far to go to the right. The second (or y) number tells how far to go up. Does your graph look like this?

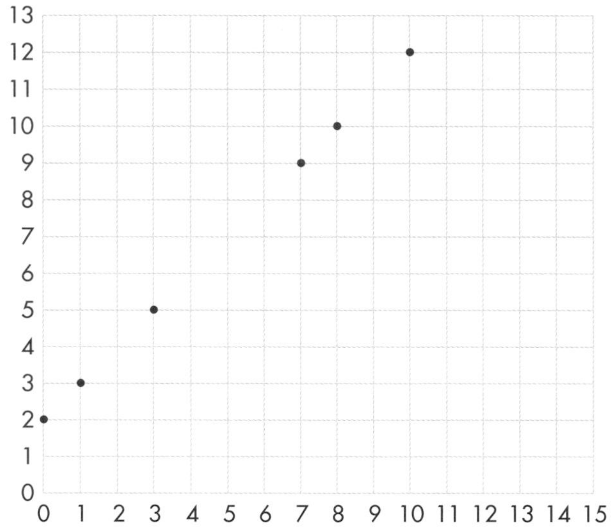

3. Do you notice anything interesting about the six points on your graph? Check with a ruler to see if they are all on the same straight line. **The six points should appear to be a straight line.**

Literature Connection For a more basic explanation of graphs, invite students to read *Help Is on the Way for Charts and Graphs* by Marilyn Berry.

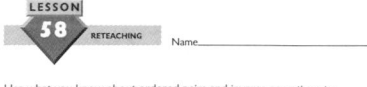

RETEACHING p. 19

LESSON 58 RETEACHING Name__________

Use what you know about ordered pairs and inverse operations to graph functions.

x —(−2)→ y	
x	y
2	0
3	1
?	2
5	?

In ordered pairs we have (2, 0), (3, 1), (x, 2), (5, y).

Let's find x: x —(−2)→ 2   2 + 2 = 4,
(4, 2) is the ordered pair.

Let's find y: 5 —(−2)→ y 5 − 2 = 3,
(5, 3) is the ordered pair.

Graph these ordered pairs on the graph.

The graph would look like this.
It is a straight line. The function
$x - 2 = y$ is a line.

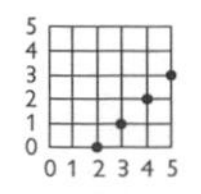

Find x and y and graph the ordered pairs.

1. x —(+2)→ y

   (1, 3), (x, 4), (3, y), (0, 2)
   (2, 4) (3, 5)

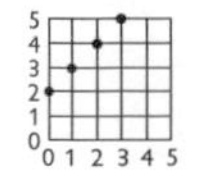

2. x —(×1)→ y

   (0, 0), (x, 2), (4, y), (5, 5)
   (2, 2) (4, 4)

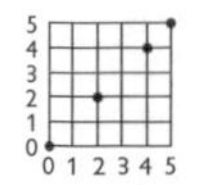

Copyright © SRA/McGraw-Hill. Permission is granted to reproduce this page for classroom use.

Math Explorations and Applications Level 4 • 19

*available separately

Look at your graph, but don't do any calculations for problems 4 and 5.

4. Think about the point that has 4 as its first coordinate.
   a. Where do you think the point ought to be? **Students should indicate (4, 6).**
   b. What is its second coordinate? **6**
   c. If 4 were put into a +2 function machine, what would come out? **6**

5. Copy each ordered pair, but replace each x or y with the number you believe would make the point fall on the line.
   a. (2, y) **4** b. (x, 11) **9** c. (x, 8) **6** d. (11, y) **13**

Copy each list of ordered pairs, but replace each *x* or *y* with the correct number. Then graph each set of ordered pairs. **Check students' graphs carefully.**

6. x —(−3)→ y (5, y) **2**, (4, y) **1**, (x, 0) **3**, (x, 5) **8**, (10, y) **7**, (x, 10) **13**

7. x —(÷2)→ y (4, y) **2**, (6, y) **3**, (20, y) **10**, (x, 4) **8**, (x, 8) **16**, (10, y) **5**

8. x —(×0)→ y (1, y) **0**, (3, y) **0**, (0, y) **0**, (10, y) **0**, (5, y) **0**, (9, y) **0**

9. x —(+0)→ y (1, y) **1**, (3, y) **3**, (0, y) **0**, (x, 9) **9**, (x, 12) **12**, (x, 8) **8**

10. x —(×1)→ y (1, y) **1**, (3, y) **3**, (0, y) **0**, (x, 9) **9**, (x, 12) **12**, (x, 8) **8**

MATH JOURNAL

Compare your graphs for problems 9 and 10. Write your observations in your Math Journal.

FANTASTIC FACT

The largest meteorite, the Hoba meteorite, still lies where it fell at Hoba West in Namibia (formerly South-West Africa). It weighs about 60 tons and measures $8\frac{1}{2}$ feet by $7\frac{1}{2}$ feet.

❷ Teach

Using the Student Pages Have students complete the ordered pairs in problem 1 on page 198. Next have them number the axes on their graph paper and locate the first point on the graph (0, 2). After students plot the six points, encourage them to compare graphs with their classmates and with the graph on page 198. The six points should appear to fall along a straight line. Have **rulers*** available.

Do problem 4 on page 199 with the class. Explain how the pattern of the points of a function can be used to estimate where other points should be. Then let students solve problems 5–10 on their own.

Note: Students may not have time to finish graphing all of these functions. Be sure to have them do problems 9 and 10 during the lesson so you can discuss them with the class. Ask students to compare their graphs for the function rules in problems 9 and 10, for which the graphs are identical. This particular function is called the *identity function* because it leaves numbers unchanged (what comes out is identical to what went in).

❸ Wrap-Up

5 MINUTES

In Closing Have students explain the convention for naming ordered pairs on a coordinate graph.

ALTERNATIVE ASSESSMENT

Informal Assessment Observe students as they make their graphs. Be sure that they label both axes of their graphs and plot points correctly. Keep anecdotal records of students' progress.

PRACTICE p. 58

LESSON 58 PRACTICE Name________

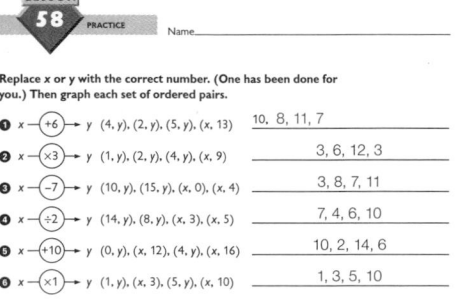

Replace x or y with the correct number. (One has been done for you.) Then graph each set of ordered pairs.

1. x —(+6)→ y (4, y), (2, y), (5, y), (x, 13) 10, 8, 11, 7
2. x —(×3)→ y (1, y), (2, y), (4, y), (x, 9) 3, 6, 12, 3
3. x —(−7)→ y (10, y), (15, y), (x, 0), (x, 4) 3, 8, 7, 11
4. x —(÷2)→ y (14, y), (8, y), (x, 3), (x, 5) 7, 4, 6, 10
5. x —(+10)→ y (0, y), (x, 12), (4, y), (x, 16) 10, 2, 14, 6
6. x —(×1)→ y (1, y), (x, 3), (5, y), (x, 10) 1, 3, 5, 10

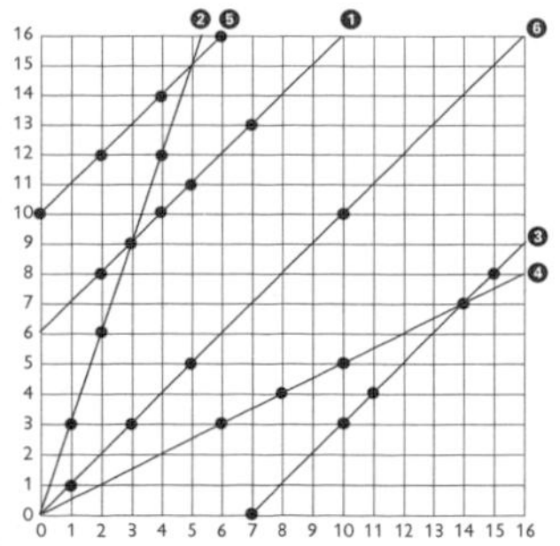

58 • Math Explorations and Applications Level 4

ENRICHMENT p. 58

LESSON 58 ENRICHMENT Name________

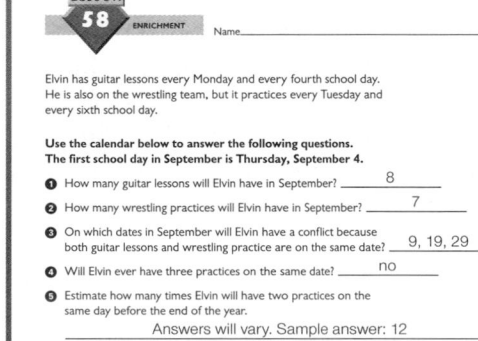

Elvin has guitar lessons every Monday and every fourth school day. He is also on the wrestling team, but it practices every Tuesday and every sixth school day.

Use the calendar below to answer the following questions. The first school day in September is Thursday, September 4.

1. How many guitar lessons will Elvin have in September? 8
2. How many wrestling practices will Elvin have in September? 7
3. On which dates in September will Elvin have a conflict because both guitar lessons and wrestling practice are on the same date? 9, 19, 29
4. Will Elvin ever have three practices on the same date? no
5. Estimate how many times Elvin will have two practices on the same day before the end of the year.
   Answers will vary. Sample answer: 12

58 • Math Explorations and Applications Level 4

Assessment Criteria

Did the student . . .

✓ correctly plot the ordered pairs?

✓ communicate understanding of the relationships among functions, ordered pairs, and a graph?

✓ explain how to solve for *x* or *y*?

Homework Have students complete any unfinished graphs. To reinforce the skill of graphing ordered pairs, assign Practice Master 58.

*available separately

LESSON 59

Student Edition pages 200–203

Identifying Scale

LESSON PLANNER

Objectives

- ▶ to demonstrate how to choose appropriate scales on axes so that graphs fit the paper
- ▶ to provide an opportunity to identify scales
- ▶ to provide practice in graphing sets of ordered pairs

Context of the Lesson This is the ninth of 13 lessons on graphing and functions.

MANIPULATIVES

calculators*
graph paper
dual dial scale*
rulers* or straightedges
objects to be measured (weight)

Program Resources

Practice Master 59
Enrichment Master 59
For extra practice:
CD-ROM* Lesson 59
Cumulative Review, page 547

1 Warm-Up (5 MINUTES)

Problem of the Day Present this problem, allowing students to use **calculators*** to solve it: On March 1, Steven began an experiment. He programmed his computer to subtract a number each day. He started at 40,000 and had the computer subtract 1 on the first day. The next day, the computer subtracted twice as much from the new difference, and on the third day it subtracted twice as much from the new difference as it had on the second day. If Steven's computer followed that pattern, what number would it display on March 15? (7233)

Problem-Solving Strategies Ask students who have solved the Problem of the Day to share how they solved it and any strategies they used.

MENTAL MATH Estimate the weight of several classroom objects. Display an object, ask for metric measurement estimates, then have a volunteer use a **scale*** to measure the object to check the estimates.

a. weight of a textbook
b. weight of several textbooks
c. weight of student's backpack

LESSON 59

Identifying Scale

ALGEBRA READINESS

Sometimes the numbers you want to graph may seem too great to fit on your paper.

Suppose you are graphing this function:

$x \rightarrow (\times 8) \rightarrow y$

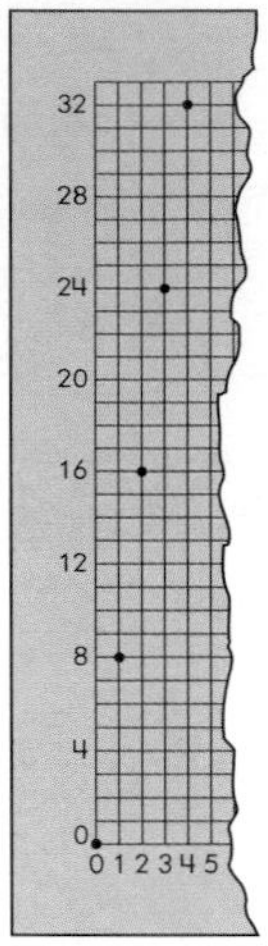

And let's say you are using these five ordered pairs:

x	y
0	0
1	8
2	16
3	24
4	32

Then you might think that you would need long, skinny graph paper, like that shown at the top right.

But there is another way to fit the five points on your graph paper.

And you don't need an unusual shape.

You can let each space in the up-and-down direction stand for more than one unit. In the graph on the bottom right, each up-and-down space stands for four units. All the points fit.

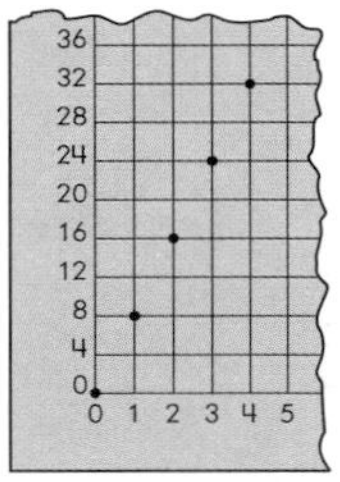

◆ Make your own graph of these points. But let each up-and-down space stand for eight units. Do the points fit? **yes**

Literature Connection Read with the class *The Magic School Bus Inside a Beehive* by Joanna Cole. Have them graph the approximate number of eggs a queen bee lays in one minute, two minutes, and so on up to ten minutes. Discuss scales that would best fit the data.

*available separately

An Ice Cream Puzzle

Alonzo surveyed the students in the fourth grade to learn their favorite ice cream flavors. There are 83 students in Alonzo's grade, and 80 of them returned the survey form.

He made a bar graph to present his data to the manager of the school cafeteria. But Alonzo forgot to write the numbers on the side of his graph that show how many students preferred each flavor.

Can you figure out how to label the side of Alonzo's graph? You may want to record the number of students who prefer each flavor.

1. How many students are represented by each line in Alonzo's graph? **2**
2. Which flavor of ice cream is most popular? How many students prefer it? **strawberry; 19**
3. How many students prefer chocolate ice cream? **13**
4. How many students prefer vanilla ice cream? **15**

Use a computer or other means to draw this chart. Then complete the chart.

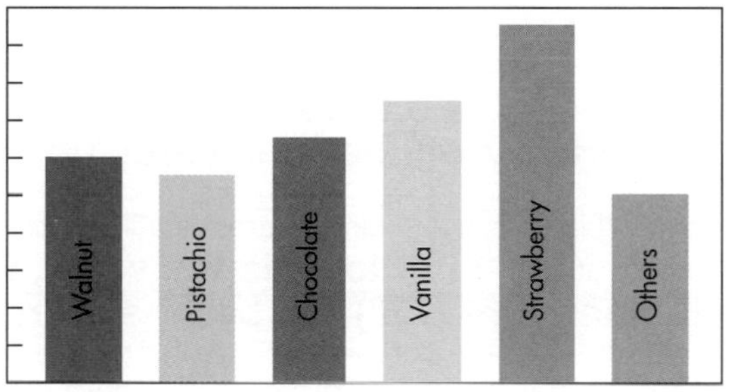

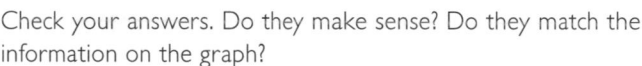

Check your answers. Do they make sense? Do they match the information on the graph?

MATH JOURNAL

In your Math Journal explain how you figured out this problem.

❷ Teach

ALGEBRA READINESS

Using the Student Pages Work through page 200 with the class. Explain that students may choose any scale for the horizontal or vertical axis that suits the data. In general, guide them to identify the greatest and least numbers that must appear on each axis. For example, if the *x*-coordinates of points to plot fall between 0 and 32, then the horizontal scale must go from at least 0 to 32. Students can calibrate the scale by ones, twos, or any reasonable increment; increments need not be identical for both axes. Remind students to clearly label whatever scale they select. When you think that most students understand that changing the scale can affect the size of a graph, let them work on the problem at the bottom of the page.

You may want to work through page 201 as a class activity or have students work on it in pairs. The graph is in increments of 2 so that all students are accounted for in the survey.

TECHNOLOGY CONNECTION

Technology Connection For more practice organizing data and constructing, modifying, and interpreting graphs, students may try the software *Graphers* from Sunburst Communications (Mac, for grades K–4). Available graph formats include pictographs, bar, circle, loop, grid-plot, and line graphs.

◆ LESSON 59 Identifying Scale

Teach

Using the Student Pages Have students work on page 202 in pairs or independently. Discuss their answers. There are several reasonable answers. For example, the scale could go from 24 to 72 in increments of 2, or from 0 to 75 in increments of 3. Then have students complete page 203 on their own. Students' graphs should have reasonable scales, and ordered pairs should be accurately graphed. Have **rulers*** and **graph paper** available.

GIFTED & TALENTED

Meeting Individual Needs

Extend the lesson by having students make a graph of average rainfall for a certain period of time. Give each student an odd-sized piece of **graph paper**, and tell students to select whatever scale is reasonable for the size of paper and the data they must plot. Display the completed graphs for students to compare and contrast, and highlight the similarities and differences among graphs based on the same data.

◆ LESSON 59 Identifying Scale

Mr. Archer's students are making a graph of the average temperature in their city for each month. Here are their data:

January	30°F
February	24°F
March	46°F
April	52°F
May	59°F
June	63°F
July	70°F
August	72°F
September	65°F
October	58°F
November	42°F
December	36°F

5. What scale should they use for the up-and-down direction on their graph if their graph paper is 25 squares tall? **For example: from 0 to 75 in increments of 3**

6. Using this scale, how many squares up will the temperature for January be? **If 0 to 75 is the scale, the temperature for January will be 10 squares up.**

7. Using this scale, how many squares up will the highest temperature be? **If 0 to 75 is the scale, the highest temperature (72°) will be 24 squares up.**

8. Create a graph using information in the above chart. You may want to use graphing software. **Check students' graphs.**

FANTASTIC FACT **The space probes sent to land on Venus had to withstand temperatures of almost 500°C (900°F), a temperature high enough to melt tin.**

202 • Algebra Readiness and Geometry

RETEACHING

No reteaching is suggested at this time. More practice with graphing and choosing scales is provided later in this unit. You may want to assign Enrichment Master 59.

*available separately

When you make a graph, think ahead. Make sure your graph will fit on your paper.

Use a computer or other means to copy and complete each chart. Then graph each set of ordered pairs. You may want to use graphing software to create your graph.

9 x —(×5)→ y

x	y
0	**0**
2	**10**
3	**15**
4	**20**
6	**30**
7	**35**
8	**40**

10 x —(×7)→ y

x	y
0	**0**
2	**14**
3	**21**
5	**35**
6	**42**
7	**49**
9	**63**

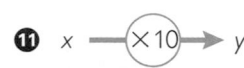

11 x —(×10)→ y

x	y
0	**0**
2	**20**
3	**30**
5	**50**
6	**60**
7	**70**
10	**100**

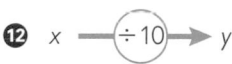

12 x —(÷10)→ y

x	y
0	**0**
20	**2**
40	**4**
50	**5**
70	**7**
80	**8**
100	**10**

13 x —(÷5)→ y

x	y
0	**0**
10	**2**
15	**3**
20	**4**
30	**6**
35	**7**
40	**8**

14 x —(−10)→ y

x	y
70	**60**
60	**50**
50	**40**
40	**30**
30	**20**
20	**10**
10	**0**

Use the Cumulative Review on page 547 after this lesson.

❸ Wrap-Up 5 MINUTES

In Closing Ask students to explain how they determine the scale for a graph.

ALTERNATIVE ASSESSMENT

Performance Assessment You might use page 203 as an assessment of students' ability to set up a graph, choose and label a reasonable scale, and accurately graph sets of ordered pairs based on function rules. If so, have students work independently. Record the results of their work in your notes.

Assessment Criteria

Did the student . . .

✓ contribute to the discussion of choosing scales for a graph?

✓ correctly solve problems based on decisions about scale?

✓ make graphs that demonstrate an understanding of scale?

✓ accurately graph sets of ordered pairs?

Homework Have students collect or research data on a topic that interests them, such as a favorite baseball player's seasonal batting average for the past ten years. Have them graph the data, a task that includes selecting a reasonable scale, and label it clearly.

SPECIAL NEEDS

Meeting Individual Needs

Some students may not be able to determine the best scale without trial and error. Allow them to try out several possibilities until they determine the scale that works best for the given data and size of graph paper. Suggest that they test their scale before they make the final draft of their graph.

PRACTICE p. 59

LESSON 59 PRACTICE Name______________

Complete each chart. Then graph each set of ordered pairs.

❶ x—(×8)→y

x	y
0	0
2	16
4	32
5	40
6	48

❷ x—(÷5)→y

x	y
60	12
50	10
40	8
30	6
20	4

❸ x—(+10)→y

x	y
5	15
10	20
15	25
20	30
25	35

❹ x—(−10)→y

x	y
50	40
40	30
30	20
20	10
10	0

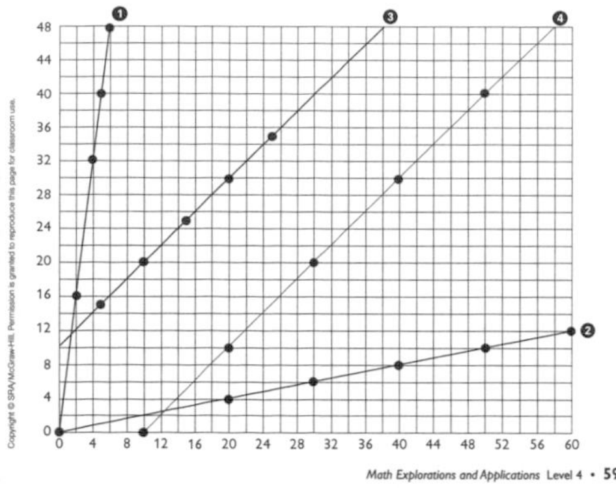

Copyright © SRA/McGraw-Hill. Permission is granted to reproduce this page for classroom use.

ENRICHMENT p. 59

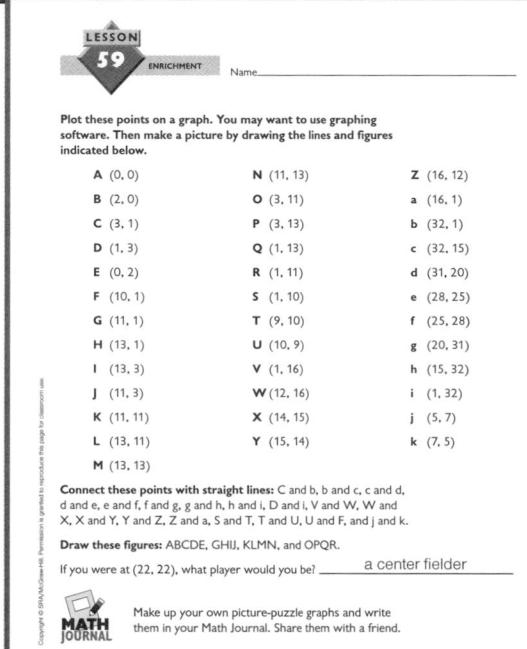

LESSON 59 ENRICHMENT Name______________

Plot these points on a graph. You may want to use graphing software. Then make a picture by drawing the lines and figures indicated below.

A (0, 0)	**N** (11, 13)	**Z** (16, 12)
B (2, 0)	**O** (3, 11)	**a** (16, 1)
C (3, 1)	**P** (3, 13)	**b** (32, 1)
D (1, 3)	**Q** (1, 13)	**c** (32, 15)
E (0, 2)	**R** (1, 11)	**d** (31, 20)
F (10, 1)	**S** (1, 10)	**e** (28, 25)
G (11, 1)	**T** (9, 10)	**f** (25, 28)
H (13, 1)	**U** (10, 9)	**g** (20, 31)
I (13, 3)	**V** (1, 16)	**h** (15, 32)
J (11, 3)	**W** (12, 16)	**i** (1, 32)
K (11, 11)	**X** (14, 15)	**j** (5, 7)
L (13, 11)	**Y** (15, 14)	**k** (7, 5)
M (13, 13)		

Connect these points with straight lines: C and b, b and c, c and d, d and e, e and f, f and g, g and h, h and i, D and i, V and W, W and X, X and Y, Y and Z, Z and a, S and T, T and U, U and F, and j and k.

Draw these figures: ABCDE, GHIJ, KLMN, and OPQR.

If you were at (22, 22), what player would you be? a center fielder

MATH JOURNAL Make up your own picture-puzzle graphs and write them in your Math Journal. Share them with a friend.

Copyright © SRA/McGraw-Hill. Permission is granted to reproduce this page for classroom use.

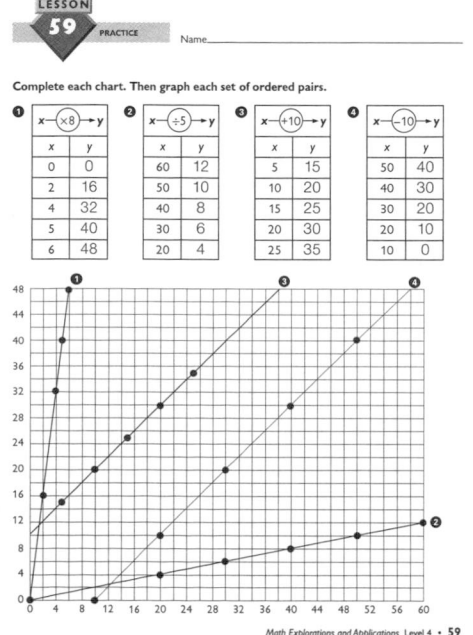

UNIT 3

Student Edition pages 204–205

Mid-Unit Review

The Mid-Unit Review pinpoints troublesome skill areas for students, allowing time for additional practice and reteaching before the unit ends. If students did not do well on the Mid-Unit Review and have completed additional practice, you may want to use the Mid-Unit Review provided on Assessment Blackline Masters pages 22–23.

Using the Student Pages Have students complete problems 1–30 on pages 204 and 205 on their own. You might treat this review as a formal assessment of students' skills and have students complete this review as a timed test. See suggestions on page 51.

Mid-Unit Review

Use the coordinate grid to answer these questions.

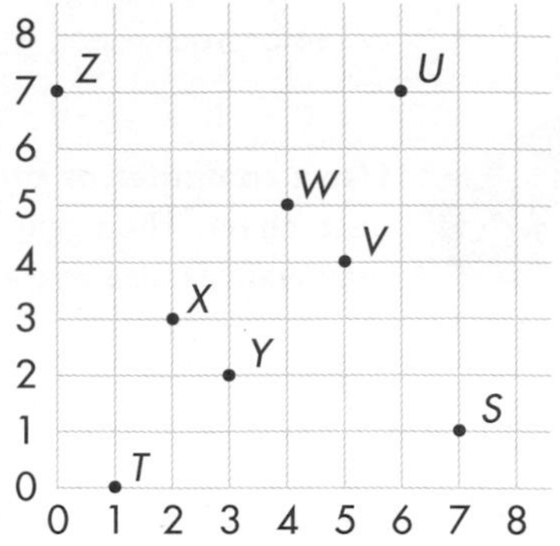

1. What are the coordinates at point *Z*? **(0, 7)**
2. What are the coordinates at point *U*? **(6, 7)**
3. What are the coordinates at point *W*? **(4, 5)**
4. What is the name of the point at (2, 3)? ***X***
5. What is the name of the point at (1, 0)? ***T***
6. What is the name of the point at (7, 1)? ***S***

Find a function rule for each set of arrow operations.

7. 3 —(?)→ 21
   6 —(?)→ 42
   8 —(?)→ 56
   9 —(?)→ 63
   x 7
8. 50 —(?)→ 5
   90 —(?)→ 9
   10 —(?)→ 1
   30 —(?)→ 3
   ÷10
9. 0 —(?)→ 8
   5 —(?)→ 13
   9 —(?)→ 17
   10 —(?)→ 18
   + 8

In each case, tell what *x* is.

10. 6 —(+5)→ *x* **11**
11. 9 —(−5)→ *x* **4**
12. 41 —(−11)→ *x* **30**
13. 54 —(÷9)→ *x* **6**
14. 8 —(×5)→ *x* **40**
15. 20 —(÷5)→ *x* **4**
16. 17 —(+8)→ *x* **25**
17. 7 —(×7)→ *x* **49**

Use the inverse arrow operation to find the value of *x*.

18. $x \rightarrow (\div 8) \rightarrow 4$ **32**
19. $x \rightarrow (-45) \rightarrow 3$ **48**
20. $x \rightarrow (+75) \rightarrow 100$ **25**
21. $x \rightarrow (\div 3) \rightarrow 9$ **27**
22. $x \rightarrow (+11) \rightarrow 20$ **9**
23. $x \rightarrow (\times 10) \rightarrow 100$ **10**
24. $x \rightarrow (-15) \rightarrow 15$ **30**
25. $x \rightarrow (\times 1) \rightarrow 0$ **0**

Copy each list of ordered pairs, but replace the *x* or *y* with the correct number.

26. $x \rightarrow (+9) \rightarrow y$ (3, 12), (6, *y*), (23, *y*), (*x*, 10), (*x*, 18) **15, 32, 1, 9**
27. $x \rightarrow (\div 4) \rightarrow y$ (16, 4), (24, *y*), (36, *y*), (*x*, 5), (*x*, 7) **6, 9, 20, 28**
28. $x \rightarrow (\times 8) \rightarrow y$ (2, 16), (1, *y*), (0, *y*), (*x*, 64), (*x*, 80) **8, 0, 8, 10**

Use a computer or other means to draw these charts. Graph each set of ordered pairs. Make sure your graph will fit on the paper. You may want to use graphing software. **Check students' graphs for accuracy.**

29. $x \rightarrow (\times 7) \rightarrow y$

x	y
4	28
6	42
9	**63**
10	70
8	**56**

30. $x \rightarrow (\div 2) \rightarrow y$

x	y
4	2
8	**4**
14	**7**
20	10
16	**8**

ASSESSMENT p. 22

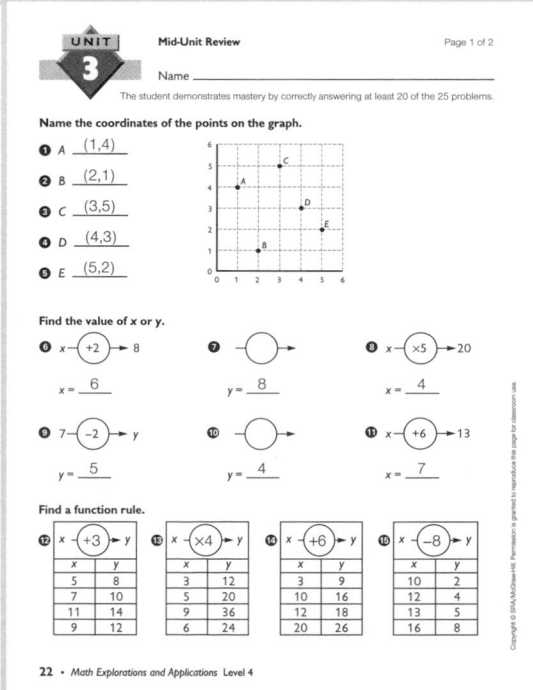

UNIT 3 **Mid-Unit Review** Page 1 of 2

Name ____________

The student demonstrates mastery by correctly answering at least 20 of the 25 problems.

Name the coordinates of the points on the graph.

1. A (1,4)
2. B (2,1)
3. C (3,5)
4. D (4,3)
5. E (5,2)

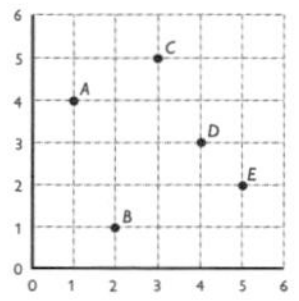

Find the value of *x* or *y*.

6. $x \rightarrow (+2) \rightarrow 8$ $x =$ 6
7. $\rightarrow (\ ) \rightarrow$ $y =$ 8
8. $x \rightarrow (\times 5) \rightarrow 20$ $x =$ 4
9. $7 \rightarrow (-2) \rightarrow y$ $y =$ 5
10. $\rightarrow (\ ) \rightarrow$ $y =$ 4
11. $x \rightarrow (+6) \rightarrow 13$ $x =$ 7

Find a function rule.

12. $x \rightarrow (+3) \rightarrow y$

x	y
5	8
7	10
11	14
9	12

13. $x \rightarrow (\times 4) \rightarrow y$

x	y
3	12
5	20
9	36
6	24

14. $x \rightarrow (+6) \rightarrow y$

x	y
3	9
10	16
12	18
20	26

15. $x \rightarrow (-8) \rightarrow y$

x	y
10	2
12	4
13	5
16	8

22 • *Math Explorations and Applications* Level 4

Copyright © SRA/McGraw-Hill. Permission is granted to reproduce this page for classroom use.

Home Connections You may want to send home the Home Connections Blackline Masters letter on pages 42–43 to provide additional activities that families can complete together. These activities apply the skills presented in this unit.

ALTERNATIVE ASSESSMENT

Portfolio Assessment As students work through the second half of this unit, the Portfolio task provided on Assessment Blackline Masters page 95 can be used to evaluate students' proficiency with using geometric transformations and graphing.

ALTERNATIVE ASSESSMENT

Performance Assessment Performance Assessment Task 1, provided on Assessment Blackline Masters pages 75–76, can be used at this time to evaluate students' proficiency with functions and graphs. You may want to administer this assessment to individual students or small groups of students.

Unit Project This would be a good time to assign the "Mathematics and Postage Stamps" project on pages 264 and 265. Students can begin working on the project in cooperative groups in their free time as they work through the unit. The Unit Project is a good opportunity for students to explore the hobby of stamp collecting, which relates to geography, history, mathematics, and art.

LESSON 60

Student Edition pages 206–209

Composite Function Rules

LESSON PLANNER

Objectives

- to introduce composite functions
- to provide a realistic situation in which a composite function is used

Context of the Lesson This is the tenth of 13 lessons on graphing and functions. Some work with composite functions was presented at the third-grade level.

MANIPULATIVES	Program Resources
graph paper	Reteaching Master
rulers* or straightedges	Practice Master 60
slips of paper (optional)	Enrichment Master 60
	For extra practice: CD-ROM* Lesson 60

1 Warm-Up

5 MINUTES

Problem of the Day Present the following problem to students. You might prepare a list of the numerical value of each letter in advance: Give each letter of the alphabet a number value—A = 1, B = 2, C = 3, and so on to Z = 26. Which has the greater value, the sum of letters in your first name or in your last name? By how much? (Answers will vary.)

Problem-Solving Strategies Ask students who have solved the Problem of the Day to share how they solved it and any strategies they used.

MENTAL MATH Present chain calculations that include all four operations. Have students work from left to right without inserting parentheses.

a. 1 + 2 – 3 + 1 = (1) **b.** 5 × 2 – 4 – 1 = (5)

c. 10 – 4 ÷ 3 + 2 = (4) **d.** 2 + 4 + 1 × 5 = (35)

e. 3 – 1 ÷ 2 + 4 = (5) **f.** 12 – 6 – 2 × 8 = (32)

g. 4 + 8 ÷ 6 × 3 = (6) **h.** 8 – 5 × 7 ÷ 3 = (7)

i. 5 + 8 – 3 – 4 = (6) **j.** 3 × 6 ÷ 9 × 2 = (4)

EXPLORE

LESSON 60

Composite Function Rules

ALGEBRA READINESS

x → in [×3] out → n → in [+5] out → y

These two function machines have been put together. A number (*x*) goes into the first machine. The number that comes out (*n*) goes into the second machine. Then a third number (*y*) comes out.

This is called a **composite function machine.**

Here's a way to write what this composite function machine does:

x —(×3)→ n —(+5)→ y

Suppose you put 6 into the first machine. What would come out of the second machine?

6 —(×3)→ n —(+5)→ y   What is *y*?

First decide what *n* is.   Then decide what *y* is.

6 —(×3)→ ~~n~~ 18 —(+5)→ y   6 —(×3)→ ~~n~~ 18 —(+5)→ ~~y~~ 23

You can do all this a short way:

6 —(×3)→ n —(+5)→ y   *n* is 18; *y* is 23.

LEARNING STYLES · MANIPULATIVES

Meeting Individual Needs Kinesthetic, interpersonal, and logical learners may benefit from acting out the operation of a composite function machine. Do a simulation with three students and **slips of paper.** Student A gives a slip of paper with a number on it to Student B, who changes the number according to his or her function rule, and then passes it to Student C, who changes the new number according to his or her rule. Record the actions by writing what students do in terms of arrows, *n*, and *y*.

*available separately

Find the value of *y*.

1. 7 → (+3) → *n* → (×8) → *y* **80**
2. 7 → (×8) → *n* → (+3) → *y* **59**
3. 4 → (+7) → *n* → (×1) → *y* **11**
4. 5 → (×5) → *n* → (−5) → *y* **20**
5. 20 → (−16) → *n* → (×3) → *y* **12**
6. 9 → (÷3) → *n* → (+2) → *y* **5**
7. 15 → (÷5) → *n* → (×4) → *y* **12**
8. 4 → (×3) → *n* → (÷2) → *y* **6**
9. 4 → (÷2) → *n* → (×3) → *y* **6**
10. 145 → (−100) → *n* → (÷5) → *y* **9**
11. 16 → (+5) → *n* → (−5) → *y* **16**
12. 8 → (×4) → *n* → (÷4) → *y* **8**
13. 6 → (×2) → *n* → (÷3) → *y* **4**
14. 5 → (+5) → *n* → (×2) → *y* **20**
15. 18 → (÷6) → *n* → (×3) → *y* **9**
16. 3 → (+3) → *n* → (×4) → *y* **24**
17. 24 → (÷4) → *n* → (×9) → *y* **54**
18. 56 → (÷7) → *n* → (×6) → *y* **48**

FANTASTIC FACT

A grasshopper can jump 20 times its own body length. If you could do that, you would be able to jump from a pitcher's mound to home plate in one hop!

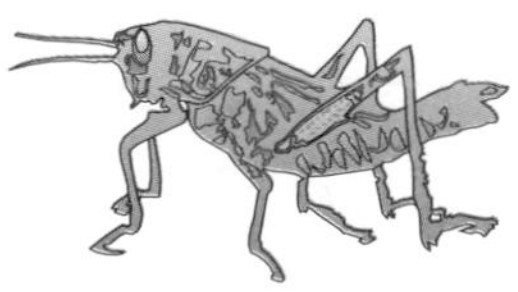

❷ Teach

ALGEBRA READINESS

Using the Student Pages Go over page 206 with the class. Emphasize that to find the value of *y*, it is necessary to find the value of *n* first because in composite function machines the order of performing the operations affects the outcome. Have students imagine putting a 6 in the composite function machine at the top of the page, but instead of multiplying by 3 and then adding 5, they first add 5 and then multiply the sum by 3. By switching the order, the output would be 33 instead of 23. Have students work independently on page 207.

There are reasons for almost everything we do in mathematics. Children should be encouraged to discover, or at least see, those reasons. Understanding the reasons will help them remember how to do the mathematics; but more important, it will help them understand that the mathematics is related to their reality and that mathematics can be used to help them understand the real world.

—Stephen S. Willoughby,
Mathematics Education for a Changing World

TECHNOLOGY CONNECTION

Technology Connection Refer students to the software *Math Football* from Gamco (Apple, IBM, for grades 4–12) for further practice with addition, subtraction, multiplication, division, and mixed operations.

◆ LESSON 60 Composite Function Rules

Teach

Using the Student Pages Discuss Sierra's price plan to be sure students understand the scenario. Go over the first two pairs of entries in Sierra's chart, then have students complete the page on their own. Alert them to choose scales that will allow them some extra room to extend the graph. After students complete page 208, they can move on to page 209 and answer those questions. Have **rulers*** and **graph paper** available.

COOPERATIVE LEARNING You may wish to have students work in pairs or small groups to solve the problems on page 209. Encourage students to discuss their solution methods as they work. You might suggest that they make an organized list or chart to help them find the various combinations of numbers of glasses of lemonade and handling charges.

◆ LESSON 60 Composite Function Rules

Sierra opened a lemonade stand. She decided to charge 3¢ for each cup of lemonade, plus a 1¢ handling charge per order.

So if you bought one cup of lemonade, Sierra would charge you 3¢ plus a 1¢ handling charge—a total of 4¢.

If you bought two cups, she would charge you 6¢ for the two cups plus the 1¢ handling charge—a total of 7¢.

To help her figure out what to charge, she started to make this function chart.

$x \rightarrow (\times 3) \rightarrow n \rightarrow (+1) \rightarrow y$

x	y
1	4¢
2	7¢
3	■ **10¢**
4	■ **13¢**
5	■ **16¢**
6	■ **19¢**

19. Help Sierra. Use a computer or other means to draw and complete the chart. Then graph the ordered pairs. You may want to use graphing software to make your graph.

20. Connect the points on your graph. Do they all lie in a straight line? **yes**

21. Look at your graph. How much would Sierra charge somebody who bought nine cups of lemonade? (You may have to extend your graph.) **28¢**

22. Devon and Brad each wanted a cup of lemonade. Brad had an idea. "Devon," he said. "Let me buy two cups and we will share them." Why did Brad think that was a good idea? **By combining their orders they pay only one handling charge and thus save 1¢.**

19 Check to be sure students have correctly completed their charts and graphs.

208 • Algebra Readiness and Geometry

Real-World Connection Discuss the meaning of "handling charges" as used on page 208. Students may have read or heard expressions such as "plus $2.95 for postage and handling" or "service charge of $3 per ticket." Discuss the purpose of a handling or service charge. Help students understand that it helps to defray the cost of materials, supplics, postage, or personnel to fill an order. Have students give examples of handling or service charges they know about.

RETEACHING p. 20

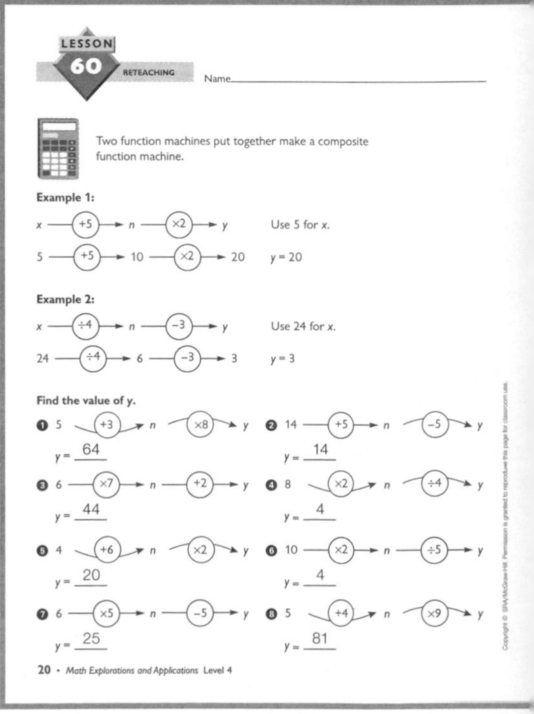

LESSON 60 RETEACHING Name______

Two function machines put together make a composite function machine.

Example 1:

$x \rightarrow (+5) \rightarrow n \rightarrow (\times 2) \rightarrow y$ Use 5 for x.

$5 \rightarrow (+5) \rightarrow 10 \rightarrow (\times 2) \rightarrow 20$ $y = 20$

Example 2:

$x \rightarrow (\div 4) \rightarrow n \rightarrow (-3) \rightarrow y$ Use 24 for x.

$24 \rightarrow (\div 4) \rightarrow 6 \rightarrow (-3) \rightarrow 3$ $y = 3$

Find the value of y.

1. $5 \rightarrow (+3) \rightarrow n \rightarrow (\times 8) \rightarrow y$ y = 64
2. $14 \rightarrow (+5) \rightarrow n \rightarrow (-5) \rightarrow y$ y = 14
3. $6 \rightarrow (\times 7) \rightarrow n \rightarrow (+2) \rightarrow y$ y = 44
4. $8 \rightarrow (\times 2) \rightarrow n \rightarrow (\div 4) \rightarrow y$ y = 4
5. $4 \rightarrow (+6) \rightarrow n \rightarrow (\times 2) \rightarrow y$ y = 20
6. $10 \rightarrow (\times 2) \rightarrow n \rightarrow (\div 5) \rightarrow y$ y = 4
7. $6 \rightarrow (\times 5) \rightarrow n \rightarrow (-5) \rightarrow y$ y = 25
8. $5 \rightarrow (+4) \rightarrow n \rightarrow (\times 9) \rightarrow y$ y = 81

20 • *Math Explorations and Applications* Level 4

Copyright © SRA/McGraw-Hill. Permission is granted to reproduce this page for classroom use.

*available separately

Solve.

23. Suppose Sierra sells ten cups of lemonade in one day.
    - **a.** What is the most she would charge? **40¢**
    - **b.** What is the least she would charge? **31¢**

24. How much will four friends save by ordering all at once instead of one at a time? **3¢**

25. Suppose Sierra collected 15¢.
    - **a.** How many cups of lemonade did she sell? **4, 2 separately and 2 together**
    - **b.** Is there more than one answer? **no**

26. Suppose Sierra collected 25¢.
    - **a.** How many cups of lemonade did she sell? **7 or 8**
    - **b.** Is there more than one answer? **yes**

27. How many different combinations of orders could Sierra have filled if she collected 20¢? **three—5 orders of 1 cup each; 2 orders of 3 cups each; 1 order of 2 cups and 1 order of 4 cups**

3 Wrap-Up

5 MINUTES

In Closing Have students describe a composite function machine and explain similarities and differences between it and a simple function machine.

ALTERNATIVE ASSESSMENT

Performance Assessment You may wish to use students' performance on page 207 as an informal assessment of their understanding of composite functions, as well as a review of basic arithmetic facts in all four operations.

Assessment Criteria

Did the student . . .

- ✓ contribute to the discussion of composite function machines?
- ✓ demonstrate understanding of the use of order in working with composite functions?
- ✓ explain how to solve for *n* and *y*?
- ✓ create an accurate graph of a composite function?
- ✓ accurately solve problems related to composite functions?

PRACTICE p. 60

LESSON 60 PRACTICE Name__________

Find the value of y.

1. 7 → (+2) → n → (×5) → y y = 45
2. 30 → (÷6) → n → (×7) → y y = 35
3. 12 → (−6) → n → (÷3) → y y = 2
4. 18 → (−8) → n → (+4) → y y = 14
5. 21 → (−1) → n → (×0) → y y = 0
6. 45 → (÷5) → n → (×4) → y y = 36
7. 9 → (+10) → n → (−4) → y y = 15
8. 8 → (×7) → n → (−6) → y y = 50
9. 8 → (×7) → n → (÷8) → y y = 7
10. 12 → (÷6) → n → (+9) → y y = 11
11. 15 → (−5) → n → (×9) → y y = 90
12. 34 → (−12) → n → (÷2) → y y = 11

PROBLEM SOLVING **Solve these problems.**

Brian mows lawns to make money. He charges $10 for each time he mows someone's lawn plus a one-time start-up fee of $5.

13. Make a function chart to show how much he will make mowing the Greenes' lawn. The function chart has been started for you.

x → (×? 10) → n → (+? 5) → y

x	y
1	15
2	25
3	35
4	45
5	55
10	105

14. How many times will Brian need to mow the Greenes' lawn to make at least $50? 5

15. Can Brian make at least $100 if he mows the Greenes' lawn ten times? yes

60 • *Math Explorations and Applications* Level 4

Copyright © SRA/McGraw-Hill. Permission is granted to reproduce this page for classroom use.

ENRICHMENT p. 60

LESSON 60 ENRICHMENT Name__________

PROBLEM SOLVING Bill's basement collects water when it rains hard. In the past, depending on how hard it has rained, between 1 and 5 inches of water have seeped into the basement every hour. Bill uses a pump that pumps out 1 inch of water in three hours.

Solve these problems.

1. After three hours, how much water will collect in the basement if it is seeping in at the rate of 1 inch every hour and the pump is working? If 1 inch is *x*, make a composite function machine to help you figure this out. 2 inches

2. How much water will collect in three hours if it is coming in at a rate of 2 inches every hour? 3 inches? 4 inches? 5 inches? Remember, the pump is still working. Plot your ordered pairs on a grid to prove your answers are right. 5 inches; 8 inches; 11 inches; 14 inches; the result would be a straight line.

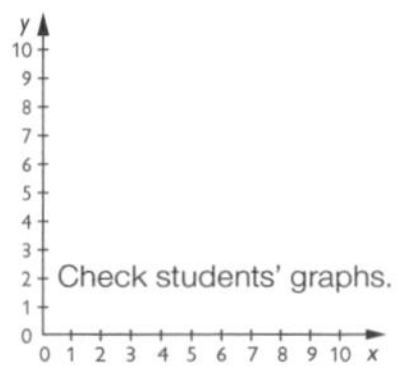

3. Bill has valuable equipment and other items stored on a platform that is 1 foot above the floor. If water comes in for three hours and the pump is working, at how many inches per hour can the water come in before it reaches the platform? a little over 4 inches per hour

4. If the pump is working, but 20 inches of water collect in the basement within three hours anyway, how many inches per hour have been seeping in? Reverse your composite function machine to figure it out. Show your work. Would this mean that the water had come in faster than ever before? 7 inches per hour; yes, 2 more inches per hour than ever before

60 • *Math Explorations and Applications* Level 4

Copyright © SRA/McGraw-Hill. Permission is granted to reproduce this page for classroom use.

Homework Have students make up five composite function problems like those on page 207.

SPECIAL NEEDS

Meeting Individual Needs

Students who have difficulty grasping the importance of order in a composite function might benefit from discussing an analogy. Have them imagine putting on their socks and shoes each morning. Ask in what order they should do things. (For each foot, sock first, then shoe.) Ask what would happen if they put the shoes on first, then the socks. (The order would be backwards and would not work.) Invite students to make up similar analogies to composite functions.

LESSON 61

Student Edition pages 210–213

Using Inverse Operations with Composite Functions

LESSON PLANNER

Objectives

- to demonstrate how to find the inverse of a composite function
- to help students develop the broad ability to use mathematical common sense

Context of the Lesson This is the 11th of 13 lessons on graphing and functions. This lesson also contains Part 3 of "The Lost Island of Addonia," a four-part Thinking Story.

MANIPULATIVES

construction paper, crayons, markers, paint, scissors, tape (optional)

Program Resources

Number Wheels
Practice Master 61
Enrichment Master 61
For career connections: Careers and Math*
For extra practice: CD-ROM* Lesson 61

1 Warm-Up

5 MINUTES

Problem of the Day Present this problem to students: Rosalie has a 3-ounce measuring cup and a 5-ounce measuring cup. Using only these two tools, how can she measure 2 ounces of popcorn? (One possible answer: Rosalie can fill the 5-oz measuring cup with popcorn, then use that quantity to fill the 3-oz measuring cup, which leaves 2 oz of popcorn in the 5-oz measuring cup.)

Problem-Solving Strategies Ask students who have solved the Problem of the Day to share how they solved it and any strategies they used.

MENTAL MATH Provide practice with pairs of problems that present inverse operations. Have students use their Number Wheels to quickly show the answers.

a. 4 × 8 = (32) 32 ÷ 8 = (4)

b. 10 × 15 = (150) 150 ÷ 10 = (15)

c. 80 + 80 = (160) 160 – 80 = (80)

(continued on page 211)

LESSON 61

Using Inverse Operations with Composite Functions

ALGEBRA READINESS

Suppose a number was put into this composite function and 23 came out. What number was put in? In other words, if *y* is 23, what is *x*?

a. What value of *n* gives 23 as the number coming out? Write the inverse arrow operation.

b. 23 − 8 = 15

So *n* is 15.

c. What value of *x* gives 15 as the value of *n*?

Write the inverse arrow operation. 15 ÷ 3 = 5

So when *y* is 23, *x* is 5.

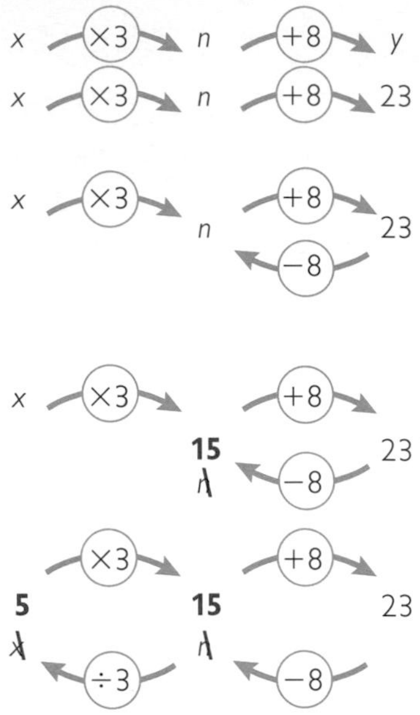

Let's check this:

5 × 3 = 15, 15 + 8 = 23. That checks.

You don't have to write all the steps.

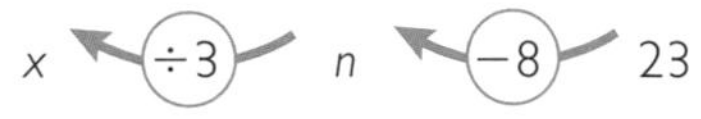

You can just write this: *n* is 15, *x* is 5.

Use inverse operations to find the value of *x*.

1 *x* (×5) *n* (+2) 37 **7**

2 *x* (−5) *n* (÷7) 1 **12**

ART CONNECTION · MANIPULATIVES

Art Connection You may wish to have students create their own function machines. Provide **scissors, tape, construction paper, paint, crayons,** and **markers,** and have students work in pairs or small groups to create colorful function "machines." Make sure they clearly label their machines with the function they perform. Then have them "run" their machines and invite classmates to put numbers into them.

*available separately

Solve these problems.

3. Mikhail's class has three students absent today. The rest of the students are divided into six groups of four students each.
   - **a.** How many students are in Mikhail's class today? **24**
   - **b.** How many students should be in Mikhail's class, counting those who are absent? **27**

4. Two fourth-grade classes are going on a field trip. Nine parents and two teachers will go with the students. All together there are ten groups of six people each.
   - **a.** How many people are going on the field trip? **60**
   - **b.** How many students are going on the field trip? **49**

5. Amanda ordered some teddy bears by mail to give as gifts, but she can't remember how many she ordered. She does know that the bears cost $9 each, plus a $4 shipping and handling fee for the order, and that her total cost was $40.
   - **a.** What was Amanda's cost before she added the shipping and handling fee? **$36**
   - **b.** How many bears did Amanda order? **4**

6. Mrs. Baez ordered teddy bears from the same company as Amanda did. Her total cost was $58.
   - **a.** What was Mrs. Baez's cost before the shipping and handling fee? **$54**
   - **b.** How many bears did Mrs. Baez order? **6**

7. Mr. Wade is ordering from a different teddy bear company that charges $10 per bear with no shipping and handling fee. Because he has ordered from this company before, he has a discount coupon that saves him $5 on his order. He wants to spend no more than $25 on his order.
   - **a.** If Mr. Wade spends $25, what would his cost be before he uses the coupon? **$30**
   - **b.** How many bears can Mr. Wade order with his coupon? **3**

Mental Math (continued)

d.	100 + 600 = (700)	700 – 600 = (100)
e.	10 x 60 = (600)	600 ÷ 10 = (60)
f.	100 – 75 = (25)	25 + 75 = (100)
g.	100 x 10 = (1000)	1000 ÷ 10 = (100)
h.	20 x 20 = (400)	400 ÷ 20 = (20)

2 Teach

ALGEBRA READINESS

Using the Student Pages Draw a composite function machine on the chalkboard to help students interpret the question "What is *x*?" Before going over steps a–c for finding *x*, ask students what number they think *x* is. Accept all answers, including guesses. Demonstrate whether or not each number works. If a student answers correctly, ask that student to explain how he or she found the answer. Assign the problems on page 210. Encourage students to use mental math, and allow those who can solve these problems without using inverse arrow operations to do so. Have students work individually or in pairs to solve the word problems on page 211.

LEARNING STYLES

Meeting Individual Needs

Students who are kinesthetic or "hands-on" learners may benefit from working with physical models of function machines. Provide models you have made or use machines students have constructed themselves (see *Art Connection* on page 210). Explain inverse operations in terms of running a function machine backwards to give students a better grasp of the concept.

. . . thinking is the ultimate basic skill in mathematics.

—Stephen S. Willoughby,
Teaching Mathematics: What Is Basic?

◆ LESSON 61 Using Inverse Operations with Composite Functions

Teach

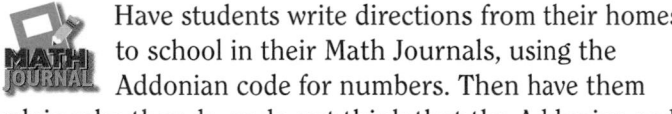

Using the Thinking Story "The Lost Island of Addonia (Part 3)" presents another situation in which students use the Addonian code of transforming numbers according to people's ages to deduce hidden information.

Answers to Thinking Story Questions:

1. Joan and Henry must be different ages. When Joan says 13 she means something different by it than Henry does.
2. If Joan was right when she said a triangle has 11 sides, her answer to the question about the square should have been one more, or 12.
3. Eight years old. If she was right when she said a triangle has 11 sides, her age must be eight, because 8 + 3 = 11.
4. Nine years old. Henry is right when he says a square has 13 sides, and 9 + 4 = 13.
5. 34 years old. She says a triangle has 37 sides, and she refers to the four visitors as 38 visitors.
6. Each child would say the other is 17 years old. Students have figured out that Joan is eight and Henry is nine. So Joan would say that Henry is 8 + 9, or 17, years old and Henry would say that Joan is 9 + 8, also 17 years old.

MATH JOURNAL Have students write directions from their homes to school in their Math Journals, using the Addonian code for numbers. Then have them explain why they do or do not think that the Addonian code is a good system.

◆ **LESSON 61 Using Inverse Operations with Composite Functions**

THINKING STORY

The Lost Island of Addonia

Part 3

You may want to refer to the previous parts of this Thinking Story, on pages 190–191 and 196–197.

The four children came to the Addonia Public School. "Let's go in here," Portia said. "Maybe this is where the library is."

Inside the school a mathematics class was going on. "Remember," said the teacher, "every triangle has 37 sides. What's the rule, Joan?"

"A triangle has 11 sides," said a girl in the front row.

"Very good, Joan. And how many sides does a square have?"

"A square has 13 sides," said Joan.

"I'm afraid that's wrong," said the teacher. "Henry, how many sides does a square have?"

"A square has 13 sides," said Henry.

"That's right," said the teacher. "And now let's welcome our 38 visitors from the United States."

. . . to be continued

Technology Connection Refer students to the software *The King's Rule* from Sunburst Communications (Apple, Mac, IBM for grades 4-8) for further practice with number rules, patterns, and relationships.

RETEACHING

Students who have trouble grasping the idea of "undoing" an operation may benefit from an analogy to wrapping and unwrapping a gift. Explain that when you wrap a gift, you perform two actions. First you put the gift in a box, then you wrap the box in paper. The person who gets the gift performs the two actions in reverse. First he or she removes the paper, then he or she takes the gift out of the box. Apply this reasoning to functions by giving a mathematical example.

Work in groups. Discuss your answers and how you figured them out. Then compare your answers with those of other groups. **Answers are in margin.**

1. How could Joan be wrong when she said a square has 13 sides and Henry be right when he said the same thing?
2. What should Joan have said about the number of sides a square has?
3. How old is Joan?
4. How old is Henry?
5. How old is the teacher?
6. **Super detective questions:** How old would Joan say that Henry is? How old would Henry say that Joan is? Why would they say the same number?

3 Wrap-Up (5 MINUTES)

In Closing Have students explain how to find an unknown number in a composite function machine.

Informal Assessment Observe students as they work through this lesson, and listen to the comments they offer during discussions. Encourage them to explain their reasoning and to "think out loud" when solving the problems so you can ascertain the level of understanding they have reached.

ALTERNATIVE ASSESSMENT

Assessment Criteria

Did the student . . .

- ✓ communicate strategies used to find the value of x?
- ✓ correctly answer at least four of the five word problems?
- ✓ contribute to the Thinking Story discussion?

Homework Have students create and solve two composite function exercises that involve inverse operations, such as those at the bottom of page 210.

PRACTICE p. 61

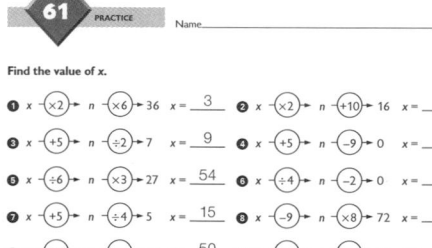

LESSON 61 PRACTICE Name__________

Find the value of x.

1. $x \xrightarrow{\times 2} n \xrightarrow{\times 6} 36$ $x =$ 3
2. $x \xrightarrow{\times 2} n \xrightarrow{+10} 16$ $x =$ 3
3. $x \xrightarrow{+5} n \xrightarrow{\div 2} 7$ $x =$ 9
4. $x \xrightarrow{+5} n \xrightarrow{-9} 0$ $x =$ 4
5. $x \xrightarrow{\div 6} n \xrightarrow{\times 3} 27$ $x =$ 54
6. $x \xrightarrow{\div 4} n \xrightarrow{-2} 0$ $x =$ 8
7. $x \xrightarrow{+5} n \xrightarrow{\div 4} 5$ $x =$ 15
8. $x \xrightarrow{-9} n \xrightarrow{\times 8} 72$ $x =$ 18
9. $x \xrightarrow{\div 10} n \xrightarrow{\times 8} 40$ $x =$ 50
10. $x \xrightarrow{\times 7} n \xrightarrow{-20} 22$ $x =$ 6
11. $x \xrightarrow{\times 7} n \xrightarrow{-8} 20$ $x =$ 4
12. $x \xrightarrow{+10} n \xrightarrow{\times 10} 100$ $x =$ 0
13. $x \xrightarrow{\times 6} n \xrightarrow{\div 6} 6$ $x =$ 6
14. $x \xrightarrow{\div 7} n \xrightarrow{\times 7} 49$ $x =$ 49
15. $x \xrightarrow{\div 7} n \xrightarrow{\times 3} 21$ $x =$ 49
16. $x \xrightarrow{-11} n \xrightarrow{\div 4} 1$ $x =$ 15
17. $x \xrightarrow{\div 6} n \xrightarrow{\times 9} 45$ $x =$ 30
18. $x \xrightarrow{\times 3} n \xrightarrow{\times 9} 81$ $x =$ 3

PROBLEM SOLVING **Solve these problems.**

19. Three students are absent from Kathleen's ballet class today. The students who are at class are divided into four groups of three students each.
    a. How many students are at ballet class today? 12
    b. How many students are in the class when no one is absent? 15

Copyright © SRA/McGraw-Hill. Permission is granted to reproduce this page for classroom use.

ENRICHMENT p. 61

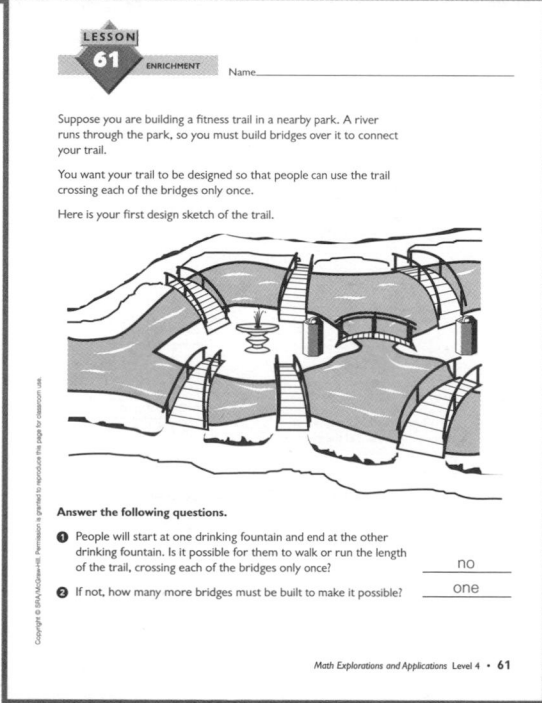

LESSON 61 ENRICHMENT Name__________

Suppose you are building a fitness trail in a nearby park. A river runs through the park, so you must build bridges over it to connect your trail.

You want your trail to be designed so that people can use the trail crossing each of the bridges only once.

Here is your first design sketch of the trail.

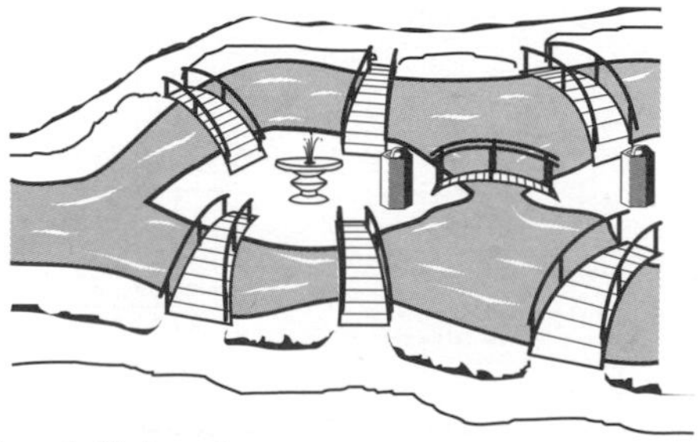

Answer the following questions.

1. People will start at one drinking fountain and end at the other drinking fountain. Is it possible for them to walk or run the length of the trail, crossing each of the bridges only once? no
2. If not, how many more bridges must be built to make it possible? one

Copyright © SRA/McGraw-Hill. Permission is granted to reproduce this page for classroom use.

LESSON 62

Student Edition pages 214–215

Graphing Composite Functions

LESSON PLANNER

Objectives

- ▶ to provide practice with finding ordered pairs of a composite function, given the second coordinates
- ▶ to demonstrate that graphs of a function will look the same even with different ordered pairs
- ✓ to assess mastery of graphing functions

Context of the Lesson This lesson, the 12th of 13 lessons on functions and graphing, contains a Mastery Checkpoint for those skills.

MANIPULATIVES
none

Program Resources
Number Wheels
Reteaching Master
Practice Master 62
Enrichment Master 62
Assessment Master
For extra practice:
CD-ROM* Lesson 62

1 Warm-Up (5 MINUTES)

Problem of the Day Present this problem: When the doorbell rang the first time, Hakim greeted one guest. On each ring after that, Hakim greeted three more guests than he did on the previous ring. If the doorbell rang five times, how many guests came to visit Hakim? (35)

Problem-Solving Strategies Ask students who have solved the Problem of the Day to share how they solved it and any strategies they used.

MENTAL MATH Have students use their Number Wheels to respond:

a. 3 × 4 = (12) 12 ÷ 4 = (3)
b. 60 – 30 = (30) 30 + 30 = (60)
c. 40 ÷ 2 = (20) 20 × 2 = (40)

MIXED PRACTICE

LESSON 62

Graphing Composite Functions

ALGEBRA READINESS

You've graphed ordered pairs from a single function rule. In this lesson you'll graph ordered pairs from composite functions.

Use inverse operations to replace each x with the correct number. Then make a graph for each set of ordered pairs. Make sure your graph will fit on your paper. You may want to use graphing software. Check students' graphs.

1. x —(×2)→ y (x, 2), (x, 10), (x, 20), (x, 0), (x, 16)
1, 5, 10, 0, 8
2. x —(+7)→ y (x, 9), (x, 17), (x, 27), (x, 7), (x, 8)
2, 10, 20, 0, 1
3. x —(−9)→ y (x, 9), (x, 7), (x, 3), (x, 8), (x, 5)
18, 16, 12, 17, 14
4. x —(÷6)→ y (x, 6), (x, 3), (x, 8), (x, 7), (x, 9)
36, 18, 48, 42, 54
5. x —(×2)→ n —(+7)→ y (x, 9), (x, 17), (x, 27), (x, 7)
1, 5, 10, 0
6. x —(×3)→ n —(−5)→ y (x, 1), (x, 7), (x, 10), (x, 25)
2, 4, 5, 10
7. x —(−5)→ n —(×3)→ y (x, 0), (x, 15), (x, 6), (x, 12)
5, 10, 7, 9
8. x —(+6)→ n —(÷2)→ y (x, 6), (x, 5), (x, 7), (x, 3)
6, 4, 8, 0
9. x —(÷3)→ n —(−3)→ y (x, 2), (x, 4), (x, 1), (x, 3)
15, 21, 12, 18
10. x —(−7)→ n —(×4)→ y (x, 28), (x, 20), (x, 16), (x, 12)
14, 12, 11, 10

RETEACHING p. 21

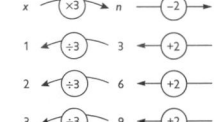

LESSON 62 RETEACHING Name________

You have already learned how to find composite functions.
Now let's graph some. Use inverse operations to find x each time.

Example:

x —(×3)→ n —(−2)→ y

1 ←(÷3)— 3 ←(+2)— 1
2 ←(÷3)— 6 ←(+2)— 4
3 ←(÷3)— 9 ←(+2)— 7
4 ←(÷3)— 12 ←(+2)— 10

Use these ordered pairs:
(x, 1), (x, 4), (x, 7), (x, 10)

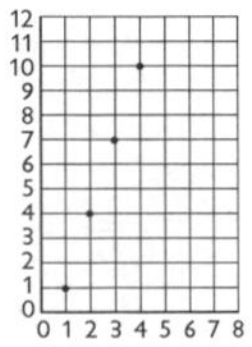

The ordered pairs found are:
(1, 1), (2, 4), (3, 7), (4, 10)

To graph the ordered pairs, remember that the x number comes first and the y number comes second.

Find the values of y. Graph the ordered pairs on a separate sheet of paper. Check students' graphs.

1. x —(+6)→ n —(÷1)→ y
(x, 6), (x, 8), (x, 10), (x, 12)
0, 2, 4, 6

2. x —(−1)→ n —(×2)→ y
(x, 2), (x, 4), (x, 6), (x, 8)
2, 3, 4, 5

Copyright © SRA/McGraw-Hill. Permission is granted to reproduce this page for classroom use.

PRACTICE p. 62

LESSON 62 PRACTICE Name________

Use inverse operations to replace x with the correct number. Graph each set of ordered pairs.

1. x —(×3)→ y (x, 6), (x, 15), (x, 30), (x, 0), (x, 24) 2, 5, 10, 0, 8
2. x —(+6)→ y (x, 10), (x, 16), (x, 26), (x, 6), (x, 24) 4, 10, 20, 0, 18
3. x —(−8)→ y (x, 8), (x, 16), (x, 4), (x, 2), (x, 5) 16, 24, 12, 10, 13
4. x —(÷2)→ y (x, 6), (x, 7), (x, 9), (x, 10), (x, 5) 12, 14, 18, 20, 10
5. x —(×2)→ n —(+6)→ y (x, 8), (x, 10), (x, 12), (x, 20) 1, 2, 3, 7
6. x —(÷4)→ n —(−4)→ y (x, 2), (x, 4), (x, 1), (x, 3) 24, 32, 20, 28

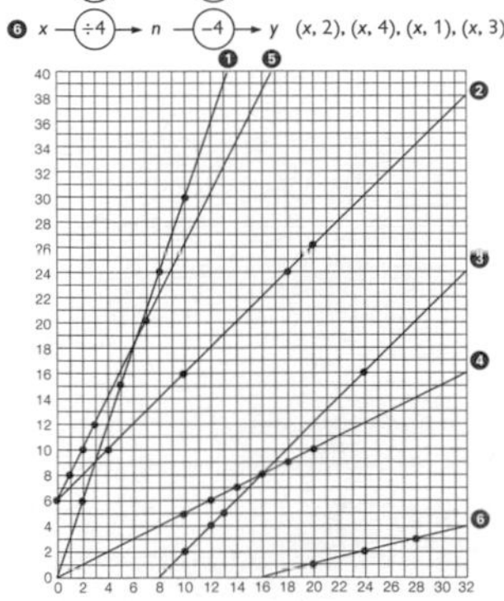

Copyright © SRA/McGraw-Hill. Permission is granted to reproduce this page for classroom use.

*available separately

Look at the following composite function. Answer the questions.

ALGEBRA READINESS

11 **a.** Pick a number between 0 and 10 for the value of x.

x —(×2)→ n —(+3)→ y

For example: (0,3), (1,5), (2,7), (3,9), (4,11)

b. Make an ordered pair of the number you used for x and the value of y.

c. Find two more ordered pairs for the same function. **For example: (5,13), (6,15)**

d. Graph the three ordered pairs you have found. **See margin.**

12 Look at your graph.

a. Pick a point that has 4 as its first (sideways) coordinate and is on the same line as the other three points.

b. What is the second coordinate of the point you picked? **11**

c. Pick a point that has 15 as its second (up-and-down) coordinate and is on the same line as the other points.

d. What is the first coordinate of the point you picked? **6**

13 Replace x and y in the ordered pairs with the correct numbers.

x —(×2)→ n —(+3)→ y (4, y), (x, 15) **11** **6**

◆ Did you use the graph to find x in the second ordered pair?

FANTASTIC FACT

The blue whale is the largest and heaviest animal on Earth. The largest elephant looks small compared to the blue whale, which is about 100 feet long and weighs as much as 400,000 pounds. That's as long as three city buses and as heavy as 200 compact cars. A newborn blue whale weighs about 6000 pounds.

❷ Teach

Using the Student Pages Do problem 1 on page 214 with the class. Then let students solve problems 2–10 on their own. Discuss the graphs on page 214. On page 215, do problem 11a with the class. In problem 11d, students will plot different sets of three points. However, all students' graphs should look like the figure below.

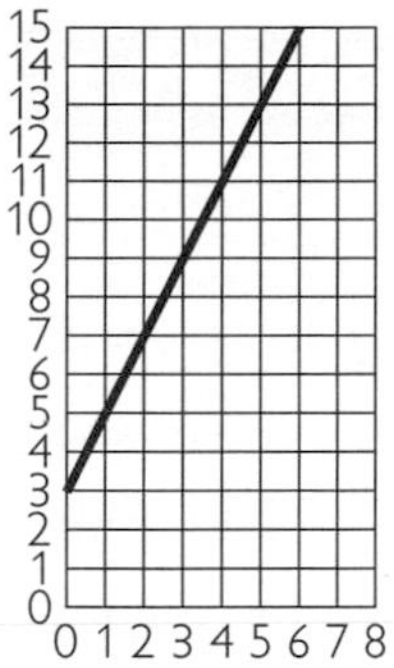

Then let students complete problem 12. Make sure they extend the vertical axis to at least 15 so they can answer problem 12c. Show how to use the graph to do problems like number 13.

❸ Wrap-Up

5 MINUTES

In Closing Have students demonstrate how to use a graph to find ordered pairs.

Mastery Checkpoint 10

By this time most students should be able to plot points on a graph, choose appropriate scales, and demonstrate understanding of the graph of a function. Students demonstrate mastery by correctly answering at least 80% of the problems on pages 214–215 or on Assessment Blackline Masters on pages 24–26.

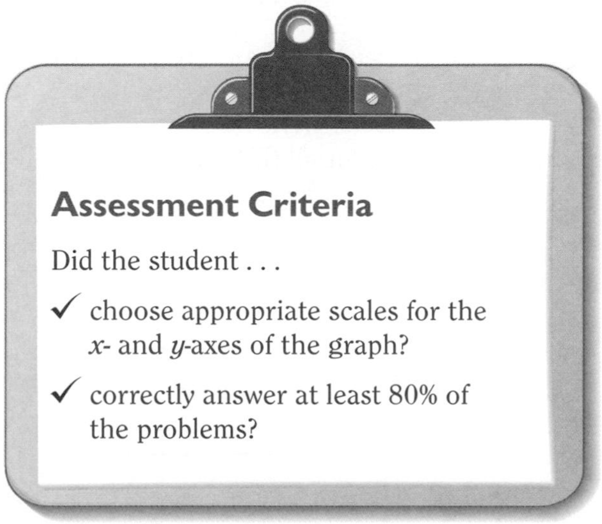

Assessment Criteria

Did the student . . .

✓ choose appropriate scales for the x- and y-axes of the graph?

✓ correctly answer at least 80% of the problems?

Homework Have students play "Cubo" (page 163 or page 15 in the Home Connections Blackline Masters) with a family member to practice mental arithmetic.

ENRICHMENT p. 62

LESSON 62 ENRICHMENT Name__________

There is a mix-up in the computer files at the Happy Pet Vet office, and the veterinarian doesn't know which pet belongs to which person.

Here are some clues:

Mr. Nakamura's pet is spotted.

Ms. Chen does not have a dog.

Mr. Nakamura's daughter has a ferret.

Ms. Chen lives next door to Mr. Nakamura.

Lisa is Mr. Nakamura's daughter.

Mr. Nakamura's daughter's pet is white.

Ms. Chen's next-door neighbor has a dog.

Someone has a black cat.

Which person owns which pet?

Mr. Nakamura spotted dog

Lisa white ferret

Ms. Chen black cat

Copyright © SRA/McGraw-Hill. Permission is granted to reproduce this page for classroom use.

62 • *Math Explorations and Applications* Level 4

ASSESSMENT p. 24

UNIT 3 **Mastery Checkpoint 10** Graphing functions (Lesson 62) Page 1 of 3

Name__________

The student demonstrates mastery by correctly answering at least 4 of the 5 problems.

Use inverse operations to replace each x with the correct number. (The first one has been done for you.) Then make a graph for each set of ordered pairs.

1 x —(+9)→ y (x, 9) 0 (x, 12) 3 (x, 18) 9 (x, 16) 7 (x, 14) 5

2 x —(−7)→ y (x, 3) 10 (x, 7) 14 (x, 0) 7 (x, 12) 19 (x, 10) 17

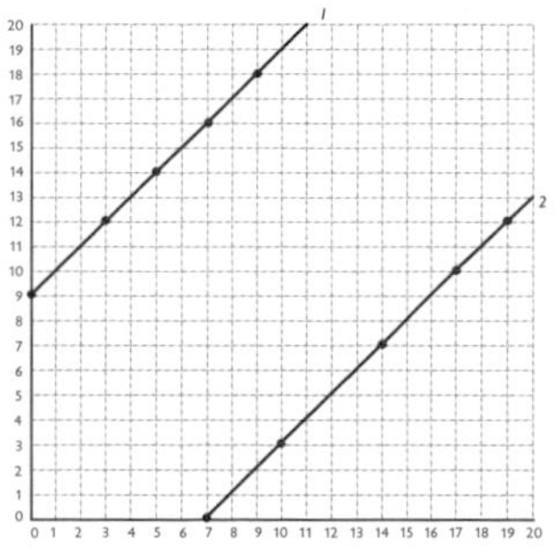

Copyright © SRA/McGraw-Hill. Permission is granted to reproduce this page for classroom use.

24 • *Math Explorations and Applications* Level 4

LESSON 63

Student Edition pages 216–219

Keeping Sharp: Facts, Computations, and Fractions

LESSON PLANNER

Objectives

- ▶ to review arithmetic facts, computations, and fractions
- ▶ to provide practice doing computations that involve parentheses and in solving word problems
- ▶ to help students develop the broad ability to use mathematical common sense

Context of the Lesson This lesson provides a review of basic facts, fractions, and problem solving. This lesson also contains Part 4 of "The Lost Island of Addonia," a four-part Thinking Story.

MANIPULATIVES

base-10 blocks*
(optional)

Program Resources

Number Wheels
Number Cubes
Practice Master 63
Enrichment Master 63
For career connections:
Careers and Math*
For extra practice:
CD-ROM* Lesson 63
Cumulative Review, page 548

1 Warm-Up

5 MINUTES

Problem of the Day Present this problem on the chalkboard: Imagine folding this net into a number cube. Write number sentences with the factors and products for all three pairs of opposite faces. (8 x 7 = 56, 6 x 5 = 30, 10 x 9 = 90)

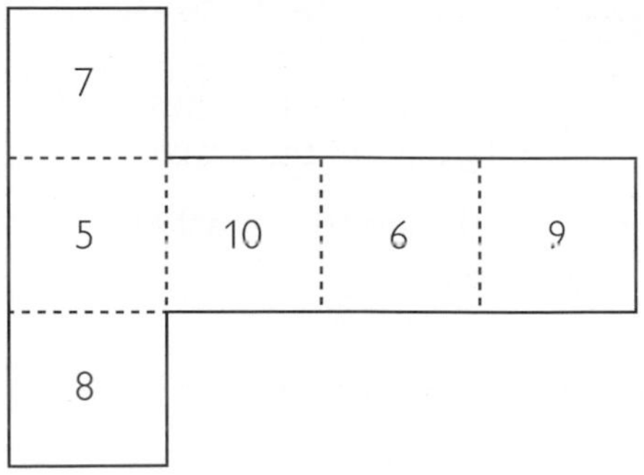

LESSON 63

Keeping Sharp: Facts, Computations, and Fractions

ALGEBRA READINESS

Keep in shape by completing this mixed review of addition, subtraction, multiplication, division, and fractions.

Watch the signs. Solve for *n*.

1. $n + 6 = 16$ **10**
2. $56 \div n = 7$ **8**
3. $n - 17 = 35$ **52**
4. $7 \times 5 = n$ **35**
5. $n \div 3 = 7$ **21**
6. $n + 9 = 31$ **22**
7. $n = 15 + 8$ **23**
8. $54 \div n = 6$ **9**
9. $63 \div n = 9$ **7**

Add or subtract.

10. $1589 + 2496 =$ **4085**
11. $329 - 167 =$ **162**
12. $1720 + 2679 =$ **4399**
13. $\$4.27 - 1.79 =$ **$2.48**
14. $\$13.56 + 8.82 =$ **$22.38**
15. $294 + 699 =$ **993**
16. $\$10.00 - 4.46 =$ **$5.54**
17. $2983 + 4799 =$ **7782**

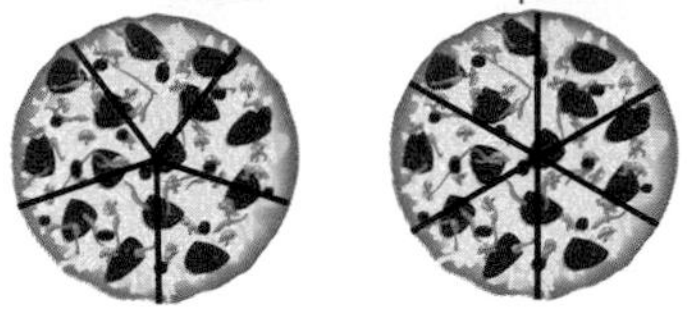

Answer these questions.

18. Which pizza has been cut into pieces that are $\frac{1}{6}$ of its size? **right pizza**
19. Which pizza has been cut into pieces that are $\frac{1}{5}$ of its size? **left pizza**
20. Which pizza has **more** pieces? **right pizza**
21. Which pizza has **bigger** pieces? **left pizza**

Solve for *n*. Watch the signs.

22. $n = 8 + 7$ **15**
23. $n = 8 \times 7$ **56**
24. $8 + n = 31$ **23**
25. $n \times 8 = 32$ **4**
26. $24 \div n = 8$ **3**
27. $n \div 10 = 7$ **70**

216 • Algebra Readiness and Geometry

Literature Connection Students can do the puzzles and problems in *Perplexing Puzzles and Tantalizing Teasers* by Martin Gardner for practice in problem solving.

*available separately

COOPERATIVE LEARNING **Work in cooperative groups to solve these problems. Be sure to explain your reasons and check that your answers make sense.**

28. Two years ago Mark was three times as old as Mia. This year he is twice as old. Is that possible? If so, how old is Mark? How old is Mia? **Mark is 8; Mia is 4**

29. Chicago, Illinois, is 291 miles from St. Louis, Missouri, and 162 miles from Davenport, Iowa. What can you tell about how far it is between St. Louis and Davenport? **can't tell**

30. Leon is 20 years old, and his sister, Yolanda, is five years old.
    - **a.** In how many years will Leon be twice as old as his sister? **10 years**
    - **b.** In how many years will Leon be five times as old as his sister? **not possible**

31. An ice cube weighs 150 grams. After the ice cube melts, about how much will the resulting water weigh? **150 grams**

32. A 7× telescope makes objects appear seven times closer than they are. If an object is 63 feet away, how far away will it seem when viewed through the telescope? **9 feet**

33. If an object appears to be about 8 feet away when viewed through a 7× telescope, how far away is it really? **56 feet**

COOPERATIVE LEARNING You may wish to have students work in pairs to complete the word problems on page 217. Students can work each problem independently and then share their results. If results agree, it is likely that both students are correct. If results disagree, students should look back at each other's work to try to detect and correct the error.

Problem-Solving Strategies Ask students who have solved the Problem of the Day to share how they solved it and any strategies they used.

MENTAL MATH In anticipation of the work with multidigit multiplication that begins in the next unit, provide practice with multiplying and dividing by 10 and 100. Have students use their Number Wheels to respond quickly.

a. 4 × 10 = (40)
4 × 100 = (400)
40 × 10 = (400)
400 ÷ 10 = (40)

b. 85 × 10 = (850)
850 ÷ 10 = (85)

c. 10 × 100 = (1000)
10 × 1000 = (10,000)
100 ÷ 10 = (10)

d. 27 × 100 = (2700)
2700 ÷ 100 = (27)

e. 5 × 100 = (500)
5000 ÷ 1000 = (5)

f. 68 × 100 = (6800)
6800 ÷ 100 = (68)

2 Teach

PROBLEM SOLVING **Using the Student Pages** Page 216 reviews skills taught in Units 1 and 2. Have students work independently on this page. As they finish, have them go on to page 217 to complete the word problems. Remind them to check that each answer fits the situation. Invite students who finish early to play a math game such as "Cubo" (page 163), which provides practice with mental arithmetic using all four operations. A copy of "Cubo" can also be found on page 15 of the Home Connections Blackline Masters.

ESL **Meeting Individual Needs**

You may wish to have students with limited proficiency in English create math vocabulary files. Have students write a word on one side of a card and its definition or illustration on the other side. Periodically review files with students, reading a word and asking them to define it. Keep the files in an easily accessible place.

◆ LESSON 63 Keeping Sharp: Facts, Computations, and Fractions

Teach

Using the Thinking Story "The Lost Island of Addonia (Part 4)" is the last part of the Thinking Story for Unit 3. Again students use the Addonian code that transforms numbers according to people's ages to solve problems. Part 4 focuses on estimating and establishing bounds.

Answers to Thinking Story Questions:

1. One or two cents a day is a good estimate. A young boy looking at books in the library would probably be at least seven years old if he took books out of the library. Students can subtract his age in years (seven) from the amount of money he said the book would cost (nine cents) to figure out that the book would probably be no more than two cents a day.
2. Yes. The boy could be eight years old.
3. No. The boy said the book cost nine cents a day. Even if the boy was only one year old, the book would not cost more than eight cents a day. A one-year-old boy would not be able to act as the boy in the story does.
4. At least 45 years old. The name of the book should be *Goldilocks and the Three Bears*. Therefore the author was 45 when the book was written (3 + 45 = 48), and may have aged since then.

MATH JOURNAL Have students write in their Math Journals a brief summary of all the children's adventures in Addonia. Have them describe a problem the children might encounter if they stayed in Addonia for another year, and suggest any possible solutions to this problem.

GIFTED & TALENTED

Meeting Individual Needs

Challenge students to create a function rule for an imaginary place called Subtractia. They can base the rule on any function they choose. Encourage them to use functions different from Addonia's function rule. Then have students write a short story that presents the rule that they have developed and takes place in Subtractia.

◆ LESSON 63 Keeping Sharp: Facts, Computations, and Fractions

THINKING STORY

The Lost Island of Addonia

Part 4

You may want to refer to previous parts of this Thinking Story, on pages 190–191, 196–197, and 212–213.

At last the children came to the library. Portia found a book to read. It was called *Goldilocks and the 48 Bears*. When Portia went to check out the book, the librarian said, "Books are not free in Addonia. You will have to pay 46¢ a day to take this book out."

"That's too much money," said Portia. "I can't pay that."

"It's not too much," said an old woman. "You should be happy to pay 73¢ a day for such a fine book."

"That's right," said a young boy. "Why, 9¢ a day is not very much. We all pay that."

"I can't figure out anything here," said Portia. "I want to go home."

"If you think things are bad here," said the librarian, "you should see what it's like in Subtractia."

. . . the end

TECHNOLOGY CONNECTION

Technology Connection Refer students to the software *The Math Majors* from Nordic Software (Mac, for grades K–6) for further practice with basic computation (addition, subtraction, multiplication, and division) and inequalities.

RETEACHING

MANIPULATIVES Provide a review of addition, subtraction, or fraction work as necessary, based on the outcome of the work students do in this lesson. Encourage students who have difficulty with mental math to use **base-10 blocks*** for further reinforcement. You may wish to have students work individually or in groups on appropriate Enrichment activities from Units 1 and 2.

*available separately

Work in groups. Discuss your answers and how you figured them out. Then compare your answers with those of other groups. **Answers are in margin.**

1. About how much does it really cost to take a book out of the Addonia Library?

2. Could it cost 1¢ a day?

3. Could it cost more than 10¢ a day?

4. **Detective question:** How old is the person who wrote the book Portia wants to read?

Use the Cumulative Review on page 548 after this lesson.

PRACTICE p. 63

LESSON 63 PRACTICE Name____________________

Solve for *n*. Watch the signs.

1. $n + 7 = 17$ __10__
2. $n - 20 = 33$ __53__
3. $n \div 4 = 8$ __32__
4. $63 \div n = 7$ __9__
5. $6 \times 3 = n$ __18__
6. $n + 8 = 27$ __19__

Add or subtract.

7. 1478 + 2496 = 3974
8. 344 − 129 = 215
9. 1820 + 2688 = 4508
10. \$4.06 − 1.68 = \$2.38
11. \$13.56 + 6.64 = \$20.20

Answer the following questions.

12. Which pie has been cut into pieces that are $\frac{1}{4}$ its size? __2__
13. Which pie has been cut into pieces that are $\frac{1}{5}$ its size? __1__
14. Which pie has more pieces? __1__
15. Which pie has bigger pieces? __2__

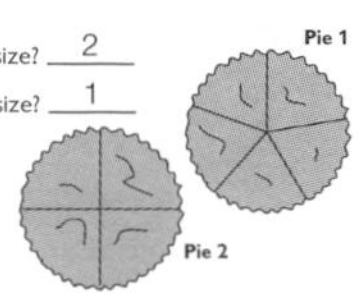

Solve for *n*. Watch the signs.

16. $n = 9 + 7$ __16__
17. $n \times 8 = 56$ __7__
18. $n \div 10 = 9$ __90__
19. $n = 8 \times 8$ __64__
20. $40 \div n = 8$ __5__
21. $n - 9 = 29$ __38__
22. $6 + n = 25$ __19__
23. $n \div 3 = 7$ __21__
24. $28 = 7 \times n$ __4__

Add or subtract.

25. 43 + 9 = 52
26. 43 − 9 = 34
27. 73 − 28 = 45
28. 334 − 83 = 251
29. 425 + 700 = 1125
30. 4126 − 2427 = 1699
31. 4000 − 1997 = 2003
32. \$5.06 + 3.04 = \$8.10
33. \$41.07 − 19.28 = \$21.79
34. \$ 4.07 + 26.93 = \$31.00

Copyright © SRA/McGraw-Hill. Permission is granted to reproduce this page for classroom use.

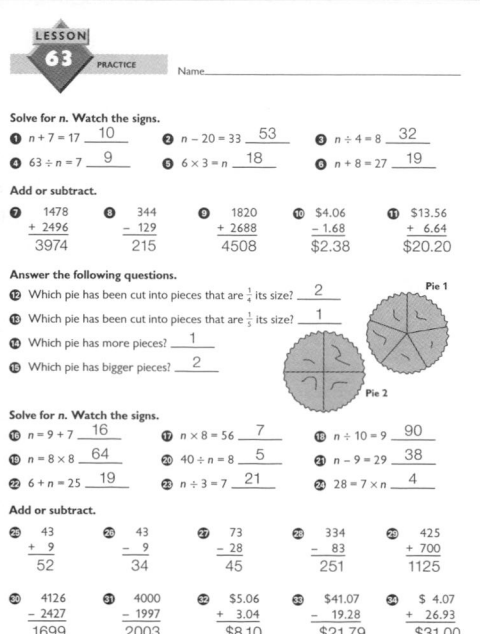

ENRICHMENT p. 63

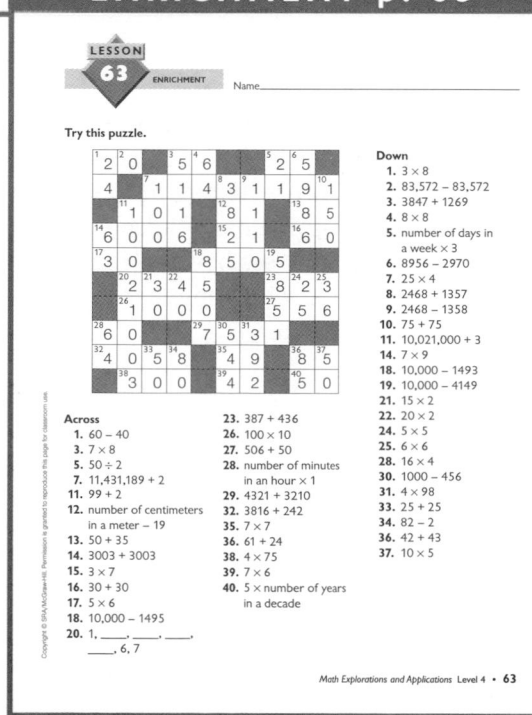

LESSON 63 ENRICHMENT Name____________________

Try this puzzle.

(1) 2	(2) 0		(3) 5	(4) 6			(5) 2	(6) 5	
4		(7) 1	1	4	(8) 3	(9) 1	1	9	(10) 1
	(11) 1	0	1		(12) 8	1		(13) 8	5
(14) 6	0	0	6		(15) 2	1		(16) 6	0
(17) 3	0			(18) 8	5	0	(19) 5		
	(20) 2	(21) 3	(22) 4	5			(23) 8	(24) 2	(25) 3
	(26) 1	0	0	0			(27) 5	5	6
(28) 6	0			(29) 7	(30) 5	(31) 3	1		
(32) 4	0	(33) 5	(34) 8		(35) 4	9		(36) 8	(37) 5
	(38) 3	0	0		(39) 4	2		(40) 5	0

Across

1. 60 − 40
3. 7 × 8
5. 50 ÷ 2
7. 11,431,189 + 2
11. 99 + 2
12. number of centimeters in a meter − 19
13. 50 + 35
14. 3003 + 3003
15. 3 × 7
16. 30 + 30
17. 5 × 6
18. 10,000 − 1495
20. 1, ____, ____, ____, ____, 6, 7
23. 387 + 436
26. 100 × 10
27. 506 + 50
28. number of minutes in an hour × 1
29. 4321 + 3210
32. 3816 + 242
35. 7 × 7
36. 61 + 24
38. 4 × 75
39. 7 × 6
40. 5 × number of years in a decade

Down

1. 3 × 8
2. 83,572 − 83,572
3. 3847 + 1269
4. 8 × 8
5. number of days in a week × 3
6. 8956 − 2970
7. 25 × 4
8. 2468 + 1357
9. 2468 − 1358
10. 75 + 75
11. 10,021,000 + 3
14. 7 × 9
18. 10,000 − 1493
19. 10,000 − 4149
21. 15 × 2
22. 20 × 2
24. 5 × 5
25. 6 × 6
28. 16 × 4
30. 1000 − 456
31. 4 × 98
33. 25 + 25
34. 82 − 2
36. 42 + 43
37. 10 × 5

Copyright © SRA/McGraw-Hill. Permission is granted to reproduce this page for classroom use.

3 Wrap-Up 5 MINUTES

In Closing Have students summarize the function used in Addonia.

ALTERNATIVE ASSESSMENT

Portfolio Assessment You can use the work students do on pages 216–217 as an informal review of arithmetic facts, computation, and fractions from Units 1 and 2. If you do so, have students date their papers and add them to their Math Portfolios as a record of ongoing learning.

Assessment Criteria

Did the student . . .

- ✓ correctly answer at least 75% of the computation problems on page 216?
- ✓ explain how to solve for *n*?
- ✓ communicate strategies used to solve the word problems?
- ✓ contribute to the Thinking Story discussion?

Homework Assign Practice Master 63 for further reinforcement of arithmetic facts and fraction skills.

AT RISK

Meeting Individual Needs

Help students to better appreciate mathematical problem solving by comparing it to real detective work. Generally, detectives work backwards from evidence they gather to figure out how an event happened. They use logical reasoning along with any data they have to solve a mystery. Students might like the *Encyclopedia Brown* series of books, in which a young person applies logical reasoning skills to solve mysteries.

LESSON 64

Student Edition pages 220–221

Graphing Functions

LESSON PLANNER

Objectives

- ▶ to provide practice in graphing functions and in identifying functions from completed graphs
- ▶ to demonstrate that all graphs of the same function are the same, no matter which ordered pairs are chosen

Context of the Lesson This is the last of 13 lessons on graphing and functions. It primarily reviews material covered in Lesson 62.

MANIPULATIVES

graph paper

rulers* or straightedges

Program Resources

Practice Master 64

Enrichment Master 64

For extra practice: CD-ROM* Lesson 64

1 Warm-Up

5 MINUTES

Problem of the Day Present this problem and suggest that students draw a picture to solve it: The gym teacher used chalk lines to mark off a 200-meter runway in an open field. She put a green ribbon at the start line, a red ribbon at the finish line, and white ribbons on stakes every 10 meters. How many white ribbons on stakes did she use? (19)

Problem-Solving Strategies Ask students who have solved the Problem of the Day to share how they solved it and any strategies they used.

MENTAL MATH Provide practice in problems that involve multiplying and dividing by 10 and 100.

a.	6 × 10 = (60)	**b.**	8 × 10 = (80)
	6 × 100 = (600)		8 × 100 = (800)
	600 ÷ 100 = (6)		800 ÷ 100 = (8)
c.	10 × 200 = (2000)	**d.**	10 × 600 = (6000)
	10 × 2000 = (20,000)		10 × 6000 = (60,000)
	2000 ÷ 10 = (200)		60,000 ÷ 10 = (6000)
e.	39 × 100 = (3900)	**f.**	50 × 100 = (5000)
	3900 ÷ 100 = (39)		5000 ÷ 50 = (100)
g.	10 × 5601 = (56,010)	**h.**	10 × 2600 = (26,000)
	56,010 ÷ 10 = (5601)		26,000 ÷ 2600 = (10)

MIXED PRACTICE

LESSON 64

Graphing Functions

You can make a graph of any function rule.

For each function rule, follow these steps:

A. Find four ordered pairs of numbers.

B. Graph the four points.

C. Try to draw a line through all four points.

1. x → (÷2) → y
2. x → (−3) → y
3. x → (÷2) → n → (−3) → y
4. x → (×1) → y
5. x → (×2) → y
6. x → (×2) → n → (÷2) → y
7. x → (−4) → y
8. x → (+4) → y

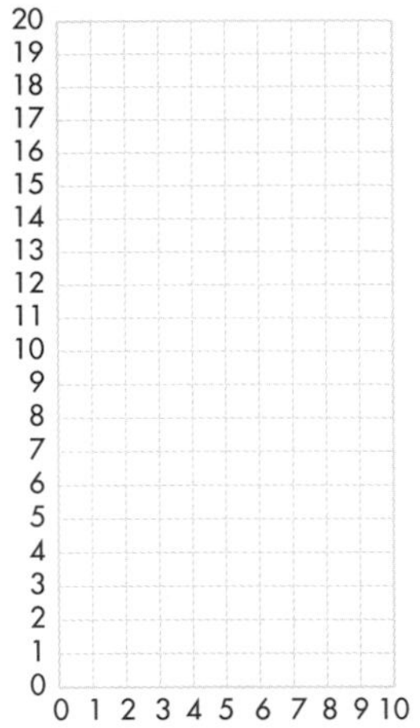

Compare your answers for problems 1 through 8 with the answers of others in your class.

- ◆ Did you choose the same numbers?
- ◆ Are the four points on your graphs the same?
- ◆ Are the lines on your graphs the same?

Points that are graphed will vary, but for each problem the students should have the same line.

MATH JOURNAL

In your Math Journal describe how you picked four points. Did you try any points that didn't work?

Literature Connection Read with students the section of *666 Jellybeans! All That?* by Malcolm E. Weiss that discusses how replacing a variable, like *x*, with a number influences the answer.

RETEACHING

Students who have difficulty selecting good values for *x* may need some guidance or hints. Suggest that they examine the function rule and pick a number compatible with it. For instance, if they pick an even number for problem 1, it will divide without a remainder; a number greater than 3 for problem 2 will avoid a negative number.

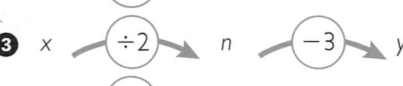

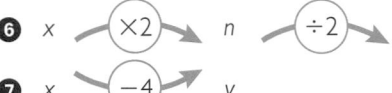

*available separately

Find a function rule for each graph.

9 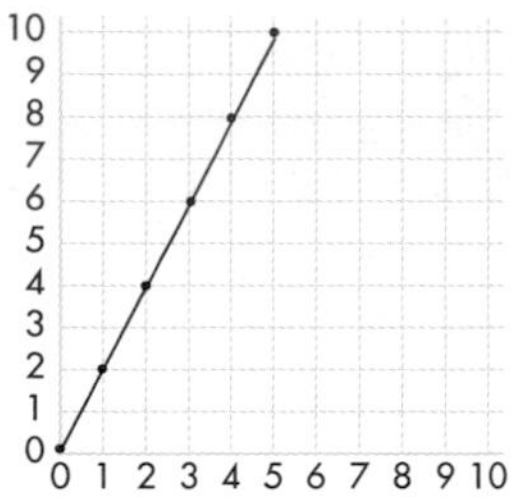

A function rule is ■ ×2

10 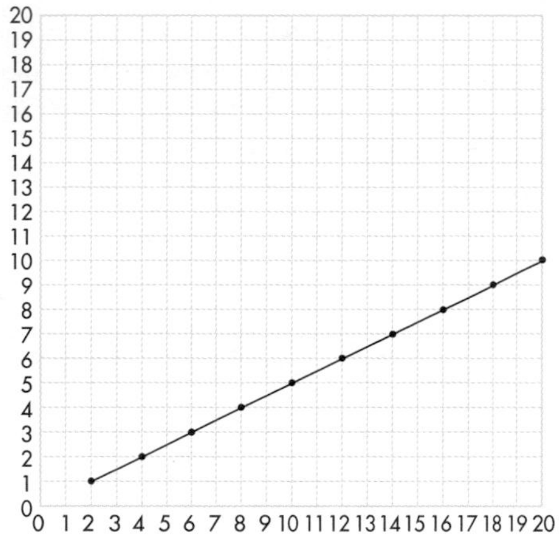

A function rule is ■ ÷2

11 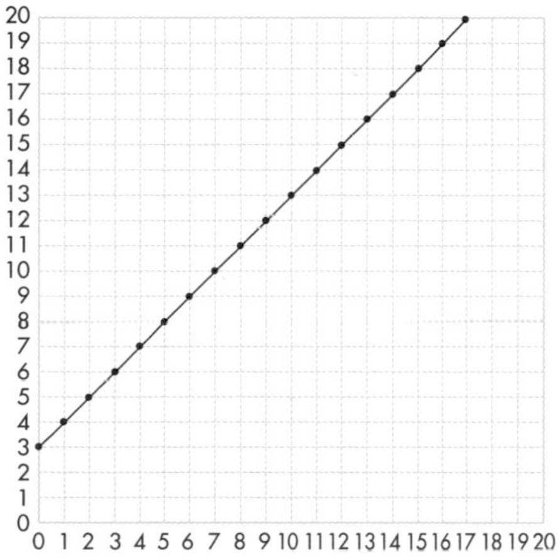

A function rule is ■ +3

12 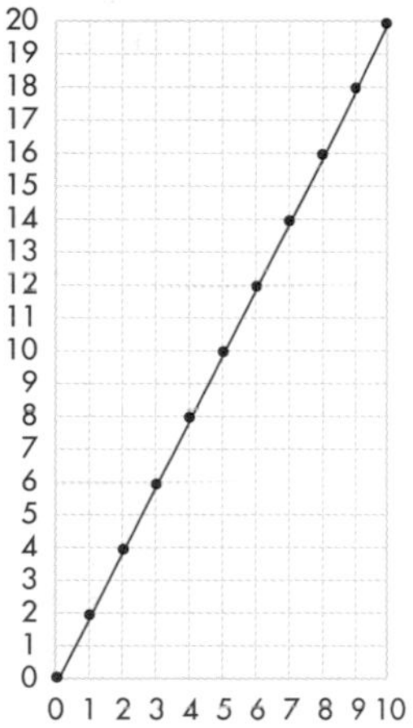

A function rule is ■ ×2

❷ Teach

ALGEBRA READINESS · MANIPULATIVES

Using the Student Pages Begin problem 1 on page 220 with the class, then let students complete the rest of the problems on the page on their own. For ease of comparison, make sure all students use a **ruler*** and the same type of **graph paper** and the same scale. Students should realize that although they choose different numbers for their ordered pairs, they will get the same straight line. They should also notice that in problem 6, $x = y$. Ask them why this is so. (The rules apply inverse functions to *n*.)

For page 221, students must work backwards from completed graphs to determine function rules. Suggest that they list the coordinates of three or more points through which a line passes. Then have them identify a consistent arithmetic relationship between the values of *x* and *y* in that set of coordinates. When they think they have determined the function rule, they should see whether it holds true for another point along the same line.

❸ Wrap-Up

5 MINUTES

In Closing Have students explain how to work backward from a graph to determine a function rule.

ALTERNATIVE ASSESSMENT

Informal Assessment Observe students as they work through this lesson. Encourage them to verbalize their reasoning, especially as they try to determine the function rules for the graphs on page 221.

PRACTICE p. 64

LESSON 64 PRACTICE Name__________

For each function rule, follow these steps.

Step 1 Find four ordered pairs of numbers.
Step 2 Graph the four points.
Step 3 Try to draw a line through all four points.

Check student's graphs.

1. $x \to (\div 1) \to y$ (1, 1), (2, 2), (3, 3), (4, 4)
2. $x \to (-5) \to y$ (10, 5), (9, 4), (8, 3), (7, 2)
3. $x \to (\div 2) \to n \to (+4) \to y$ (0, 4), (2, 5), (4, 6), (6, 7)
4. $x \to (\times 2) \to y$ (0, 0), (1, 2), (2, 4), (3, 6)

For each graph find a function rule.

5. A function rule is ×1.

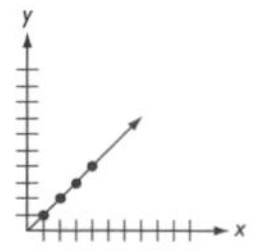

6. A function rule is +3.

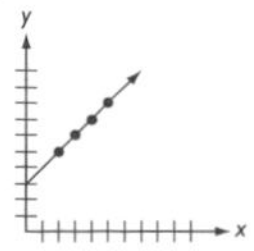

7. A function rule is ×2.

8. A function rule is +5.

Copyright © SRA/McGraw-Hill. Permission is granted to reproduce this page for classroom use.

64 • *Math Explorations and Applications* Level 4

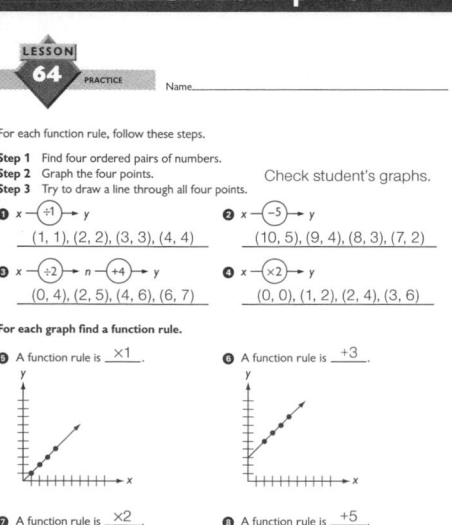

ENRICHMENT p. 64

LESSON 64 ENRICHMENT Name__________

Imagine you are going to have a birthday party. What is the least number of people you should invite to be sure that two people have birthdays in the same month? 13

Copyright © SRA/McGraw-Hill. Permission is granted to reproduce this page for classroom use.

64 • *Math Explorations and Applications* Level 4

Assessment Criteria

Did the student . . .

✓ accurately graph functions?

✓ contribute to the discussion of comparing graphs?

✓ accurately identify missing function rules when given completed graphs?

Homework Have students create four composite function rules and graph them.

*available separately

LESSON 65

Student Edition pages 222–225

Working with Graphs

LESSON PLANNER

Objectives

- to provide applications for organizing and analyzing data
- to provide practice interpreting graphs and selecting appropriate graph formats

Context of the Lesson This lesson provides data analysis activities. The next lesson continues work with choosing and interpreting graphs.

MANIPULATIVES

graph paper

Program Resources

Reteaching Master

Practice Master 65

Enrichment Master 65

For extra practice:
CD-ROM* Lesson 65

1 Warm-Up

5 MINUTES

Problem of the Day Present this problem and suggest that students draw a picture to solve it: Kevin is hanging drawings on a bulletin board. Each drawing needs a tack in every corner. Because there are so many drawings to hang, Kevin decides to overlap the corners to save space and tacks. Figure out the least number of tacks he needs to hang six drawings. (12, when there are two rows of three pictures each)

Problem-Solving Strategies Ask students who have solved the Problem of the Day to share how they solved it and any strategies they used.

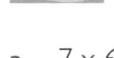

MENTAL MATH Provide a fast-paced review of basic arithmetic facts in all four operations:

a. 7 × 6 = (42)	**b.** 7 + 6 = (13)
c. 15 ÷ 3 = (5)	**d.** 11 − 3 = (8)
e. 8 + 7 = (15)	**f.** 8 × 7 = (56)
g. 8 − 7 = (1)	**h.** 48 ÷ 6 = (8)
i. 18 − 9 = (9)	**j.** 18 ÷ 9 = (2)
k. 28 ÷ 7 = (4)	**l.** 13 − 7 = (6)
m. 8 + 8 = (16)	**n.** 8 × 8 = (64)
o. 0 + 4 = (4)	**p.** 9 × 7 = (63)

PRACTICE

LESSON 65

Working with Graphs

Juan wanted to collect information about how many books New City residents read per month. He made a survey asking people about how many books they check out of the local library each month.

To complete the survey, he spent two afternoons at the library, asking the same question to people as they left. Juan's results are shown in the table.

Number of People	Number of Books per Month
1	15
8	13
12	10
14	9
20	8
25	7
51	6
35	5
24	4
4	3
3	2
2	1
1	0

Answer these questions.

1. How fairly do Juan's results describe the reading habits of the people who live in New City? **Not very fairly; his information is limited.**
2. Did Juan's survey reach only people who use the library often? **Perhaps; however, some infrequent users may have gone to the library while Juan was conducting his survey.**

MATH JOURNAL **In your Math Journal explain what you might have done differently if you were conducting the survey.**

Why teach it at this time?

Data analysis and graphing are closely related to functions. Also, these pages may serve as a review and extension of the Unit 1 project, in which students analyzed their school library.

*available separately

As part of his report, Juan decided to make a picture graph of the results of his survey. Here's what his picture graph looked like.

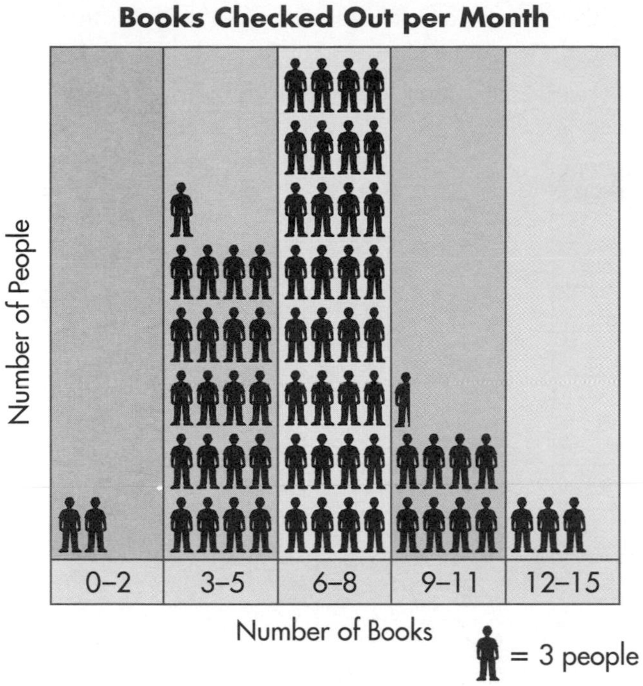

Study Juan's picture graph. Make up questions that can be answered with the information in the graph. **Sample questions: Does anyone read more than 15 books? How many books do most people read?**

Answer these questions.

3. Which shows the results of Juan's survey better, the table or the picture graph? **picture graph**
4. What is the advantage of the table? **All of the data is available.**
5. What is the advantage of the picture graph? **It is easier to use and makes it easier to see the overall results.**
6. If you wanted to show that your community needs a larger library, what kind of information would you collect? **the number of people who use the library each day, the number of books that are checked out when people request them, and so on**

❷ Teach

COOPERATIVE LEARNING **Using the Student Pages** Have students work in cooperative groups to discuss the data on these pages and to solve the problems. Groups should prepare to report back to the class for a follow-up discussion. In discussing problem 1, guide students to realize that Juan's data probably do not reflect the reading habits of the town because he asked only people who already use the library. A better survey would include people who do not use the library or who use it rarely. Juan might have tapped a broader cross-section of the population if he had surveyed people as they left a supermarket or gas station.

Encourage students to challenge quick assumptions by offering logical explanations that would not appear in raw data. For example, in problem 2, students may say that someone who takes out only one book does not necessarily underuse the library. Perhaps that person was too busy to read much that week or checked out one long book. One person claimed not to have checked out any books. Possibly that person was a service person who was in the library on business or someone who simply returned a book. Discuss the differences between a picture graph and a table. Guide students to notice that some data are more easily understood in picture graph form, but a table can give data with great precision.

COOPERATIVE LEARNING Have each cooperative group prepare a written report on how they might survey people in their community to discover patterns of library usage. Each report should include an explanation of who will be surveyed; how that group accurately represents the community; and a plan for how, when, and where the survey might be distributed. Encourage groups to prepare a sample survey questionnaire to include in the report.

◆ LESSON 65 Working with Graphs

Teach

Using the Student Pages Briefly discuss the concept of seed germination (sprouting). Help students understand that a seed can lie dormant over time and will sprout only under the right conditions for that kind of seed. You might do these pages as a class activity, or have students continue working in their cooperative groups. Have **graph paper** available.

Note: The key idea on pages 224 and 225 is to compare two line graphs: one that gives the number of seeds that sprouted each day (frequency distribution) and another that gives the running total of all the seeds that have sprouted (cumulative frequency distribution). The cumulative frequency distribution better shows the total number of seeds that germinated and how quickly they sprouted. The frequency distribution better shows how many seeds germinated on any given day.

For page 225, have students discuss the differences between the old and the new seeds. Discuss reasons why the old seeds took longer to germinate than the new seeds. Discuss how the graphs illustrate this difference. Check students' graphs for accuracy.

◆ LESSON 65 Working with Graphs

Carlos was doing experiments to see how the age of seeds affects how they sprout. He made sprouting trays with wet towels, plastic wrap, and exactly 100 seeds.

Each day Carlos checked his trays and removed the seeds that had sprouted. He planted those seeds in his garden.

Carlos began by doing a trial with new seeds to make sure his experiment would work. Here's how the new seeds sprouted.

Day	Seeds Sprouted
1	0
2	1
3	18
4	45
5	13
6	4
7	0
8	1
9	0
10	0

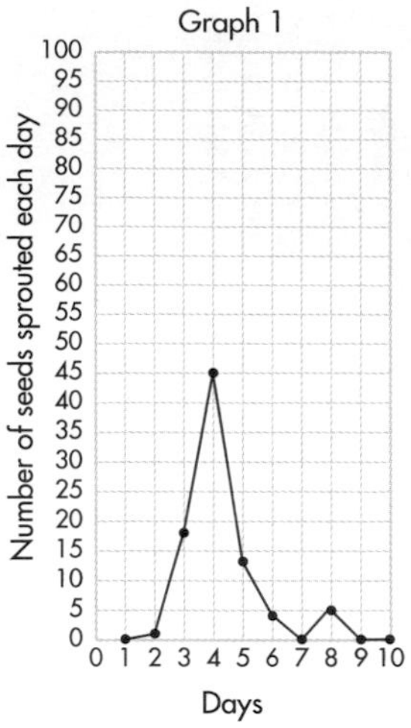

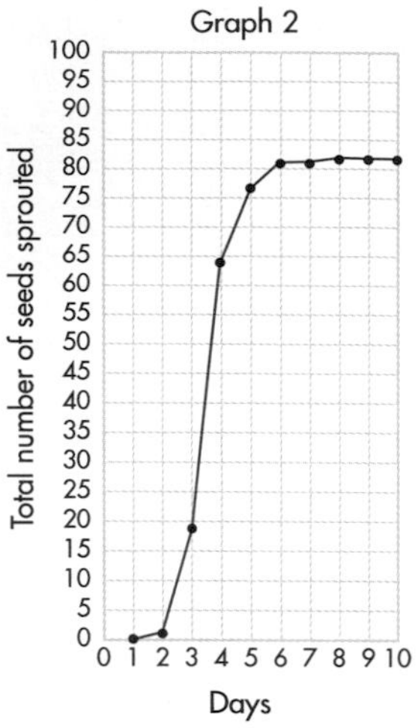

Answer these questions.

7. How many seeds sprouted? **82**
8. Do you think more seeds will sprout if the experiment goes beyond ten days? **probably not**
9. Carlos made two graphs to present his results. Which graph do you think Carlos should use? **Both are useful but for different purposes.**
10. Which graph better shows the day on which most seeds sprouted? **Graph 1**
11. Which graph better shows the total number of seeds that sprouted? **Graph 2**

Science Connection

Help students do their own seed germination experiments in class or at home. Have them write a proposal for the experiment. Guide them to include a statement of what the experiment will investigate. Students should tell what type of seeds they will use. They should also specify how many seeds will be in each sample. One hundred seeds per group is enough. The same number of seeds in each group facilitates analysis. Have students conduct the experiment, record the results, and present their findings.

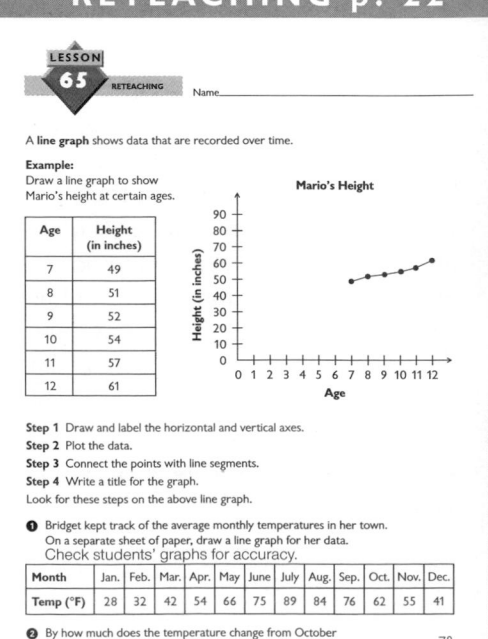

RETEACHING p. 22

LESSON 65 RETEACHING Name________________

A **line graph** shows data that are recorded over time.

Example:
Draw a line graph to show Mario's height at certain ages.

Age	Height (in inches)
7	49
8	51
9	52
10	54
11	57
12	61

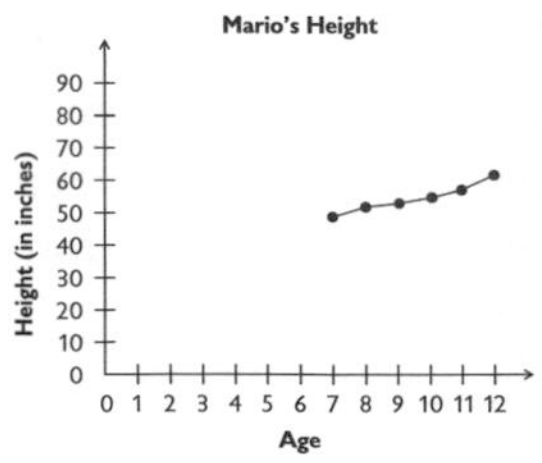

Step 1 Draw and label the horizontal and vertical axes.
Step 2 Plot the data.
Step 3 Connect the points with line segments.
Step 4 Write a title for the graph.
Look for these steps on the above line graph.

1. Bridget kept track of the average monthly temperatures in her town. On a separate sheet of paper, draw a line graph for her data. Check students' graphs for accuracy.

Month	Jan.	Feb.	Mar.	Apr.	May	June	July	Aug.	Sep.	Oct.	Nov.	Dec.
Temp (°F)	28	32	42	54	66	75	89	84	76	62	55	41

2. By how much does the temperature change from October to November? 7°

22 • *Math Explorations and Applications* Level 4

Copyright © SRA/McGraw-Hill. Permission is granted to reproduce this page for classroom use.

Next Carlos set up two sprouting trays. One had new seeds and the other had the same kind of seeds that were 20 years old. He recorded his results in a chart.

Seeds Sprouted

Day	New	Old
1	0	0
2	3	0
3	15	0
4	47	1
5	11	4
6	7	25
7	1	16
8	1	13
9	0	10
10	0	10
11	0	5
12	0	1
13	0	0
14	0	1
15	0	0

Carlos decided to present information about both groups of seeds on the same graph. Here is one of his graphs.

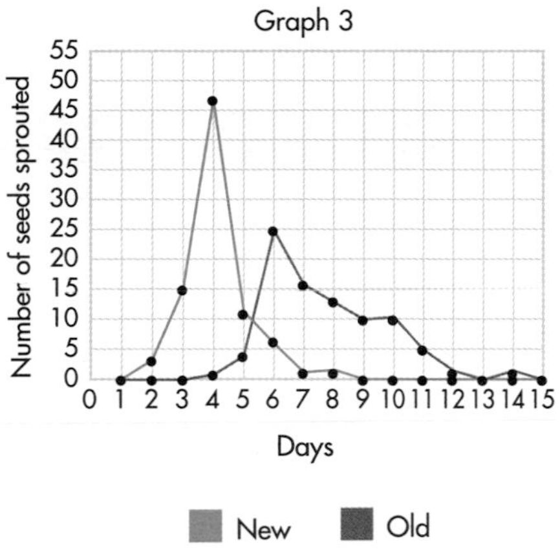

Use the above data to create a graph showing the total amount of seeds sprouted each day (like Graph 2).

12. Which graph better shows the days on which the most seeds sprouted? **Graph 3**
13. Which graph better shows how quickly each group of seeds sprouted? **Graph 3**
14. Which graph better shows how many seeds of each group sprouted? **the new graph**

MATH JOURNAL

Study the results of Carlos's experiment. In your Math Journal write how the age of the seeds seemed to affect their growth.

3 Wrap-Up 5 MINUTES

In Closing Have students discuss some differences between picture graphs and line graphs.

ALTERNATIVE ASSESSMENT

Informal Assessment Observe and listen as students work through the activities in this lesson. Encourage them to verbalize their ideas and observations about graphs, tables, and ways to present data. Help them make analytical observations about the data, but insist that the data support their comments.

Assessment Criteria

Did the student . . .

- ✓ contribute to the discussion of the data in table and graph form?
- ✓ communicate strategies used to analyze and interpret the data?
- ✓ support his or her conclusions based on the data?

Homework Have students devise an experiment on seed germination. Have them bring their ideas to class and discuss them. Use the best ideas as science projects for ongoing research.

PRACTICE p. 65

LESSON 65 PRACTICE Name________

Alexa keeps a record of the books she sells in her bookstore each month. Then she prints a bar graph to show her employees.

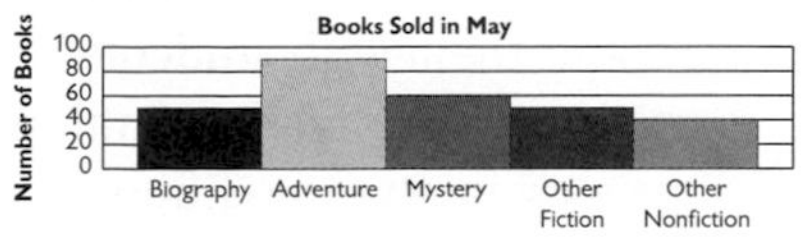

Use the bar graph to answer questions 1–3.

1. How many mystery books were sold this month? 60
2. For which two types of books were the same number of books sold? Biography and Other Fiction
3. For which type of book was the most copies sold? Adventure

The sporting goods store made a line graph to show the number of sales for the first six months of the year.

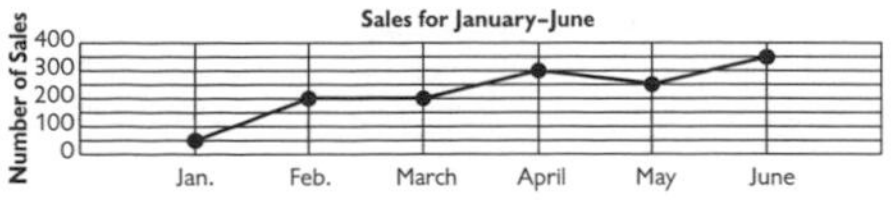

Use the line graph to answer questions 4–6.

4. During which month was the number of sales greatest? June
5. During which month was the number of sales least? January
6. How many sales were there in April? 300

Copyright © SRA/McGraw-Hill. Permission is granted to reproduce this page for classroom use.

Math Explorations and Applications Level 4 • 65

ENRICHMENT p. 65

LESSON 65 ENRICHMENT Name________

REAL-WORLD CONNECTION

You can use graphs to help you examine all sorts of information—including your own eating habits.

Use The Cruncher: *How Much Do We Eat and Drink in a Year?* project to look at information about the quantity of foods and drinks consumed in a year. Look at the graph that compares milk and soft drink consumption.

1. What does the graph tell you? Soft drink consumption has increased, while milk consumption has decreased.
2. What do you think are some of the reasons for the trend? Answers will vary. Possible answers: Soft drinks are more easily available and are heavily advertised.
3. Use the information about milk and soft drink consumption to make a line graph on a separate sheet of paper. See students' graphs.
4. Which displays the information best, a bar graph or a line graph? Why do you think so? Answers will vary. Possible answers: Students may prefer a line graph because it clearly shows upward and downward trends. Students may prefer a bar graph because it shows a clear comparison of quantities.
5. Check the figures to see how your own consumption of these foods and drinks measures up.
6. Take a survey of nine classmates. Include your own answers and make a bar graph or line graph on a separate sheet of paper. How does your graph compare to those of your classmates? See students' graphs.

Copyright © SRA/McGraw-Hill. Permission is granted to reproduce this page for classroom use.

Math Explorations and Applications Level 4 • 65

LESSON 66

Student Edition pages 226–227

Choosing an Appropriate Graph

LESSON PLANNER

Objective

▶ to provide practice for interpreting graphic data

Context of the Lesson This is a continuation of the data analysis activities from the previous lesson. In this lesson, students learn how graphs can be constructed to mislead.

MANIPULATIVES

graphs, various (optional)

graph paper

rulers* or straightedges

magazines, newspapers, or printed materials (optional)

Program Resources

Number Wheels

Practice Master 66

Enrichment Master 66

For extra practice: CD-ROM* Lesson 66

1 Warm-Up

5 MINUTES

Problem of the Day Present this problem to students: Three consecutive numbers have a sum of 6000. What are the numbers? (1999, 2000, 2001)

Problem-Solving Strategies Ask students who have solved the Problem of the Day to share how they solved it and any strategies they used.

MENTAL MATH Provide practice with place-value chain calculations. Have students add 10, then 100, then 1000 to each number. Then, from the original number, have them subtract 10, then 100, then 1000. You might have a volunteer record the answers on the chalkboard and ask students to use Number Wheels to show answers.

a. 2470 (2480, 2580, 3580; 2460, 2360, 1360)

b. 9081 (9091, 9191, 10,191; 9071, 8971, 7971)

c. 3005 (3015, 3115, 4115; 2995, 2895, 1895)

d. 1199 (1209, 1309, 2309; 1189, 1089, 89)

e. 4613 (4623, 4723, 5723; 4603, 4503, 3503)

LESSON 66

Choosing an Appropriate Graph

Mr. Sly owns a small business. Each year he must report the amount of sales and earnings for his business.

Sales is the amount of money received.

Earnings is the amount of money left after all expenses are paid.

The chart shows the sales and earnings for Mr. Sly's business for the years 1989–1996.

Year	Sales (Dollars)	Earnings (Dollars)
1989	995,000	85,000
1990	1,021,000	83,500
1991	1,300,000	79,000
1992	1,210,000	74,500
1993	1,450,000	72,000
1994	1,820,000	74,000
1995	1,950,000	71,500
1996	2,150,000	68,300

Answer the following questions using the information in the chart. You may use a calculator.

1. How much did Mr. Sly's sales increase from 1989 to 1990? **$26,000**
2. In what year was the greatest amount of money received through sales? **1996**
3. In what year did Mr. Sly earn the least? **1996**
4. What was the total amount of money in sales from 1989 to 1996? **$11,896,000**
5. What were Mr. Sly's earnings from 1989 to 1996? **$607,800**

Real-World Connection Have students take a **graph** that accurately represents its data and rework it to give a different impression. You might provide graphs of population, sales or earnings, stock prices, or other data that could be presented with other scales. You might also present data in table form and have students make different graphs of that data to see the possible variations.

RETEACHING

Prepare three graphs of the same data, each with a different scale, so that the slopes of the lines or lengths of the bars vary. Present the three graphs and talk about them with students. Encourage students to notice similarities and differences among the graphs.

*available separately

Mr. Sly decided to report his data using separate graphs for sales and earnings. Here are Mr. Sly's graphs.

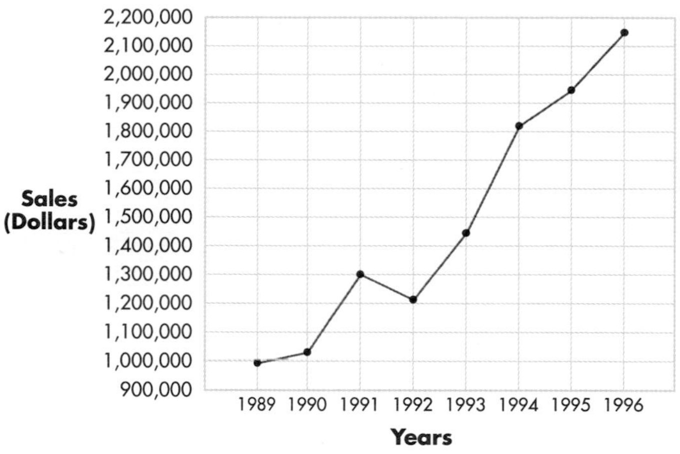

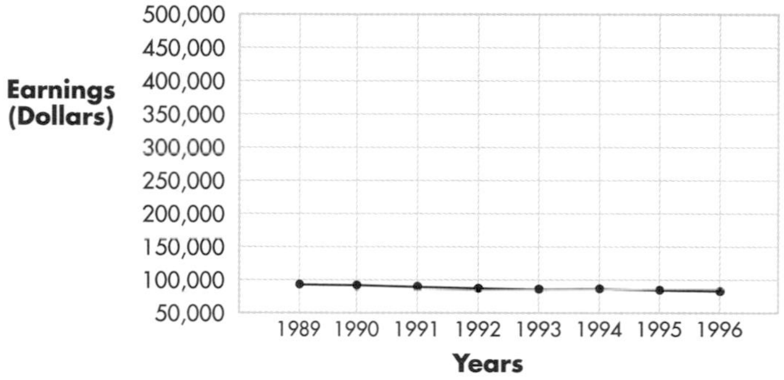

Study Mr. Sly's graphs. Write about how fairly or unfairly they present the information. Make a graph for earnings that shows the change in earnings more fairly. **These charts unfairly present Mr. Sly's earnings. He should change the scale on the second graph to reflect the actual range of his earnings (about 65,000 to 85,000).**

❷ Teach

Using the Student Pages Go over the data presented to be sure students understand the nature of the information. Students can use **calculators*** and work independently or in pairs on pages 226 and 227. Have **rulers*** and **graph paper** available. When students have finished, bring the class together to review their conclusions. Point out that Mr. Sly did two questionable things. First, he put sales and earnings data on separate graphs so that people would not notice that earnings were trending lower while sales were trending higher. Second, he chose vertical axis scales that would show a steep upward slope for sales but a very gentle downward slope for earnings. To help students see why Mr. Sly's earnings graph is misleading, prepare another graph of the data on the chalkboard or an overhead transparency. Calibrate the vertical axis from $68,000 to $85,000. The line will then slope sharply downward. Then make another sales graph whose vertical axis goes from $0 to $10 million. The line will show a gentle upward slope, and it will not be immediately apparent that sales doubled over the eight-year period.

❸ Wrap-Up

5 MINUTES

In Closing Discuss with students why someone would display correct data in a misleading way.

SELF ASSESSMENT

Have students write a brief statement in which they evaluate their ability to analyze data from graphs. Encourage them to tell what they can learn from a graph, what they should look for, and where they might expect to encounter graphs in real life.

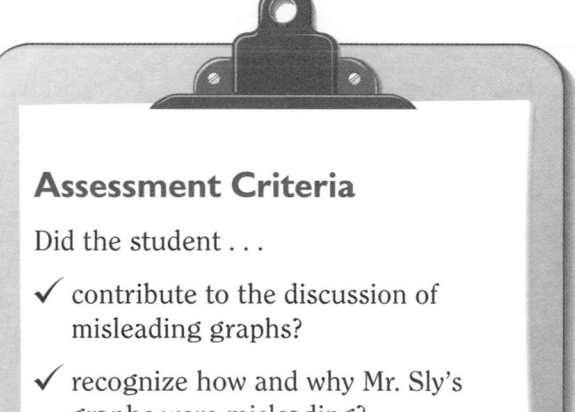

Assessment Criteria

Did the student . . .

- ✓ contribute to the discussion of misleading graphs?
- ✓ recognize how and why Mr. Sly's graphs were misleading?

Homework Have students look for three examples of graphs in **magazines, newspapers,** or **other printed materials** and study the graphs so they can present an oral summary of the information to classmates. Display the graphs on a bulletin board.

PRACTICE p. 66

LESSON 66 PRACTICE Name__________

Mr. Greenley owns Computers Are Fun, Inc. The chart below shows the sales and earnings for the first seven months he was in business.

Year	Sales (Dollars)	Earnings (Dollars)
January	63,500	6300
February	50,900	4750
March	50,750	4500
April	62,000	5700
May	69,350	3100
June	74,725	5900
July	76,200	4900

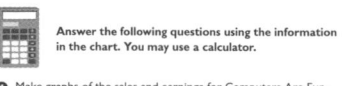

Answer the following questions using the information in the chart. You may use a calculator.

1. Make graphs of the sales and earnings for Computers Are Fun, Inc. over the first seven months. Check students' graphs.
2. What were Mr. Greenley's earnings from January to April? $21,250
3. What were Mr. Greenley's earnings from January to July? $35,150
4. In what month did Mr. Greenley earn the most? January
5. In which month were sales the least? March
6. How much did sales decrease from January to February? $12,600
7. Make a graph for earnings that shows the change in earnings more fairly. Check students' graphs.

66 • *Math Explorations and Applications* Level 4

Copyright © SRA/McGraw-Hill. Permission is granted to reproduce this page for classroom use.

ENRICHMENT p. 66

LESSON 66 ENRICHMENT Name__________

Graphs help us make sense of information easily and quickly. Graphs are used for many purposes.

Look through some newspapers and magazines at home for graphs. Find one pictograph, one bar graph, one line graph, and one circle graph. Draw these graphs on a piece of poster board. Then answer these questions.

1. What kind of a graph is it? Label each graph.
2. What does each graph show?
Answers will vary depending on the graphs each student chooses. Be sure students have correctly identified each type of graph.
3. What doesn't each graph tell you that you would like to know about the subject?
4. What, if anything, is confusing about the graphs?
5. Could the information in the graphs be shown better in a chart, table, diagram, or different kind of graph? Why do you think so?
6. When would you use a pictograph? A bar graph? A line graph? A circle graph?

66 • *Math Explorations and Applications* Level 4

Copyright © SRA/McGraw-Hill. Permission is granted to reproduce this page for classroom use.

*available separately

LESSON 67

Student Edition pages 228–229

Revisiting Number Facts

LESSON PLANNER

Objectives

✓ to assess mastery of the basic arithmetic facts

▶ to provide realistic problems involving finding the best buy (considering more than unit cost)

Context of the Lesson This lesson reviews basic number facts and contains a Mastery Checkpoint to assess this skill. The next lesson begins a seven-lesson sequence on geometry topics.

MANIPULATIVES

none

Program Resources

Practice Master 67

Enrichment Master 67

Assessment Master

For extra practice:
CD-ROM* Lesson 67

1 Warm-Up

5 MINUTES

Problem of the Day Present this problem orally or on the chalkboard. There is more than one answer: In the following problem, each letter stands for a different number: I T + T O = O O H. If the letter repeats, it stands for the same number each time. Find numbers that work to make the number sentence true. (Possible answers: 38 + 81 = 119; 56 + 61 = 117; 47 + 71 = 118)

Problem-Solving Strategies Ask students who have solved the Problem of the Day to share how they solved it and any strategies they used.

MENTAL MATH Practice the basic addition, subtraction, multiplication, and division facts, emphasizing accuracy and speed.

a. 10 + 7 = (17)	**b.** 9 × 4 = (36)	**c.** 42 ÷ 6 = (7)
d. 13 – 10 = (3)	**e.** 24 ÷ 4 = (6)	**f.** 15 ÷ 3 = (5)
g. 7 × 3 = (21)	**h.** 4 + 1 = (5)	**i.** 9 + 6 = (15)
j. 6 × 10 = (60)	**k.** 6 × 2 = (12)	**l.** 4 + 5 = (9)
m. 10 × 2 = (20)	**n.** 8 × 3 = (24)	**o.** 9 + 9 = (18)
p. 4 + 9 = (13)	**q.** 35 ÷ 7 = (5)	**r.** 16 ÷ 4 = (4)

LESSON 67

Revisiting Number Facts

Keep in shape by practicing your number facts. Watch the signs.

SELF ASSESSMENT

Are You Shiny or Rusty?

Very shiny	29 or more right
Shiny	24–28 right
A bit rusty	19–23 right
Rusty	Fewer than 19 right

ALGEBRA READINESS

Solve for *n*. Watch the signs.

1. 40 ÷ *n* = 8 **5**	2. *n* + 8 = 14 **6**	3. 7 + 5 = *n* **12**
4. *n* − 7 = 10 **17**	5. *n* = 72 ÷ 8 **9**	6. 12 − *n* = 7 **5**
7. 7 × 9 = *n* **63**	8. 9 + 6 = *n* **15**	9. *n* × 4 = 32 **8**
10. *n* ÷ 3 = 7 **21**	11. 7 × *n* = 49 **7**	12. *n* + 9 = 12 **3**
13. 24 = *n* × 8 **3**	14. *n* ÷ 7 = 4 **28**	15. 13 − *n* = 10 **3**
16. *n* ÷ 5 = 9 **45**	17. 5 + 8 = *n* **13**	18. 6 × 9 = *n* **54**
19. *n* × 5 = 30 **6**	20. 13 − 7 = *n* **6**	21. *n* ÷ 5 = 6 **30**
22. 8 + *n* = 15 **7**	23. *n* = 5 × 8 **40**	24. *n* − 2 = 9 **11**

Solve these problems. Watch the signs.

25. 9 × 8 = **72**
26. 13 − 5 = **8**
27. 5 + 7 = **12**
28. 35 − 5 = **30**
29. $6\overline{)36}$ **6**

30. 18 − 9
31. 4 × 6
32. 7 + 9
33. 20 − 12
34. $6\overline{)54}$ **9**

30. **9**
31. **24**
32. **16**
33. **8**

RETEACHING

For students who have not yet mastered the basic facts, assign Practice Master 67 for further reinforcement.

PRACTICE p. 67

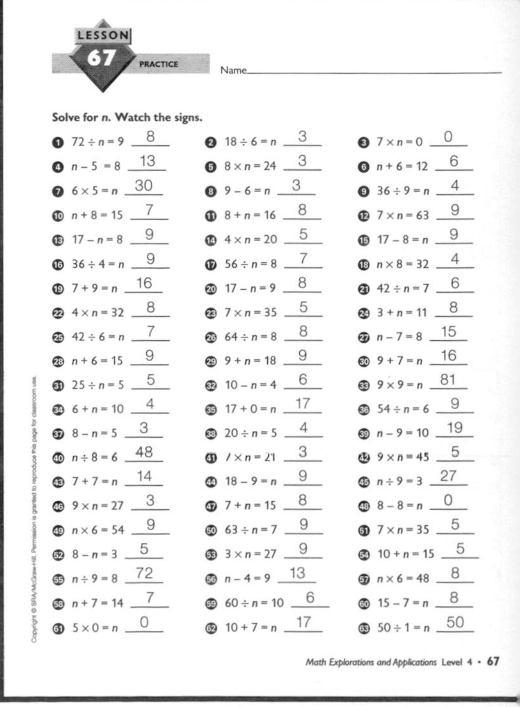
LESSON 67 PRACTICE Name______

Solve for *n*. Watch the signs.

1. 72 ÷ *n* = 9 __8__	2. 18 ÷ 6 = *n* __3__	3. 7 × *n* = 0 __0__
4. *n* – 5 = 8 __13__	5. 8 × *n* = 24 __3__	6. *n* + 6 = 12 __6__
7. 6 × 5 = *n* __30__	8. 9 – 6 = *n* __3__	9. 36 ÷ 9 = *n* __4__
10. *n* + 8 = 15 __7__	11. 8 + *n* = 16 __8__	12. 7 × *n* = 63 __9__
13. 17 – *n* = 8 __9__	14. 4 × *n* = 20 __5__	15. 17 – 8 = *n* __9__
16. 36 ÷ 4 = *n* __9__	17. 56 ÷ *n* = 8 __7__	18. *n* × 8 = 32 __4__
19. 7 + 9 = *n* __16__	20. 17 – *n* = 9 __8__	21. 42 ÷ *n* = 7 __6__
22. 4 × *n* = 32 __8__	23. 7 × *n* = 35 __5__	24. 3 + *n* = 11 __8__
25. 42 ÷ 6 = *n* __7__	26. 64 ÷ *n* = 8 __8__	27. *n* – 7 = 8 __15__
28. *n* + 6 = 15 __9__	29. 9 + *n* = 18 __9__	30. 9 + 7 = *n* __16__
31. 25 ÷ *n* = 5 __5__	32. 10 – *n* = 4 __6__	33. 9 × 9 = *n* __81__
34. 6 + *n* = 10 __4__	35. 17 + 0 = *n* __17__	36. 54 ÷ *n* = 6 __9__
37. 8 – *n* = 5 __3__	38. 20 ÷ *n* = 5 __4__	39. *n* – 9 = 10 __19__
40. *n* ÷ 8 = 6 __48__	41. 7 × *n* = 21 __3__	42. 9 × *n* = 45 __5__
43. 7 + 7 = *n* __14__	44. 18 – 9 = *n* __9__	45. *n* ÷ 9 = 3 __27__
46. 9 × *n* = 27 __3__	47. 7 + *n* = 15 __8__	48. 8 – 8 = *n* __0__
49. *n* × 6 = 54 __9__	50. 63 ÷ *n* = 7 __9__	51. 7 × *n* = 35 __5__
52. 8 – *n* = 3 __5__	53. 3 × *n* = 27 __9__	54. 10 + *n* = 15 __5__
55. *n* ÷ 9 = 8 __72__	56. *n* – 4 = 9 __13__	57. *n* × 6 = 48 __8__
58. *n* + 7 = 14 __7__	59. 60 ÷ *n* = 10 __6__	60. 15 – 7 = *n* __8__
61. 5 × 0 = *n* __0__	62. 10 + 7 = *n* __17__	63. 50 ÷ 1 = *n* __50__

Copyright © SRA/McGraw-Hill. Permission is granted to reproduce this page for classroom use.

Math Explorations and Applications Level 4 • 67

*available separately

Discuss the questions based on the above information.

- Which of the batteries is the best buy? Why do you think so? **See comments in margin.**
- Which of the tires is the best buy? Why do you think so?
- Which of the mufflers is the best buy? Why do you think so?

❷ Teach

SELF ASSESSMENT

Using the Student Pages Have students complete page 228 independently. You may wish to time this exercise. Before you begin page 229, let students know that there are no clear-cut right and wrong answers to the questions on this page. Encourage students to think about what determines a "best buy." Is price the only factor? Is a five-year guarantee important? Raise these questions to stimulate students' thinking. Have students work in groups, similar to the way they work on Thinking Stories, or keep the entire class together for discussion.

❸ Wrap-Up

5 MINUTES

In Closing Ask students what factors they would consider if they were buying a new computer.

Mastery Checkpoint 11

By this time most students should demonstrate mastery of the basic facts by correctly answering at least 80% of the problems on page 228 or on Assessment Blackline Masters page 27 in a reasonable amount of time. You can record the results of this assessment on the Mastery Checkpoint Chart.

Assessment Criteria

Did the student . . .

✓ contribute to the "best buy" discussion?

✓ communicate strategies used to make wise shopping decisions?

✓ correctly answer at least 80% of the computation problems?

MATH JOURNAL

Homework Have students determine the best buy for a product of their choice from two or more stores, or from among two or more similar models, and present their reasons in writing in their Math Journals.

ENRICHMENT p. 67

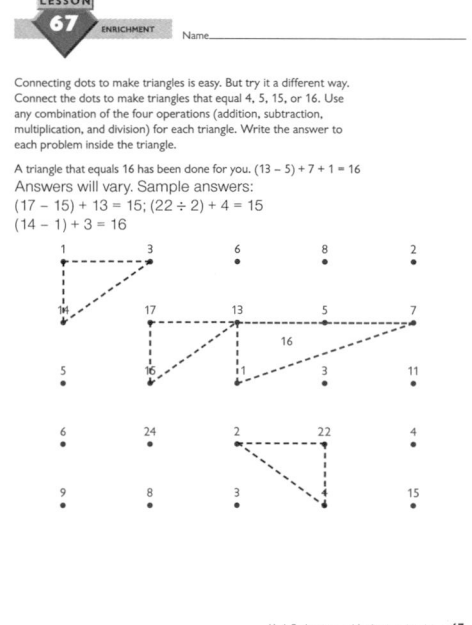

LESSON 67 ENRICHMENT Name______________________

Connecting dots to make triangles is easy. But try it a different way. Connect the dots to make triangles that equal 4, 5, 15, or 16. Use any combination of the four operations (addition, subtraction, multiplication, and division) for each triangle. Write the answer to each problem inside the triangle.

A triangle that equals 16 has been done for you. (13 – 5) + 7 + 1 = 16

Answers will vary. Sample answers:
(17 – 15) + 13 = 15; (22 ÷ 2) + 4 = 15
(14 – 1) + 3 = 16

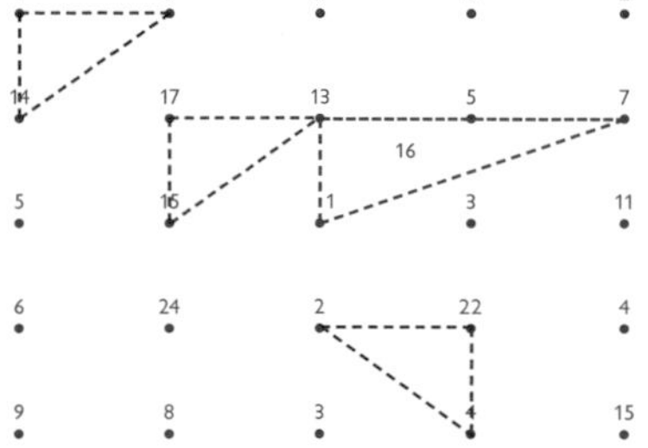

Copyright © SRA/McGraw-Hill. Permission is granted to reproduce this page for classroom use.

Math Explorations and Applications Level 4 • **67**

ASSESSMENT p. 27

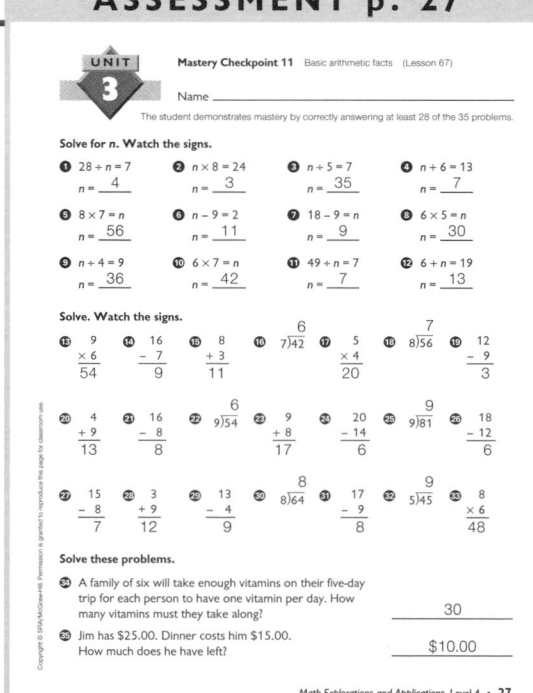

UNIT 3 **Mastery Checkpoint 11** Basic arithmetic facts (Lesson 67)

Name______________________

The student demonstrates mastery by correctly answering at least 28 of the 35 problems.

Solve for *n*. Watch the signs.

1. $28 \div n = 7$ $n =$ 4
2. $n \times 8 = 24$ $n =$ 3
3. $n \div 5 = 7$ $n =$ 35
4. $n + 6 = 13$ $n =$ 7
5. $8 \times 7 = n$ $n =$ 56
6. $n - 9 = 2$ $n =$ 11
7. $18 - 9 = n$ $n =$ 9
8. $6 \times 5 = n$ $n =$ 30
9. $n \div 4 = 9$ $n =$ 36
10. $6 \times 7 = n$ $n =$ 42
11. $49 \div n = 7$ $n =$ 7
12. $6 + n = 19$ $n =$ 13

Solve. Watch the signs.

13. $9 \times 6 = 54$
14. $16 - 7 = 9$
15. $8 + 3 = 11$
16. $42 \div 7 = 6$
17. $5 \times 4 = 20$
18. $56 \div 8 = 7$
19. $12 - 9 = 3$
20. $4 + 9 = 13$
21. $16 - 8 = 8$
22. $54 \div 9 = 6$
23. $9 + 8 = 17$
24. $20 - 14 = 6$
25. $81 \div 9 = 9$
26. $18 - 12 = 6$
27. $15 - 8 = 7$
28. $3 + 9 = 12$
29. $13 - 4 = 9$
30. $64 \div 8 = 8$
31. $17 - 9 = 8$
32. $45 \div 5 = 9$
33. $8 \times 6 = 48$

Solve these problems.

34. A family of six will take enough vitamins on their five-day trip for each person to have one vitamin per day. How many vitamins must they take along? 30
35. Jim has $25.00. Dinner costs him $15.00. How much does he have left? $10.00

Copyright © SRA/McGraw-Hill. Permission is granted to reproduce this page for classroom use.

Math Explorations and Applications Level 4 • **27**

LESSON 68

Student Edition pages 230–233

Lines and Angles

LESSON PLANNER

Objectives

- to introduce the terms *line segment* and *ray*
- to allow students to explore relationships among points, lines, and angles
- to teach or review the properties of right angles
- to demonstrate how to construct right angles using a paper-folding technique

Context of the Lesson This lesson begins a series of seven lessons in which students explore topics in geometry. Students studied right angles in Lesson 31 in the context of right triangles.

MANIPULATIVES

plain white paper for the folding activity

flashlight (optional)

magazines, catalogs, and pamphlets (optional)

Program Resources

Practice Master 68

Enrichment Master 68

For extra practice:

CD-ROM* Lesson 68

Cumulative Review, page 549

1 Warm-Up

5 MINUTES

Problem of the Day Present the following problem. Have groups discuss it together: Tom's present is not next to Ellen's. Ellen's present is smaller than Sam's. Who has the striped present? (Ellen)

Problem-Solving Strategies Ask students who have solved the Problem of the Day to share how they solved it and any strategies they used.

MENTAL MATH Provide practice in multiplying by multiples of 10 and 100:

a. 2 × 10 = (20) **b.** 7 × 60 = (420)

c. 8 × 50 = (400) **d.** 2 × 20 = (40)

e. 70 × 6 = (420) **f.** 8 × 500 = (4000)

g. 2 × 40 = (80) **h.** 7 × 600 = (4200)

EXPLORE

LESSON 68

Lines and Angles

You know what a point, a line, and an angle are. Sometimes we wish to refer to just a part of a line. If the part has two endpoints, we call it a **line segment** (see line segment *AB* in the picture below).

If the part has only one endpoint and goes on forever in the other direction, we call it a **ray,** or sometimes we call it a **half line** (see ray *DE*).

The first letter in the name of the ray is its **endpoint.** We sometimes draw arrows on our pictures of lines to show that they go on forever in both directions.

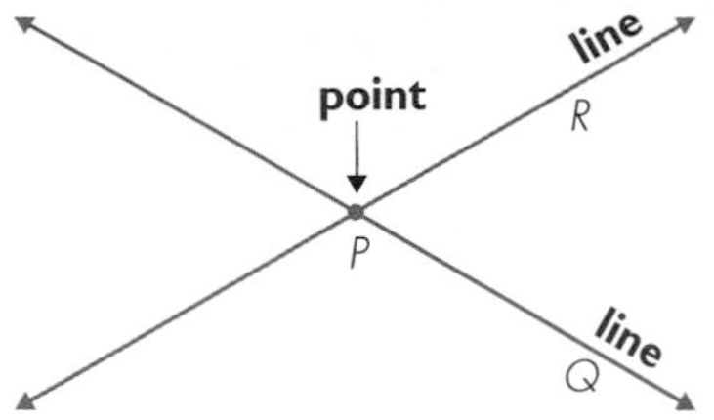

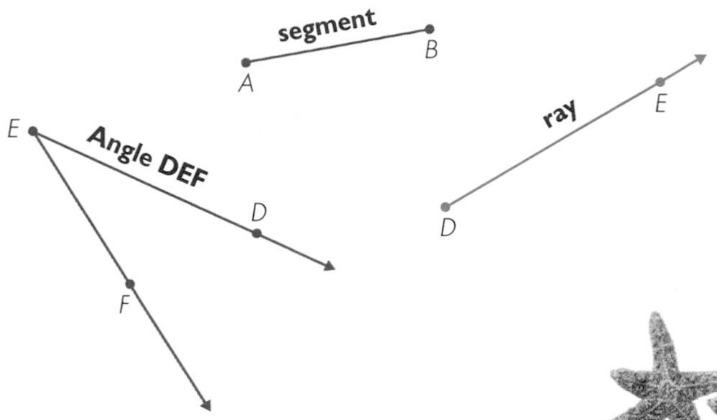

FANTASTIC FACT

Starfish come in all sizes. The largest is the sunflower star. It has more than 26 arms. When a starfish loses an arm, another one grows in its place. In fact, a starfish can grow a whole new body from just one arm.

230 • Algebra Readiness and Geometry

Why teach it this way?

The informal approach of allowing students to explore geometric concepts is more appropriate at Level 4 than taking a more formal approach. Geometry will be studied more formally in Level 6.

*available separately

Answer the following questions.

1. Suppose two different lines meet at point *P*.
   a. Could they also meet at some other point? At point *T*? **no**
   b. Discuss this with your friends. Decide what you think.
2. Suppose there are two points. How many lines do you think you could draw that go through both points? **one**
3. On your paper draw two lines that meet in as many points as possible. How many points is that? **one**
4. On your paper make two points.
   a. Draw as many different lines through them as you can.
   b. How many lines is that? **one**
5. Look at angle *DEF* in the picture on page 230.
   a. Is it made up of two rays? **yes**
   b. What is the endpoint of each ray? **point *E***

We usually name an angle with a point on one of its sides (rays), then the common endpoint of its rays (sometimes called the **vertex**), and then a point on the other ray. However, in some cases we just name the vertex.

6. Do you know which angle is angle *E*? **yes**
7. Do you know which angle is angle *P*? Explain. **no; angle P could be any one of four angles**

Name the following in two ways. Remember to use only two letters.

8. 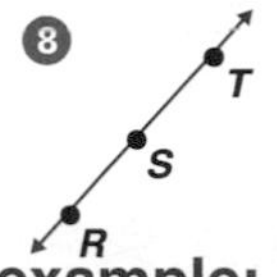

9. 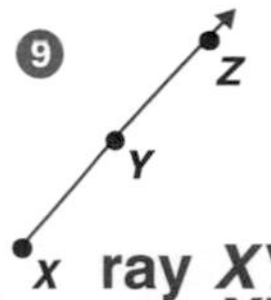

10. 

For example: **line *RS*** **line *ST*** | **ray *XY*** **ray *XZ*** | **line segment *AC*** **line segment *CA***

11. Which is longer, a line segment or a line? Explain.
   A line is longer because it continues on, as indicated by the arrows. A line segment has two endpoints and is only part of a line.

❷ Teach

COOPERATIVE LEARNING **Using the Student Pages** Go over the information presented at the top of page 230. If necessary, review the definitions of *points, lines,* and *angles* and have volunteers identify or draw examples of them. Have students work in pairs or small groups to answer the questions on page 231. Encourage students to draw enough examples to ensure that they have adequately resolved each problem. Bring groups together to discuss the problems as a class.

Note: Throughout this and future lessons at this level, assume that a line is a straight line unless otherwise indicated.

SPECIAL NEEDS

Meeting Individual Needs

Students may need a concrete example of a ray to help them distinguish it from a line segment. Perform a simple demonstration with a basic **flashlight.** Point out that the beam (ray) begins at the bulb (the endpoint) and shines away from the flashlight in one general direction, which represents the one-way, ongoing portion of the ray.

TECHNOLOGY CONNECTION

Technology Connection For practice with angles, shapes, similarity, *x* and *y* coordinates, motions and symmetry, probability, and computation, students may try the software *Turtle Math* from LCSI (Mac, for grades 3–6).

◆ LESSON 68 Lines and Angles

Teach

Using the Student Pages Have students work on problems 12 and 13 on page 232, then discuss their answers. In problem 13, note that signs whose corners have been rounded off do not, technically, have angles. However, for discussion purposes, guide students to envision any corners as being sharp. You should discuss *acute* and *obtuse* angles and have students try to identify each. Acute angles are angles that are smaller than right angles. Obtuse angles are larger than right angles. Then go on to page 233. Provide students with **plain paper.** Have them follow the steps of the folding activity on page 233 as you demonstrate it for them. Check around the room to see that students are following the steps correctly. If students make an incorrect fold, provide fresh paper to avoid any later confusion that superfluous creases could cause.

◆ LESSON 68 Lines and Angles

Remember, a **right angle** is an angle like the one in the figure. The corners of this page are right angles.

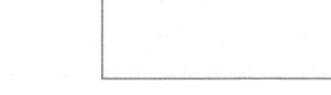

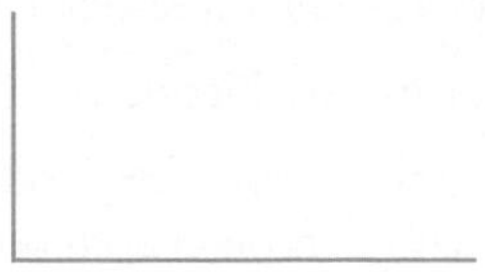

12 Look around you.

a. Identify other right angles in the classroom. **corner of poster, chalkboard, window**

b. Make a list of at least five examples of right angles other than the corners of the page.

13 Look at the traffic signs below.

a. Which of these traffic signs have at least one right angle? **Do Not Enter, Deer Crossing, School Zone, Road Construction Ahead, Minimum 40, Detour, One Way**

b. Try to name the shape of each sign.

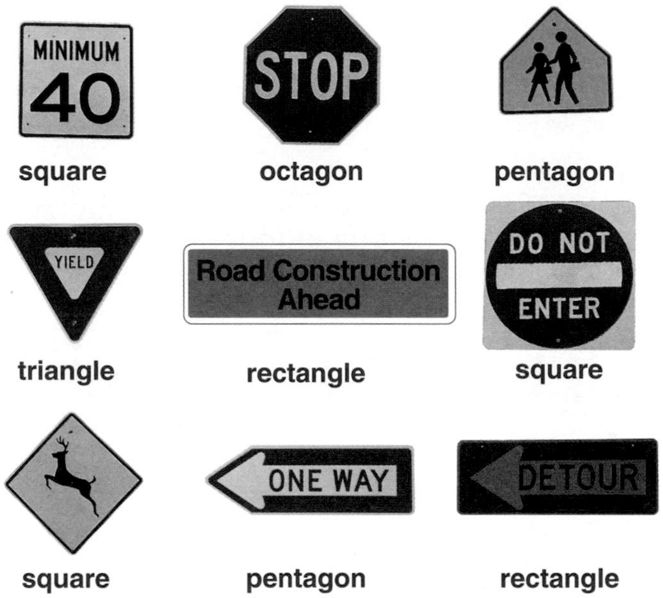

Real-World Connection Have students look through old **magazines, catalogs, pamphlets,** or other sources for pictures of real-life objects whose shapes suggest points, rays, line segments, or right angles. Have students cut out the pictures, sort them by types of geometric figures, and display them on a bulletin board.

RETEACHING

Students who have difficulty naming angles may benefit from a simple mnemonic trick. Have them trace over an angle in one continuous motion with their fingers. They must give the letters that name the angle in the same order that their fingers moved. So, the letter at the vertex must be the middle one of the three letters, just as the vertex is in the middle position of the angle as it is traced.

Follow these steps to make right angles.

A. Get a piece of paper. Imagine a line like this dotted one.

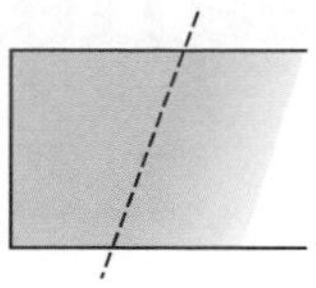

B. Fold along the line.

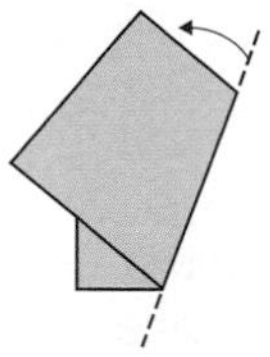

C. Your paper should look like this. Rub with your finger or a pencil to make a sharp crease.

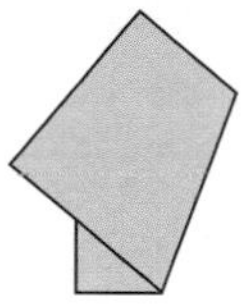

D. Imagine a line like the dotted one. Start to fold along the line.

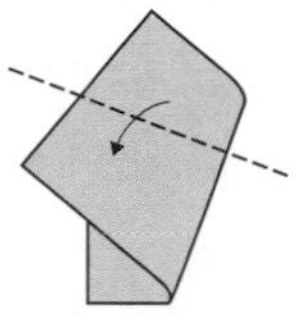

E. As you fold, make sure you line up the edges on the right.

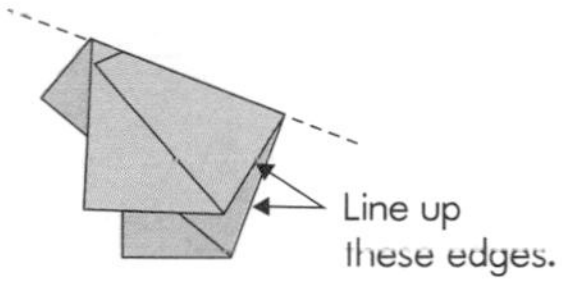

F. Your paper should look like this.

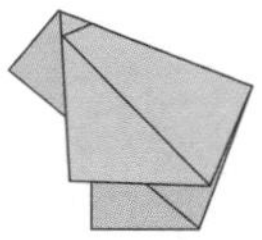

◆ Unfold your paper. How many right angles did you make? **4**

Use the Cumulative Review on page 549 after this lesson.

❸ Wrap-Up (5 MINUTES)

In Closing Have students identify examples of points, line segments, rays, and right angles in the classroom.

ALTERNATIVE ASSESSMENT

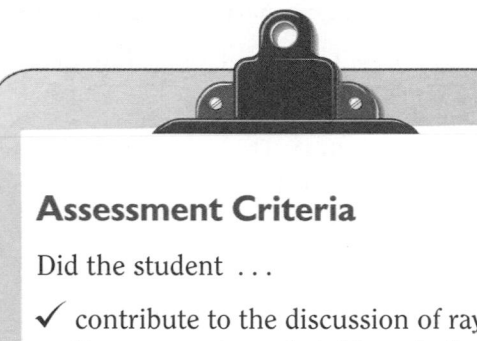

Informal Assessment Observe students as they work on the activities in this lesson. To ascertain whether they can recognize these geometric figures, have them give other examples of points, rays, line segments, and right angles.

Assessment Criteria

Did the student . . .

- ✓ contribute to the discussion of rays, line segments, and right angles?
- ✓ identify right angles in the classroom?
- ✓ follow the sequence of instructions in the folding activity?

Homework Have students identify and list five examples each of points, rays, line segments, and right angles at home or in their neighborhood.

PRACTICE p. 68

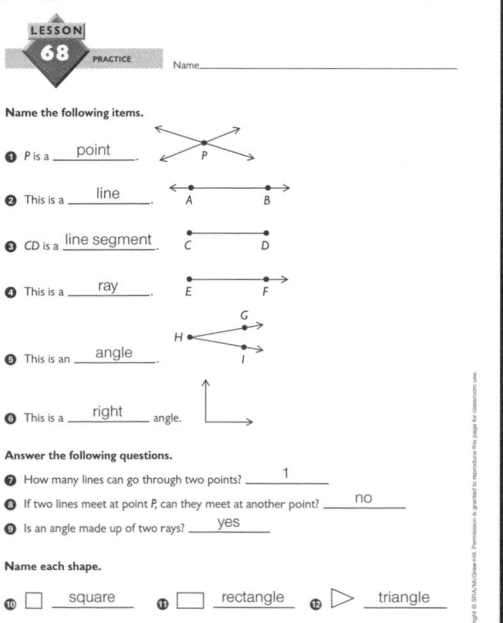

LESSON 68 PRACTICE Name________

Name the following items.

1. P is a point.
2. This is a line. (A, B)
3. CD is a line segment. (C, D)
4. This is a ray. (E, F)
5. This is an angle. (G, H, I)
6. This is a right angle.

Answer the following questions.

7. How many lines can go through two points? 1
8. If two lines meet at point P, can they meet at another point? no
9. Is an angle made up of two rays? yes

Name each shape.

10. □ square
11. ▭ rectangle
12. ▷ triangle

Copyright © SRA/McGraw-Hill. Permission is granted to reproduce this page for classroom use.

68 • *Math Explorations and Applications* Level 4

ENRICHMENT p. 68

LESSON 68 ENRICHMENT Name________

Look around your classroom, bedroom, and other rooms at school and at home for examples of right angles. In the space below write and describe or draw as many examples as you can find.

Look around outdoors at buildings, signs, vehicles, telephone poles and wires, and anything else you see for examples of right angles. Write and describe or draw as many examples as you can in the space below. Show the right angles.

Now look around in nature for examples of right angles. Can you find many? Write and describe or draw these examples.

Are there more right angles in human-made things or in nature? Why do you think that is?

Answers will vary. Right angles indoors might include door frames, window panes, table corners, and so on. Right angles outdoors might include telephone poles and wires, street signs, corners of houses, and so on. Right angles in nature might include a branch of a tree or an angle of a leaf. There are more right angles in human-made things.

Copyright © SRA/McGraw-Hill. Permission is granted to reproduce this page for classroom use.

68 • *Math Explorations and Applications* Level 4

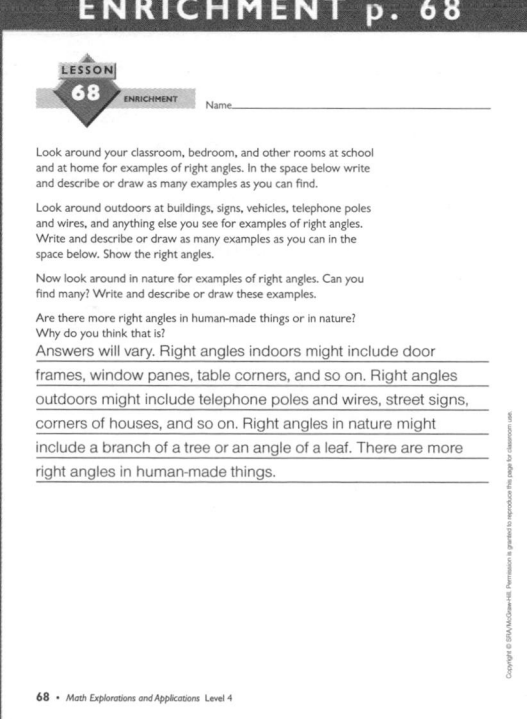

LESSON 69

Student Edition pages 234–237

Perpendicular and Parallel Lines

LESSON PLANNER

Objectives

- to teach or review recognizing parallel and perpendicular lines
- to teach or review the properties of parallel lines
- to help students explore the classification of polygons, especially quadrilaterals

Context of the Lesson This is the second of seven lessons on geometry topics. Parallel lines were covered in Level 3.

MANIPULATIVES

rulers* or straightedges

dictionary (optional)

Program Resources

Practice Master 69

Enrichment Master 69

For extra practice:
CD-ROM* Lesson 69

1 Warm-Up

5 MINUTES

Problem of the Day Present this problem: Margo is four years older than Barrett and 16 years younger than Rosa. Rosa is three times as old as Margo. What are their ages? (Margo, 8; Barrett, 4; Rosa, 24)

Problem-Solving Strategies Ask students who have solved the Problem of the Day to share how they solved it and any strategies they used.

MENTAL MATH Provide practice in multiplying greater numbers. Encourage students to answer quickly.

a. 3 x 10 = (30); 3 x 30 = (90); 3 x 29 = (87)

b. 4 x 10 = (40); 2 x 40 = (80); 2 x 41 = (82)

c. 4 x 100 = (400); 5 x 100 = (500); 5 x 99 = (495)

d. 6 x 100 = (600); 7 x 100 (700); 7 x 99 = (693)

e. 8 x 100 = (800); 9 x 100 = (900); 9 x 101 = (909)

f. 5 x 20 = (100); 6 x 20 = (120); 6 x 19 = (114)

EXPLORE

LESSON 69

Perpendicular and Parallel Lines

In this lesson you'll learn to identify two special kinds of lines using what you already know about points and angles.

Any two lines are **perpendicular** if the angles they make when they meet are right angles.

These lines are perpendicular.

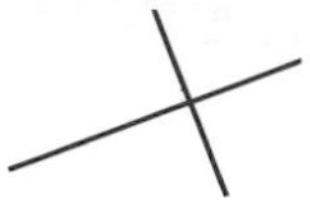

1. Try to draw two lines that meet with one right angle and with the other three angles not right angles. The two lines must be straight and must continue straight through the point where they meet. Can you do it? **no**
2. If two lines meet so that one angle formed is a right angle, what kind of angles will the other three angles be? **right angles**
3. By folding paper, make two lines that are perpendicular. Draw the lines in two different colors.
4. Suppose you fold a piece of paper twice.
   a. What is the least number of right angles you can make? **0**
   b. The greatest number? **4—counting only those angles formed by edges of paper and creases**

In each case, tell whether the two lines are perpendicular.

5.  **yes**
6.  **no**
7.  **no**
8.  **yes**

◆ Suppose you fold a piece of paper three times. What is the least number of right angles you can make? The greatest number? **0; 12**

◆ Suppose you fold a piece of paper four times. What is the least number of right angles you can make? The greatest number? **0; 36**

Language Arts Connection

Have students use a **dictionary** to find the derivation of the word *polygon*. Help them extend their understanding by brainstorming other words that use the same suffix. Discuss their meanings.

*available separately

Parallel lines are lines that go in the same direction. The lines in this figure are parallel lines.

9. Do the two lines look as though they will ever meet each other? **no**
10. Do the lines look as though they stay the same distance apart? **yes**

Parallel lines never meet. They remain the same distance apart no matter how far they are extended.

In each case, tell whether the two lines are *parallel, perpendicular,* or *neither.*

11. 
neither

12. 
neither

13. 
parallel

14. 
parallel

15. 
perpendicular

16. Draw a line. Now draw two more lines, each perpendicular to the first. What do you think is true of these last two lines? **parallel**

In your Math Journal list several examples of parallel and perpendicular lines that you see every day.

Technology Connection Refer students to the software *Quadrominoes* from Sunburst Communications (Mac, for grades 4–8) for more practice with congruence, probability theory, geometric concepts, transformations, and strategic planning.

2 Teach

Using the Student Pages Go over page 234 with the class, or have students do the problems on their own and discuss the answers with the class afterward. Be sure students use the paper-folding procedure from the previous lesson to solve questions 3 and 4 and the bulleted questions at the bottom of the page. Alert them that the bulleted questions are difficult. Provide extra paper so they feel free to use a trial-and-error approach. These examples show the least and greatest number of right angles for paper folded three and four times.

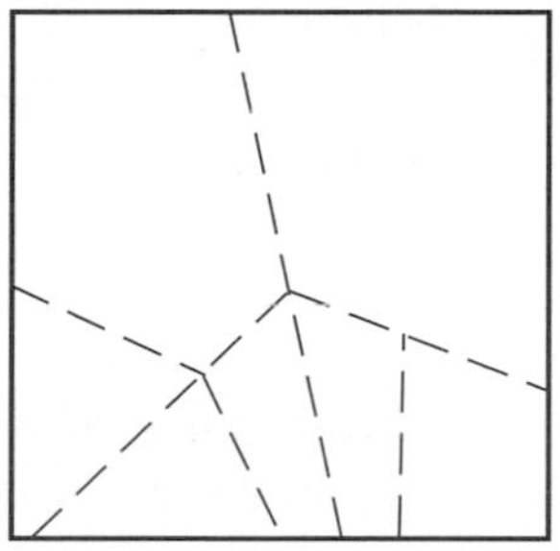
3 folds, 0 right angles

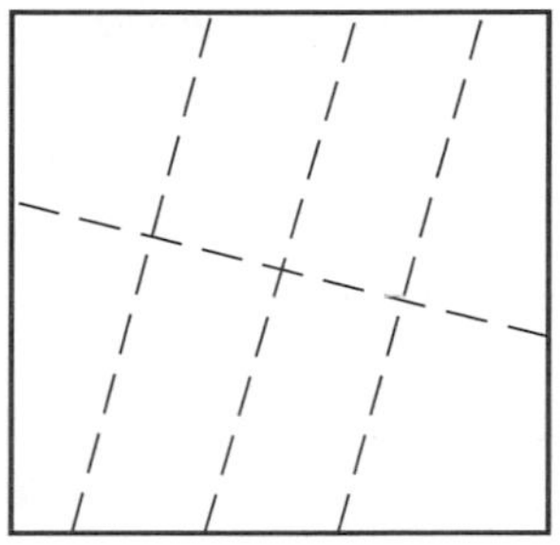
3 folds, 12 right angles

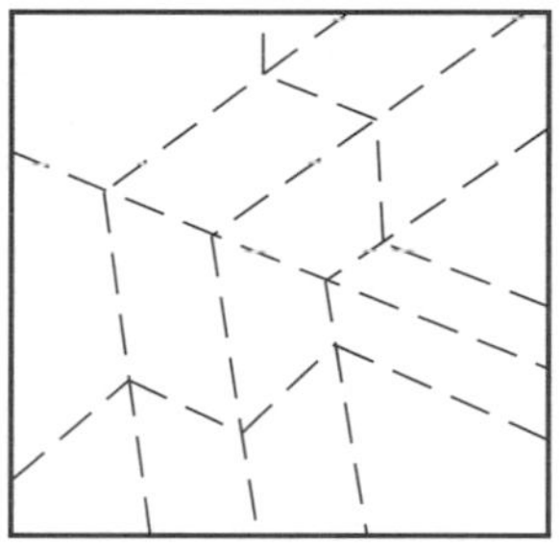
4 folds, 0 right angles

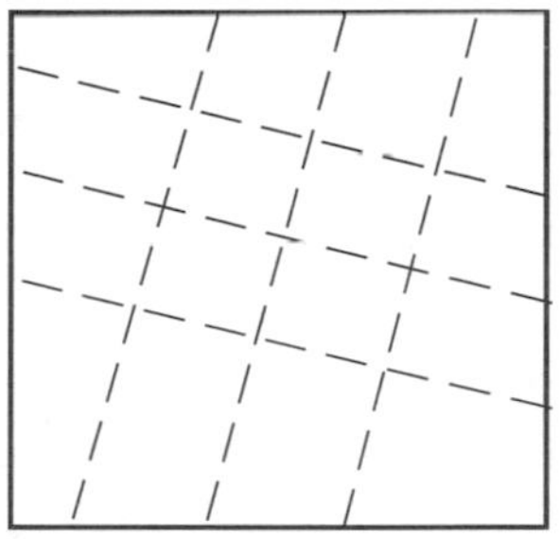
4 folds, 36 right angles

Discuss the questions on page 235. Ask for real-life examples of parallel lines, such as railroad tracks, the double yellow lines in the center of a road, or two sides of a picture frame. Clarify the meaning of parallel lines "going in the same direction" by explaining that parallel lines always stay the same distance apart, no matter how far they extend. You might introduce the term *intersecting lines* to describe lines or segments that cross (or would cross if extended far enough). Point out that intersecting lines that are not perpendicular will not form a right angle.

◆ LESSON 69 Perpendicular and Parallel Lines

Teach

Using the Student Pages Go over the information presented on these two pages. Explain that the term *polygon* is a broad term that can be applied to many geometric figures, even irregular ones that have no specific name. You might work with the class to compile a chart that gives the names of polygons and the number of sides each has. Begin with triangle, the polygon with the fewest number of sides, and go on to list quadrilateral, pentagon, hexagon, heptagon, octagon, nonagon, and decagon. Invite students to use **rulers*** to draw examples of each polygon. Then go over the distinctions among the quadrilaterals on page 237. Guide students to notice, for example, that a rectangle is a particular kind of parallelogram and a square is a particular kind of rectangle. Then have students complete the page on their own.

ESL **Meeting Individual Needs**

Students with limited proficiency in English may have difficulty with some of the vocabulary in this lesson. Help them pronounce the words and identify clues within the words to signal their meaning. For instance, the double *l*s in para*ll*el suggest parallel lines. You might highlight the suffix *-gon* at the ends of the various polygon names.

GIFTED & TALENTED **Meeting Individual Needs**

Students may enjoy learning the formal mathematical symbols used to indicate parallel $||$ and perpendicular $\perp$ lines. Explain how to use these symbols to write geometric statements, such as $AB \perp EF$ (line *AB* is perpendicular to line *EF*) or $JK \; || \; YZ$ (line *JK* is parallel to line *YZ*). Challenge students to draw accurate geometric figures based on such statements.

◆ LESSON 69 Perpendicular and Parallel Lines

Look at the figures below. Count the sides in each figure. Write the number of sides for each on your paper. Write "T−3" and so on for each figure. Can you guess how the letters for the various figures were chosen?

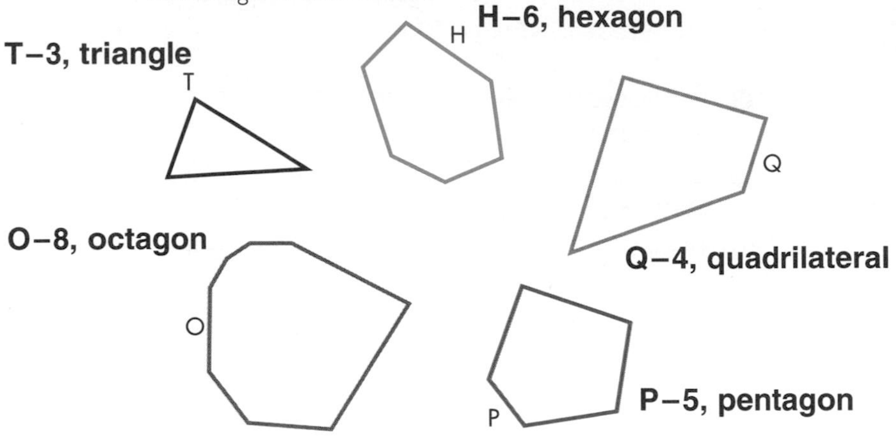

All of the figures shown are called **polygons.** A polygon is a closed plane figure with three or more line segments as sides. In a closed figure, every side shares its endpoints with two other sides. Think of a polygon as a fence with no break in it. Somebody inside can't get out without climbing the fence.

A polygon with five sides is called a **pentagon** (*penta-* means "five"). A polygon with six sides is a **hexagon.** A polygon with eight sides is an **octagon.**

The names for three- and four-sided polygons don't include "gon." They are **triangle** and **quadrilateral.** Sometimes people say eight-gon to mean an octagon, ten-gon to mean a ten-sided polygon, and so on. **Drawings may vary. Possibilities include:**

17. Draw an octagon. 
18. Draw a seven-gon (called a **heptagon**). 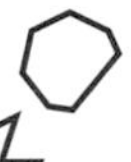
19. Draw a ten-gon (called a **decagon**). 
20. Draw a triangle with two of its sides the same length. 

Literature Connection Display a copy of *Round Trip* by Ann Jonas. Have students identify parallel and perpendicular lines in the illustrations.

RETEACHING

Although no reteaching strategy is suggested at this time, continue to draw attention to examples of parallel and perpendicular lines and specific polygons. You may want to assign Enrichment Master 69.

*available separately

21. Draw a quadrilateral with two of its sides parallel but the other two sides not parallel. 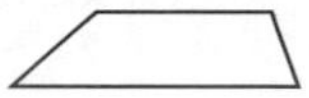

22. Draw a quadrilateral with both pairs of opposite sides parallel. 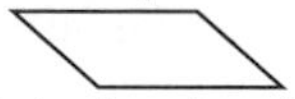

23. Draw a quadrilateral with both pairs of opposite sides parallel and with all its sides the same length. 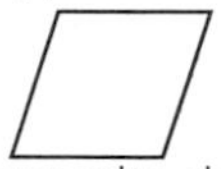

24. Draw a quadrilateral with both pairs of opposite sides parallel and with all its angles the same size. 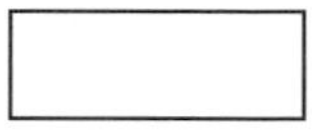

25. Draw a quadrilateral with both pairs of opposite sides parallel and with all its sides and all its angles the same size. 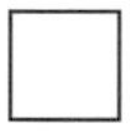

Do your answers for problems 21–25 look like the quadrilaterals shown below? These figures have special names that are given here.

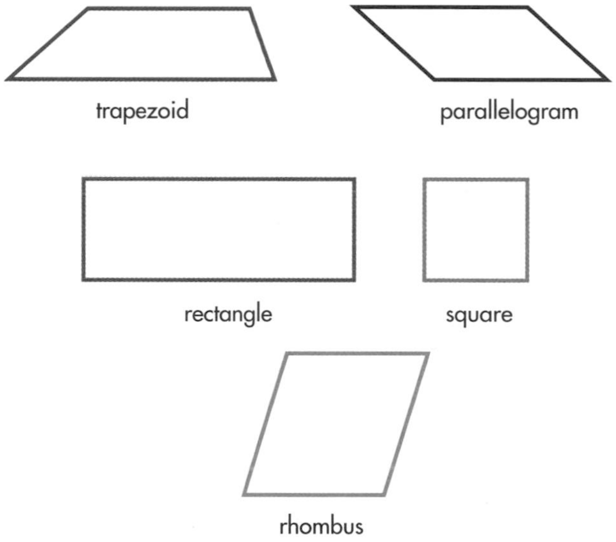

❸ Wrap-Up

5 MINUTES

In Closing Have students explain the meaning of *parallel* and *perpendicular* and identify parallel and perpendicular lines in polygons.

ALTERNATIVE ASSESSMENT

Portfolio Assessment Have students write a statement about the meaning of *parallel lines* and *perpendicular lines.* Then have them draw and label examples of the various polygons they examined in this lesson. Ask them to date and add this statement to their Math Portfolios as evidence of ongoing learning.

Assessment Criteria

Did the student . . .

- ✓ communicate an understanding of parallel and perpendicular lines?
- ✓ identify and discuss characteristics of polygons?
- ✓ distinguish differences among quadrilaterals?

Homework Have students identify and list five different examples of parallel and perpendicular lines in their room at home. Also have them identify five specific polygons in the classroom.

PRACTICE p. 69

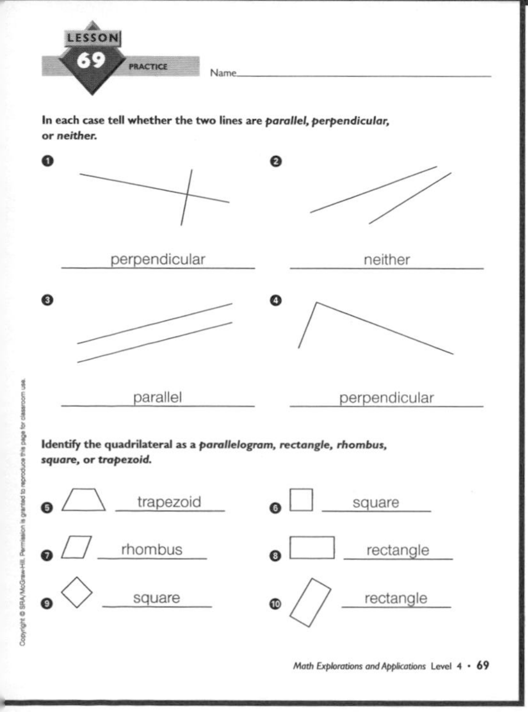

LESSON 69 PRACTICE Name______

In each case tell whether the two lines are *parallel, perpendicular,* or *neither.*

1. perpendicular
2. neither
3. parallel
4. perpendicular

Identify the quadrilateral as a *parallelogram, rectangle, rhombus, square,* or *trapezoid.*

5. trapezoid
6. square
7. rhombus
8. rectangle
9. square
10. rectangle

Copyright © SRA/McGraw-Hill. Permission is granted to reproduce this page for classroom use.

Math Explorations and Applications Level 4 • 69

ENRICHMENT p. 69

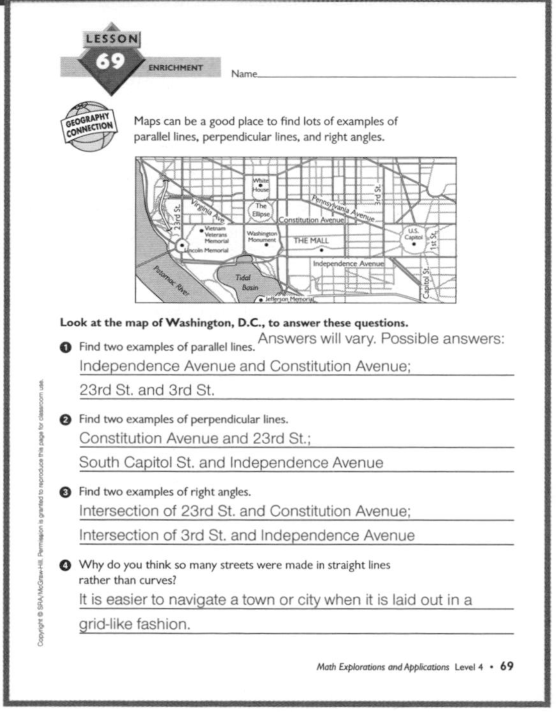

LESSON 69 ENRICHMENT Name______

GEOGRAPHY CONNECTION

Maps can be a good place to find lots of examples of parallel lines, perpendicular lines, and right angles.

Look at the map of Washington, D.C., to answer these questions.

1. Find two examples of parallel lines. Answers will vary. Possible answers:
Independence Avenue and Constitution Avenue;
23rd St. and 3rd St.
2. Find two examples of perpendicular lines.
Constitution Avenue and 23rd St.;
South Capitol St. and Independence Avenue
3. Find two examples of right angles.
Intersection of 23rd St. and Constitution Avenue;
Intersection of 3rd St. and Independence Avenue
4. Why do you think so many streets were made in straight lines rather than curves?
It is easier to navigate a town or city when it is laid out in a grid-like fashion.

Copyright © SRA/McGraw-Hill. Permission is granted to reproduce this page for classroom use.

Math Explorations and Applications Level 4 • 69

LESSON 70

Student Edition pages 238–239

Congruence and Similarity

LESSON PLANNER

Objective

- ▶ to introduce the geometric concepts of congruence and similarity

Context of the Lesson This is the third of seven lessons on geometry topics.

MANIPULATIVES

tracing paper

Program Resources

Number Wheels

Reteaching Master

Practice Master 70

Enrichment Master 70

For extra practice:
CD-ROM* Lesson 70

1 Warm-Up

5 MINUTES

Problem of the Day Present the following problem: Figure out the pattern. Then give the next three numbers. 1, 2, 3, 5, 8, 13, . . . (21, 34, 55; the numbers in the pattern, starting with 3, are the sum of the two previous numbers.)

Problem-Solving Strategies Ask students who have solved the Problem of the Day to share how they solved it and any strategies they used.

MENTAL MATH Review the number of sides in polygons. Name a polygon and have students use Number Wheels to show how many sides the polygon has.

a.	triangle (3)	**b.**	hexagon (6)
c.	octagon (8)	**d.**	quadrilateral (4)
e.	pentagon (5)	**f.**	parallelogram (4)
g.	rectangle (4)	**h.**	circle (not a polygon)

EXPLORE

LESSON 70

Congruence and Similarity

Two figures are **congruent** if they are the same size and same shape. If one figure fits exactly on top of another, they are congruent.

If two figures are the same shape but not the same size we say they are **similar.**

1. List all the figures below that look congruent to figure A. **E, G, I**
2. List all the figures below that look similar to figure A but not congruent to it. **D, K**
3. List all the figures below that look congruent to figure B. **C, F, H, J**
4. List all the figures below that look similar to figure B but not congruent to it. **L, M**

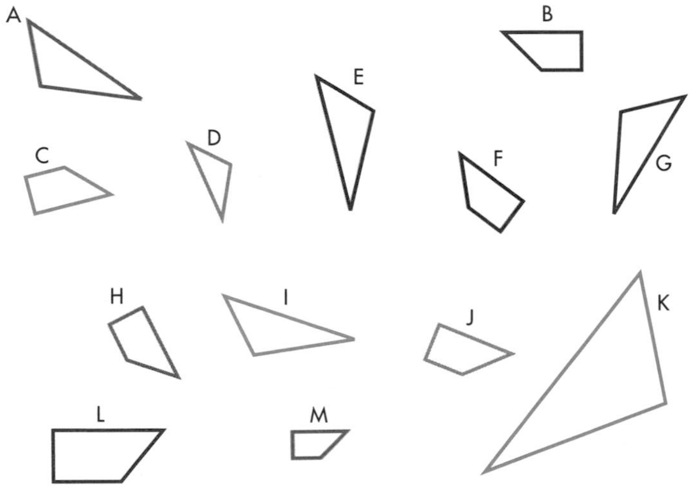

238 • Algebra Readiness and Geometry

Why teach it at this time?

As with previous and subsequent lessons in this sequence, our informal approach to the development of geometric concepts allows for much exploration. Formal proofs for congruence and similarity are taken up in later grade levels.

RETEACHING p. 23

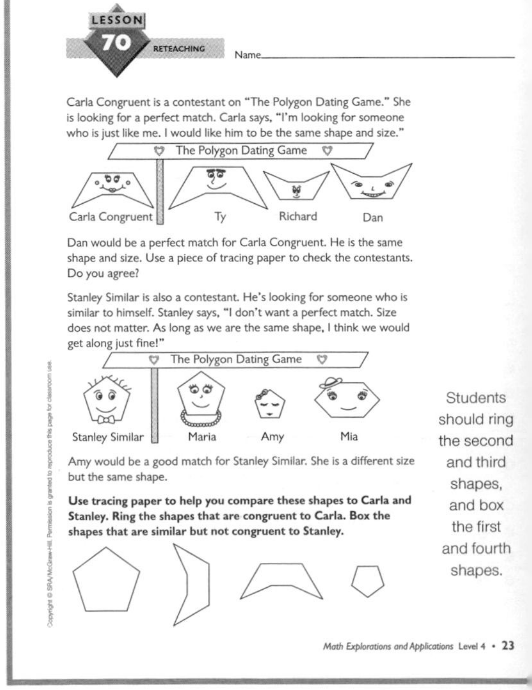
LESSON 70 RETEACHING Name________________

Carla Congruent is a contestant on "The Polygon Dating Game." She is looking for a perfect match. Carla says, "I'm looking for someone who is just like me. I would like him to be the same shape and size."

The Polygon Dating Game

Carla Congruent Ty Richard Dan

Dan would be a perfect match for Carla Congruent. He is the same shape and size. Use a piece of tracing paper to check the contestants. Do you agree?

Stanley Similar is also a contestant. He's looking for someone who is similar to himself. Stanley says, "I don't want a perfect match. Size does not matter. As long as we are the same shape, I think we would get along just fine!"

The Polygon Dating Game

Stanley Similar Maria Amy Mia

Amy would be a good match for Stanley Similar. She is a different size but the same shape.

Use tracing paper to help you compare these shapes to Carla and Stanley. Ring the shapes that are congruent to Carla. Box the shapes that are similar but not congruent to Stanley.

Copyright © SRA/McGraw-Hill. Permission is granted to reproduce this page for classroom use.

Math Explorations and Applications Level 4 • 23

Students should ring the second and third shapes, and box the first and fourth shapes.

*available separately

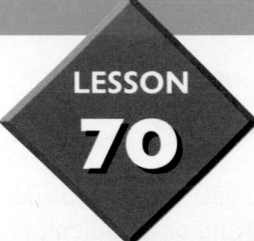

5. List five examples of congruent objects. **Examples: tires on a car; checkers in a game set**
6. List five examples of similar objects. **Examples: different sizes of the same item of clothing; small plate and large plate**
7. Before factories began producing items, do you think there were as many good examples of congruent objects as there are today? Why? **no; because items were duplicated by hand, they were subject to human error**

◆ Consider three similar squares. The first one is 1 cm on a side. The second is 2 cm on a side. The third is 3 cm on a side.

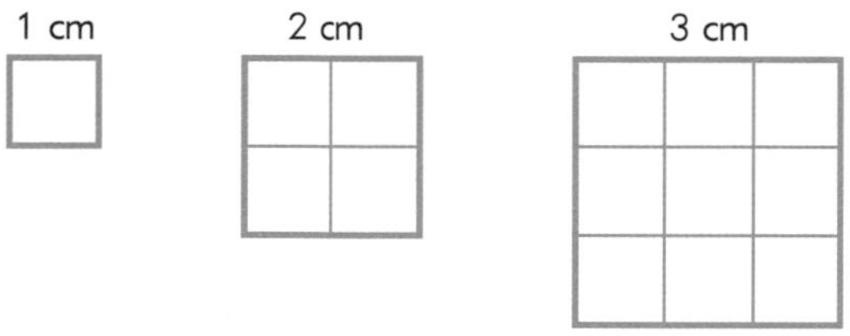

8. Solve the following problems.
   - **a.** What is the area of the smallest square? **1 square cm**
   - **b.** What is the area of the middle square? **4 square cm**
   - **c.** What is the area of the largest square? **9 square cm**
   - **d.** What is the perimeter of the smallest square? **4 cm**
   - **e.** What is the perimeter of the middle square? **8 cm**
   - **f.** What is the perimeter of the largest square? **12 cm**
9. What pattern do you see as the area of the squares increases? What do you see as the perimeter increases? **When the side length doubles, the area quadruples and the perimeter doubles.**

In your Math Journal continue this exercise using measures from 5 centimeters to 10 centimeters as the side lengths. Write about the relationship you see between area and perimeter.

PRACTICE p. 70

LESSON 70 PRACTICE

Name____________________

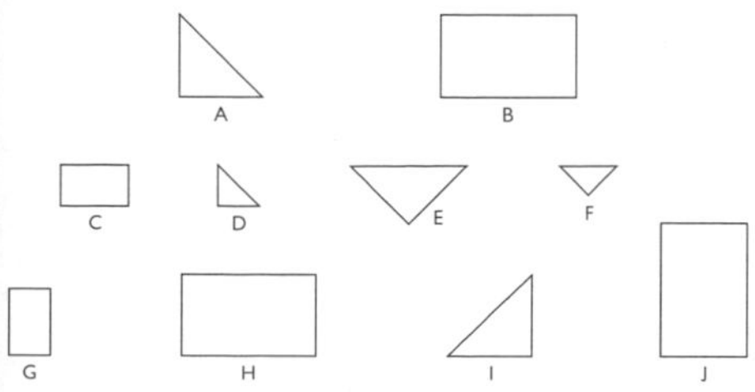

Answer the following questions.

1. Which figures are congruent to A? E, I
2. Which figures are similar to A? D, F
3. Which figures are congruent to B? H, J
4. Which figures are similar to B? C, G
5. Which figures are similar to I? D, F

Consider these rectangles. Answer the following questions.

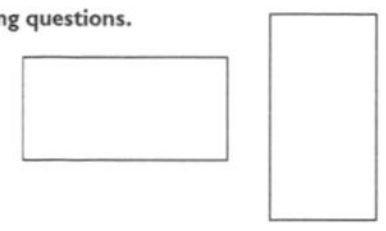

6. Are they similar? yes
7. Are they congruent? yes
8. Do they have the same area? yes

Copyright © SRA/McGraw-Hill. Permission is granted to reproduce this page for classroom use.

ENRICHMENT p. 70

LESSON 70 ENRICHMENT

Name____________________

A wood-block engraver carves away wood to reveal shapes or pictures on a wood block. When the block is covered with ink and pressed on paper, the shape or picture on the block is printed on the paper.

A block carved like this looks like this **S** when it is printed.

A block carved like this looks like this when it is printed.

Answer these questions.

1. Look at the M above. How will you carve it on your block? Ring your answer.
   a. as you see it **b.** upside down **c.** as if you saw it in a mirror
   a., b. (then rotate the block halfway to print), or c.
2. Look at the hand above. How would you carve it to make your block print look exactly like the hand?
   You must carve the hand as a mirror image in order for it to print correctly. Rotating the block after carving it as you see it will not help.
3. Look at the crescent moon. How many ways can you carve it on your block? What effect does rotating the block have on the way the moon is printed?
   You could carve the crescent moon as you see it or as its mirror image. If you carve it as you see it, you must rotate the block halfway around before printing with it. If you carve it as a mirror image, you can print without rotating the block.

Copyright © SRA/McGraw-Hill. Permission is granted to reproduce this page for classroom use.

2 Teach

Using the Student Pages Go over the information given on page 238. Help students read and pronounce the words *congruent, congruence,* and *similar.* Discuss several examples with the class. Then have students work independently. You may wish to provide **tracing paper** for them to use to check for congruence. Some examples of congruent objects include new pencils of the same brand, copies of this textbook, and dollar bills. Some examples of similar objects include an image on an overhead transparency and its projected image, model trains and real trains, and all squares that are not congruent.

Note: Strictly speaking, all congruent figures are similar, but similar figures are not necessarily congruent. At this level, we define similarity as congruent in shape but not in size. Students will explore these concepts in more depth in higher levels of mathematics.

3 Wrap-Up

5 MINUTES

In Closing Have students summarize the meaning of *similar* and *congruent.*

ALTERNATIVE ASSESSMENT

Performance Assessment You might use students' work on this lesson to assess their understanding of similarity and congruence. You might also have them identify alphabet letters that are similar, such as an upper- and lowercase *X,* or they can draw sets of polygons that are similar and congruent.

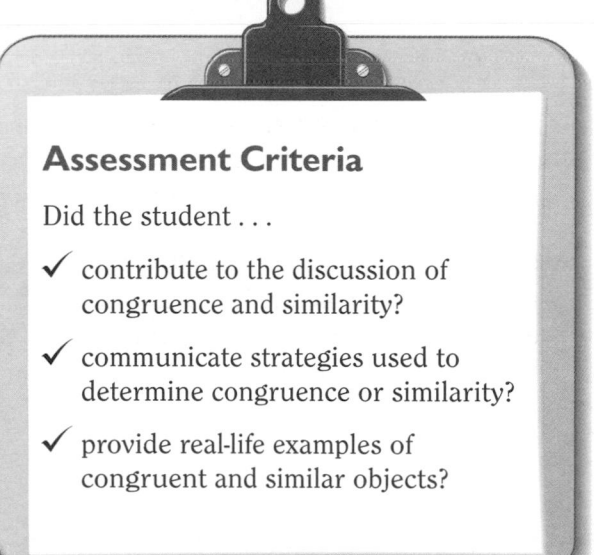

Assessment Criteria

Did the student . . .

- ✓ contribute to the discussion of congruence and similarity?
- ✓ communicate strategies used to determine congruence or similarity?
- ✓ provide real-life examples of congruent and similar objects?

Homework Assign Practice Master 70 for further practice with congruence and similarity.

LESSON 71

Student Edition pages 240–241

Rotation, Reflection, and Translation

LESSON PLANNER

Objective

▶ to have students explore congruence by translation, rotation, and reflection

Context of the Lesson This is the fourth of seven lessons on topics in geometry. This lesson extends the idea of congruence that was introduced in the last lesson.

MANIPULATIVES

overhead projector and transparencies

tracing paper or waxed paper

Program Resources

Number Wheels

Practice Master 71

Enrichment Master 71

For extra practice:
CD-ROM* Lesson 71

1 Warm-Up

5 MINUTES

Problem of the Day Present the following problem. Suggest that students draw a picture to solve it: Wanda is planning a design for a six-by-six grid. She plans to make a star in every third square. She will make a border around every sixth square. How many squares in the grid will remain empty? (24)

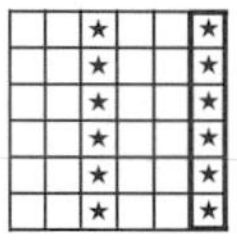

Problem-Solving Strategies Ask students who have solved the Problem of the Day to share how they solved it and any strategies they used.

MENTAL MATH Provide practice for basic addition, subtraction, multiplication, and division facts, emphasizing accuracy and speed. Have students use Number Wheels to show answers.

a. 7 + 6 = (13)	**b.** 11 – 3 = (8)	**c.** 4 × 8 = (32)
d. 72 ÷ 8 = (9)	**e.** 9 + 7 = (16)	**f.** 6 × 7 = (42)
g. 10 – 9 = (1)	**h.** 27 ÷ 3 = (9)	**i.** 6 + 3 = (9)
j. 4 × 6 = (24)	**k.** 16 ÷ 8 = (2)	**l.** 14 – 8 = (6)
m. 0 × 5 = (0)	**n.** 5 – 0 = (5)	**o.** 7 ÷ 7 = (1)

EXPLORE

LESSON 71

Rotation, Reflection, and Translation

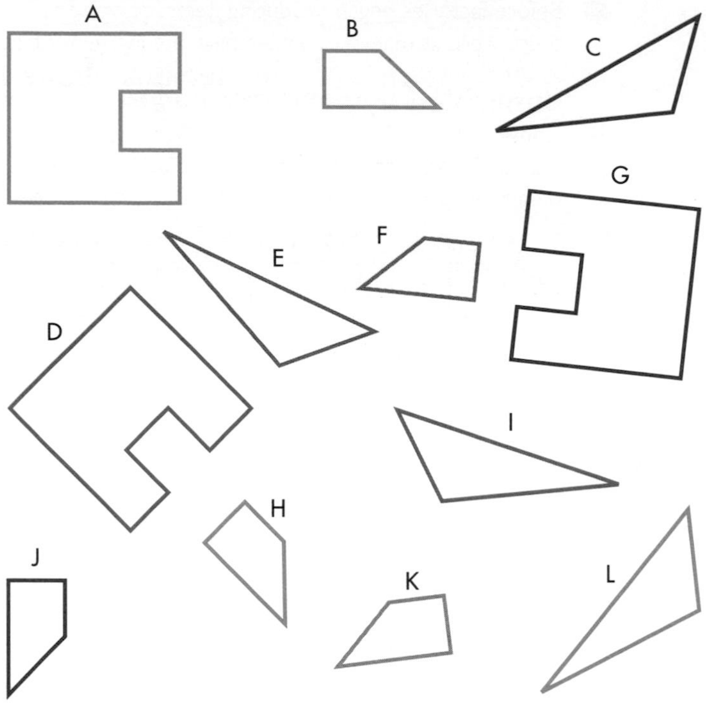

Use tracing paper or waxed paper. Then answer the questions.

1. Trace figures A, B, and C on your paper.
2. List the figures you think are congruent to figure A. **D, G**
3. Slide your paper so that your copy of figure A is directly over each figure you thought was congruent to figure A. Does your figure fit on top of each of them? **yes**

Why teach it at this time?

The study of reflections, rotations, and translations (or flips, turns, and slides) is formally known as transformational geometry. Transformational geometry is a suitable topic of discussion during this sequence of lessons because it directly relates to the concept of congruence.

RETEACHING

No reteaching is suggested at this time. You may wish to assign Enrichment Master 71.

*available separately

When you slide the paper in a straight line without turning it, you make a **translation** of figure A. If you turn the paper, that move is called a **rotation.**

4. Look at figure B.
   - **a.** List the figures you think are congruent to figure B. **F, H, J, K**
   - **b.** Slide your paper (translating and rotating) to see if your tracing fits on top of each figure you thought was congruent to figure B.
   - **c.** Can you make your tracing fit on each of them with only translations and rotations? Why not? **no; some of them are mirror images of figure B**
   - **d.** Can you think of something to do with the tracing to make your copy of figure B fit on the figures that appear to be congruent to it? **Turn over the tracing paper.**

◆ Discuss your idea with classmates.

5. Look at figure C.
   - **a.** List the figures you think are congruent to figure C. **E, I, L**
   - **b.** Can you make your tracing of figure C fit on each of them? **yes**
   - **c.** Did you have to turn the paper over for some of those figures? **yes**

Turning the tracing over makes a figure into a mirror image of itself. This is called a **reflection.** You get the same effect by holding a mirror beside the figure and looking only at the mirror image rather than at the figure.

6. Why did you not have to turn the tracing over to check for congruency with figure A? **The mirror image of figure A is the same as figure A.**

FANTASTIC FACT **Colorado and Wyoming are the only two states that are perfect rectangles.**

PRACTICE p. 71

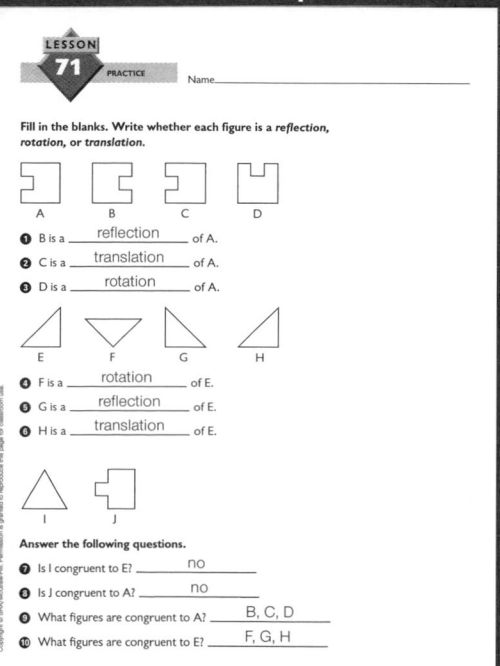

LESSON 71 PRACTICE Name____________

Fill in the blanks. Write whether each figure is a *reflection, rotation, or translation.*

1. B is a reflection of A.
2. C is a translation of A.
3. D is a rotation of A.

4. F is a rotation of E.
5. G is a reflection of E.
6. H is a translation of E.

Answer the following questions.

7. Is I congruent to E? no
8. Is J congruent to A? no
9. What figures are congruent to A? B, C, D
10. What figures are congruent to E? F, G, H

Copyright © SRA/McGraw-Hill. Permission is granted to reproduce this page for classroom use.

Math Explorations and Applications Level 4 • 71

ENRICHMENT p. 71

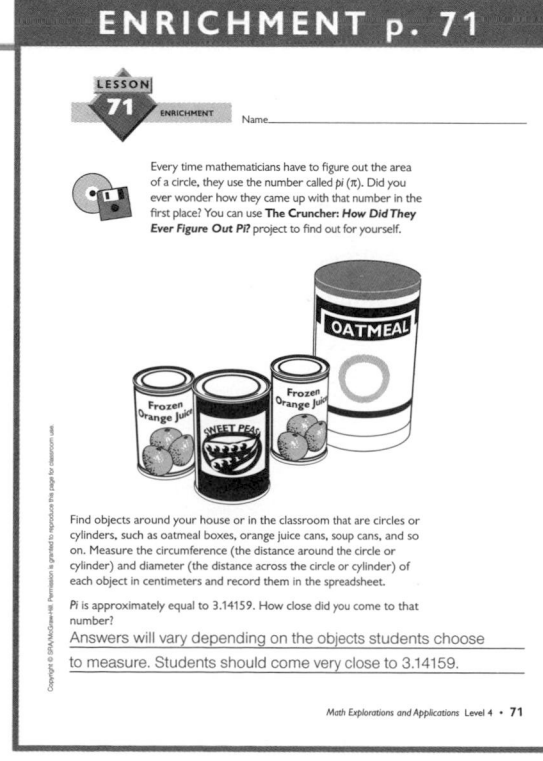

LESSON 71 ENRICHMENT Name____________

Every time mathematicians have to figure out the area of a circle, they use the number called *pi* (π). Did you ever wonder how they came up with that number in the first place? You can use **The Cruncher: *How Did They Ever Figure Out Pi?*** project to find out for yourself.

Find objects around your house or in the classroom that are circles or cylinders, such as oatmeal boxes, orange juice cans, soup cans, and so on. Measure the circumference (the distance around the circle or cylinder) and diameter (the distance across the circle or cylinder) of each object in centimeters and record them in the spreadsheet.

Pi is approximately equal to 3.14159. How close did you come to that number?
Answers will vary depending on the objects students choose to measure. Students should come very close to 3.14159.

Copyright © SRA/McGraw-Hill. Permission is granted to reproduce this page for classroom use.

Math Explorations and Applications Level 4 • 71

2 Teach

Using the Student Pages With an **overhead projector,** demonstrate several problems similar to the ones on these pages before having students complete the lesson on their own. Include at least one example of a translation, a rotation, and a reflection that demonstrates congruence. Also include one or two examples of figures that are not congruent even when they are reflected, rotated, and translated. Have **tracing paper** or waxed paper available.

Note: Slide a figure in the same plane to make a translation. Turn or rotate a figure around a point to make a rotation. Flip a figure over an imaginary line of symmetry to make a reflection.

3 Wrap-Up

5 MINUTES

In Closing Have students demonstrate how to use translation, reflection, and rotation to determine congruence.

ALTERNATIVE ASSESSMENT

Informal Assessment Observe students as they work through this lesson. Have them verbalize their discoveries and demonstrate and explain rotations, translations, and reflections as methods to test for congruence.

Assessment Criteria

Did the student . . .

✓ communicate strategies used to test for congruency using tracing paper?

✓ explain the distinctions among rotation, reflection, and translation?

Homework Assign Practice Master 71 for further practice with rotation, reflection, and translation.

LOOKING AHEAD For the next lesson you will need a variety of objects shaped like prisms, spheres, pyramids, and cylinders.

LESSON 72

Student Edition pages 242–245

Identifying Solid Figures

LESSON PLANNER

Objectives

- ▶ to introduce names and properties of solid objects: prism, cylinder, sphere, and pyramid
- ▶ to have students create two-dimensional patterns (nets) that fold into three-dimensional figures

Context of the Lesson This is the fifth of seven lessons on topics in geometry.

MANIPULATIVES

- acetate (optional)
- clock, analog*
- common objects shaped like prisms, spheres, pyramids, and cylinders
- geometric set*
- overhead projector
- paper, tracing or white
- scissors
- tape
- gift boxes, cardboard toys, and party decorations (optional)
- cardboard boxes (optional)

Program Resources

- Practice Master 72
- Enrichment Master 72
- For extra practice: CD-ROM* Lesson 72

1 Warm-Up

5 MINUTES

Problem of the Day Present the following problem and display an **analog clock*** that students can look at: During a normal school morning, at what times do the clock's hands form a right angle? (Times include 7:56 A.M., 8:28 A.M., 9:00 A.M., 9:33 A.M., 10:06 A.M., 11:11 A.M., and 11:44 A.M.)

Problem-Solving Strategies Ask students who have solved the Problem of the Day to share how they solved it and any strategies they used.

LESSON 72

Identifying Solid Figures

There are mathematical names for many of the objects we see and use in our everyday lives. Four of those names are **sphere, cylinder, pyramid,** and **prism.**

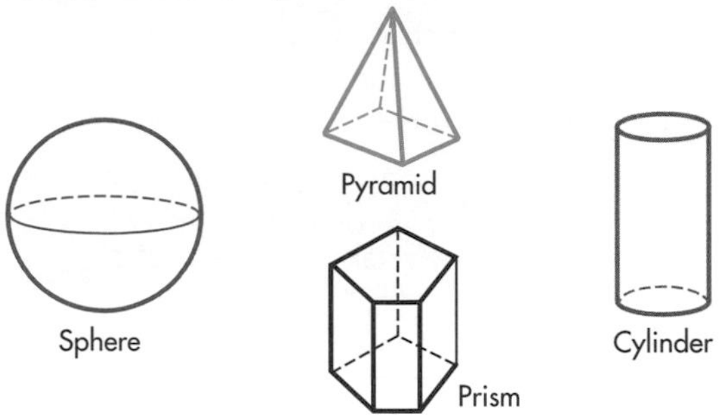

The points on the surface of a **sphere** are all exactly the same distance from a point called the **center** of the sphere. Does that remind you of a circle?

1. Name at least four objects that are like a sphere. Compare your list with your classmates' lists. **a globe, a basketball, an orange**

A **cylinder** is a solid object with two congruent curved bases. We usually think of cylinders as having circles for their bases.

2. Name four objects that are like a cylinder. **a tennis ball container, a can of juice, a glass**

A **pyramid** is a solid object with only one base that is a polygon. The sides of a pyramid are triangles, all of which meet in a point.

3. Try to name four objects that are like a pyramid. **a mountain, the Louvre, pyramids in Egypt**

A **prism** is a solid object with two congruent bases. The sides of a prism are parallelograms.

4. Name four objects that are like a prism. Remember, the bases can be any polygons, such as triangles, squares, rectangles, and so on. **a book, a box, a die**

Technology Connection Refer students to the software *KidCAD* from Davidson (IBM, for grades 3-6) for practice with 3D geometry and architectural design.

*available separately

There are many special kinds of prisms.

5. Does a regular cardboard box have two congruent bases? **yes**

6. Are the sides of a box parallelograms? (Remember that a rectangle is a special kind of parallelogram.) **yes**

7. Is a box a prism? **yes**

8. Look at the room you are in. Is it a prism? **yes**

Sometimes we make solid (or three-dimensional) figures out of flat (or two-dimensional) material. We draw a pattern for the figure on some flat, foldable material like cardboard. Then we cut, fold, and tape the pattern together to make the solid. The pattern is sometimes called a **net.**

9. Look at the following pattern.
   a. Would it make a cube if it were folded along the lines? **yes**
   b. Make a pattern like this one. Cut it out, fold it, and tape it together. Does it make a cube? **yes**

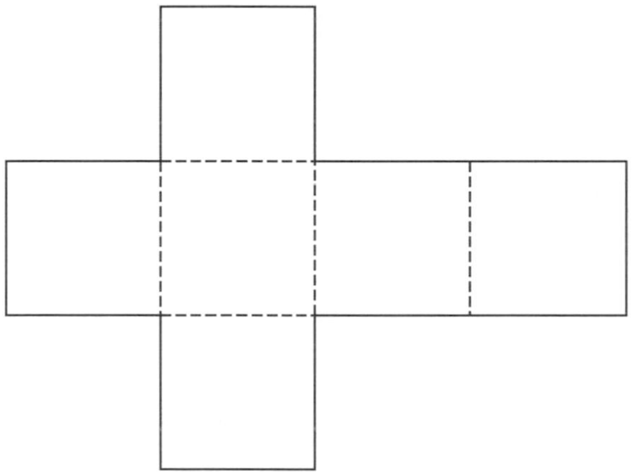

10. Is a cube a prism? **yes**

AT RISK

Meeting Individual Needs

Discuss with students that many everyday objects are manufactured as two-dimensional flat figures designed to be folded into three-dimensional objects. Common examples include **gift boxes**, **cardboard toys**, and **party decorations**. Collect examples of such objects and allow students to fold and form them. Or, gather assorted boxes that students can deconstruct to see their flat net shapes.

MENTAL MATH Provide mixed practice with approximation problems in which answers range from 0 to 999. Have students show thumbs up if the answer is more than 500 and thumbs down if the answer is less than 500. They can stand if the answer is equal to 500.

a. 752 – 444 (thumbs down)
b. 37 × 11 (thumbs down)
c. 4032 – 3087 (thumbs up)
d. 199 + 301 (stand up)
e. 1300 – 482 (thumbs up)
f. 1000 ÷ 2 (stand up)
g. 6 × 52 (thumbs down)
h. 666 – 555 (thumbs down)
i. 99 + 422 (thumbs up)
j. 248 + 842 (thumbs up)

2 Teach

Using the Student Pages Display the assortment of common and **geometric three-dimensional objects*** that you collected. Ask students to find ways to sort the objects and describe the characteristics they observe to do so. For instance, students might group all spheres because they look like balls. List students' examples on the chalkboard. Have students answer problems 1–4 on page 242. Then as you discuss the page with the class, sort or resort objects into groups based on their mathematical properties. Go over the names of each kind of object.

Have students do page 243 independently or in small groups. Provide **paper, scissors,** and **tape** so students can trace, cut, fold, and fasten the net to see what figure it forms. You may want to trace the figures from the student page onto a piece of **acetate** and enlarge them on an **overhead projector.**

Note: Although pyramid-shaped objects are not common, you might obtain models from an upper-grade math or science teacher. Pyramids are often included in sets of polyhedrons used to generate random numbers.

*available separately

◆ LESSON 72 Identifying Solid Figures

Teach

COOPERATIVE LEARNING **Using the Student Pages** Before you begin page 244, you may want to introduce the terms *vertex, edge,* and *face* to help students visualize a cube. Have students work in cooperative groups to complete these pages. You might set aside extra time so that students can explore and experiment more extensively. Make sure that students construct the cube so that the faces are in proper position and edges are aligned.

LEARNING STYLES · MANIPULATIVES

Meeting Individual Needs Although spatial and logical learners may find this lesson well within their grasp, students with other learning styles may have difficulty visualizing the correlations between two-dimensional nets and the three-dimensional figures they form. Provide adequate time for hands-on manipulation. If possible, provide sturdy **cardboard boxes** that students can fold and unfold until they become more familiar with the characteristics of the patterns.

◆ LESSON 72 Identifying Solid Figures

Are there other nets from which you could make a cube?

Consider each net shown here. Decide whether the net would make a cube. Compare your answers with those of your classmates. If you disagree, the person who thinks it is possible should make the net out of paper and try to show that it will make a cube.

11
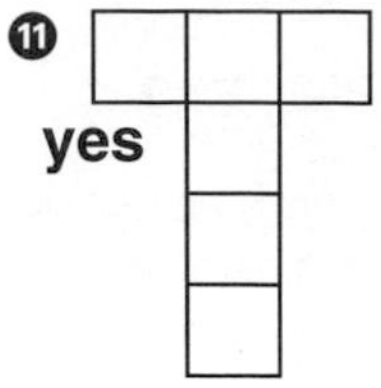

12
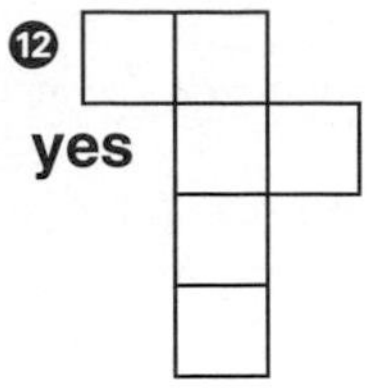

13
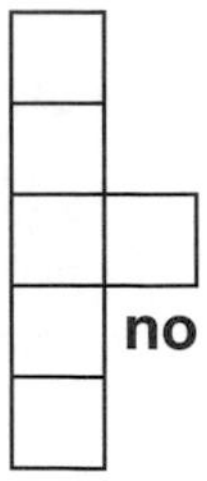

14
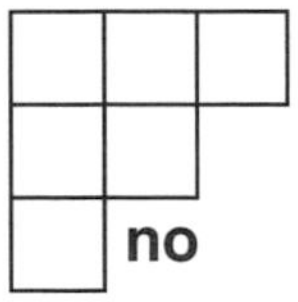

15
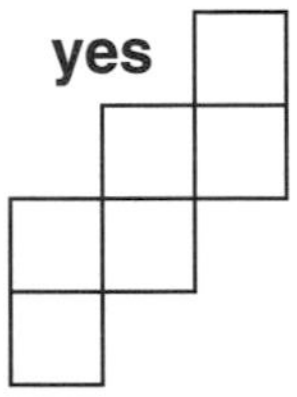

16
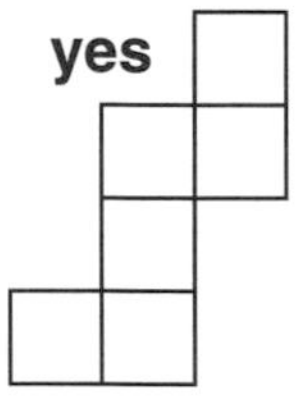

17
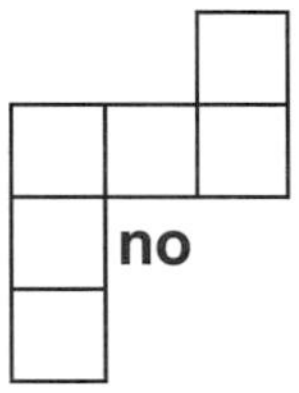

18
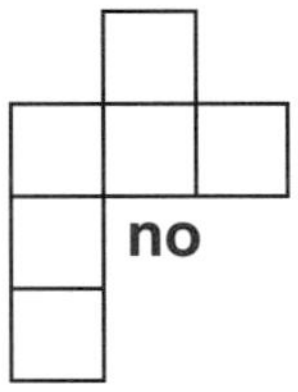

19
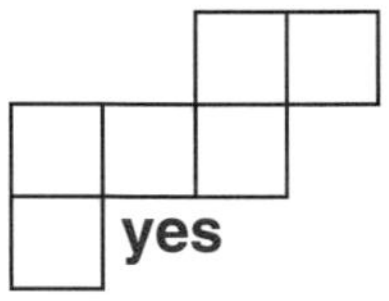

LANGUAGE ARTS CONNECTION

Language Arts Connection Have each student create a logical, orderly set of directions that someone could follow to fold a net into a three-dimensional figure. Have students include a list of necessary materials. Remind them to try out the directions as written to be sure that they are clear and that they present all necessary steps in the proper order.

RETEACHING

Students may benefit from wrapping solid figures with paper and then unfolding the paper so that the nets can be seen.

⑳ What figures do you think you could make from the following nets?

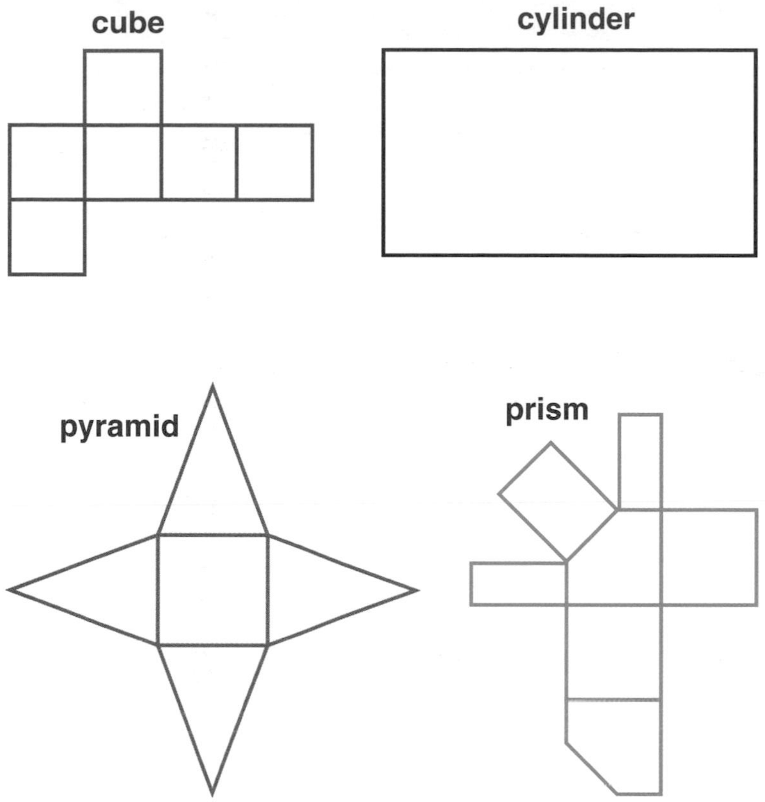

MATH JOURNAL **In your Math Journal design your own nets for figures you would like to make. Then create them.**

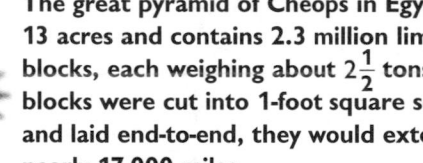

FANTASTIC FACT **The great pyramid of Cheops in Egypt covers 13 acres and contains 2.3 million limestone blocks, each weighing about $2\frac{1}{2}$ tons. If all the blocks were cut into 1-foot square segments and laid end-to-end, they would extend for nearly 17,000 miles.**

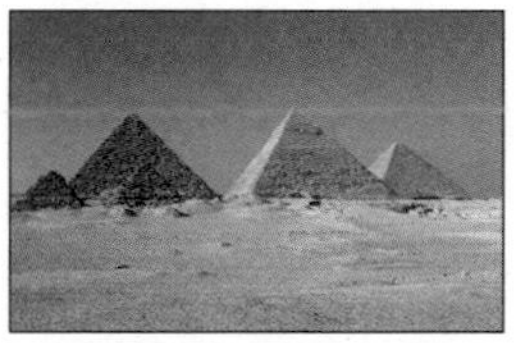

PRACTICE p. 72

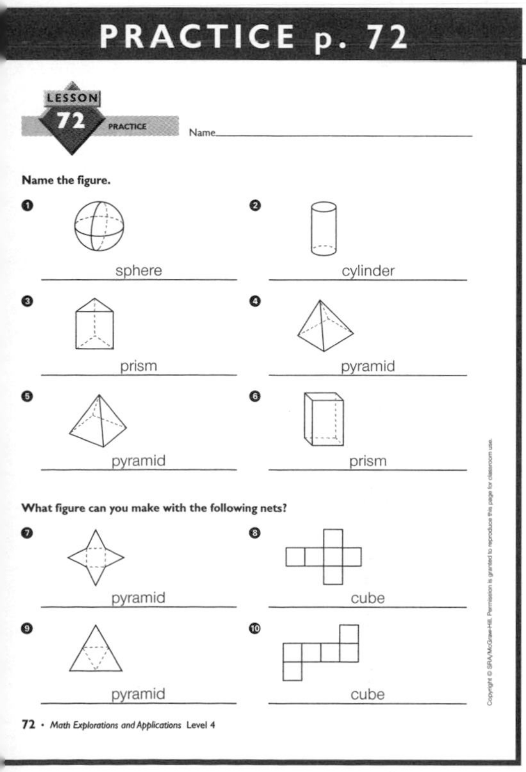

LESSON 72 PRACTICE Name________

Name the figure.

1. sphere
2. cylinder
3. prism
4. pyramid
5. pyramid
6. prism

What figure can you make with the following nets?

7. pyramid
8. cube
9. pyramid
10. cube

72 • *Math Explorations and Applications* Level 4

Copyright © SRA/McGraw-Hill. Permission is granted to reproduce this page for classroom use.

ENRICHMENT p. 72

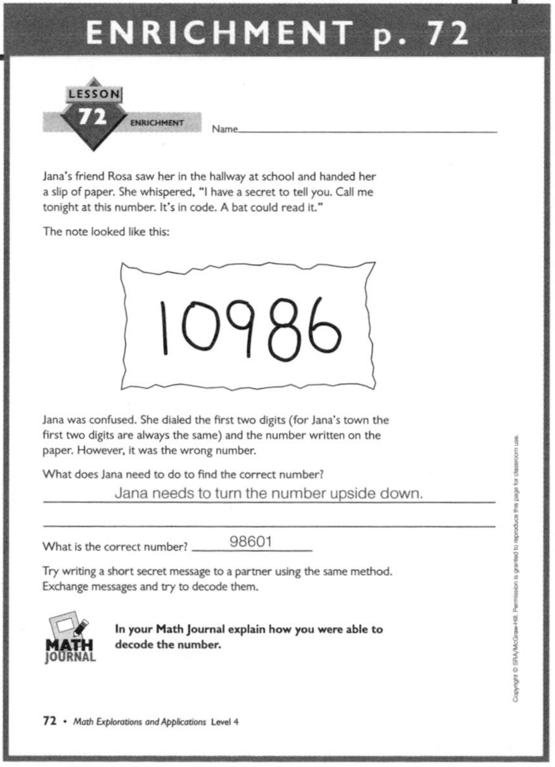

LESSON 72 ENRICHMENT Name________

Jana's friend Rosa saw her in the hallway at school and handed her a slip of paper. She whispered, "I have a secret to tell you. Call me tonight at this number. It's in code. A bat could read it."

The note looked like this:

10986

Jana was confused. She dialed the first two digits (for Jana's town the first two digits are always the same) and the number written on the paper. However, it was the wrong number.

What does Jana need to do to find the correct number? Jana needs to turn the number upside down.

What is the correct number? 98601

Try writing a short secret message to a partner using the same method. Exchange messages and try to decode them.

MATH JOURNAL **In your Math Journal explain how you were able to decode the number.**

72 • *Math Explorations and Applications* Level 4

Copyright © SRA/McGraw-Hill. Permission is granted to reproduce this page for classroom use.

③ Wrap-Up (5 MINUTES)

In Closing Have students identify the properties of a sphere, cylinder, pyramid, and prism and give examples of each.

ALTERNATIVE ASSESSMENT **Portfolio Assessment** Have students explain how they visualize a two-dimensional net to figure out what three-dimensional shape it folds into. Encourage them to describe any clues or techniques they use. Ask them to include a self-evaluation statement assessing this task as easy, medium, or difficult for them, and have them include their pieces in their Math Portfolios as a record of ongoing learning.

Assessment Criteria

Did the student . . .

✓ contribute to the discussion and identification of solid objects?

✓ demonstrate understanding of the mathematical properties of solid objects?

✓ communicate strategies used to analyze nets?

Homework Have students look around their homes for examples of the **solid objects** they explored in this lesson. Compile a class list of objects, and set aside a special area in the classroom in which to display examples of various objects. Invite students to add to the display as they find objects, or pictures of them, that they can bring to class.

LESSON 73

Student Edition pages 246–249

Lines of Symmetry

LESSON PLANNER

Objectives

- to provide experience in finding lines of symmetry
- to teach or review the properties and names of some common polygons
- to demonstrate a relationship between geometry and fractions: how parallel lines that are the same distance apart can be used to divide a line segment into equal parts

Context of the Lesson This is the sixth of seven lessons on topics in geometry. Students have worked with lines of symmetry in previous levels of *Math Explorations and Applications.*

MANIPULATIVES

analog clock*
crayons
paper
pattern blocks
scissors
rulers* or straightedges
tracing paper
graph paper (optional)
mirror (optional)

Program Resources

Practice Master 73
Enrichment Master 73
For extra practice:
CD-ROM* Lesson 73
Cumulative Review, page 550

Note: This lesson may take more than one day.

PRACTICE

LESSON 73

Lines of Symmetry

You can easily make a square out of a rectangular piece of paper. Just fold it diagonally, matching the edge of the short side to the edge of the long side, and cut off the leftover part. Unfold the paper, and you have a square!

A **line of symmetry** in a figure cuts the figure into two parts that are mirror images of each other. That is, the line of symmetry will form two congruent parts.

If you fold a figure on a line of symmetry, the two sides will fall exactly on top of each other.

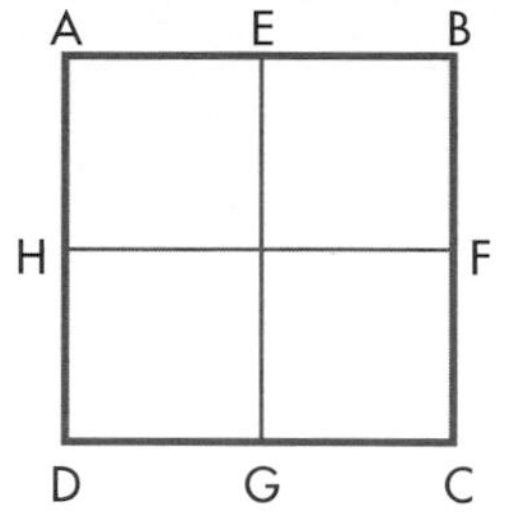

- In the heart-shaped figure, is the dashed line a line of symmetry? **yes**
- *HF* is a line of symmetry. Fold a square along a line like *HF*. Do the two sides fall exactly on top of each other? **yes**
- Find another line of symmetry in your square. Is there a line like it in the square above? **See margin.**
- Try to find two more lines of symmetry in your square. Fold to make sure they are lines of symmetry. **See margin.**
- Are there any more lines of symmetry in your square? Check any line you think might be a line of symmetry by folding along it. **no**
- How many lines of symmetry are there in your square? **4**
- How many lines of symmetry do you think there are in other squares? **4**

1 Warm-Up

5 MINUTES

Problem of the Day Students may use an **analog clock*** to solve the following problem: Between 8:00 A.M. and 4:00 P.M., at about what times do the clock hands form straight line segments? (8:10 A.M., 9:15 A.M., 10:20 A.M., 11:25 A.M., 12:30 P.M., 1:38 P.M., 2:44 P.M., 3:49 P.M.)

Problem-Solving Strategies Ask students who have solved the Problem of the Day to share how they solved it and any strategies they used.

COOPERATIVE LEARNING

This lesson is well-suited to small-group learning. Students can help each other trace and match figures, compare and discuss their findings regarding lines of symmetry, and divide a line segment using parallel lines. For instance, one student can hold the **tracing paper** steady while a partner marks the intersections.

*available separately

Trace the figures. Then find out how many lines of symmetry there are in each. Watch your numbering.

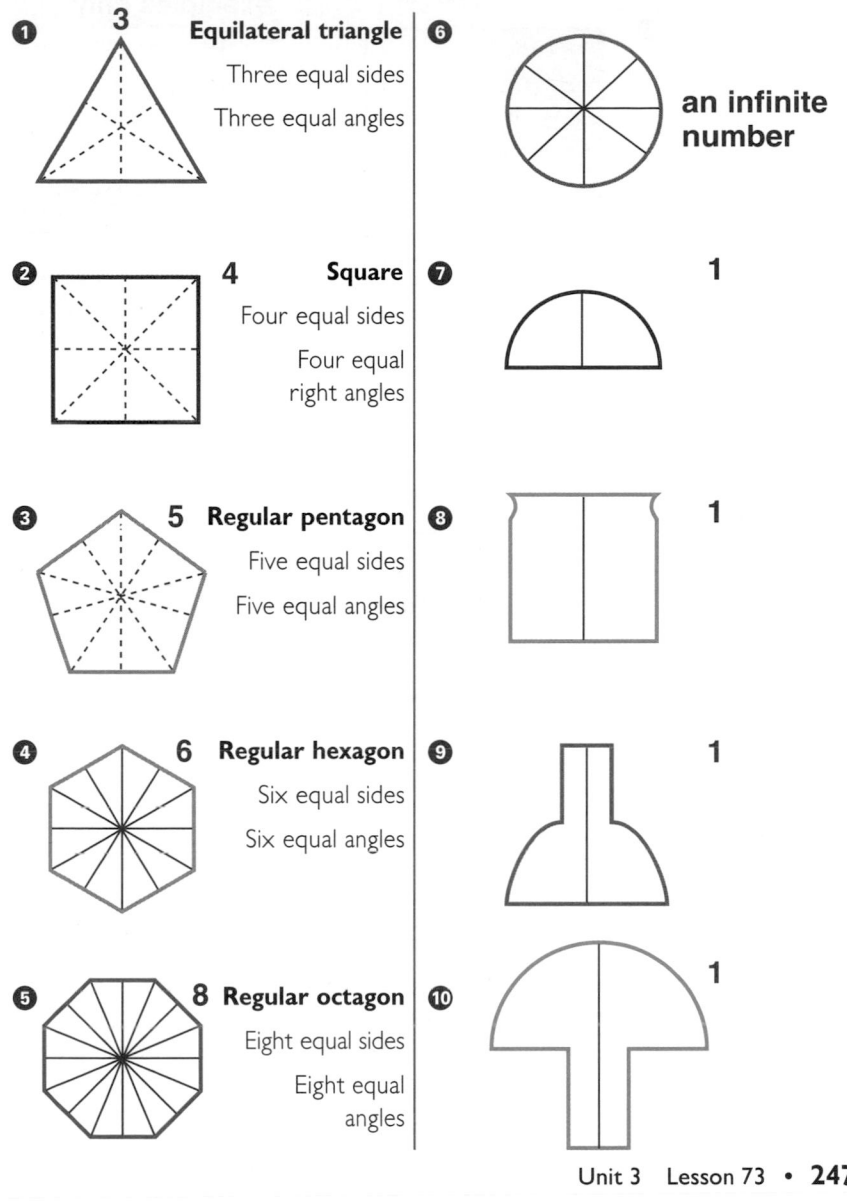

1 3 **Equilateral triangle**
Three equal sides
Three equal angles

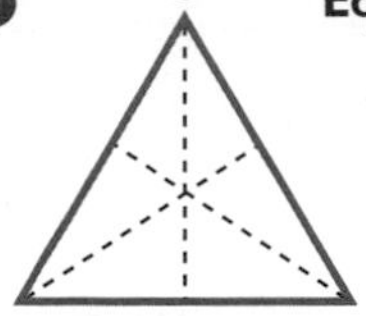

2 4 **Square**
Four equal sides
Four equal right angles

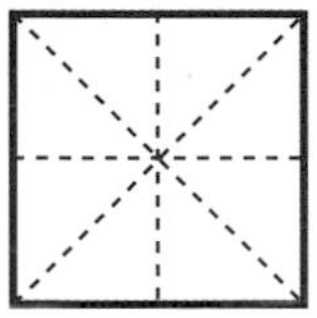

3 5 **Regular pentagon**
Five equal sides
Five equal angles

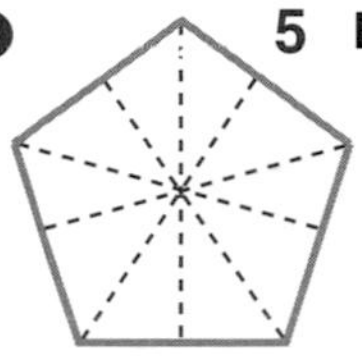

4 6 **Regular hexagon**
Six equal sides
Six equal angles

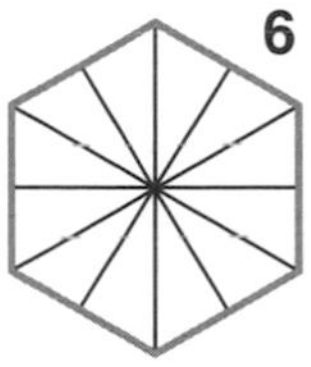

5 8 **Regular octagon**
Eight equal sides
Eight equal angles

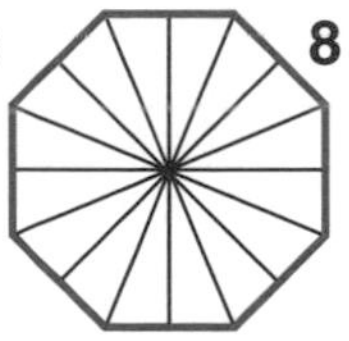

6 an infinite number

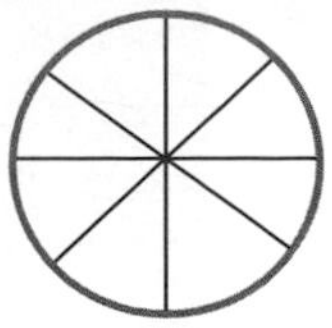

7 1

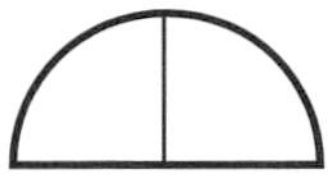

8 1

9 1

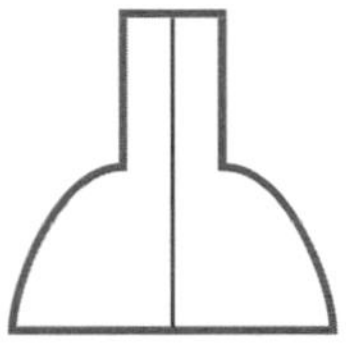

10 1

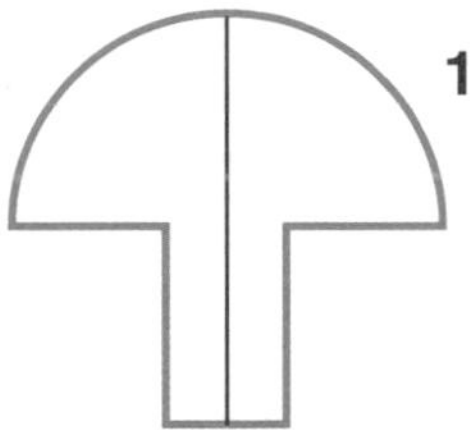

CULTURAL DIVERSITY Symmetry is a common element in many designs that appear in Islamic art. Display examples of tile work, rugs, mosaics, or architecture, and have students identify the lines of symmetry they see.

Art Connection

Encourage students to create their own symmetrical designs on **graph paper.** They can color in boxes around one or more lines of symmetry to create an original symmetrical pattern or figure. Display the finished products in the classroom.

MENTAL MATH Provide practice with approximation problems, but extend the number range from 500 to 1000. Have students show "thumbs up" if the answer is more than 1000 and "thumbs down" if the answer is less than 1000. They should stand up if the answer is equal to 1000.

a.	50 × 200 (thumbs up)	**b.**	8300 – 8000 (thumbs down)
c.	60 × 80 (thumbs up)	**d.**	6000 ÷ 5 (thumbs up)
e.	60 × 5 (thumbs down)	**f.**	780 + 25 (thumbs down)
g.	50 × 20 (stand up)	**h.**	540 + 450 (thumbs down)
i.	980 + 90 (thumbs up)	**j.**	990 – 90 (thumbs down)

2 Teach

Using the Student Pages Have students use the squares they make to answer the discussion questions about lines of symmetry in squares. Explain to students how to use two letters (such as *AB*) to name a line or line segment. Then go over the problems on page 246 with the class. Explain that when something is folded so that its two halves match exactly, the crease is a line of symmetry.

Answers to Discussion Questions (page 246):

Third Question. For those students who find a line of symmetry like EG, the answer is yes; for those who choose a diagonal, the answer is no.

Fourth Question. The four lines of symmetry in the square on student page 246 are HF, EG, AC, and BD.

For page 247, students may cut out their tracings of the figures to check for lines of symmetry. Discuss answers with the class and have students check for symmetry by folding. Students may notice that for regular polygons the number of lines of symmetry is equal to the number of sides.

◆ LESSON 73 Lines of Symmetry

Teach

Using the Student Pages Have students work independently on page 248. Students can draw any line of symmetry (see answers for page 247) and then shade half the figure. There is only one line of symmetry for the isosceles triangle and for figure 14.

Answers for problem 15 will vary. Possible answers for figures 13 and 14 might look like this:

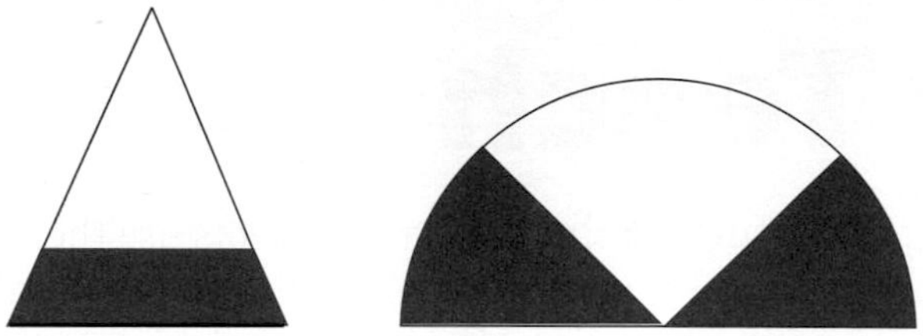

Before beginning page 249, tell students that they are going to learn how to use parallel lines to divide a line segment into several equal parts. Have them trace the segment very carefully using their **rulers*** or **straightedges.** While they follow the procedure on page 249, check around the room; you may need to help students place the traced segment correctly. You may also need to help students hold the **tracing paper** steady while they mark the intersections. With care, students should be able to divide the 12-centimeter line segment into six 2-centimeter parts.

◆ LESSON 73 Lines of Symmetry

Trace the figures. Divide each figure into halves, using a line of symmetry. Shade $\frac{1}{2}$ of each figure. **Answers shown are examples only.**

11

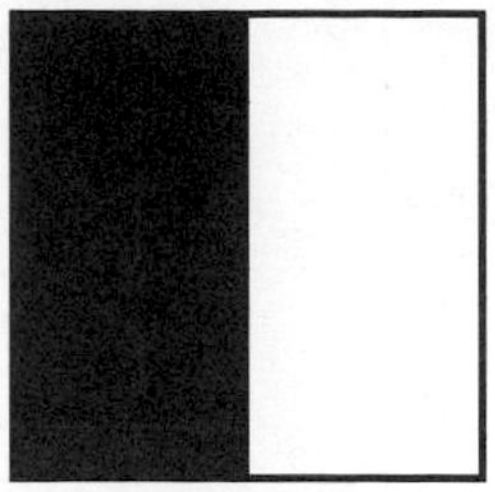

Square

12

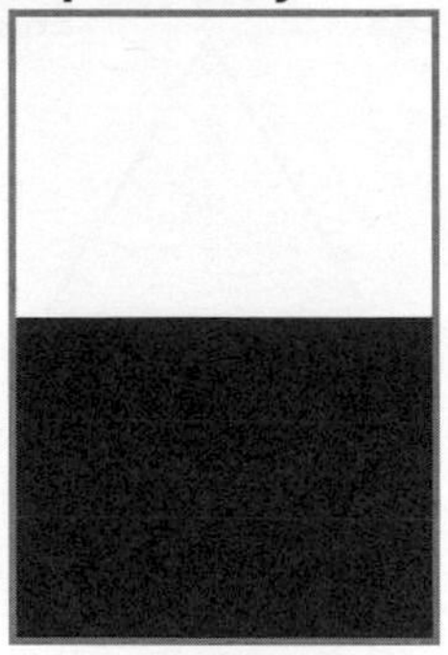

Rectangle

13

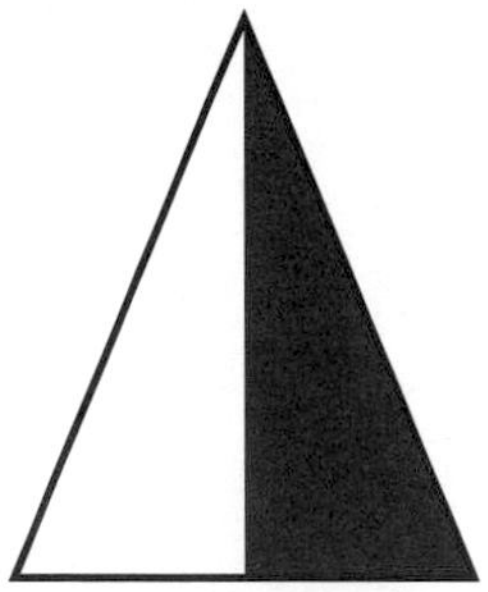

Isosceles triangle

Two equal sides

Two equal angles

14

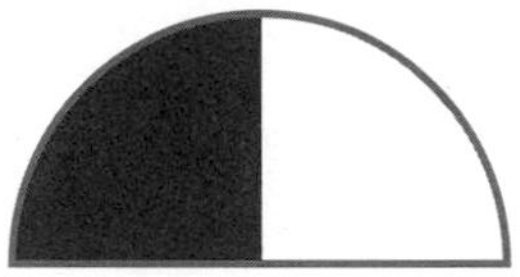

Semicircle

15 Trace each figure again. Try to shade $\frac{1}{2}$ the area of each figure in such a way that there is not a line of symmetry between the shaded and the unshaded parts. (This is hard for figures 13 and 14. Do the best you can.) **Answers will vary. Check to be sure that the students have divided each figure into precise halves.**

MATH JOURNAL

In your Math Journal explain how you can find a line of symmetry without folding a figure.

Literature Connection Invite students to read *Rechenka's Eggs* by Patricia Polacco. Have them find examples of symmetry and parallel lines in the design of Rechenka's eggs.

RETEACHING

Demonstrate two ways to check for symmetry. Fold a figure along the line being checked. If the parts match, then the line is a line of symmetry. Or, place a **mirror** along the line. If the reflection is such that the half of the figure showing together with its reflection looks like the entire original figure, then the line is a line of symmetry.

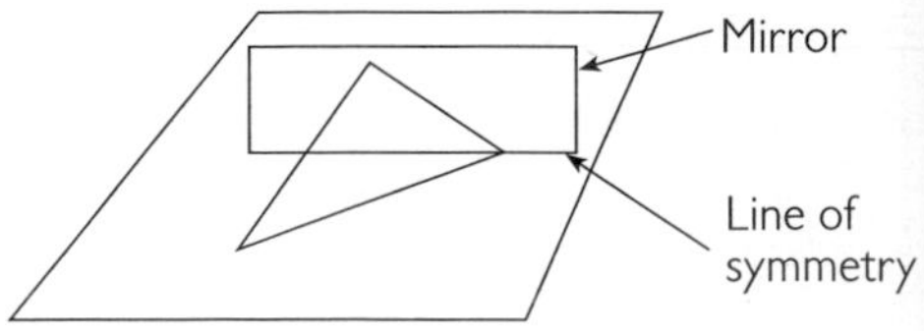

*available separately

Parallel lines can be used to divide line segments into equal parts.

The seven lines above are parallel, so the distances between them are the same.

Copy the line segment below on a sheet of tracing paper.

Place your paper with the line segment over the seven parallel lines at the top of this page. Move the paper so that one end of the line segment just touches the top line and the other just touches the bottom line.

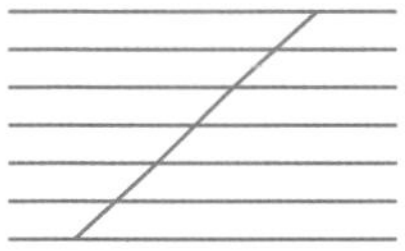

Mark the points where the line segment crosses each of the parallel lines.

- Into how many parts has your line segment been divided? **6**
- Do the parts seem about equal in length? **yes**
- Is each part $\frac{1}{6}$ of the length of the segment? **yes**
- How many centimeters long is the segment? **12**
- How many centimeters long is each small part of the segment? **2**
- What is $\frac{1}{6}$ of 12? **2**

Copy the line segment again. Divide the segment into four equal parts by placing it across five of the parallel lines.

- Measure to find how many centimeters there are in $\frac{1}{4}$ of the segment. **3**
- What is $\frac{1}{4}$ of 12? **3**

Use the Cumulative Review on page 550 after this lesson.

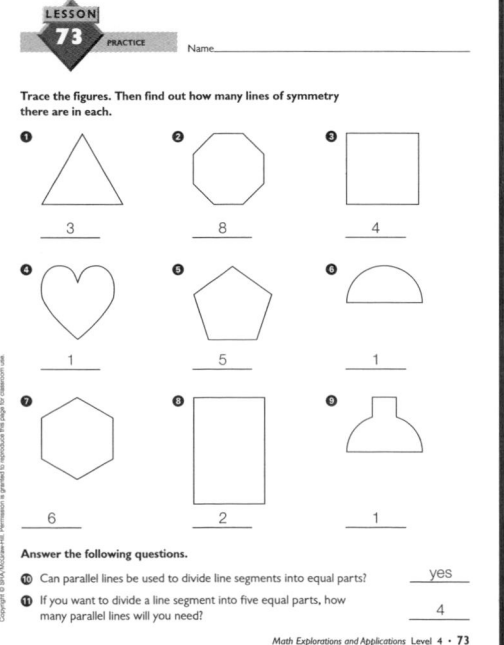

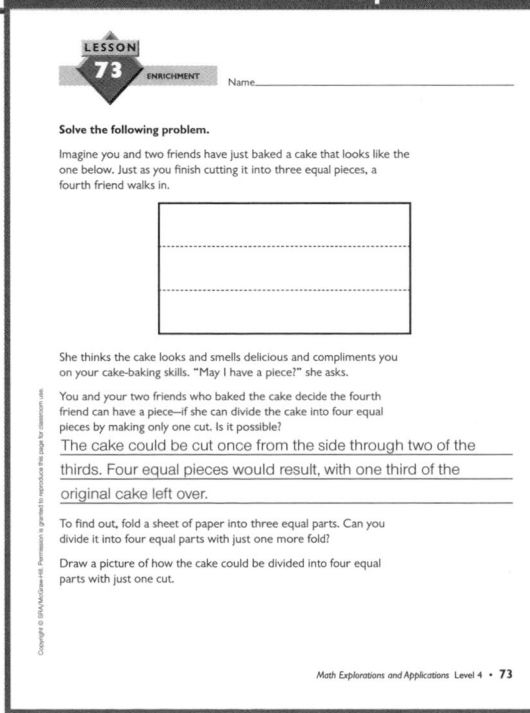

❸ Wrap-Up

5 MINUTES

In Closing Have students define *line of symmetry.* Also have them explain how to use parallel lines to divide a line segment into equal parts.

ALTERNATIVE ASSESSMENT

Informal Assessment Circulate around the room to observe students as they work. Ask individuals to explain what they are doing and to demonstrate their understanding of lines of symmetry.

Assessment Criteria

Did the student . . .

- ✓ contribute to the discussion about symmetry?
- ✓ demonstrate understanding of symmetry by folding and tracing?
- ✓ identify the lines of symmetry in various geometric figures?
- ✓ communicate understanding of the relationship between fractions and geometry?

Homework Have students use pattern blocks to create a design that has two lines of symmetry.

PRACTICE p. 73

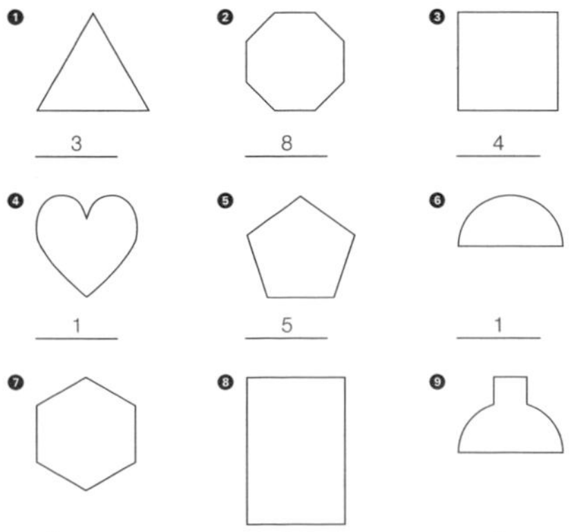
LESSON 73 PRACTICE Name________

Trace the figures. Then find out how many lines of symmetry there are in each.

1. 3
2. 8
3. 4
4. 1
5. 5
6. 1
7. 6
8. 2
9. 1

Answer the following questions.

10. Can parallel lines be used to divide line segments into equal parts? yes
11. If you want to divide a line segment into five equal parts, how many parallel lines will you need? 4

Copyright © SRA/McGraw-Hill. Permission is granted to reproduce this page for classroom use.

Math Explorations and Applications Level 4 • 73

ENRICHMENT p. 73

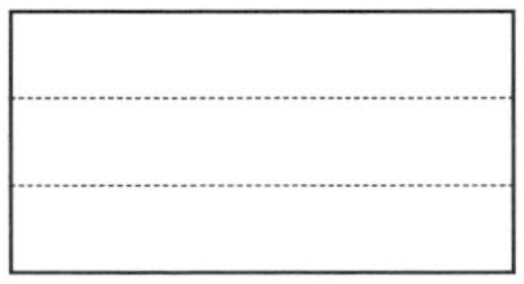
LESSON 73 ENRICHMENT Name________

Solve the following problem.

Imagine you and two friends have just baked a cake that looks like the one below. Just as you finish cutting it into three equal pieces, a fourth friend walks in.

She thinks the cake looks and smells delicious and compliments you on your cake-baking skills. "May I have a piece?" she asks.

You and your two friends who baked the cake decide the fourth friend can have a piece—if she can divide the cake into four equal pieces by making only one cut. Is it possible?

The cake could be cut once from the side through two of the thirds. Four equal pieces would result, with one third of the original cake left over.

To find out, fold a sheet of paper into three equal parts. Can you divide it into four equal parts with just one more fold?

Draw a picture of how the cake could be divided into four equal parts with just one cut.

Copyright © SRA/McGraw-Hill. Permission is granted to reproduce this page for classroom use.

Math Explorations and Applications Level 4 • 73

LESSON 74

Student Edition pages 250–251

Area and Perimeter: Practice

LESSON PLANNER

Objectives

- to demonstrate that the ratio of perimeters of similar figures is the same as the ratio of any of their corresponding lengths
- to demonstrate that the ratio of areas of similar figures is the square of the ratio of any of their corresponding lengths

Context of the Lesson This is the last lesson of this unit. The next lesson begins the end-of-unit sequence of review, practice, and testing.

MANIPULATIVES

none

Program Resources

Practice Master 74

Enrichment Master 74

For extra practice:
CD-ROM* Lesson 74

1 Warm-Up

5 MINUTES

Problem of the Day Present the following problem. Tell students that there are several possible answers: Think of three words that have a horizontal line of symmetry if you print them in uppercase letters. Think of two words that have a vertical line of symmetry if you print them in uppercase letters. (Answers include HOOK, DID, BOB; WOW, TOT.)

Problem-Solving Strategies Ask students who have solved the Problem of the Day to share how they solved it and any strategies they used.

MENTAL MATH Provide fast-paced drill on multiplication facts.
.

a.	4 x 4 = (16)	**b.**	7 x 9 = (63)
c.	8 x 8 = (64)	**d.**	9 x 4 = (36)
e.	8 x 7 = (56)	**f.**	6 x 8 = (48)
g.	6 x 6 = (36)	**h.**	4 x 6 = (24)
i.	7 x 7 = (49)	**j.**	9 x 6 = (54)
k.	4 x 8 = (32)	**l.**	9 x 9 = (81)
m.	7 x 4 = (28)	**n.**	5 x 0 = (0)
o.	6 x 7 = (42)	**p.**	9 x 3 = (27)

MIXED PRACTICE

LESSON 74

Area and Perimeter: Practice

Review what you know about area and perimeter by answering the following questions.

1. Look at the rectangles shown here.
   a. Which ones seem similar to each other? **A, D and E**
   b. How did you decide? **Two rectangles are similar if their corresponding sides are proportional.**

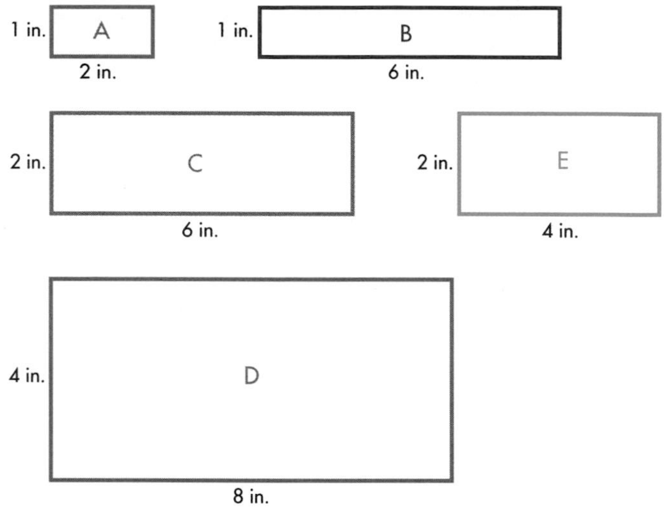

2. You know that to find the perimeter of, or distance around, a polygon, you add the lengths of all the sides. How do you find the area of a rectangle?
   Multiply the length by the width.

Let's look at Rick's garden. It's shaped like a rectangle. The short side measures 3 meters. The long side measures 7 meters.

3. What is the perimeter? **20 m**
4. What is the area? **21 square m**

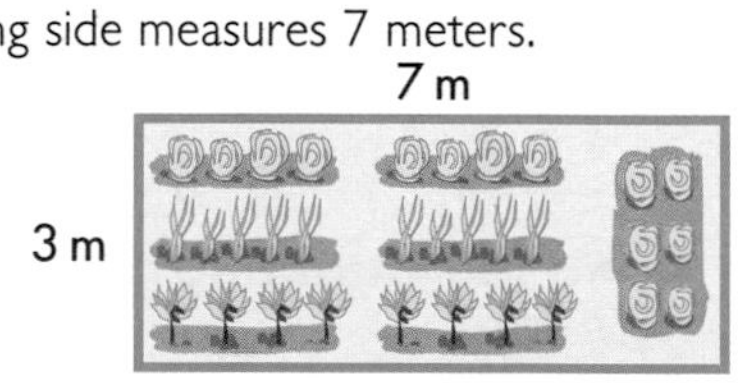

RETEACHING

No reteaching strategy is suggested at this time. You may wish to assign Enrichment Master 74.

*available separately

❺ Find the perimeter and the area for each of the three similar rectangles on page 250. Then make a chart like the following. Fill in the missing numbers.

Rectangle	Length of Short Side (in inches)	Perimeter (in inches)	Area (in square inches)
A	1	**6**	**2**
B	**1**	**14**	**6**
C	**2**	**16**	**12**
D	**4**	**24**	**32**
E	**2**	**12**	**8**

Answer the following questions.

❻ Examine your chart.

a. For the similar rectangles, if you double the length of a side, what happens to the perimeter? **It is doubled.**

b. Is that what you would expect? **yes**

❼ As you double the length of a side in similar rectangles, what happens to the area? **It is multiplied by 4.**

❽ If you triple the length of a side,

a. What happens to the perimeter? **It is tripled.**

b. What happens to the area? **It is multiplied by 9.**

❾ If you multiply the length of a side by 4,

a. What happens to the perimeter? **It is multiplied by 4.**

b. What happens to the area? **It is multiplied by 16.**

❿ Another rectangle is similar to rectangle A, but its short side is 5 inches long.

a. What would be its perimeter? **30 inches**

b. What would be its area? **50 square inches**

❷ Teach

COOPERATIVE LEARNING **Using the Student Pages** Have students work in small groups to discuss and analyze the figures on page 250 and to complete the chart and answer the questions on page 251. Encourage groups to try to formulate general rules about the areas and perimeters of similar figures. Such statements should convey the basic messages stated in the lesson objectives. If students have trouble with the problems on page 251, have them use numerical examples to answer the questions.

❸ Wrap-Up

5 MINUTES

In Closing Ask representatives of the groups to state their general rules about the relationship between the perimeter and area of similar figures.

ALTERNATIVE ASSESSMENT

Informal Assessment Have students explain in their own words general rules that relate the perimeter and area of similar figures to the ratio of corresponding lengths.

Assessment Criteria

Did the student . . .

✓ contribute to the discussion of the perimeters and areas of similar figures?

✓ communicate the reasoning used to determine rules about the ratio of areas and perimeters in similar figures?

✓ produce two correct and comprehensible rules that relate ratios of perimeters and areas to ratios of corresponding lengths in similar figures?

Homework Assign Practice Master 74 for further practice with area and perimeter.

PRACTICE p. 74

LESSON 74 PRACTICE

Name________________

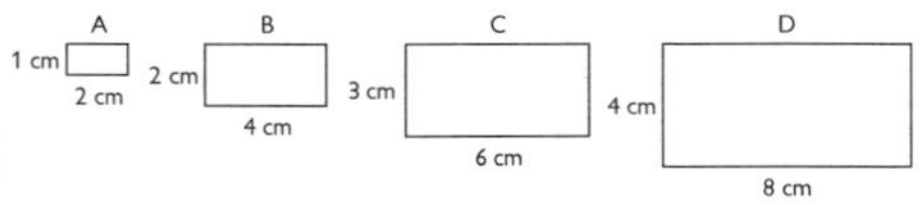

Consider the similar rectangles above. Complete the chart.

Rectangle	Perimeter	Area
A	❶ 6 cm	❷ 2 sq cm
B	❸ 12 cm	❹ 8 sq cm
C	❺ 18 cm	❻ 18 sq cm
D	❼ 24 cm	❽ 32 sq cm

Use your chart to answer the questions below.

❾ As you double the length of the sides, what happens to the perimeter? doubles

❿ As you double the length of the sides, what happens to the area? increases by factor of 4 (2 × 2)

⓫ As you triple the length of the sides, what happens to the perimeter? triples

⓬ As you triple the length of the sides, what happens to the area? increases by factor of 9 (3 × 3)

⓭ As you multiply the length of the sides by 4, what happens to the perimeter? increases by factor of 4

⓮ As you multiply the length of the sides by 4, what happens to the area? increases by factor of 16 (4 × 4)

Copyright © SRA/McGraw-Hill. Permission is granted to reproduce this page for classroom use.

74 • *Math Explorations and Applications* Level 4

ENRICHMENT p. 74

LESSON 74 ENRICHMENT

Name________________

Pick a number—12, 15, 18, 24, or 30. Use the dot paper below to make as many different shapes as you can that have the area of the number you picked. Drawings will vary depending on the shapes students choose to draw.

Copyright © SRA/McGraw-Hill. Permission is granted to reproduce this page for classroom use.

74 • *Math Explorations and Applications* Level 4

LESSON 75

Student Edition pages 252–253

Unit 3 Review

Using the Student Pages Use this Unit 3 Review as a preliminary unit test to indicate areas in which each student is having difficulty or in which the entire class may need help. If students do well on the Unit 3 Review, you may wish to skip directly to the next unit. If not, you may spend a day or so helping students overcome their individual difficulties before they take the Unit Test.

Next to each set of problems is a list of the lessons in the unit covered in those problems. Students can refer to a specific lesson for additional instruction if they need help. You can also use this information to make additional assignments based on the previous lesson concepts.

Problems 1–6 If students miss more than one of these naming-coordinates problems, check to see whether there is a pattern to the errors. Try to correct consistent errors with an appropriate reteaching strategy.

Problems 7–12 If students miss more than one of these arrow arithmetic problems, try to establish the source of the problem. Determine whether the problem is with the basic facts or with arrow notation itself and reteach as necessary.

GAME **Problems 13–15** To help students who miss one of these problems, check to see that they know they are looking for a rule that will change the first number into the second. The same rule must work for all pairs. For more practice, suggest the "Function" game on page 194, which provides practice with mental arithmetic and mathematical reasoning, or the "Snake" Game Mat, which reinforces the skills of solving missing-term problems and mental arithmetic.

Problems 16–18 If students miss one or more of these function chart and graph problems, try to establish why. Determine whether the problem is with basic facts or with confusion over graphing ordered pairs on the x and y axes. Reteach as necessary.

LESSON 75

Unit 3 Review

Lessons 51, 52

Look at the graph. Name the coordinates of these points.

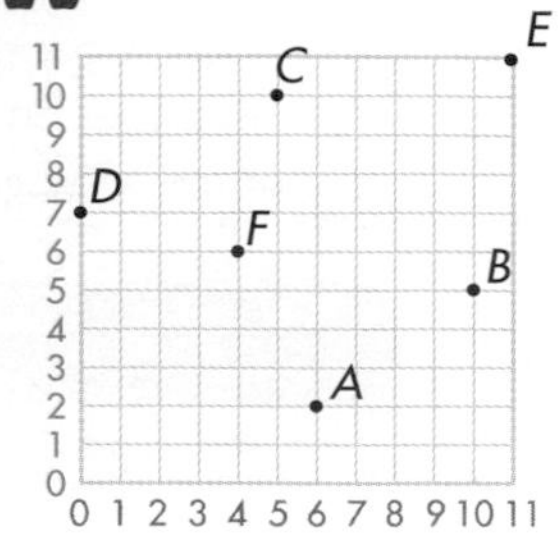

1. A **(6, 2)**
2. B **(10, 5)**
3. C **(5, 10)**
4. D **(0, 7)**
5. E **(11, 11)**
6. F **(4, 6)**

Lessons 53, 54

Find the value of x or y.

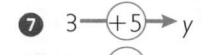

7. 3 —(+5)→ y **8**
8. 12 —(−5)→ n **7** —(×3)→ y **21**
9. 8 —(−2)→ y **6**
10. 4 —(÷2)→ n **2** —(+9)→ y **11**
11. x —(×6)→ 42 **7**
12. x **32** —(÷4)→ n **8** —(−6)→ 2

Lessons 53–56

What is a possible function rule for each of these?

13. x —(?)→ y **+6**

x	y
7	13
10	16
24	30
0	6

14. x —(?)→ y **÷3**

x	y
15	5
12	4
30	10
3	1

15. x —(?)→ y **×9**

x	y
3	27
5	45
1	9
8	72

Lessons 56, 58–59

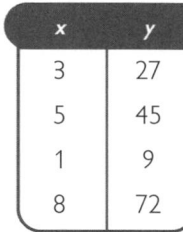

Use a computer to copy and complete these charts. Then graph each set of ordered pairs. Make sure your graph will fit on your paper.

16. x —(×3)→ y

x	y
6	18
9	27
5	**15**
4	12

17. x —(÷4)→ y

x	y
28	**7**
12	**3**
20	5
16	**4**

18. x —(+10)→ y

x	y
25	**35**
5	15
7	**17**
12	**22**

RETEACHING

Students who have difficulty with this Unit Practice should have further opportunity to review and to practice the skills before they proceed on with the next unit. For each set of problems there are specific suggestions for reteaching. These suggestions can be found in the margins.

Lesson 70 ⑲ Which of the following figures are congruent to figure A? **B**

Solve these problems.

Lesson 63

⑳ Habib saves $3 a week. How long will it take him to save $24? **8 weeks**

㉑ Heather lives 2 kilometers from her school. Laura lives 1 kilometer from the school. How far does Laura live from Heather? **can't tell**

㉒ Steve's tenth birthday was in 1996. In what year was his second birthday? **1988**

Lesson 68 ㉓ Identify these parts of a line.

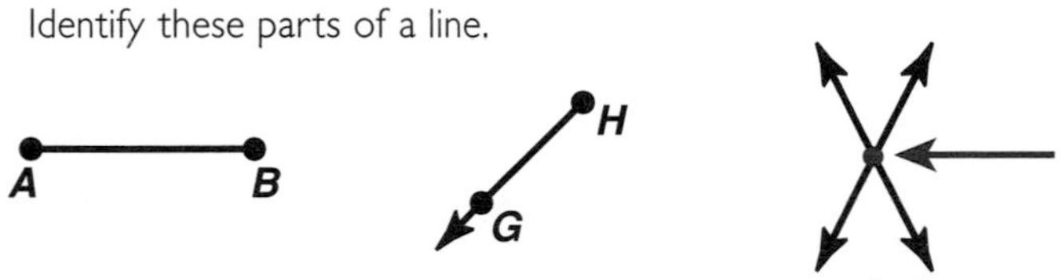

segment **ray** **point**

Lesson 69 **For each pair of lines, tell whether the lines are *parallel*, *perpendicular*, or *neither*.**

㉔ **neither** ㉕ **perpendicular** ㉖ **parallel**

Lesson 73 **How many lines of symmetry can be drawn in each figure?**

㉗ **1** ㉘ **6** ㉙ **1**

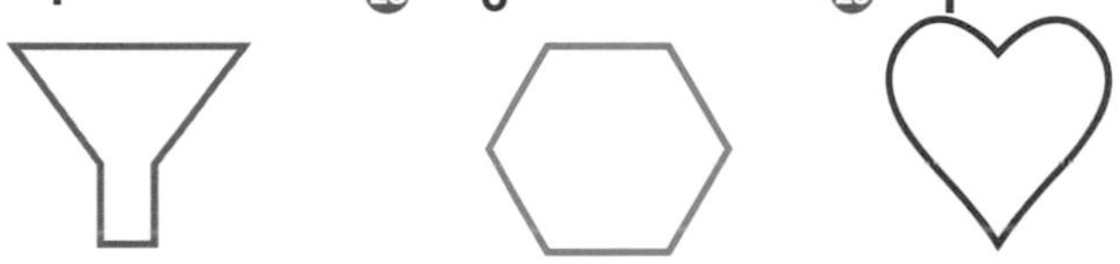

Lesson 74 ㉚ Find the perimeter and area of a rectangle with a long side that measures 8 meters and a short side that measures 3 meters.
perimeter = 22 m; area = 24 square m

Problem 19 For students who have problems distinguishing congruent figures, refer to Lesson 70 for reteaching.

Problems 20–22 For students who miss more than one of these problems, reteach as necessary. Determine whether students have difficulty with the basic arithmetic facts or reading the problems. Allow students to use drawings to help solve the problems.

Problems 23–30 Students who miss more than one of these problems about identifying parts of a line, recognizing parallel and perpendicular lines, finding lines of symmetry, and finding area and perimeter should be assessed individually. Check to see that they know the definitions of the terms. Use examples when explaining to these students.

ALTERNATIVE ASSESSMENT

Portfolio Assessment If you have not already completed the Portfolio Assessment task provided on Assessment Blackline Masters page 95, it can be used at this time to evaluate students' proficiency with using geometric transformations and graphing.

ALTERNATIVE ASSESSMENT

Performance Assessment Performance Assessment Task 2, provided on Assessment Blackline Masters pages 77–78, can be used at this time to evaluate students' proficiency with geometry. You may want to administer this assessment to individual students or small groups of students.

Unit Project If you have not already assigned the "Mathematics and Postage Stamps" project on pages 264 and 265, you may want to do so at this time. This project is a good opportunity for students to explore the hobby of stamp collecting, which can relate to geography, history, mathematics, and art.

PRACTICE p. 75

LESSON 75 PRACTICE Name________

Look at the graph. What are the coordinates of these points?

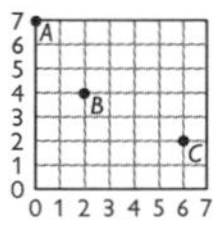

❶ A (0, 7)
❷ B (2, 4)
❸ C (6, 2)

Find the value of *x* or *y*.

❹ $x \rightarrow (+7) \rightarrow 15$ $x =$ 8

❺ $14 \rightarrow (-6) \rightarrow n \rightarrow (\times 3) \rightarrow y$ $y =$ 24

Solve for *n*.

❻ $56 \div n = 7$ 8   ❼ $6 \times n = 30$ 5   ❽ $n + 7 = 20$ 13
❾ $n - 7 = 16$ 23   ❿ $8 + n = 27$ 19   ⓫ $25 - n = 16$ 9

Add or subtract. Watch the signs.

⓬ $847 + 793 = 1640$ ⓭ $584 - 98 = 486$ ⓮ $326{,}398 - 22{,}509 = 303{,}889$ ⓯ $83{,}218 + 15{,}647 = 98{,}865$

Solve this problem.

⓰ Susan saves $5 a month. How long will it take her to save $40? 8 months

Tell whether each angle is a right angle. Write *yes* or *no*.

⓱ 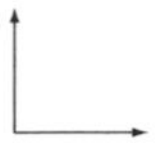 yes

⓲ 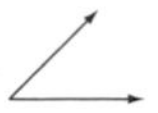 no

Copyright © SRA/McGraw-Hill. Permission is granted to reproduce this page for classroom use.

Math Explorations and Applications Level 4 • 75

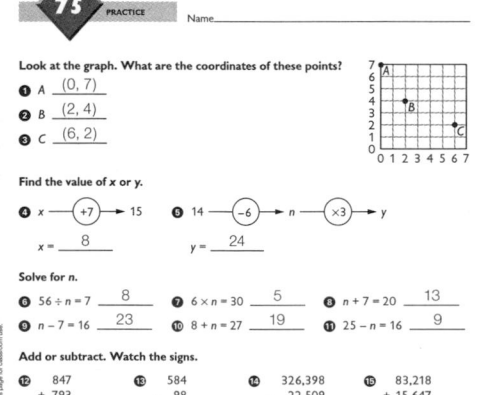

ENRICHMENT p. 75

LESSON 75 ENRICHMENT Name________

COOPERATIVE LEARNING

Work in a small group. Read the story and then discuss the questions at the bottom of the page. You may want to act out this story after you discuss it.

Larry found a baseball card. It was an old one, and nobody else in his neighborhood had one like it.

He showed the card to his sister Sara. "I'll give you 5¢ for it," Sara said, and Larry sold it.

The next day Larry decided he would like to have the baseball card back. "I'll give you 10¢ for it," he told Sara. "That will be a 5¢ profit for you." Sara sold the card to Larry for 10¢.

On the following day Sara changed her mind and asked Larry if she could buy the baseball card for 15¢. Larry sold the card to her.

Each day for the next two weeks Larry and Sara sold the baseball card back and forth. Each time the price went up by 5¢.

Then one day Larry asked Sara to sell him the card for 90¢. "I'm sorry," Sara said, "but I sold the card to my friend Terri today for 95¢."

"What!" said Larry. "How could you do such a thing? We were both making so much money from that card. How could you go and sell it?"

Discuss: Did Larry and Sara really make money each time the card was sold? Why or why not?
Both Larry and Sara have made money. Whoever sold the card made money, but lost money when he or she bought it back.

Copyright © SRA/McGraw-Hill. Permission is granted to reproduce this page for classroom use.

Math Explorations and Applications Level 4 • 75

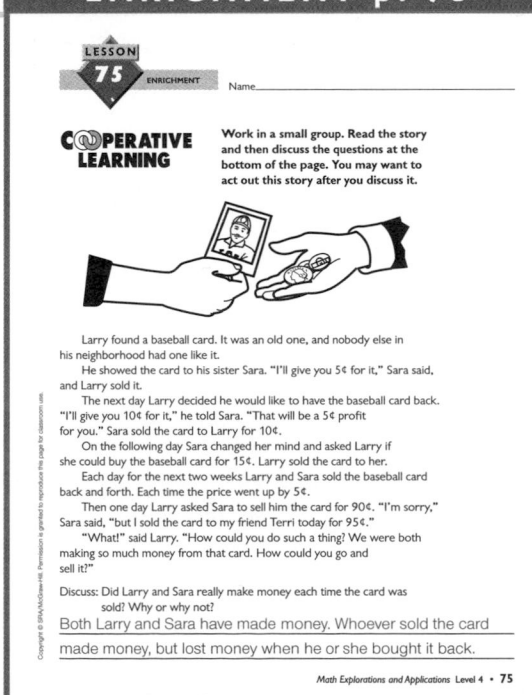

Unit 3 Review 253

LESSON 76

Student Edition pages 254–257

Unit 3 Practice

Using the Student Pages The purpose of these pages is to provide additional practice for those students who demonstrated a need for it on the Unit Review. You may wish to assign only the specific exercises in this Unit Practice in which students need further reinforcement. Listed in the margin beside each instruction line are the lessons covered in the unit so that you or the students can refer to the specific lesson for additional review and instruction.

GAME Students who do not require additional practice on specific concepts may enjoy playing the "Cubo Challenge" game on page 261. This game provides practice with mental math, use of parentheses, and mathematical reasoning. These students may also help by practicing **flash card** drills and playing appropriate games with students who need remedial practice or by actually teaching certain procedures to other students.

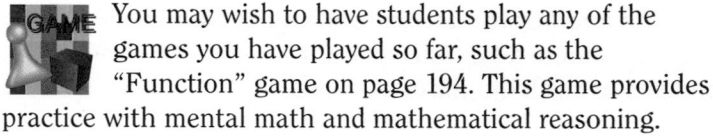

GAME You may wish to have students play any of the games you have played so far, such as the "Function" game on page 194. This game provides practice with mental math and mathematical reasoning.

MIXED **PRACTICE**

LESSON 76

Unit 3 Practice

Translate the messages by using the Code Graph to translate ordered pairs to letters.

Lessons 51, 52

1. (12, 4), (9, 5), (28, 16), (8, 9), (24, 9), (12, 4), (9, 5), (28, 16), (3, 11), (18, 0), (1, 6) (3, 11), (1, 6) (20, 13), (20, 8), (9, 17). **MATHEMATICS IS FUN**
2. (15, 15), (9, 5), (1, 6), (8, 9), (3, 11), (9, 17), (14, 9), (28, 16), (17, 6), (9, 17) (15, 15), (9, 5), (1, 6) (28, 16), (8, 9), (24, 9) (20, 13), (3, 11), (3, 2), (1, 6), (28, 16) (26, 12), (3, 2), (24, 9), (1, 6), (3, 11), (21, 3), (24, 9), (9, 17), (28, 16) (17, 6), (20, 13) (28, 16), (8, 9), (24, 9) (20, 8). (1, 6). **WASHINGTON WAS THE FIRST PRESIDENT OF THE U.S.**
3. (15, 15), (9, 5), (1, 6), (8, 9), (3, 11), (9, 17), (14, 9), (28, 16), (17, 6), (9, 17) (3, 11), (1, 6) (28, 16), (8, 9), (24, 9) (18, 0), (9, 5), (26, 12), (3, 11), (28, 16), (9, 5), (6, 15) (17, 6), (20, 13) (28, 16), (8, 9), (24, 9) (20, 8). (1, 6). **WASHINGTON IS THE CAPITAL OF THE U.**

Code Graph

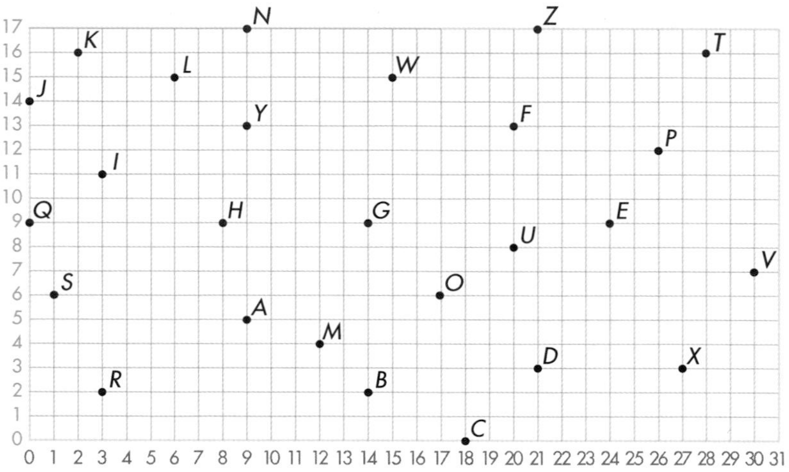

What is the value of *y*?

Lessons 53, 54

4. 24 → (+7) → y **31**
5. 2956 → (+0) → y **2956**
6. 18 → (−3) → y **15**
7. 0 → (+2) → y **2**
8. 7 → (×8) → y **56**
9. 3 → (×6) → y **18**
10. 8 → (×0) → y **0**
11. 7 → (+98) → y **105**
12. 36 → (−9) → y **27**
13. 63 → (÷7) → y **9**
14. 36 → (÷4) → y **9**
15. 82 → (−0) → y **82**

What is the value of *x*?

Lessons 53, 54

16. x → (−8) → 0 **8**
17. x → (+0) → 0 **0**
18. x → (÷2) → 7 **14**
19. x → (+3) → 56 **53**
20. x → (+2) → 5 **3**
21. x → (÷6) → 8 **48**
22. x → (÷4) → 7 **28**
23. x → (−2) → 12 **14**
24. x → (+5) → 26 **21**
25. x → (×0) → 0 **any number**
26. x → (×1) → 179 **179**
27. x → (+9) → 20 **11**

Solve the following problems.

Lessons 70, 74

28. Find the perimeter and area of a rectangle with a long side that measures 6 cm and a short side that measures 2 cm. **16 cm; 12 sq. cm**
29. Which of the following polygons are similar to figure A? **B and C**

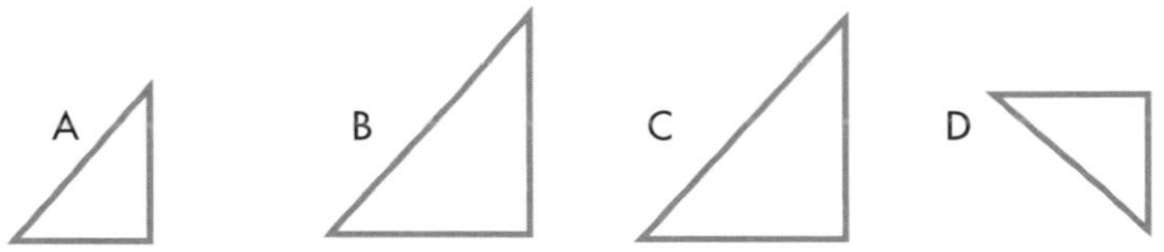

Unit 3 Practice 255

◆ LESSON 76 Unit 3 Practice

◆ LESSON 76 Unit 3 Practice

Give a possible function rule for each set of ordered pairs.

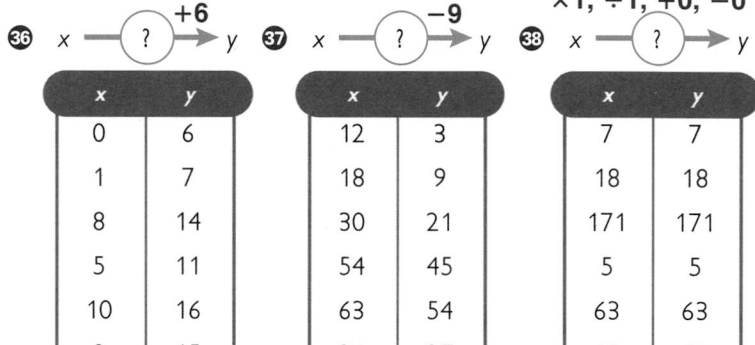

Lesson 53

30 x → (?) → y **÷3**

x	y
0	0
6	2
15	5
30	10

31 x → (?) → y **×8**

x	y
0	0
1	8
7	56
10	80

32 x → (?) → y **−3**

x	y
5	2
34	31
52	49
8	5

33 x → (?) → y **+4**

x	y
9	13
1	5
6	10
12	16

34 x → (?) → y **×7**

x	y
8	56
9	63
7	49
6	42

35 x → (?) → y **×9**

x	y
8	72
9	81
6	54
7	63

36 x → (?) → y **+6**

x	y
0	6
1	7
8	14
5	11
10	16
9	15

37 x → (?) → y **−9**

x	y
12	3
18	9
30	21
54	45
63	54
36	27

38 x → (?) → y **×1, ÷1, +0, −0**

x	y
7	7
18	18
171	171
5	5
63	63
45	45

RETEACHING

Students who have difficulty with this Unit Practice should have further opportunity to review and to practice the skills before they proceed on with the next unit. Beside each set of problems is a reference to the lesson or lessons from which the problems were taken. You may want to review the individual lessons with students who are having difficulty with them.

Use a computer or other means to draw each table of ordered pairs. Then graph each set of points. Make sure your graph will fit on your paper. You may want to use graphing software.

eck students' phs for :uracy.

Lessons 56, 58–60

39 x —(×4)→ y

x	y
0	**0**
3	**12**
2	8
1	**4**
4	16

40 x —(+7)→ y

x	y
0	**7**
12	**19**
8	15
4	**11**
16	23

41 x —(÷2)→ y

x	y
6	**3**
12	6
10	5
16	**8**
20	10

42 x —(×4)→ n —(+7)→ y

x	y
0	**7**
3	**19**
2	15
1	**11**
4	23

43 x —(−3)→ n —(×2)→ y

x	y
3	0
6	**6**
4	2
8	**10**
5	4

44 x —(÷2)→ n —(−3)→ y

x	y
6	**0**
12	**3**
10	2
16	**5**
20	7

Lesson 68

45 Which of the following are right angles? **A**

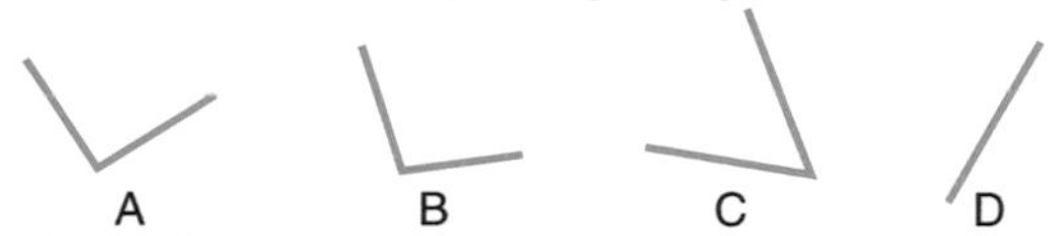

A B C D

Lesson 57

In each problem, two of the answers are clearly wrong and one is correct. Choose the correct answer.

46 180 + 437
a. 417
(b.) 617
c. 697

47 938 + 85
(a.) 1023
b. 123
c. 7357

48 180 + 437
a. 175
b. 1117
(c.) 617

49 927 + 97
a. 206
(b.) 1024
c. 200

50 290 + 180
(a.) 470
b. 110
c. 10

Unit 3 Practice • **257**

PRACTICE p. 76

LESSON 76 PRACTICE Name________

What is the value of y?

1 17 —(+8)→ y y = 25
2 19 —(−6)→ y y = 13
3 6 —(×8)→ y y = 48
4 32 —(÷4)→ y y = 8
5 4 —(+15)→ y y = 19
6 20 —(−10)→ y y = 10

What is the value of x?

7 x —(−7)→ 0 x = 7
8 x —(÷3)→ 7 x = 21
9 x —(+5)→ 25 x = 20
10 x —(×1)→ 44 x = 44
11 x —(−12)→ 59 x = 71
12 x —(×9)→ 63 x = 7

Give a possible function rule for each set of ordered pairs.

13 x —(+5)→ y

x	y
1	6
4	9
8	13

14 x —(÷3)→ y

x	y
12	4
18	6
30	10

15 x —(×2)→ y

x	y
7	14
5	10
10	20

Copyright © SRA/McGraw-Hill. Permission is granted to reproduce this page for classroom use.

76 • *Math Explorations and Applications* Level 4

ENRICHMENT p. 76

LESSON 76 ENRICHMENT Name________

Place a small mirror on this figure. What do you see? Move the mirror. Now what do you see?

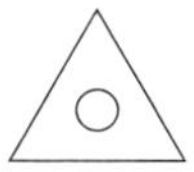

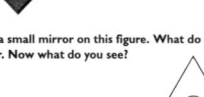

Mark the mirror pictures that can be seen with a mirror and the figure shown just above.

Check marks indicate possible mirror pictures.

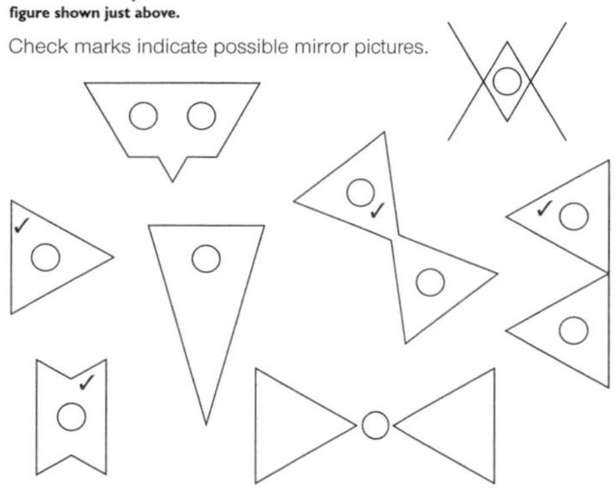

What other mirror pictures can you see? Draw them.

76 • *Math Explorations and Applications* Level 4

Copyright © SRA/McGraw-Hill. Permission is granted to reproduce this page for classroom use.

LESSON 77

Student Edition pages 258–261

More Unit 3 Practice

Using the Student Pages The purpose of these pages is to provide additional practice for those students who demonstrated a need for it on the Unit Review. You may wish to assign only the specific exercises in this Unit Practice in which students need further reinforcement. Listed in the margin beside each instruction line are the lessons covered in the unit so that you or the students can refer to the specific lesson for additional review and instruction.

GAME You may want to demonstrate the "Cubo Challenge" game on page 261 for practice with all four operations. You may also wish to have students play any other games you have played so far, such as the "Function" game on page 194. This game provides practice with mental math and mathematical reasoning.

You may want to use the Cumulative Review on page 551 after this lesson.

LESSON 77

More Unit 3 Practice

ALGEBRA READINESS

Lessons 63, 67

Solve for *n*. Watch the signs.

1. $21 - n = 7$ **14**	2. $n = 5 + 27$ **32**	3. $7 + n = 36$ **29**
4. $49 \div 7 = n$ **7**	5. $27 - 16 = n$ **11**	6. $42 - 24 = n$ **18**
7. $n = 8 \times 5$ **40**	8. $n \times 4 = 16$ **4**	9. $n \div 3 = 24$ **72**
10. $13 + 4 = n$ **17**	11. $n = 27 \div 3$ **9**	12. $6 \times n = 36$ **6**
13. $4 = n \div 9$ **36**	14. $21 + 39 = n$ **60**	15. $n = 15 + 18$ **33**
16. $6 \times 7 = n$ **42**	17. $63 \div n = 9$ **7**	18. $n - 28 = 13$ **41**
19. $37 - 18 = n$ **19**	20. $n = 9 \times 9$ **81**	21. $n + 18 = 32$ **14**

Lesson 63

Add or subtract.

22. 312 − 154 = **158**	23. 782 + 429 = **1211**	24. 294 − 123 = **171**	25. 781 + 317 = **1098**	26. 7642 − 3295 = **4347**
27. 238 + 513 = **751**	28. 508 − 274 = **234**	29. 3089 − 666 = **2423**	30. 341 + 265 = **606**	31. 4579 − 1238 = **3341**
32. 731 − 245 = **486**	33. 665 + 306 = **971**	34. 156 + 179 = **335**	35. 7376 − 6127 = **1249**	36. 7649 − 219 = **7430**
37. 23 + 38 = **61**	38. 48 − 29 = **19**	39. 614 + 327 = **941**	40. $43.10 − 23.20 = **$19.90**	41. $105.76 − 59.38 = **$46.38**
42. $27.30 + 4.62 = **$31.92**	43. $14.14 + 1.70 = **$15.84**	44. $6.87 − 1.90 = **$4.97**	45. $324.17 + 79.43 = **$403.60**	46. $2.93 + 8.41 = **$11.34**

Solve these problems.

Lessons 61, 63

47. Martin saves $10 each week. How long will it take him to save enough money to buy hockey skates that cost $70? **7 weeks**

48. Bernelle is six years younger than her sister. They were both born in October. Bernelle was born in 1990. In what year was her sister born? **1984**

49. Petra had a stack of baseball cards. Then Luis gave her 20 cards and Emily gave her 35 cards. How many cards does Petra have now? **not enough information**

50. Thea bought six pencils that cost 9¢ each. She gave the clerk a $1 bill. How much change should she get? **46¢**

51. Nolan had a package of 100 star stickers. He wanted to make a pattern of six rows with eight stars in each row. Did he have enough stars to make two of these patterns? **yes**

52. Olivia runs 7 kilometers every day. How many days will it be before she has run at least 50 kilometers? **8**

53. Victor bought nine erasers that cost 7¢ each. He gave the cashier three quarters. How much change should he get? **12¢**

54. Mackenzie collects rocks. Jake gave her 31 rocks and Max gave her 27.

    a. How many more rocks does Mackenzie have now than before? **58**

    b. How many rocks does Mackenzie have? **not enough information**

◆ LESSON 77 More Unit 3 Practice

◆ LESSON 77 More Unit 3 Practice

Lesson 68 **Answer these questions about right angles.**

55 Which of these angles are right angles? **b. and e.**

a. **b.** **c.** **d.** **e.**

56 Draw a right angle. 

57 Find five right angles in your classroom. **Examples: corner of desk, frame of door**

Lesson 69 **For each pair of lines, tell whether the lines are *parallel*, *perpendicular*, or *neither*.**

58 59 60 61

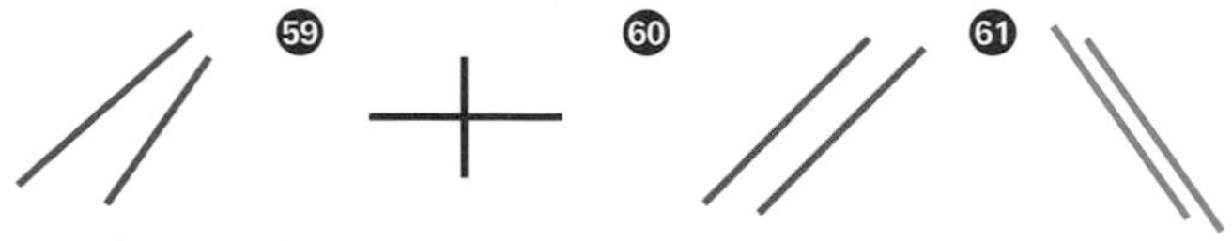

neither **perpendicular** **parallel** **parallel**

62 63 64 65

neither **perpendicular** **perpendicular** **neither**

66 Find three pairs of perpendicular lines in your classroom.

66 Example: the ceiling and the wall

67 Find three pairs of parallel lines in your classroom.

Example: the top and bottom of the chalkboard

Lesson 73 **How many lines of symmetry can be drawn in each figure?**

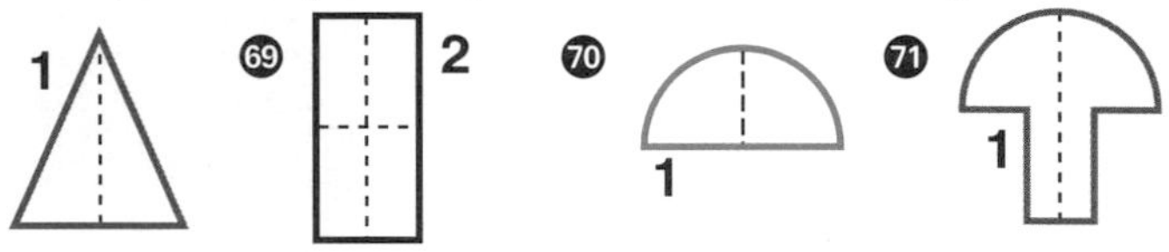

68 **1** 69 **2** 70 **1** 71 **1**

Lesson 63 **Answer the following questions.**

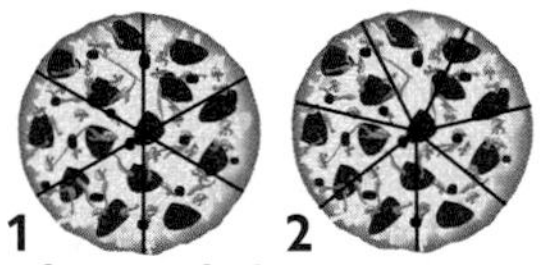

1 **2**

72 Which pizza has **more** pieces? **2**

73 Which pizza has **bigger** pieces? **1**

74 Which pizza has been cut into pieces $\frac{1}{6}$ of its size? **1**

75 Which pizza has been cut into pieces $\frac{1}{7}$ of its size? **2**

RETEACHING

Students who have difficulty with this Unit Practice should have further opportunity to review and to practice the skills before they proceed on with the next unit. Beside each set of problems is a reference to the lesson or lessons from which the problems were taken. You may want to review the individual lessons with students who are having difficulty with them.

Cubo Challenge Game

COOPERATIVE LEARNING

GAME

Players: Two or more
Materials: Two 0–5 cubes, two 5–10 cubes
Object: To make numbers from 1 to 20
Math Focus: Mental math (with all four operations) and mathematical reasoning

Using only the numbers 1, 2, 6, and 10, try to make each number from 0 to 20 by the rules of the "Cubo" game (page 163).

Remember that you must use each number only once and may combine numbers using addition, subtraction, multiplication, and division.

Keep track of **how** you make each number. You may use parentheses, if necessary.

Challenge problem: Following the rules of Cubo, what is the greatest number you can make from 1, 2, 6, and 10?

Superchallenge problem: Try to make as many numbers as you can between 0 and 40 by following the rules of Cubo, using 1, 2, 6, and 10. (All but two of the numbers from 0 to 40 are possible.)

Super-duper challenge problem: Try to make as many numbers as you can between 0 and 64. (All but eight of the numbers from 0 to 64 are possible.)

Roll the four cubes until you find another set of four numbers that you think will work well. Then use those numbers in the challenge problems.

Use the same numbers as other people in the class and compare your results with theirs.

Use the Cumulative Review on page 551 after this lesson.

PRACTICE p. 77

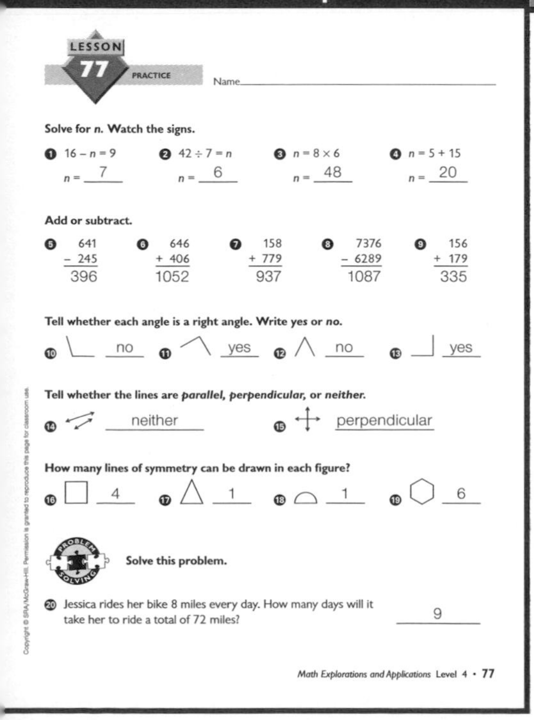
LESSON 77 PRACTICE Name

Solve for *n*. Watch the signs.

1. $16 - n = 9$ $n =$ 7
2. $42 \div 7 = n$ $n =$ 6
3. $n = 8 \times 6$ $n =$ 48
4. $n = 5 + 15$ $n =$ 20

Add or subtract.

5. 641 − 245 = 396
6. 646 + 406 = 1052
7. 158 + 779 = 937
8. 7376 − 6289 = 1087
9. 156 + 179 = 335

Tell whether each angle is a right angle. Write *yes* or *no*.

10. no
11. yes
12. no
13. yes

Tell whether the lines are *parallel, perpendicular,* or *neither*.

14. neither
15. perpendicular

How many lines of symmetry can be drawn in each figure?

16. 4
17. 1
18. 1
19. 6

PROBLEM SOLVING **Solve this problem.**

20. Jessica rides her bike 8 miles every day. How many days will it take her to ride a total of 72 miles? 9

Copyright © SRA/McGraw-Hill. Permission is granted to reproduce this page for classroom use.

Math Explorations and Applications Level 4 • 77

ENRICHMENT p. 77

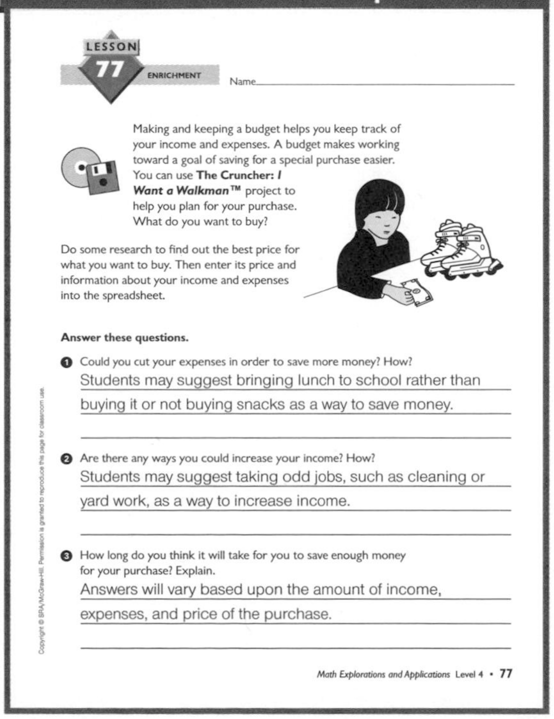
LESSON 77 ENRICHMENT Name

Making and keeping a budget helps you keep track of your income and expenses. A budget makes working toward a goal of saving for a special purchase easier. You can use **The Cruncher: *I Want a Walkman™*** project to help you plan for your purchase. What do you want to buy?

Do some research to find out the best price for what you want to buy. Then enter its price and information about your income and expenses into the spreadsheet.

Answer these questions.

1. Could you cut your expenses in order to save more money? How?
Students may suggest bringing lunch to school rather than buying it or not buying snacks as a way to save money.
2. Are there any ways you could increase your income? How?
Students may suggest taking odd jobs, such as cleaning or yard work, as a way to increase income.
3. How long do you think it will take for you to save enough money for your purchase? Explain.
Answers will vary based upon the amount of income, expenses, and price of the purchase.

Copyright © SRA/McGraw-Hill. Permission is granted to reproduce this page for classroom use.

Math Explorations and Applications Level 4 • 77

GAME **Using the Student Pages** Consider letting the entire class work on the "Cubo Challenge" game since all students will benefit from this challenge. "Cubo Challenge" provides practice with mental math using all four operations. For the Challenge problem the answer is 180.

Possible Solutions:

$0 = (10 \div 2) + 1 - 6$
$1 = (6 \times 2) - 10 - 1$
$2 = 10 - 6 - (2 \times 1)$
$3 = 10 - 6 - 2 + 1$
$4 = (10 - 6) \times (2 - 1)$
$5 = 10 + 2 - 6 - 1$
$6 = 10 - (6 \div 2) - 1$
$7 = 10 + 1 + 2 - 6$
$8 = 10 - (6 \div 2) + 1$
$9 = [(10 - 6) \times 2] + 1$
$10 = (10 \div 2) + 6 - 1$
$11 = (10 \div 2) + (6 \times 1)$
$12 = (10 \div 2) + 6 + 1$
$13 = (10 \times 2) - 6 - 1$
$14 = (10 \times 2) - (6 \times 1)$
$15 = 10 - 2 + 6 + 1$
$16 = (10 + 6) \times (2 - 1)$
$17 = 10 + 6 + 2 - 1$
$18 = (10 + 6 + 2) \times 1$
$19 = 10 + 6 + 2 + 1$
$20 = 10 \times [6 \div (2 + 1)]$
$21 = 10 - 1 + (6 \times 2)$
$22 = (6 \times 2) + (10 \times 1)$
$23 = 10 + 1 + (6 \times 2)$
$24 = [(10 - 1) \times 2] + 6$
$25 = (10 \times 2) - 1 + 6$
$26 = (10 \times 2) + (6 \times 1)$
$27 = (10 \times 2) + 6 + 1$
$28 = [6 \times (2 + 1)] + 10$
$29 = [10 \times (6 \div 2)] - 1$
$30 = [(10 \div 2) \times 6] \times 1$
$31 = 10 \times (6 \div 2) + 1$
$32 = [(10 \times 1) + 6] \times 2$
$33 = (10 + 1) \times (6 \div 2)$
$34 = (10 + 6 + 1) \times 2$
$35 = (10 \div 2) \times (6 + 1)$
$36 = [(10 \div 2) + 1] \times 6$
37 = no solution
38 = no solution
$39 = 10 \times (6 - 2) - 1$
$40 = (10 - 2) \times (6 - 1)$
$41 = [10 \times (6 - 2)] + 1$
$42 = (10 - 2 - 1) \times 6$
43 = no solution
$44 = (10 + 1) \times (6 - 2)$
45 = no solution
46 = no solution
$47 = [(10 - 2) \times 6] - 1$
$48 = [(10 - 2) \times 1] \times 6$
$49 = [(10 - 2) \times 6] + 1$
$50 = 10 \times [6 - (2 - 1)]$
51 = no solution
$52 = 10 \times (6 - 1) + 2$
53 = no solution
$54 = (10 - 2 + 1) \times 6$
55 = no solution
$56 = (10 - 2) \times (6 + 1)$
$57 = (10 \times 6) - (2 + 1)$
$58 = (10 \times 6) - (2 \times 1)$
$59 = (10 \times 6) + 1 - 2$
$60 = (10 + 2) \times (6 - 1)$
$61 = (10 \times 6) + (2 - 1)$
$62 = (10 \times 6) + (2 \times 1)$
$63 = (10 \times 6) + (2 + 1)$
$64 = [(10 + 1) \times 6] - 2$

UNIT 3

Student Edition pages 262–263

Unit Test

Using the Student Pages The Unit 3 Test on Student Edition pages 262 and 263 provides an opportunity to formally evaluate your students' proficiency with concepts developed in this unit. It is similar in content and format to the Unit 3 Review. Students who did well on the Unit 3 Review may not need to take this test. Students who did not do well on the Unit 3 Review should be provided with additional practice opportunities, such as the Unit 3 Practice pages, before taking the Unit 3 Test. For further evaluation, you may wish to have these students also take the Unit 3 Test in standardized format, provided on Assessment Blackline Masters pages 121–128 or the Unit 3 Test on Assessment Blackline Masters pages 28–31.

UNIT 3

Unit Test

What are the coordinates of these points?

1. *A* **(3, 10)** 2. *B* **(11, 9)** 3. *C* **(10, 3)** 4. *D* **(5, 0)** 5. *E* **(1, 4)**

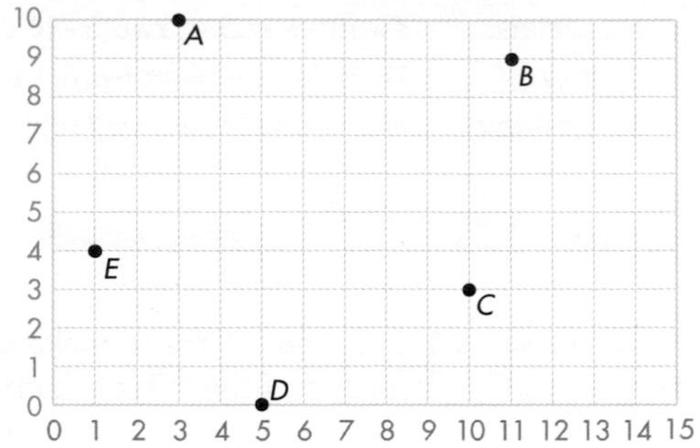

Find the value of *x* or *y*.

6. 8 → (+9) → *y* **17**
7. 17 → (−7) → *n* **10** → (÷2) → *y* **5**
8. *x* **6** → (×4) → 24
9. *x* **21** → (÷3) → *n* **7** → (−5) → 2
10. 42 → (÷7) → *y* **6**
11. 18 → (−2) → *n* **16** → (÷8) → *y* **2**

What is a possible function rule for each chart?

12. *x* → (?) → *y* **×3**

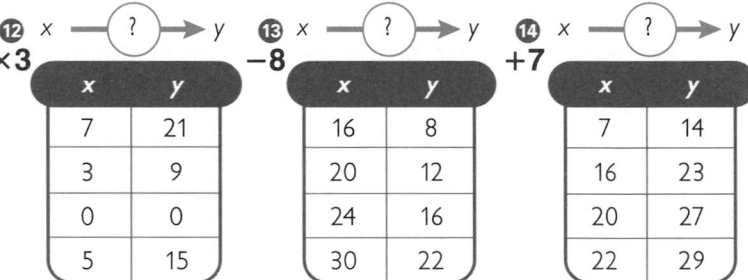

x	*y*
7	21
3	9
0	0
5	15

13. *x* → (?) → *y* **−8**

x	*y*
16	8
20	12
24	16
30	22

14. *x* → (?) → *y* **+7**

x	*y*
7	14
16	23
20	27
22	29

Solve for *n*.

15. $20 \div 4 = n$ **5**
16. $56 \div 7 = n$ **8**
17. $7 - n = 0$ **7**
18. $7 \times n = 42$ **6**
19. $5 \times n = 45$ **9**
20. $16 + n = 32$ **16**
21. $n - 2 = 8$ **10**
22. $n \times 3 = 18$ **6**
23. $n - 15 = 30$ **45**

Add or subtract.

24. 67 + 49 = **116**
25. 324 − 98 = **226**
26. 706 + 214 = **920**
27. 404 − 187 = **217**
28. 3509 − 2654 = **855**

Solve these problems.

29. Kim is saving to buy a birdcage that costs $14. She saves $2 each week. How many weeks will it take her to save enough money to buy the birdcage? **7**

30. Carl is reading a book about parrots. This morning he was on page 39. By the end of the day he reached page 72. How many pages are in the book? **not enough information given**

31. Bella was born in May of 1987. Her brother, Alex, was born in May of 1993. When Bella was nine years old, how old was Alex? **3 years old**

32. Paul went to see his friend give a puppet show. He noticed that there were four rows with six chairs in each row. There was also a row of three chairs. How many people could be seated? **27**

Tell whether each is a right angle.

33. **no**

34. **yes**

For each pair of lines, tell whether the lines are *parallel, perpendicular,* or *neither.*

35. **perpendicular**

36. **parallel**

37. **neither**

How many lines of symmetry can be drawn in each figure?

38. **2**

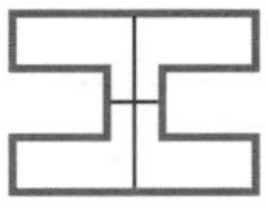

39. **3**

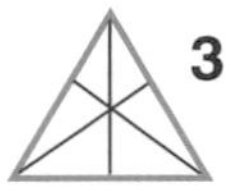

40. Which of the following figures look congruent to figure A? **E**

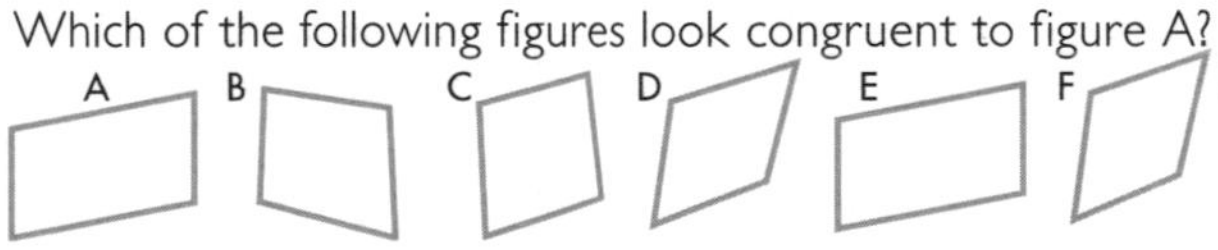

ASSESSMENT p. 28

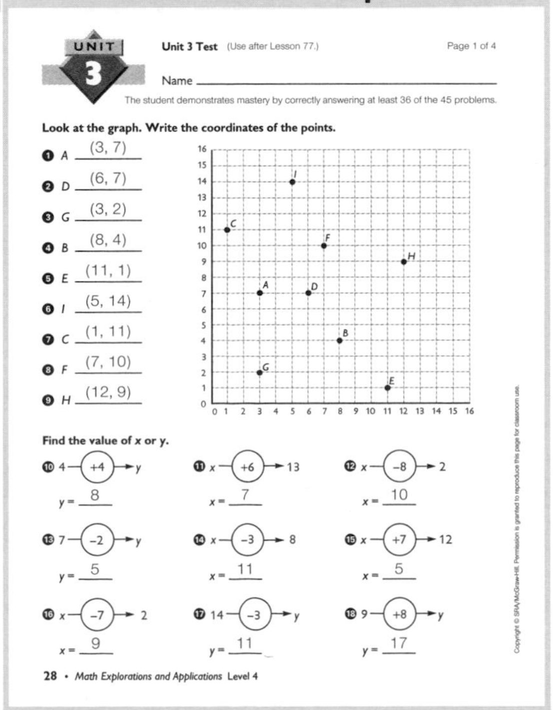

UNIT 3

Unit 3 Test (Use after Lesson 77.) Page 1 of 4

Name ______

The student demonstrates mastery by correctly answering at least 36 of the 45 problems.

Look at the graph. Write the coordinates of the points.

1. A (3, 7)
2. D (6, 7)
3. G (3, 2)
4. B (8, 4)
5. E (11, 1)
6. I (5, 14)
7. C (1, 11)
8. F (7, 10)
9. H (12, 9)

Find the value of *x* or *y*.

10. 4 → (+4) → y; y = 8
11. x → (+6) → 13; x = 7
12. x → (−8) → 2; x = 10
13. 7 → (−2) → y; y = 5
14. x → (−3) → 8; x = 11
15. x → (+7) → 12; x = 5
16. x → (−7) → 2; x = 9
17. 14 → (−3) → y; y = 11
18. 9 → (+8) → y; y = 17

28 • *Math Explorations and Applications* Level 4

Copyright © SRA/McGraw-Hill. Permission is granted to reproduce this page for classroom use.

UNIT 3

Student Edition pages 264–265

Wrap-Up

PRESENTING THE PROJECT

Project Objective

- to introduce students to the hobby of stamp collecting, which can relate to geography, history, mathematics, and art

Materials

information about stamp collecting from the United States Postal Service

large collection of used, common postage stamps, preferably from many countries

Begin the project with a brief discussion about postage stamps. Then have students work in small groups, each with a collection of stamps. Ask the students to classify their stamps in different ways. After a while, bring the class together and have each group report on ways in which they classified their stamps. Possible categories might include United States stamps, foreign stamps, animals, plants, famous people, sports, and space travel.

Allow students to discuss topics in which they might be interested. Provide information from the United States Postal Service and other sources for those students who appear interested. Have those students begin a long-term project collecting these stamps.

COOPERATIVE LEARNING **Minds on Math** *Minds on Math* is a series of units covering Problem Solving, Data Collection, Number Sense, Measurement, Money, and Geometry and Spatial Relations. Each unit provides a series of open-ended projects for individuals or small groups. These projects develop problem-solving and critical-thinking skills. Use projects from *Shape, Movement, and Location* to examine maps and floor plans and look at objects from a different perspective.

SCIENCE CONNECTION **Science, Math & YOU** *Weather Counts* is one of four units in a program published by SRA that provides a variety of hands-on projects that integrate real-world math and science. Individual students or small groups of students can complete these projects. The four units in *Science, Math & YOU* are *Weather Counts, Life Adds Up, Motion Measures,* and *Circling the Sun.* Use projects from *Weather Counts* with this unit to help students graph coordinates.

COOPERATIVE LEARNING

Mathematics and Postage Stamps

People have been sending mail for thousands of years. In ancient times messengers on foot or horseback delivered mail. But this was an expensive service.

In the 1840s mail service changed. A new idea to put glue on the back of paper stamps made it easy and cheap for people to mail their own letters. The new stamps got to be so popular that people started collecting them.

Many people still enjoy collecting postage stamps as a hobby.

Some people collect stamps from a single country.

Some people collect stamps about a special topic.

How do you find stamps? Many businesses get mail from all over the world. Often they will save the stamps for schoolchildren. Most people simply buy stamps from a dealer. You can often buy a large number of used stamps for a few dollars.

264 • Algebra Readiness and Geometry

Start a stamp collection that features mathematics. You can start one collection for the whole class, or you can build individual or small group collections.

Before you begin, decide on the details. You could collect stamps of all mathematics topics, including famous mathematicians, geometry, maps, and space travel.

◆ What other topics in mathematics can you think of?
Examples: patterns, algebra, graphs

Design Your Own Stamp

Design your own stamp that relates to a topic in mathematics. Display your stamp along with your classmates' stamps.

If you are really proud of your stamp design, send it to the United States Postal Service. Write a letter to ask them to consider your design for a new stamp.

COOPERATIVE LEARNING **Minds on Math** SRA'S *Minds on Math* is a series of units covering Problem Solving, Data Collection, Number Sense, Measurement, Money, and Geometry and Spatial Relations. Each unit provides a series of open-ended projects for individuals or small groups. These projects develop problem-solving and critical-thinking skills, utilize real-world materials, emphasize language, and integrate cross-curricular connections. Use projects from this series for practice with translation, reflection, and rotation.

What Is a Math Project? If this is the first time you have used math projects in your classroom, you may want to refer to pages 96–97 in this Teacher's Guide for more detailed information about effectively implementing and assessing projects.

Homework Much of the stamp collection and research can be done outside the classroom.

Wrapping Up the Project Initiate a discussion about how governments decide on the topics for stamps. In general, the topics reflect the interests of the people and their government at a particular time in history.

Assessing the Project Note those students who take a genuine interest in building a collection of stamps. Provide help and encouragement as they embark on what might become a lifetime hobby.

ART CONNECTION **Art Connection** Have the students design their own stamps and invite them to submit their designs to the Postal Service.

COOPERATIVE LEARNING **Math CrossSections** SRA'S *Math CrossSections* consists of eight units that provide real-world math projects related to famous places in the United States. These open-ended projects focus on problem solving and reinforce reading, research, and study skills. The eight units are as follows:

The White House (Washington, D.C.)
747 DFW (Texas)
California's Giant Sequoias (California)
Pencil Making (Tennessee)
Barging Through the Locks (Michigan)
Atlanta's Olympic Stadium (Georgia)
Madison Square Garden (New York)
The Denver Mint (Colorado)

Use projects from *Pencil Making* to provide extra practice with the four basic operations.

PACING

PACING THE REST OF THE YEAR

Perhaps you have less than 45 minutes to devote to each lesson. Perhaps you have a slower-than-average class that needs extra time on various lessons. Or, perhaps you simply feel comfortable proceeding at a more leisurely pace. Whatever the reason, a few tips will help you trim the program with the fewest consequences.

Because each unit should take up about one sixth of the school year, you can use the units somewhat as mileposts. From time to time, after each unit or halfway though each unit, do a rough calculation to see whether your pace will allow you to finish the program. If it appears that you won't finish, check the suggestions given below; but don't speed up at the expense of students' understanding. If you are moving at an appropriate pace and yet won't finish the program, that is all right. The material in Unit 6 is reviewed in depth or retaught in Level 5.

MORE THAN 80 DAYS LEFT AFTER UNIT 3

If more than 80 days remain, you'll probably be able to finish the Level 4 program, so you won't need to significantly modify the lesson plans for the rest of the year.

60–80 DAYS LEFT AFTER UNIT 3

If, after you finish Unit 3, 60–80 days remain in the school year, go though the lesson list below and decide which lessons or portions of lessons to omit. The lessons listed may be omitted without creating undue difficulty for students when they enter the fifth grade. Any of these lessons may be omitted, but if you have to skip only a few lessons, try to choose lessons from later in the year rather than earlier. This will minimize disruption of the lesson continuity. Whenever possible, do the Mental Math exercises of the lessons you omit.

Unit 4

Lesson 97	Perimeter and Area
Lesson 100	Using Multiplication

Unit 5

Lesson 116	Practicing Division: Missing Digits
Lesson 117	Multiply and Divide
Lesson 119	Prime and Composite Numbers

Unit 6

Lesson 148	Addition and Subtraction of Decimals: Applications
Lesson 150	Multiplying a Decimal by a Whole Number

If you omit any material from a unit, be sure to modify the Unit Review and Unit Test to take into account the deleted material.

FEWER THAN 60 DAYS LEFT AFTER UNIT 3

If, after you finish Unit 3, fewer than 60 days remain in the school year, omit the items listed below.

Unit 4

Lesson 97	Perimeter and Area
Lesson 100	Using Multiplication

Unit 5

Lesson 116	Practicing Division: Missing Digits
Lesson 117	Multiply and Divide
Lesson 119	Prime and Composite Numbers
Lesson 120	Using a Bar Graph
Lesson 121	More Division Review
Lesson 123	Division Revisited: Missing Digits

Unit 6

Lesson 148	Addition and Subtraction of Decimals: Applications
Lesson 150	Multiplying a Decimal by a Whole Number

Allow plenty of time for remediation outlined in Lesson 155. Depending on how much remediation you foresee, you'll spend from three days to two weeks on this. Be sure you go through the final review and diagnostic test early enough to leave as much time as you think you'll need for remediation.

IF YOU ADMINISTER STANDARDIZED TESTS

You might want to review the test that you will be administering to your students at this time. Note any topics that will be assessed that you have not covered in your mathematics curriculum. You might want to introduce a series of lessons earlier to accommodate your testing schedule.

UNIT 4

Multidigit Multiplication

APPROXIMATION AND APPLICATION

OVERVIEW

This unit develops the algorithm for multiplication. It begins with multiplying by powers and multiples of 10. Practice is provided in rounding and approximating. Students progress from multiplying a two-digit number by a one-digit number through multiplying a three-digit number by a three-digit number. Students convert measurements and solve a variety of problems, including perimeter and area problems, and are introduced to scientific notation.

Integrated Topics in This Unit Include:

- multiplying by powers of 10
- converting metric units
- multiplying by multiples of 10
- rounding and approximating
- using scientific notation
- using the standard algorithm for multiplication
- applying multiplication
- converting customary units of measures
- solving perimeter and area problems

USING SCIENTIFIC NOTATION
ROUNDING AND APPROXIMATING

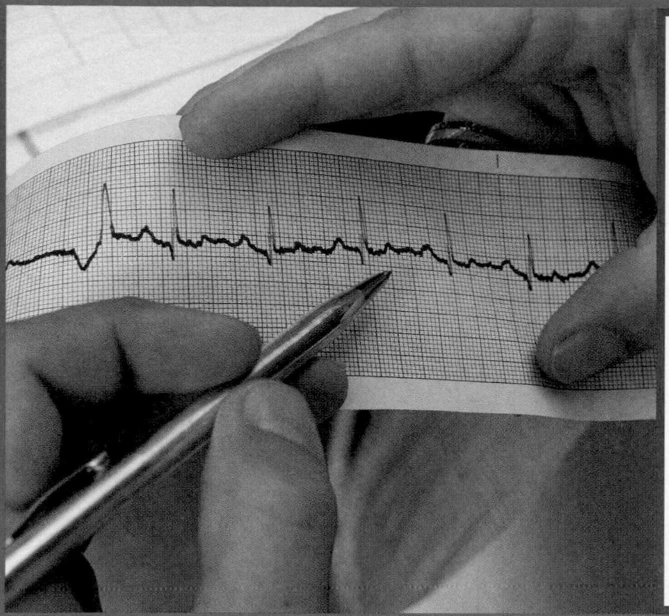

"A developmental approach to computation fosters a problem-solving atmosphere in which children are actively involved in using materials, discussing their work, validating solutions, and raising questions. Placing computation in a problem-solving context motivates students to learn computational skills and serves as an impetus for the mastery of paper-and-pencil algorithms."

—NCTM Curriculum and Evaluation Standards for School Mathematics

GAMES

Motivating Mixed Practice

Games provide **basic math skills** practice in cooperative groups. Playing the games also helps students develop **mathematical reasoning**.

Harder Shopping Game Mat	Lesson 85	page 288
Cube 100	Lesson 87	page 293
Four Cube Multiplication	Lesson 89	page 304
(Multiplication) Roll a Problem	Lesson 95	page 325
More or Less	Lesson 100	page 339

THINKING STORY

Integrated Problem Solving

Thinking Stories provide opportunities for students to work in **cooperative groups** and develop **logical reasoning** while they integrate **reading skills** with mathematics.

The Treasure of Mugg Island

Part 1	Lesson 81	pages 276–277
Part 2	Lesson 87	pages 294–295
Part 3	Lesson 90	pages 308–309
Part 4	Lesson 96	pages 328–329
Part 5	Lesson 99	pages 336–337
Part 6	Lesson 101	pages 342–343

Story Summary In "The Treasure of Mugg Island," a queen asks four children to help her find a royal treasure on Mugg Island. As the story progresses, the children must first create a map to locate the island using written directions. They then must use an incomplete map of the land and a series of clues to navigate their way around the island. Students will use mapping, measuring, and geometry to evaluate the children's methods and help decide how the children should proceed.

PROJECT

Making Connections

The Unit 4 Project makes real-world connections. Students work in **cooperative groups** to problem solve and to communicate their findings.

The project presented in the Unit 4 Wrap-Up asks students to learn about the human heart. Show students how to take their pulse and then how to calculate how many times their hearts have beaten in their lifetimes. This project can be started any time throughout the unit during students' free time.

UNIT 4

MULTIDIGIT MULTIPLICATION LESSON PLANS

	LESSON	PACING	PRIMARY OBJECTIVES	FEATURE	RESOURCES	NCTM STANDARDS
78	**Multiplying by Powers of 10** 268–269	1 day	to provide practice using the rule for multiplying by 10 and powers of 10		Reteaching Strategy Practice Master 78 Enrichment Master 78	7
79	**Converting Metric Units** 270–271	1 day	to review converting from one metric unit to another		Reteaching Master Practice Master 79 Enrichment Master 79	7, 10
80	**Multiplying by Multiples of 10** 272–273	1 day	to develop a procedure for multiplying multiples of 10		Reteaching Master Practice Master 80 Enrichment Master 80	7, 8
81	**Practice with Multiples of 10** 274–277	1 day	✓ to assess students' mastery of multiplying multiples of 10 and multiplying by powers of 10	Thinking Story	Reteaching Strategy Practice Master 81 Enrichment Master 81 Assessment Master	1, 2, 3, 4, 8
82	**Rounding and Approximating** 278–281	1 day	to use rounding and approximation to solve word problems		Reteaching Master Practice Master 82 Enrichment Master 82	1, 2, 3, 4, 5
83	**Approximating Answers** 282–283	1 day	✓ to assess mastery of approximating answers to multidigit multiplication problems		Reteaching Master Practice Master 83 Enrichment Master 83 Assessment Master	5, 8
84	**Practice with Approximating** 284–285	1 day	to use scientific notation to approximate answers		Reteaching Strategy Practice Master 84 Enrichment Master 84	6, 7
85	**Multiply: Two-Digit Numbers by One-Digit Numbers** 286–289	1 day	to teach the standard algorithm for multiplying a two-digit number by a one-digit number	ACT IT OUT Game	Reteaching Master Practice Master 85 Enrichment Master 85	7, 8
86	**Multiply: Three-Digit Numbers by One-Digit Numbers** 290–291	1 day	to teach an algorithm for multiplying a three-digit number by a one-digit number	ACT IT OUT	Reteaching Strategy Practice Master 86 Enrichment Master 86	8
87	**Multiplication Review** 292–295	1 day	✓ to assess students' ability to multiply two- or three-digit numbers by a one-digit number	Thinking Story Game	Reteaching Master Practice Master 87 Enrichment Master 87 Assessment Master	1, 2, 3, 4, 8
88	**Multiply: Two-Digit Numbers by Two-Digit Numbers** 296–299	2 days	to teach an algorithm for multiplying two two-digit numbers	ACT IT OUT	Reteaching Strategy Practice Master 88 Enrichment Master 88	8
	Mid-Unit Review 300–301	1 day			Assessment Masters	
89	**Applying Multiplication** 302–305	1 day	to provide practice in multidigit multiplication	Game	Reteaching Master Practice Master 89 Enrichment Master 89	8, 9
90	**Multiplication Practice** 306–309	1 day	✓ to assess students' mastery of multiplying two-digit numbers	Thinking Story	Reteaching Strategy Practice Master 90 Enrichment Master 90 Assessment Master	1, 2, 3, 4, 8

LESSON		PACING	PRIMARY OBJECTIVES	FEATURE	RESOURCES	NCTM STANDARDS
91	**Multiply: Three-Digit Numbers by Two-Digit Numbers** **310–313**	1 day	to introduce an algorithm for multiplying two- and three-digit numbers		Reteaching Strategy Practice Master 91 Enrichment Master 91	8, 9
92	**Converting Customary Units of Measure** **314–315**	1 day	to review converting between customary units of measure		Reteaching Master Practice Master 92 Enrichment Master 92	1, 2, 3, 4, 10
93	**Applications of Multiplication** **316–319**	1 day	to approximate products		Reteaching Strategy Practice Master 93 Enrichment Master 93	1, 2, 3, 4, 5, 8
94	**Multiply: Three-Digit Numbers by Three-Digit Numbers** **320–323**	1 day	to introduce an algorithm for multiplying a three-digit number by a three-digit number		Reteaching Strategy Practice Master 94 Enrichment Master 94	5, 8
95	**Multiplication Uses** **324–325**	1 day	to provide some practical applications of multiplication	Game	Reteaching Strategy Practice Master 95 Enrichment Master 95	1, 2, 3, 4, 8
96	**Keeping Sharp: Functions, Facts, and Computation** **326–329**	1 day	to review working with functions and basic arithmetic operations	Thinking Story	Reteaching Strategy Practice Master 96 Enrichment Master 96	1, 2, 3, 4, 11, 13
97	**Perimeter and Area** **330–331**	1 day	to provide practice in solving problems that involve perimeter and area		Reteaching Strategy Practice Master 97 Enrichment Master 97	1, 2, 3, 4, 9, 10
98	**Multiply: Multidigit Numbers** **332–333**	2 days	✓ to assess students' mastery of the general multidigit multiplication algorithm		Reteaching Master Practice Master 98 Enrichment Master 98 Assessment Master	8
99	**Reviewing the Facts** **334–337**	1 day	to provide practice with basic facts and multidigit arithmetic	Thinking Story	Reteaching Strategy Practice Master 99 Enrichment Master 99	1, 2, 3, 4, 8
100	**Using Multiplication** **338–339**	1 day	to provide practice in approximating products and using relation signs	Game	Reteaching Strategy Practice Master 100 Enrichment Master 100	1, 2, 3, 4, 5, 8
101	**Approximating Products** **340–343**	1 day	to provide practice in using approximation to solve arithmetic problems	Thinking Story	Reteaching Strategy Practice Master 101 Enrichment Master 101	1, 2, 3, 4, 5, 8
102	**Unit 4 Review** **344–345**		to review multiplication		Practice Master 102 Enrichment Master 102	
103	**Unit 4 Practice** **346–349**		to practice multiplication		Practice Master 103 Enrichment Master 103	
	Unit 4 Test **350–351**		to review multiplication		Assessment Masters	
	Unit 4 Wrap-Up . . . . . **352–353** Your Heart at Work			**Project**		

UNIT CONNECTIONS

INTERVENTION STRATEGIES

In this Teacher's Guide there are specific strategies suggested for students with individual needs. These strategies appear with icons under the headings ESL, Gifted and Talented, Special Needs, Learning Styles, and At Risk, and are provided at the point of use. Following are the icons to look for and the types of strategies that will accompany them:

English as a Second Language

These strategies, designed for students who do not speak the English language fluently, suggest meaningful ways to present the lesson concepts and vocabulary.

Gifted and Talented

These strategies are designed to enrich and extend the lessons and offer further challenges to students who have easily mastered the concepts already presented.

Special Needs

Students who are physically challenged or who have learning disabilities may require alternative ways to complete activities, record answers, use manipulatives, and so on. The strategies labeled with this icon offer appropriate methods of teaching lesson concepts to these students.

Learning Styles

Each student has his or her individual approach to learning. The strategies labeled with this icon suggest ways to present lesson concepts so that various learning modalities—such as tactile/kinesthetic, visual, and auditory—can be addressed.

At Risk

These strategies highlight the relevancy of the skills presented by making the connection between school and real life. They are directed toward students who appear to be at risk of dropping out of school before graduation.

TECHNOLOGY CONNECTIONS

The following materials, designed to reinforce and extend lesson concepts, are referred to throughout this Teacher's Guide. It might be helpful to either order the software and video or check them out of the school media center or community library. If your school does not provide Internet access, consider visiting a local library, college, or business specializing in Internet services. Some students may be able to access the Internet at home.

Look for this **Technology Connection** *icon.*

- *Number Munchers,* from MECC; Mac, IBM, for grades 2–6 (software)
- *Rounding,* from Gamco; Mac, IBM, for grades 4–10 (software)
- *Math Mystery Theatre: Multiplication Maniac,* from EdCon/Imperial International; VHS, for grades 2–8 (video)
- *Calculating Crew,* from Edmark; Mac, IBM, for grades 3–5 (software)
- *Number Heroes,* from Edmark; Mac, IBM, for grades 3–5 (software)
- *Math/Geometry Forum,* http://forum.swarthmore.edu (Internet)
- *The Quarter-Mile Estimation & Math Tricks,* from Barnum Software; IBM, for grades 3–9 (software)
- *The Math Map Trip,* from Educational Activities; Mac, IBM, for grades 4–8 (software)
- *Knowledge Quest: Mathematics,* from CBE Services; Mac, IBM, for grades 4–12 (software)
- *In the Neighborhood,* from Critical Thinking Software & Books; Mac, IBM, for grades 2–12 (software)

CROSS-CURRICULAR CONNECTIONS

This Teacher's Guide offers specific suggestions on ways to connect the math concepts presented in this unit with other subjects that students are studying. Students can connect math concepts with topics they already know about, and they can find examples of math in other subjects and in real-world situations. These strategies are provided at the point of use.

Look for these icons:

- Geography
- Health
- Social Studies
- Music
- Science
- Math
- Art
- Physical Education
- Language Arts
- Careers

LITERATURE CONNECTIONS

The following books are referenced throughout this Teacher's Guide at points where they can be used to introduce, reinforce, or extend specific lesson concepts. You may want to locate these books in your school or community library.

Look for this **Literature Connection** *icon.*

- *Jason and the Money Tree* by Sonia Levitin. Harcourt Brace Jovanovich, 1974.
- *Building Tables on Tables on Tables: A Book About Multiplication* by John V. Trivett. Crowell, 1975.
- *The Magic School Bus Lost in the Solar System* by Joanna Cole. Scholastic, 1990.
- *The 329th Friend* by Marjorie Weinman Sharmat. Four Winds Press, 1979.
- *The Toothpaste Millionaire* by Jean Merrill. Houghton Mifflin, 1972.
- "Do Too Much Homework" in *Math Wizardry for Kids* (p. 199) by Martha Kenda and Phyllis S. Williams. Barron's Educational Series, 1995.
- *Pumpkins* by Mary Lynn Ray. Harcourt Brace Jovanovich, 1992.
- *Anno's Hat Tricks* by Mitsumasa Anno and Akihiro Nozaki. Philomel Books, 1985.
- *Calculator Riddles* by David A. Adler. Holiday House, 1995.
- *Cookies* by William Jaspersohn. Macmillan, 1993.
- *Math Fun with a Pocket Calculator* by Rose Wyler and Mary Elting. Julian Messner, 1992.
- *Take Me to Your Liter: Science and Math Jokes* by Charles Keller. Pippin Press, 1991.

ASSESSMENT OPPORTUNITIES AT-A-GLANCE

LESSON	PORTFOLIO	PERFORMANCE	FORMAL	SELF	INFORMAL	CUMULATIVE REVIEWS	MULTIPLE-CHOICE	MASTERY CHECKPOINTS	ANALYZING ANSWERS
78					✓				
79				✓					
80	✓								
81			✓					✓	
82						✓			✓
83			✓					✓	
84					✓				
85		✓							
86				✓					✓
87			✓					✓	✓
88					✓	✓			
Mid-Unit Review	✓	✓	✓						
89		✓							
90			✓					✓	
91				✓		✓			✓
92		✓							✓
93					✓				
94		✓							
95		✓				✓			
96	✓								
97		✓							
98			✓	✓				✓	
99				✓					
100					✓	✓			
101		✓							
102	✓	✓	✓						
103						✓			
Unit Test			✓				✓		

ASSESSMENT OPTIONS

PORTFOLIO ASSESSMENT

Throughout this Teacher's Guide are suggestions for activities in which students draw pictures, make graphs, and write about mathematics. Keep students' work to assess growth of understanding as the year progresses.

Lessons 80, Mid-Unit Review, 96, and 102

PERFORMANCE ASSESSMENT

Performance Assessment items focus on evaluating how students think and work as they solve problems. Opportunities for performance assessment can be found throughout the unit. Rubrics and guides for grading can be found in the front of the Assessment Blackline Masters.

Lessons 85, Mid-Unit Review, 89, 92, 94, 95, 97, 101, and 102

FORMAL ASSESSMENT

A Mid-Unit Review, Unit Review, and Unit Test help assess students' understanding of concepts, skills, and problem-solving ability. The *Math Explorations and Applications* CD-ROM Test Generator can create additional unit tests at three ability levels. Also Mastery Checkpoints are provided periodically throughout the unit.

Lessons 81, 83, 87, Mid-Unit Review, 90, 98, 102, and Unit Test

SELF ASSESSMENT

Throughout the program students are given the opportunity to check their own math skills.

Lessons 79, 86, 91, 98, and 99

INFORMAL ASSESSMENT

A variety of assessment suggestions are provided throughout the unit, including interviews, oral questions or presentations, and debates. Also, each lesson includes Assessment Criteria, a list of questions about each student's progress, understanding, and participation.

Lessons 78, 84, 88, 93, and 100

CUMULATIVE REVIEW

Cumulative Reviews, covering material presented thus far in the year, are provided in the unit for use as either assessment or practice.

Lessons 82, 88, 91, 95, 100, and 103

MULTIPLE-CHOICE TESTS (STANDARDIZED FORMAT)

Each unit provides a Unit Test in standardized format, giving students many opportunities to practice taking tests in this format.

MASTERY CHECKPOINTS

Mastery Checkpoints are provided throughout the unit to assess student proficiency in specific skills. Checkpoints reference appropriate Assessment Blackline Masters and other assessment options. Results of these evaluations can be recorded on the Mastery Checkpoint Chart.

Lessons 81, 83, 87, 90, and 98

ANALYZING ANSWERS

Analyzing Answers items suggest possible sources of student error and offer teaching strategies for addressing difficulties.

Lessons 82, 86, 87, 91, and 92

Look for these icons:

ALTERNATIVE ASSESSMENT ANALYZING ANSWERS SELF ASSESSMENT

> ***"Large pieces of work, like performance tasks, projects, and portfolios, provide opportunities for students to demonstrate growth in mathematical power."***
>
> *—NCTM Assessment Standards*

MASTERY CHECKPOINTS

WHAT TO EXPECT FROM STUDENTS AS THEY COMPLETE THIS UNIT

⑫ MULTIPLYING BY POWERS OF 10 AND MULTIPLYING BY MULTIPLES OF 10—LESSON 81

By this time most students should demonstrate mastery of multiplying by powers of 10 and multiplying by multiples of 10 by correctly answering at least 80% of the problems on page 274 or a similar page. Record the results of this assessment on the Mastery Checkpoint Chart. You may also wish to assign Assessment Blackline Masters page 32 to determine mastery.

⑬ APPROXIMATING ANSWERS TO MULTIDIGIT MULTIPLICATION PROBLEMS—LESSON 83

By this time most students should be able to approximate answers to multidigit multiplication problems and correctly answer 80% of the problems on page 283. You can assess this ability by observing students during the Mental Math exercise in Lesson 83 or by assigning Assessment Blackline Masters page 33. Results of this assessment may be recorded on the Mastery Checkpoint Chart.

⑭ MULTIPLYING TWO- AND THREE-DIGIT NUMBERS BY ONE-DIGIT NUMBERS—LESSON 87

By this time most students should demonstrate mastery of multiplying two- and three-digit numbers by one-digit numbers by correctly answering at least 80% of the problems on page 292 or a similar page. Record the results of this assessment on the Mastery Checkpoint Chart. You may also wish to assign Assessment Blackline Masters page 34 to determine mastery.

⑮ MULTIPLYING TWO-DIGIT NUMBERS—LESSON 90

By this time most students should demonstrate mastery of multiplying two two-digit numbers by correctly answering at least 80% of the problems on page 306 or a similar page. Record the results of this assessment on the Mastery Checkpoint Chart. You may also wish to assign Assessment Blackline Masters page 37 to determine mastery.

⑯ MULTIPLYING MULTIDIGIT NUMBERS—LESSON 98

By this time most students should demonstrate mastery of multiplying any two whole numbers by correctly solving and using correct procedures on at least 20 of the 25 problems on page 333 or a similar page. You may want to use Assessment Blackline Masters page 38 and record the results in the Mastery Checkpoint Chart.

UNIT 4

PROGRAM RESOURCES

THESE ADDITIONAL COMPONENTS OF *MATH EXPLORATIONS AND APPLICATIONS* CAN BE PURCHASED SEPARATELY FROM SRA/MCGRAW-HILL.

LESSON	BASIC MANIPULATIVE KIT	GAME MAT PACKAGE	TEACHER MANIPULATIVE KIT	INTERMEDIATE MANIPULATIVE KIT	INTERMEDIATE OVERHEAD MANIPULATIVE KIT	*THE CRUNCHER* SOFTWARE	*MATH EXPLORATIONS AND APPLICATIONS* CD-ROM
78	Number Cubes	play money		base-10 blocks place value pad	bills, coins base-10 blocks		Lesson 78
79							Lesson 79
80	Number Cubes Number Wheels					spreadsheet	Lesson 80
81		play money		angle rulers	bills, coins		Lesson 81
82				place value pad			Lesson 82
83							Lesson 83
84	Number Wheels						Lesson 84
85		Harder Shopping game					Lesson 85
86				base-10 blocks interlocking cubes	base-10 blocks		Lesson 86
87	Number Cubes Number Wheels						Lesson 87
88							Lesson 88
89	Number Cubes		scale	angle rulers			Lesson 89
90					coins		Lesson 90
91							Lesson 91
92							Lesson 92
93		play money	clock	clock faces	bills, coins clock faces	spreadsheet	Lesson 93
94							Lesson 94
95	Number Cubes	play money			bills, coins		Lesson 95
96				tape measure		spreadsheet	Lesson 96
97				tape measure angle rulers		spreadsheet	Lesson 97
98							Lesson 98
99	Number Cubes						Lesson 99
100	Number Cubes						Lesson 100
101	Number Wheels			angle ruler			Lesson 101
102							Lesson 102
103							Lesson 103

UNIT 4

Student Edition pages 266–267

Multidigit Multiplication

INTRODUCING THE UNIT

Using the Student Pages Begin your discussion of the opening unit photo by asking students, "When does a medical technician or doctor interpret photographs? When do they use multiplication and approximation?" Then read aloud the paragraph on the student page that highlights medicine as a career. This helps make the connection between school and work and encourages students to explore how math is used in the real world.

ACTIVITY On **paper,** have students brainstorm a list of types of photographs and charts that doctors interpret when making a diagnosis.

FYI Medicine has been practiced as a science for thousands of years. Even long ago, people performed complex surgeries and learned how to treat illnesses with naturally occurring drugs. As long ago as 10,000 years, people in South America were treating headaches with an operation called trephining. The trephine was an iron or copper blade that was used to cut a small hole in the human skull, relieving pressure on the blood vessels around the brain. There is evidence that, while sometimes fatal, this operation was occasionally a success. People long ago also knew how to use a range of roots and other plants to cure patients. Willow bark was used by ancient people for a variety of illnesses and is now known to contain an ingredient found in aspirin. By 2650 B.C. an Egyptian doctor named Imhotep wrote a textbook on how to set broken limbs and treat wounds. The science of medicine was further advanced by the ancient Israelites, who recorded their discoveries for future generations. The ancient Greek Hippocrates was another early doctor who, in the 400s B.C., developed a philosophy that is still used as an oath by modern doctors. By taking the Hippocratic oath, physicians vow to put the patient's well-being first.

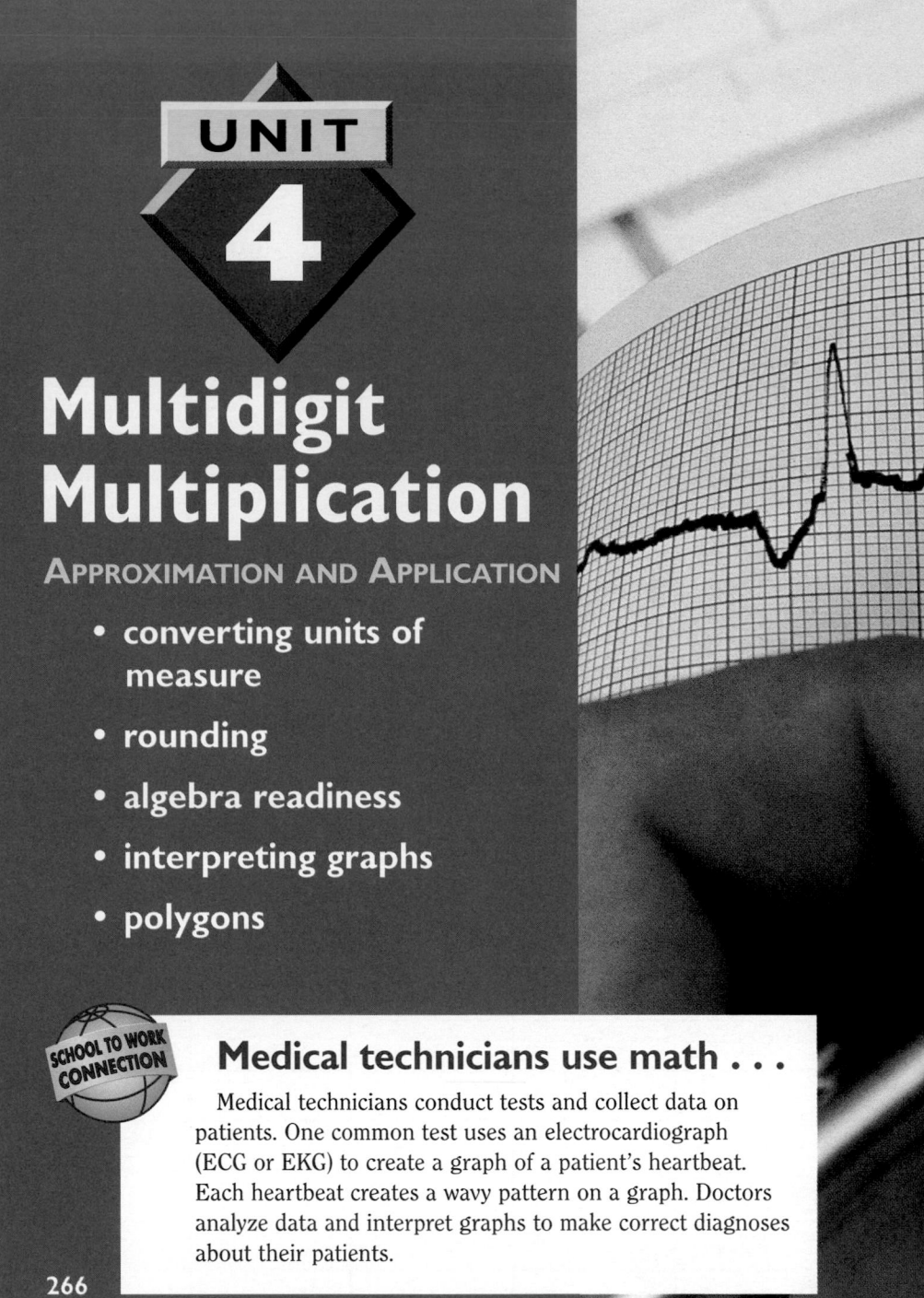

UNIT 4

Multidigit Multiplication

APPROXIMATION AND APPLICATION

- converting units of measure
- rounding
- algebra readiness
- interpreting graphs
- polygons

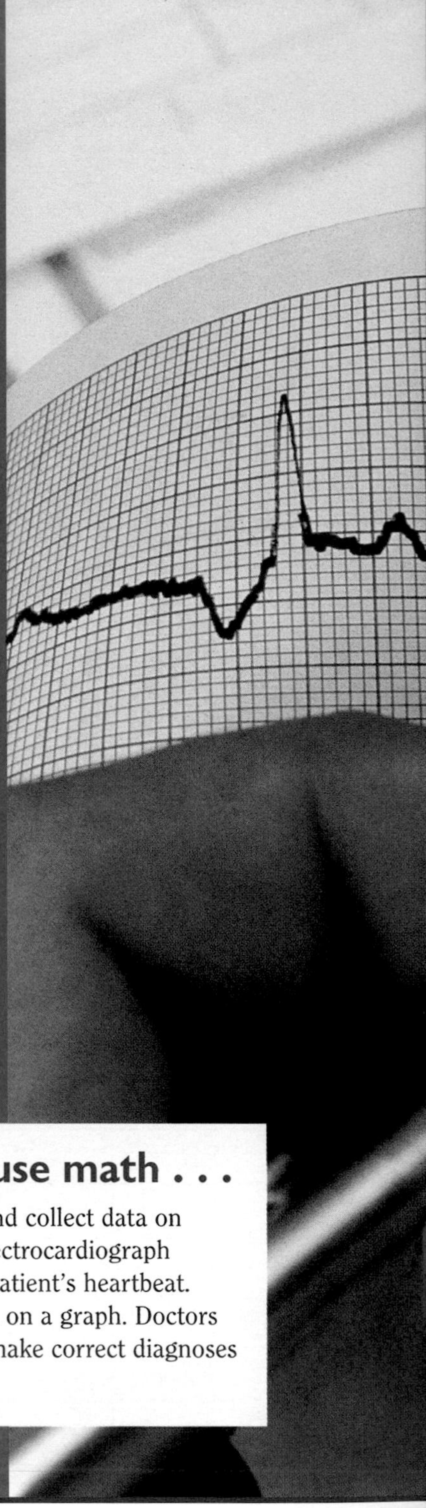

Medical technicians use math . . .

Medical technicians conduct tests and collect data on patients. One common test uses an electrocardiograph (ECG or EKG) to create a graph of a patient's heartbeat. Each heartbeat creates a wavy pattern on a graph. Doctors analyze data and interpret graphs to make correct diagnoses about their patients.

266

Thinklab™

SRA's *Thinklab*™ provides a series of creative and logical problem-solving opportunities for individual students. The problems are designed to appeal to different cognitive abilities.

- Use Problems 61–70 with this unit to reinforce creative insight (developing abstract relationships from given data).
- Use Problems 71–80 with this unit to reinforce perceiving image patterns (analysis of pattern and structure).

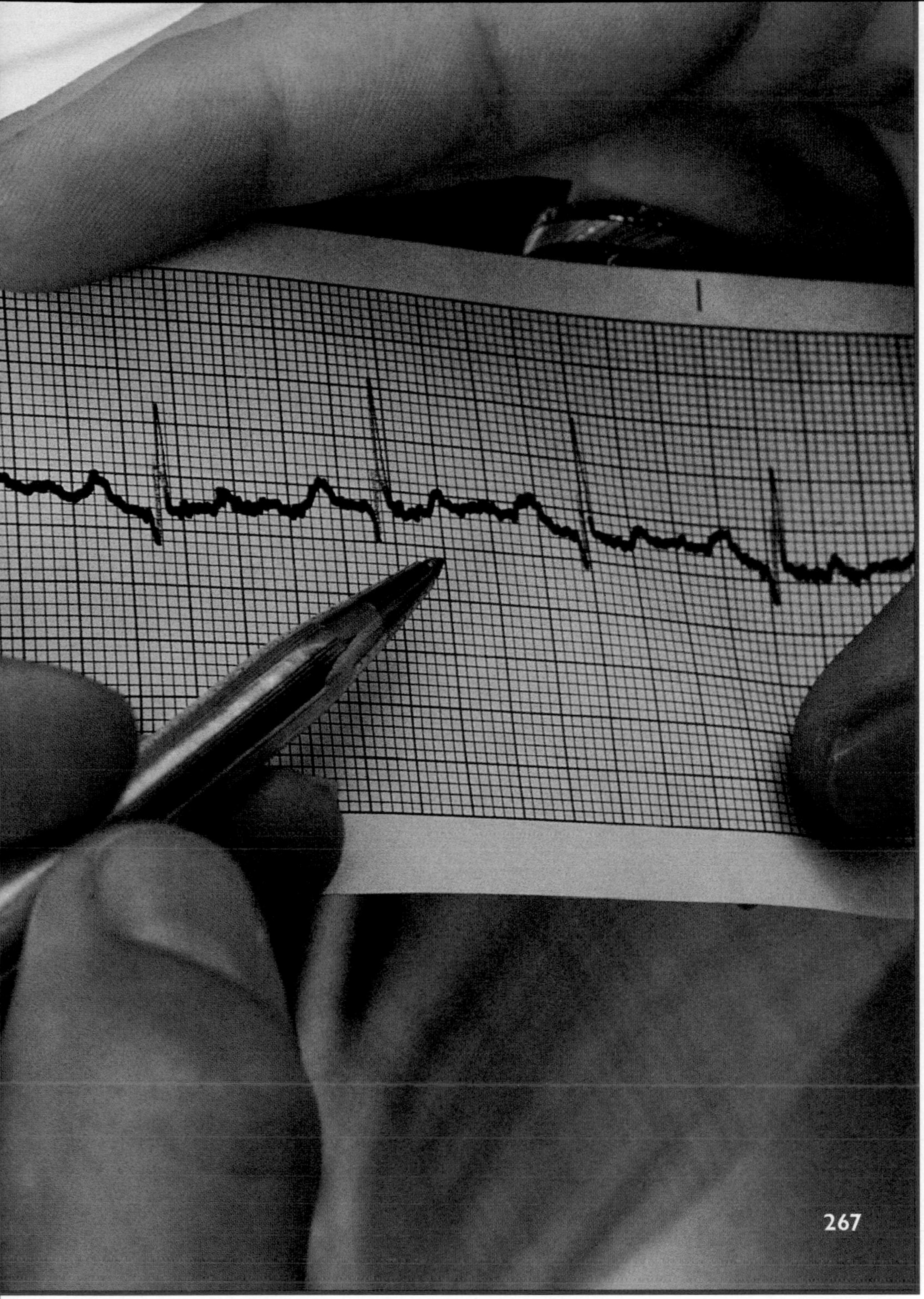

A profession in medicine begins with a firm grounding in math and science. Chemistry and biology are critical subjects for anyone considering a future in this field. Mastering these disciplines requires a solid knowledge of math. Once a doctor is treating patients, he or she must be able to collect and interpret data produced by machines like the EKG, and to calculate blood pressure and heart rate quickly and accurately. Make clear to students that a doctor must also be more than a scientist or a mathematician, and a doctor's ability to treat patients with concern is regarded as a vital skill.

Home Connections You may want to send the Home Connections Blackline Masters letter on pages 44–45 home to introduce this unit.

Unit Project This would be a good time to assign the "Your Heart at Work" project on pages 352 and 353. Students can begin working on the project in cooperative groups in their free time as they work through the unit. The Unit Project is a good opportunity for students to learn how to measure pulse rate, relate it to the beating of the heart, and give an indication of how much the heart works during one's lifetime.

Cooperate 1

Cooperate 1, published by SRA, provides a series of creative and logical problem-solving opportunities for cooperative groups. The problems are designed to provide practice in problem solving, communication, reasoning, and making connections. *Cooperate 1* presents the following cognitive strategies–perceiving spatial relations, ordering and sequencing, logical deduction, establishing and testing hypotheses, sequential exploration, identifying starting points, attending to detail, organizing information, and screening irrelevant information.

Each Problem Card emphasizes a principal strategy as well as reinforcing other strategies.

- Use Problem Card 16 with this unit to emphasize perceiving spatial relations.
- Use Problem Cards 17–18 with this unit to emphasize logical deduction.
- Use Problem Cards 19–20 with this unit to emphasize sequential exploration.

LESSON 78

Student Edition pages 268–269

Multiplying by Powers of 10

LESSON PLANNER

Objectives

- ▶ to develop a rule for multiplying by 10 and powers of 10
- ▶ to provide practice using the rule for multiplying by 10 and powers of 10

Context of the Lesson This is the first of seven lessons on multiplying by powers of 10, multiplying multiples of 10, and approximating products. This sequence, which precedes work with multidigit multiplication algorithms beginning in Lesson 85, will help students know whether their answers to general multidigit multiplication problems make sense. Multiplying by 10, 100, and 1000 was formally introduced in Level 3.

MANIPULATIVES

base-10 blocks* (optional)

play money* (optional)

place-value pads* (optional)

Program Resources

Number Cubes (0–5 and 5–10)

Practice Master 78

Enrichment Master 78

For extra practice:
CD-ROM* Lesson 78

1 Warm-Up 5 MINUTES

Problem of the Day Ask students: If you had a choice, would you rather have 5 dollars, 50 dimes, or 500 pennies? Explain your reasoning. (Answers may vary, but all three choices have the same value.)

Problem-Solving Strategies Ask students who have solved the Problem of the Day to share how they solved it and any strategies they used.

MENTAL MATH Provide practice with the multiplication facts and with multiplying by powers of 10. Make the practice fast-paced and mixed.

a. 100 x 6 = (600); 1000 x 6 = (6000)

b. 100 x 5 = (500); 1000 x 5 = (5000)

c. 100 x 7 = (700); 1000 x 7 = (7000)

d. 100 x 4 = (400); 1000 x 4 = (4000)

EXPLORE

LESSON 78

Multiplying by Powers of 10

"I can add 0 to 3 and get 30," said Kenji. "I just write 3 and then I add the 0 after it." He wrote 30 on the board.

"You aren't really adding 0," answered Carol. "You're multiplying by 10 when you write that 0 after the 3."

- ◆ When Kenji writes 0 after 3, is he adding 0 to 3 or multiplying 3 × 10? **multiplying 3×10**
- ◆ How can you multiply 3 by 100? **Write 2 zeros after the 3.**
- ◆ How can you multiply 3 by 1000? **Write 3 zeros after the 3.**
- ◆ How can you multiply 3 by 10,000? **Write 4 zeros after the 3.**

MATH JOURNAL **Write a general rule for multiplying by numbers like 10, 100, 1000, and so on in your Math Journal.**

- ◆ Discuss your rule with others. Why does your rule work? **Sample rule: count how many zeros there are in the power of 10 and write that many zeros after the other factor.**

268 • Multidigit Multiplication

Why teach it this way?

You may find that some students have not yet developed a solid understanding of place value, but they can still learn the rules for multiplying and dividing by powers of 10. At this time, you should emphasize learning the rules. You may wish to begin a program of extra help for students who demonstrate weakness in understanding place value.

RETEACHING

Reinforce students' understanding of place value by using assorted base-10 manipulative materials, such as **base-10 blocks*, play money*,** and **place-value pads*.** Students may also benefit from playing the "Harder Rummage Sale" game from Level 3 of the *Math Explorations and Applications* program. This game provides practice with changing money ($1, $10, $100).

*available separately

Use your rule to solve for *n*. Watch your numbering.

1. $10 \times 7 = n$ **70**
2. $100 \times 7 = n$ **700**
3. $1000 \times 7 = n$ **7000**
4. $1000 \times 6 = n$ **6000**
5. $1000 \times 65 = n$ **65,000**
6. $100 \times 73 = n$ **7300**
7. $10 \times 583 = n$ **5830**
8. $583 \times 10 = n$ **5830**
9. $68 \times 100 = n$ **6800**
10. $10{,}000 \times 583 = n$ **5,830,000**
11. $657 \times 10 = n$ **6570**
12. $100 \times 783 = n$ **78,300**
13. $594 \times 1000 = n$ **594,000**
14. $86 \times 100 = n$ **8600**
15. $503 \times 10 = n$ **5030**
16. $100 \times 10 = n$ **1000**
17. $100 \times 496 = n$ **49,600**
18. $10 \times 392 = n$ **3920**
19. $16 \times 1000 = n$ **16,000**
20. $497 \times 1000 = n$ **497,000**
21. $709 \times 10 = n$ **7090**
22. $649 \times 1000 = n$ **649,000**
23. $200 \times 1000 = n$ **200,000**
24. $800 \times 100 = n$ **80,000**

◆ How many 0s are there in your answer to problem 16? Did you write two 0s after the 10 or did you write one 0 after the 100? Does it make a difference in your answer? **3; no**

Multiply. Watch your numbering.

25. 100×100 **10,000**
26. 1000×10 **10,000**
27. 1000×1000 **1,000,000**
28. $10{,}000 \times 100$ **1,000,000**
29. $10{,}000 \times 10{,}000$ **100,000,000**
30. 100×1000 **100,000**
31. $100{,}000 \times 10$ **1,000,000**
32. $1{,}000{,}000 \times 1{,}000$ **1,000,000,000**
33. $100{,}000 \times 1{,}000$ **100,000,000**

PROBLEM SOLVING

Solve these problems.

34. How many years are there in ten centuries? **1000**
35. The Packard family made a patio out of bricks. There are 20 rows of bricks, with 100 bricks in each row. How many bricks are there all together? **2000**

Unit 4 Lesson 78 • **269**

PRACTICE p. 78

LESSON 78 PRACTICE Name________________

Multiply.

1. $100 \times 5 =$ 500
2. $89 \times 10 =$ 890
3. $10 \times 10 =$ 100
4. $6 \times 1000 =$ 6000
5. $1000 \times 6 =$ 6000
6. $41 \times 10{,}000 =$ 410,000
7. $1000 \times 8 =$ 8000
8. $12 \times 10 =$ 120
9. $80 \times 10 =$ 800
10. $50 \times 100 =$ 5000
11. $421 \times 10 =$ 4210
12. $81 \times 1000 =$ 81,000
13. $824 \times 100 =$ 82,400
14. $64 \times 10 =$ 640
15. $1000 \times 417 =$ 417,000
16. $6 \times 10{,}000 =$ 60,000
17. $100 \times 10 =$ 1000
18. $608 \times 100 =$ 60,800
19. $98 \times 100 =$ 9800
20. $137 \times 1000 =$ 137,000
21. $10 \times 2731 =$ 27,310
22. $75 \times 10{,}000 =$ 750,000
23. $1000 \times 86 =$ 86,000
24. $11 \times 100 =$ 1100
25. $31 \times 100 =$ 3100
26. $307 \times 10 =$ 3070
27. $18 \times 10{,}000 =$ 180,000
28. $8 \times 1000 =$ 8000
29. $49 \times 100 =$ 4900
30. $89 \times 10{,}000 =$ 890,000
31. $14 \times 10 =$ 140
32. $100 \times 100 =$ 10,000
33. $138 \times 100 =$ 13,800
34. $10 \times 10{,}000 =$ 100,000
35. $7 \times 1000 =$ 7000
36. $1000 \times 1000 =$ 1,000,000
37. $246 \times 10 =$ 2460
38. $1{,}000{,}000 \times 10 =$ 10,000,000
39. $48 \times 100 =$ 4800
40. $4000 \times 1000 =$ 4,000,000
41. $167 \times 10{,}000 =$ 1,670,000
42. $10 \times 100 =$ 1000

78 • *Math Explorations and Applications* Level 4

Copyright © SRA/McGraw-Hill. Permission is granted to reproduce this page for classroom use.

ENRICHMENT p. 78

LESSON 78 ENRICHMENT Name________________

PROBLEM SOLVING

How powerful are the powers of 10? Apply the powers of 10 to some situations and see for yourself. Be ready to discuss how you solved each problem.

1. Does 3 miles per hour seem slow to you? That is about how fast people walk. What if you could walk faster by a power of 10 every day? How fast would you be walking
   a. on the second day? 30 mph
   b. on the fifth day? 30,000 mph
   c. on the tenth day? 3,000,000,000 mph
2. If someone offered you a choice between $1.00 that would increase by a power of 10 every day for a week or $1,000,000 right now, which would you take? Explain your answer. If you took $1,000,000 now, you wouldn't have to wait for the $1,000,000 you would get in a week.
3. If you could tell ten people a secret every day, how many people could you tell in two days? 20
4. If you could tell ten people a secret in one day, and those people told another ten people the next day, how many people would know the secret in two days? 111 (including the student)
5. How many people would know the secret in two days if you could tell 100 people in one day, who in turn could each tell 100 people the next day? 10,101

78 • *Math Explorations and Applications* Level 4

Copyright © SRA/McGraw-Hill. Permission is granted to reproduce this page for classroom use.

2 Teach

Using the Student Pages Discuss the story and the five questions on page 268 with the class. Point out that Kenji does not use the word *add* in the arithmetic sense; he uses it to mean "to put next to or attach." In the fifth discussion question on page 268, it is important to acknowledge different ways to state the rule.

Have students work independently on problems 1–35 on page 269. Discuss problem 16 with the class. Point out that either method gives the correct answer. After students complete page 269, have them play the "Roll a Number" game (page 11) or the "Order" game (page 13). Both games provide practice with place value.

3 Wrap-Up

5 MINUTES

In Closing Have students summarize how to multiply a number by 10, by 100, and by 1000.

ALTERNATIVE ASSESSMENT

Informal Assessment Observe students as they work through this lesson. Ask them to verbalize the rule for multiplying by 10, by 100, or by 1000 and to show you how they know they have written the correct product.

Assessment Criteria

Did the student . . .

✓ contribute to the discussion of the situation?

✓ communicate a rule for multiplying by 10, by 100, and by 1000?

✓ explain how to apply the rule to solve for *n*?

✓ correctly answer at least 75% of the computation problems?

Homework Assign Practice Master 78 to reinforce the skill of multiplying by powers of 10.

LESSON 79

Student Edition pages 270–271

Converting Metric Units

LESSON PLANNER

Objectives

- ▶ to review converting from one metric unit to another
- ▶ to provide practice with estimating metric measures

Context of the Lesson This is the second of seven lessons on multiplying by powers of 10, multiplying multiples of 10, and approximating products. This sequence, which precedes work with multidigit multiplication algorithms, will help students check their answers to multidigit multiplication problems.

MANIPULATIVES

none

Program Resources

Reteaching Master

Practice Master 79

Enrichment Master 79

For extra practice:

CD-ROM* Lesson 79

1 Warm-Up

5 MINUTES

Problem of the Day Present the following problem and discuss students' solution methods: A snail fell into a well that was 15 feet deep. Starting at noon, the snail slowly inched up the side of the well to get out. The snail climbed steadily for 45 minutes, got 3 feet closer to the top, and then rested for 15 minutes. During the rest, the snail slowly slid back down 1 foot. At this rate, what time will it be when the snail gets out of the well? (7:00 P.M.)

Problem-Solving Strategies Ask students who have solved the Problem of the Day to share how they solved it and any strategies they used.

MENTAL MATH Provide practice multiplying by 10, 100, and 1000:

a. 8 × 10 = (80)	**b.** 8 × 100 = (800)
c. 8 × 1000 = (8000)	**d.** 24 × 10 = (240)
e. 24 × 100 = (2400)	**f.** 24 × 1000 = (24,000)
g. 10 × 36 = (360)	**h.** 100 × 36 = (3600)
i. 1000 × 36 = (36,000)	**j.** 44 × 100 = (4400)
k. 51 × 1000 = (51,000)	**l.** 10 × 345 = (3450)

MIXED PRACTICE

LESSON 79

Converting Metric Units

Remember: 100 centimeters (cm) = 1 meter (m)
1000 meters = 1 kilometer

Answer the following questions.

1. How many centimeters are there in 1 kilometer? **100,000**
2. How many centimeters are there in 7 kilometers? **700,000**
3. How many centimeters are there in 7 meters? **700**
4. How many meters are there in 7 kilometers? **7000**
5. How many centimeters are there in 73 meters? **7300**
6. How many centimeters are there in 73 kilometers? **7,300,000**

Remember: 1000 milliliters = 1 liter

Answer the following questions.

7. How many milliliters are there in 7 liters? **7000**
8. How many milliliters are there in 73 liters? **73,000**
9. How many cents are worth seven dollars? **700**
10. How many cents are worth $73? **7300**
11. How many milliliters are in 13 liters? **13,000**
12. How many cents are worth eighteen dollars? **1800**

Remember: 1000 grams (g) = 1 kilogram

Answer the following questions.

13. How many grams are there in 10 kilograms? **10,000**
14. How many grams are there in 7 kilograms? **7000**
15. How many grams are there in 73 kilograms? **73,000**

SPECIAL NEEDS

Meeting Individual Needs

Students who have difficulty recalling or applying metric relationships may benefit from using a metric place-value chart that gives the metric prefixes in order from greatest to least: *kilo-, hecto-, deca-, deci-, centi-,* and *milli-* (liter, meter, and gram).

RETEACHING p. 24

LESSON 79 RETEACHING Name________________

The metric system is based on units of 10. Each unit of measure is ten times less or ten times greater than the next unit.

Prefixes have specific meanings related to the size of the unit. Understanding the metric system is easy if you know what all the prefixes mean.

Prefixes and Their Meanings	
Prefix	*Meaning*
kilo-	1000
hecto-	100
deca-	10
deci-	$\frac{1}{10}$
centi-	$\frac{1}{100}$
milli-	$\frac{1}{1000}$

Units of Length, Weight, and Volume	
1 meter	1000 millimeters
1 millimeter	$\frac{1}{1000}$ meter
1 meter	100 centimeters
1 centimeter	$\frac{1}{100}$ meter
1 kilometer	1000 meters
1 kilogram	1000 grams
1 milligram	$\frac{1}{1000}$ gram
1000 milligrams	1 gram
1 milliliter	$\frac{1}{1000}$ liter
1000 milliliters	1 liter

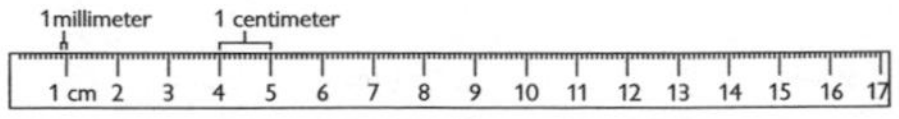

This shows you part of a meterstick, a tool used to measure length. A meterstick is divided into 100 equal parts. Each part is 1 centimeter.

Each centimeter is divided into ten equal parts. Each part is 1 millimeter.

Use the information to answer these questions.

1. Choose an object in the classroom. Measure it in millimeters and centimeters. Students may measure books, desks, etc.
2. What fraction of a meter is 1 centimeter? $\frac{1}{100}$ 1 millimeter? $\frac{1}{1000}$
3. How many kilograms do 5000 grams equal? 5

24 • *Math Explorations and Applications* Level 4

Copyright © SRA/McGraw-Hill. Permission is granted to reproduce this page for classroom use.

*available separately

Answer these questions.

Jim rode his bicycle all day, from 8:00 A.M. until 5:00 P.M. At the end of the day he said, "I must have ridden more than 60 centimeters today."

16. Do you think Jim probably rode more than 60 cm? **yes**
17. How far do you think Jim was trying to say he had ridden? **60 km** How far is that in centimeters? **6,000,000 cm**

Mary said she thinks she weighs about 45 grams.

18. Do you think Mary really weighs about 45 grams? **no**
19. How much do you think Mary was trying to say she weighs? How many grams is that? **45 kilograms; 45,000 g**

Pete said he thinks he is at least 120 kilometers tall.

20. Do you think Pete is at least 120 kilometers tall? **no**
21. What do you think he meant to say? **120 centimeters**
22. If Pete were 120 kilometers tall, how many meters would that be? How many centimeters would that be? **120,000; 12,000,000**
23. Do you know of anything that is 120 kilometers tall? If so, name it. **no**
24. Name something that is about 100 meters tall. How many centimeters is that? **skyscraper; 10,000**

② Teach

Using the Student Pages Have students complete page 270 individually. Call attention to the repeated use of the metric prefixes *kilo-*, *centi-*, and *milli-*. Students should be able to use these patterns to estimate how many grams there are in a kilogram. (1000)

You may want to do page 271 as a class or small-group activity. Allow time to discuss the reasoning students used to determine whether the given measurements made sense.

③ Wrap-Up

5 MINUTES

In Closing Discuss the patterns students use to make metric conversions.

SELF ASSESSMENT

Have students write a statement about converting within the metric system in their Math Journals. Ask them to explain how to do it and how easy or difficult it is.

Assessment Criteria

Did the student . . .

✓ correctly convert from one metric unit to another?

✓ contribute to the discussion of metric conversions and sensible units of metric measure?

✓ write a comprehensible statement about conversion within the metric system?

Homework Have students write three reasonable statements that involve estimates of metric measure. They can use the problems on page 271 as models for the kind of statements to formulate.

PRACTICE p. 79

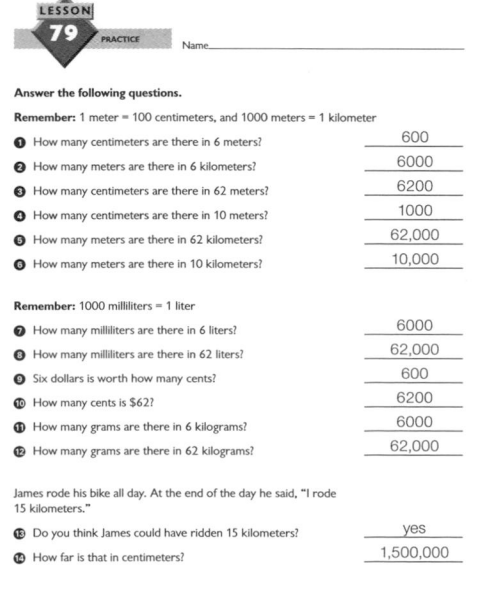

LESSON 79 PRACTICE Name______

Answer the following questions.

Remember: 1 meter = 100 centimeters, and 1000 meters = 1 kilometer

1. How many centimeters are there in 6 meters? 600
2. How many meters are there in 6 kilometers? 6000
3. How many centimeters are there in 62 meters? 6200
4. How many centimeters are there in 10 meters? 1000
5. How many meters are there in 62 kilometers? 62,000
6. How many meters are there in 10 kilometers? 10,000

Remember: 1000 milliliters = 1 liter

7. How many milliliters are there in 6 liters? 6000
8. How many milliliters are there in 62 liters? 62,000
9. Six dollars is worth how many cents? 600
10. How many cents is $62? 6200
11. How many grams are there in 6 kilograms? 6000
12. How many grams are there in 62 kilograms? 62,000

James rode his bike all day. At the end of the day he said, "I rode 15 kilometers."

13. Do you think James could have ridden 15 kilometers? yes
14. How far is that in centimeters? 1,500,000

Copyright © SRA/McGraw-Hill. Permission is granted to reproduce this page for classroom use.

ENRICHMENT p. 79

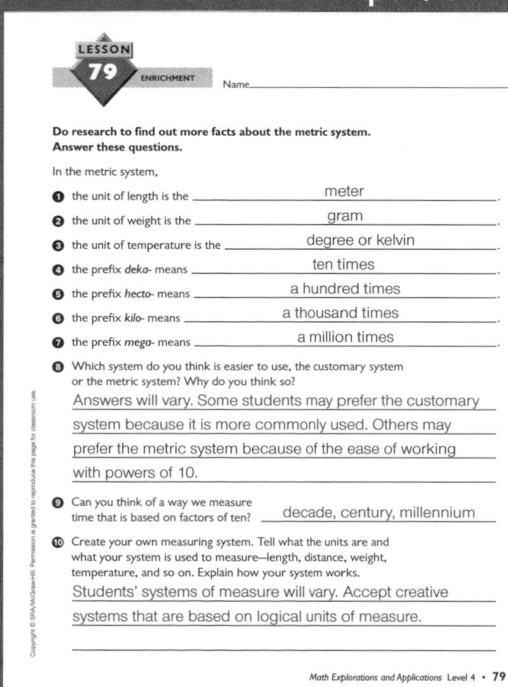

LESSON 79 ENRICHMENT Name______

Do research to find out more facts about the metric system. Answer these questions.

In the metric system,

1. the unit of length is the meter.
2. the unit of weight is the gram.
3. the unit of temperature is the degree or kelvin.
4. the prefix *deka-* means ten times.
5. the prefix *hecto-* means a hundred times.
6. the prefix *kilo-* means a thousand times.
7. the prefix *mega-* means a million times.
8. Which system do you think is easier to use, the customary system or the metric system? Why do you think so? Answers will vary. Some students may prefer the customary system because it is more commonly used. Others may prefer the metric system because of the ease of working with powers of 10.
9. Can you think of a way we measure time that is based on factors of ten? decade, century, millennium
10. Create your own measuring system. Tell what the units are and what your system is used to measure—length, distance, weight, temperature, and so on. Explain how your system works. Students' systems of measure will vary. Accept creative systems that are based on logical units of measure.

Copyright © SRA/McGraw-Hill. Permission is granted to reproduce this page for classroom use.

LESSON 80

Student Edition pages 272–273

Multipying by Multiples of 10

LESSON PLANNER

Objectives

- to develop a procedure for multiplying multiples of 10 that have only one nonzero digit (such as 300 x 7000)
- to provide practice in using this procedure

Context of the Lesson This is the third of seven lessons on multiplying by powers and multiples of 10 and on approximating products. This sequence will help prepare students for the work with multidigit multiplication algorithms that begins in Lesson 85.

MANIPULATIVES

none

Program Resources

Number Cubes (0–5)
Number Wheels
Reteaching Master
Practice Master 80
Enrichment Master 80
The Cruncher*
For extra practice:
CD-ROM* Lesson 80

1 Warm-Up

5 MINUTES

Problem of the Day Present this problem on the chalkboard and encourage students to draw a picture to solve it: Ms. Klein's driveway is 60 feet long. She wants to put a reflector on a metal post at the beginning and end of both sides of her driveway. She also wants reflectors every 10 feet along both sides. If reflectors on posts cost $10 each, how much money will Ms. Klein spend on materials? ($140)

Problem-Solving Strategies Ask students who have solved the Problem of the Day to share how they solved it and any strategies they used.

MENTAL MATH Provide practice with multiplication facts, multiplying by powers of 10, and multiplying multiples of 10 with these problems. Have students respond with their Number Wheels.

a. 30 x 100 = (3000) **b.** 300 x 100 = (30,000)
c. 700 x 4 = (2800) **d.** 9 x 80 = (720)
e. 8 x 900 = (7200) **f.** 80 x 80 = (6400)
g. 8000 x 8 = (64,000) **h.** 500 x 30 = (15,000)
i. 300 x 500 = (150,000) **j.** 100 x 100 = (10,000)

LESSON 80

Multiplying by Multiples of 10

The Albany Parks Department has bought land for a new public sports park. The large, open field is 400 meters wide and 800 meters long. What is the area of the field? You can multiply to find out.

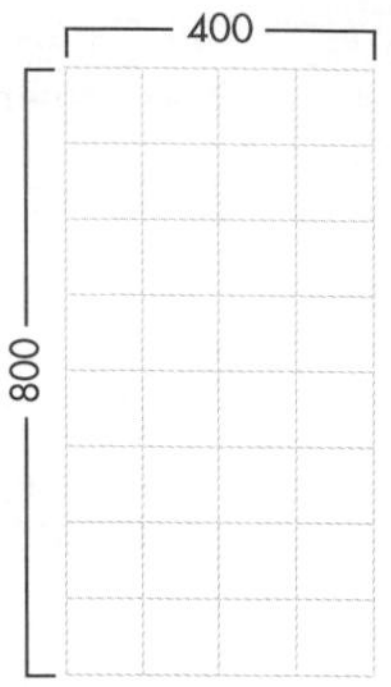

Multiply 400 × 800.

Think of a rectangle that is 800 units long and 400 units wide.

Now think of separating the rectangle into squares, so that each square is 100 units by 100 units.

- How many squares are there? **32**
- What is the area of each square? **10,000 square units**
- What is the area of the entire rectangle? **320,000 square units**
- What is 400 × 800?

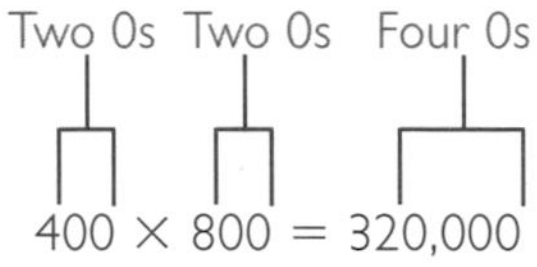

Notice that the number of 0s in the answer is the sum of the numbers of 0s in the two factors.

Multiply 300 × 60.

Look at another rectangle separated into rectangular sections.

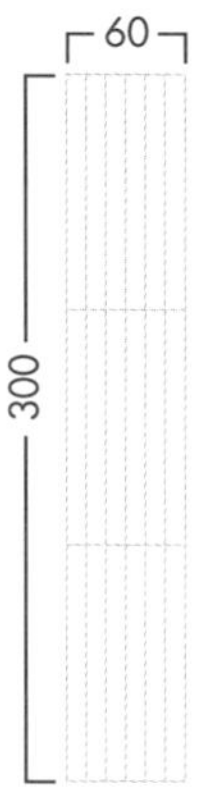

- How many small rectangles are there? **18**
- What is the area of each small rectangle? **1000 square units**
- What is the area of the entire rectangle? **18,000 square units**
- What is 300 × 60? **18,000**

Literature Connection Invite students to read *Jason and the Money Tree* by Sonia Levitin, in which Jason is surprised when he plants a ten-dollar bill that grows into a money tree. Have students figure out the cash value of a whole crop of these plants.

RETEACHING p. 25

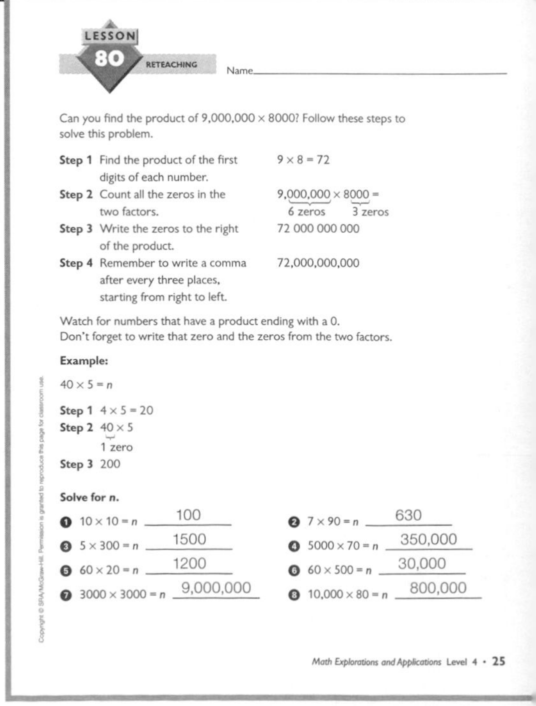
LESSON 80 RETEACHING Name__________

Can you find the product of 9,000,000 × 8000? Follow these steps to solve this problem.

Step 1 Find the product of the first digits of each number. 9 × 8 = 72
Step 2 Count all the zeros in the two factors. 9,000,000 × 8000 = (6 zeros, 3 zeros)
Step 3 Write the zeros to the right of the product. 72 000 000 000
Step 4 Remember to write a comma after every three places, starting from right to left. 72,000,000,000

Watch for numbers that have a product ending with a 0.
Don't forget to write that zero and the zeros from the two factors.

Example:

40 × 5 = *n*

Step 1 4 × 5 = 20
Step 2 40 × 5 (1 zero)
Step 3 200

Solve for *n*.

1. 10 × 10 = *n* 100
2. 7 × 90 = *n* 630
3. 5 × 300 = *n* 1500
4. 5000 × 70 = *n* 350,000
5. 60 × 20 = *n* 1200
6. 60 × 500 = *n* 30,000
7. 3000 × 3000 = *n* 9,000,000
8. 10,000 × 80 = *n* 800,000

Copyright © SRA/McGraw-Hill. Permission is granted to reproduce this page for classroom use.

Math Explorations and Applications Level 4 • 25

*available separately

Multiply 90,000 × 2,000,000.

The answer is 9 × 2 with many 0s after it. Here's how to find out how many 0s.

Count the number of 0s in the two factors.

There are **four 0s** in 90,000.

There are **six 0s** in 2,000,000.

There are **ten 0s** in all in the two factors.

So the answer is 9 × 2 with ten 0s after it.

The answer is 180,000,000,000.

(Read it "one hundred eighty billion.")

Multiply.

❶	❷	❸	❹	❺	❻
30 × 50	80 × 40	600 × 700	8000 × 30	60 × 50	800 × 400
1500	**3200**	**420,000**	**240,000**	**3000**	**320,000**

Multiply. Solve for *n*.

❼ 900 × 200 = *n* **180,000**

❽ 200 × 4000 = *n* **800,000**

❾ 5 × 4 = *n* **20**

❿ 300 × 40 = *n* **12,000**

⓫ 50 × 4 = *n* **200**

⓬ 4 × 7000 = *n* **28,000**

⓭ 5 × 40 = *n* **200**

⓮ 30 × 90 = *n* **2700**

⓯ 500 × 4 = *n* **2000**

⓰ 800 × 4000 = *n* **3,200,000**

⓱ 5000 × 4000 = *n* **20,000,000**

⓲ 90 × 5000 = *n* **450,000**

⓳ 60 × 50 = *n* **3000**

⓴ 80 × 30 = *n* **2400**

㉑ 20 × 500 = *n* **10,000**

㉒ 3 × 500 = *n* **1500**

㉓ 600 × 30 = *n* **18,000**

㉔ 4000 × 7000 = *n* **28,000,000**

㉕ 900 × 80 = *n* **72,000**

㉖ 90 × 500 = *n* **45,000**

㉗ 8000 × 7000 = *n* **56,000,000**

㉘ 600 × 40 = *n* **24,000**

㉙ 1000 × 4000 = *n* **4,000,000**

㉚ 8 × 500 = *n* **4000**

㉛ 10,000 × 60 = *n* **600,000**

㉜ 90 × 400 = *n* **36,000**

❷ Teach

Using the Student Pages Discuss page 272 with students. If they have trouble answering the second discussion question, draw a simple square. Ask them to imagine that there are 100 small squares in the first row and in each of the other 99 rows. Then ask how many small squares are in the 100 × 100 square. (100 × 100 = 10,000) Students can use a blank **Cruncher*** spreadsheet to show the pattern for multiplying multidigit numbers by powers of 10.

Discuss the top of page 273 with the class. Then have students work independently on the page. As they finish, they can play the "Add the Products" game (page 110), which provides practice with multiplication and addition, or another game of their choice.

❸ Wrap-Up

5 MINUTES

In Closing Have students tell the rules for multiplying by multiples of 10.

ALTERNATIVE ASSESSMENT

Portfolio Assessment Have students write a step-by-step explanation that tells how to find the product of 600 × 500. Have them date this work and add it to their Math Portfolios for a record of ongoing learning.

Assessment Criteria

Did the student . . .

- ✓ contribute to the discussion?
- ✓ communicate a rule for multiplying by multiples of 10?
- ✓ accurately apply the rule to solve for *n*?
- ✓ correctly answer at least 75% of the computation problems?

Homework Assign Practice Master 80 to reinforce the skill of multiplying by multiples of 10.

PRACTICE p. 80

LESSON 80 PRACTICE Name__________

Multiply.

❶ 60 × 4 = 240	❷ 60 × 60 = 3600
❸ 6 × 40 = 240	❹ 8 × 80 = 640
❺ 60 × 40 = 2400	❻ 90 × 300 = 27,000
❼ 600 × 400 = 240,000	❽ 20 × 50 = 1000
❾ 6000 × 4000 = 24,000,000	❿ 8 × 900 = 7200
⓫ 30 × 700 = 21,000	⓬ 600 × 700 = 420,000
⓭ 80 × 4000 = 320,000	⓮ 300 × 90 = 27,000
⓯ 9 × 800 = 7200	⓰ 6 × 9000 = 54,000
⓱ 70 × 5000 = 350,000	⓲ 40 × 500 = 20,000
⓳ 400 × 700 = 280,000	⓴ 7 × 700 = 4900
㉑ 8 × 3000 = 24,000	㉒ 2 × 3000 = 6000
㉓ 60 × 7000 = 420,000	㉔ 50 × 50 = 2500
㉕ 800 × 5 = 4000	㉖ 8 × 40 = 320
㉗ 7000 × 60 = 420,000	㉘ 9 × 200 = 1800
㉙ 50 × 300 = 15,000	㉚ 400 × 80 = 32,000
㉛ 9 × 5000 = 45,000	㉜ 90 × 7000 = 630,000
㉝ 90 × 90 = 8100	㉞ 20 × 60 = 1200
㉟ 600 × 300 = 180,000	㊱ 8 × 60 = 480
㊲ 70 × 8000 = 560,000	㊳ 30 × 4000 = 120,000
㊴ 6 × 50 = 300	㊵ 9 × 600 = 5400
㊶ 30 × 30 = 900	㊷ 4 × 700 = 2800

80 • *Math Explorations and Applications* Level 4

Copyright © SRA/McGraw-Hill. Permission is granted to reproduce this page for classroom use.

ENRICHMENT p. 80

LESSON 80 ENRICHMENT Name__________

PROBLEM SOLVING **Solve these problems.**

❶ Imagine you have a large square made up of 400 smaller squares. How many small squares are in each row of the large square? How many rows are there? 20; 20

❷ If you hid a key under one of the smaller squares, what are the chances that someone would find it in one try? Ring the correct answer.

a. 1 in 40 (**b.**) 1 in 400

c. 1 in 4000 **d.** 1 in 4,000,000

❸ What if each of the small squares were made up of 10,000 tiny squares? If you hid a tiny key under one of the tiny squares, what are the chances someone would find it in one try? Ring the correct answer.

a. 1 in 40,000 **b.** 1 in 80,000

c. 1 in 100,000 (**d.**) 1 in 4,000,000

❹ Imagine you hid two keys, one gold and one silver, under two different squares on the square of 10,000 tiny squares.

a. What are the chances someone would find the gold key in one try? 1 in 4,000,000

b. What are the chances someone would find the silver key in one try? 1 in 4,000,000

c. What are the chances someone would find one of the keys in one try? 2 in 4,000,000

80 • *Math Explorations and Applications* Level 4

Copyright © SRA/McGraw-Hill. Permission is granted to reproduce this page for classroom use.

*available separately

LESSON 81

Student Edition pages 274–277

Practice with Multiples of 10

LESSON PLANNER

Objectives

- ✓ to assess students' mastery of multiplying multiples of 10 and multiplying by powers of 10
- ▶ to provide practice with solving word problems based on powers and multiples of 10
- ▶ to help students develop the broad ability to use mathematical common sense

Context of the Lesson This is the fourth of seven lessons on multiplying by powers of 10, multiplying multiples of 10, and approximating products. It includes a Mastery Checkpoint for assessing mastery of multiplying by powers of 10 and multiplying multiples of 10. This lesson also contains the first part of "The Treasure of Mugg Island," a six-part Thinking Story.

MANIPULATIVES

centimeter rulers*
drawing paper
meterstick
play money*

Program Resources

Practice Master 81
Enrichment Master 81
Assessment Master
For career connections:
Careers and Math*
For extra practice:
CD-ROM* Lesson 81

1 Warm-Up

5 MINUTES

Problem of the Day Present this problem for students to work on as a class to find all the solutions: Arianna can buy batteries in packs of two, four, six, or ten. Using all possible combinations of packs, how many different ways can she buy 20 batteries? (19 ways)

Problem-Solving Strategies Ask students who have solved the Problem of the Day to share how they solved it and any strategies they used.

MENTAL MATH Present a drill in which you present the following problems and a range of 100–200 in which answers should fall. Students show thumbs up if the answer falls within the stated range or thumbs down if it is outside the range.

a. 28 + 32 (thumbs down)

b. 33 x 10 (thumbs down)

(continued on page 275)

MIXED PRACTICE

LESSON 81

Practice with Multiples of 10

Be careful when you multiply by multiples of 10. Remember to count the number of 0s in the two factors.

Multiply.

1 100 × 10 **1000**	2 100 × 1000 **100,000**	3 10 × 1000 **10,000**
4 1000 × 1000 **1,000,000**	5 10,000 × 1,000 **10,000,000**	6 10,000 × 100 **1,000,000**
7 1000 × 100 **100,000**	8 1,000 × 10,000 **10,000,000**	9 10 × 100,000 **1,000,000**
10 600 × 300 **180,000**	11 10 × 200 **2000**	12 200 × 600 **120,000**
13 300 × 400 **120,000**	14 70 × 400 **28,000**	15 60 × 400 **24,000**
16 90 × 30 **2700**	17 8000 × 50 **400,000**	18 4000 × 60 **240,000**
19 4000 × 8000 **32,000,000**	20 50 × 400 **20,000**	21 70 × 80 **5600**
22 200 × 200 **40,000**	23 300,000 × 20 **6,000,000**	24 200 × 70 **14,000**
25 300 × 50 **15,000**	26 6000 × 500 **3,000,000**	27 500 × 500 **250,000**
28 1,000,000 × 10 **10,000,000**	29 10 × 100,000 **1,000,000**	30 480 × 100 **48,000**
31 100 × 40 **4000**	32 100 × 100 **10,000**	33 1000 × 100 **100,000**
34 5000 × 900 **4,500,000**	35 603 × 100 **60,300**	36 740 × 100 **74,000**
37 150 × 10 **1500**	38 70,000 × 80 **5,600,000**	39 35 × 1000 **35,000**

274 • Multidigit Multiplication

Literature Connection Invite students to look through *Building Tables on Tables on Tables: A Book About Multiplication* by John V. Trivett, to learn more about the basic structure and principles of multiplication tables. Or you might read with the class sections that pertain to multiples.

*available separately

Answer the following questions.

You know that there are 100 centimeters in 1 meter and 1000 meters in 1 kilometer.

40. How many centimeters are there in 1 kilometer? **100,000**

41. How many centimeters are there in 5 kilometers? **500,000**

You know that there are 100 cents in a dollar and 1000 dollars in a 1000-dollar bill.

42. How many cents are there in 1000 dollars? **100,000**

43. How many cents are there in $5000? **500,000**

44. How many nickels are there in $5000? **100,000**

45. How many dimes are there in $5000? **50,000**

There are 10 decimeters in 1 meter.

46. How many decimeters are in 1 kilometer? **10,000**

47. How many decimeters are in 5 kilometers? **50,000**

48. Name an object that is about 1 decimeter long. **a measuring spoon**

49. How many decimeters are there in 50 kilometers? **500,000**

50. How many decimeters are there in 100 kilometers? **1,000,000**

FANTASTIC FACT

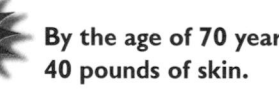

By the age of 70 years, the human body has shed 40 pounds of skin.

Mental Math (continued)

c. 48 + 53 (thumbs up)

d. 8 x 40 (thumbs down)

e. 1200 ÷ 3 (thumbs down)

f. 480 – 350 (thumbs up)

g. 49 x 4 (thumbs up)

h. 730 – 540 (thumbs up)

i. 8000 ÷ 20 (thumbs down)

2 Teach

Using the Student Pages Have students work independently on page 274. Observe how they solve the problems. Note those who do not use an efficient method for obtaining correct answers, and provide extra help as needed. Then assign the word problems on page 275. You may wish to have students work in pairs to solve the problems. Encourage them to discuss the problems, verify that they both get the same answer, and check that the solution makes sense. You might provide some hands-on materials, such as **centimeter rulers*, metersticks,** and **play money*** for students who wish to use them.

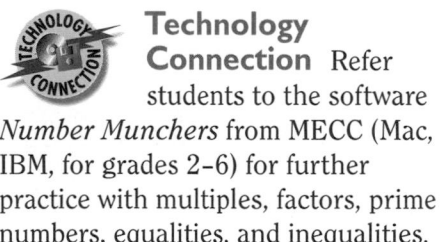

Technology Connection Refer students to the software *Number Munchers* from MECC (Mac, IBM, for grades 2–6) for further practice with multiples, factors, prime numbers, equalities, and inequalities.

*available separately

◆ LESSON 81 Practice with Multiples of 10

Teach

Using the Thinking Story "The Treasure of Mugg Island (Part 1)" is the first part of the six-part Thinking Story in Unit 4. The story centers on drawing a map based on verbal descriptions. In Part 1, the children begin to help the queen of Addonia find the Royal Treasure, which is hidden on Mugg Island. Have students read the story, compare maps, discuss the questions, and draw the map in small groups. Have **drawing paper** available.

Answers to Thinking Story Questions:

1. The island map should look roughly like this:

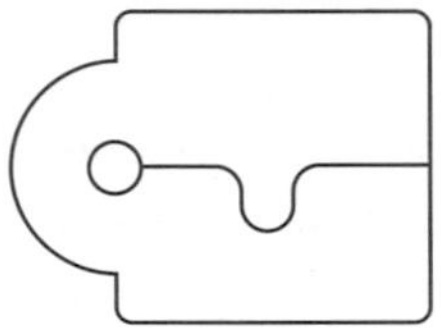

You might take the best map students draw and duplicate it, or have it redrawn larger and posted in the classroom.

It will be helpful if students have a good map to refer to during future episodes of the story. If all the maps are inaccurate, work together with students to make a correct one.

2. Mugg Island resembles a mug.

MATH JOURNAL Have students describe in their Math Journals the task of making a map from written directions. Invite them to evaluate how well they did, how hard or easy they found the task to be, and how they might do better in similar attempts in the future.

◆ LESSON 81 Practice with Multiples of 10

THINKING STORY

The Treasure of Mugg Island

Part 1

In this story the children leave the island of Addonia. Therefore numbers are now said in the usual way.

The queen of Addonia called Manolita, Marcus, Ferdie, and Portia to her castle. "I need your help," she said. "Years ago pirates stole the Royal Treasure. Now I have learned that it is hidden on Mugg Island. Will you go there with me to help find it?"

The children were happy to help. This sounded like an adventure! Soon they were flying over the sea in the royal helicopter. The queen herself was the pilot.

"Where is Mugg Island?" Portia asked.

"I don't know," said the queen. "We'll just have to fly around until we see it."

"But how will we know which island it is?" Portia asked. "There are dozens and dozens of islands out here."

"This should help," said the queen.

RETEACHING

Difficulty with multiplying by powers or multiples of 10 often centers on determining the correct number of 0s to affix to the product. Encourage students to place tally marks above the 0s as they count.

PRACTICE p. 81

LESSON 81 PRACTICE Name________

Multiply.

1. 10 × 100 = 1000	2. 10 × 10,000 = 100,000
3. 100 × 100 = 10,000	4. 10,000 × 10,000 = 100,000,000
5. 10,000 × 10 = 100,000	6. 100 × 1000 = 100,000
7. 1000 × 1000 = 1,000,000	8. 1000 × 10 = 10,000
9. 100,000 × 100 = 10,000,000	10. 10,000 × 1000 = 10,000,000
11. 20 × 20 = 400	12. 1000 × 600 = 600,000
13. 400 × 100 = 40,000	14. 200 × 800 = 160,000
15. 1000 × 30 = 30,000	16. 70 × 70 = 4900
17. 800 × 300 = 240,000	18. 9000 × 10,000 = 90,000,000
19. 17 × 10 = 170	20. 40,000 × 5000 = 200,000,000
21. 704 × 100 = 70,400	22. 60 × 700 = 42,000
23. 328 × 1000 = 328,000	24. 6000 × 6000 = 36,000,000
25. 50,000 × 600 = 30,000,000	26. 10,000 × 740 = 7,400,000
27. 808 × 10 = 8080	28. 90 × 60 = 5400
29. 72 × 10 = 720	30. 280 × 700 = 196,000

Answer the following questions.

31. There are 10 centimeters in a decimeter and 10 decimeters in a meter. How many centimeters are there in a meter? 100
32. How many centimeters are there in 6 meters? 600
33. There are 1000 meters in a kilometer. How many meters are there in 5 kilometers? 5000

Copyright © SRA/McGraw-Hill. Permission is granted to reproduce this page for classroom use.

Math Explorations and Applications Level 4 • 81

"She handed them a note. It said:

"Mugg Island. The south shore of Mugg Island is straight and about 1 kilometer long. On the east side, the shore goes straight north for 2 kilometers. Then the shore goes west for 1 kilometer. Then the shore turns south for a short distance. Then there is a large bulge of land, about 1 kilometer across, sticking out toward the west. After the bulge, the shore goes straight south again until it meets the south shore. In the middle of the bulge is a small round lake. Out of the lake comes a stream, which flows eastward to the sea. The stream makes a line like a human face, with a pointy nose pointing south."

"This is no help," said Ferdie. "I can't tell what the island looks like from reading this!"

"Try drawing a map," said the queen.

. . . to be continued

Work in groups. Discuss your answers and how you figured them out. Then compare your answers with those of other groups. **Answers are in margin.**

1. Draw a map of Mugg Island. Try to use every fact that the story gives you. See which group can make the best map.
2. How would you describe the shape of Mugg Island?

ENRICHMENT p. 81

LESSON 81 ENRICHMENT Name

Sometimes it's hard to picture in your mind what a number means or looks like. Think of a number fact for every number below. Your fact can be about any subject. One has been done for you.

10 ______

100 ______

1000 ______

10,000 Mitchell Peak in King's Canyon National Park is 10,365 feet high.

100,000 ______

1,000,000 ______

1,000,000,000 ______

Share your facts with the class. Discuss how you found them.
Students' facts will vary. Sources may include an atlas, an encyclopedia, an astronomy guide, a general reference book, a globe, and so on.

Copyright © SRA/McGraw-Hill. Permission is granted to reproduce this page for classroom use.

ASSESSMENT p. 32

UNIT 4 **Mastery Checkpoint 12** Multiplying by powers of 10 and multiplying multiples of 10 (Lesson 81)

Name

The student demonstrates mastery by correctly answering at least 24 of the 30 problems.

Multiply. Watch your numbering.

1. 10 × 10 = 100	14. 10,000 × 100 = 1,000,000
2. 10 × 100 = 1000	15. 1,000,000 × 10 = 10,000,000
3. 1000 × 10 = 10,000	16. 10,000 × 10,000 = 100,000,000
4. 100 × 100 = 10,000	17. 10,000 × 10 = 100,000
5. 1000 × 100 = 100,000	18. 1000 × 1000 = 1,000,000
6. 200 × 500 = 100,000	19. 60 × 700 = 42,000
7. 80 × 40 = 3200	20. 6000 × 50 = 300,000
8. 3000 × 7000 = 21,000,000	21. 40 × 500 = 20,000
9. 300 × 300 = 90,000	22. 200,000 × 300 = 60,000,000
10. 400 × 30 = 12,000	23. 7000 × 50 = 350,000
11. 10 × 500 = 5000	24. 200 × 100 = 20,000
12. 4000 × 800 = 3,200,000	25. 507 × 1000 = 507,000
13. 170 × 100 = 17,000	26. 60,000 × 30 = 1,800,000

Solve these problems.

27. If paper comes 100 sheets to a package and Mrs. Morris wants to buy 30 packages, how many sheets of paper will she get? 3000
28. There are about 2000 split peas in a pack. Ida wants 300 packs. How many split peas will she have? 600,000
29. Simon had twelve ten-dollar bills. Which item(s) can he buy?
    a. the stereo $89.95
    b. the TV $329.95
    c. the bureau $189.95
    a
30. Mark wants to give 100 jelly beans to each person in his class. There are 28 people in his class. How many jelly beans must he buy? 2800

Copyright © SRA/McGraw-Hill. Permission is granted to reproduce this page for classroom use.

3 Wrap-Up (5 MINUTES)

In Closing Ask students why it is important to be able to use a map. Have them suggest some real-life examples of situations in which map-reading is useful.

Mastery Checkpoint 12

By this time most students should demonstrate mastery of multiplying by powers of 10 and multiplying multiples of 10 by correctly answering at least 80% of the problems on page 274 or a similar page. Record the results of this assessment on the Mastery Checkpoint Chart. You may also wish to assign Assessment Blackline Masters page 32 to determine mastery.

Assessment Criteria

Did the student . . .

- ✓ correctly answer at least 80% of the multiplication problems on page 274?
- ✓ correctly solve at least eight of the 11 word problems on page 275?
- ✓ contribute to the Thinking Story discussion?
- ✓ demonstrate or explain how to draw a map from written instructions?

Homework Have students draw a map of the school playground or of part of their neighborhood. Remind them to label major objects or landmarks.

LESSON 82

Student Edition pages 278–281

Rounding and Approximating

LESSON PLANNER

Objectives

- to help students explore how precisely to express a number based on the situation in which it is used
- to use rounding and approximation to solve word problems

Context of the Lesson This is the fifth of seven lessons on multiplying powers and multiples of 10 and on approximating products. Approximation was included in previous levels of *Math Explorations and Applications* and in earlier lessons within Level 4.

MANIPULATIVES

magazines and newspapers (optional)

place-value pad*

Program Resources

Reteaching Master

Practice Master 82

Enrichment Master 82

For extra practice:
CD-ROM* Lesson 82
Cumulative Review, page 552

1 Warm-Up

5 MINUTES

Problem of the Day Present the following problem: Lucy sold some raffle tickets. If she rounded the number of tickets she sold to the nearest ten, she sold about 150 tickets. If she rounded the number of tickets she sold to the nearest hundred, she sold about 200 tickets. Give all possible exact numbers of raffle tickets Lucy could have sold. (150, 151, 152, 153, 154)

Problem-Solving Strategies Ask students who have solved the Problem of the Day to share how they solved it and any strategies they used.

MENTAL MATH Provide a mixed arithmetic drill in which students show thumbs up if answers fall within the bounds 100–200 and thumbs down if they do not.

a.	86 + 20 (thumbs up)	**b.**	30 × 3 (thumbs down)
	86 + 40 (thumbs up)		30 × 5 (thumbs up)
	86 + 80 (thumbs up)		30 × 6 (thumbs up)
	86 + 150 (thumbs down)		30 × 7 (thumbs down)

(continued on page 279)

LESSON 82

Rounding and Approximating

Sometimes you use numbers to mean *about* how many. You might say that *about* 5000 people live in Steelton, or a book has *about* 200 pages. In this lesson you'll learn an important skill known as rounding.

◆ Which number in each pair is usually easier to work with?

61 or 60? 214 or 200? 4971 or 5000?

Multiples of 10, 100, 1000, and so on are usually easier to work with than other numbers.

When we say, write, or use numbers, we often do not have to be exact. So we can replace a number by the nearest multiple of 10, or 100, or 1000, and so on. We call this **rounding.** How exact we need to be depends on what the numbers will be used for.

For each statement, choose the most appropriate answer. Use each answer only once.

1. **a.** The train will arrive **2**
   b. Aunt Mary is coming for dinner **3**
   c. The rocket will be launched **1**

   (1) at 6:03 and 11 seconds.
   (2) at 6:03.
   (3) at about 6:00.

2. **a.** A mapmaker said the distance between those cities is **2**
   b. Dad said that the trip to Wisconsin is **1**
   c. The mechanic said to change the oil in the car **3**

   (1) about 2900 miles.
   (2) 2873 miles.
   (3) every 3000 miles.

REAL-WORLD CONNECTION **Read newspaper articles. Watch and listen to news reports. Can you find examples of rounded numbers?**

LANGUAGE ARTS CONNECTION **Language Arts Connection** Discuss with students the nuances of the terms *exact* and *precise.* Guide them to recognize that *precise* implies an attempt to be as accurate as possible but allows some room for sensible approximation. By contrast, *exact* implies total agreement with all known details or facts. Talk about possible examples to help students grasp the distinctions.

*available separately

GEOGRAPHY CONNECTION

Round each of the numbers in the chart to a reasonable estimate. Use no more than two nonzero digits.

	1994 Population		
3	Alaska	606,276	**600,000**
4	California	31,430,697	**31,000,000**
5	Delaware	706,351	**700,000**
6	Florida	13,952,714	**14,000,000**
7	New Jersey	7,903,925	**8,000,000**
8	New York	18,169,051	**18,000,000**
9	Ohio	11,102,198	**11,000,000**
10	Texas	18,378,185	**18,000,000**
11	Vermont	580,209	**600,000**
12	Wyoming	475,981	**500,000**
13	United States (total)	260,340,990	**260,000,000**

Using your rounded figures, answer the following questions.

14. Which state had the smallest population? **Wyoming**

15. About how many more people were there in Alaska than in Wyoming? **about 100,000**

16. Which state had the greatest population? **California**

17. About how many more people were there in California than in New York? **about 13,000,000**

18. Which of the following fractions is the best approximation of the fraction of people in the United States who lived in California? $\frac{1}{2}$, $\frac{1}{4}$, $\frac{1}{8}$, $\frac{1}{20}$, $\frac{1}{40}$, or $\frac{1}{50}$ $\mathbf{\frac{1}{8}}$

19. Which of the following fractions is the best approximation of the fraction of people in the United States who lived in Wyoming? $\frac{1}{50}$, $\frac{1}{80}$, $\frac{1}{100}$, $\frac{1}{200}$, $\frac{1}{400}$, or $\frac{1}{550}$ $\mathbf{\frac{1}{550}}$

Mental Math (continued)

c. 300 – 250 (thumbs down)
300 – 150 (thumbs up)
300 – 50 (thumbs down)

d. 400 ÷ 1 (thumbs down)
400 ÷ 2 (thumbs up)
400 ÷ 4 (thumbs up)

2 Teach

PROBLEM SOLVING

Using the Student Pages Complete page 278 with the class. Students may disagree on some statements, which is acceptable as long as they offer valid reasons for their choices. Help them grasp why different situations call for different degrees of precision. The key point is that to report a figure in a real situation, one must determine an appropriate degree of precision. Begin using the term *precise* instead of *exact* to differentiate between a general sense of precision and an exact fact. Have students solve the problems on page 279 independently or in pairs. You may want to go over the figures students rounded in the population chart before they answer questions 14–19.

TECHNOLOGY CONNECTION

Technology Connection Refer students to the software *Rounding* from Gamco (Apple, IBM, for grades 4–10) for further practice with rounding whole numbers and decimals; rounding to tens, hundreds, and thousands; and rounding 9s and multidigit numbers.

◆ LESSON 82 Rounding and Approximating

Teach

COOPERATIVE LEARNING **Using the Student Pages** Complete page 280 with the class. Be sure that everyone understands how it is possible and easier to answer the question without calculating exactly how much the packages of balsa wood will cost. Discuss two or three of the word problems to get students started. For example, in problem 20, if the toothbrushes cost $2 each, they would cost $50 in all. Because the toothbrushes actually cost only $1.69 each, Dr. Fleisch certainly has enough money. In problem 21, help students see that 30 shirts at $8 each would cost $240. Because this is far greater an amount of money than Mr. Gomez has to spend, students might estimate what he would spend for 20 shirts at $8 each ($160). Because $160 is more than $140, Mr. Gomez can afford fewer than 20 shirts.

Have students work in pairs or small groups to complete the problems on page 281. Explain that for each problem, students might have to try several approximations to answer the question. Encourage group members to talk to each other as they work to share their reasoning and solution strategies. For problem 24, remind students that one year has 365 days (366 days in a leap year). Problem 25 may cause some difficulties. By always rounding the numbers down, one can report that there are more than 3000 seconds in an hour, more than 60,000 seconds in a day (20 × 3000), and more than 18,000,000 seconds in a year (300 × 60,000).

◆ LESSON 82 Rounding and Approximating

Rounding is also useful when you do not need an exact answer to a calculation.

Alex wants to buy seven packages of balsa wood for $2.97 (297 cents) each. He has $25. Does he have enough money for this much balsa wood?

The answer is yes. You can figure that out without finding the exact cost.

The cost of each package of balsa wood is less than $3. So the cost of seven packages is less than 7 × 3, or $21. Because $25 is greater than $21, Alex has enough money to buy seven packages of balsa wood.

Approximate. You don't need an exact answer to solve these problems.

20. Dr. Fleisch wants to buy 25 toothbrushes for $1.69 (169 cents) each. She has $50. Is that enough to buy the toothbrushes? **yes**

21. Mr. Gomez wants to buy 27 baseball shirts for his team. The shirts cost $7.98 (798 cents) each. He has $140 to spend. Is that enough money to buy the shirts? **no**

Real-World Connection Have students look through **magazines** and **newspapers** for examples of statistical reports that include rounded or exact numbers. Ask them to evaluate whether the numbers are exact or approximated and which figures may have been reported with more precision than necessary. For instance, in reality, census figures are not exact to the nearest one, yet they are often reported that way.

RETEACHING p. 26

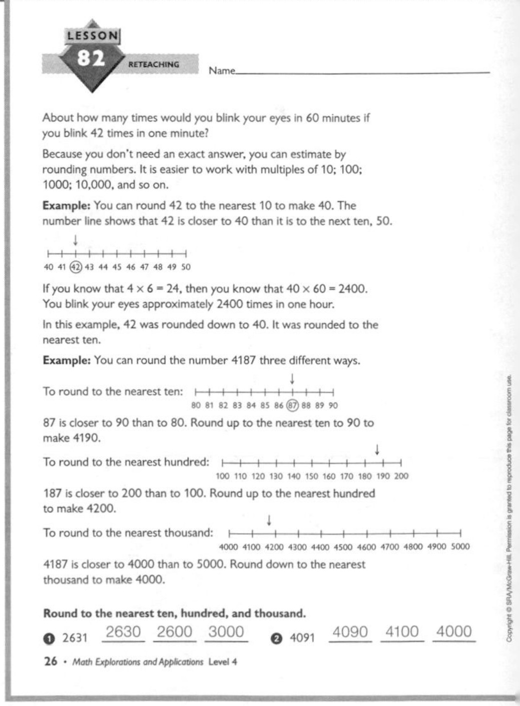

LESSON 82 RETEACHING Name________________

About how many times would you blink your eyes in 60 minutes if you blink 42 times in one minute?

Because you don't need an exact answer, you can estimate by rounding numbers. It is easier to work with multiples of 10; 100; 1000; 10,000, and so on.

Example: You can round 42 to the nearest 10 to make 40. The number line shows that 42 is closer to 40 than it is to the next ten, 50.

40 41 (42) 43 44 45 46 47 48 49 50

If you know that 4 × 6 = 24, then you know that 40 × 60 = 2400. You blink your eyes approximately 2400 times in one hour.

In this example, 42 was rounded down to 40. It was rounded to the nearest ten.

Example: You can round the number 4187 three different ways.

To round to the nearest ten: 80 81 82 83 84 85 86 (87) 88 89 90

87 is closer to 90 than to 80. Round up to the nearest ten to 90 to make 4190.

To round to the nearest hundred: 100 110 120 130 140 150 160 170 180 190 200

187 is closer to 200 than to 100. Round up to the nearest hundred to make 4200.

To round to the nearest thousand: 4000 4100 4200 4300 4400 4500 4600 4700 4800 4900 5000

4187 is closer to 4000 than to 5000. Round down to the nearest thousand to make 4000.

Round to the nearest ten, hundred, and thousand.

1. 2631 2630 2600 3000
2. 4091 4090 4100 4000

26 • *Math Explorations and Applications* Level 4

Copyright © SRA/McGraw-Hill. Permission is granted to reproduce this page for classroom use.

22 Caitlin wants to buy nine postcards that cost 18¢ each. She has $2.00 (200 cents). Does she have enough money to buy the postcards? **yes**

23 Chris wants to buy 30 pencils. The pencils cost 12¢ each. Chris has $3.00. Does he have enough money to buy the pencils? **no**

24 Greta is nine years old. She wants to know if she's more than 2500 days old. Is she? **yes**

25 Armando says there are more than ten million seconds in a year. Is he right? (There are 60 seconds in one minute, 60 minutes in one hour, 24 hours in one day, and about 365 days in one year.) **yes**

26 The auditorium in Jan's school has 48 rows with 24 seats in each row. Can 750 people be seated for a school play? **yes**

27 Omar says that his school used more than 10,000 cans of soup last year for meals. A case of soup contains 24 cans. Omar's school used 831 cases last year. Is he right? **yes**

28 Dorleta delivers 36 newspapers every day. Does she deliver more than 300 newspapers in a week (seven days)? **no**

29 Suzy sells peanuts at football games for $0.95 a bag. If she sells 280 bags, will she take in $300? **no**

30 Patrick collected 82 seashells last summer. If he sells all of them for 35¢ each, will he earn enough money to buy swim goggles that cost $23.99? **yes**

MATH JOURNAL

In your Math Journal create your own word problem in which rounding is more useful than using an exact calculation. Give this problem to a classmate to solve.

Use the Cumulative Review on page 552 after this lesson.

PRACTICE p. 82

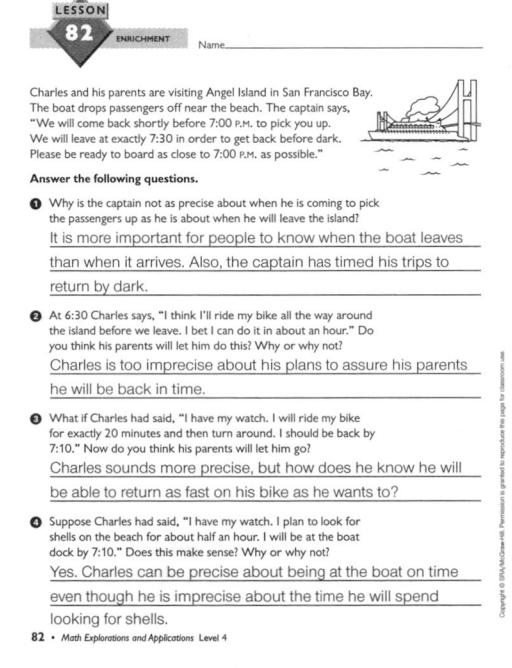

LESSON 82 PRACTICE Name________________

Approximate to solve these problems.

1. Ken needs $10.00. He has six jars of fishing worms he can sell for $1.95 each. If he sells all six jars, will he have at least $10.00? yes
2. The students at Kennedy School need 2000 soup labels to win a prize for the school. If each of the six classes turns in about 200 labels, will they have enough to win the prize? no
3. Lian wants to buy ten apples that cost 10¢ each. Does she have enough money if she has exactly $1.10? yes
4. Ricardo is eight years old. Is he more than 5000 days old? no
5. A baseball stadium has 50 rows of seats with 420 seats in a row. Will the stadium hold at least 2000 people? yes
6. At a basketball game Pam sells large bags of popcorn for 75¢ each. If she sells 200 bags, will she take in at least $200? no
7. Doug wants to buy 200 sheets of paper that are sold at 45¢ for a packet of 50. Will $1.50 cover the cost of 200 sheets? no
8. JoAnn wants to run 250 kilometers each month. Can she do this by running 6 kilometers each day? no
9. Claire earns $9.00 an hour working at a store. If she works ten hours, will she have earned enough money to buy a watch that costs $80.00? yes

For each statement choose the most appropriate answer. Use each answer only once.

10 a. The plane will arrive 2 — 1. at around 12:00.
b. Chris is coming to lunch 1 — 2. at 12:04.
c. The timed math test ended 3 — 3. at 12:04 and 30 seconds.

82 • *Math Explorations and Applications* Level 4

Copyright © SRA/McGraw-Hill. Permission is granted to reproduce this page for classroom use.

ENRICHMENT p. 82

LESSON 82 ENRICHMENT Name________________

Charles and his parents are visiting Angel Island in San Francisco Bay. The boat drops passengers off near the beach. The captain says, "We will come back shortly before 7:00 P.M. to pick you up. We will leave at exactly 7:30 in order to get back before dark. Please be ready to board as close to 7:00 P.M. as possible."

Answer the following questions.

1. Why is the captain not as precise about when he is coming to pick the passengers up as he is about when he will leave the island?
It is more important for people to know when the boat leaves than when it arrives. Also, the captain has timed his trips to return by dark.
2. At 6:30 Charles says, "I think I'll ride my bike all the way around the island before we leave. I bet I can do it in about an hour." Do you think his parents will let him do this? Why or why not?
Charles is too imprecise about his plans to assure his parents he will be back in time.
3. What if Charles had said, "I have my watch. I will ride my bike for exactly 20 minutes and then turn around. I should be back by 7:10." Now do you think his parents will let him go?
Charles sounds more precise, but how does he know he will be able to return as fast on his bike as he wants to?
4. Suppose Charles had said, "I have my watch. I plan to look for shells on the beach for about half an hour. I will be at the boat dock by 7:10." Does this make sense? Why or why not?
Yes. Charles can be precise about being at the boat on time even though he is imprecise about the time he will spend looking for shells.

82 • *Math Explorations and Applications* Level 4

Copyright © SRA/McGraw-Hill. Permission is granted to reproduce this page for classroom use.

*available separately

3 Wrap-Up (5 MINUTES)

In Closing Ask students for examples of situations in which it is appropriate to round numbers for convenience.

ANALYZING ANSWERS — MANIPULATIVES

If students make errors, check to determine the nature of the problem. Is there a misunderstanding about when to round up or round down? If this is the case, have students write down the rule and use it for reference as they go through the problems. Is there a problem in regard to place value? If this is the case, have the students use a **place-value pad.***

Assessment Criteria

Did the student . . .

- ✓ contribute to the discussion of the usefulness of approximation?
- ✓ accurately apply rounding and approximation skills to solve realistic problems?
- ✓ explain how to determine when an approximate answer is adequate?

Homework Have students formulate three word problems similar to those on page 281, in which they ask a question that can be answered by rounding or approximation.

LEARNING STYLES

Meeting Individual Needs

Social or interpersonal learners may benefit from playing a game to practice approximation and rounding skills. Teach students how to play "Tic-Tac-Toe—Rounding in a Row," which appears on page 243 of *Family Math* by Jean Stenmark, Virginia Thompson, and Ruth Cossey. In this game students apply their skills to play a game similar to tic-tac-toe.

LESSON 83

Student Edition pages 282–283

Approximating Answers

LESSON PLANNER

Objectives

- ▶ to show how to find upper and lower bounds for multiplication problems
- ✓ to assess mastery of approximating answers to multidigit multiplication problems

Context of the Lesson This is the sixth of seven lessons on multiplying powers and multiples of 10 and on approximating products. The approximating procedures learned here will help students get an idea of what size product to expect and to check whether answers make sense. This lesson contains a Mastery Checkpoint for approximating answers to multidigit multiplication problems.

MANIPULATIVES

geode (optional)

Program Resources

Reteaching Master

Practice Master 83

Enrichment Master 83

Assessment Master

For extra practice:
CD-ROM* Lesson 83

1 Warm-Up (5 MINUTES)

Problem of the Day Present this problem orally or on the chalkboard. If necessary, display a picture of a **geode:** Hallie saw two geodes she liked at a rock shop. The more expensive geode cost four times as much as the other one. Together, both geodes cost $150. Figure out the price of each geode. ($30 and $120)

Problem-Solving Strategies Ask students who have solved the Problem of the Day to share how they solved it and any strategies they used.

MENTAL MATH Conduct an approximation drill similar to the Mental Math drill in Lesson 82, but change the bounds to 500–600. Have students show thumbs up if the sum is between 500 and 600 and thumbs down if it is greater or less than this range.

a. 540 – 50 (thumbs down) **b.** 4000 ÷ 8 (thumbs up)

c. 840 ÷ 10 (thumbs down) **d.** 700 – 150 (thumbs up)

e. 62 x 10 (thumbs down) **f.** 990 ÷ 9 (thumbs down)

g. 300 + 295 (thumbs up) **h.** 460 + 50 (thumbs up)

MIXED PRACTICE

LESSON 83

Approximating Answers

When you **approximate** an answer, you don't have to give just one number. You can give two numbers and say that the answer is between those two numbers.

Example:

A calendar is 56 centimeters long and 27 centimeters wide. About how large is the calendar?

The answer must be less than 60 × 30 square centimeters. So it must be less than 1800 square centimeters.

The answer must also be greater than 50 × 20 square centimeters. So it must be greater than 1000 square centimeters.

The answer must be between 1000 and 1800 square centimeters.

Answer these questions.

1. An office is 28 meters long and 12 meters wide. Approximate the area by finding two numbers that it must be between.
   - **a.** Can the area be 600 square meters? **no**
   - **b.** Suppose you calculated the area and got an answer of 278 square meters. How would you know that you had made a mistake? **The answer must be greater than 28 × 10, or 280.**
2. A rug is 261 centimeters long and 194 centimeters wide. Approximate the area by finding two numbers that it must be between. (You may round to whole numbers of hundreds.) Which of these could be the actual area?
   - **a.** 15,824 square centimeters
   - (**b.**) 50,494 square centimeters
   - **c.** 63,774 square centimeters

RETEACHING p. 27

LESSON 83 RETEACHING Name__________

When approximating an answer, you can say that it is between two numbers.

Example:

The town wants to build a new playground. It will be 43 feet long and 27 feet wide. The new jungle gym covers an area of 500 square feet. Will the new playground be large enough for the jungle gym to fit?

1. If you round down, 43 rounds to 40, and 27 rounds to 20. The approximate area is 40 × 20 = 800 square feet.
2. If you round up, 43 rounds to 50, and 27 rounds to 30. The approximate area is 50 × 30 = 1500 square feet.
3. The approximate area of the new playground is between 800 and 1500 square feet. Yes, the jungle gym will fit.

Solve these problems.

1. Suppose you are buying nine books. Each book costs $3.75. The clerk tells you that the total is $47.25. How would you know that the clerk made a mistake? 9 × $4 = $36; the total should be about $36.
2. The kitchen is 13 feet by 18 feet. About how many square feet of vinyl flooring needs to be ordered to cover the kitchen floor? about 200 square feet

Choose the correct answer for each problem.

3. 117 × 389 = c	a. 4500	b. 400,000	c. 45,513
4. 977 × 8 = a	a. 7816	b. 9871	c. 72,519
5. 23 × 822 = b	a. 1639	b. 18,906	c. 27,906

Copyright © SRA/McGraw-Hill. Permission is granted to reproduce this page for classroom use.

PRACTICE p. 83

LESSON 83 PRACTICE Name__________

In each problem two of the answers are clearly wrong and one is correct. Choose the correct answer.

1. 42 × 16 = b	a. 342	b. 672	c. 1912
2. 12 × 37 = a	a. 444	b. 682	c. 1042
3. 84 × 61 = b	a. 2824	b. 5124	c. 3512
4. 92 × 59 = c	a. 6418	b. 829	c. 5428
5. 702 × 48 = c	a. 2839	b. 432,142	c. 33,696
6. 32 × 645 = a	a. 20,640	b. 2140	c. 200,740
7. 602 × 501 = b	a. 540,212	b. 301,602	c. 721,800
8. 45 × 66 = b	a. 1970	b. 2970	c. 3970
9. 1402 × 76 = c	a. 1,841,200	b. 10,500	c. 106,552
10. 8447 × 340 = a	a. 2,871,980	b. 1,000,847	c. 4,200,500
11. 122 × 333 = a	a. 40,626	b. 562,406	c. 4250
12. 999 × 27 = c	a. 4842	b. 36,823	c. 26,973
13. 201 × 55 = a	a. 11,055	b. 9050	c. 152,005
14. 562 × 26 = c	a. 8142	b. 34,006	c. 14,612
15. 904 × 878 = b	a. 427,282	b. 793,712	c. 127,602
16. 709 × 75 = c	a. 65,175	b. 43,175	c. 53,175
17. 87 × 39 = a	a. 3393	b. 3893	c. 2093
18. 31 × 31 = b	a. 691	b. 961	c. 1331
19. 201 × 79 = a	a. 15,879	b. 25,879	c. 35,879
20. 35 × 53 = b	a. 1455	b. 1855	c. 1055

Copyright © SRA/McGraw-Hill. Permission is granted to reproduce this page for classroom use.

*available separately

3. A parking lot is 92 meters long and 53 meters wide. Approximate the area by finding two numbers that it must be between. Which of these could be the actual area?

   a. 4266 square meters
   b. 6376 square meters
   (c.) 4906 square meters

In each problem, two of the answers are clearly wrong and one is correct. Choose the correct answer.

4	32 × 17 = ■	**a.** 264	**(b.)** 544	**c.** 914
5	46 × 61 = ■	**(a.)** 2806	**b.** 2316	**c.** 2026
6	28 × 195 = ■	**(a.)** 5460	**b.** 6140	**c.** 7440
7	206 × 38 = ■	**a.** 5828	**(b.)** 7828	**c.** 4828
8	74 × 803 = ■	**(a.)** 59,422	**b.** 592,222	**c.** 5,942,222
9	284 × 579 = ■	**a.** 13,896	**(b.)** 164,436	**c.** 187,296
10	612 × 559 = ■	**(a.)** 342,108	**b.** 3,116,608	**c.** 3,402,108
11	527 × 312 = ■	**a.** 1,826,394	**b.** 15,204	**(c.)** 164,424
12	111 × 8901 = ■	**a.** 890,901	**b.** 89,011	**(c.)** 988,011
13	72 × 501 = ■	**(a.)** 36,288	**b.** 3888	**c.** 396,288
14	632 × 59 = ■	**a.** 373,588	**b.** 353,288	**(c.)** 37,288
15	125 × 8888 = ■	**a.** 222,200	**b.** 111,000	**(c.)** 1,111,000
16	574 × 896 = ■	**a.** 49,364	**b.** 794,644	**(c.)** 514,304
17	994 × 9735 = ■	**(a.)** 9,676,590	**b.** 9,981,910	**c.** 9,872,540
18	762 × 7450 = ■	**a.** 533,400	**(b.)** 5,676,900	**c.** 6,438,900

ENRICHMENT p. 83

LESSON 83 ENRICHMENT Name________

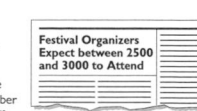

REAL-WORLD CONNECTION **Answer the following questions.**

Festival Organizers Expect between 2500 and 3000 to Attend

1. Look at this headline. Why do you think the festival organizers do not give an exact number of people they expect to attend their festival?
   Answers will vary. Organizers may still be selling tickets, people who have tickets may not show up, weather on the day of the festival might affect attendance, and so on.
2. How can knowing the fewest (2500) and the greatest (3000) number of people who might attend help the organizers?
   Answers will vary. Having lower and upper bounds helps the organizers plan. They should have enough food, seating, and programs for at least 2500, but no more than 3000.
3. How do the organizers know how many people might attend? Answers will vary. They may base their prediction on past attendance.
4. How could the organizers make sure no more than 3000 people attend?
   Answers will vary. They could sell no more than 3000 tickets.
5. Look in newspapers, magazines, and advertisements for examples of approximations. Glue three examples on a separate sheet of paper. Tell why you think an approximate number was used instead of an exact number.
   Answers will vary. Numbers could be rounded up or down, depending on the desired impression. For example, "300 attend" sounds more impressive than "271 attend."

Copyright © SRA/McGraw-Hill. Permission is granted to reproduce this page for classroom use.

Math Explorations and Applications Level 4 • **83**

ASSESSMENT p. 33

UNIT 4 **Mastery Checkpoint 13** Approximating answers to multidigit multiplication problems (Lesson 83)

Name ________

The student demonstrates mastery by correctly answering at least 10 of the 13 problems.

In each problem two of the answers are clearly wrong and one is correct. Ring the correct answer.

1	23 × 16 = c	**a.** 968	**b.** 168	**c.** 368
2	37 × 72 = a	**a.** 2664	**b.** 2064	**c.** 2149
3	26 × 184 = a	**a.** 4784	**b.** 2484	**c.** 5784
4	305 × 27 = b	**a.** 6235	**b.** 8235	**c.** 2235
5	73 × 702 = c	**a.** 49,246	**b.** 45,336	**c.** 51,246
6	392 × 687 = c	**a.** 180,304	**b.** 207,204	**c.** 269,304
7	523 × 668 = b	**a.** 309,364	**b.** 349,364	**c.** 253,364
8	436 × 213 = a	**a.** 92,868	**b.** 12,868	**c.** 10,868
9	7819 × 111 = b	**a.** 7819	**b.** 867,909	**c.** 781,909
10	82 × 605 = c	**a.** 40,610	**b.** 45,610	**c.** 49,610

Solve these problems.

11. A music speaker has a front face that measures 24 inches tall and 14 inches wide. Approximate the area of the front face.
    (a.) 300 sq. in. **b.** 200 sq. in. **c.** 400 sq. in.
12. A painting measures 21 inches by 25 inches. Approximately how much wall area will it cover?
    a. 400 sq. in. **(b.)** 500 sq. in. **c.** 600 sq. in.
13. Julie wants to put a rectangular trampoline in her backyard. It is 12 feet wide by 16 feet long. Approximately how much area will it cover?
    a. 160 sq. ft. **(b.)** 190 sq. ft. **c.** 200 sq. ft.

Copyright © SRA/McGraw-Hill. Permission is granted to reproduce this page for classroom use.

Math Explorations and Applications Level 4 • **33**

2 Teach

Using the Student Pages Before discussing the example at the top of page 282, ask students to think of a situation in which it would be useful to identify a range in which an answer must fall. Discuss the example on page 282 in which students approximate 56 x 27. After this discussion, have students work in groups or individually to do problems 1–3. Note that for problems 2 and 3, although one choice in each case is reasonable, all three choices are incorrect. Even if an answer falls within approximated bounds, it can still be incorrect. Have students work independently on problems 4–18 on page 283.

3 Wrap-Up

5 MINUTES

In Closing Ask students to approximate how much carpet would be needed to cover a floor that measures 17 feet by 27 feet.

Mastery Checkpoint 13

By this time most students should be able to approximate answers to multidigit multiplication problems and correctly answer at least 80% of the problems on page 283. You can assess this ability by observing students during the Mental Math exercise or by assigning Assessment Blackline Masters page 33. Results of this assessment may be recorded on the Mastery Checkpoint Chart.

Assessment Criteria

Did the student . . .

- ✓ contribute to the approximation discussion?
- ✓ communicate strategies used to approximate answers to multidigit multiplication problems?
- ✓ correctly answer at least 80% of the approximation problems?

Homework Have students play the "Don't Go Over 1000" game with a family member to reinforce the skill of approximating. A copy of this game can also be found on page 10 of the Home Connections Blackline Masters.

LESSON 84

Student Edition pages 284–285

Practice with Approximating

LESSON PLANNER

Objectives

- ▶ to introduce the use of scientific notation to approximate answers to multidigit multiplication problems
- ▶ to teach students to investigate properties of multiplication of multidigit numbers

Context of the Lesson This is the last of seven lessons on multiplying powers and multiples of 10 and on approximating products.

MANIPULATIVES

calculators*

Program Resources

Number Wheels

Practice Master 84

Enrichment Master 84

For extra practice:
CD-ROM* Lesson 84

1 Warm-Up

5 MINUTES

Problem of the Day Present this problem orally or on the chalkboard: Use the factors 2, 4, 6, and 8, repeating them as often as you wish. Find all the different products you can by multiplying any two factors. (There are nine different products: 2 x 2 = 4, 2 x 4 = 8, 2 x 6 = 12, 2 x 8 and 4 x 4 = 16, 4 x 6 = 24, 4 x 8 = 32, 6 x 6 = 36, 6 x 8 = 48, and 8 x 8 = 64.)

Problem-Solving Strategies Ask students who have solved the Problem of the Day to share how they solved it and any strategies they used.

MENTAL MATH Provide practice multiplying multiples of 10 with these problems. Have students use their Number Wheels to respond.

a. 40 x 70 = (2800)

b. 400 x 700 = (280,000)

c. 4000 x 70 = (280,000)

d. 80 x 70 = (5600)

e. 80 x 700 = (56,000)

f. 800 x 7000 = (5,600,000)

MIXED **PRACTICE**

LESSON 84

Practice with Approximating

Use a computer or other means to copy the chart on page 285. Approximate the answer to each problem. Then use your calculator to find the answer.

Compare each approximation with each answer. Comment on whether you could have made a better approximation for each problem. Here are some examples:

Example 1: 378 × 591 ≈ 400 × 600 = 240,000

Approximation: 240,000
Answer: 223, 398
Comment: Because both factors were rounded up and were too great, 230,000 or 220,000 would have been a better approximation.

Example 2: 408 × 523 ≈ 400 × 500 = 200,000

Approximation: 200,000
Answer: 213,384
Comment: Because both factors were rounded down and were too low, 210,000 would have been a better approximation.

Example 3: 32 × 8796 ≈ 30 × 9000 = 270,000

Approximation: 270,000
Answer: 281,472
Comment: One factor was rounded down and the other up. The factor rounded up changed more than the one rounded down, so the estimate will have to be adjusted up to 280,000.

RETEACHING

At this time it is not necessary for students to become proficient at the fine points of adjusting initial estimates. However, encourage them to consider and use this skill when appropriate. You may want to assign Enrichment Master 84.

*available separately

	Standard Form	Approximation	Answer	Comment
1	654 × 865	$7 \times 10^2 \times 9 \times 10^2$ $= 63 \times 10^4$ = 630,000	565,710	Since both factors were rounded up, the approximation is too high.
2	78,596 × 8,492	$8 \times 10^4 \times 8 \times 10^3$ $= 64 \times 10^7$ = 640,000,000	667,437,232	Since the lesser factor was rounded down, the approximation is too low. See margin.
3	650 × 75,000	$7 \times 10^2 \times 8 \times 10^4$ $= 56 \times 10^6$ = 56,000,000	48,750,000	Rounding one factor down and the other up will give a better approximation.
4	6497 × 7496	$6 \times 10^3 \times 7 \times 10^3$ $= 42 \times 10^6$ = 42,000,000	48,701,512	Rounding one factor up and the other down will give a better approximation than rounding both down.
5	12 × 3482	$1 \times 10^1 \times 3 \times 10^3$ $= 3 \times 10^4$ = 30,000	41,784	The approximation is low, since the lesser factor was rounded down.
6	100,000 × 40,000	$1 \times 10^5 \times 4 \times 10^4$ $= 4 \times 10^9$ = 4,000,000,000	4,000,000,000	Since no rounding was done with either factor, the approximation is correct. See margin.
7	29 × 31	$3 \times 10^1 \times 3 \times 10^1 =$ 9×10^2 = 900	899	The approximation is slightly high because the lesser factor was rounded up.
8	700,000 × 34	$7 \times 10^5 \times 3 \times 10^1$ $= 21 \times 10^6$ = 21,000,000	23,800,000	The approximation is low because the lesser factor was rounded down.
9	1089 × 8905	$1 \times 10^3 \times 9 \times 10^3$ $= 9 \times 10^6$ = 9,000,000	9,697,545	The approximation is low since the lesser factor was rounded down.
10	456 × 7038	$5 \times 10^2 \times 7 \times 10^3$ $= 35 \times 10^5$ = 3,500,000	3,209,328	Even though one factor was rounded down and one was rounded up, the approximation is a bit high.

Solve these problems.

11. The snack bar at the movie theater used 36 boxes of napkins last weekend. There are 500 napkins in each box. About how many napkins were used? **approximately 20,000; exactly 18,000**

12. In one day about 300 bags of popcorn are sold at the movie theater. About how many bags are sold in a 31-day month? **approximately 9000; exactly 9300**

FANTASTIC FACT

The best-selling children's book of all time is *The Tale of Peter Rabbit* by Beatrix Potter. More than 9 million copies have been sold since it was first published in 1902.

❷ Teach

Using the Student Pages Review the approximation examples on page 284. Have students use their **calculators*** to help them complete the chart on page 285. Note that problems 2 and 6 on page 285 have answers that will not fit on an eight-digit calculator display. Accept calculator approximations for these exercises. Discuss the exercises on page 285, raising the following points:

1. There is no single best approximation method.
2. When both factors are rounded up, the approximation is likely to be too high. When both are rounded down, the approximation is likely to be too low. Either way, students should usually adjust the approximation.
3. If two factors are rounded in opposite directions, the one that is rounded more is likely to have the greater effect.
4. Rounding the lesser factor is likely to have a greater effect than rounding the greater factor.

❸ Wrap-Up

5 MINUTES

In Closing Have students explain the effects of rounding factors up or down to approximate products.

ALTERNATIVE ASSESSMENT

Informal Assessment Observe students as they complete this lesson. Have them verbalize their thinking, and encourage them to explain their comments as fully as possible.

Assessment Criteria

Did the student . . .

- ✓ contribute to the discussion?
- ✓ demonstrate understanding of approximation techniques?
- ✓ apply and describe approximation techniques to complete the chart?

Homework Assign Practice Master 84 for further reinforcement of the skill of approximating.

PRACTICE p. 84

LESSON 84 PRACTICE Name_______________

Complete the chart below. Approximate the answer to each problem using scientific notation. Then use your calculator to find the answer. Comment on whether you could have made a better approximation for each problem.

	Standard Form	Approximation	Answer	Comment
1	756 × 763	$8 \times 10^2 \times 8 \times 10^2 =$ 640,000	576,828	Both factors were rounded up. Estimate too great.
2	68,589 × 7,496	$7 \times 10^4 \times 7 \times 10^3 =$ 490,000,000	514,143,144	Rounded one up and one down. Good approximation.
3	550 × 85,000	$6 \times 10^2 \times 9 \times 10^4 =$ 54,000,000	46,750,000	Both rounded up. Estimate too high.
4	5496 × 6498	$5 \times 10^3 \times 6 \times 10^3 =$ 30,000,000	35,713,008	Both rounded down. Estimate too low.
5	12 × 4490	$1 \times 10 \times 4 \times 10^3 =$ 40,000	53,880	Both rounded down. Estimate too low.
6	200,000 × 30,000	$2 \times 10^5 \times 3 \times 10^4 =$ 6,000,000,000	6,000,000,000	Rounding gives same result as exact answer.
7	39 × 41	$4 \times 10 \times 4 \times 10 =$ 1600	1599	Rounded one up and one down. Good approximation.
8	699 × 31	$7 \times 10^3 \times 3 \times 10 =$ 21,000	21,669	Rounded one up and one down. Good approximation.
9	545 × 649	$5 \times 10^2 \times 6 \times 10^2 =$ 300,000	353,705	Both numbers were rounded down. Estimate too low.
10	800 × 900	$8 \times 10^2 \times 9 \times 10^2 =$ 720,000	720,000	Rounding gives same result as exact answer.

Copyright © SRA/McGraw-Hill. Permission is granted to reproduce this page for classroom use.

84 • *Math Explorations and Applications* Level 4

ENRICHMENT p. 84

LESSON 84 ENRICHMENT Name_______________

SCIENCE CONNECTION

In scientific notation, $150 = 1.5 \times 10^2$, $1500 = 1.5 \times 10^3$, $15,000 = 1.5 \times 10^4$, $150,000 = 1.5 \times 10^5$, $1,500,000 = 1.5 \times 10^6$. Can you see how scientific notation works?

Solve these problems.

The planet Pluto has the smallest diameter (distance across) of the nine planets. Its diameter is 1500 miles, or 1.5×10^3.

1. The diameter of Mercury is about twice that of Pluto. Give the approximate diameter of Mercury in miles. Then write it in scientific notation.
   about 3000 miles; 3×10^3
2. The diameters of Neptune and Uranus are about 20 times that of Pluto. Give the approximate diameters of Neptune and Uranus in miles. Then write the diameter in scientific notation.
   about 30,000 miles; 3×10^4
3. The diameter of Venus is about five times that of Pluto. Give the approximate diameter of Venus in miles. Then write it in scientific notation.
   about 7500 miles; 7.5×10^3
4. Research to check your approximations. How close were they? Now write the diameters of each planet in miles and scientific notation.

Mercury 3100 miles; 3.1×10^3
Venus 7700 miles; 7.7×10^3
Earth 7920 miles; 7.92×10^3
Mars 4200 miles; 4.2×10^3
Jupiter 88,640 miles; 8.864×10^4
Saturn 74,500 miles; 7.45×10^4
Uranus 32,000 miles; 3.2×10^4
Neptune 31,000 miles; 3.1×10^4
Pluto 1500 miles; 1.5×10^3

Copyright © SRA/McGraw-Hill. Permission is granted to reproduce this page for classroom use.

84 • *Math Explorations and Applications* Level 4

*available separately

LESSON 85

Student Edition pages 286–289

Multiply: Two-Digit Numbers by One-Digit Numbers

LESSON PLANNER

Objectives

- to teach the standard algorithm for multiplying a two-digit number by a one-digit number
- to provide a story that shows why the algorithm works

Context of the Lesson This is the first of 17 lessons on multidigit multiplication. Before students proceed to multiplying two two-digit numbers in Lesson 88, they should become reasonably proficient in multiplying by one-digit numbers.

MANIPULATIVES

multiplication table (optional)

Program Resources

"Harder Shopping" Game Mat

Reteaching Master

Practice Master 85

Enrichment Master 85

For additional math integration: Math Throughout the Day*

For extra practice: CD-ROM* Lesson 85

1 Warm-Up (5 MINUTES)

Problem of the Day Present this problem orally or on the chalkboard: Eric went to a parade at the local riding school. There were ten horses in the parade. Half of the horses had one rider, and the other half had two riders. How many legs did Eric see? (70 legs)

Problem-Solving Strategies Ask students who have solved the Problem of the Day to share how they solved it and any strategies they used.

EXPLORE

LESSON 85

ACT IT OUT

Multiply: Two-Digit Numbers by One-Digit Numbers

The Case of the Soda Bottle Cases *Episode 1*

Adam, Malik, Darryl, and Vernon want to earn some money. They can get money at the store for each soda bottle they recycle.

They collect lots of bottles and put them into cases like this one.

◆ How many bottles are in this case? **24**

286 • Multidigit Multiplication

Why teach it this way?

Multidigit multiplication was introduced near the end of Level 3. Those lessons included only the partial-product algorithm. Teaching shorter algorithms was suggested only as an option in Level 3. At this point, the standard algorithm is taught with the assumption that students have not learned it before. Short algorithms are stressed so that students will be prepared for more advanced work on multidigit multiplication.

*available separately

The boys filled eight cases with bottles. Each case had 24 bottles. They wanted to know how many bottles they had all together.

Malik said, "If there were only 20 bottles in a case, we would have 160 bottles."

"How do you know?" asked Darryl.

"Because $8 \times 2 = 16$, so 8×2 tens is 16 tens. And that's 160," answered Malik.

"But you didn't count all the bottles," said Vernon. "You counted only 20 for each case."

"I left out only four from each case," Malik said.

"But that means there are 32 bottles that you didn't count," said Vernon.

"I've got it!" said Adam. "If we add the 32 that Malik didn't count to the 160 he did count, we would have the answer."

"That's it," said Darryl. "We have 192 bottles."

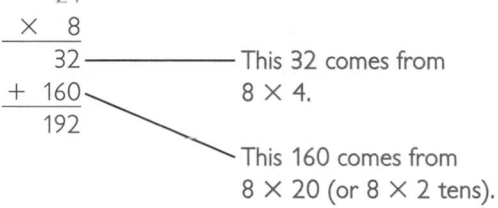

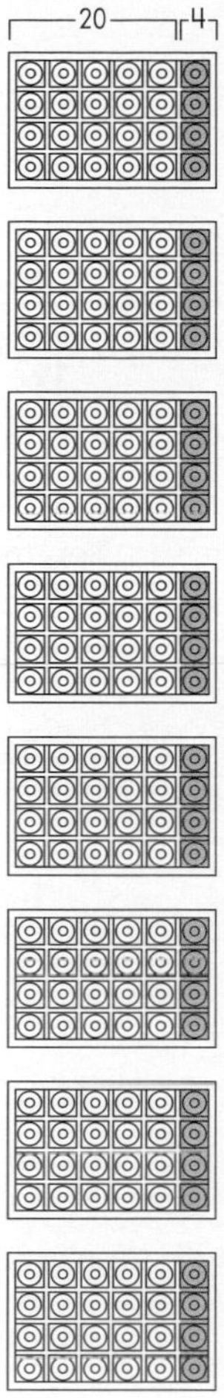

$$\begin{array}{r} 24 \\ \times\ 8 \\ \hline 32 \\ +\ 160 \\ \hline 192 \end{array}$$

This 32 comes from 8×4.

This 160 comes from 8×20 (or 8×2 tens).

Literature Connection Invite students to read *The Magic School Bus Lost in the Solar System* by Joanna Cole. Have them determine what a 170-pound person would weigh on each of the planets.

MENTAL MATH Complete this drill using the bounds 500–600. Have students show thumbs up for answers that are between 500 and 600 and thumbs down for answers that are not.

a. 445 + 20 (down); 445 + 40 (down); 445 + 80 (up); 445 + 200 (down)

b. 900 – 250 (down); 900 – 350 (up); 900 – 450 (down)

c. 65 × 10 (down); 55 × 10 (up); 45 × 10 (down); 53 × 10 (up)

d. 5170 ÷ 10 (up); 4350 ÷ 10 (down); 56,700 ÷ 100 (up); 31,200 ÷ 100 (down)

2 Teach

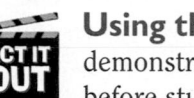

ACT IT OUT **Using the Student Pages** You might want to demonstrate the "Harder Shopping" Game Mat before students begin pages 286–289 so that they can play as soon as they finish. This game provides practice with multidigit multiplication.

The story on pages 286–287 develops an algorithm for multiplying a two-digit number by a one-digit number. Read the story with the class. Encourage students to make suggestions about how to solve 24 x 8. Use the standard algorithm if suggested, but encourage students to discuss why it works.

Note that the order in which the story characters perform the multiplication is the reverse of the standard algorithm. Approximation is usually done this way, and most students find this way to be more natural. The algorithm is done here in the opposite order because the shortcut on page 288 works only if you work from lesser to greater place values.

LEARNING STYLES **Meeting Individual Needs**

Some students like to record the carried number as they learn the multiplication algorithm until it becomes more automatic to them. For students who benefit from this approach, have them write the carried numbers or use their fingers as needed until they can solve problems without using such aids.

◆ LESSON 85 Multiply: Two-Digit Numbers by One-Digit Numbers

Teach

Using the Student Pages Review the steps at the top of page 288. You may wish to follow these steps with several other examples. Discourage students from writing "carried" numbers because it may become cumbersome and confusing in multidigit multiplication.

At the bottom of page 289, go through the example for checking whether an answer makes sense. Point out that this procedure shows only whether the answer makes sense, not whether it is correct. Emphasize that it is not always necessary to do both steps of the check. Problem 16 is a good example of a case in which only one step is enough. Because 3 x 89 is a little less than 3 x 90, which is 270, an answer a little less than 270 should make sense. Have students complete page 289 on their own.

Using the "Harder Shopping" Game Mat Have students play this game to provide practice with multiplication and forming amounts of money and change. It is similar to the "Shopping" game, but it involves multidigit numbers. Complete instructions can be found on the Game Mat. A copy of this Game Mat can also be found on page 602 of this Teacher's Guide.

SPECIAL NEEDS

Meeting Individual Needs

Students who are still having difficulty with the basic multiplication facts should continue to practice them until they become automatic. Practice procedures may vary, depending on each student. You might also want to let students consult a **multiplication table** as needed so they can practice the algorithm.

◆ LESSON 85 Multiply: Two-Digit Numbers by One-Digit Numbers

ACT IT OUT

Here's a shorter way to multiply 8 × 24.

24 × **8** **2**	Start at the right. Multiply the ones digit by 8. 8 × 4 = 32 (that's 3 tens and 2) Write the 2 and **remember the 3 tens** for the next column.
24 × **8** **19**2	Multiply the tens digit by 8. 8 × 2 = 16 16 tens **plus the 3 tens you remembered** is 19 tens. Write 19.

You may have trouble remembering the number that you saved from the previous column. If you do, you may use one of these methods to help:

a. Keep track of the number on your fingers. If the number is greater than 5, use both hands; you won't have to write until you've used that number.

b. You may write the number you are remembering in the place you will write the next part of the answer. Cross off the number as soon as you use it.

24 × 8 → 24 × 8 = (3 written below the line) 2 → 24 × 8 = (3 crossed off) 192

c. Write the number above the next digit of the top number. Cross it off when you use it.

24 × 8 → (3 above) 24 × 8 = 2 → (3 crossed off above) 24 × 8 = 192

If you write the numbers, be sure to make them small and neat so you don't get confused.

Technology Connection You might want to refer students to the video *Math Mystery Theatre: Multiplication Maniac,* from EdCon/Imperial International (VHS, for grades 2–8) for further practice with multidigit multiplication.

RETEACHING p. 28

LESSON 85 RETEACHING Name______________________

Mr. Krasner's class wants to plant a garden. In one section the students want to plant nine rows of lettuce. Each row can fit 13 plants. The students need to know how many lettuce seeds to plant.

One way to find out is to make a drawing or use counters. Circle groups of ten.

How many tens are there? 11

How many ones are left over? 7

How many lettuce seeds should the students plant? 117

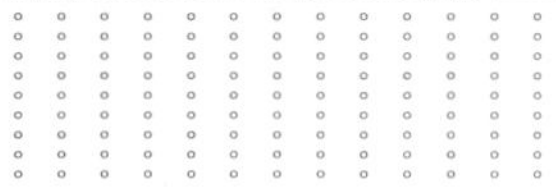

Another way to solve the problem is to multiply.
Change 13 into tens and ones.
Multiply each by 9. 9 × 1 ten = 90 9 × 3 ones = 27
Add the products. 90 + 27 = 117

The problem can be written like this:

13 × 9 27 from 3 × 9 90 from 10 × 9 117	← Once you are comfortable multiplying, you can leave out this step. Write the problem like this. →	2 13 × 9 117	(9 × 3 = 27) (9 × 1 + 2 = 11)	Write 7. Write 11.

Multiply. Use counters or sticks to help you find the products.

1. 10 × 6 = *n* 60
2. 36 × 4 = *n* 144
3. 85 × 2 = *n* 170
4. 18 × 8 = *n* 144
5. 25 × 6 = *n* 150
6. 50 × 5 = *n* 250

28 • *Math Explorations and Applications* Level 4

Copyright © SRA/McGraw-Hill. Permission is granted to reproduce this page for classroom use.

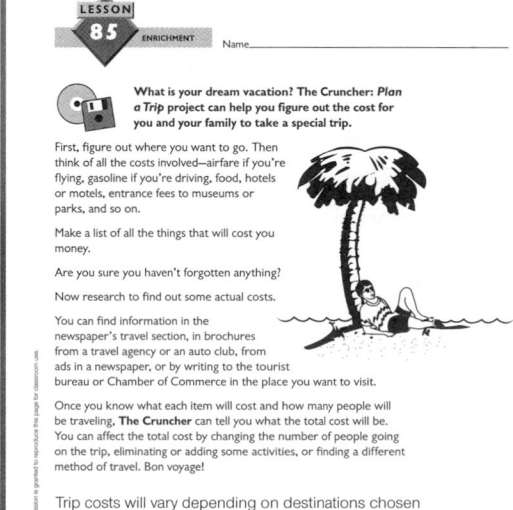

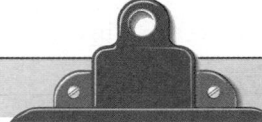

Multiply. Use shortcuts when you can.

❶ 24 × 6 **144**	❷ 26 × 9 **234**	❸ 43 × 3 **129**	❹ 60 × 8 **480**	❺ 90 × 3 **270**	❻ 83 × 4 **332**
❼ 24 × 8 **192**	❽ 46 × 7 **322**	❾ 65 × 4 **260**	❿ 19 × 4 **76**	⓫ 78 × 9 **702**	⓬ 57 × 7 **399**
⓭ 25 × 4 **100**	⓮ 87 × 2 **174**	⓯ 51 × 7 **357**	⓰ 89 × 3 **267**	⓱ 95 × 6 **570**	⓲ 28 × 4 **112**
⓳ 72 × 8 **576**	⓴ 29 × 6 **174**	21 43 × 9 **387**	22 27 × 2 **54**	23 39 × 5 **195**	24 72 × 6 **432**

25 68 × 3 **204**	26 26 × 9 **234**	27 6 × 39 **234**	28 72 × 8 **576**
29 37 × 5 **185**	30 7 × 49 **343**	31 68 × 5 **340**	32 27 × 6 **162**
33 4 × 70 **280**	34 6 × 27 **162**	35 8 × 54 **432**	36 74 × 3 **222**
37 29 × 3 **87**	38 99 × 8 **792**	39 91 × 2 **182**	40 85 × 4 **340**
41 77 × 8 **616**	42 40 × 3 **120**	43 4 × 72 **288**	44 6 × 58 **348**

Check to see that your answers make sense.

Example: The answer to problem 1 should be less than 6 × 30, which is 180.

The answer to problem 1 should be greater than 6 × 20, which is 120.

Is your answer to problem 1 less than 180 and greater than 120?

If so, the answer makes sense. (That does not tell you it is correct. But if it does not make sense, it must be wrong.)

Unit 4 Lesson 85 • **289**

PRACTICE p. 85

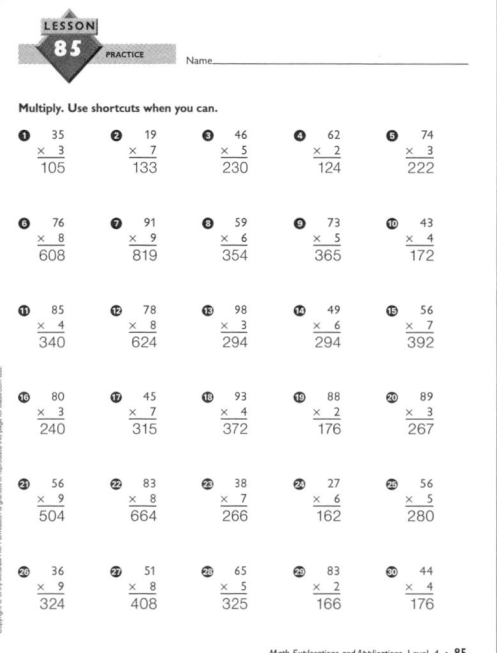

LESSON 85 PRACTICE Name________

Multiply. Use shortcuts when you can.

❶ 35 × 3 = 105	❷ 19 × 7 = 133	❸ 46 × 5 = 230	❹ 62 × 2 = 124	❺ 74 × 3 = 222
❻ 76 × 8 = 608	❼ 91 × 9 = 819	❽ 59 × 6 = 354	❾ 73 × 5 = 365	❿ 43 × 4 = 172
⓫ 85 × 4 = 340	⓬ 78 × 8 = 624	⓭ 98 × 3 = 294	⓮ 49 × 6 = 294	⓯ 56 × 7 = 392
⓰ 80 × 3 = 240	⓱ 45 × 7 = 315	⓲ 93 × 4 = 372	⓳ 88 × 2 = 176	⓴ 89 × 3 = 267
21 56 × 9 = 504	22 83 × 8 = 664	23 38 × 7 = 266	24 27 × 6 = 162	25 56 × 5 = 280
26 36 × 9 = 324	27 51 × 8 = 408	28 65 × 5 = 325	29 83 × 2 = 166	30 44 × 4 = 176

Copyright © SRA/McGraw-Hill. Permission is granted to reproduce this page for classroom use.

Math Explorations and Applications Level 4 • **85**

ENRICHMENT p. 85

LESSON 85 ENRICHMENT Name________

What is your dream vacation? The Cruncher: *Plan a Trip* project can help you figure out the cost for you and your family to take a special trip.

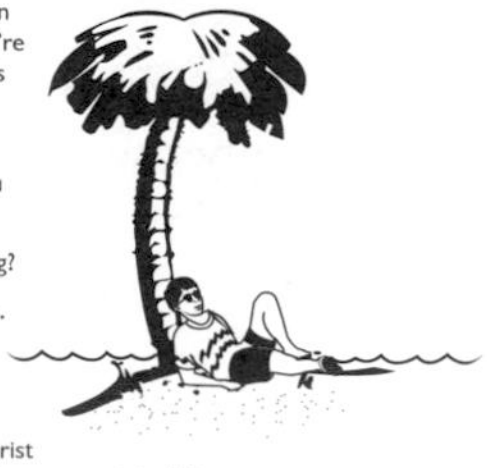

First, figure out where you want to go. Then think of all the costs involved—airfare if you're flying, gasoline if you're driving, food, hotels or motels, entrance fees to museums or parks, and so on.

Make a list of all the things that will cost you money.

Are you sure you haven't forgotten anything?

Now research to find out some actual costs.

You can find information in the newspaper's travel section, in brochures from a travel agency or an auto club, from ads in a newspaper, or by writing to the tourist bureau or Chamber of Commerce in the place you want to visit.

Once you know what each item will cost and how many people will be traveling, **The Cruncher** can tell you what the total cost will be. You can affect the total cost by changing the number of people going on the trip, eliminating or adding some activities, or finding a different method of travel. Bon voyage!

Trip costs will vary depending on destinations chosen and activities planned.

Copyright © SRA/McGraw-Hill. Permission is granted to reproduce this page for classroom use.

Math Explorations and Applications Level 4 • **85**

3 Wrap-Up (5 MINUTES)

In Closing Have students list steps for multiplying a two-digit number by a one-digit number.

ALTERNATIVE ASSESSMENT

Performance Assessment Have students role-play teaching each other how to multiply a two-digit number by a one-digit number. Listen and watch as the "teacher" explains the steps to the "student," who should feel free to ask questions. Then have students switch roles.

Assessment Criteria

Did the student . . .

- ✓ contribute to the discussion of the story?
- ✓ demonstrate understanding of the multiplication algorithm?
- ✓ apply the algorithm to the practice exercises?
- ✓ correctly answer at least 75% of the multiplication problems?

Homework Have students make up six multiplication problems of their own to solve, each of which uses a different one-digit multiplier. Have them use numbers that yield three even-numbered products and three odd-numbered products.

LESSON 86

Student Edition pages 290–291

Multiply: Three-Digit Numbers by One-Digit Numbers

LESSON PLANNER

Objective

- ▶ to teach an algorithm for multiplying a three-digit number by a one-digit number

Context of the Lesson This is the second of 17 lessons on multidigit multiplication.

MANIPULATIVES

base-10 blocks*, craft sticks, or interlocking cubes* (optional)

Program Resources

Practice Master 86

Enrichment Master 86

For extra practice: CD-ROM* Lesson 86

1 Warm-Up

5 MINUTES

Problem of the Day Present this problem orally or on the chalkboard: The Earth Club bought a volcano kit for $14. All members chipped in to pay for it. Each member gave at least 50¢ but less than $1. Figure out the greatest and least possible number of members of the Earth Club. (28 members, 15 members)

Problem-Solving Strategies Ask students who have solved the Problem of the Day to share how they solved it and any strategies they used.

MENTAL MATH Provide practice with detecting obviously wrong answers. Students should respond with thumbs down for obviously wrong answers and thumbs up for possibly correct ones.

a. 100 x 8 = 108 (thumbs down)

b. 600 x 4 = 2800 (thumbs down)

c. 70 + 30 = 100 (thumbs up)

d. 400 x 5 = 2400 (thumbs down)

e. 300 x 6 = 1800 (thumbs up)

f. 510 x 7 = 3017 (thumbs down)

g. 200 + 40 = 240 (thumbs up)

EXPLORE

LESSON 86

ACT IT OUT

Multiply: Three-Digit Numbers by One-Digit Numbers

The Case of the Soda Bottle Cases *Episode 2*

Remember that Adam, Malik, Darryl, and Vernon collected 192 soda bottles. "I think we can get nine cents at the store for each bottle we recycle," said Adam. "I wonder how much money we can get all together."

"Let's see," said Darryl, "192 is the same amount as 100 + 90 + 2. For 100 bottles we get 900 cents. For 90 bottles we get 810 cents. For two bottles we get 18 cents. How much is that all together?"

"That's 1728 cents," said Vernon, "which is $17.28."

"Let's go get our money," they all said.

Look:

```
    192
  ×   9
     18 —This 18 comes from 9 × 2.
+   810 —This 810 comes from 9 × 90 (or 9 × 9 tens).
+   900 —This 900 comes from 9 × 100 (or 9 × 1 hundred).
   1728 —This 1728 comes from 18 + 810 + 900.
```


Literature Connection Invite students to read *The 329th Friend* by Marjorie Weinman Sharmat. They can multiply the number of friends by the number of individual preparations made by the host.

RETEACHING

Have students use **base-10 materials*** to model the steps of the multiplication algorithm. For example, use 30 bundles of 10 to illustrate the problem 100 x 3 = 300. First take 10 bundles of 10 to illustrate 100. Then explain that to multiply by 3 means to have 3 groups of 100. Show how many bundles of 10 are in 3 groups of 100, and then run through the steps on paper. Continue with several other problems until students understand the concept, and then work at practicing with only the algorithm.

*available separately

Here's a shorter way to multiply 9 × 192.

192 × 9 8	Start at the right. Multiply the ones digit by 9. 9 × 2 = 18 18 = 1 ten and 8 Write the 8 and remember the 1 ten.
192 × 9 28	Multiply the tens digit by 9. 9 × 9 = 81 81 tens and 1 ten is 82 tens. 82 tens = 8 hundreds and 2 tens Write the 2 and remember the 8 hundreds.
192 × 9 1728	Multiply the hundreds digit by 9. 9 × 1 = 9 9 hundreds and 8 hundreds is 17 hundreds. 17 hundreds is 1 thousand and 7 hundreds. Write the 17.

Multiply. Use shortcuts when you can.

1. 352 × 8 **2816**
2. 643 × 8 **5144**
3. 721 × 2 **1442**
4. 684 × 7 **4788**
5. 987 × 6 **5922**
6. 7 × 367 **2569**
7. 47 × 6 **282**
8. 453 × 4 **1812**
9. 800 × 6 **4800**
10. 308 × 7 **2156**
11. 795 × 5 **3975**
12. 505 × 3 **1515**
13. 200 × 9 **1800**
14. 497 × 2 **994**
15. 7 × 607 **4249**

Check to see that your answers make sense.

Example: The answer to problem 1 should be less than 8 × 400, which is 3200. It should be greater than 8 × 300, which is 2400. Is your answer to problem 1 less than 3200 and greater than 2400? If so, the answer makes sense.

Unit 4 Lesson 86 • **291**

❷ Teach

Using the Student Pages Read through the story with the class. When going over the shorter multiplication algorithm on page 291, point out to students that the steps are the same as those they have been using to solve problems like 68 × 8. Here the process is extended to include the hundreds place. Remind students to check their answers by approximating.

❸ Wrap-Up

5 MINUTES

In Closing Have students review the algorithm for multiplying a three-digit number by a one-digit number by verbalizing the steps for finding the product of 587 × 6.

ANALYZING ANSWERS

Be sure students realize that even when an answer falls within the upper and lower bounds of the approximated products, it is not necessarily correct. Emphasize the importance of checking that answers are reasonable.

SELF ASSESSMENT

Have students each write a brief statement in which they evaluate their ability to multiply a two- or three-digit number by a one-digit number. Encourage them to include aspects of the process that they may find difficult or tricky. You might have students include their statements in their Math Portfolios as a measure of ongoing learning.

Assessment Criteria

Did the student . . .

- ✓ contribute to the story discussion?
- ✓ explain and apply the multiplication algorithm?
- ✓ correctly answer at least 75% of the multiplication problems?

Homework Assign Practice Master 86 for further reinforcement of the skill of multiplying three-digit numbers by one-digit numbers.

PRACTICE p. 86

LESSON 86 PRACTICE

Name____________

Multiply. Use shortcuts when you can.

1. 453 × 8 = 3624
2. 400 × 7 = 2800
3. 569 × 5 = 2845
4. 436 × 4 = 1744
5. 585 × 7 = 4095
6. 568 × 3 = 1704
7. 600 × 8 = 4800
8. 382 × 9 = 3438
9. 64 × 6 = 384
10. 821 × 5 = 4105
11. 521 × 2 = 1042
12. 400 × 9 = 3600
13. 409 × 7 = 2863
14. 401 × 8 = 3208
15. 646 × 7 = 4522
16. 458 × 6 = 2748
17. 88 × 5 = 440
18. 986 × 6 = 5916
19. 823 × 4 = 3292
20. 85 × 9 = 765
21. 300 × 4 = 1200
22. 697 × 9 = 6273
23. 689 × 3 = 2067
24. 751 × 8 = 6008
25. 193 × 9 = 1737
26. 505 × 7 = 3535
27. 469 × 6 = 2814
28. 469 × 3 = 1407
29. 200 × 4 = 800
30. 844 × 2 = 1688

Copyright © SRA/McGraw-Hill. Permission is granted to reproduce this page for classroom use.

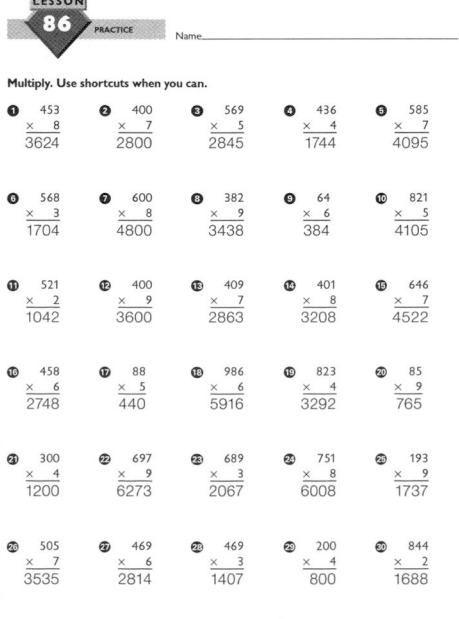

ENRICHMENT p. 86

LESSON 86 ENRICHMENT

Name____________

Recycling is one way to help clean and protect the environment and to earn some money. Does your school need supplies for a special project? Does your class need money for a field trip? **The Cruncher: *Recycling*** project can help you keep track of the money you earn and the money you still need.

Imagine you need $40 for art supplies. The table below shows what recycling different items pays and what you will have collected after a week.

	Aluminum Cans	Glass Bottles	Plastic Bottles
Cash per pound at recycling center	$1	$0.05	$0.25
Number of pieces per pound	25	2	7
Value of one container	$0.04	$0.03	$0.04
Number of pieces collected	100	100	100
Cash from recycling center	$4.00	$2.50	$3.57

1. How much money have you made so far? $10.07
2. How much more money do you need? $29.93
3. Start a recycling project of your own. Find out what your local recycling center pays for each item that can be recycled. Set a dollar-amount goal, and start collecting.
Answers will vary depending on what items your local recycling center accepts and what the center pays per item.

Copyright © SRA/McGraw-Hill. Permission is granted to reproduce this page for classroom use.

LESSON 87

Student Edition pages 292–295

Multiplication Review

LESSON PLANNER

Objectives

✓ to assess students' ability to multiply two- or three-digit numbers by a one-digit number

▶ to help students develop the broad ability to use mathematical common sense

Context of the Lesson This lesson, the third of 17 lessons on multidigit multiplication, contains a Mastery Checkpoint for assessing mastery of multiplying two- or three-digit numbers by one-digit numbers. This lesson also contains Part 2 of "The Treasure of Mugg Island," a six-part Thinking Story.

MANIPULATIVES

map from Lesson 81

jigsaw puzzle (optional)

Program Resources

Number Cubes (0–5 and 5–10)

Number Wheels

Reteaching Master

Practice Master 87

Enrichment Master 87

Assessment Master

For career connections: Careers and Math*

For extra practice: CD-ROM* Lesson 87

MIXED PRACTICE

LESSON 87

Multiplication Review

Practice multiplying two-digit and three-digit numbers by a one-digit number. Check to see that your answers make sense.

Multiply.

1. 64×7 = **448**	2. 308×4 = **1232**	3. 99×5 = **495**	4. 726×8 = **5808**	5. 394×2 = **788**
6. 501×8 = **4008**	7. 663×7 = **4641**	8. 48×3 = **144**	9. 90×9 = **810**	10. 307×9 = **2763**

11. 56×7 **392**	12. 321×4 **1284**	13. 872×7 **6104**
14. 434×3 **1302**	15. 82×5 **410**	16. 49×4 **196**
17. 72×6 **432**	18. 19×8 **152**	19. 6×481 **2886**
20. 840×9 **7560**	21. 28×6 **168**	22. 2×917 **1834**
23. 107×5 **535**	24. 730×4 **2920**	25. 5×489 **2445**

Solve these problems.

26. Jamie rides her bike 3 kilometers every day. How far does she ride in 15 days? **45 km**

27. Judy gets eight ride tickets in every ticket book she buys. How many ride tickets will she get in nine books? **72**

28. Antonio is packing supplies for a camping trip. He will bake biscuits five times. He will use four packages of biscuit mix each time he bakes biscuits. How many packages of biscuit mix should he pack? **20, if he wants to take just enough**

29. Allison works 15 hours a week at the video store. How many hours will she work in six weeks? **90**

30. Mrs. Winter is buying crayons for her students. She wants to buy a box of eight crayons for each student. There are 35 students in her class. How many crayons is that all together? **280**

292 • Multidigit Multiplication

1 Warm-Up

5 MINUTES

Problem of the Day Present this problem to the class. Explain to students that there are many answers: Ed's seven-digit phone number starts and ends with a 9. It has two 7s in it. All the other digits are odd numbers, but no other digits repeat. What might Ed's phone number be? (One possible answer is 973-7519.)

Problem-Solving Strategies Ask students who have solved the Problem of the Day to share how they solved it and any strategies they used.

Literature Connection Read *The Toothpaste Millionaire* by Jean Merrill with the class, or have students read it on their own. This novel, about an eighth-grade boy who starts a business and finds success, provides many opportunities for students to apply their multiplication skills.

*available separately

COOPERATIVE LEARNING

Cube 100 Game

Players: Two
Materials: Two 0–5 cubes, two 5–10 cubes
Object: To score as close to 100 as possible without going over
Math Focus: Adding, multiplying, and mathematical reasoning

GAME

RULES

1. Roll the cubes one at a time, adding the numbers as you roll.
2. After any roll, instead of adding that number you may multiply it by the sum of the previous numbers. But once you multiply, your turn is over.
3. The player with the score closer to, but not over, 100 wins the round.

SAMPLE GAME

Wendy rolled 6, then 3.	Todd rolled 5, then 5.
6 + 3 = 9	5 + 5 = 10
Then she rolled 9.	Then he rolled 6.
9 × 9 = 81	10 + 6 = 16
She stopped after three rolls.	He rolled 6 again.
	16 × 6 = 96
Wendy's score was 81.	Todd's score was 96.
	Todd won the round.

MATH JOURNAL

In your Math Journal explain your strategy for playing the game.

Unit 4 Lesson 87 • **293**

Technology Connection Refer students to the software *Calculating Crew* from Edmark (Mac, IBM, for grades 3–5) for further practice with one- to three-digit addition, subtraction, multiplication and division; 3D geometry (solids and nets); estimation and rounding; money transactions; problem solving; and reasoning.

MENTAL MATH Provide mixed practice with addition, subtraction, and multiplication. Have students use Number Wheels to quickly show their answers.

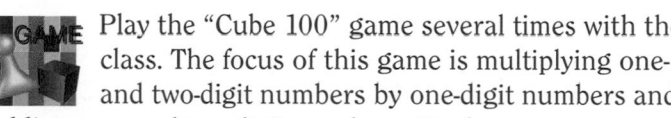

a. 45 + 200 = (245)
b. 750 – 250 = (500)
c. 20 × 600 = (12,000)
d. 970 – 370 = (600)
e. 614 × 100 = (61,400)
f. 4307 + 501 = (4808)
g. 392 × 10 = (3920)
h. 33 + 66 = (99)
i. 800 – 399 = (401)
j. 1500 + 1500 = (3000)
k. 100 – 54 = (46)
l. 70 × 80 = (5600)

2 Teach

PROBLEM SOLVING **Using the Student Pages** Demonstrate the "Cube 100" game on page 293 before students begin the problems on page 292. This game provides practice with multiplying and adding using one- and two-digit numbers. Then have students work on page 292 independently. As they finish, have them play the game in pairs.

GAME Play the "Cube 100" game several times with the class. The focus of this game is multiplying one- and two-digit numbers by one-digit numbers and adding one- and two-digit numbers. Students may remember the game from the third-grade level. As you demonstrate the game, call attention to the available possibilities with each roll, as shown in the sample game.

ESL **Meeting Individual Needs**
Students with limited proficiency in English may have difficulty understanding spoken instructions and discussion about math problems. Pair these students for about a month with students who are fluent in English. Partners should take responsibility for checking with each other after each class activity to verify that both have the same understanding of teacher instructions and class discussions. You may wish to have these pairs of students sit together.

◆ LESSON 87 Multiplication Review

Teach

Using the Thinking Story "The Treasure of Mugg Island (Part 2)" centers on making deductions from a seemingly unintelligible fragment of a map. Display the **map** students created when they read Part 1 of the story.

Answers to Thinking Story Questions:

1. The map is obviously a fragment because it doesn't show a complete path from the starting point to the hollow tree.
2. The trail seems to follow the stream and then cross it at some rocks.
3. From the fact that the stream cuts across both corners of the map, students can figure out that the hollow tree must be at a place where there is a sharp bend in the stream. This would put it in the part shaped like a nose.

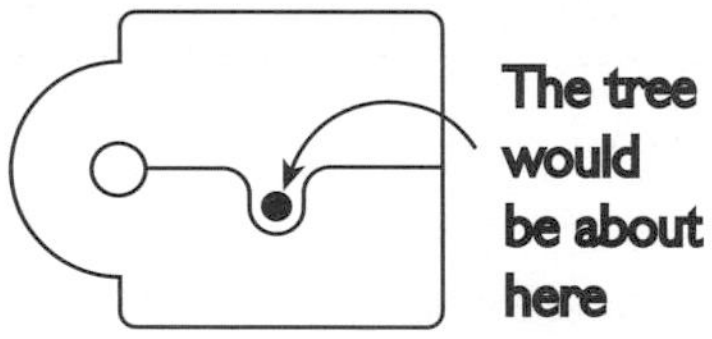

MATH JOURNAL Have students write in their Math Journals about what they would do if they were part of the treasure-hunting group on Mugg Island.

AT RISK **MANIPULATIVES**

Meeting Individual Needs

Students would apply many of the same reasoning skills used in the Thinking Story to solve a **jigsaw puzzle**. Obtain a jigsaw puzzle of a subject that would interest students and make it available in the classroom. Allow them to work on the puzzle in their spare time. Encourage them to work together and share their problem-solving strategies with each other.

◆ LESSON 87 Multiplication Review

THINKING STORY

The Treasure of Mugg Island

Part 2

You may want to refer to the first part of this Thinking Story, on pages 276–277.

Soon the Royal Helicopter came to an island that had the shape of a coffee mug. "This is it," said Manolita. "Mugg Island."

The island was rocky and full of trees. At first they could not find any place to land. Then they found a place where the land was flat and there were no trees. So they landed there.

They all climbed out of the royal helicopter. "Now," said the queen, "we must find the hollow tree. The dotted line on the map shows the trail to follow." Here is the map she showed them:

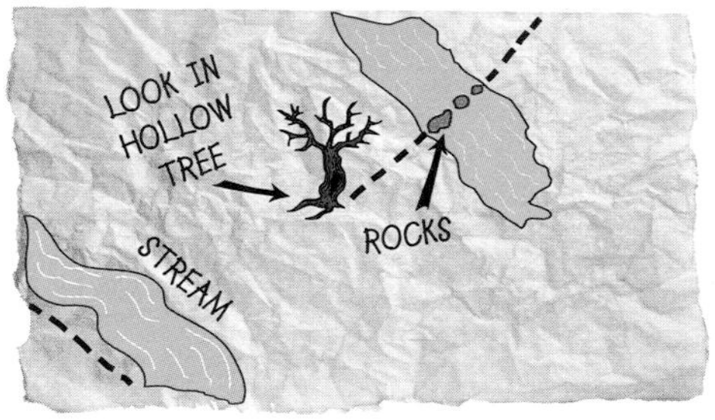

RETEACHING p. 29

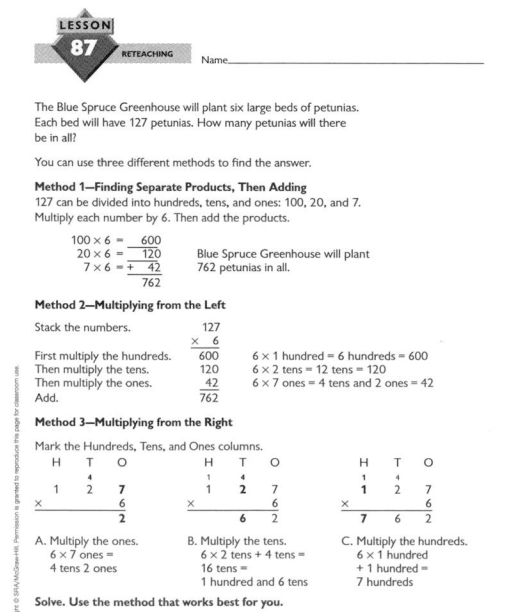

LESSON 87 RETEACHING Name__________

The Blue Spruce Greenhouse will plant six large beds of petunias. Each bed will have 127 petunias. How many petunias will there be in all?

You can use three different methods to find the answer.

Method 1—Finding Separate Products, Then Adding
127 can be divided into hundreds, tens, and ones: 100, 20, and 7.
Multiply each number by 6. Then add the products.

$100 \times 6 = 600$
$20 \times 6 = 120$
$7 \times 6 = +\ 42$
762

Blue Spruce Greenhouse will plant 762 petunias in all.

Method 2—Multiplying from the Left

Stack the numbers.	127 × 6	
First multiply the hundreds.	600	6 × 1 hundred = 6 hundreds = 600
Then multiply the tens.	120	6 × 2 tens = 12 tens = 120
Then multiply the ones.	42	6 × 7 ones = 4 tens and 2 ones = 42
Add.	762	

Method 3—Multiplying from the Right

Mark the Hundreds, Tens, and Ones columns.

H	T	O		H	T	O		H	T	O
	4			1	4			1	4	
1	2	7		1	2	7		1	2	7
×		6		×		6		×		6
		2			6	2		7	6	2

A. Multiply the ones.
6 × 7 ones =
4 tens 2 ones

B. Multiply the tens.
6 × 2 tens + 4 tens =
16 tens =
1 hundred and 6 tens

C. Multiply the hundreds.
6 × 1 hundred
+ 1 hundred =
7 hundreds

Solve. Use the method that works best for you.

1. 653 × 4 = 2612
2. 897 × 8 = 7176
3. 324 × 5 = 1620

Copyright © SRA/McGraw-Hill. Permission is granted to reproduce this page for classroom use.

PRACTICE p. 87

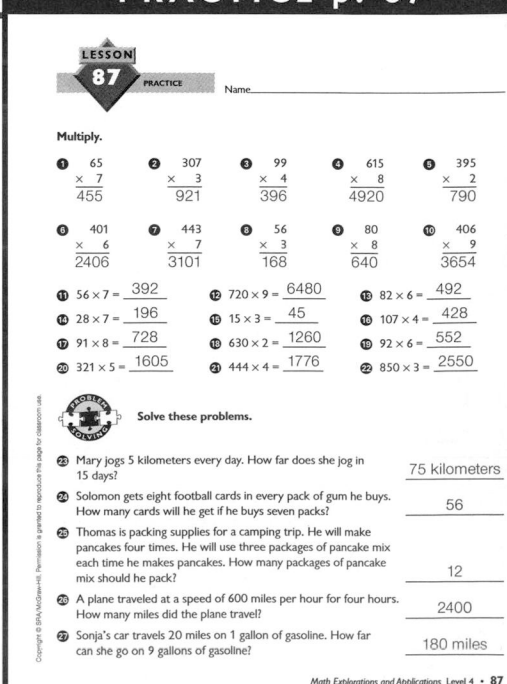

LESSON 87 PRACTICE Name__________

Multiply.

1. 65 × 7 = 455
2. 307 × 3 = 921
3. 99 × 4 = 396
4. 615 × 8 = 4920
5. 395 × 2 = 790
6. 401 × 6 = 2406
7. 443 × 7 = 3101
8. 56 × 3 = 168
9. 80 × 8 = 640
10. 406 × 9 = 3654
11. 56 × 7 = 392
12. 720 × 9 = 6480
13. 82 × 6 = 492
14. 28 × 7 = 196
15. 15 × 3 = 45
16. 107 × 4 = 428
17. 91 × 8 = 728
18. 630 × 2 = 1260
19. 92 × 6 = 552
20. 321 × 5 = 1605
21. 444 × 4 = 1776
22. 850 × 3 = 2550

PROBLEM SOLVING **Solve these problems.**

23. Mary jogs 5 kilometers every day. How far does she jog in 15 days? 75 kilometers
24. Solomon gets eight football cards in every pack of gum he buys. How many cards will he get if he buys seven packs? 56
25. Thomas is packing supplies for a camping trip. He will make pancakes four times. He will use three packages of pancake mix each time he makes pancakes. How many packages of pancake mix should he pack? 12
26. A plane traveled at a speed of 600 miles per hour for four hours. How many miles did the plane travel? 2400
27. Sonja's car travels 20 miles on 1 gallon of gasoline. How far can she go on 9 gallons of gasoline? 180 miles

Copyright © SRA/McGraw-Hill. Permission is granted to reproduce this page for classroom use.

"This can't be the whole map," said Marcus.

"It's all I have," said the queen. "That's why I need your help. If I had the whole map, I could find the hollow tree myself."

. . . to be continued

Work in groups. Discuss your answers and how you figured them out. Then compare your answers with those of other groups. **Answers are in margin.**

1. How could Marcus tell that this was only part of the map showing how to find the hollow tree?
2. Why might the trail show up in two different places on the map?
3. Where is the hollow tree on the island? Use the map of the whole island to help you.

3 Wrap-Up

5 MINUTES

In Closing Have a volunteer plot the location of the hollow tree on the classroom map of Mugg Island.

ANALYZING ANSWERS When you evaluate students' work on page 292, determine the nature of the errors they make. If the problem is with multiplication facts, provide extra drill to help students memorize the facts. If the problem is with understanding or carrying out the algorithm, focus on the steps.

Mastery Checkpoint 14

By this time most students should demonstrate mastery of multiplying two- and three-digit numbers by one-digit numbers by correctly answering at least 80% of the first 25 problems on page 292 or a similar page. Record the results of this assessment on the Mastery Checkpoint Chart. You may also wish to assign Assessment Blackline Masters page 34 to determine mastery.

Assessment Criteria

Did the student . . .

- ✓ correctly answer at least 80% of the multiplication problems on page 292?
- ✓ actively participate in the "Cube 100" game?
- ✓ contribute to the Thinking Story discussion?
- ✓ explain how to determine the location of the hollow tree?

Homework Have students play the "Cube 100" game with a family member for further practice with addition and multiplication facts. A copy of this game can also be found on page 18 of the Home Connections Blackline Masters.

ENRICHMENT p. 87

LESSON 87 ENRICHMENT

Name____________________

Carlos and Maria are making garden beds in a fenced space that is 50 feet long and 29 feet wide. They want the garden beds to be narrow enough so that they can reach into the middle of them without walking on the beds (between 3 feet and 5 feet wide if there is a path on both sides). Paths between the beds should be about $1\frac{1}{2}$ to 2 feet wide.

Draw a plan of the garden in the area below. Let $\frac{1}{8}$ inch on your paper equal 1 foot in the garden.

Now figure out how to arrange the beds to make the most space possible for growing vegetables. Use a ruler to measure and draw the beds and walkways. Show the measurements of each bed on your garden plan.

What is the total area of your garden beds? What is the total area of your paths?

Garden plans will vary. A good way to take advantage of the fences is to make a 2-foot-wide bed along the fences (two 100-square-foot beds and two 50-square-foot beds). An entrance will take about 4 square feet out of one of the border beds.

The space between the border beds (approximately 46 feet by 25 feet) can accommodate six wide beds that are 5 feet by 20 feet (100 square feet each) with 2-foot-wide paths between each. The space between the ends and sides of each wide bed and the fence beds will be about $2\frac{1}{2}$ feet and 3 feet respectively.

The total area of beds and paths will vary.

Copyright © SRA/McGraw-Hill. Permission is granted to reproduce this page for classroom use.

Math Explorations and Applications Level 4 • 87

ASSESSMENT p. 34

UNIT 4

Mastery Checkpoint 14 Multiplying two- and three-digit numbers (Lesson 87)

Name ____________________

The student demonstrates mastery by correctly answering at least 24 of the 30 problems.

Multiply.

1. 85×6 = 510
2. 406×3 = 1218
3. 88×4 = 352
4. 382×7 = 2674
5. 485×5 = 2425
6. 420×3 = 1260
7. 602×2 = 1204
8. 774×8 = 6192
9. 39×9 = 351
10. 80×8 = 640
11. 409×8 = 3272
12. 68×7 = 476
13. $47 \times 6 =$ 282
14. $890 \times 7 =$ 6230
15. $680 \times 5 =$ 3400
16. $18 \times 9 =$ 162
17. $82 \times 7 =$ 574
18. $76 \times 8 =$ 608
19. $432 \times 5 =$ 2160
20. $29 \times 6 =$ 174
21. $570 \times 3 =$ 1710
22. $383 \times 4 =$ 1532
23. $350 \times 8 =$ 2800
24. $487 \times 6 =$ 2922
25. $850 \times 3 =$ 2550
26. $52 \times 4 =$ 208
27. $785 \times 9 =$ 7065

Solve these problems.

28. Susan runs 6 miles every day. How far will she have run in 20 days? 120 miles
29. Jay collects football cards. There are six in each pack. If he buys eight packs how many cards will he have? 48
30. Martin builds a block structure with 120 blocks. If he builds two more identical structures, how many blocks will he have used in all? 360

Copyright © SRA/McGraw-Hill. Permission is granted to reproduce this page for classroom use.

34 • *Math Explorations and Applications* Level 4

LESSON 88

Student Edition pages 296–299

Multiply: Two-Digit Numbers by Two-Digit Numbers

LESSON PLANNER

Objective

- ▶ to teach an algorithm for multiplying two two-digit numbers

Context of the Lesson This is the fourth of 17 lessons on multidigit multiplication and the first in which students compute with a two-digit multiplier. This algorithm was previously introduced in Level 3.

MANIPULATIVES

multiplication table (optional)

Program Resources

Practice Master 88

Enrichment Master 88

For extra practice:

CD-ROM* Lesson 88

Cumulative Review, page 553

Note: This lesson may take more than one day.

1 Warm-Up

5 MINUTES

Problem of the Day Challenge students with this problem: Using the digits 1, 2, 3, and 4 once each for each equation, form an addition equation, a subtraction equation, a multiplication equation, and a division equation. (One possible set of answers: 4 + 1 = 3 + 2; 2 – 1 = 4 – 3; 4 x 3 = 12; 12 ÷ 3 = 4)

Problem-Solving Strategies Ask students who have solved the Problem of the Day to share how they solved it and any strategies they used.

MENTAL MATH Conduct a speed drill on basic multiplication facts.

a. 4 x 6 = (24)	**b.** 3 x 7 = (21)	**c.** 9 x 9 = (81)
d. 5 x 6 = (30)	**e.** 7 x 2 = (14)	**f.** 7 x 8 = (56)
g. 4 x 9 = (36)	**h.** 6 x 6 = (36)	**i.** 4 x 8 = (32)
j. 7 x 7 = (49)	**k.** 8 x 8 = (64)	**l.** 3 x 6 = (18)

EXPLORE

LESSON 88

ACT IT OUT

Multiply: Two-Digit Numbers by Two-Digit Numbers

Cutting a Problem Down to Size

Mr. Ogata needs fertilizer for his garden. The garden is 57 meters long and 36 meters wide. Each bag of fertilizer covers 100 square meters. He must find the area of the garden to know how many bags of fertilizer to get. Emiko wants to help her father. She draws a picture of the garden.

"But I don't know how to multiply 57 × 36," she says.

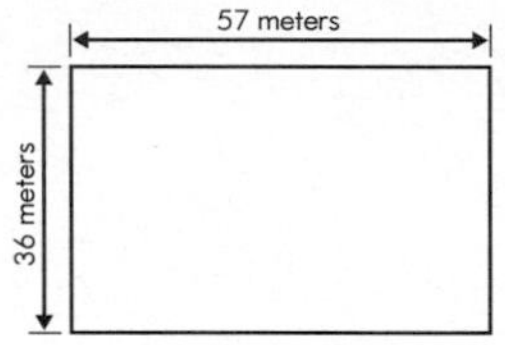

"Wait! I have an idea," Emiko says suddenly. "I'll draw lines to make sections, like this."

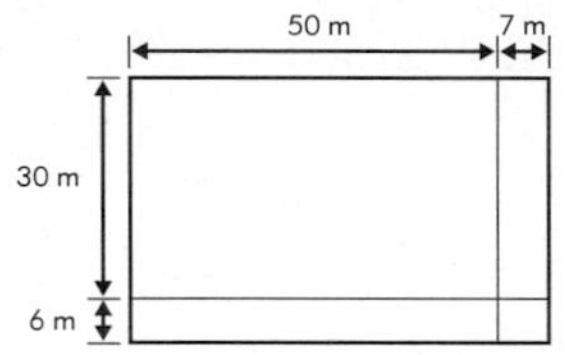

"Then I can figure out the area of each section and add them up."

COOPERATIVE LEARNING Have small groups of students solve problems together in round-robin fashion. One student makes up a problem, the next student multiplies by the ones digit of the multiplier, the next student multiplies by the tens digit of the multiplier, the next student adds the partial products, and two students approximate upper and lower bounds to check that the answer makes sense.

*available separately

Follow Emiko's thinking. The diagrams can help you.

The area of the small section is 6 × 7, or 42 square meters.

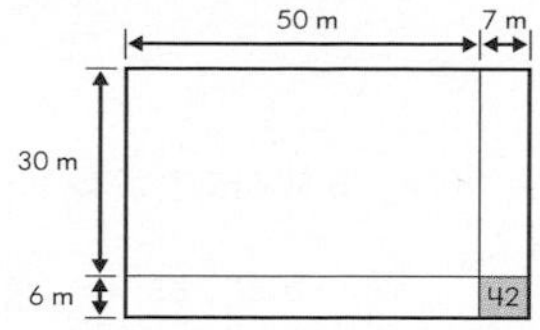

The area of the section on the bottom is 50 × 6, or 300 square meters.

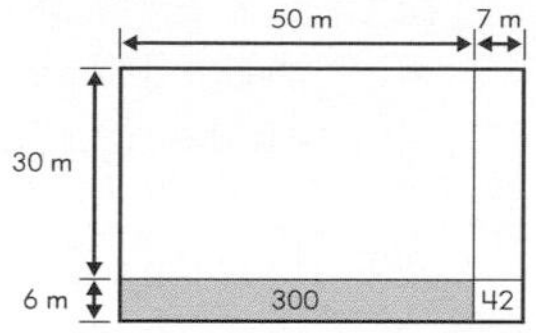

The area of the section on the side is 30 × 7, or 210 square meters.

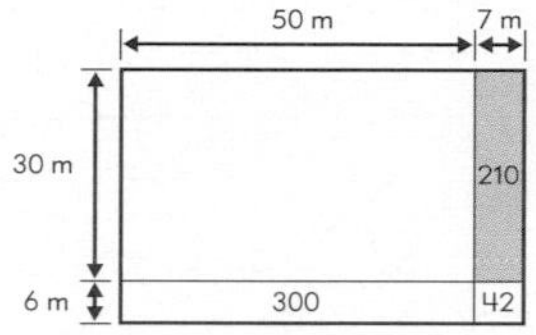

The area of the large section is 50 × 30, or 1500 square meters.

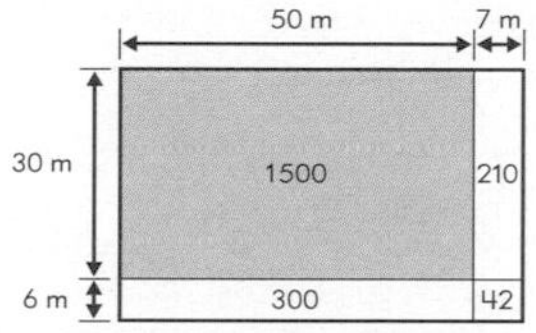

"Now I can add up the areas of the four sections to find the area of the garden," says Emiko. "42 + 300 + 210 + 1500 is 2052. So the area is 2052 square meters," she announces to her father.

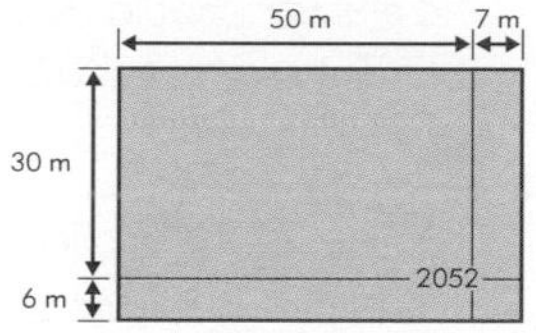

❷ Teach

ACT IT OUT **Using the Student Pages** The story on pages 296–297 develops an algorithm for multiplying two two-digit numbers. You might begin by drawing a diagram of the garden. Make sure students recognize that the Ogatas must find the area of their garden so they can figure out how much fertilizer to buy.

Ask the class to suggest ways to find the area of the garden. Follow through on any suggestions students make, including those that may lead to incorrect answers. Make sure students know how the standard algorithm works if they suggest it. Ask how students think Emiko will solve the problem without knowing the standard algorithm. As you discuss Emiko's idea, point out that dividing the garden into smaller sections does not change its total area. Go over the dimensions of each section and ensure that students can see how Emiko determined the total area by adding the areas of the smaller sections.

> ***. . . one of the most important parts of problem solving is deciding whether there is a problem in the first place, and the people who are most in need of practicing problem solving are the people who aren't naturally good at it.***
>
> –Stephen S. Willoughby, *Mathematics Education for a Changing World*

Literature Connection Invite students to read "Do Too Much Homework" on page 199 of *Math Wizardry for Kids* by Martha Kenda and Phyllis Williams. Encourage students to work out a set of multiplication steps to determine how long it would take to do one million pages of homework.

◆ LESSON 88 Multiply: Two-Digit Numbers by Two-Digit Numbers

Teach

Using the Student Pages When reviewing Emiko's record, relate each step to the appropriate part of page 297 so that students see that each step is simply a calculation of the area of one of the sections in the garden. Then, explain how each step in this shortcut simply combines two steps of the long form. Tell students that because they know how to multiply 57 x 6 and 57 x 3, they can use this shortcut.

Make sure students write the partial product directly beneath the digit of the multiplier they are using. Have students explain in their own words why, for example, 171 is written with the right-hand digit in the tens column. Review the checking procedure at the bottom of page 298. Continue to encourage the habit of checking to be sure that answers make sense.

Have students complete problems 1–28 on page 299 on their own. Again, discourage students from writing carried numbers. Remind them to check answers by approximating upper and lower bounds or, when appropriate, just one bound.

◆ LESSON 88 Multiply: Two-Digit Numbers by Two-Digit Numbers

Emiko kept the following record:

```
   57
 × 36
   42
  300
  210
 1500
 2052
```

Here's a shorter way to multiply 36 × 57.

```
   57
 × 36
  342
```

Start at the right. Multiply the top number by the **ones** digit.
6 × 57 = 342
Write 342 so that the digit on the right (2) is in the **ones** column.

```
   57
 × 36
  342
 171
```

Multiply the top number by the **tens** digit.
3 × 57 = 171
There are 171 tens.
Write 171 so that the digit on the right (1) is in the **tens** column.

```
   57
 × 36
  342
 171
 2052
```

Add to get the final answer.

Check to see that the answer makes sense.

The answer should be less than 40 × 60, which is 2400.
The answer should be greater than 30 × 50, which is 1500.
2052 is less than 2400 and greater than 1500, so the answer makes sense.

The area of the garden is 2052 square meters. Remember that each bag of fertilizer covers 100 square meters. So Mr. Ogata needs 21 bags of fertilizer.

Technology Connection You may wish to have students try the software *Number Heroes* from Edmark (Mac and IBM) for further practice with one- to three-digit multiplication.

RETEACHING

No reteaching is recommended at this time. You may want to assign Enrichment Master 88.

Multiply. Use shortcuts when you can.

❶ 43 × 54 **2322**	❷ 96 × 27 **2592**	❸ 18 × 67 **1206**	❹ 420 × 20 **8400**	❺ 86 × 59 **5074**
❻ 47 × 35 **1645**	❼ 53 × 8 **424**	❽ 64 × 9 **576**	❾ 58 × 5 **290**	❿ 21 × 20 **420**
⓫ 39 × 9 **351**	⓬ 75 × 8 **600**	⓭ 67 × 51 **3417**	⓮ 64 × 39 **2496**	⓯ 58 × 50 **2900**
⓰ 39 × 90 **3510**	⓱ 21 × 21 **441**	⓲ 13 × 29 **377**	⓳ 84 × 84 **7056**	⓴ 68 × 56 **3808**
㉑ 50 × 50 **2500**	㉒ 54 × 79 **4266**	㉓ 29 × 75 **2175**	㉔ 21 × 38 **798**	㉕ 50 × 51 **2550**

Check to see that your answers make sense.

Solve these problems.

㉖ Students from Kennedy School are going on a field trip. There are 525 people going. Each bus can seat 45 people. It costs $85 to rent each bus for a day.

a. Will 12 buses be too few, just enough, or too many? **just enough**

b. How many extra seats will there be? **15**

c. How much will it cost to rent 12 buses for a day? **$1020**

㉗ Sam bought 16 stamps that cost 32¢ each. How much did Sam pay? Give your answer in cents, then in dollars and cents. **512¢, $5.12**

㉘ A hotel room costs $46 for one night. How much would it cost to stay at the hotel for 11 nights? **$506**

Use the Cumulative Review on page 553 after this lesson.

PRACTICE p. 88

LESSON 88 PRACTICE Name__________

Multiply. Use shortcuts when you can.

❶ 27 × 5 135	❷ 91 × 8 728	❸ 72 × 7 504	❹ 43 × 6 258	❺ 78 × 74 5772
❻ 18 × 20 360	❼ 43 × 40 1720	❽ 47 × 48 2256	❾ 80 × 80 6400	❿ 64 × 13 832
⓫ 99 × 34 3366	⓬ 95 × 36 3420	⓭ 28 × 46 1288	⓮ 21 × 89 1869	⓯ 65 × 87 5655
⓰ 91 × 24 2184	⓱ 53 × 27 1431	⓲ 92 × 28 2576	⓳ 69 × 15 1035	⓴ 77 × 77 5929

Solve these problems.

㉑ Ann is setting up chairs for the assembly. She knows that there are 525 students in the school. She sets up chairs in rows of 25.

a. Will 20 rows be too few, just enough, or too many? too few

b. If only 498 students are present that day, how many extra seats are there (in 20 rows of 25 chairs)? 2

Copyright © SRA/McGraw-Hill. Permission is granted to reproduce this page for classroom use.

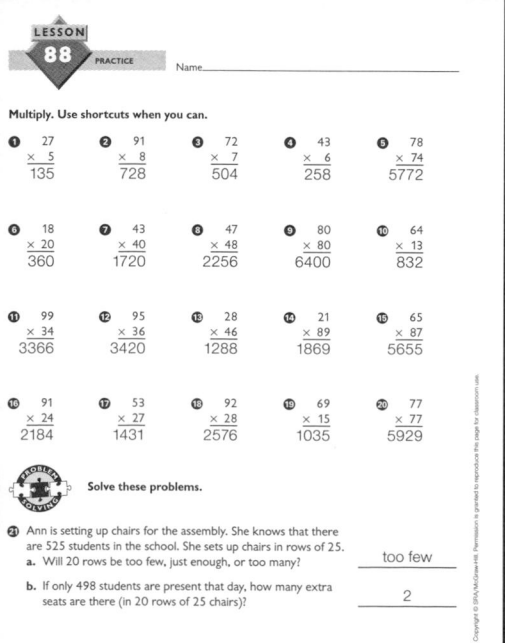

ENRICHMENT p. 88

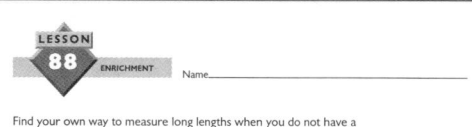

LESSON 88 ENRICHMENT Name__________

Find your own way to measure long lengths when you do not have a yardstick or tape measure.

First, borrow a tape measure. With the help of a friend or family member, measure 100 feet in a straight line. Mark both ends of the line with objects or stakes.

Now walk the 100 feet. Count your steps. Did you come closest to 50, 40, or 33 steps? It depends on the length of your stride. Practice walking the 100 feet until you can do it in about the same number of steps. Remember how it feels. These are your measuring steps.

If you walk the length in 33 steps, how many feet is each step? If you walk it in 40 steps, how many feet is each step? 50 steps?

33 steps in 100 feet = 3 feet per step

40 steps in 100 feet = $2\frac{1}{2}$ feet per step

50 steps in 100 feet = 2 feet per step

Now you have learned to walk your own measuring step. You can apply your new skill by measuring rooms in your house or school building, a driveway, a yard, or any other space. Choose three spaces to measure. What are their approximate areas?

What if you or a friend uses a wheelchair? Can you think of a way to find a measuring roll instead of a measuring step? How?

Write your ideas below.

Using a wheelchair: Measure the circumference of a wheel. Place a chalk mark near the inside edge of the wheel. Count the number of times the chalk mark appears at the top of the wheel as the chair moves. Multiply the circumference of the wheel by the number of times the chalk appears at the top to find the distance rolled.

Copyright © SRA/McGraw-Hill. Permission is granted to reproduce this page for classroom use.

❸ Wrap-Up 5 MINUTES

In Closing Have students explain how the process of multiplying by a two-digit number is similar to and different from multiplying by a one-digit number.

ALTERNATIVE ASSESSMENT

Informal Assessment Observe students as they work through the problems on page 299. Encourage them to verbalize their thinking. You might wish to point out any errors you notice and help students identify and correct them. Although students may not be proficient with the algorithm for two-digit multipliers at this point in the sequence, they will be getting significant practice in applying these rules in subsequent lessons.

Assessment Criteria

Did the student . . .

- ✓ contribute to the story discussion?
- ✓ correctly apply the steps of the algorithm?
- ✓ check to be sure his or her answers made sense?
- ✓ correctly answer at least 75% of the multiplication problems?

Homework Have students use the following two-digit numbers, in any combination, as the factors in six different multiplication exercises: 78, 64, 59, 47, 36. (Answers may vary but some examples are 78 x 64 = 4992, 59 x 64 = 3776, 47 x 64 = 3008, 59 x 36 = 2124, 64 x 64 = 4096, 36 x 78 = 2808.)

SPECIAL NEEDS

Meeting Individual Needs

Some students have difficulty that stems from a weak grasp of the basic multiplication facts. Allow these students to refer to a **multiplication table** while they are learning the algorithm so they will not have to deal with two difficulties at once.

UNIT 4

Student Edition pages 300–301

Mid-Unit Review

The Mid-Unit Review pinpoints troublesome skill areas for students, allowing time for additional practice and reteaching before the unit ends. If students did not do well on the Mid-Unit Review and have completed additional practice, you may want to use the Mid-Unit Review provided on Assessment Blackline Masters pages 35–36.

Using the Student Pages Have students complete problems 1–60 on pages 300 and 301 on their own. You might treat this review as a formal assessment of students' skills and have students complete this review as a timed test. See suggestions on page 51.

UNIT 4

ASSESSMENT

Mid-Unit Review

Multiply.

1. 1000 × 100 **100,000**
2. 10 × 100,000 **1,000,000**
3. 100 × 4 **400**
4. 53 × 1000 **53,000**
5. 281 × 100 **28,100**
6. 709 × 10 **7090**
7. 800 × 500 **400,000**
8. 40 × 700 **28,000**
9. 10,000 × 300 **3,000,000**
10. 500 × 6000 **3,000,000**
11. 500 × 600 **300,000**
12. 50 × 60 **3000**
13. 300 × 600 **180,000**
14. 70 × 800 **56,000**
15. 100 × 504 **50,400**

Remember: 1000 grams = 1 kilogram and 1000 milliliters = 1 liter

16. How many milliliters are there in 5 liters? **5000**
17. How many milliliters are there in 54 liters? **54,000**
18. How many grams are there in 8 kilograms? **8000**
19. How many grams are there in 80 kilograms? **80,000**

Approximate. You don't need an exact answer to solve these problems.

20. Mr. Romano wants to buy 26 rulers for $1.09 (109 cents) each. He has $25. Is that enough to buy the rulers? **no**
21. The Plaza Theater has 36 rows with 32 seats in each row. Can the theater seat 900 people? **yes**
22. Jacqui is 11 years old. Is she more than 3600 days old? **yes**

In each problem, two of the answers are clearly wrong and one is correct. Choose the correct answer.

23. 12 × 37	24. 402 × 58	25. 123 × 321	26. 695 × 777
a. 429	(**a.**) 23,316	**a.** 394,833	**a.** 560,005
b. 864	**b.** 2316	(**b.**) 39,483	**b.** 54,015
(**c.**) 444	**c.** 24,000	**c.** 3983	(**c.**) 540,015

Multiply. Use shortcuts when you can.

27. 44×5 = **220**
28. 72×5 = **360**
29. 19×7 = **133**
30. 50×6 = **300**
31. 74×7 = **518**
32. 26×4 = **104**
33. 39×8 = **312**
34. 18×9 = **162**
35. 64×1 = **64**
36. 87×6 = **522**
37. 46×9 **414**
38. 71×6 **426**
39. 39×5 **195**
40. 18×3 **54**
41. 66×4 **264**
42. 7×324 **2268**
43. 294×8 **2352**
44. 345×6 **2070**
45. 152×7 **1064**
46. 605×2 **1210**
47. 791×8 **6328**
48. 200×6 **1200**

Multiply.

49. 64×46 = **2944**
50. 72×63 = **4536**
51. 58×76 = **4408**
52. 86×90 = **7740**
53. 72×84 = **6048**
54. 247×60 = **14,820**
55. 603×87 = **52,461**
56. 173×26 = **4498**
57. 400×98 = **39,200**
58. 425×30 = **12,750**

PROBLEM SOLVING

Solve.

59. Ethan gets six raffle tickets in each booklet he buys. How many tickets will he get in seven booklets? **42**
60. Next week 47 students from Zoller School are going to the science museum. Each student will pay $4 to cover the cost of bus fare and admission. How much money will they pay all together? **$188**

Home Connections You may want to send home the Home Connections Blackline Masters letter on pages 46–47 to provide additional activities that families can complete together. These activities apply the skills presented in this unit.

ALTERNATIVE ASSESSMENT

Portfolio Assessment The Portfolio Assessment Blackline Masters on page 96 can be used at this time to evaluate students' ability to use multidigit multiplication to solve problems.

ALTERNATIVE ASSESSMENT

Performance Assessment Performance Assessment Task 1, provided on Assessment Blackline Masters pages 79–80, can be used at this time to evaluate students' proficiency with multidigit multiplication. You may want to administer this assessment to individual students or small groups of students.

Unit Project This would be a good time to assign the "Your Heart at Work" project on pages 352 and 353. Students can begin working on the project in cooperative groups in their free time as they work through the unit. The Unit Project is a good opportunity for students to learn how to measure pulse rate, relate it to the beating of the heart, and give an indication of how much the heart works during one's lifetime.

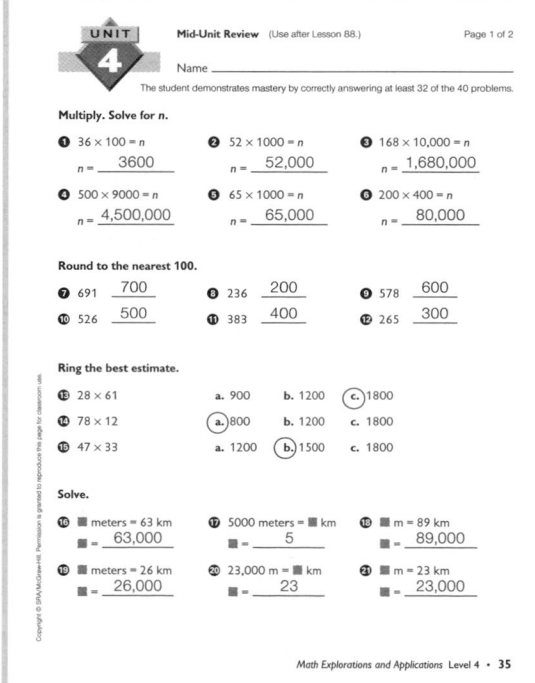

ASSESSMENT p. 35

UNIT 4

Mid-Unit Review (Use after Lesson 88.) Page 1 of 2

Name ______________________

The student demonstrates mastery by correctly answering at least 32 of the 40 problems.

Multiply. Solve for *n*.

1. $36 \times 100 = n$ $n =$ 3600
2. $52 \times 1000 = n$ $n =$ 52,000
3. $168 \times 10{,}000 = n$ $n =$ 1,680,000
4. $500 \times 9000 = n$ $n =$ 4,500,000
5. $65 \times 1000 = n$ $n =$ 65,000
6. $200 \times 400 = n$ $n =$ 80,000

Round to the nearest 100.

7. 691 700
8. 236 200
9. 578 600
10. 526 500
11. 383 400
12. 265 300

Ring the best estimate.

13. 28×61 a. 900 b. 1200 (c.) 1800
14. 78×12 (a.) 800 b. 1200 c. 1800
15. 47×33 a. 1200 (b.) 1500 c. 1800

Solve.

16. ■ meters = 63 km ■ = 63,000
17. 5000 meters = ■ km ■ = 5
18. ■ m = 89 km ■ = 89,000
19. ■ meters = 26 km ■ = 26,000
20. 23,000 m = ■ km ■ = 23
21. ■ m = 23 km ■ = 23,000

Copyright © SRA/McGraw-Hill. Permission is granted to reproduce this page for classroom use.

Math Explorations and Applications Level 4 • 35

LESSON 89

Student Edition pages 302–305

Applying Multiplication

LESSON PLANNER

Objectives

- to provide practice with solving word problems that involve multiplication and other operations
- to review geometric figures in a drawing
- to provide practice with multidigit multiplication

Context of the Lesson This is the fifth of 17 lessons on multidigit multiplication.

MANIPULATIVES	Program Resources
rulers*	Number Cubes (0–5 and 5–10)
dual dial scale*	Reteaching Master
objects to be weighed	Practice Master 89
audiocassette/ recorder (optional)	Enrichment Master 89
	For extra practice: CD-ROM* Lesson 89

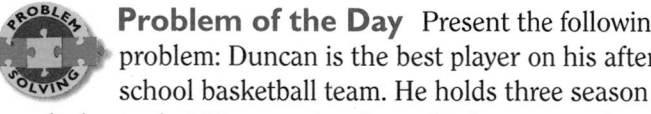

1 Warm-Up

5 MINUTES

Problem of the Day Present the following problem: Duncan is the best player on his after-school basketball team. He holds three season records: he made 156 two-point shots, 47 three-point shots, and 132 one-point free throws. What is Duncan's total number of points scored during his record-setting season? (585 points)

Problem-Solving Strategies Ask students who have solved the Problem of the Day to share how they solved it and any strategies they used.

MENTAL MATH · MANIPULATIVES

Provide practice in estimating weight using customary units of measure. After each estimate, have volunteers measure the object with a **scale*** to check students' estimates. (Estimates should improve after each object is measured.)

a. weight of a textbook

b. weight of several textbooks

c. weight of a student's backpack

PROBLEM SOLVING

LESSON 89

Applying Multiplication

In this lesson you'll use multiplication in real-life situations in many of the problems.

Solve these problems.

1. A rectangle is 63 meters long and 42 meters wide.
   a. What is the area of the rectangle? **2646 square m**
   b. What is the perimeter of the rectangle? **210 m**
2. A rectangle is 63 centimeters long and 42 centimeters wide.
   a. What is the area of the rectangle? **2646 square cm**
   b. What is the perimeter of the rectangle? **210 cm**
3. Yusef bought six quarts of milk. Each quart costs 77¢ each.
   a. How many cents did he pay for the six quarts? **462¢**
   b. How much is that in dollars and cents? **$4.62**
4. Tara bought five muffins. Each muffin cost 72¢. How much did she pay for the five muffins? Give your answer in cents and then in dollars and cents. **360¢; $3.60**
5. Matt owns six dogs. Each dog weighs about 32 kilograms. Do they weigh more than 240 kilograms all together? **no**
6. Each of Matt's dogs can jump a stream that is 350 centimeters wide without getting wet. About how wide a stream can they jump together? **about 350 cm**
7. There are 12 eggs in a carton. How many eggs are there in six cartons? **72**
8. There are 100 centimeters in a meter. How many centimeters are there in 7 meters? **700**
9. A school has 15 buses. Each bus seats 66 students. How many students can be seated on the buses at once? **990**

302 • Multidigit Multiplication

CULTURAL DIVERSITY

Students who come from places that do not participate in recycling may not understand the situation described in the problems on page 303. Explain that the purpose of recycling is to reuse materials that would otherwise create enormous amounts of wasted material. Ask students who have lived in other places to explain what they customarily did with trash. If possible, visit a recycling center in your area to help students learn more about the goals of recycling, the kinds of materials that are recycled, and what happens to recycled materials.

*available separately

A bottle of soda costs 25 cents at Terwilliger's Drugstore. You must also pay 10 cents deposit on the bottle. If you return the bottle, you get back the 10 cents. At the One-Stop Food Shop, you can buy a case of 24 bottles of soda for $6.96, including the 10 cent deposit on each bottle.

Answer these questions.

10. Bryan wants to buy 48 bottles of soda. How much will he have to pay, including the deposit, at Terwilliger's Drugstore? **1680¢ = $16.80**
11. How much will 48 bottles cost at the One-Stop Food Shop? **$13.92**
12. How much would Bryan save by buying his soda at the One-Stop Food Shop instead of at Terwilliger's? **$2.88**
13. How much money will Bryan get back when he returns the 48 bottles? **$4.80**
14. Boyd and Niki have found 13 empty soda bottles from Terwilliger's Drugstore. When they return them to Terwilliger's, will they get enough money to buy three bottles of soda at Terwilliger's? **yes**

Technology Connection Direct students to the Internet's *Math/Geometry Forum* (http://forum.swarthmore.edu) for interactive problem solving including "Ask Dr. Math."

❷ Teach

Using the Student Pages Demonstrate the "Four Cube Multiplication" game on page 305 so students can play it when they complete pages 302–304. This game provides practice with multidigit multiplication.

Before students begin working on these pages, tell them that they will encounter problems that may involve operations other than multiplication. Alert students to read each problem carefully and think about the question it asks. Students should notice, for example, that they do not need to perform any calculations for problem 2. Also tell them that they may use shortcuts. For example, in problem 8, students need not use the multiplication algorithm because they can do 7 x 100 mentally. Students can go on to page 303 as soon as they finish page 302.

> ***Carefully conceived educational games provide one of the most effective methods of practice. Practice with people or even machines or cards that give positive, immediate feedback can also be effective for some learners. Projects or activities that require mathematical skills and concepts to help students reach some goal they wish to reach can provide excellent practice and can have the additional advantage of encouraging learners to see mathematics as useful.***
>
> –Stephen S. Willoughby, *Mathematics Education for a Changing World*

◆ LESSON 89 Applying Multiplication

Teach

Using the Student Pages The geometry problems on page 304 involve visual and spatial problem solving. Remind students that they can look back to Unit 3 if they need to refresh their memories about geometric figures and ideas. Have them complete the page on their own.

The "Four Cube Multiplication" game provides practice with multidigit multiplication, place value, and mathematical reasoning. Students may remember this as the "Roll Four Multiplication" game from Level 3. Roll the cubes, write the four digits on the chalkboard, and ask students what they think is the greatest product they can get. Work out their suggestions together so that students can get an idea of the effect a variety of number combinations will have on the product.

Meeting Individual Needs

Students with limited proficiency in English may have difficulty solving the word problems. Help them read and understand the problems. You can act out or draw pictures using **rulers***, or help students to do so, to verify that they understand the situations or to help pinpoint which parts of a problem they may not understand. Alternatively, you might prepare an **audiocassette** of the problems so that students who better comprehend spoken rather than written English may work independently.

◆ LESSON 89 Applying Multiplication

Look at the two figures. Try to find as many different geometric figures as possible. Tell how many of each you find. Remember to use such names as *right triangle, trapezoid, parallelogram,* and *pentagon.*

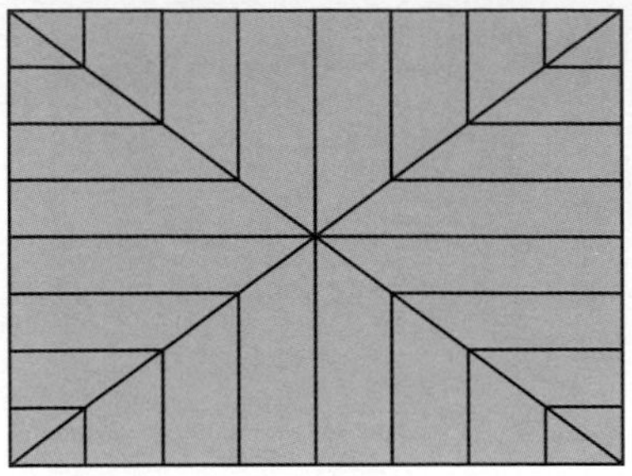

Rt. triangles 36
Trapezoids 24
Pentagons 36
Rectangles 21
Triangles 4

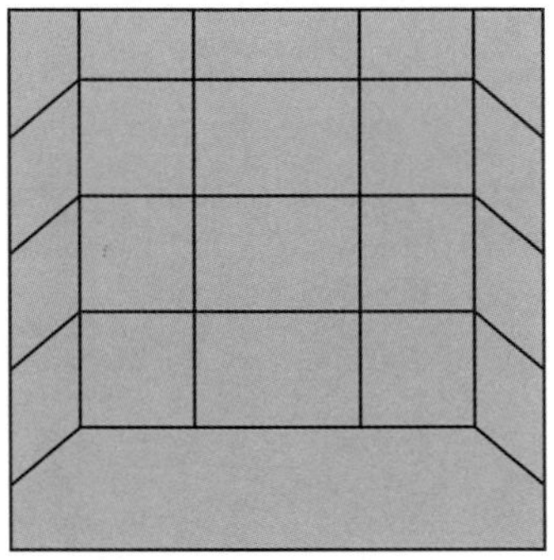

Trapezoids 8
Rectangles 55
Parallelograms 12
Squares 6

Compare your answers with those of your classmates to see if together you can identify more.

Try to find more examples of geometric figures in art, architecture, and other places. In your Math Journal make a list of interesting places where you have found geometric figures, and name the figures.

304 • Multidigit Multiplication

Literature Connection Read *Pumpkins* by Mary Lynn Ray to the class. Have students create multiplication problems based on the story of a man's abundant pumpkin harvest.

RETEACHING p. 30

LESSON 89 RETEACHING Name__________

The area of a rectangle equals the length times the width.

Example:

A rectangle measures 27 meters long and 16 meters wide.

What is the area of the rectangle?

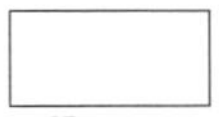

To find the area of a rectangle, multiply the length and the width. The answer will always be a square unit of measure.

Step 1	**Step 2**	**Step 3**
4 27 × 16 162	27 × 16 162 27	27 × 16 162 27 432
Multiply the ones.	Multiply the tens.	Add the two products.

The area of the rectangle is 432 square meters. What is the perimeter of the rectangle? To find the perimeter of a rectangle, add the length twice and the width twice. Then add these two sums.

Step 1	**Step 2**	**Step 3**
27 + 27 54	16 + 16 32	54 + 32 86

The perimeter of the rectangle is 86 meters.

Solve these problems.

A garden is shaped like a rectangle. The length of the garden is 36 feet and the width is 17 feet.

1. What is the area of the garden? 612 square feet
2. What is the perimeter of the garden? 106 feet

30 • *Math Explorations and Applications* Level 4

Copyright © SRA/McGraw-Hill. Permission is granted to reproduce this page for classroom use.

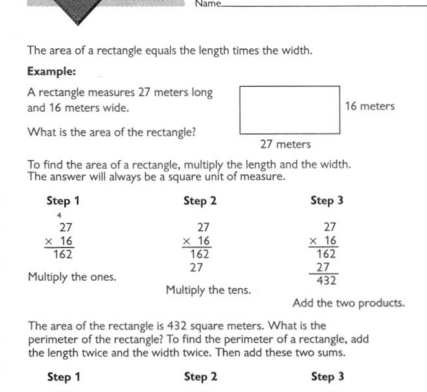

*available separately

GAME

COOPERATIVE LEARNING

Four Cube Multiplication Game

Players: Two or more
Materials: Two 0–5 cubes, two 5–10 cubes
Object: To get the greatest product
Math Focus: Multidigit multiplication, place value, and mathematical reasoning

RULES

1. Take turns rolling all four cubes. If a 10 is rolled, roll that cube again.
2. Combine the numbers you rolled to make a two-digit by two-digit or a three-digit by one-digit multiplication problem.

If you rolled:

These are some problems you could make:

853	73	753	75
× 7	× 85	× 8	× 83

3. The player with the greatest product wins. (Find the exact products only if you need to.)

SAMPLE GAME

Terri rolled: 4 2 7 8
She made this problem:

$$\begin{array}{r} 82 \\ \times\ 74 \\ \hline \end{array}$$

Earl rolled: 3 0 6 5
He made this problem:

$$\begin{array}{r} 53 \\ \times\ 60 \\ \hline \end{array}$$

Terri won the round. (Terri and Earl did not have to find the exact products to see that Terri's product was greater.)

PRACTICE p. 89

LESSON 89 PRACTICE Name__________

PROBLEM SOLVING **Solve these problems.**

1. Jim bought five folders that cost 78¢ each, including tax.
   a. How much did the five folders cost all together? $3.90
   b. If Jim gave the cashier $5.00, how much change would he get back? $1.10
2. Ruth is knitting a scarf. She needs 98 pieces of yarn that are each 3 meters long. Will 250 meters of yarn be enough? no
3. If seven children each weigh 35 kilograms, do they weigh more than 200 kilograms all together? yes
4. A rectangle is 52 centimeters long and 36 centimeters wide.
   a. What is its area? 1872 sq cm
   b. What is its perimeter? 176 cm
5. Juan needs to buy 12 cans of soda, four loaves of bread, and two packages of cheese. The soda is 50¢ a can; the bread is 90¢ a loaf; and the cheese is $1.50 a package. Will $20 be enough money for him to buy what he needs? yes
6. Name the polygons you can find in the diagram below.

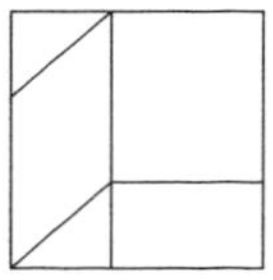

a. triangle **b.** square
c. rectangle **d.** parallelogram
e. trapezoid **f.** hexagon
g. pentagon

Copyright © SRA/McGraw-Hill. Permission is granted to reproduce this page for classroom use.

ENRICHMENT p. 89

LESSON 89 ENRICHMENT Name__________

Read each statement. Write a question for each.

1. Jamie has 34¢, and Matthew has 67¢. Answers will vary. Sample answers:
   How much do Jamie and Matthew have all together?
2. Marty bought three pencils at the school bookstore for 92¢.
   How much did each pencil cost?
3. Emily left her house at 8:30 A.M. It took her 15 minutes to walk to school.
   At what time did Emily arrive at school?
4. The school lunch costs $1.50, and extra milk is 35¢.
   How much does lunch with two extra milks cost?
5. Make up your own story problem that involves multiplication.
   a. Write your problem in the space below. If you need to, draw pictures to help explain it. Make the problem as challenging as you can.
   Problems will vary. Make sure students' problems involve multiplication.
   b. On a separate sheet of paper, write the answer to the problem and show how you found it.
   c. Now give your problem to a partner to solve. Then check his or her answer. Ask your partner about the problem. Was it too easy? Too difficult?

Copyright © SRA/McGraw-Hill. Permission is granted to reproduce this page for classroom use.

3 Wrap-Up

5 MINUTES

In Closing Have students explain their strategy for playing the "Four Cube Multiplication" game.

ALTERNATIVE ASSESSMENT

Performance Assessment You may wish to use students' work on pages 302–304 as an informal assessment of their ability to solve word problems involving multiplication and other operations, as well as their ability to solve visual problems involving geometry. If so, be sure students work independently.

Assessment Criteria

Did the student . . .

- ✓ apply his or her skills in multiplication and other operations to solve word problems?
- ✓ communicate strategies used to solve the problems?
- ✓ explain how he or she identified hidden geometric figures in an illustration?
- ✓ actively participate in playing the "Four Cube Multiplication" game?

Homework Have students play the "Four Cube Multiplication" game with a family member for further practice with multidigit multiplication and place value. A copy of this game can also be found on page 19 of the Home Connections Blackline Masters.

LESSON 90

Student Edition pages 306–309

Multiplication Practice

LESSON PLANNER

Objectives

✓ to assess students' mastery of multiplying two-digit numbers

▶ to help students develop the broad ability to use mathematical common sense

Context of the Lesson This is the sixth of 17 lessons on multidigit multiplication. It includes a Mastery Checkpoint for assessing mastery of multiplying two-digit numbers. This lesson also includes Part 3 of "The Treasure of Mugg Island," a six-part Thinking Story.

MANIPULATIVES

nickels

treasure map (optional)

Program Resources

Practice Master 90

Enrichment Master 90

Assessment Master

For career connections: Careers and Math*

For extra practice: CD-ROM* Lesson 90

1 Warm-Up

5 MINUTES

Problem of the Day Present this problem to the class: If you made a stack of **nickels** as tall as one nickel standing on edge, how many nickels would be in the stack? How much would the stack be worth? (11 nickels; 55¢)

Problem-Solving Strategies Ask students who have solved the Problem of the Day to share how they solved it and any strategies they used.

MENTAL MATH Provide practice with addition facts by asking students to approximate whether $100 is enough money to buy a pair of items. Have students show thumbs down for "no" and thumbs up for "yes."

a. a radio for $77.00 + a coat for $81.00? (thumbs down)

b. a sleeping bag for $50.00 + a pocket knife for $15.00? (thumbs up)

c. a radio for $77.00 + a book for $8.00? (thumbs up)

d. a coat for $81.00 + a CD for $13.00? (thumbs up)

e. a sleeping bag for $50.00 + a tent for $60.00? (thumbs down)

LESSON 90

Multiplication Practice

You've been learning to multiply by two-digit numbers. Keep sharp by solving these problems. Remember to check that your answers make sense.

Multiply. Use shortcuts when you can.

1. 26 × 35 = **910**	2. 68 × 49 = **3332**	3. 96 × 17 = **1632**	4. 32 × 90 = **2880**	5. 55 × 25 = **1375**
6. 38 × 43 = **1634**	7. 72 × 95 = **6840**	8. 87 × 70 = **6090**	9. 17 × 36 = **612**	10. 63 × 91 = **5733**
11. 18 × 22 = **396**	12. 30 × 31 = **930**	13. 66 × 36 = **2376**	14. 76 × 41 = **3116**	15. 57 × 43 = **2451**
16. 70 × 70 = **4900**	17. 53 × 53 = **2809**	18. 27 × 58 = **1566**	19. 82 × 91 = **7462**	20. 17 × 71 = **1207**
21. 39 × 46 = **1794**	22. 71 × 70 = **4970**	23. 77 × 11 = **847**	24. 67 × 24 = **1608**	25. 90 × 90 = **8100**

Solve these problems.

26. The ice-cube maker in Zack's refrigerator makes 14 ice cubes every hour. How many ice cubes can it produce in 12 hours? **168**

27. Yuki's soccer team is selling magazine subscriptions to raise money. They can keep $0.35 for each subscription they sell. If the 14 members sell one subscription each, how much money will they raise? **$4.90**

28. Billy's grandfather plans to plant 12 rows of elm trees. Each row will contain 21 trees. How many trees will Billy's grandfather plant? **252**

Geography Connection Have students work in pairs or small groups to make a **treasure map** that would take hunters from the classroom to a spot somewhere on the school grounds. Have them use direction words, such as *north, south, east,* and *west,* and units of measure, such as meters, feet, paces, or steps. Encourage students to try out their maps to be sure that they work. Then groups can exchange and follow each other's maps.

*available separately

There are many ways to recognize that the answer to a problem is wrong. Sometimes the size of the answer is so far off that it is impossible. Sometimes the last digit of an answer is impossible.

Decide which of the given answers is correct by showing that the other two could not be correct. Be prepared to explain your answers.

29	42 × 16 =	**a.** 640	(**b.**) 672	**c.** 58
30	395 × 87 =	(**a.**) 34,365	**b.** 334,305	**c.** 43,427
31	145 × 15 =	**a.** 2320	**b.** 2160	(**c.**) 2175
32	79 × 2583 =	**a.** 21,344	**b.** 312,054	(**c.**) 204,057
33	3598 + 8745 =	**a.** 21,344	**b.** 18,433	(**c.**) 12,343
34	872,558 − 4,444 =	**a.** 888,113	(**b.**) 868,114	**c.** 8,214
35	7682 + 297 =	(**a.**) 7979	**b.** 7385	**c.** 7987
36	482,100 − 165,000 =	**a.** 647,100	**b.** 342,000	(**c.**) 317,100
37	8742 − 2952 =	(**a.**) 5790	**b.** 5802	**c.** 5831
38	852 + 258 =	**a.** 1111	**b.** 111	(**c.**) 1110
39	64 × 38 =	**a.** 2470	(**b.**) 2432	**c.** 2560
40	35 × 4 =	**a.** 160	(**b.**) 140	**c.** 120

Literature Connection

Display a copy of *Anno's Hat Tricks* by Mitsumasa Anno and Akihiro Nozaki. Encourage students to select and solve problems from the book that involve logical reasoning.

❷ Teach

Using the Student Pages Have students work on page 306 independently. Discuss the directions at the top of page 307. Encourage students to share methods they use to determine when an answer is obviously wrong. Then do one or two problems with the class. Have students complete the page on their own. When you discuss the problems, invite volunteers to present the reasoning they used to eliminate wrong answers.

> *No matter how well children understand the basis for the addition facts, they will need lots of practice to make them automatic. Unless these facts are automatic, children will use their time and creativity to reconstruct the addition facts when they should have gone on to bigger and better things. Thus, practice is essential.*
>
> —Stephen S. Willoughby, *Mathematics Education for a Changing World*

◆ LESSON 90 Multiplication Practice

Teach

Using the Thinking Story "The Treasure of Mugg Island (Part 3)" continues the story of a search for buried treasure. In this part, students solve problems by eliminating absurd possibilities and by using geometric intuition.

Answers to Thinking Story Questions:

1. The missing part of the note would give the complete number instead of just the first two digits (13); it would tell whether the number referred to paces, meters, or some other unit; and it would tell what direction to go from the spider rock.
2. Among various possibilities, spider rock could be 13, approximately 130, or perhaps about 1300 paces from the tree. Or the unit might be feet, yards, or meters.
3. a. 13 cm makes little sense, because it would put spider rock right next to the tree.

   b. 132 km is impossible, given the size of the island described in Part 1 of the story (it is only 2 km on its longest side).

   c. 132 paces would be a reasonable distance—far enough that a person would not see the rock without knowing what direction to look, yet close enough that a person would have a reasonable chance of getting to it by pacing off the distance.
4. Simply start heading northwest from the hollow tree and keep going until the rock is found.
5. It is not known what direction the peg is from the rock.
6. Go 23 paces away from the rock and then walk in a circle around the rock, thus covering all the possible directions.

MATH JOURNAL Have students list in their Math Journals tools or equipment they would find useful if they were participating in this treasure-hunting expedition. Have them keep in mind that their equipment must be portable and fit in a backpack or pocket. Encourage them to explain how they would use these tools.

THINKING STORY

◆ LESSON 90 Multiplication Practice

The Treasure of Mugg Island

Part 3

You may want to refer to previous parts of this Thinking Story, on pages 276–277 and 294–295.

"There is the hollow tree, just where we figured out it would be!" Willy yelled.

Ferdie ran over the bridge of rocks so that he would be the first to find the treasure in the hollow tree. "No treasure here," he moaned. "Somebody else must have found it first."

"Wait," said Manolita. "There is a piece of paper in the tree."

"Let me see," said the queen.

Here is the piece of paper they found in the hollow tree:

From tree go NW13
to spider rock.
From spider rock go
23 paces to peg.

RETEACHING

GAME Have students play the "Four Cube Multiplication" game (page 305) for extra practice with multidigit multiplication.

PRACTICE p. 90

LESSON 90 PRACTICE Name________

Multiply. Use shortcuts when you can.

❶ 32 × 46 = 1472	❷ 84 × 21 = 1764	❸ 45 × 16 = 720	❹ 58 × 37 = 2146	❺ 83 × 94 = 7802
❻ 72 × 30 = 2160	❼ 67 × 56 = 3752	❽ 25 × 38 = 950	❾ 49 × 29 = 1421	❿ 60 × 50 = 3000
⓫ 29 × 18 = 522	⓬ 79 × 64 = 5056	⓭ 26 × 21 = 546	⓮ 17 × 15 = 255	⓯ 64 × 63 = 4032

Choose the answer that is most reasonable for the following multiplication problems.

⓰ 82 × 37 = a	a. 3034	b. 2418	c. 30,304
⓱ 53 × 53 = c	a. 28,009	b. 2806	c. 2809
⓲ 40 × 62 = b	a. 248	b. 2480	c. 102
⓳ 74 × 45 = b	a. 280	b. 3330	c. 33,000
⓴ 92 × 80 = c	a. 736	b. 7216	c. 7360

90 • *Math Explorations and Applications* Level 4

Copyright © SRA/McGraw-Hill. Permission is granted to reproduce this page for classroom use.

"Dear me," said the queen. "It seems that some animal has eaten part of the note. Now we'll never find the treasure."

. . . to be continued

Work in groups. Discuss your answers and how you figured them out. Then compare your answers with those of other groups. **Answers are in margin.**

1. What would the missing parts of the note tell you? (Be careful. Try to think of all that is missing.)
2. How far might the spider rock be from the tree? What are some possible distances?
3. Which of these makes sense for the distance from the tree to the spider rock: (a) 13 centimeters, (b) 132 kilometers, or (c) 132 paces? Why?
4. NW means northwest—a direction halfway between north and west. Knowing this, how could you find the spider rock?
5. What don't you know about where the peg is?
6. How could you find the peg anyway?

❸ Wrap-Up 5 MINUTES

In Closing Have students describe multiplication shortcuts they use to solve two-digit by two-digit multiplication problems.

Mastery Checkpoint 15

At about this time most students should demonstrate mastery of multiplying two two-digit numbers by correctly answering at least 80% of the problems on page 306 or a similar page. Record the results of this assessment on the Mastery Checkpoint Chart. You may also wish to assign Assessment Blackline Masters page 37 to determine mastery.

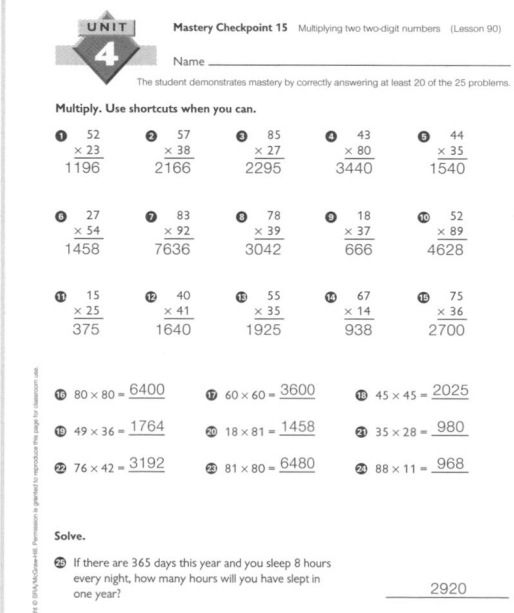

Assessment Criteria

Did the student . . .

- ✓ correctly answer at least 80% of the multiplication problems?
- ✓ communicate strategies used to identify obviously wrong answers?
- ✓ contribute to the Thinking Story discussion?

ENRICHMENT p. 90

LESSON 90 ENRICHMENT Name________

Are you good at solving mysteries? Sometimes numbers can give us important clues, but we must also rely on our common sense and knowledge in other areas.

In **The Cruncher: *Mystery Population*** project, data from a special census taken in a region of the United States during a unique time in the history of the country are presented.

Answer these questions.

1. Look at the numbers on the spreadsheet. What do you observe? What can you conclude?
   Answers will vary; students should notice that men greatly outnumber women, and young men outnumber older men.
2. How do the numbers of men and women compare?
   There are 1981 men and 80 women.
3. Follow the directions in **The Cruncher** to create graphs that display the data. Can you guess where and when this mystery population existed? Give reasons to support your theory.
   Answers will vary. Students should be able to conclude that it was an early part of the country's history and in an undeveloped part of the country.
4. How do the numbers for men and women in the 1990 census compare?
   They are about the same.

Copyright © SRA/McGraw-Hill. Permission is granted to reproduce this page for classroom use.

ASSESSMENT p. 37

UNIT 4 **Mastery Checkpoint 15** Multiplying two two-digit numbers (Lesson 90)

Name ________

The student demonstrates mastery by correctly answering at least 20 of the 25 problems.

Multiply. Use shortcuts when you can.

1. 52 × 23 = 1196	2. 57 × 38 = 2166	3. 85 × 27 = 2295	4. 43 × 80 = 3440	5. 44 × 35 = 1540
6. 27 × 54 = 1458	7. 83 × 92 = 7636	8. 78 × 39 = 3042	9. 18 × 37 = 666	10. 52 × 89 = 4628
11. 15 × 25 = 375	12. 40 × 41 = 1640	13. 55 × 35 = 1925	14. 67 × 14 = 938	15. 75 × 36 = 2700

16. 80 × 80 = 6400
17. 60 × 60 = 3600
18. 45 × 45 = 2025
19. 49 × 36 = 1764
20. 18 × 81 = 1458
21. 35 × 28 = 980
22. 76 × 42 = 3192
23. 81 × 80 = 6480
24. 88 × 11 = 968

Solve.

25. If there are 365 days this year and you sleep 8 hours every night, how many hours will you have slept in one year? 2920

Copyright © SRA/McGraw-Hill. Permission is granted to reproduce this page for classroom use.

Homework Have students play the "Four Cube Multiplication" game on page 305 (also on page 19 of the Home Connections Blackline Masters) with a family member for further practice with multidigit multiplication.

SPECIAL NEEDS Meeting Individual Needs

Some students have difficulty applying deductive reasoning or visual/spatial reasoning to a problem-solving situation such as the one in this part of the Thinking Story. To help these students, offer hints or partial information so they can participate in solving the problems.

LESSON 91

Student Edition pages 310–313

Multiply: Three-Digit Numbers by Two-Digit Numbers

LESSON PLANNER

Objectives

- ▶ to introduce an algorithm for multiplying two- and three-digit numbers
- ▶ to provide practice using calculators to solve problems that involve area and perimeter

Context of the Lesson This is the seventh of 17 lessons on multidigit multiplication. This is the first time in the program that the three-digit by two-digit multiplication algorithm is taught, but the algorithm itself is similar to previous algorithms taught in this unit.

MANIPULATIVES

calculators*

multiplication table (optional)

Program Resources

Practice Master 91

Enrichment Master 91

For extra practice:
CD-ROM* Lesson 91
Cumulative Review, page 554

1 Warm-Up (5 MINUTES)

Problem of the Day Present the following problem and have students work in groups to solve it: A square number is the product of a factor multiplied by itself. For example, 4 is a square number because it is the product of 2 x 2. What is the product of the first two two-digit square numbers? Find the factors for which that product is a square number. (16 x 25 = 400; 400 = 20 x 20)

Problem-Solving Strategies Ask students who have solved the Problem of the Day to share how they solved it and any strategies they used.

MENTAL MATH Provide mixed practice on problems for which students indicate obviously wrong answers with thumbs down and possibly correct answers with thumbs up.

a. 35 + 300 = 605 (thumbs down)
b. 2 x 401 = 802 (thumbs up)
c. 600 – 199 = 401 (thumbs up)
d. 8 x 300 = 513 (thumbs down)

(continued on page 311)

EXPLORE

LESSON 91

Multiply: Three-Digit Numbers by Two-Digit Numbers

The telephone book for Marla's community has 49 pages of listings. Each page lists 376 names. How many listings are in the entire book? Marla can multiply to find out.

Multiply: 49 × 376

```
  376
×  49
 3384
```

Start at the right. Multiply the top number by the **ones** digit.
9 × 376 = 3384
Write 3384 so that the digit on the right (4) is in the **ones** column.

```
  376
×  49
 3384
1504
```

Multiply by the **tens** digit.
4 × 376 = 1504
There are 1504 tens.
Write 1504 so that the digit on the right (4) is in the **tens** column.

```
   376
×   49
  3384
 1504
18,424
```

Add to get the final answer.

The telephone book lists 18,424 names.

Check to see that the answer makes sense.

The answer should be less than 50 × 400, which is 20,000.

The answer should be greater than 40 × 300, which is 12,000.

18,424 is less than 20,000 and greater than 12,000. So the answer makes sense.

310 • Multidigit Multiplication

COOPERATIVE LEARNING One way students can practice the algorithm for multiplying three-digit numbers by two-digit numbers is to work in groups. Group members work in round-robin fashion to solve a problem. The first student begins the problem, then hands off the pencil or chalk to the next student, who picks up at that point and continues the computation, and so on until the problem is solved.

*available separately

Multiply: 30 × 312

Here's how you would multiply using the way shown on page 310.

312 × **3**0 **0**	Multiply the top number by the **ones** digit. 0 × 312 = 0 Write 0 in the **ones** column.
312 × **3**0 0 **936**	Multiply by the **tens** digit. 3 × 312 = 936 There are 936 tens. Write 936 so that the digit on the right (6) is in the **tens** column.
312 × 30 0 936 **9360**	Add.

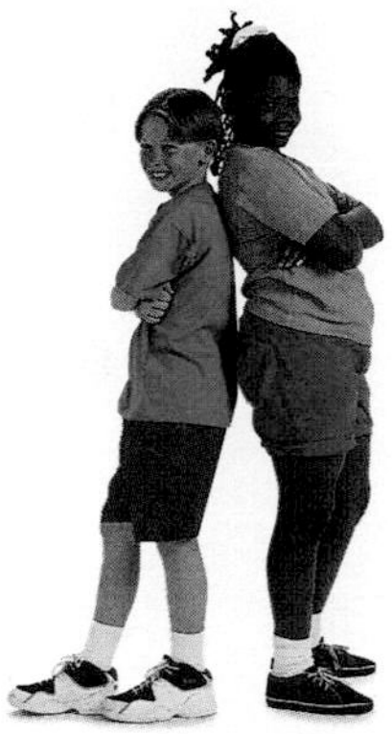

Here's a shorter way to multiply 30 × 312.

312 × 3**0** **0**	Multiply the top number by the **ones** digit. 0 × 312 = 0 Write 0 in the **ones** column.
312 × **3**0 **936**0	Multiply by the **tens** digit. 3 × 312 = 936 There are 936 tens. Write the 936 next to the 0.

Remember:

387 × 46	→ 387 × 4**6** **2322**	→ 387 × **4**6 2322 **1548**	→ 387 × 46 2322 1548 **17,802**

Mental Math (continued)

e. 600 ÷ 3 = 200 (thumbs up)

f. 350 x 2 = 452 (thumbs down)

g. 335 + 100 = 345 (thumbs down)

h. 800 ÷ 4 = 200 (thumbs up)

i. 700 – 350 = 350 (thumbs up)

j. 500 + 50 = 605 (thumbs down)

2 Teach

Using the Student Pages Go through the steps on page 310 with the class. Emphasize correct placement of each partial product. Also stress the final step—checking that the answer makes sense. Repeat the steps with one or two more examples, and then go on to page 311. Go through the regular algorithm for multiplying 30 x 312. Then show the class the shorter way to do the same problem. Encourage students to use the shorter form whenever there is a 0 in the multiplier. Students may understand the short form more readily if they see that it is the same as thinking 3 x 312 = 936, so 30 x 312 = 936 tens, or 9360.

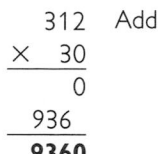

SPECIAL NEEDS

Meeting Individual Needs

Allow students who have weak recall of multiplication facts, but understand the steps of the algorithm, to consult a **multiplication table** as they work. This enables them to practice the algorithm without getting bogged down by having to figure out each fact as they need it.

◆ LESSON 91 Multiply: Three-Digit Numbers by Two-Digit Numbers

Teach

Using the Student Pages Have students work on page 312 independently. Draw their attention to problems 7 and 8. Ask them to identify a relationship between the problems and predict a relationship between their products. Students will see that the multipliers are 7 and 70, so the product in problem 8 should be ten times greater than the product in problem 7. Alert them that they will encounter other pairs of problems that are related in a similar way. Point out that several of the problems can be done mentally. Provide **calculators*** so that students can solve the problems on page 313. You might have students work in pairs so that they can discuss their strategies. Stress the importance of checking if the dimensions that they discover for each rectangle really work.

LEARNING STYLES

Meeting Individual Needs Students who are visual or artistic learners may benefit from sketching possible rectangles as they attempt to solve the problems on page 313.

◆ LESSON 91 Multiply: Three-Digit Numbers by Two-Digit Numbers

Multiply. Use shortcuts when you can.

1. 247 × 26 = **6422**	2. 813 × 59 = **47,967**	3. 512 × 64 = **32,768**	4. 256 × 32 = **8192**	5. 243 × 27 = **6561**
6. 806 × 37 = **29,822**	7. 281 × 7 = **1967**	8. 281 × 70 = **19,670**	9. 394 × 8 = **3152**	10. 394 × 80 = **31,520**
11. 38 × 27 = **1026**	12. 380 × 27 = **10,260**	13. 7 × 8 = **56**	14. 70 × 8 = **560**	15. 700 × 8 = **5600**
16. 70 × 80 = **5600**	17. 700 × 80 = **56,000**	18. 6 × 7 = **42**	19. 60 × 70 = **4200**	20. 600 × 70 = **42,000**
21. 163 × 31 = **5053**	22. 287 × 15 = **4305**	23. 641 × 10 = **6410**	24. 269 × 34 = **9146**	25. 377 × 21 = **7917**

Check to see that your answers make sense.

PROBLEM SOLVING

Solve these problems.

26. There are 42 rows of bleachers in the school gym. At the pep rally there were 30 people sitting in each row. How many people were sitting at the pep rally? **1260**

A rectangle's length measures 139 cm, and its width measures 81 cm.

27. What is the perimeter of the rectangle? **440 cm**

28. What is the area of the rectangle? **11,259 square cm**

29. Andrew's family drove 264 miles to the beach for summer vacation. They returned home two weeks later, using the same route. How many miles did they travel? **528**

Literature Connection Have students solve the problems in *Calculator Riddles* by David A. Adler with paper and pencil and then use their **calculators*** to find the answers to the riddles.

RETEACHING

Have students work on lined paper turned sideways so that they have columns in which to line up partial products.

*available separately

Each problem below gives the perimeter of a rectangle in inches and the area of the same rectangle in square inches.

Give the dimensions of a rectangle that fits these numbers. If there is no such rectangle, explain why. Use a calculator if needed.

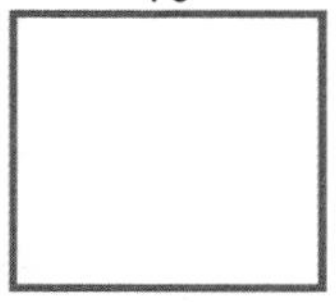

Example:

perimeter = 38, area = 90

Answer: length = 10, width = 9

Check: 10 + 9 + 10 + 9 = 38, and 10 × 9 = 90

30. perimeter = 20, area = 24 **length = 6 width = 4**
31. perimeter = 202, area = 100 **length = 100 width = 1**
32. perimeter = 26, area = 36 **length = 9 width = 4**
33. perimeter = 24, area = 36 **length = 6 width = 6**
34. perimeter = 36, area = 81 **length = 9 width = 9**
35. perimeter = 30, area = 56 **length = 8 width = 7**
36. perimeter = 4, area = 1 **length = 1 width = 1**
37. perimeter = 16, area = 16 **length = 4 width = 4**
38. perimeter = 40, area = 36 **length = 18 width = 2**
39. perimeter = 74, area = 36 **length = 36 width = 1**
40. perimeter = 30, area = 36 **length = 12 width = 3**
41. perimeter = 50, area = 24 **length = 24 width = 1**
42. perimeter = 28, area = 24 **length = 12 width = 2**
43. perimeter = 22, area = 24 **length = 8 width = 3**

Solve these problems.

Tim's vegetable garden is 14 meters long and 11 meters wide.

44. What is the perimeter of Tim's garden? **50 meters**
45. What is the area of Tim's garden? **154 square meters**

A rectangle has a length of 496 centimeters and a width of 24 centimeters.

46. What is the perimeter of the rectangle? **1040 centimeters**
47. What is the area of the rectangle? **11,904 square centimeters**

Use the Cumulative Review on page 554 after this lesson.

PRACTICE p. 91

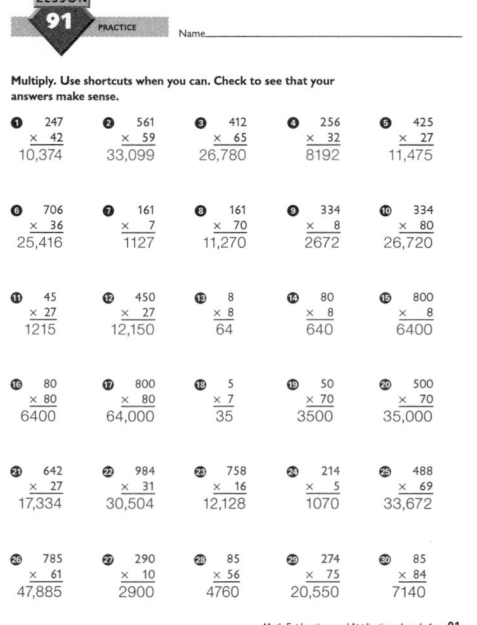

LESSON 91 PRACTICE Name____________________

Multiply. Use shortcuts when you can. Check to see that your answers make sense.

1. 247 × 42 = 10,374
2. 561 × 59 = 33,099
3. 412 × 65 = 26,780
4. 256 × 32 = 8192
5. 425 × 27 = 11,475
6. 706 × 36 = 25,416
7. 161 × 7 = 1127
8. 161 × 70 = 11,270
9. 334 × 8 = 2672
10. 334 × 80 = 26,720
11. 45 × 27 = 1215
12. 450 × 27 = 12,150
13. 8 × 8 = 64
14. 80 × 8 = 640
15. 800 × 8 = 6400
16. 80 × 80 = 6400
17. 800 × 80 = 64,000
18. 5 × 7 = 35
19. 50 × 70 = 3500
20. 500 × 70 = 35,000
21. 642 × 27 = 17,334
22. 984 × 31 = 30,504
23. 758 × 16 = 12,128
24. 214 × 5 = 1070
25. 488 × 69 = 33,672
26. 785 × 61 = 47,885
27. 290 × 10 = 2900
28. 85 × 56 = 4760
29. 274 × 75 = 20,550
30. 85 × 84 = 7140

Copyright © SRA/McGraw-Hill. Permission is granted to reproduce this page for classroom use.

ENRICHMENT p. 91

LESSON 91 ENRICHMENT Name____________________

Work in groups to answer the following questions.

1. Find out how many people live in your city, town, or village. How long would it take you to shake hands with them all? (Hint: How long does it take you to shake hands with ten people?)
   Answers will vary. If, for example, it takes the student 20 seconds to shake hands with 10 people and there are about 5000 people in the town, it would take about 10,000 seconds, or about 2.8 hours to shake hands with everyone.

2. Find out how many people live in your state. How long would it take you to shake hands with them all?
   Answers will vary. If, for example, it takes the student 12 seconds to shake hands with 10 people and there are about 4,000,000 people in the state, it would take about 4,800,000 seconds, or about 56 days, if the student doesn't sleep.

3. Find out how many people live in the United States. How long would it take you to shake hands with them all?
   Answers will vary. If, for example, it takes the student 10 seconds to shake hands with 10 people and there are about 248,709,873 people in the country, it would take about 248,709,873 seconds, or about 7.9 years, with no time for sleep.

Copyright © SRA/McGraw-Hill. Permission is granted to reproduce this page for classroom use.

3 Wrap-Up (5 MINUTES)

In Closing Ask students to describe how they solved the rectangle problems on page 313. Also have them explain how to check that an answer makes sense.

ANALYZING ANSWERS If students make errors, check to determine the nature of the problem. If the trouble stems from difficulty with the one-digit multiplication algorithm, review that process. If the trouble lies mainly with the two-digit algorithm, go over the steps slowly in several examples. Before each step, ask, "What should you do next?" Watch for students who write partial products in the wrong columns. For example, ask them to put special emphasis on the word *tens* when they say "Multiply by the *tens* digit" or "The digit on the right goes in the *tens* column."

SELF ASSESSMENT Have students write evaluations in their Math Portfolios of their performance on this lesson. Have them tell whether they think they have a solid grasp of the multiplication algorithm and can apply it consistently to different sets of factors.

Assessment Criteria

Did the student . . .

- ✓ contribute to the discussion of the algorithm?
- ✓ apply the algorithm to multiply three-digit by two-digit numbers?
- ✓ correctly answer at least 75% of the computation problems?
- ✓ apply logical problem-solving skills to solve the area and perimeter problems?

Homework Have students make up five three-digit by two-digit multiplication problems and solve them. Ask students to use five different digits in each problem.

LESSON 92

Student Edition pages 314–315

Converting Customary Units of Measure

LESSON PLANNER

Objectives

- to review converting between customary units of measure
- to provide practice estimating measures in the customary measurement system
- to provide practice with solving word problems using customary units of measure

Context of the Lesson This is the eighth of 17 lessons that involve multidigit multiplication. In this lesson, the multiplication situations apply to converting customary units of measure.

MANIPULATIVES
yardstick

Program Resources
Reteaching Master
Practice Master 92
Enrichment Master 92
For extra practice:
CD-ROM* Lesson 92

1 Warm-Up

5 MINUTES

Problem of the Day Present the following problem: A square window is made of four smaller square panes of glass. The perimeter of one small pane is 60 centimeters. What is the perimeter of the entire window? (120 cm)

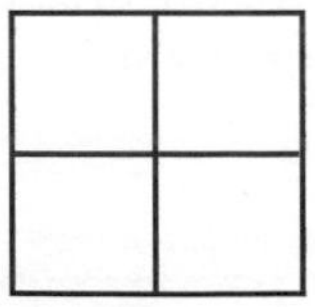

Problem-Solving Strategies Ask students who have solved the Problem of the Day to share how they solved it and any strategies they used.

MIXED **PRACTICE**

LESSON 92

Converting Customary Units of Measure

Remember: 12 inches = 1 foot
3 feet = 1 yard

Answer these questions.

1. How many inches are there in 1 yard? **36**
2. How many inches are there in 7 yards? **252**
3. How many inches are there in 7 feet? **84**
4. How many feet are there in 7 yards? **21**
5. How many inches are there in 73 feet? **876**
6. How many inches are there in 73 yards? **2628**
7. How many feet are there in 18 yards? **54**

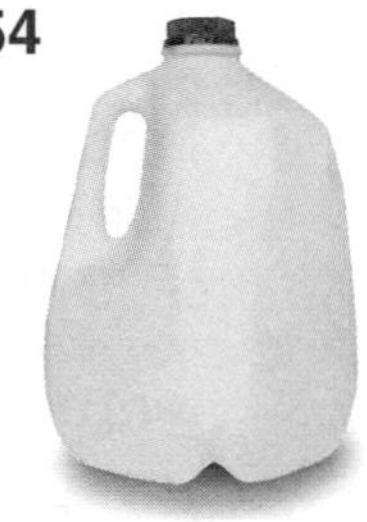

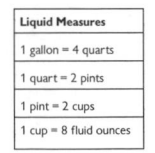

Remember: 8 fluid ounces = 1 cup
2 cups = 1 pint
2 pints = 1 quart
4 quarts = 1 gallon

Answer these questions.

8. How many fluid ounces are there in 7 cups? **56**
9. How many fluid ounces are there in 1 pint? **16**
10. How many fluid ounces are there in 1 quart? **32**
11. How many fluid ounces are there in 1 gallon? **128**
12. How many fluid ounces are there in 7 gallons? **896**
13. How many pints are there in 1 gallon? **8**
14. How many pints are there in 73 gallons? **584**

Why teach it at this time?

This lesson provides an opportunity for students to review customary units of measure and practice the multiplication algorithm to perform conversions between them.

RETEACHING p. 31

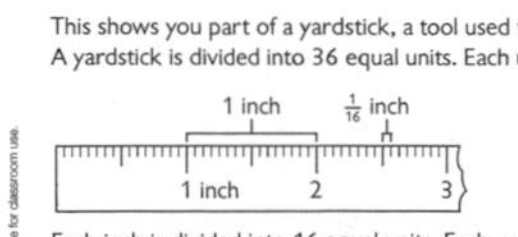

LESSON 92 RETEACHING Name__________

The customary system of measurement is not based on a system of 10 like the metric system. Use these charts to see relationships between units in the customary system.

Linear Measures
1 foot = 12 inches
1 yard = 3 feet

Weight Measures
1 pound = 16 ounces

Liquid Measures
1 gallon = 4 quarts
1 quart = 2 pints
1 pint = 2 cups
1 cup = 8 fluid ounces

This shows you part of a yardstick, a tool used to measure length. A yardstick is divided into 36 equal units. Each unit is 1 inch.

Each inch is divided into 16 equal units. Each unit is $\frac{1}{16}$ inch.

Answer these questions.

1. Choose an object and measure it in inches. Choose another object and measure it in yards. When is it better to use inches? Answers will vary. Students may suggest using inches for objects that are less than 1 ft in length.
2. How many ounces are there in 20 pounds? 320
3. How many cups are in
   a. $1\frac{1}{2}$ gallons? 24 **b.** 3 quarts? 12
4. How many fluid ounces are in 3 quarts? 96

Copyright © SRA/McGraw-Hill. Permission is granted to reproduce this page for classroom use.

*available separately

Remember: 16 ounces = 1 pound

Answer these questions.

15. How many ounces are there in 7 pounds? **112**
16. How many ounces are there in 73 pounds? **1168**

Juan said, "I'm pretty sure I weigh about 100 ounces."

17. Do you think Juan weighs about 100 ounces? **no**
18. What do you think Juan meant to say he weighs? How many ounces is that? **100 pounds; 1600**

Solve these problems.

19. In math class Angie sits 30 inches from Mrs. Packard's computer. Jenny sits $2\frac{1}{2}$ feet from Mrs. Packard's computer. Who sits closer to the computer, Angie or Jenny? **They sit the same distance from it.**
20. Paul had a new 5-pound bag of flour. He used 8 ounces of flour to make cookies. How many ounces of flour does Paul have left? **72**
21. Todd drank 1 cup of orange juice at breakfast. He drank 1 cup of juice at lunch, and 1 cup of juice before he went to bed. Did Todd drink 1 quart of juice that day? **no**
22. Abby bought some groceries. In her bag she had 2 pounds of cheese, a 16-ounce loaf of bread, and a 15-ounce box of cereal. How much does her food weigh in pounds? **3 pounds 15 ounces**
23. Mrs. Fisher bought some ribbon. She got 2 feet of plaid ribbon, 5 inches of green ribbon, 1 yard of purple ribbon, and 1 foot of red ribbon. How many yards of ribbon did Mrs. Fisher buy? **2 yards 5 inches**

MATH JOURNAL

Look at Lesson 79, in which you explored metric measures. Compare what you have done in this lesson with what you did in Lesson 79. Do you see any similarities? Write a paragraph in your Math Journal about your observations.

MENTAL MATH Provide problems in all four operations in which students indicate obviously wrong answers with thumbs down and possibly correct answers with thumbs up.

a. 45 + 400 = 805 (thumbs down)
b. 3 x 302 = 906 (thumbs up)
c. 800 – 299 = 501 (thumbs up)
d. 7 x 600 = 420 (thumbs down)
e. 800 ÷ 2 = 400 (thumbs up)

2 Teach

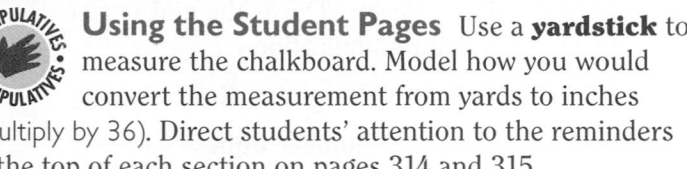

Using the Student Pages Use a **yardstick** to measure the chalkboard. Model how you would convert the measurement from yards to inches (multiply by 36). Direct students' attention to the reminders at the top of each section on pages 314 and 315.

3 Wrap-Up

5 MINUTES

In Closing Have students compare converting from one unit to another in the customary system with conversions in the metric system.

ANALYZING ANSWERS Determine whether students' errors stem from computational mistakes or from using the wrong relationship between units.

ALTERNATIVE ASSESSMENT **Performance Assessment** You may wish to use students' work on this lesson as an informal assessment of their ability to use multiplication to convert between units in the customary system of measure. If so, be sure they work independently.

PRACTICE p. 92

LESSON 92 PRACTICE Name__________

Answer these questions.

1. How many ounces are there in 12 pounds? 192
2. How many pounds are there in 320 ounces? 20
3. How many inches are there in 5 feet? 60
4. How many inches are there in 5 yards? 180
5. How many feet are there in 11 yards? 33
6. How many feet are there in 96 inches? 8
7. How many pints are there in 8 gallons? 64
8. How many quarts are there in 8 gallons? 32

Solve these problems.

9. Mr. Wong bought 6 feet of wood. He cut off a piece that was 18 inches long. How many feet of wood does he have left? $4\frac{1}{2}$
10. Stella bought a gallon of milk. Her family drank 56 ounces for breakfast. How many ounces of milk are left? 72
11. Mrs. Finn bought $3\frac{3}{4}$ yards of fabric. Mrs. Pine bought 13 feet of fabric. Who bought more fabric? Mrs. Pine
12. Marge bought pints of ice cream for a party. She bought 1 pint of strawberry, 3 pints of chocolate, and 3 pints of vanilla. Did she buy a gallon of ice cream all together? no
13. Mrs. Smith is baking brownies. She bought a 5-pound bag of sugar. The recipe called for 8 ounces of sugar. Mrs. Smith is making four batches of brownies. How many ounces of sugar will she have left? 48

Copyright © SRA/McGraw-Hill. Permission is granted to reproduce this page for classroom use.

92 • *Math Explorations and Applications* Level 4

ENRICHMENT p. 92

LESSON 92 ENRICHMENT Name__________

Estimating is a skill that people use every day.

Find some objects around your home or classroom and measure or weigh them. Try to find objects as close to 1 pound and 1 foot as you can. The more objects you weigh and measure, the better your estimates should become.

Record the weights in pounds, then record the weights in ounces. Record the lengths of the objects in feet, then record the lengths in inches.

Object ___ Answers will vary depending on
Weight in pounds ___ objects students choose to weigh
Weight in ounces ___ and measure and on their own
Object ___ weights and measures.
Weight in pounds ___
Weight in ounces ___
Object ___
Length or height in feet ___
Length or height in inches ___
Object ___
Length or height in feet ___
Length or height in inches ___
How tall are you in feet (rounded to the nearest $\frac{1}{2}$ foot)? ___
How tall are you in inches? ___

Copyright © SRA/McGraw-Hill. Permission is granted to reproduce this page for classroom use.

92 • *Math Explorations and Applications* Level 4

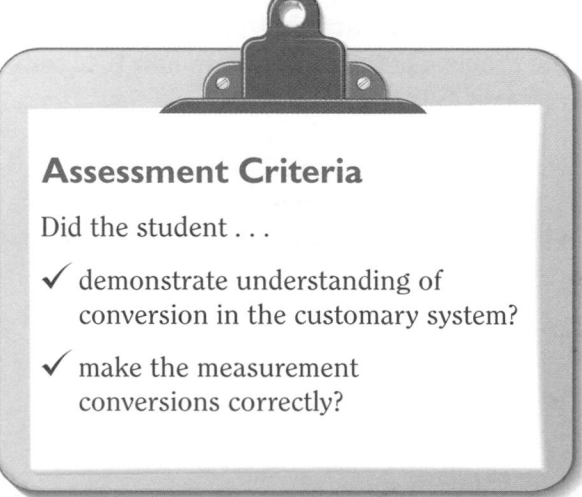

Assessment Criteria

Did the student . . .

✓ demonstrate understanding of conversion in the customary system?

✓ make the measurement conversions correctly?

Homework Have students interview five adults to get their views on using the metric system versus the customary system of measure. Discuss students' findings to formulate a general statement about how adults view the two systems of measure.

LESSON 93

Student Edition pages 316–319

Applications of Multiplication

LESSON PLANNER

Objectives

- to help students approximate products
- to provide further practice with multiplication
- to provide practice in solving word problems

Context of the Lesson This is the ninth of 17 lessons on multidigit multiplication.

MANIPULATIVES

calculators*

play money* (optional)

clock with movable hands* (optional)

paper (optional)

calendar (optional)

Program Resources

Number Cubes

Practice Master 93

Enrichment Master 93

The Cruncher*

For extra practice:
CD-ROM* Lesson 93

1 Warm-Up

5 MINUTES

Problem of the Day Present the following problem: Dean dropped his math book. It landed open, showing two page numbers whose product is 930. What two pages were showing? (pages 30 and 31)

Problem-Solving Strategies Ask students who have solved the Problem of the Day to share how they solved it and any strategies they used.

MENTAL MATH Provide problems in all four operations. Have students show thumbs up if an answer falls between the bounds 2000 and 3000 and thumbs down if it does not.

a. 1860 + 200 (thumbs up)

1860 + 400 (thumbs up)

1860 + 800 (thumbs up)

1860 + 1500 (thumbs down)

(continued on page 317)

MIXED PRACTICE

LESSON 93

Applications of Multiplication

If you know that the length of a rectangle is 293 feet and the width is 21 feet, you can approximate the area by multiplying 300 × 20. You would get 6000, so the area is about 6000 square feet. Even though the exact answer is 6153, your answer of 6000 might be acceptable. This is because when things are measured, it is often impossible for the measurements to be absolutely precise.

Answers may vary.

Approximate the answers to the following problems.

1. 489 × 71 **35,000 (34,719)**
2. 101 × 51 **5000 (5151)**
3. 56 × 88 **4800 (4928)**
4. 888 × 52 **45,000 (46,176)**
5. 45 × 451 **25,000 (20,295)**
6. 352 × 60 **24,000 (21,120**
7. 61 × 498 **30,000 (30,378)**
8. 64 × 271 **18,000 (17,344)**
9. 21 × 480 **10,000 (10,080**
10. Use your calculator to find the precise answers to questions 1–9, and compare them with your approximated answers. What happens if you round one number up and one down? Can you think of other ways to make better approximations? **Rounding one number up and one down usually brings your approximation closer to the precise answer.**
11. At the beginning of the lesson you learned that because of possible errors in the measurement, 6000 square feet might be as good an answer as 6153 square feet.

    a. Do you think this is true? Why? **Yes; Due to possible measurement errors, 6000 square feet might be equally as accurate as 615 square feet**

    b. Assume that both measurements are short by 1 foot, so the true measures are 294 feet and 22 feet. Then assume that both are long by 1 foot, so the true measures are 292 feet and 20 feet. Do you think reporting the result as about 6000 square feet or as 6153 square feet is more reasonable? Why? **about 6000 square feet; range of error: from 5840 to 6468 square feet**

COOPERATIVE LEARNING Students can work on approximate products in groups of four. Two students should collaborate in determining an approximate perimeter of a desk. The other two should measure the perimeter. Then the foursome should figure the precise answer.

*available separately

12 Ms. Jones's class wants to take a field trip. They know that the total cost is going to be $500. There are 28 students in the class. They decide to collect $12 from each student.

a. Will that be enough to pay for the trip? **no**

b. After reconsidering, they decide to ask each student to contribute $20. Will that be enough to pay for the trip? **yes**

Solve these problems.

13 Chuck earns $9.00 per hour as a short-order cook. He works 27 hours a week. How much does he earn in a week? **$243.00**

14 Elliot's dog Pudgy eats about 275 grams of dog food per day. About how many grams will Pudgy eat in April (30 days)? **8250**

15 The chart shows how much time Carlos spends eating each day. Use a computer or other means to copy and complete the chart. There are 365 days in a year.

Meal	Time Carlos Spends Eating		
	Daily	Yearly	
Breakfast	15 minutes	■	**5475**
Lunch	25 minutes	■	**9125**
Dinner	45 minutes	■	**16,425**
Total	■ **85**	■	**31,025**

16 Martina has gone to school for five years (including kindergarten). She has spent about 180 days in school each year. About how many days has she gone to school? **900**

17 Oleta is nine years old today.

a. Assuming 365 days in each year, how many days old is she? **3285**

b. If there have been two leap years (366 days each) since she was born, how many days old is she? **3287**

Mental Math (continued)

b. 300 x 6 (thumbs down)
300 x 7 (thumbs up)
300 x 8 (thumbs up)
300 x 9 (thumbs up)
300 x 11 (thumbs down)

c. 2300 – 350 (thumbs down)
2300 – 150 (thumbs up)
2300 – 0 (thumbs up)

d. 8000 ÷ 1 (thumbs down)
8000 ÷ 2 (thumbs down)
8000 ÷ 3 (thumbs up)
8000 ÷ 4 (thumbs up)

2 Teach

Using the Student Pages Go over the introductory material on page 316 with the class. Ask students to give another reason why the approximated area of 6000 square feet makes sense. Students might say that sometimes only an estimate, not an exact answer, is needed. You may want to do problems 1–12 with the class, or have students work on them independently or in pairs. Discuss the answers with the class when students finish. Assign the rest of page 317 for students to do on their own. Students can use a **calculator*** or a blank **Cruncher*** spreadsheet to help solve questions using multiplication.

Technology Connection Refer students to the software *The Quarter-Mile Estimation & Math Tricks* from Barnum Software (IBM, for grades 3–9), which allows players to compete against their own "best score" as they sharpen estimation skills.

*available separately

◆ LESSON 93 Applications of Multiplication

Teach

Using the Student Pages Go over the first paragraph with the class to check that students understand the situation. Then do the first few problems with them. Have students assume that the paper in question is standard $8\frac{1}{2}" \times 11"$ paper. Then have students work in pairs or small groups to do the rest of the problems on these pages. Be sure students realize that problems 22–25 all relate to the school magazine project. As students finish, they may play the "Four Cube Multiplication" game on page 305 for practice with multidigit multiplication. A copy of this game can also be found on page 19 of the Home Connections Blackline Masters.

◆ LESSON 93 Applications of Multiplication

Monica's class is publishing a newspaper for the school. The newspaper will have 24 pages. The students will print 650 copies, enough for everyone in the school to get one. They have to buy paper, which comes in packages of 500 sheets. Each package costs $6.

Answer these questions.

18. The students will print on both sides of each sheet. How many sheets of paper will they need for each copy of the newspaper? **12**
19. About how many sheets of paper will they need all together? **7800**
20. Will ten packages of paper be enough? 15 packages? 16 packages? **no; no; yes**
21. How much will the paper cost? **$96**

318 • Multidigit Multiplication

Art Connection Have students interview the school art teacher to find out how many different types of paper he or she stocks for art projects. Have them find out the standard sizes and weights of the **paper**, the quantities each kind of paper comes in, and about how much paper is used during a school year. Have students summarize the information they learn, using multiplication when appropriate, and present their findings. If possible, students might make a cost comparison of art paper at different stores in the area or at stores versus mail-order art supply companies.

RETEACHING

Have students restate problems in their own words so you can ascertain whether they understand the situation and can identify the correct operation to use to find the answer. Ask them leading questions to help them comprehend what they must do.

22. If the students charge 10¢ for a copy of the newspaper, and if they sell all 650 copies, will they make a profit? **no**

23. The students decide to sell advertising space in the newspaper to make extra money. They sell 47 advertisements at 95¢ each. How much is that in cents? In dollars and cents? **4465¢; $44.65**

24. How much money will the students make if they charge 10¢ for a copy of the newspaper and also sell advertising space? If paper is their only cost, will the class make a profit? **They will take in $109.65, which will yield a profit of $13.65.**

25. If the school charges $10 for the use of the copy machine for printing the newspaper, will the class make a profit? **yes**

Multiply.

26. 672 × 54 = **36,288**
27. 849 × 21 = **17,829**
28. 240 × 15 = **3600**
29. 493 × 89 = **43,877**
30. 796 × 29 = **23,084**
31. 216 × 55 = **11,880**
32. 463 × 41 = **18,983**
33. 291 × 11 = **3201**
34. 444 × 83 = **36,852**
35. 100 × 10 = **1000**
36. 117 × 61 = **7137**
37. 211 × 49 = **10,339**
38. 855 × 5 = **4275**
39. 763 × 9 = **6867**
40. 290 × 10 = **2900**

PRACTICE p. 93

LESSON 93 PRACTICE Name__________

If you know that the length of a rectangle is 394 meters and the width is 22 meters, you can approximate the area by multiplying 400 × 20. Your estimate would be 8000 square meters. The exact area is 8668 square meters.

Approximate the answers to these problems. Then use your calculator to find the precise answers. Compare these answers with your approximated answers.

1. 389 × 61 24,000, 23,729
2. 52 × 777 40,000, 40,404
3. 51 × 597 30,000, 30,447
4. 89 × 73 6300, 6497
5. 98 × 305 30,000, 29,890
6. 101 × 41 4000, 4141
7. 35 × 352 16,000, 12,320
8. 74 × 163 14,000, 12,062
9. 87 × 754 72,000, 65,598
10. 63 × 77 4800, 4851
11. 256 × 12 3000, 3072
12. 75 × 234 20,000, 17,550
13. 26 × 136 3000, 3536
14. 58 × 30 1800, 1740
15. 29 × 34 900, 986
16. 23 × 46 1000, 1058
17. 16 × 140 2000, 2240
18. 27 × 276 9000, 7452

Solve these problems.

The drama club decided to sell candy bars to raise money. Each box of candy bars contains 20 candy bars. The drama club must pay $10 for each box and must buy at least ten boxes.

19. The drama club members decide to charge $1 per candy bar. If they buy ten boxes and sell all ten boxes, will they make a profit? How much? yes; $100
20. If they buy ten boxes, how many candy bars will they have to sell to break even? Give the answer in candy bars and boxes. 100 candy bars; 5 boxes

Copyright © SRA/McGraw-Hill. Permission is granted to reproduce this page for classroom use.

Math Explorations and Applications Level 4 • 93

ENRICHMENT p. 93

LESSON 93 ENRICHMENT Name__________

You can use **The Cruncher: *Make a Calendar*** project to design your own calendar to keep track of your days. Make a monthly calendar for the next few months. Use it to keep track of birthdays, holidays, and other special days.

Answer these questions. Show your work.

1. What does a day equal in hours? 24 hours
2. How many hours are in one week? 168
3. About how many hours are in one month? 672–744 (28–31 days)
4. How are calendars useful? Answers will vary. Possible answers: Calendars can help us remember important occasions, events, and appointments.

Copyright © SRA/McGraw-Hill. Permission is granted to reproduce this page for classroom use.

Math Explorations and Applications Level 4 • 93

*available separately

3 Wrap-Up

5 MINUTES

In Closing Have students look back at their work in this lesson to determine which problems required exact answers and which did not.

ALTERNATIVE ASSESSMENT

Informal Assessment Circulate through the classroom as students work on the problems in this lesson and note what they say and how they approach the various problems. Have them verbalize their solution methods and explain how they verify that their answers make sense.

Assessment Criteria

Did the student . . .

- ✓ contribute to the discussion of approximations and exact answers?
- ✓ accurately apply multiplication skills to solve word problems?
- ✓ communicate the strategies she or he used to solve the word problems?
- ✓ correctly answer at least 75% of the computation problems?

Homework Assign Practice Master 93 for further practice with multiplication applications.

LEARNING STYLES • MANIPULATIVES

Meeting Individual Needs

Students who are interpersonal or visual learners may benefit from drawing or acting out the situations in the word problems to better grasp what they need to do to solve them. For example, they might use **play money***, a **clock with movable hands***, or a **calendar** to work through some of the problems on page 317.

LESSON 94

Student Edition pages 320–323

Multiply: Three-Digit Numbers by Three-Digit Numbers

LESSON PLANNER

Objectives

- ▶ to introduce an algorithm for multiplying a three-digit number by a three-digit number
- ▶ to provide practice in finding errors in multiplication computations

Context of the Lesson This is the tenth of 17 lessons on multidigit multiplication, and the last multidigit multiplication algorithm for a specific case. Lesson 98 presents a general algorithm for any multidigit multiplication.

MANIPULATIVES

graph paper (optional)

calculators* (optional)

Program Resources

Practice Master 94

Enrichment Master 94

For extra practice:
CD-ROM* Lesson 94

1 Warm-Up

5 MINUTES

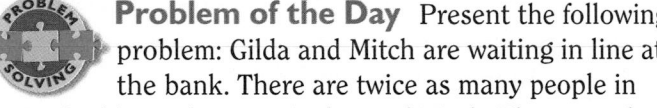

Problem of the Day Present the following problem: Gilda and Mitch are waiting in line at the bank. There are twice as many people in front of Gilda as there are in front of Mitch. There are three people between Gilda and Mitch. How many people are in front of Gilda? (8 people)

Problem-Solving Strategies Ask students who have solved the Problem of the Day to share how they solved it and any strategies they used.

MENTAL MATH Provide practice finding products of factors that are multiples of 10. Encourage prompt responses.

a. 40 x 60 = (2400)

b. 80 x 70 = (5600)

c. 5 x 80 = (400)

d. 500 x 80 = (40,000)

e. 500 x 8000 = (4,000,000)

EXPLORE

LESSON 94

Multiply: Three-Digit Numbers by Three-Digit Numbers

Miyoko is an airline pilot. She flies between two airports that are 749 miles apart. Last year, she flew that route 583 times. What is the total number of miles Miyoko flew on that route? You can multiply to find out.

Multiply: 749 × 583

```
  583
× 749
 5247
```

Multiply 583 by the **ones** digit. 9 × 583 = 5247
Write 5247 so that the digit on the right (7) is in the **ones** column.

```
  583
× 749
 5247
2332
```

Multiply 583 by the **tens** digit. 4 × 583 = 2332
There are 2332 tens. Write 2332 so that the digit on the right (2) is in the **tens** column.

```
  583
× 749
 5247
2332
4081
```

Multiply 583 by the **hundreds** digit.
7 × 583 = 4081
There are 4081 hundreds. Write 4081 so that the digit on the right (1) is in the **hundreds** column.

```
    583
  × 749
   5247
  2332
 4081
436,667
```

Add to get the final answer.

Check to see that the answer makes sense.

The answer should be less than 800 × 600, which is 480,000.
The answer should be greater than 700 × 500, which is 350,000.
436,667 is less than 480,000 and greater than 350,000.
The answer makes sense.

Literature Connection Read *Cookies* by William Jaspersohn with the class. Have students determine the quantities of the ingredients they would need to mass-produce a particular recipe.

*available separately

When there is a 0 in the multiplier, you can save time by using a shorter way. Look at these two examples.

Example 1:

624	Multiply by the **ones** digit.
× 37**0**	0 × 624 = 0
0	Write the 0 in the **ones** column.

624	Multiply by the **tens** digit.
× 3**7**0	7 × 624 = 4368
43680	There are 4368 **tens.**
	Write 4368 next to the 0.

624	Multiply by the **hundreds** digit.
× **3**70	3 × 624 = 1872
43680	There are 1872 hundreds.
1872	Write 1872 so that the digit on the right (2) is in the
230,880	**hundreds** column. Add.

Example 2:

624	Multiply by the **ones** digit.
× 30**7**	7 × 624 = 4368
4368	Write 4368 so that the digit on the right (8) is in the
	ones column.

624	Multiply by the **tens** digit.
× 3**0**7	0 × 624 = 0
4368	There are 0 tens.
0	Write the 0 in the **tens** column.

624	Multiply by the **hundreds** digit.
× **3**07	3 × 624 = 1872
4368	There are 1872 hundreds.
18720	Write the 1872 next to the 0.
191,568	Add.

❷ Teach

Using the Student Pages Because the algorithm in this case is so similar to the previous ones, ask students to suggest how to multiply 583 x 749 *before* they look at the lesson. The new step involves using a third partial product and correctly placing it. Students may be able to determine what to do in such a situation using the algorithms they have already learned.

Go over the presentation on page 320 with the class. Discuss that the 1 in the partial product 4081 belongs in the hundreds column, directly below the 7 in the multiplier, because 4081 is the product of 583 times 7 hundreds. Students should see that the answer from multiplying the ones digit by any digit in the multiplier always belongs directly below that digit of the multiplier. Do several more examples as students follow along. The placement of partial products should become a fairly mechanical process for students.

Go on to page 321 and discuss the examples with the class. Most students will readily see how the first problem was done. The shortcut in the second example may require more explanation. In that case, the 0 appears in the middle of the multiplier. Some students may want to omit writing anything for the second partial product, but that decision is ill-advised at this stage. Such an omission may lead to serious mistakes, such as dropping the 0 when it occurs in the ones digit or misplacing partial products.

> ***The main purpose of teaching mathematics is to educate people to use mathematical thought to solve real problems.***
>
> —Stephen S. Willoughby, *Teaching Mathematics: What Is Basic?*

◆ LESSON 94 Multiply: Three-Digit Numbers by Three-Digit Numbers

Teach

Using the Student Pages Have students work on page 322 independently. Alert them to look for patterns and shortcuts they can use to complete the exercises quickly and accurately. Have students work in pairs to complete page 323. Encourage partners to discuss their thinking together so they can benefit from each other's observations.

LEARNING STYLES

Meeting Individual Needs

Students who are rhythmic or musical learners might enjoy making up a rap or song that gives the steps of the algorithm for multiplying multidigit numbers. Invite students to share their rap or song with classmates to help them multiply accurately.

◆ LESSON 94 Multiply: Three-Digit Numbers by Three-Digit Numbers

Remember:

721 × 365	721 × 36**5** **3605**	721 × 3**6**5 3605 **4326**	721 × **3**65 3605 4326 **2163**	721 × 365 3605 4326 2163 **263,165**
498 × 603	498 × 60**3** **1494**	498 × 6**0**3 1494 **0**	498 × **6**03 1494 **29880**	498 × 603 1494 29880 **300,294**

Multiply. Use shortcuts when you can.

❶ 287 × 596 **171,052**	❷ 831 × 609 **506,079**	❸ 434 × 292 **126,728**	❹ 816 × 333 **271,728**	❺ 417 × 28 **11,676**
❻ 604 × 17 **10,268**	❼ 604 × 170 **102,680**	❽ 365 × 108 **39,420**	❾ 9 × 6 **54**	❿ 90 × 6 **540**
⓫ 900 × 6 **5400**	⓬ 9 × 60 **540**	⓭ 9 × 600 **5400**	⓮ 90 × 60 **5400**	⓯ 900 × 60 **54,000**
⓰ 90 × 600 **54,000**	⓱ 900 × 600 **540,000**	⓲ 901 × 599 **539,699**	⓳ 902 × 598 **539,396**	⓴ 903 × 507 **457,821**
㉑ 547 × 392 **214,424**	㉒ 281 × 61 **17,141**	㉓ 307 × 409 **125,563**	㉔ 215 × 17 **3655**	㉕ 649 × 501 **325,149**

Check to see that your answers make sense.

RETEACHING

Have students work on **graph paper**, writing each digit in a separate box. This technique can help those who have difficulty aligning partial products.

Below are ten multiplication problems that have been worked out. Six of them have errors. Use what you know about multiplication to find the errors.

List the six problems that are wrong. Be prepared to explain how you know they are wrong without doing the computations. **Problems 26, 29, 30, 31, 32 and 34 are incorrect.**

26	27	28	29	30
274	379	497	139	486
× 861	× 814	× 555	× 257	× 395
472	1516	2485	973	3418
1644	379	2485	685	4374
2192	3032	2485	278	1458
236,112	308,506	275,835	35,723	192,958

31	32	33	34	35
874	879	258	258	536
× 69	× 951	× 379	× 973	× 123
7866	879	2322	774	1608
5241	4395	1806	1806	1072
60,276	7911	774	2322	536
	84,384	97,782	25,800	65,928

PROBLEM SOLVING

Solve these problems.

36. Mrs. Berry ordered 15 boxes of pens. There are 120 pens in each box. How many pens did she order? **1800**

37. Mr. Andrews is building a brick wall. He wants 15 rows of bricks, with 90 bricks in each row. How many bricks does he need for the wall? **1350**

38. The Gala Concert Hall has 110 rows of seats. There are 100 seats in each row. How many seats are in the concert hall? **11,000**

FANTASTIC FACT **In Australia, kangaroos outnumber people 10 to 1.**

3 Wrap-Up (5 MINUTES)

In Closing Have students explain some strategies they used to identify errors in worked-out multiplication exercises.

ALTERNATIVE ASSESSMENT

Performance Assessment You might wish to use students' work on page 322 as an informal assessment of their understanding of the algorithm for multiplying by a three-digit multiplier. If so, have students complete the page independently.

Assessment Criteria

Did the student . . .

- ✓ contribute to the discussion of the multiplication algorithm?
- ✓ communicate strategies used to identify errors in worked-out multiplication exercises?
- ✓ correctly answer at least 75% of the computation problems?

Homework Have students make up four exercises that involve multiplying two three-digit factors and then solve them. Students should use six different digits in each problem.

PRACTICE p. 94

LESSON 94 PRACTICE Name______________________

Multiply. Use shortcuts when you can.

1	2	3	4
258 × 325	604 × 283	912 × 456	278 × 61
83,850	170,932	415,872	16,958

5	6	7	8
823 × 649	925 × 683	264 × 172	808 × 27
534,127	631,775	45,408	21,816

9	10	11	12
987 × 8	548 × 7	295 × 592	703 × 333
7896	3836	174,640	234,099

Below are four multiplication problems that have been worked out. Two of them have errors. Ring the numbers that are errors. Write correct below the problems that are correct.

13	14	15	16
335	728	419	549
× 57	× 627	× 307	× 126
2345	5096	2(8)(6)3	329(5)
1675	1456	12570	10(8)8
19,095	4368	128,563	549
correct	456,456		69,074
	correct		

Copyright © SRA/McGraw-Hill. Permission is granted to reproduce this page for classroom use.

ENRICHMENT p. 94

LESSON 94 ENRICHMENT Name______________________

One way that food, products, and other goods get from the part of the country where they are produced to another part of the country where they will be used or sold is by truck. Truck drivers cover great distances in a short amount of time.

Suppose a truck driver in the Midwest drives between seven cities. He can travel from any city below to any other city, using a direct route.

Solve.

How many different highways can the truck driver use? ___20___

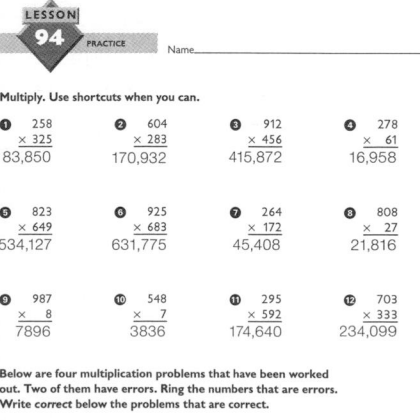

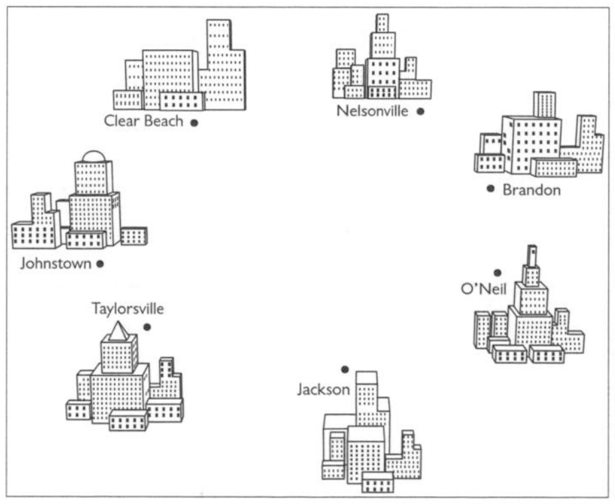

Copyright © SRA/McGraw-Hill. Permission is granted to reproduce this page for classroom use.

AT RISK

Meeting Individual Needs Nowadays, in most situations in which people multiply multidigit numbers, they use a **calculator*** or the calculator function on a computer. Challenge students by asking them how they think computers perform multiplication. Provide appropriate reference materials that explain how computers function. Have students work out multiplication problems like those in this lesson and then use a calculator or computer to do the same problems. Discuss the advantages and disadvantages of using technology to do computations.

*available separately

LESSON 95 Multiplication Uses

Student Edition pages 324–325

LESSON PLANNER

Objectives

- ▶ to provide some practical applications of multiplication
- ▶ to provide practice in multiplication

Context of the Lesson This is the 11th of 17 lessons on multidigit multiplication.

MANIPULATIVES	Program Resources
calculators*	Number Cubes (0–5 and 5–10)
graph paper	Practice Master 95
play money* (optional)	Enrichment Master 95
	For extra practice: CD-ROM* Lesson 95 Cumulative Review, page 555

1 Warm-Up (5 MINUTES)

Problem of the Day Have students use a **calculator*** to solve this problem: Using the digits 2, 3, 4, 5, and 6 once each, what two factors can you form that give the greatest possible product? (542 x 63 = 34,146)

Problem-Solving Strategies Ask students who have solved the Problem of the Day to share how they solved it and any strategies they used.

MENTAL MATH Provide approximation exercises in all four operations. Have students indicate obviously wrong answers with thumbs down and possibly correct answers with thumbs up.

a. 6 x 80 = 1480 (thumbs down)

b. 389 + 428 = 817 (thumbs up)

c. 41 x 26 = 526 (thumbs down)

d. 410 ÷ 10 = 41 (thumbs up)

2 Teach

Using the Student Pages Before beginning the problems on page 324, you may wish to introduce the

PROBLEM SOLVING

LESSON 95 Multiplication Uses

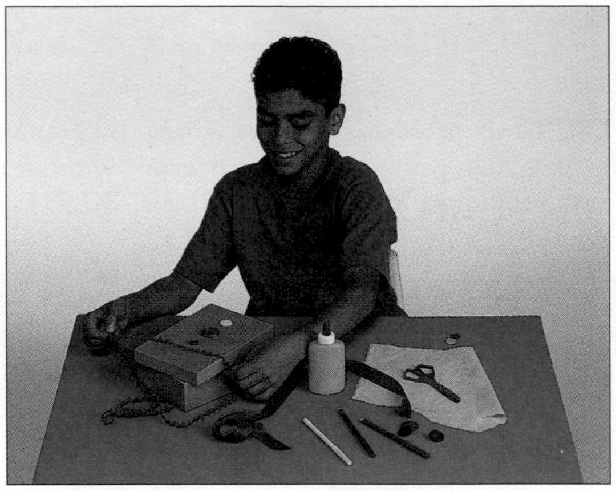

Marco's class is making and selling decorated pencil boxes. Each box requires a rectangular piece of cloth 20 centimeters long and 15 centimeters wide. The students in the class buy the cloth in large pieces that are 80 centimeters long and 60 centimeters wide.

Answer these questions.

1. Draw a picture to find out how many pencil boxes they can make from one piece of cloth. How many boxes? **16**

Marco's class buys five pieces of cloth.

2. How many pencil boxes can the students make? **80**

Each piece of cloth costs $6.79 (679 cents), including tax.

3. How much did the students pay for the five pieces they bought? **$33.95**

The students sold each pencil box for 98 cents, and they sold every one.

4. How much money did the class take in? **$78.40**

The class also paid for other supplies besides the cloth. The other supplies cost $5.73 all together.

5. How much profit did the class make? **$38.72**

324 • Multidigit Multiplication

ESL Meeting Individual Needs

Students with limited English proficiency may need help with the word problems on page 324. You may want to group them with native English speakers or have volunteers act out or draw pictures of the situations.

RETEACHING

MANIPULATIVES Students who have difficulty with the money problems should use **play money*** to act out those problems and keep a written record of their actions.

*available separately

COOPERATIVE LEARNING

GAME

(Multiplication) Roll a Problem Game

Players: Two or more
Materials: One 0–5 cube
Object: To get the greatest product
Math Focus: Multidigit multiplication, place value, and mathematical reasoning

RULES

1. Use blanks to outline a multiplication problem on your paper, like this:

$$\begin{array}{r} \_\_\_\ \ \_\_\_ \\ \times\ \_\_\_\ \ \_\_\_ \\ \hline \end{array}$$

2. The first player rolls the cube four times.
3. Each time the cube is rolled, write that number in one of the blanks in your outline.
4. When all the blanks have been filled in, find the product of the two numbers.
5. The player with the greatest product wins the round.

OTHER WAYS TO PLAY THIS GAME

1. Try to get the least product.
2. Multiply a one-digit number and a three-digit number.
3. Multiply two three-digit numbers.
4. Use a 5–10 cube. If you roll a 10, roll again.

MATH JOURNAL

How did you play this game? Explain your strategies in your Math Journal.

Use the Cumulative Review on page 555 after this lesson.

PRACTICE p. 95

LESSON 95 PRACTICE Name__________

PROBLEM SOLVING **Solve these problems.**

Janelle's club is making and selling doll blankets. Each blanket requires a rectangular piece of fabric 15 inches long and 10 inches wide. The members of the club buy the fabric in large pieces that are 75 inches long and 50 inches wide.

1. Draw a picture to find out how many doll blankets they can make from one large piece of fabric. How many blankets can they make? 25
2. Janelle's club bought ten pieces of fabric. How many doll blankets can the club members make? 250
3. Each large piece of fabric cost $9.98 (998 cents), including tax. How much did the club members pay for the ten large pieces of fabric they bought? $99.80
4. The club members sold each doll blanket for $4.00, and they sold all of them. How much money did the club take in? $1000.00
5. The club also paid for other supplies besides the fabric. The other supplies cost $10.20 all together. How much profit did the club make? $890.00
6. The next month the fabric they bought was on sale for $8.50 (850 cents), including tax. They bought 20 large pieces of fabric. How much did they pay? $170.00
7. How many doll blankets can they make from these 20 large pieces of fabric? 500
8. The club members sold all of these blankets for $3.00 each. How much money did they take in? $1500.00
9. If their other supplies cost $25.00, how much profit did they make? $1305.00

Copyright © SRA/McGraw-Hill. Permission is granted to reproduce this page for classroom use.

Math Explorations and Applications Level 4 • **95**

ENRICHMENT p. 95

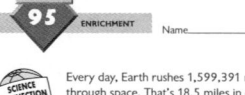

LESSON 95 ENRICHMENT Name__________

SCIENCE CONNECTION Every day, Earth rushes 1,599,391 miles through space. That's 18.5 miles in one second!

Use a calculator to solve the following problems.

1. How far is Earth moving every minute? 1110 miles
2. How many miles per hour is that? 66,600
3. When you are traveling 60 miles per hour in a car, how many miles per minute is that? 1
4. A satellite must go at least 300 miles per minute to keep from falling back to Earth. How fast is that per hour? 18,000 miles
5. Why do you think we can't feel how fast Earth is moving? Compare it to riding in a car. When do you notice movement most? When do you least notice the speed? Does it depend on how fast you are going?
The speed of Earth remains constant. It never speeds up, slows down, or changes direction. Because we see nothing rushing by, it's as if we're riding in a car with our eyes shut. We are aware of movement only if we change speed or direction.
6. Do you think we would notice if Earth changed speed or direction? How?
Yes. The length of seasons and amount of daylight would change.

Copyright © SRA/McGraw-Hill. Permission is granted to reproduce this page for classroom use.

Math Explorations and Applications Level 4 • **95**

"(Multiplication) Roll a Problem" game (page 325) so that students can play as they finish. This game provides practice with multidigit multiplication.

MANIPULATIVES Go over the introduction on page 324 with students. Provide **graph paper** so students can complete problem 1. You may want students to work in groups to solve these problems.

GAME Demonstrate the "(Multiplication) Roll a Problem" game for the class. This game provides practice with multidigit multiplication, place value, and mathematical reasoning. Have students play all together or in groups of four or more. Also encourage them to play game variations 3 and 4 as soon as possible.

3 Wrap-Up

5 MINUTES

In Closing Discuss other possible variations of the "(Multiplication) Roll a Problem" game.

ALTERNATIVE ASSESSMENT **Performance Assessment** Observe students as they play the "(Multiplication) Roll a Problem" game and solve the problems they create. Notice whether they apply good strategies for creating the problems and solve problems accurately.

Assessment Criteria

Did the student . . .

✓ contribute to the discussion of the word problems?

✓ choose the right operation to solve the applications problems?

✓ actively participate in the "(Multiplication) Roll a Problem" game?

Homework Have students play the "(Multiplication) Roll a Problem" game with family members for further practice with multidigit multiplication. A copy of this game can also be found on page 20 of the Home Connections Blackline Masters.

LESSON 96

Student Edition pages 326–329

Keeping Sharp: Functions, Facts, and Computation

LESSON PLANNER

Objectives

- to review working with functions and basic arithmetic operations
- to provide practice interpreting graphs
- to help students develop the broad ability to use mathematical common sense

Context of the Lesson This lesson, the 12th of 17 lessons on multidigit multiplication, contains Part 4 of "The Treasure of Mugg Island," a six-part Thinking Story.

MANIPULATIVES

graph paper

meterstick or tape measure*

objects to be measured

Program Resources

Practice Master 96

Enrichment Master 96

The Cruncher*

For career connections: Careers and Math*

For extra practice: CD-ROM* Lesson 96

1 Warm-Up

5 MINUTES

Problem of the Day Present this problem and provide **graph paper** on which students can work: Draw a capital letter H that has a perimeter of 22 units. (Answers will vary.)

Problem-Solving Strategies Ask students who have solved the Problem of the Day to share how they solved it and any strategies they used.

MENTAL MATH Have students estimate the measurements of these objects using metric units of measure. After each estimate is made, use a **meterstick** or **tape measure*** and measure to check for accuracy. (Estimates should improve after each object is measured.)

a. height and width of a map

b. height of a doorway

c. length of the chalkboard

d. length of a room

MIXED PRACTICE

LESSON 96

Keeping Sharp: Functions, Facts, and Computation

Copy and complete these function machine charts.

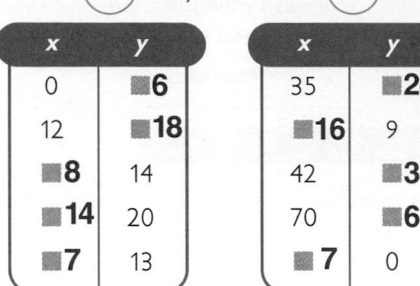

1. $x \rightarrow (+6) \rightarrow y$

x	y
0	■ **6**
12	■ **18**
■ **8**	14
■ **14**	20
■ **7**	13

2. $x \rightarrow (-7) \rightarrow y$

x	y
35	■ **28**
■ **16**	9
42	■ **35**
70	■ **63**
■ **7**	0

3. $x \rightarrow (\times 26) \rightarrow y$

x	y
13	■ **338**
10	■ **260**
0	■ **0**
6	■ **156**
1	■ **26**

ALGEBRA READINESS

Solve for *n*.

4. $n = 9 + 6$ **15**
5. $n = 9 \times 7$ **63**
6. $7 \times n = 56$ **8**
7. $7 + n = 22$ **15**
8. $27 \div n = 9$ **3**
9. $36 \div 4 = n$ **9**
10. $9 \times 6 = n$ **54**
11. $n \div 8 = 8$ **64**
12. $n \div 10 = 60$ **600**
13. $n = 63 \div 7$ **9**
14. $n - 8 = 8$ **16**
15. $n - 9 = 47$ **56**

Solve for *n*. Watch the signs.

16. $49 + 13 = n$ **62**
17. $49 - 13 = n$ **36**
18. $49 \times 13 = n$ **637**
19. $419 - 394 = n$ **25**
20. $519 \times 304 = n$ **157,776**
21. $439 + 396 = n$ **835**
22. $10 \times 25 = n$ **250**
23. $256 \times 100 = n$ **25,600**
24. $367 \times 1000 = n$ **367,000**
25. $1000 \times 99 = n$ **99,000**
26. $100 \times 15 = n$ **1500**
27. $5 \times 100 = n$ **500**
28. $5 \times 10{,}000 = n$ **50,000**
29. $51 \times 1000 = n$ **51,000**
30. $100 \times 969 = n$ **96,900**
31. $479 \times 23 = n$ **11,017**
32. $648 \times 251 = n$ **162,648**
33. $216 \times 415 = n$ **89,640**

Math Connection Help students learn about other nonstandard units of length that were used in the past, such as thumbs, cubits, palms, and spans, as well as units that were less familiar then but became standardized, such as the foot, yard, fathom, furlong, and rod. One resource is *History of Mathematics, Volume II* by David Eugene Smith.

*available separately

Janice and Nakia decided to get up early and take a long hike. The trail had mile markers so they could tell how far they were from home. They made a graph of how far they were away from home each hour. Look at their graph.

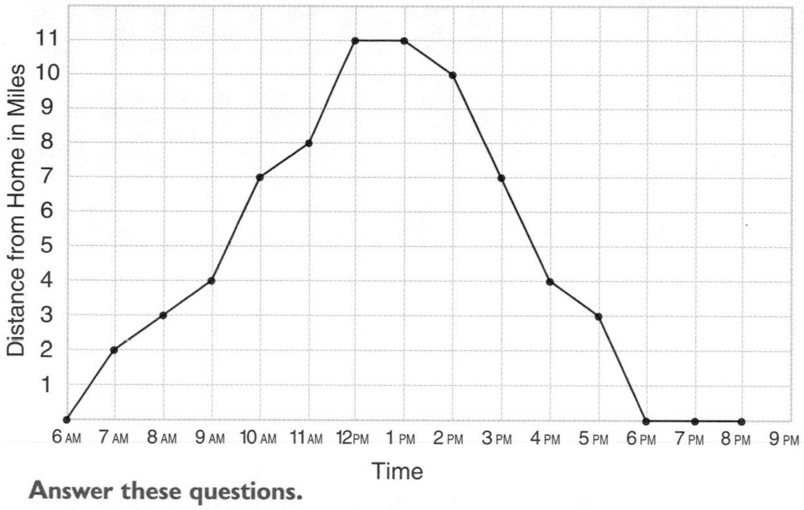

Answer these questions.

34. Where were they at 7:00 A.M.? **about 2 miles from home**
35. How far were they from home at 9:00 A.M.? **4 miles**
36. What was the greatest distance they had been from home? **about 11 miles**
37. Could they have gone farther from home at some time when they didn't record it? If so, when do you think that might have happened? If not, why do you think they didn't go farther from home? **yes; sometime between 12 P.M. and 1 P.M.**
38. About how fast do you think they walked? **about 2 miles per hour**

MATH JOURNAL

Write a story in your Math Journal about what Janice and Nakia did on their hike and when they did it. Be sure that your story agrees with the information shown on the graph.

❷ Teach

ALGEBRA READINESS

Using the Student Pages Review the types of problems on page 326 with students before they begin working on their own. Help them get started, if necessary, by doing the first problem. Students can use a blank **Cruncher*** spreadsheet to create a function machine and find the missing numbers.

Work through the problems on page 327 with the class, or have students work in small groups to discuss and solve the problems together. Review how to read information from a line graph. Be sure that students' stories in their Math Journals are consistent with the information provided in the graph.

> *There are four important steps that children should follow to learn mathematics and to be willing and able to use it effectively to solve problems of all kinds: (1) derive the mathematics from their own reality, (2) discover and use the power of abstract thought, (3) practice, and (4) apply the mathematics to something that is of interest to them.*
>
> —Stephen S. Willoughby, *Mathematics Education for a Changing World*

*available separately

◆ LESSON 96 Keeping Sharp: Functions, Facts, and Computation

Teach

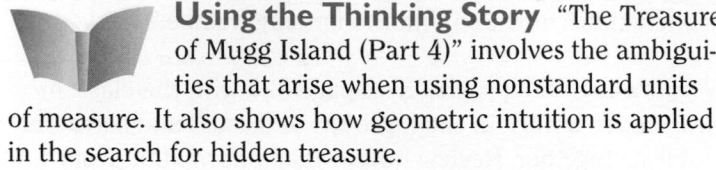

Using the Thinking Story "The Treasure of Mugg Island (Part 4)" involves the ambiguities that arise when using nonstandard units of measure. It also shows how geometric intuition is applied in the search for hidden treasure.

Answers to Thinking Story Questions:

1. Portia must have taken somewhat smaller steps than Manolita because it took her more steps to get to the rock. Marcus took larger steps, and the queen took much smaller steps. No one knows what size steps Ferdie took. Manolita apparently took steps of about the same size as the person who made up the directions, because they both came to a number starting with 13. (It is unlikely that anyone could cover the distance in 13 steps or would require 1300 steps.)
2. No matter what direction the peg is from the rock, it should be passed by if the rock is circled at the right distance.
3. Manolita should find the peg because, as noted above, she seems to take steps about the size of those made by the person who wrote the directions.

MATH JOURNAL Have students predict in their Math Journals what the treasure hunters may have to do next to find the hidden treasure.

THINKING STORY

◆ LESSON 96 Keeping Sharp: Functions, Facts, and Computation

The Treasure of Mugg Island

Part 4

You may wish to refer to the earlier parts of this Thinking Story, on pages 276–277, 294–295, and 308–309.

Remember the note in the hollow tree?

From tree go NW13
to spider rock.
From spider rock go
23 paces to peg.

Manolita had a good idea. She said, "Let's all walk northwest and count our steps. Maybe one of us will find the spider rock."

The queen had a compass. They used it to find northwest. Then they all started walking in the same direction. Soon they found a rock that had marks on it like a spider web.

Technology Connection Students can use the software *The Math Map Trip* from Educational Activities (Mac, IBM, for grades 4–8) to tour the United States as they solve problems involving area, perimeter, average, estimation, basic geometry, fractions, graphing, geography (directions, distance, maps, etc.), and science (temperature, scales, weights, etc.).

RETEACHING

Continue to provide additional practice in whatever algorithms or facts students need to review. You may want to assign Enrichment Master 96.

"This must be it," said Manolita. "And I walked 134 steps."

"That's funny," said Portia. "I walked 172 steps to get here."

Marcus walked 105 giant steps, the queen walked 324 dainty steps, and Ferdie forgot to count.

"Now," said Marcus, "I have an idea. The peg is 23 paces from the spider rock. But we don't know in what direction. So let's walk all around the rock, 23 paces away from it."

Everyone did that. The queen walked 23 dainty steps away from the rock and then went around it in a circle. Marcus walked 23 giant steps from the rock and then went around it in a circle. Manolita and Portia, each in her own way, walked 23 steps away from the rock and then went around it in a circle. Ferdie went away from the rock, but he forgot how many paces. Then he went around it in a circle. Finally one of them said, "I found it! Here is the peg in the ground."

. . . to be continued

Work in groups. Discuss your answers and how you figured them out. Then compare your answers with those of other groups. **Answers are in margin.**

1. What size steps did the different people take in getting to the spider rock? Explain.
2. How could Marcus's idea work for finding the peg?
3. If all the treasure hunters took the same size steps as they did before, who do you think would find the peg? Why do you think so?

PRACTICE p. 96

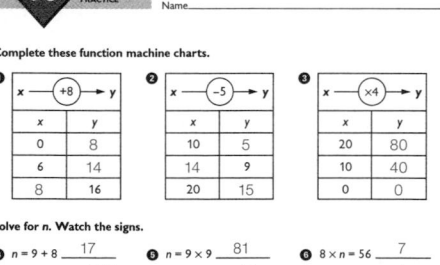

LESSON 96 PRACTICE Name__________

Complete these function machine charts.

1. x → (+8) → y

x	y
0	8
6	14
8	16

2. x → (−5) → y

x	y
10	5
14	9
20	15

3. x → (×4) → y

x	y
20	80
10	40
0	0

Solve for *n*. Watch the signs.

4. $n = 9 + 8$ 17
5. $n = 9 \times 9$ 81
6. $8 \times n = 56$ 7
7. $n \div 10 = 50$ 500
8. $5 + n = 20$ 15
9. $32 \div n = 8$ 4
10. $36 \div 6 = n$ 6
11. $n - 9 = 38$ 47
12. $n \times 6 = 54$ 9

Solve for *n*. Watch the signs.

13. $35 + 13 = n$ 48
14. $35 - 13 = n$ 22
15. $35 \times 13 = n$ 455
16. $417 - 396 = n$ 21
17. $405 \times 35 = n$ 14,175
18. $428 + 394 = n$ 822
19. $10 \times 24 = n$ 240
20. $156 \times 100 = n$ 15,600
21. $223 \times 1000 = n$ 223,000
22. $32 \times 10{,}000 = n$ 320,000

Add.

23. 37 + 39 + 57 = 133
24. 423 + 412 + 501 = 1336
25. 1006 + 952 + 228 = 2186
26. 15 + 28 + 25 = 68
27. 29 + 40 + 60 = 129

96 • *Math Explorations and Applications* Level 4

Copyright © SRA/McGraw-Hill. Permission is granted to reproduce this page for classroom use.

ENRICHMENT p. 96

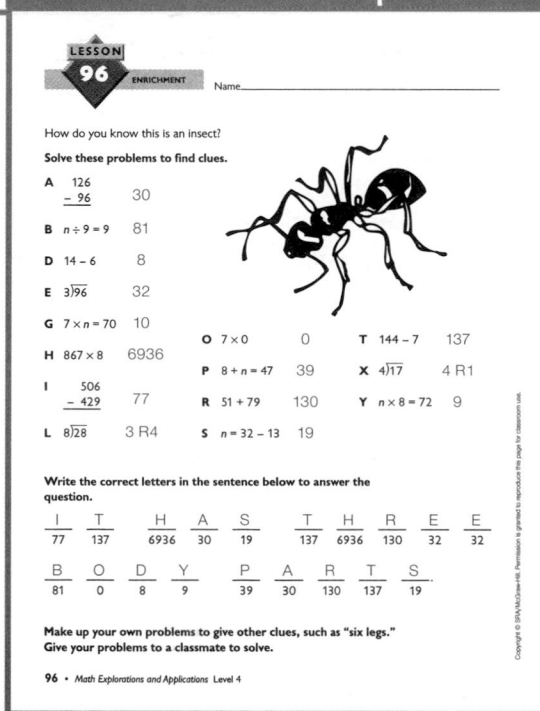

LESSON 96 ENRICHMENT Name__________

How do you know this is an insect?

Solve these problems to find clues.

- **A** 126 − 96 = 30
- **B** $n \div 9 = 9$ 81
- **D** 14 − 6 = 8
- **E** 3)96 32
- **G** $7 \times n = 70$ 10
- **H** 867 × 8 = 6936
- **I** 506 − 429 = 77
- **L** 8)28 3 R4
- **O** 7 × 0 = 0
- **P** $8 + n = 47$ 39
- **R** 51 + 79 = 130
- **S** $n = 32 - 13$ 19
- **T** 144 − 7 = 137
- **X** 4)17 4 R1
- **Y** $n \times 8 = 72$ 9

Write the correct letters in the sentence below to answer the question.

I T H A S T H R E E (77 137 6936 30 19 137 6936 130 32 32)

B O D Y P A R T S. (81 0 8 9 39 30 130 137 19)

Make up your own problems to give other clues, such as "six legs." Give your problems to a classmate to solve.

96 • *Math Explorations and Applications* Level 4

Copyright © SRA/McGraw-Hill. Permission is granted to reproduce this page for classroom use.

3 Wrap-Up (5 MINUTES)

In Closing Ask students why paces are an unreliable way to describe measures of length.

ALTERNATIVE ASSESSMENT

Portfolio Assessment You may wish to use students' work on pages 326 and 327 to check their mastery of functions, facts, computation, and problem solving. If so, have students correct any errors they may make, date their papers, and add them to their Math Portfolios as a record of ongoing review.

Assessment Criteria

Did the student . . .

- ✓ correctly answer at least 75% of the computation problems on page 326?
- ✓ explain how to interpret the graph to solve the problems related to it?
- ✓ contribute to the Thinking Story discussion?
- ✓ communicate strategies used to answer the questions?

Homework Have students make a map of a room in their home and find its dimensions in paces. Then have them ask a family member to pace off the same dimensions and record both nonstandard measurements of the room to show why paces are an unreliable way to describe measures of length.

LESSON 97

Student Edition pages 330–331

Perimeter and Area

LESSON PLANNER

Objectives

- ▶ to provide practice with solving word problems that involve perimeter and area
- ▶ to demonstrate that one rectangle can have a greater perimeter but a smaller area than another rectangle

Context of the Lesson This is the 13th of 17 lessons on multidigit multiplication.

MANIPULATIVES

measuring tools* (rulers, tape measures)

square pieces of paper

objects to be measured

rectangular or square objects

Program Resources

Practice Master 97

Enrichment Master 97

The Cruncher*

For extra practice: CD-ROM* Lesson 97

1 Warm-Up

5 MINUTES

Problem of the Day Present this problem on the chalkboard: Fill in the blanks in the equation below with different digits to create a three-digit number multiplied by a one-digit number with a product of 3720.

____ × ____ = 3720

(Possible answers are: 465 × 8, 620 × 6, 744 × 5, 930 × 4)

Problem-Solving Strategies Ask students who have solved the Problem of the Day to share how they solved it and any strategies they used.

MENTAL MATH **MANIPULATIVES** Have students estimate the area of the objects. After each estimate, have students use **measuring tools*** to measure to check for accuracy. (Estimates should improve after each object is measured.)

a. area of a sheet of paper

b. area of a notebook cover

c. area of a chalkboard

(continued on page 331)

PRACTICE

LESSON 97

Perimeter and Area

Both Ray and Clara have backyards. They wanted to know whose yard was bigger. They measured and got the following results:

"My yard is longer!" Ray shouted.

"But mine is wider," said Clara.

"Let's measure the distance around them," said Ray.

- ◆ What is the perimeter of Ray's yard? **26 m**
- ◆ What is the perimeter of Clara's yard? **24 m**

"My yard is bigger," bragged Ray.

"Let's find the areas," said Clara.

"Why?" asked Ray. "Yours can't have more area if it's smaller around."

- ◆ What is the area of Ray's yard? **30 square m**
- ◆ What is the area of Clara's yard? **36 square m**
- ◆ Can a yard with a smaller perimeter than another yard have a larger area? **yes**

"You see," said Clara, "my yard is bigger."

"I still say mine is bigger," Ray insisted.

- ◆ Who is right? What does "bigger" mean? ← **Either child could be right, depending on what is meant by "bigger." Depending on the context, "bigger" can refer to different aspects of size.**
- ◆ Whose yard is bigger if they're talking about how much topsoil is needed? **Clara's**
- ◆ Whose yard is bigger if they're talking about how much fencing is needed? **Ray's**
- ◆ Try to draw two rectangles so that one has a larger area and the other has a larger perimeter. **For example:**

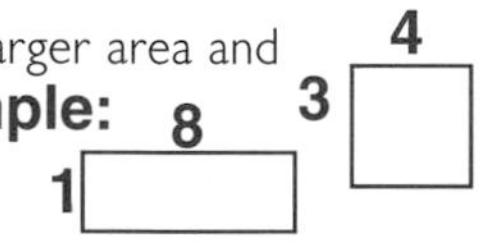

COOPERATIVE LEARNING Have students work in pairs or small groups to complete this activity. First have the group approximate the length of each side of a rectangular figure. Then have one student measure it and give hints to the others so they can improve the estimate. Getting and giving hints can help students sharpen their own approximation skills. Students can then use the estimated values to approximate perimeter by adding and approximate area by multiplying.

RETEACHING

Extra teaching or practice in the material introduced in this lesson is not essential at this time. Area and perimeter are discussed in varying contexts throughout the year. Encourage students to complete Enrichment Master 97.

*available separately

Solve these problems.

John lives in Weston. The public swimming pool there is 30 meters long and 20 meters wide. Carter lives in Easton. The pool there is 40 meters long and 15 meters wide.

1. Each boy has agreed to paint the bottom of the pool in his town before the pool is filled with water for the summer. Who has the bigger job? **The areas are equal (600 sq. m).**
2. When someone swims up and down the length of a pool, we say they have swum one lap of the pool. John swims 24 laps of the Weston pool every day. How many meters does he swim each day? **1440 m**
3. Carter swims in the Easton pool. But he doesn't swim up and down the length of the pool. He swims around the pool 12 times every day. How many meters does he swim each day? **1320 m (actually less; he doesn't swim on the pool's edge)**
4. When Carter visits John, the boys go to the Weston pool for their daily swim.
   - **a.** Suppose Carter swims 12 times around the Weston pool. Will he swim more or less than the distance he usually swims? **less than his usual distance**
   - **b.** About how many times do you think Carter should swim around the Weston pool to equal the distance he usually swims? **Answers will vary. (for example: about 13 times around, or a little more than 13 times)**

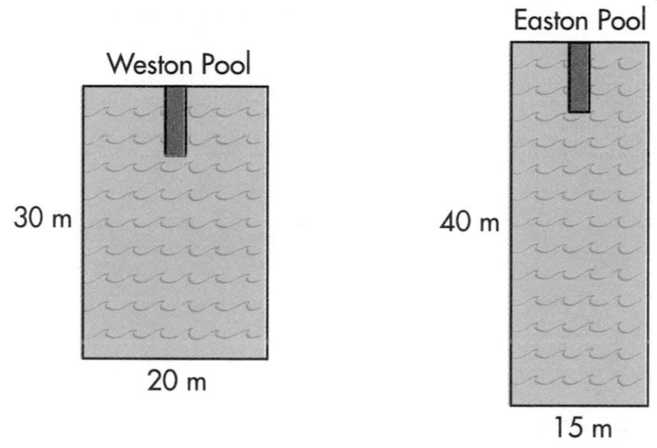

Mental Math (continued)

d. area of a door

e. area of the classroom floor

2 Teach

Using the Student Pages Discuss the problems on page 330 with the class. Point out that one rectangle can have a greater area than another rectangle while also having a smaller perimeter. In discussing the last set of questions on page 330, help students realize that it is better to use a more precise term, such as *greater* area or *greater* perimeter, rather than *bigger.* Students can use a blank **Cruncher*** spreadsheet to create a chart for comparing length, width, and area. Do page 331 with the class, or have students work in groups.

MANIPULATIVES Have students estimate and then measure the perimeters and areas of different **rectangular** or **square classroom objects**. The goal of this activity is for each student to find ways to improve his or her approximation skills.

3 Wrap-Up

5 MINUTES

In Closing Have students draw a labeled diagram to prove that two rectangles with the same area can have different perimeters.

ALTERNATIVE ASSESSMENT **Performance Assessment** Observe as students complete the activity. Suggest ways for students to improve their approximations, such as making sure they estimate the lengths of the sides correctly and add the sides correctly.

Assessment Criteria

Did the student . . .

- ✓ contribute to the discussion about area and perimeter?
- ✓ communicate strategies used to solve the word problems?
- ✓ perform calculations accurately?

Homework Provide each student with eight **square pieces of paper** to manipulate. Have students use the squares to create and record as many rectangular figures as they can that have different perimeters but always an area of eight square units.

PRACTICE p. 97

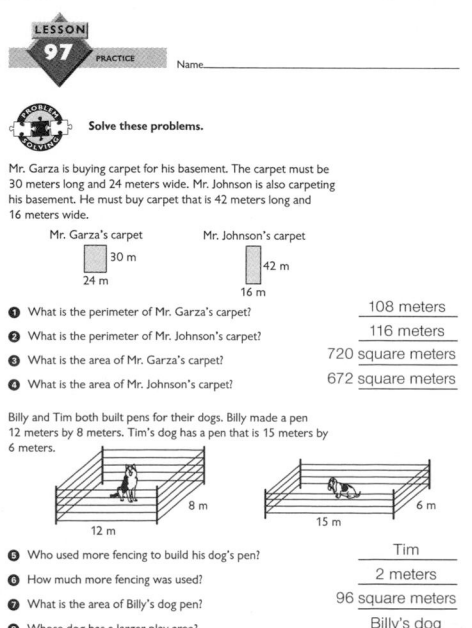

LESSON 97 PRACTICE Name________________

Solve these problems.

Mr. Garza is buying carpet for his basement. The carpet must be 30 meters long and 24 meters wide. Mr. Johnson is also carpeting his basement. He must buy carpet that is 42 meters long and 16 meters wide.

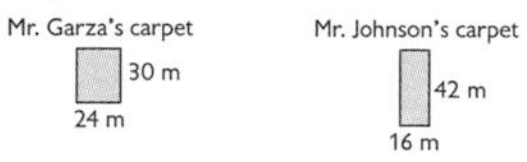

1. What is the perimeter of Mr. Garza's carpet? 108 meters
2. What is the perimeter of Mr. Johnson's carpet? 116 meters
3. What is the area of Mr. Garza's carpet? 720 square meters
4. What is the area of Mr. Johnson's carpet? 672 square meters

Billy and Tim both built pens for their dogs. Billy made a pen 12 meters by 8 meters. Tim's dog has a pen that is 15 meters by 6 meters.

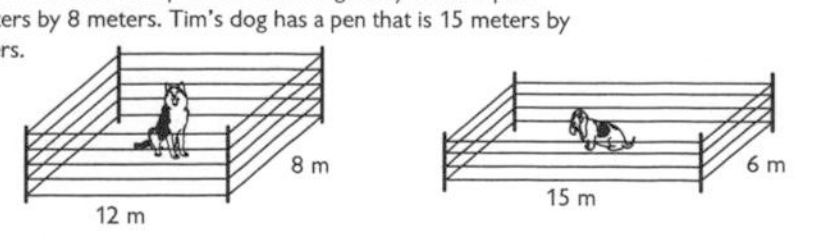

5. Who used more fencing to build his dog's pen? Tim
6. How much more fencing was used? 2 meters
7. What is the area of Billy's dog pen? 96 square meters
8. Whose dog has a larger play area? Billy's dog

Copyright © SRA/McGraw-Hill. Permission is granted to reproduce this page for classroom use.

Math Explorations and Applications Level 4 • 97

ENRICHMENT p. 97

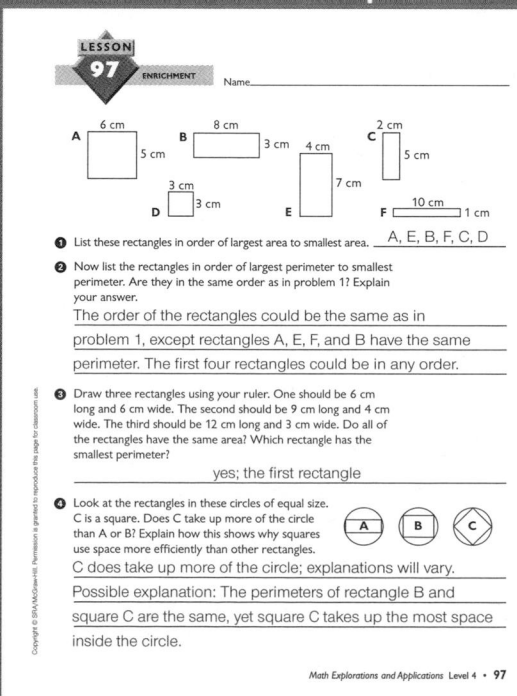

LESSON 97 ENRICHMENT Name________________

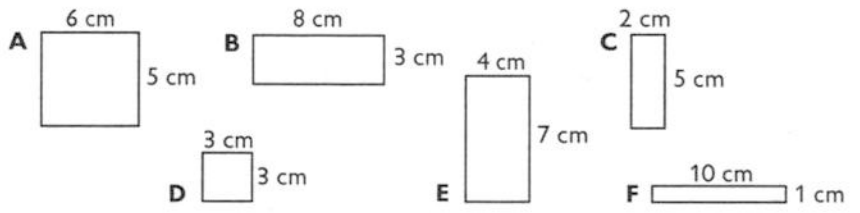

1. List these rectangles in order of largest area to smallest area. A, E, B, F, C, D
2. Now list the rectangles in order of largest perimeter to smallest perimeter. Are they in the same order as in problem 1? Explain your answer.
   The order of the rectangles could be the same as in problem 1, except rectangles A, E, F, and B have the same perimeter. The first four rectangles could be in any order.
3. Draw three rectangles using your ruler. One should be 6 cm long and 6 cm wide. The second should be 9 cm long and 4 cm wide. The third should be 12 cm long and 3 cm wide. Do all of the rectangles have the same area? Which rectangle has the smallest perimeter?
   yes; the first rectangle
4. Look at the rectangles in these circles of equal size. C is a square. Does C take up more of the circle than A or B? Explain how this shows why squares use space more efficiently than other rectangles.

C does take up more of the circle; explanations will vary. Possible explanation: The perimeters of rectangle B and square C are the same, yet square C takes up the most space inside the circle.

Copyright © SRA/McGraw-Hill. Permission is granted to reproduce this page for classroom use.

Math Explorations and Applications Level 4 • 97

*available separately

LESSON 98

Student Edition pages 332–333

Multiply: Multidigit Numbers

LESSON PLANNER

Objectives

- ▶ to teach how to multiply any pair of whole numbers
- ✓ to assess students' mastery of the general multidigit multiplication algorithm

Context of the Lesson This is the 14th of 17 lessons on multidigit multiplication. A Mastery Checkpoint for this skill is provided in this lesson.

MANIPULATIVES

none

Program Resources

Reteaching Master
Practice Master 98
Enrichment Master 98
Assessment Master
For extra practice:
CD-ROM* Lesson 98

Note: This lesson may take more than one day.

1 Warm-Up (5 MINUTES)

Problem of the Day Present this problem on the chalkboard: Figure out the missing digits. There are two possible answers.

```
  2■,576
×      ■
11■,■04
```

(29,576 × 4 = 118,304 or 28,576 × 4 = 114,304)

Problem-Solving Strategies Ask students who have solved the Problem of the Day to share how they solved it and any strategies they used.

MENTAL MATH Give students this fast-paced practice with the basic facts. Encourage automatic responses.

- **a.** 5 × 3 = *n* (15)
- **b.** *n* – 2 = 9 (11)
- **c.** 14 – 7 = *n* (7)
- **d.** 9 – 6 = *n* (3)
- **e.** 2 × 3 = *n* (6)
- **f.** 72 ÷ n = 8 (9)
- **g.** 8 + 9 = *n* (17)
- **h.** 36 ÷ 6 = *n* (6)
- **i.** 12 – 5 = *n* (7)
- **j.** *n* + 6 = 14 (8)

EXPLORE

LESSON 98

Multiply: Multidigit Numbers

You can multiply any two whole numbers. Use the same procedures you have been using.

Multiply: 8924 × 5306

```
  8924
× 5306
 53544
```

Start at the right. Multiply by the **ones** digit. Write the answer so that the digit on the right is in the **ones** column.

```
  8924
× 5306
 53544
     0
```

Multiply by the **tens** digit. If it happens to be a 0, write a 0 in the **tens** column.

```
  8924
× 5306
 53544
267720
```

Multiply by the **hundreds** digit. Write the answer so that the digit on the right is in the **hundreds** column. Continue in the same way.

```
  8924
× 5306
 53544
267720
44620
```

The next digit is in the **thousands** column. So multiply by the **thousands** digit. Write the answer so that the digit on the right is in the **thousands** place.

```
      8924
    × 5306
     53544
    267720
    44620
47,350,744
```

When you have gone through every digit in the multiplier, add to get the final answer.

RETEACHING p. 32

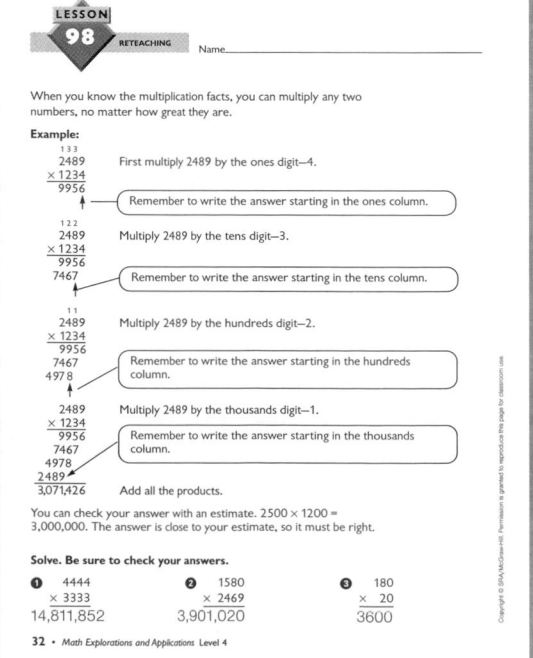

LESSON 98 RETEACHING Name________

When you know the multiplication facts, you can multiply any two numbers, no matter how great they are.

Example:

```
   133
  2489
× 1234
  9956
```

First multiply 2489 by the ones digit—4.

Remember to write the answer starting in the ones column.

```
   122
  2489
× 1234
  9956
 7467
```

Multiply 2489 by the tens digit—3.

Remember to write the answer starting in the tens column.

```
    11
  2489
× 1234
  9956
 7467
4978
```

Multiply 2489 by the hundreds digit—2.

Remember to write the answer starting in the hundreds column.

```
     2489
   × 1234
     9956
    7467
   4978
  2489
3,071,426
```

Multiply 2489 by the thousands digit—1.

Remember to write the answer starting in the thousands column.

Add all the products.

You can check your answer with an estimate. 2500 × 1200 = 3,000,000. The answer is close to your estimate, so it must be right.

Solve. Be sure to check your answers.

❶ 4444 × 3333 = 14,811,852	❷ 1580 × 2469 = 3,901,020	❸ 180 × 20 = 3600

Copyright © SRA/McGraw-Hill. Permission is granted to reproduce this page for classroom use.

PRACTICE p. 98

LESSON 98 PRACTICE Name________

Multiply. Use shortcuts when you can.

❶ 7631 × 204 = 1,556,724	❷ 3700 × 16 = 59,200	❸ 909 × 475 = 431,775	❹ 8034 × 6003 = 48,228,102
❺ 6132 × 5194 = 31,849,608	❻ 2483 × 6195 = 15,382,185	❼ 7200 × 3500 = 25,200,000	❽ 27 × 53 = 1431
❾ 6320 × 57 = 360,240	❿ 795 × 90 = 71,550	⓫ 3703 × 404 = 1,496,012	⓬ 9603 × 156 = 1,498,068
⓭ 408 × 715 = 291,720	⓮ 2650 × 830 = 2,199,500	⓯ 361 × 872 = 314,792	⓰ 1304 × 3485 = 4,544,440
⓱ 4600 × 3901 = 17,944,600	⓲ 210 × 285 = 59,850	⓳ 5036 × 243 = 1,223,748	⓴ 7108 × 4320 = 30,706,560
㉑ 649 × 298 = 193,402	㉒ 2851 × 1649 = 4,701,299	㉓ 7934 × 628 = 4,982,552	㉔ 2740 × 4919 = 13,478,060

Copyright © SRA/McGraw-Hill. Permission is granted to reproduce this page for classroom use.

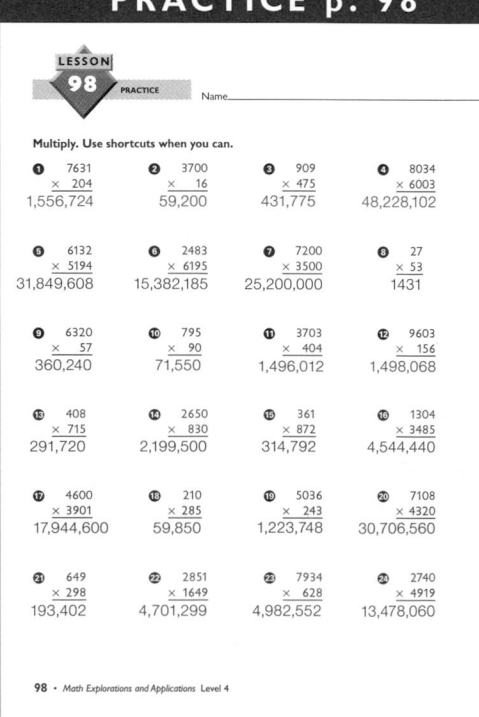

*available separately

Check to see that the answer makes sense.

The answer should be less than 9000 × 6000, which is 54,000,000.

The answer should be greater than 5000 × 8000, which is 40,000,000.

47,350,744 is less than 54,000,000 and greater than 40,000,000. So the answer makes sense.

Multiply. Use shortcuts when you can.

❶ 160 × 18 = **2880**	❷ 8134 × 305 = **2,480,870**	❸ 2132 × 4422 = **9,427,704**	❹ 5139 × 2041 = **10,488,699**	❺ 24,682 × 385 = **9,502,570**
❻ 16 × 18 = **288**	❼ 5432 × 678 = **3,682,896**	❽ 1600 × 18 = **28,800**	❾ 1600 × 1800 = **2,880,000**	❿ 1000 × 1000 = **1,000,000**
⓫ 24 × 26 = **624**	⓬ 2400 × 2006 = **4,814,400**	⓭ 864 × 365 = **315,360**	⓮ 86,400 × 365 = **31,536,000**	⓯ 2000 × 2000 = **4,000,000**
⓰ 147 × 121 = **17,787**	⓱ 28,476 × 641 = **18,253,116**	⓲ 257 × 245 = **62,965**	⓳ 4962 × 2185 = **10,841,970**	⓴ 764 × 311 = **237,604**
㉑ 84 × 56 = **4704**	㉒ 110 × 57 = **6270**	㉓ 293 × 481 = **140,933**	㉔ 27,635 × 857 = **23,683,195**	㉕ 649 × 297 = **192,753**

Check to see that your answers make sense.

FANTASTIC FACT **By the time a person is 30 years old, he or she will have spent 12 years sleeping.**

❷ Teach

Using the Student Pages Explain to students that they can multiply two factors by applying the same rules they have been using with lesser numbers. Present a multiplication problem on the chalkboard that has two four-digit factors, and work through each step.

Go over several more examples. Vary the number of digits. Review the example that begins on page 332. Then have students work independently on the 25 problems on page 333.

❸ Wrap-Up

5 MINUTES

In Closing Have students tell how to multiply any two whole numbers, regardless of the number of digits.

Mastery Checkpoint 16

By this time most students should demonstrate mastery of multiplying any two whole numbers by correctly solving at least 20 of the 25 problems on page 333 or on Assessment Blackline Masters page 38. Assessment results may be recorded on the Mastery Checkpoint Chart.

SELF ASSESSMENT Have students write statements that assess their multiplication skills. Encourage students to tell what they know, how they can check their work, and what aspects of multiplication, if any, may require further attention. Have students place their statements in their Math Portfolios as a means of ongoing evaluation.

ENRICHMENT p. 98

LESSON 98 ENRICHMENT Name__________

Look at each group of objects. For each group write what is the same about the objects in it. Then list three other objects that could go in that group.

❶ 

Each object is something frozen. Answers will vary. Possible answers: package of meat, carton of ice cream, can of juice

❷ 

Each object has a picture or drawing of a person on it. Answers will vary. Possible answers: baseball card, greeting card, driver's license

❸ 

Each object requires electricity. Answers will vary. Possible answers: toaster, coffee maker, computer

❹ 

Each object belongs to a pair. Answers will vary. Possible answers: salt and pepper shakers, gloves, eyes

Copyright © SRA/McGraw-Hill. Permission is granted to reproduce this page for classroom use.

ASSESSMENT p. 38

UNIT 4 **Mastery Checkpoint 16** Multiplying multidigit numbers (Lesson 98)

Name__________

The student demonstrates mastery by correctly answering at least 16 of the 20 problems.

Multiply. Use shortcuts when you can.

❶ 250 × 16 = 4000	❷ 7245 × 207 = 1,499,715	❸ 3246 × 5533 = 17,960,118	❹ 6249 × 3052 = 19,071,948
❺ 17 × 19 = 323	❻ 6523 × 876 = 5,714,148	❼ 1500 × 19 = 28,500	❽ 1500 × 1900 = 2,850,000
❾ 25 × 27 = 675	❿ 2500 × 2007 = 5,017,500	⓫ 486 × 359 = 174,474	⓬ 7830 × 478 = 3,742,740
⓭ 346 × 218 = 75,428	⓮ 284 × 109 = 30,956	⓯ 763 × 23 = 17,549	⓰ 2002 × 491 = 982,982
⓱ 853 × 178 = 151,834	⓲ 1443 × 395 = 569,985	⓳ 431 × 16 = 6896	⓴ 954 × 48 = 45,792

Copyright © SRA/McGraw-Hill. Permission is granted to reproduce this page for classroom use.

Assessment Criteria

Did the student . . .

- ✓ apply the general rules of the multiplication algorithm to multidigit numbers?
- ✓ check to see that his or her answers make sense?
- ✓ correctly answer at least 80% of the multiplication problems?

Homework Have students create a six-digit by five-digit multiplication problem to solve at home.

LESSON 99

Student Edition pages 334–337

Reviewing the Facts

LESSON PLANNER

Objectives

- to provide practice with basic facts and multidigit arithmetic
- to help students develop the broad ability to use mathematical common sense

Context of the Lesson This is the 15th of 17 lessons on multidigit multiplication. This lesson also contains Part 5 of "The Treasure of Mugg Island," a six-part Thinking Story.

MANIPULATIVES

calculators*

Program Resources

Number Cubes (0–5 and 5–10)

Practice Master 99

Enrichment Master 99

For career connections:
Careers and Math*

For extra practice:
CD-ROM* Lesson 99

1 Warm-Up

5 MINUTES

Problem of the Day When presenting the following problem, provide **calculators*** or do the first calculations with the class: Look for a pattern in the three sets of factors and products. Then use the pattern to give the next two sets of factors and products.

33 x 37 = (1221)

333 x 37 = (12,321)

3333 x 37 = (123,321)

The next two sets are: (33,333 x 37 = 1,233,321 and 333,333 x 37 = 12,333,321)

Problem-Solving Strategies Ask students who have solved the Problem of the Day to share how they solved it and any strategies they used.

MENTAL MATH Play several rounds of "Cubo" (page 163) with the class to provide practice with basic arithmetic facts. Encourage students to use mental math to find the best combination of operations.

LESSON 99

Reviewing the Facts

Keep in shape by practicing your number facts on this page.

SELF ASSESSMENT

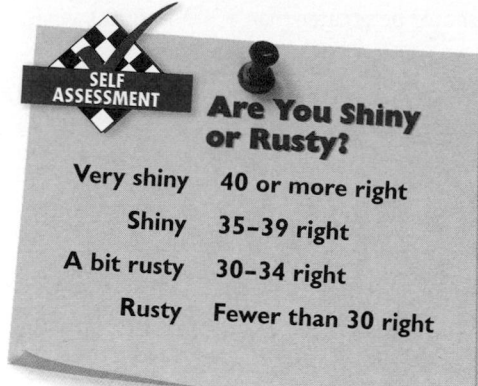

Are You Shiny or Rusty?

Very shiny	40 or more right
Shiny	35–39 right
A bit rusty	30–34 right
Rusty	Fewer than 30 right

Solve for *n*. Watch the signs.

1 $7 + 6 = n$ **13**	2 $n = 5 + 5$ **10**	3 $n = 17 + 5$ **22**
4 $14 - 5 = n$ **9**	5 $6 \times 6 = n$ **36**	6 $38 = n - 2$ **40**
7 $n = 6 + 3$ **9**	8 $6 + 6 = n$ **12**	9 $6 \times n = 18$ **3**
10 $n = 7 \times 5$ **35**	11 $6 \div 6 = n$ **1**	12 $21 \div n = 7$ **3**
13 $n = 6 \times 8$ **48**	14 $6 - 6 = n$ **0**	15 $10 \times n = 10$ **1**
16 $5 \times 9 = n$ **45**	17 $n - 7 = 12$ **19**	18 $4 \times 0 = n$ **0**
19 $4 \div 1 = n$ **4**	20 $12 + 19 = n$ **31**	21 $9 \times 8 = n$ **72**
22 $27 - 3 = n$ **24**	23 $11 = n + 7$ **4**	24 $6 + n = 15$ **9**
25 $10 \times 5 = n$ **50**	26 $n = 3 \times 7$ **21**	27 $2 \times n = 18$ **9**
28 $n = 6 \times 8$ **48**	29 $n + 6 = 20$ **14**	30 $7 \times n = 49$ **7**
31 $14 + 3 = n$ **17**	32 $5 + n = 13$ **8**	33 $54 \div n = 6$ **9**
34 $17 - 9 = n$ **8**	35 $28 \div 4 = n$ **7**	36 $21 \div 7 = n$ **3**
37 $n = 6 \times 3$ **18**	38 $n = 10 \times 6$ **60**	39 $10 + n = 21$ **11**
40 $n = 30 \div 6$ **5**	41 $7 + 9 = n$ **16**	42 $18 - n = 12$ **6**
43 $n = 7 \times 7$ **49**	44 $n = 2 \times 9$ **18**	45 $16 + 4 = n$ **20**

COOPERATIVE LEARNING Have students work in pairs or small groups to make up sets of directions for classmates to follow. The directions should include direction words and standard or nonstandard units of length. You might plan to have a treasure hunt day when all groups trade directions.

*available separately

Solve. Watch the signs.

46. 742 + 243 = **985**
47. 742 − 243 = **499**
48. 65 × 7 = **455**
49. 89 × 25 = **2225**
50. 314 × 5 = **1570**
51. 36 + 92 = **128**
52. 47 − 39 = **8**
53. 362 + 279 = **641**
54. 87 × 87 = **7569**
55. 341 × 265 = **90,365**
56. 877 − 392 = **485**
57. 52 + 99 = **151**
58. 73 × 6 = **438**
59. 901 − 723 = **178**
60. 327 × 18 = **5886**
61. 597 + 623 = **1220**
62. 382 + 469 = **851**
63. 777 − 209 = **568**
64. 73 × 8 = **584**
65. 563 − 384 = **179**

Solve these problems.

66. Find the perimeter and area of a rectangle whose long side measures 43 centimeters and whose short side measures 21 centimeters. **perimeter = 128 cm; area = 903 sq. cm**
67. There are 100 rows of chairs in the auditorium. Each row has 50 chairs. How many chairs are in the auditorium? **5000**
68. Andrea has 23 CDs, and Jason has 16 CDs. How many CDs do Andrea and Jason have? **39**
69. Tara's mother bought three bags of balloons for Tara's birthday party. Each bag had 15 balloons. How many balloons did Tara's mother buy? **45**

Technology Connection Students can answer over 1000 questions on topics from whole numbers, fractions, geometry, and pre-algebra in the quiz-show game software *Knowledge Quest: Mathematics* from CBE Services (Mac, IBM, for grades 4–12).

❷ Teach

Using the Student Pages Have students work independently on pages 334 and 335. After they complete the exercises, have them correct any errors they may have made.

Whether through formal courses in school or through simpler mathematical learning combined with an ability and willingness to think, mathematical problem solving can certainly be more useful in our everyday lives than most of us allow it to be.

—Stephen S. Willoughby,
Teaching Mathematics: What Is Basic?

◆ LESSON 99 Reviewing the Facts

Teach

Using the Thinking Story In "The Treasure of Mugg Island (Part 5)" the group follows a path described by compass directions and nonstandard units of distance.

Answers to Thinking Story Questions:

1. The map should be in this shape:

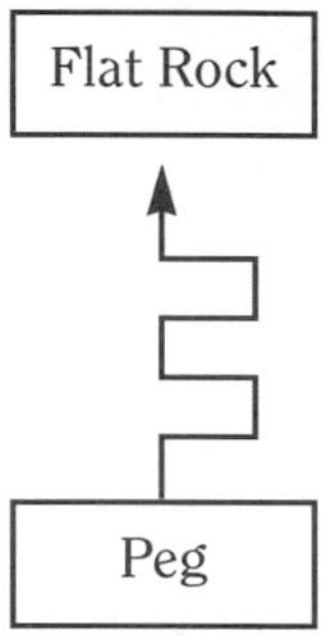

2. Ferdie could have gone straight north, eliminating all the jogs. By this route he would have to go only 100 paces; the others would have to go 160 paces if they followed the instructions.
3. The reason for the jogs in the route was to avoid obstacles such as the quicksand Ferdie encountered.

Have students write a character sketch of Ferdie in their Math Journals. Encourage them to reread previous parts of the Thinking Story to recall his actions and comments so far in the treasure hunt.

◆ LESSON 99 Reviewing the Facts

THINKING STORY

The Treasure of Mugg Island

Part 5

You may want to review the earlier parts of this Thinking Story, on pages 276–277, 294–295, 308–309, and 328–329.

When the children found the peg in the ground they thought the treasure was there. But it wasn't. On the peg was another note. Here is what the note said:

Go N 20 paces
Go E 15
Go N 20
Go W 15
Go N 30
Go E 15
Go N 20
Go W 15
Go N 10

Look under
flat rock.

Literature Connection Invite students to select a game or trick from *Math Fun with a Pocket Calculator* by Rose Wyler and Mary Elting and follow the instructions to play it with a **calculator***.

RETEACHING

If students made a significant number of errors on a particular type of problem on pages 334–335, assign specific games to provide further practice with that skill. For example, you may want to assign the "Roll a Problem" game, which provides practice with adding and subtracting multidigit numbers. Consult the Game Directory of this Teacher's Guide to help you select appropriate games.

*available separately

"This is hard," they all said. Then they started off walking, first north, then east, then north, then west, then north, and so on. But Ferdie didn't do that.

"I know how to get to the flat rock a shorter way," he said. He started walking straight north.

In a little while Ferdie called, "Hey, come quick!" Everyone came running. "I found out why you have to go in such a funny zigzag way," Ferdie said.

"Why is that?" the queen asked.

"First pull me out of this quicksand and then I'll tell you," said Ferdie.

. . . to be continued

Work in groups. Discuss your answers and how you figured them out. Then compare your answers with those of other groups. **Answers are in margin.**

1. Draw a map showing the way from the peg to the flat rock.
2. What shorter way could Ferdie have gone? How far would he have to go by that way? How far would the others have to go, if they followed all the directions of the note?
3. What could be a reason for going the way the note said, instead of going by Ferdie's shorter way?

❸ Wrap-Up 5 MINUTES

In Closing Ask students to explain the procedure they used to multiply a three-digit number by a two-digit number.

SELF ASSESSMENT Have students write an honest evaluation of their ability to solve missing-term equations with basic facts and multidigit addition, subtraction, and multiplication problems based on the results of their work on pages 334 and 335. Have them identify areas in which they need more work or discuss related math goals that they hope to reach in the future.

Assessment Criteria

Did the student . . .

- ✓ explain how to solve for *n*?
- ✓ correctly answer at least 80% of the computation problems on pages 334 and 335?
- ✓ contribute to the Thinking Story discussion?
- ✓ communicate strategies used to understand the directions?

PRACTICE p. 99

LESSON 99 PRACTICE Name________________

ALGEBRA READINESS **Solve for *n*. Watch the signs.**

1. $8 \times 7 = n$, $n =$ 56	2. $9 + 6 = n$, $n =$ 15	3. $10 \times 4 = n$, $n =$ 40	4. $n = 20 \div 5$, $n =$ 4	5. $16 - 9 = n$, $n =$ 7
6. $32 \div 8 = n$, $n =$ 4	7. $n = 9 \times 5$, $n =$ 45	8. $20 - n = 7$, $n =$ 13	9. $n = 6 \times 7$, $n =$ 42	10. $n + 7 = 15$, $n =$ 8
11. $4 \times 6 = n$, $n =$ 24	12. $20 - 4 = n$, $n =$ 16	13. $9 \times 3 = n$, $n =$ 27	14. $n = 10 \div 2$, $n =$ 5	15. $12 - 4 = n$, $n =$ 8
16. $25 \div n = 5$, $n =$ 5	17. $n = 4 \times 3$, $n =$ 12	18. $11 - n = 2$, $n =$ 9	19. $n = 7 \times 7$, $n =$ 49	20. $n + 3 = 13$, $n =$ 10
21. $34 - 6 = n$, $n =$ 28	22. $9 \div 9 = n$, $n =$ 1	23. $n = 10 \times 8$, $n =$ 80	24. $n = 12 - 12$, $n =$ 0	25. $n = 40 \div 5$, $n =$ 8
26. $4 \times 10 = n$, $n =$ 40	27. $24 \div 4 = n$, $n =$ 6	28. $n = 6 \times 5$, $n =$ 30	29. $8 + 8 = n$, $n =$ 16	30. $17 = n + 9$, $n =$ 8

Solve. Watch the signs.

31. $37 \times 8 =$ 296	32. $116 + 245 =$ 361	33. $29 \times 4 =$ 116	34. $43 - 18 =$ 25	35. $42 \times 7 =$ 294
36. $248 + 723 =$ 971	37. $835 + 516 =$ 1351	38. $365 - 209 =$ 156	39. $33 \times 51 =$ 1683	40. $231 - 161 =$ 70
41. $923 - 899 =$ 24	42. $126 + 493 =$ 619	43. $407 - 188 =$ 219	44. $83 \times 7 =$ 581	45. $463 + 187 =$ 650

Copyright © SRA/McGraw-Hill. Permission is granted to reproduce this page for classroom use.

Math Explorations and Applications Level 4 • **99**

ENRICHMENT p. 99

LESSON 99 ENRICHMENT Name________________

Use this chart to help you answer the questions about the ages of students at Lincoln Elementary. Use the tally marks to find the number of students.

Age in Months	Tally	Number of Students	Age in Months	Tally	Number of Students
106	II	2	113	卌 卌 卌 III	18
107	I	1	114	卌 卌 卌	15
108	卌 卌 卌 I	16	115	卌 卌 卌 卌 I	21
109	卌 卌 卌 卌	20	116	卌 卌 卌 IIII	19
110	卌 卌 卌 II	17	117	卌 卌 卌 卌	20
111	卌 卌 卌 卌 I	21	118	卌 卌 卌 IIII	19
112	卌 卌 卌 卌 卌 I	26	119	卌 卌 IIII	14

1. How many students were
   a. 110 months old? 17
   b. 117 months old? 20
   c. 118 months old? 19
2. One of the students had celebrated her ninth birthday the day before Manuel made his survey. How many months old was she? 108
3. Had any of the students reached their tenth birthday? no
4. What grade do you think Manuel is in? fourth grade
5. If there are about 29 students in each class, how many classes does his school have at that grade level? 8 to 11
6. Why do you think so few students were 106 or 107 months old? Possible answers: they are transfer students or they skipped second or third grade.

Copyright © SRA/McGraw-Hill. Permission is granted to reproduce this page for classroom use.

Math Explorations and Applications Level 4 • **99**

Homework Have students make up a set of directions similar to the ones in the Thinking Story that would lead someone from one point to another around obstacles. They can plan a route for the classroom, the schoolyard, or the playground.

ESL **Meeting Individual Needs**

Students with limited proficiency in English may have difficulty with some of the vocabulary used when directions are given orally. Have them work with a partner who is fluent in English to practice using words such as *right, left, north, south, turn,* and *follow*. Ask each student to choose a route in the classroom and give simple directions for his or her partner to follow.

LESSON 100

Student Edition pages 338–339

Using Multiplication

LESSON PLANNER

Objectives

- to provide practice in applying multiplication to travel situations
- to provide practice in approximating products and using relation signs

Context of the Lesson This is the 16th of 17 lessons on multidigit multiplication.

MANIPULATIVES

none

Program Resources

Number Cubes (0–5 and 5–10)

Practice Master 100

Enrichment Master 100

For extra practice:

CD-ROM* Lesson 100

Cumulative Review, page 556

1 Warm-Up

5 MINUTES

Problem of the Day Present this problem orally or on the chalkboard: A three-digit number and a one-digit number have a product of 1500. The same two numbers have a difference of 244 and a sum of 256. What are the two numbers? (250 and 6)

Problem-Solving Strategies Ask students who have solved the Problem of the Day to share how they solved it and any strategies they used.

MENTAL MATH Provide mixed practice with approximation, but extend the range to 5000–10,000. Have students show thumbs up for an answer that falls within the bounds and thumbs down for one that does not.

a. 900 x 10 (thumbs up)

b. 862 x 10 (thumbs up)

c. 6598 x 3 (thumbs down)

d. 39,000 – 29,000 (thumbs up)

e. 7699 x 4 (thumbs down)

f. 388 x 100 (thumbs down)

g. 15,000 ÷ 300 (thumbs down)

h. 6000 + 6000 (thumbs down)

i. 9000 – 5000 (thumbs down)

PROBLEM SOLVING

LESSON 100

Using Multiplication

Multiplication is useful in planning a car trip.

Solve these problems.

On the highway, Hank travels about 65 miles in one hour. His car can go about 23 miles on one gallon of gasoline. The tank holds 18 gallons.

1. About how far can Hank travel on one tankful of gasoline? **about 414 miles**
2. About how far does he travel in three hours on the highway? **about 195 miles**
3. At the speed Hank drives, it's about 14 hours of driving time from his home to his cousin's house in Denver. About how many miles long is the trip? **about 910 miles**
4. Can Hank make it there on two tankfuls of gasoline? **no**

Hank's neighbor, Isabel, has the same kind of car as Hank. But Isabel drives slower. She goes about 55 miles in one hour. But, because she goes slower, her car gets about 27 miles to one gallon of gasoline.

5. About how far does Isabel travel on one tankful of gasoline? **about 486 miles**
6. Who travels farther on one tankful, Hank or Isabel? About how much farther? **Isabel; about 72 miles**
7. Who travels farther in one hour, Hank or Isabel? About how much farther? **Hank; about 10 miles**
8. Can Isabel make the 910-mile trip to Denver on two tankfuls of gasoline? **yes**

FANTASTIC FACT **Pollution has become such a problem in Mexico City that fresh air is sold at sidewalk oxygen booths for $1.15 per minute.**

COOPERATIVE LEARNING Encourage each group of students to discuss their ideas, strategies, and solution methods after working together to complete the problems on page 338.

Social Studies Connection Students who live in urban areas may be less familiar with traveling by car. Help students find out the travel costs per passenger of the typical types of public transportation available in your area. Students might also find out how much fuel a bus holds and its mileage per gallon.

RETEACHING

Reteaching of the material introduced in this lesson is not essential at this time. Encourage all students to complete Enrichment Master 100.

*available separately

COOPERATIVE LEARNING

More or Less Game

Players: Two
Materials: Two 0–5 cubes, two 5–10 cubes
Object: To make a product greater than or less than the product made by the other player
Math Focus: Multiplying two-digit numbers, identifying inequalities, and using relation signs

RULES

1. Make a game form like this one: _____ < _____
2. Roll the four cubes and use the numbers rolled to make two two-digit numbers. If you roll a 10, roll that cube again.
3. Write the two two-digit numbers with a multiplication sign on the game form on either side of the < sign.
4. The other player rolls the four cubes, makes two two-digit numbers, and writes them with a multiplication sign on the game form on the other side of the < sign.
5. If the number sentence made by the other player is not true, you win the round. If it is true, the other player wins the round.
6. You don't have to multiply unless the products are too close to approximate.
7. Take turns being the first player.

SAMPLE GAME

Keiko rolled: 1 4 7 9	Lawrence rolled: 3 2 6 7
She wrote 91×74.	He wrote 72×63.
$91 \times 74 <$ _____	$91 \times 74 < 72 \times 63$

Keiko and Lawrence agreed that this number sentence is not true. (They didn't need to multiply to know that.) So Keiko won this round.

Use the Cumulative Review on page 556 after this lesson.

❷ Teach

Using the Student Pages You may wish to introduce the "More or Less" game on page 339 before students begin page 338 so they can play as they finish their work. This game focuses on multiplying two-digit numbers.

Have students work individually or in groups to solve problems 1–8 on page 338. Discuss students' solution methods and results when they finish. Point out in the discussion that Isabel spends more time traveling, but Hank uses more gas. Explain that, in general, cars burn more gas at faster speeds than they do at slower speeds.

GAME Demonstrate the "More or Less" game at the chalkboard with students. This game gives students practice with multiplication, approximation, and identifying inequalities.

❸ Wrap-Up

5 MINUTES

In Closing Have students determine which car would have the greater range: Model X, which holds 18 gallons of gas and gets 24 miles to the gallon, or Model Y, which holds 15 gallons of gas and gets 28 miles to the gallon. (Model X)

ALTERNATIVE ASSESSMENT

Informal Assessment Observe students as they solve the problems on page 338 and as they play the "More or Less" game. Encourage students to verbalize their solution methods and game strategies.

Assessment Criteria

Did the student . . .

- ✓ accurately solve at least six of the eight word problems?
- ✓ actively participate in the game?
- ✓ demonstrate understanding of approximating products?

Homework Have students play the "More or Less" game with a family member for further practice with multiplication and approximation. A copy of this game can also be found on page 21 of the Home Connections Blackline Masters.

PRACTICE p. 100

LESSON 100 PRACTICE Name______________________

PROBLEM SOLVING **Solve these problems.**

Fred travels about 65 kilometers in one hour on the highway. His van goes about 17 kilometers on 1 liter of gasoline. The gas tank holds 36 liters. Mike drives more slowly. Mike travels about 55 kilometers in one hour on the highway. Mike's car goes about 21 kilometers on 1 liter of gasoline, and his gas tank holds 28 liters.

1. About how far can Fred travel on one tankful of gasoline? 612 km
2. About how far can Fred travel in four hours on the highway? 260 km
3. About how far can Mike travel on one tankful of gasoline? 588 km
4. Who travels farther on one tankful, Fred or Mike? About how much farther? Fred; 24 km
5. Who travels farther in one hour, Fred or Mike? About how much farther? Fred; 10 km

Harold and Samantha have the same kind of car. Harold drives faster. Harold goes 80 kilometers in one hour but he gets only about 14 kilometers to one liter of gasoline. Harold's tank holds 24 liters. Samantha travels about 55 kilometers in one hour but she gets 20 kilometers to one liter of gasoline.

6. About how far does Samantha travel on one tank of gasoline? 480 kilometers
7. Who travels farther on one tankful, Harold or Samantha? Samantha
8. Can Samantha make a 1200-kilometer trip on three tankfuls of gasoline? yes
9. Who travels farther in one hour, Harold or Samantha? Harold

Copyright © SRA/McGraw-Hill. Permission is granted to reproduce this page for classroom use.

100 • *Math Explorations and Applications* Level 4

ENRICHMENT p. 100

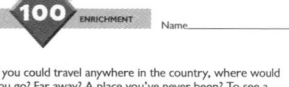

LESSON 100 ENRICHMENT Name______________________

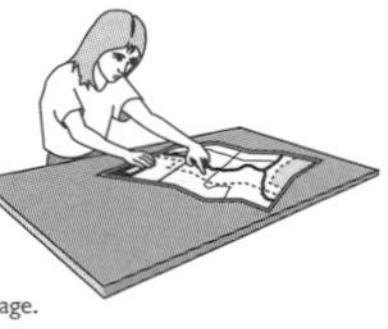

If you could travel anywhere in the country, where would you go? Far away? A place you've never been? To see a friend, grandparent, or other relative?

Find a road map of your state or of the United States. Find where you live and where you would like to travel. Plan your route on the map. Most road maps show mileage as small numbers near the lines for highways. As you follow the highway lines to your destination, record these numbers, then add them together for your total mileage.

Use a colored marker or pencil to show your route. Will you take the shortest way or the scenic route?

Now imagine you have a car that you will drive at an average speed of 55 miles per hour. Your car can go about 35 miles on one gallon of gas. The gas tank holds 13 gallons of gas when full. Gas costs $1.25 per gallon.

Answer the following questions.

1. How many miles is it to your destination? Answers will vary. Mileage should be calculated correctly.
2. How many miles can you go on a full tank of gas? 455
3. How many times will you have to buy gas on your trip? Each fill-up will cost $16.25.
4. What will be the total cost for gas for your trip? Answers will vary.
5. Estimate how long it will take you to drive to your destination. Remember to include time for resting, sleeping, getting gas, eating, and so on. Answers will vary.

Copyright © SRA/McGraw-Hill. Permission is granted to reproduce this page for classroom use.

100 • *Math Explorations and Applications* Level 4

Student Edition pages 340–343

LESSON 101

Approximating Products

LESSON PLANNER

Objectives

- ▶ to provide practice with using approximation to solve arithmetic problems in which the complete numbers are unknown
- ▶ to help students develop the broad ability to use mathematical common sense

Context of the Lesson This is the last of 17 lessons on multidigit multiplication. The end-of-unit sequence begins in the next lesson. This lesson includes problems presented in the same paint-spill format used in Lesson 17. It also contains Part 6 of "The Treasure of Mugg Island," a six-part Thinking Story.

MANIPULATIVES

classroom map made by students in Lesson 81 (optional)

ruler*

masking tape (optional)

Program Resources

Number Wheels

Practice Master 101

Enrichment Master 101

For career connections:
Careers and Math*

For extra practice:
CD-ROM* Lesson 101

1 Warm-Up (5 MINUTES)

Problem of the Day Present this problem for which there are several possible answers: Jenna and Lucy live in different states. Both of their five-digit ZIP codes use the same five numbers, but no number appears in the same position in both ZIP codes. Jenna's ZIP code is even; Lucy's is odd. The sum of the five numbers is a multiple of 7. What might the two ZIP codes be? (One possible answer is 74012 and 42701.)

Problem-Solving Strategies Ask students who have solved the Problem of the Day to share how they solved it and any strategies they used.

PROBLEM SOLVING

LESSON 101

Approximating Products

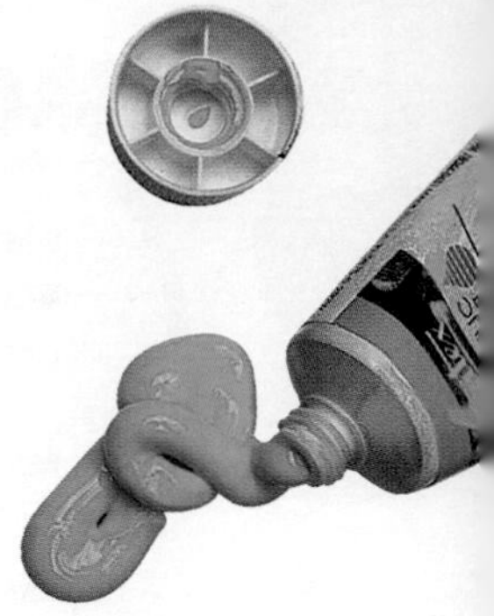

Paint has spilled on this page.
Choose the correct answer in each case.

Example:
307
× 5

a. 14,10
b. 179,902
c. 15,108,507

The answer must be greater than 500 × 300, which is 150,000.

The answer must be less than 600 × 400, which is 240,000.

The answer is b.

1. 8,7 × 6,
 a. 247,508
 b. 4,821,643
 (c.) 56,995,947

2. 50, × 86
 a. 3,089,666
 (b.) 4,333,884
 c. 5,402,220

3. 238 × 5
 a. 41,
 (b.) 12,
 c. 3,

4. 0 ×
 a. 43
 (b.) 370
 c. ,595

5. 00 × 0
 a. ,650
 (b.) ,000
 c. 53,100

6. 36 × 2
 a. 720
 b. 5,648
 (c.) 8,760

340 • Multidigit Multiplication

Real-World Connection Have students plan an imaginary party for the entire school. Have them determine the number of classrooms and the average number of students per classroom to estimate how many guests would attend. Then ask them to plan how many cups, plates, beverages, pieces of fruit, and other snacks they would need for the party. Tell them to assume that each guest would consume more than one drink and several snacks.

*available separately

Paint has spilled on this page of mixed addition, subtraction, and multiplication problems. Choose the correct answer in each case.

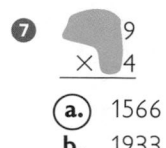

7. 9 × 4
   - (a.) 1566
   - b. 1933
   - c. 98,901

8. 473 869
   - (a.) 1342
   - b. 347,190
   - c. 411,037

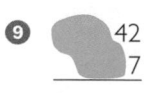

9. 42 7
   - (a.) 475
   - b. 2208
   - c. 1,163,512

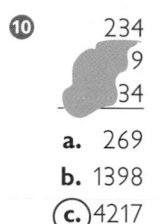

10. 234 9 34
   - a. 269
   - b. 1398
   - (c.) 4217

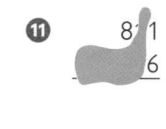

11. 8 1 6
   - a. 542
   - b. 1744
   - (c.) 832,676

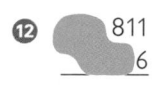

12. 811 6
   - a. 453
   - (b.) 1827
   - c. 832,667

Solve these problems.

13. Find the perimeter and area of a rectangular garden with a long side that measures 10 meters and a short side that measures 8 meters. **perimeter = 36 m; area = 80 sq. m**

14. There are 752 students at McKinley Elementary School. The school secretary needs to order notebooks for the supply room. There are 60 notebooks in a box. If the secretary orders 12 boxes, will there be enough notebooks for each student to have one? **no (there will only be 720)**

15. Jan's family traveled 489 miles to their family reunion. Her aunt traveled 802 miles, and her uncle drove 264 miles. How many miles did these relatives travel all together? **1555**

Technology Connection Refer students to the software *In the Neighborhood* from Critical Thinking Software and Books (Apple, Mac, IBM, for grades 2–12) for further practice with finding unknowns, mental computation, problem solving, logical thinking, and probability.

MENTAL MATH Provide a drill on basic number facts. Emphasize speedy recall and have students use their Number Wheels to show the answers.

a. 1 × 2 = (2)	b. 9 + 8 = (17)
c. 21 ÷ 3 = (7)	d. 7 + 5 = (12)
e. 9 + 5 = (14)	f. 64 ÷ 8 = (8)
g. 3 × 9 = (27)	h. 5 × 9 = (45)
i. 56 ÷ 8 = (7)	j. 4 + 8 = (12)

2 Teach

COOPERATIVE LEARNING **Using the Student Pages** Treat these pages as a challenging puzzle you can do with the class. Although students did similar problems with addition and subtraction in Lesson 17 (pages 58–59), the multiplication problems are more difficult and require a wider variety of techniques, such as using bounds. Students must determine the right-hand digits of the product rather than estimate its value. After you work through page 340 with the class, you may want to have students work in pairs or trios to solve the additional paint-spill problems on page 341. Encourage group members to share their reasoning as they try to solve the problems.

> *Students should be encouraged to produce their own lists of strategies, to think about their own and other people's strategies, and then to continue solving many interesting and difficult problems using whatever strategies they wish. But after solving such problems, they should be encouraged to rethink and discuss what they have done, decide which strategies have been useful and which have not, and continually reexamine their own and other people's methods of solving problems.*
>
> —Stephen S. Willoughby, *Mathematics Education for a Changing World*

◆ LESSON 101 Approximating Products

Teach

Using the Thinking Story

"The Treasure of Mugg Island (Part 6)" is the last part of the Thinking Story for this unit. It centers on making a scale drawing using a **ruler*** to find alternate routes from one point to another once you know the way.

Answers to Thinking Story Questions:

1. Drawing a right triangle to scale shows that the straight-line distance to the treasure is about 500 paces. Students may also do this by using the Pythagorean theorem, which was illustrated in Lesson 31 (pages 108–109).
2. Students need to know what direction to go from the flat rock. The direction would be roughly northwest.
3. By first going 400 paces west and then 300 paces north, instead of the reverse, Manolita could arrive at the same point as the directions indicated.

MATH JOURNAL: Have students write a description in their Math Journals of what they imagine to be inside the trunk that holds the Royal Treasure. Have them tell what reward, if any, they think the queen should present to Ferdie, Portia, Manolita, and Marcus for their help.

◆ LESSON 101 Approximating Products

THINKING STORY

The Treasure of Mugg Island

Part 6

You may want to review the earlier parts of this Thinking Story, on pages 276–277, 294–295, 308–309, 328–329, and 336–337.

Finally, after going back and forth many paces, the children found the flat rock. Under the rock they found a bottle. In it was another note. It read:

To find the treasure,
go 300 paces north and
400 paces west.

"At last we're near my treasure," said the queen. But it was not so easy. They could go 300 paces north, all right. But then they came to a huge pile of rocks. There had been a landslide. The side of a mountain had fallen down. They could not walk west at all.

Literature Connection Invite students to look through *Take Me to Your Liter: Science and Math Jokes* by Charles Keller. Have students choose math jokes they like, or choose some of your favorites to share with the class.

RETEACHING

No extra reteaching or practice is recommended at this time. More practice with approximation, given in various formats, will be provided throughout the year. You may want to assign Enrichment Master 101.

*available separately

They went back to the flat rock. "I have an idea," said Portia. "Let's draw a map. Let's try to figure out how to go straight to the treasure instead of going first north and then west."

Ferdie had a ruler. They used his ruler to draw the lines on a map. Then they used his ruler to figure out how far it was to the treasure, if they went in a straight line. But Manolita didn't help. She started off walking straight west. A little while later she called to them. "You can stop figuring. I found the treasure! It's right here, where the note said it would be!"

. . . the end

Work in groups. Discuss your answers and how you figured them out. Then compare your answers with those of other groups. **Answers are in margin.**

1. Draw lines. Use a ruler. Try to figure out how far it is from the flat rock to the treasure, if you go in a straight line.
2. After you know how far it is, what else do you have to know to find the treasure?
3. How could Manolita find the treasure by starting off walking straight west? What way would she go? Why would it work?

❸ Wrap-Up (5 MINUTES)

In Closing Ask students to explain how the solution to Part 6 of the Thinking Story is similar to plotting points on a coordinate grid.

ALTERNATIVE ASSESSMENT

Performance Assessment Observe students as they solve the paint-spill problems on pages 340 and 341. Ask them to share their thinking with you so you can evaluate the reasoning they use to determine correct answers. Have students verbalize what they know and do not know about any given problem and what strategies they might use to solve it.

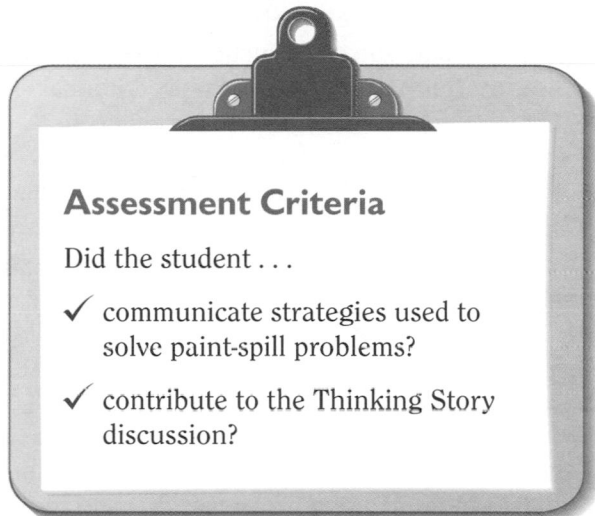

Assessment Criteria

Did the student . . .

✓ communicate strategies used to solve paint-spill problems?

✓ contribute to the Thinking Story discussion?

Homework Have students play the "More or Less" game on page 339 (also on page 21 of the Home Connections Blackline Masters) with a family member for further practice with approximation.

PRACTICE p. 101

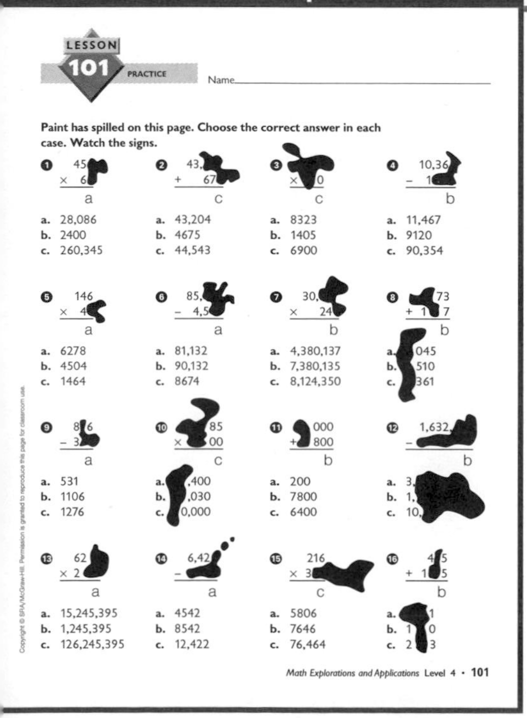

LESSON 101 PRACTICE Name__________

Paint has spilled on this page. Choose the correct answer in each case. Watch the signs.

1. 45 × 6 — a
   a. 28,086 b. 2400 c. 260,345
2. 43, + 67 — c
   a. 43,204 b. 4675 c. 44,543
3. × 0 — c
   a. 8323 b. 1405 c. 6900
4. 10,36 − 1 — b
   a. 11,467 b. 9120 c. 90,354
5. 146 × 4 — a
   a. 6278 b. 4504 c. 1464
6. 85, − 4,5 — a
   a. 81,132 b. 90,132 c. 8674
7. 30, × 24 — b
   a. 4,380,137 b. 7,380,135 c. 8,124,350
8. 73 + 1 7 — b
   a. 045 b. 510 c. 361
9. 8 6 − 3 — a
   a. 531 b. 1106 c. 1276
10. 85 × 00 — c
    a. ,400 b. ,030 c. 0,000
11. 000 + 800 — b
    a. 200 b. 7800 c. 6400
12. 1,632, − — b
    a. 3, b. 1, c. 10,
13. 62 × 2 — a
    a. 15,245,395 b. 1,245,395 c. 126,245,395
14. 6,42 − — a
    a. 4542 b. 8542 c. 12,422
15. 216 × 3 — c
    a. 5806 b. 7646 c. 76,464
16. 4 5 + 1 5 — b
    a. 1 b. 1 0 c. 2 3

Copyright © SRA/McGraw-Hill. Permission is granted to reproduce this page for classroom use.

Math Explorations and Applications Level 4 • **101**

ENRICHMENT p. 101

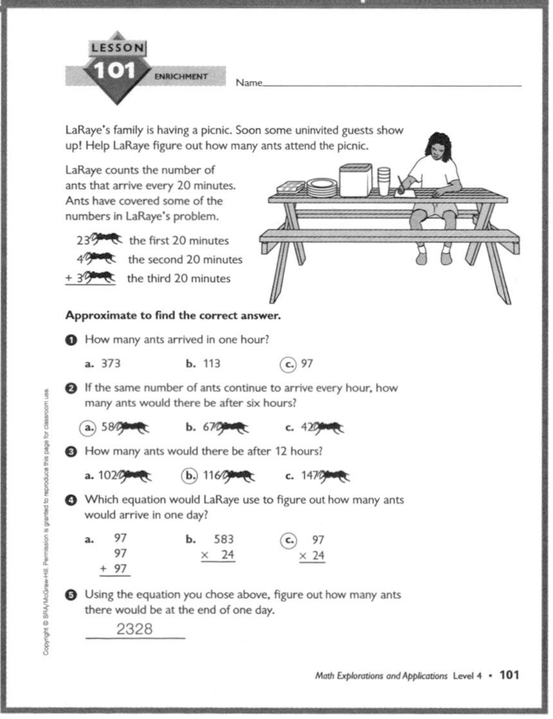

LESSON 101 ENRICHMENT Name__________

LaRaye's family is having a picnic. Soon some uninvited guests show up! Help LaRaye figure out how many ants attend the picnic.

LaRaye counts the number of ants that arrive every 20 minutes. Ants have covered some of the numbers in LaRaye's problem.

23 the first 20 minutes
4 the second 20 minutes
+ 3 the third 20 minutes

Approximate to find the correct answer.

1. How many ants arrived in one hour?
   a. 373 b. 113 (c.) 97
2. If the same number of ants continue to arrive every hour, how many ants would there be after six hours?
   (a.) 58 b. 67 c. 42
3. How many ants would there be after 12 hours?
   a. 102 (b.) 116 c. 147
4. Which equation would LaRaye use to figure out how many ants would arrive in one day?
   a. 97 + 97 + 97 b. 583 × 24 (c.) 97 × 24
5. Using the equation you chose above, figure out how many ants there would be at the end of one day.
   2328

Copyright © SRA/McGraw-Hill. Permission is granted to reproduce this page for classroom use.

Math Explorations and Applications Level 4 • **101**

LEARNING STYLES MANIPULATIVES

Meeting Individual Needs Physical or kinesthetic learners may be best able to solve the problems in the Thinking Story by acting out the story. You might have them role-play the characters and situations. Put **masking tape** on the floor to represent the landslide area. Display the original **classroom map** students made when they read "The Treasure of Mugg Island (Part 1)" so they can better understand what Ferdie did with his ruler.

LESSON 102

Student Edition pages 344–345

Unit 4 Review

Using the Student Pages Use this Unit 4 Review as a preliminary unit test to indicate areas in which each student is having difficulty or in which the entire class may need help. If students do well on the Unit 4 Review, you may wish to skip directly to the next unit. If not, you may spend a day or so helping students overcome their individual difficulties before they take the Unit Test.

Next to each set of problems is a list of the lessons in the unit covered in those problems. Students can refer to a specific lesson for additional instruction if they need help. You can also use this information to make additional assignments based on the previous lesson concepts.

Problems 1–12 If students miss more than three of these multiplication facts problems, you might want to give extra practice with the facts using **flash cards,** oral practice, and games. "Add the Products" on page 110 provides practice with multiplication and addition and "Cubo" on page 163 reinforces the skill of using mental arithmetic.

Problems 13–24 If students miss more than two of these multidigit multiplication problems, check to see whether the difficulty is with the facts or the algorithm. Also check for patterns of errors such as multidigit multipliers, 0s in a factor, misplacing partial products, incorrect carrying, or poor alignment. Reteach as necessary.

Problems 25–29 If students miss more than one of these mixed multidigit computation problems, check to see whether they performed the wrong computation. Encourage them to watch the signs carefully.

Problems 30–33 Students who miss any of these approximation problems or who do them by calculating the exact answer should be checked individually. Give appropriate help as necessary.

ASSESSMENT

LESSON 102

Unit 4 Review

Multiply to solve for *n*.

Lesson 96

1. $n = 6 \times 8$ **48**
2. $8 \times 7 = n$ **56**
3. $n = 6 \times 6$ **36**
4. $5 \times 7 = n$ **35**
5. $5 \times 8 = n$ **40**
6. $9 \times 6 = n$ **54**
7. $4 \times 9 = n$ **36**
8. $9 \times 8 = n$ **72**
9. $n = 8 \times 5$ **40**
10. $n = 3 \times 6$ **18**
11. $7 \times 7 = n$ **49**
12. $9 \times 9 = n$ **81**

Multiply. Use shortcuts when you can.

Lessons 80, 85, 87, 91, 98

13. 20×7 **140**
14. 600×8 **4800**
15. 91×89 **8099**
16. 14×3 **42**
17. 504×7 **3528**
18. 60×80 **4800**
19. 11×6 **66**
20. 90×90 **8100**
21. 213×31 **6603**
22. 243×6 **1458**
23. 38×43 **1634**
24. 127×58 **7366**

Watch the signs.

Lesson 96

25. $57 + 14$ = **71**
26. $57 - 14$ = **43**
27. 57×14 = **798**
28. 834×555 = **462,870**
29. $834 + 555$ = **1389**

In each problem, two of the answers are clearly wrong and one is correct. Choose the correct answer.

Lessons 94, 98, 101

30. 367×93
    - (a.) 34,131 (circled)
    - b. 47,281
    - c. 26,911
31. 8121×375
    - a. 286,575
    - (b.) 3,045,375 (circled)
    - c. 2,319,875
32. 702×311
    - a. 207,152
    - b. 249,982
    - (c.) 218,322 (circled)
33. 7903×614
    - a. 5,628,442
    - b. 496,372
    - (c.) 4,852,442 (circled)

ALGEBRA READINESS

Solve for *n*. Watch the signs.

Lesson 99

34. $n \div 8 = 4$ **32**
35. $n + 15 = 41$ **26**
36. $87 + n = 93$ **6**
37. $6 \times n = 42$ **7**
38. $9 \times n = 27$ **3**
39. $n \times 7 = 63$ **9**

344 • Multidigit Multiplication

RETEACHING

Students who have difficulty with this Unit Review should have further opportunity to review and to practice the skills before they proceed on with the next unit. For each set of problems there are specific suggestions for reteaching. These suggestions can be found in the margins.

Solve for *n*.

Lesson 78

(40) 1000 × 100 = *n* **100,000**
(41) 1000 × 10 = *n* **10,000**
(42) 10,000 × 10,000 = *n* **100,000,000**
(43) 1000 × 1000 = *n* **1,000,000**

Solve these problems.

Lessons 79, 82, 87, 92, 93, 97

(44) One roll costs 73¢. Ike buys two rolls each day.

a. How many cents does Ike spend on rolls each day? **146¢**

b. How much money will he spend on rolls in six days? **$8.76**

(45) A rectangle is 23 centimeters wide and 47 centimeters long.

a. What is the area of the rectangle, in square centimeters? **1081 sq. cm**

b. What is the perimeter of the rectangle? **140 cm**

(46) An auditorium has 36 rows with 36 seats in each row. Can 2000 people be seated? **no**

(47) There are 100 centimeters in 1 meter.

a. How many centimeters are there in 100 meters? **10,000**

b. How many centimeters are there in 1000 meters? **100,000**

(48) Georgia plays the piano 45 minutes each day. About how many minutes will she play the piano in a year (365 days)? **16,425**

(49) In a certain book there are about 350 words per page. The book has 512 pages. About how many words are in the book? **about 179,200**

(50) A bag of dried peas costs 58¢. Ramón uses four bags to make a kettle of pea soup.

a. How much do the dried peas cost for one kettle of soup? **$2.32**

b. Ramón cooks a kettle of pea soup twice a month. How much do the dried peas cost for a year? **$55.68**

Problems 34–39 Students who miss more than two of these missing-term problems should be checked to determine the nature of the difficulty. Model the problems with manipulatives such as **craft sticks**, or work with arrow notation.

Problems 40–43 If students miss more than one of these problems involving multiplication by powers of 10, check to see whether the difficulty is with writing the correct number of 0s. Provide reteaching if necessary.

Problems 44–50 If students miss more than two of these word problems, give extra help similar to that you have given before for word problems. Students may use manipulatives or diagrams to help them.

ALTERNATIVE ASSESSMENT

Portfolio Assessment If you have not already completed the Portfolio Assessment task provided on Assessment Blackline Masters page 96, it can be used at this time to evaluate students' ability to use multidigit multiplication to solve problems.

ALTERNATIVE ASSESSMENT

Performance Assessment Performance Assessment Task 2, provided on Assessment Blackline Masters pages 81–82, can be used at this time to evaluate students' proficiency with multidigit multiplication. You may want to administer this assessment to individual students or small groups of students.

Unit Project If you have not already assigned the "Your Heart at Work" project on pages 352 and 353, you may want to do so at this time. The Unit Project is a good opportunity for students to learn how to measure pulse rate, relate it to the beating of the heart, and give an indication of how much the heart works over a lifetime.

PRACTICE p. 102

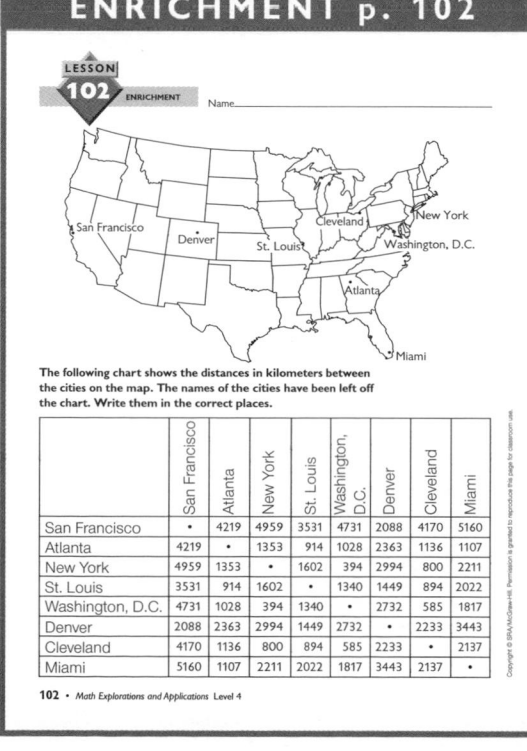

LESSON 102 PRACTICE Name________

Solve for *n*. Watch the signs.

(1) $n \times 7 = 63$, n = 9
(2) $9 + n = 45$, n = 36
(3) $n \times 4 = 28$, n = 7
(4) $8 = n \div 4$, n = 32
(5) $16 - n = 9$, n = 7
(6) $45 \div n = 5$, n = 9
(7) $n = 10 \times 5$, n = 50
(8) $n - 18 = 41$, n = 59

Multiply. Use shortcuts when you can.

(9) 12 × 7 = 84
(10) 70 × 90 = 6300
(11) 312 × 5 = 1560
(12) 146 × 36 = 5256
(13) 3000 × 40 = 120,000
(14) 27 × 84 = 2268

Solve. Watch the signs.

(15) 43 × 18 = 774
(16) 43 + 18 = 61
(17) 43 − 18 = 25
(18) 645 − 519 = 126
(19) 645 × 519 = 334,755
(20) 645 + 519 = 1164
(21) 205 + 836 = 1041
(22) 836 − 205 = 631
(23) 836 × 205 = 171,380
(24) 214 × 14 = 2996

Solve these problems.

A rectangular garden is 5 meters wide and 12 meters long.

(25) What is the area of the garden? 60 square meters

(26) What is the perimeter of the garden? 34 meters

Copyright © SRA/McGraw-Hill. Permission is granted to reproduce this page for classroom use.

102 • *Math Explorations and Applications* Level 4

ENRICHMENT p. 102

LESSON 102 ENRICHMENT Name________

The following chart shows the distances in kilometers between the cities on the map. The names of the cities have been left off the chart. Write them in the correct places.

	San Francisco	Atlanta	New York	St. Louis	Washington, D.C.	Denver	Cleveland	Miami
San Francisco	•	4219	4959	3531	4731	2088	4170	5160
Atlanta	4219	•	1353	914	1028	2363	1136	1107
New York	4959	1353	•	1602	394	2994	800	2211
St. Louis	3531	914	1602	•	1340	1449	894	2022
Washington, D.C.	4731	1028	394	1340	•	2732	585	1817
Denver	2088	2363	2994	1449	2732	•	2233	3443
Cleveland	4170	1136	800	894	585	2233	•	2137
Miami	5160	1107	2211	2022	1817	3443	2137	•

Copyright © SRA/McGraw-Hill. Permission is granted to reproduce this page for classroom use.

102 • *Math Explorations and Applications* Level 4

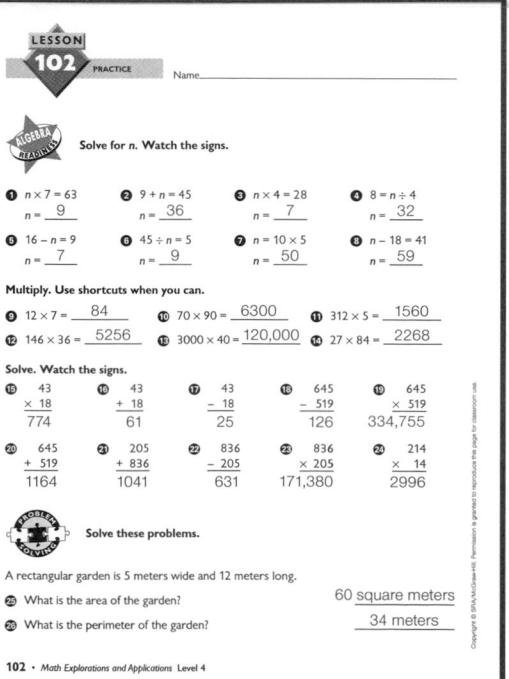

LESSON 103

Student Edition pages 346–349

Unit 4 Practice

Using the Student Pages The purpose of these pages is to provide additional practice for those students who demonstrated a need for it on the Unit 4 Review. You may wish to assign only the specific exercises in this Unit 4 Practice in which students need further reinforcement. Listed in the margin beside each instruction line are the lessons covered in the unit so that you or the students can refer to the specific lesson for additional review and instruction.

GAME Students who do not require additional practice on specific concepts may enjoy playing any of the games you have played so far, such as the "Cube 100" game on page 293. This game provides practice with addition, multiplication, and mathematical reasoning. These students may also help by practicing flash card drills and playing appropriate games with students who need remedial practice or by actually teaching certain procedures to other students.

You may want to use the Cumulative Review on page 557 after this lesson.

LESSON 103

Unit 4 Practice

Multiply to solve for *n*.

Lesson 96

1. $3 \times 7 = n$ **21**	2. $2 \times 6 = n$ **12**	3. $7 \times 8 = n$ **56**
4. $8 \times 1 = n$ **8**	5. $n = 9 \times 4$ **36**	6. $1 \times 7 = n$ **7**
7. $10 \times 6 = n$ **60**	8. $n = 2 \times 5$ **10**	9. $n = 4 \times 8$ **32**
10. $n = 5 \times 8$ **40**	11. $n = 4 \times 4$ **16**	12. $9 \times 10 = n$ **90**
13. $3 \times 8 = n$ **24**	14. $10 \times 5 = n$ **50**	15. $7 \times 4 = n$ **28**
16. $6 \times 0 = n$ **0**	17. $0 \times 7 = n$ **0**	18. $6 \times 4 = n$ **24**
19. $n = 3 \times 9$ **27**	20. $n = 4 \times 5$ **20**	21. $n = 6 \times 5$ **30**
22. $n = 9 \times 8$ **72**	23. $9 \times 7 = n$ **63**	24. $9 \times 2 = n$ **18**

ALGEBRA READINESS

Solve for *n*. Watch the signs.

Lesson 99

25. $n \div 5 = 7$ **35**	26. $8 \times 9 = n$ **72**	27. $47 + 29 = n$ **76**
28. $8 \times n = 40$ **5**	29. $28 \div n = 7$ **4**	30. $27 \div n = 9$ **3**
31. $n \div 7 = 28$ **196**	32. $35 + 62 = n$ **97**	33. $n + 78 = 97$ **19**

Multiply.

Lessons 80, 85, 87, 91, 98

34. 1203×114 = **137,142**	35. 376×204 = **76,704**	36. 2013×68 = **136,884**	37. 4135×77 = **318,395**	38. 847×29 = **24,563**
39. 643×792 = **509,256**	40. $98,765 \times 7$ = **691,355**	41. 12×9 = **108**	42. 123×9 = **1107**	43. 1234×9 = **11,106**
44. 8643×25 = **216,075**	45. 649×285 = **184,965**	46. $12,345 \times 9$ = **111,105**	47. $123,456 \times 9$ = **1,111,104**	48. $142,857 \times 7$ = **999,999**

Solve these problems. Watch the signs.

Lessons 80, 85, 87, 91, 96, 98

49. 90 × 80 = **7200**	50. 1221 − 819 = **402**	51. 2457 + 407 = **2864**	52. 4906 − 997 = **3909**	53. 258 × 321 = **82,818**
54. 30 × 40 = **1200**	55. 4906 + 997 = **5903**	56. 87 × 39 = **3393**	57. 87 + 39 = **126**	58. 7295 + 6481 = **13,776**
59. 87 − 39 = **48**	60. 101 + 99 = **200**	61. 7024 + 889 = **7913**	62. 65 × 65 = **4225**	63. 15 × 12 = **180**

In each problem, two of the answers are clearly wrong and one is correct. Choose the correct answer.

Lesson 83

64. 27 × 89
a. 2753
b. 1093
(c.) 2403

65. 121 × 47
a. 3887
(b.) 5687
c. 54,767

66. 37 × 89
(a.) 3293
b. 36,593
c. 1803

67. 709 × 374
a. 26,526
b. 2,651,666
(c.) 265,166

68. 45 × 99
(a.) 4455
b. 34,555
c. 2425

69. 507 × 92
(a.) 46,644
b. 44,874
c. 448,794

70. 53 × 18
a. 7824
(b.) 954
c. 434

71. 407 × 29
(a.) 11,803
b. 7143
c. 23,003

72. 43 × 81
a. 32,863
b. 3193
(c.) 3483

73. 457 × 91
a. 34,927
(b.) 41,587
c. 46,587

74. 612 × 559
(a.) 342,108
b. 3,416,608
c. 3,402,108

75. 9735 × 994
(a.) 9,676,590
b. 9,981,910
c. 9,872,540

◆ LESSON 103 Unit 4 Practice

◆ LESSON 103 Unit 4 Practice

Solve these problems.

Lessons 79, 82, 85, 86, 87, 92, 93, 97

76 A 2-liter bottle of water costs 89¢.

a. How much do seven bottles cost? **$6.23**

b. When the bottles are full, how much water do they contain all together? **14 liters**

c. Ava buys three bottles of water each day for a week (seven days). How much money does she spend all together? **$18.69**

77 A rectangle is 89 meters wide and 97 meters long.

a. What is the area of the rectangle in square meters? **8633 sq. m**

b. What is the perimeter of the rectangle? **372 m**

78 One can of paint will cover about 50 square meters. Mrs. Andrews is going to paint a wall that is 57 meters long and 11 meters high. Will ten cans of paint be enough? **no**

79 There are 1000 grams in a kilogram. There are 1000 kilograms in a metric ton. How many grams are there in a metric ton? **1,000,000**

80 There are 12 inches in 1 foot. How many inches are there in 160 feet? **1920**

81 Some baby whales drink about 200 liters of milk each day for about seven months. About how many liters of milk is this? (Assume that one month is 30 days.) **about 42,000 L**

82 A shrew weighs about 3 grams. It eats about eight times its own weight every day. About how many grams of food does a shrew eat in a year (365 days)? **8760 g**

83 Cliff used a shoelace 67 centimeters long to measure a room. The room is about 14 shoelaces long. About how many centimeters long is the room? **938 cm**

RETEACHING

Students who have difficulty with this Unit Practice should have further opportunity to review and to practice the skills before they proceed on with the next unit. Beside each set of problems is a reference to the lesson or lessons from which the problems were taken. You may want to review the individual lessons with students who are having difficulty with them.

Solve these problems.

84 A rectangle is 120 meters wide and 200 meters long.

a. What is the area of the rectangle? **24,000 square meters**

b. What is the perimeter of the rectangle? **640 meters**

85 How many cents are worth 18 dollars? **1800 cents**

Jim said he thinks he is at least 130 kilometers tall.

86 Do you think Jim is 130 kilometers tall? **no**

87 What do you think he meant to say? **130 centimeters**

SCIENCE CONNECTION

About how much is 4,962,100 × 37,942,614?

An approximate answer is 5,000,000 × 40,000,000. That is, 5 × 4 followed by the number of 0s in the two factors.

So, an approximate answer is 20 followed by 13 0s: 200,000,000,000,000.

Solve these problems by approximating.

Lessons 82–84

88 Light travels 299,792,500 meters in one second. There are 31,556,926 seconds in one year. About how many meters does light travel in one year? (That is, about how many meters are there in one light-year?) **about 9,000,000,000,000,000 (9 quadrillion)**

89 The sun is about 150,000,000,000 meters from Earth. Suppose you read that it takes light about eight minutes (or 480 seconds) to reach Earth from the sun. Would that figure make sense? **yes**

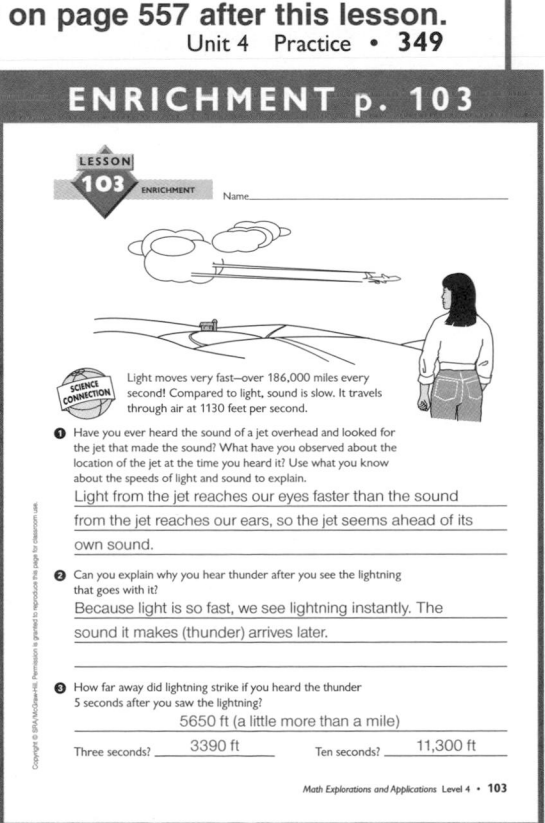

90 Our galaxy is about 80,000 light-years across.

a. About how many meters is that? **about 720,000,000,000,000,000,000 (720 quintillion)**

b. About how many years would it take light to travel across our galaxy? **about 80,000**

Use the Cumulative Review on page 557 after this lesson.

Unit 4 Practice • **349**

PRACTICE p. 103

LESSON 103 PRACTICE Name____________

ALGEBRA READINESS **Solve for *n*. Watch the signs.**

1. $48 + 16 = n$ $n =$ 64
2. $5 \times 8 = n$ $n =$ 40
3. $n + 26 = 84$ $n =$ 58
4. $3 \times n = 27$ $n =$ 9
5. $n - 34 = 9$ $n =$ 43
6. $n \times 9 = 54$ $n =$ 6
7. $39 + n = 76$ $n =$ 37
8. $6 \times n = 30$ $n =$ 5

Multiply.

9. $1045 \times 36 =$ 37,620
10. $312 \times 240 =$ 74,880
11. $436 \times 18 =$ 7848
12. $83,625 \times 8 =$ 669,000
13. $135,211 \times 6 =$ 811,266

Solve. Watch the signs.

14. $35 \times 35 =$ 1225
15. $64 + 97 =$ 161
16. $6043 - 718 =$ 5325
17. $4145 - 567 =$ 3578
18. $60 \times 50 =$ 3000
19. $3723 + 685 =$ 4408
20. $2805 + 495 =$ 3300
21. $64 - 25 =$ 39
22. $608 \times 75 =$ 45,600
23. $132 \times 46 =$ 6072

PROBLEM SOLVING **Solve these problems.**

A pound of apples costs 98¢. Jo uses 4 pounds to make an apple pie.

24. What is the cost in cents for enough apples to make one apple pie? 392¢
25. What is the cost in dollars for one apple pie? $3.92

Copyright © SRA/McGraw-Hill. Permission is granted to reproduce this page for classroom use.

Math Explorations and Applications Level 4 • **103**

ENRICHMENT p. 103

LESSON 103 ENRICHMENT Name____________

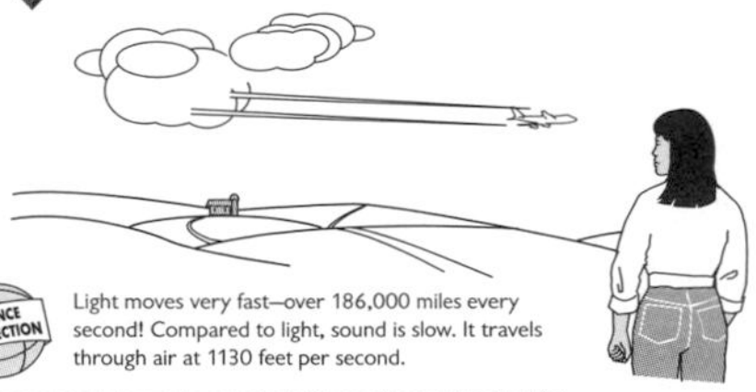

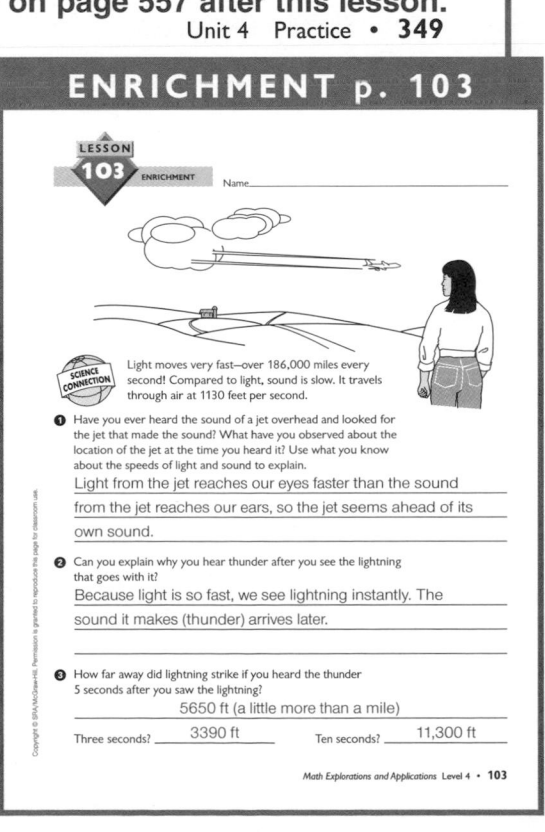

SCIENCE CONNECTION Light moves very fast—over 186,000 miles every second! Compared to light, sound is slow. It travels through air at 1130 feet per second.

1. Have you ever heard the sound of a jet overhead and looked for the jet that made the sound? What have you observed about the location of the jet at the time you heard it? Use what you know about the speeds of light and sound to explain.
   Light from the jet reaches our eyes faster than the sound from the jet reaches our ears, so the jet seems ahead of its own sound.
2. Can you explain why you hear thunder after you see the lightning that goes with it?
   Because light is so fast, we see lightning instantly. The sound it makes (thunder) arrives later.
3. How far away did lightning strike if you heard the thunder 5 seconds after you saw the lightning? 5650 ft (a little more than a mile)
   Three seconds? 3390 ft   Ten seconds? 11,300 ft

Copyright © SRA/McGraw-Hill. Permission is granted to reproduce this page for classroom use.

Math Explorations and Applications Level 4 • **103**

UNIT 4

Student Edition pages 350–351

Unit Test

Using the Student Pages The Unit 4 Test on Student Edition pages 350 and 351 provides an opportunity to formally evaluate your students' proficiency with concepts developed in this unit. It is similar in content and format to the Unit 4 Review. Students who did well on the Unit 4 Review may not need to take this test. Students who did not do well on the Unit 4 Review should be provided with additional practice opportunities, such as the Unit 4 Practice pages, before taking the Unit 4 Test. For further evaluation, you may wish to have these students also take the Unit 4 Test in standardized format, provided on Assessment Blackline Masters pages 129–140 or the Unit 4 Test on Assessment Blackline Masters pages 39–43.

UNIT 4

ASSESSMENT

Unit Test

Multiply to solve for *n*.

1. 8 × 7 = *n* **56**
2. 9 × 9 = *n* **81**
3. 9 × 7 = *n* **63**
4. *n* = 4 × 4 **16**
5. *n* = 7 × 6 **42**
6. 3 × 8 = *n* **24**
7. *n* = 8 × 5 **40**
8. 5 × 4 = *n* **20**
9. 6 × 8 = *n* **48**
10. *n* = 7 × 4 **28**
11. 7 × 7 = *n* **49**
12. 6 × 4 = *n* **24**
13. 9 × 5 = *n* **45**
14. 6 × 6 = *n* **36**
15. *n* = 8 × 8 **64**
16. 6 × 8 = *n* **48**

Multiply. Use shortcuts when you can.

17. 52 × 56 = **2912**
18. 43 × 29 = **1247**
19. 31 × 24 = **744**
20. 60 × 25 = **1500**
21. 203 × 54 = **10,962**
22. 876 × 9 = **7884**
23. 28 × 431 = **12,068**
24. 500 × 700 = **350,000**
25. 346 × 210 = **72,660**
26. 142,857 × 7 = **999,999**

Solve these problems. Watch the signs.

27. 35 − 25 = **10**
28. 35 + 25 = **60**
29. 35 × 25 = **875**
30. 407 − 209 = **198**
31. 407 + 209 = **616**

In each problem, two of the answers are clearly wrong and one is correct. Choose the correct answer.

32. 76 × 67
    - **a.** 6763
    - **b.** 6776
    - **(c.)** 5092
33. 407 × 209
    - **(a.)** 85,063
    - **b.** 8563
    - **c.** 65,630
34. 305 × 13
    - **a.** 318
    - **b.** 1305
    - **(c.)** 3965
35. 595 × 129
    - **a.** 140,755
    - **b.** 40,755
    - **(c.)** 76,755

ALGEBRA READINESS

Solve for *n*. Watch the signs.

36. *n* + 16 = 53 **37**
37. 36 ÷ 4 = *n* **9**
38. *n* = 42 + 21 **63**
39. 7 × *n* = 56 **8**
40. 7 × *n* = 49 **7**
41. 89 − *n* = 52 **37**

350 • Multidigit Multiplication

Solve these problems.

42. A high-speed train travels 160 kilometers in one hour. At that rate, how far can it go in 15 hours? **2400 km**
43. What is the area of a playground that is 85 meters long and 47 meters wide? **3995 sq. m**
44. A rectangle measures 215 centimeters long and 112 centimeters wide. What is the perimeter of the rectangle? What is the area of the rectangle? **perimeter = 654 cm; area = 24,080 sq. cm**
45. Pokey the cat eats about 215 grams of cat food per day. About how many grams of cat food will Pokey eat during the month of May (31 days)? **6665 g**
46. A pint of milk costs 51¢, and a pint of cola costs 68¢. Which costs more? How much more? **A pint of cola costs 17¢ more.**
47. A pint of milk costs 51¢, and a loaf of bread costs \$1.45. How much do they cost together? **\$1.96**
48. One can of tuna costs 83¢. How much will 16 cans of tuna cost? Give your answer in cents. Also give your answer in dollars and cents. **1328¢; \$13.28**
49. Cans of tuna are packed in cartons that have eight rows with 12 cans in each row. How many cans are there in ten cartons? **960**
50. Liam wants to put his stamp collection in a scrapbook. Each page of the scrapbook will hold 15 stamps. There are 38 pages. How many stamps will the scrapbook hold? **570**

ASSESSMENT p. 39

UNIT 4

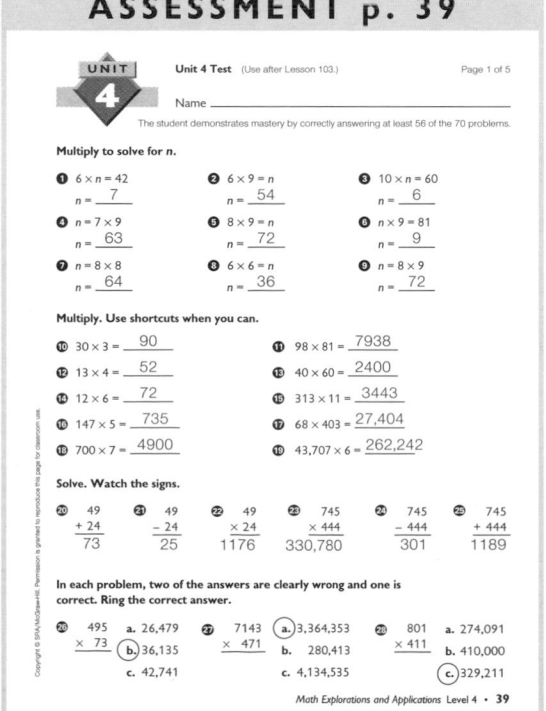

Unit 4 Test (Use after Lesson 103.) Page 1 of 5

Name ______________________

The student demonstrates mastery by correctly answering at least 56 of the 70 problems.

Multiply to solve for *n*.

1. $6 \times n = 42$ — $n =$ 7
2. $6 \times 9 = n$ — $n =$ 54
3. $10 \times n = 60$ — $n =$ 6
4. $n = 7 \times 9$ — $n =$ 63
5. $8 \times 9 = n$ — $n =$ 72
6. $n \times 9 = 81$ — $n =$ 9
7. $n = 8 \times 8$ — $n =$ 64
8. $6 \times 6 = n$ — $n =$ 36
9. $n = 8 \times 9$ — $n =$ 72

Multiply. Use shortcuts when you can.

10. $30 \times 3 =$ 90
11. $98 \times 81 =$ 7938
12. $13 \times 4 =$ 52
13. $40 \times 60 =$ 2400
14. $12 \times 6 =$ 72
15. $313 \times 11 =$ 3443
16. $147 \times 5 =$ 735
17. $68 \times 403 =$ 27,404
18. $700 \times 7 =$ 4900
19. $43{,}707 \times 6 =$ 262,242

Solve. Watch the signs.

20. $49 + 24 =$ 73
21. $49 - 24 =$ 25
22. $49 \times 24 =$ 1176
23. $745 \times 444 =$ 330,780
24. $745 - 444 =$ 301
25. $745 + 444 =$ 1189

In each problem, two of the answers are clearly wrong and one is correct. Ring the correct answer.

26. 495×73 — a. 26,479 (b.) 36,135 c. 42,741
27. 7143×471 — (a.) 3,364,353 b. 280,413 c. 4,134,535
28. 801×411 — a. 274,091 b. 410,000 (c.) 329,211

Copyright © SRA/McGraw-Hill. Permission is granted to reproduce this page for classroom use.

Math Explorations and Applications Level 4 • 39

UNIT 4

Student Edition pages 352–353

Wrap-Up

PRESENTING THE PROJECT

Project Objective

- to show how to measure pulse rate, relate it to the beating of the heart, and give an indication of how hard the heart works over a lifetime

To begin the project, initiate a discussion about the human heart, its function in the body, and its importance. You may want to use your health textbook as a guide, if available. Then show the students how to measure the rate at which their hearts beat by taking their pulse.

To find their pulse rate, students can count the number of beats in 15 seconds and multiply by 4, or count the beats in 30 seconds and multiply by 2, or count the beats in one minute. Use **The Cruncher*** to help calculate heartbeats.

If students are interested, you might allow them to measure their pulse rate before and after exercising. Usually, jogging in one place for one minute will raise the pulse significantly.

COOPERATIVE LEARNING **Math CrossSections** SRA's *Math CrossSections* consists of eight units that provide real-world math projects related to famous places in the United States. These open-ended projects focus on problem solving and reinforce reading, research, and study skills. The eight units are as follows:

The White House (Washington, D.C.)
747 DFW (Texas)
California's Giant Sequoias (California)
Pencil Making (Tennessee)
Barging Through the Locks (Michigan)
Atlanta's Olympic Stadium (Georgia)
Madison Square Garden (New York)
The Denver Mint (Colorado)

Use projects from *California's Giant Sequoias* to provide extra practice with multidigit multiplication.

PROJECT

UNIT 4 WRAP-UP

Your Heart at Work

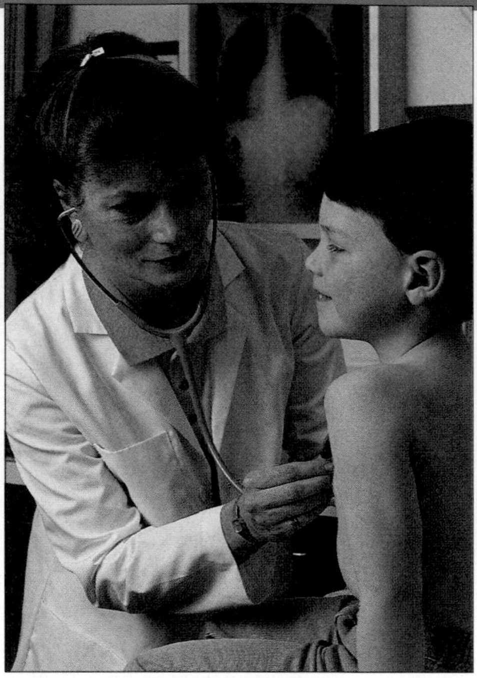

SCIENCE CONNECTION

The human heart works to pump blood to all parts of the body. It is always working. Some people's hearts beat about 50 times each minute. Other people's hearts beat 75 times each minute. Both speeds can be normal. It is not unusual to have a higher or lower heartbeat rate and still be normal. It is also normal for your heart to beat faster when you are exercising than when you are resting.

You can measure how many times your heart beats in one minute by taking your pulse. Your pulse is caused by blood vessels, called arteries, stretching as blood is forced through them after each heartbeat.

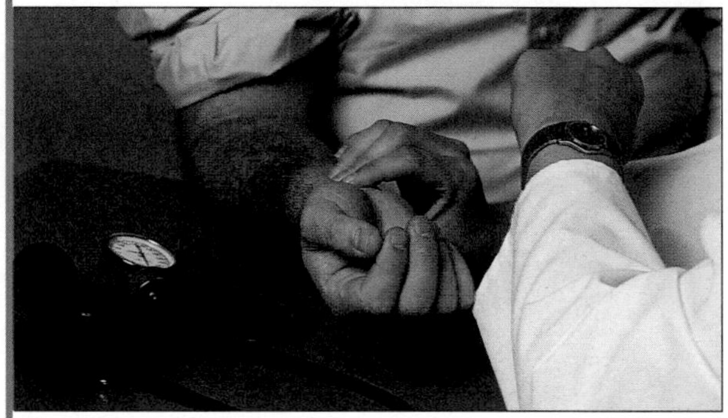

An artery that is often used to measure pulse rate is found on the inside of your wrist. Ask your teacher to demonstrate how to measure your pulse rate.

352 • Multidigit Multiplication

*available separately

Adam measured his pulse. He found that his pulse rate was 70. That means that his heart beats 70 times in one minute.

Answer these questions. You may use a calculator.

1. How many times will Adam's heart beat in one hour? **4200**
2. How many times will Adam's heart beat in one day? **100,800**
3. How many times will Adam's heart beat in one year? **36,792,000**

Challenge: How many times has your heart beat in your lifetime? **See margin.**

Your answer to this question may not be accurate, because we know that young children's hearts beat quickly and slow down with age. It is not unusual for a newborn baby to have a heartbeat rate of over 100 beats per minute.

You can take care of your heart by eating healthful foods and by exercising regularly.

Take care of your heart. It still has much more work to do.

Why teach it at this time?

Although this project might be introduced at any time, we do it now because it provides applications for multidigit multiplication, the main topic of this unit.

What Is a Math Project? If this is the first time you have used math projects in your classroom, you may want to refer to pages 96–97 in this Teacher's Guide for more detailed information about effectively implementing and assessing projects.

Answer for Challenge Question Children should explain their rationale for their calculations. There are two premises: the average number of times a heart beats per minute and one's age. For example, an eight-year-old with a pulse rate of 60 would calculate 8 × 60 × 60 × 24 × 365 (252,288,000). A ten-year-old with a pulse rate of 75 would calculate 10 × 75 × 60 × 24 × 365 (394,200,000). Answers for most fourth graders should fall within this range.

Homework Have students take the pulse rate of members of their family and record their family members' ages at the same time. You may wish to have them graph their data. If there is interest, have the class make a graph that relates age to heart rate using all their data. (The graph should show a general trend toward lower pulse rate as one gets older.)

Wrapping Up the Project Have students brainstorm ways to take care of their hearts, an important organ that works very hard. You may wish to use a health textbook as a guide.

Assessing the Project Note students who take a special interest in measuring and interpreting pulse rates. Have books available for them to read more on the subject.

COOPERATIVE LEARNING **Minds on Math** SRA's *Minds on Math* is a series of units covering Problem Solving, Data Collection, Number Sense, Measurement, Money, and Geometry and Spatial Relations. Each unit provides a series of open-ended projects for individuals or small groups. These projects develop problem-solving and critical-thinking skills, utilize real-world materials, emphasize language, and integrate cross-curricular connections. Use projects from *Problems to Think About* to illustrate that problems can have more than one correct answer.

UNIT 5

Division

PATTERNS AND RELATIONSHIPS

OVERVIEW

This unit begins with an introduction to the division algorithm for one-digit divisors. Students explore why the algorithm works and investigate the inverse relationship between multiplication and division. Students apply division to a variety of problems, including finding unit costs and averages. Students learn how to find the mean, median, and mode and how to use a bar graph. They are also introduced to finding factors and to prime and composite numbers.

Integrated Topics in This Unit Include:

- dividing by a one-digit divisor
- finding missing digits
- finding unit costs and determining the best buy
- using the short form of division
- applying division
- finding averages
- finding the mean, median, and mode
- relating multiplication and division
- identifying factors of a number
- identifying prime and composite numbers
- using bar graphs

FINDING MISSING DIGITS
FINDING THE MEAN, MEDIAN, AND MODE

"A climate should be established in the classroom that places critical thinking at the heart of instruction. Both teachers' and children's statements should be open to question, reaction, and elaboration from others in the classroom."

—NCTM Curriculum and Evaluation Standards for School Mathematics

GAMES

Motivating Mixed Practice

Games provide **basic math skills** practice in cooperative groups. Playing the games also helps students develop **mathematical reasoning**.

Diviso	Lesson 107	page 367
Diviso	Lesson 108	page 371
Four Cube Division	Lesson 110	page 375
Four Cube Division	Lesson 111	page 379
Diviso	Lesson 115	page 393
Four Cube Division	Lesson 115	page 393
Harder Snake Game Mat	Lesson 120	page 409
Cubo	Lesson 122	page 415
Diviso	Lesson 122	page 415
Four Cube Division	Lesson 122	page 415
Harder Snake Game Mat	Lesson 122	page 415

THINKING STORY

Integrated Problem Solving

Thinking Stories provide opportunities for students to work in **cooperative groups** and develop **logical reasoning** while they integrate **reading skills** with mathematics.

Estimating Is Rough

Part 1	Lesson 107	pages 368–369
Part 2	Lesson 110	pages 376–377
Part 3	Lesson 116	pages 398–399
Part 4	Lesson 120	pages 410–411
Part 5	Lesson 123	pages 418–419

Story Summary "Estimating Is Rough" focuses on Mr. Muddle's adventures in his new job as chief estimator. As the story progresses and Mr. Muddle is faced with a series of challenges, students refine their understanding of estimation and are asked to use their averaging skills. Students have an opportunity to discuss the differences between guessing and estimating, and they determine on what kind of information a good estimate is based.

PROJECT

Making Connections

The Unit 5 Project makes real-world connections. Students work in **cooperative groups** to problem solve and to communicate their findings.

The project presented in the Unit 5 Wrap-Up asks students to study the fictional broad-jump contest in the text. Working in small groups, students should decide who is the winner. Then they can design their own contest. This project can be worked on during students' free time throughout the unit.

UNIT 5 DIVISION LESSON PLANS

LESSON		PACING	PRIMARY OBJECTIVES	FEATURE	RESOURCES	NCTM STANDARDS
104	**Dividing by a One-Digit Divisor 356–361**	2 days	to introduce a division algorithm for one-digit divisors	ACT IT OUT	Reteaching Strategy Practice Master 104 Enrichment Master 104	7, 8
105	**Keeping Records of Division 362–363**	1 day	to develop further student understanding of the division algorithm		Reteaching Master Practice Master 105 Enrichment Master 105	7, 8
106	**Practicing Division ... 364–365**	1 day	✓to assess mastery of dividing by one-digit divisors	✓	Reteaching Strategy Practice Master 106 Enrichment Master 106 Assessment Master	7, 8
107	**Division Review: Missing Digits 366–369**	1 day	to provide practice with multiplication facts and division with one-digit divisors	Thinking Story Game	Reteaching Strategy Practice Master 107 Enrichment Master 107	1, 2, 3, 4, 6, 8
108	**Using Division: Unit Cost 370–371**	1 day	to provide practice in using division to find unit costs and determine better buys	Game	Reteaching Strategy Practice Master 108 Enrichment Master 108	1, 2, 3, 4, 8
109	**Dividing by a One-Digit Divisor: Short Form 372–373**	1 day	to introduce the "short form" division algorithm		Reteaching Strategy Practice Master 109 Enrichment Master 109	7, 8
110	**More Division Practice 374–377**	1 day	to provide experience in estimating answers to division problems	Thinking Story Game	Reteaching Strategy Practice Master 110 Enrichment Master 110	1, 2, 3, 4, 5, 8
111	**Applying Division 378–379**	1 day	to provide practice in solving word problems that focus on multiplication and division	Game	Reteaching Strategy Practice Master 111 Enrichment Master 111	1, 2, 3, 4, 8
112	**Finding Averages 380–383**	1 day	to teach the concept of average (mean) and how to compute it		Reteaching Master Practice Master 112 Enrichment Master 112	8, 11
113	**Mean, Median, and Mode............ 384–385**	1 day	to provide practice computing and thinking about means, medians, and modes		Reteaching Master Practice Master 113 Enrichment Master 113	11
	Mid-Unit Review..... 386–389	1 day		✓	Assessment Masters	
114	**Division Patterns 390–391**	1 day	✓ to assess students' mastery of dividing by one-digit divisors and to provide practice in dividing with one-digit divisors	✓	Reteaching Strategy Practice Master 114 Enrichment Master 114 Assessment Master	8
115	**Using Division 392–395**	1 day	to develop the meaning of and to begin to make predictions based on average	Game	Reteaching Strategy Practice Master 115 Enrichment Master 115	1, 2, 3, 4, 10, 11
116	**Practicing Division: Missing Digits 396–399**	1 day	to provide practice in dividing by one-digit divisors	Thinking Story	Reteaching Strategy Practice Master 116 Enrichment Master 116	1, 2, 3, 4, 8, 9
117	**Multiply and Divide................ 400–403**	1 day	to review the inverse relationship of multiplication and division	ACT IT OUT	Reteaching Master Practice Master 117 Enrichment Master 117	7, 11, 13

LESSON		PACING	PRIMARY OBJECTIVES	FEATURE	RESOURCES	NCTM STANDARDS
118	**Multiplying to Find Quotients** **404–405**	1 day	to provide practice for applying the inverse relationship between multiplication and division to solve division problems		Reteaching Strategy Practice Master 118 Enrichment Master 118	7
119	**Prime and Composite Numbers** **406–407**	1 day	to introduce the concepts of factors, prime numbers, and composite numbers		Reteaching Strategy Practice Master 119 Enrichment Master 119	6
120	**Using a Bar Graph** . . . **408–411**	1 day	to provide practice in reading a bar graph and in solving problems based on it	Thinking Story Game	Reteaching Strategy Practice Master 120 Enrichment Master 120	1, 2, 3, 4, 11
121	**More Division Review** **412–413**	1 day	to provide practice in reading a telephone bill and solving problems based on it		Reteaching Strategy Practice Master 121 Enrichment Master 121	1, 2, 3, 4, 8
122	**Division Applications** **414–415**	1 day	to provide practice in approximating answers to division problems, using the inverse operation of multiplication	Game	Reteaching Strategy Practice Master 122 Enrichment Master 122	1, 2, 3, 4, 5, 7
123	**Division Revisited: Missing Digits** **416–419**	1 day	to provide practice with basic facts and multidigit arithmetic	Thinking Story	Reteaching Strategy Practice Master 123 Enrichment Master 123	1, 2, 3, 4, 8
124	**Unit 5 Review** **420–421**		to review division		Practice Master 124 Enrichment Master 124	
125	**Unit 5 Practice** **422–425**		to practice division		Practice Master 125 Enrichment Master 125	
	Unit 5 Test **426–427**		to review division		Assessment Masters	
	Unit 5 Wrap-Up . . . . . **428–429** The Broad-Jump Contest			Project		

UNIT CONNECTIONS

INTERVENTION STRATEGIES

In this Teacher's Guide there are specific strategies suggested for students with individual needs. These strategies appear with icons under the headings ESL, Gifted and Talented, Special Needs, Learning Styles, and At Risk, and are provided at the point of use. Following are the icons to look for and the types of strategies that will accompany them:

ESL

English as a Second Language

These strategies, designed for students who do not speak the English language fluently, suggest meaningful ways to present the lesson concepts and vocabulary.

GIFTED & TALENTED

Gifted and Talented

These strategies are designed to enrich and extend the lessons and offer further challenges to students who have easily mastered the concepts already presented.

SPECIAL NEEDS

Special Needs

Students who are physically challenged or who have learning disabilities may require alternative ways to complete activities, record answers, use manipulatives, and so on. The strategies labeled with this icon offer appropriate methods of teaching lesson concepts to these students.

LEARNING STYLES

Learning Styles

Each student has his or her individual approach to learning. The strategies labeled with this icon suggest ways to present lesson concepts so that various learning modalities—such as tactile/kinesthetic, visual, and auditory—can be addressed.

AT RISK

At Risk

These strategies highlight the relevancy of the skills presented by making the connection between school and real life. They are directed toward students who appear to be at risk of dropping out of school before graduation.

TECHNOLOGY CONNECTIONS

The following materials, designed to reinforce and extend lesson concepts, are referred to throughout this Teacher's Guide. It might be helpful to either order the software and videos or check them out of the school media center or community library. If your school does not provide Internet access, consider visiting a local library, college, or business specializing in Internet services. Some students may be able to access the Internet at home.

TECHNOLOGY CONNECTION

Look for this **Technology Connection** *icon.*

- *Intermediate Math,* from Queue; Mac, IBM, for grades 3–9 (software)
- *Math Blaster: In Search of Spot,* from Davidson; IBM, for grades 1–6 (software)
- *The Wonderful Problems of Fizz & Martina, Volume 3: Fizz and Martina Do Hollywood,* from Tom Snyder Productions; VHS, for grades 3–6 (video)
- *Mystery Math Island,* from Lawrence Productions; Mac, IBM, for grades 3–8 (software)
- NASA Home Page, http://www.gsfc.nasa.gov (Internet)
- *Mega Math,* www.c3.lanl.gov/mega-math/menu.html (Internet)
- *New Math Blaster Plus,* from Davidson; IBM, for grades 1–6 (software)

CROSS-CURRICULAR CONNECTIONS

This Teacher's Guide offers specific suggestions on ways to connect the math concepts presented in this unit with other subjects that students are studying. Students can connect math concepts with topics they already know about, and they can find examples of math in other subjects and in real-world situations. These strategies are given at the point of use.

Look for these icons:

Geography	Health
Social Studies	Music
Science	Math
Art	Physical Education
Language Arts	Careers

LITERATURE CONNECTIONS

The following books are referenced throughout this Teacher's Guide at the points where they can be used to introduce, reinforce, or extend specific lesson concepts. You may want to locate these books in your school or community library.

Look for this **Literature Connection** *icon.*

- *A Remainder of One* by Elinor J. Pinczes. Houghton Mifflin, 1995.
- "Divisors," in *Mathematics* (p. 23) by Irving Adler. Doubleday, 1990.
- *Sadako and the Thousand Paper Cranes* by Elenor Coerr. Putnam, 1977.
- *The Doorbell Rang* by Pat Hutchins. Greenwillow Books, 1986.
- *Averages* by Jane Srivastava. Crowell, 1975.
- *The Sneaky Square + 113 Other Math Activities for Kids* by Richard Sharp and Seymour Metzner. TAB Books, 1990.
- *Math Curse* by Jon Scieska. Viking, 1995.
- "Prime Numbers," in *Mathematics* (p. 22) by Irving Adler. Doubleday, 1990.
- "Bar Graphs," in *Math for Every Kid* (pp. 129–136) by Janice Van Cleave. Wiley, 1991.
- *Making Cents: Every Kid's Guide to Money* by Elizabeth Wilkinson. Little, Brown, 1989.
- "Five Fruit Jars," in *Gold and Silver, and Silver and Gold* (pp. 49–50) by Alvin Schwartz. Farrar Straus Giroux, 1988.
- *I Hate Mathematics Book!* by Marilyn Burns. Little, Brown, 1975.

ASSESSMENT OPPORTUNITIES AT-A-GLANCE

LESSON	PORTFOLIO	PERFORMANCE	FORMAL	SELF	INFORMAL	CUMULATIVE REVIEWS	MULTIPLE-CHOICE	MASTERY CHECKPOINTS	ANALYZING ANSWERS
104				✓					
105					✓				
106			✓					✓	✓
107					✓	✓			
108		✓							
109					✓				
110					✓				
111		✓							
112	✓					✓			
113				✓					
Mid-Unit Review	✓	✓	✓						
114			✓					✓	✓
115		✓							✓
116		✓				✓			
117					✓				
118		✓							
119	✓								
120				✓					
121				✓					
122					✓	✓			✓
123					✓				
124	✓	✓	✓						
125						✓			
Unit Test			✓				✓		

ASSESSMENT OPTIONS

PORTFOLIO ASSESSMENT

Throughout this Teacher's Guide are suggestions for activities in which students draw pictures, make graphs, and write about mathematics. Keep students' work to assess growth of understanding as the year progresses.

Lessons 112, Mid-Unit Review, 119, and 124

PERFORMANCE ASSESSMENT

Performance Assessment items focus on evaluating how students think and work as they solve problems. Opportunities for performance assessment can be found throughout the unit. Rubrics and guides for grading can be found in the front of the Assessment Blackline Masters.

Lessons 108, 111, Mid-Unit Review, 115, 116, 118, and 124

FORMAL ASSESSMENT

A Mid-Unit Review, Unit Review, and Unit Test help assess students' understanding of concepts, skills, and problem-solving ability. The *Math Explorations and Applications* CD-ROM Test Generator can create additional unit tests at three ability levels. Also, Mastery Checkpoints are provided periodically throughout the unit.

Lessons 106, Mid-Unit Review, 114, 124, and Unit Test

SELF ASSESSMENT

Throughout the program students are given the opportunity to check their own math skills.

Lessons 104, 113, 120, and 121

INFORMAL ASSESSMENT

A variety of assessment suggestions are provided throughout the unit, including interviews, oral questions or presentations, debates, and so on. Also, each lesson includes Assessment Criteria, a list of questions about each student's progress, understanding, and participation.

Lessons 105, 107, 109, 110, 117, 122, and 123

CUMULATIVE REVIEW

Cumulative Reviews, covering material presented thus far in the year, are provided in the unit for use as either assessment or practice.

Lessons 107, 112, 116, 122, and 125

MULTIPLE-CHOICE TESTS (STANDARDIZED FORMAT)

Each unit provides a Unit Test in standardized format, giving students many opportunities to practice taking tests in this format.

MASTERY CHECKPOINTS

Mastery Checkpoints are provided throughout the unit to assess student proficiency in specific skills. Checkpoints reference appropriate Assessment Blackline Masters and other assessment options. Results of these evaluations can be recorded on the Mastery Checkpoint Chart.

Lessons 106 and 114

ANALYZING ANSWERS

Analyzing Answers items suggest possible sources of student error and offer teaching strategies for addressing difficulties.

Lessons 106, 114, 115, and 122

Look for these icons:

ALTERNATIVE ASSESSMENT · ANALYZING ANSWERS · SELF ASSESSMENT

> ***"Grades based on demonstrated depth of mathematical knowledge communicate more about students' developing mathematical understanding than grades based on a student's relative position in the class or on percentage points."***
>
> *—NCTM Assessment Standards*

MASTERY CHECKPOINTS

WHAT TO EXPECT FROM STUDENTS AS THEY COMPLETE THIS UNIT

17a DIVIDING BY A ONE-DIGIT DIVISOR—LESSON 106

At about this time most students should demonstrate mastery of dividing a whole number by a one-digit divisor by correctly answering at least 80% of the problems on page 364 or on Assessment Blackline Masters page 44. Results of this assessment may be recorded on the Mastery Checkpoint Chart.

17b DIVIDING BY A ONE-DIGIT DIVISOR—LESSON 114

At this time most students should demonstrate mastery of division with one-digit divisors using short forms. Although this skill was assessed in Lesson 106, students have now learned a shorter method. Students should correctly answer 80% of the problems on pages 390–391 or on Assessment Blackline Masters page 46. Results of this assessment may be recorded on the Mastery Checkpoint Chart.

UNIT 5

PROGRAM RESOURCES

These additional components of *Math Explorations and Applications* can be purchased separately from SRA/McGraw-Hill.

LESSON	BASIC MANIPULATIVE KIT	GAME MAT PACKAGE	TEACHER MANIPULATIVE KIT	INTERMEDIATE MANIPULATIVE KIT	INTERMEDIATE OVERHEAD MANIPULATIVE KIT	*THE CRUNCHER* SOFTWARE	*MATH EXPLORATIONS AND APPLICATIONS* CD-ROM
104		play money			bills, coins		Lesson 104
105		play money		counters	bills, coins, counters		Lesson 105
106		play money		base-10 blocks	bills, coins, base-10 blocks		Lesson 106
107	Number Cubes						Lesson 107
108	Number Cubes	play money			bills, coins		Lesson 108
109							Lesson 109
110	Number Cubes						Lesson 110
111	Number Cubes						Lesson 111
112			tape measures		counters	spreadsheet	Lesson 112
113							Lesson 113
114							Lesson 114
115	Number Cubes		beakers				Lesson 115
116				angle rulers			Lesson 116
117				counters	counters		Lesson 117
118							Lesson 118
119							Lesson 119
120		Harder Snake game, play money		interlocking cubes	bills, coins, interlocking cubes	spreadsheet	Lesson 120
121				counters, interlocking cubes	counters, interlocking cubes	project	Lesson 121
122	Number Cubes	Harder Snake game		counters, interlocking cubes	bills, coins		Lesson 122
123	Number Wheels		scale				Lesson 123
124		play money		base-10 blocks	base-10 blocks, bills, coins		Lesson 124
125						spreadsheet	Lesson 125

UNIT 5

Student Edition pages 354–355

Division

INTRODUCING THE UNIT

Using the Student Pages Begin your discussion of the opening unit photo by asking students, "Did you know that teachers of all subjects need to know how to average?" Then read the paragraph on the student page aloud that highlights teaching as a career. This helps make the connection between school and work and encourages students to explore how math is used in the real world.

ACTIVITY Ask students to tell whether they would like the teacher to use mean, median, or mode to determine their grades. On **paper,** have them explain their choices.

FYI Teaching has a history that stretches back to ancient times. A Greek named Socrates, who lived in Athens in the 800s B.C., was famous in his day for teaching young people by asking questions. This kind of teaching came to be called the Socratic method and was described in the writings of Plato, a student of Socrates. Throughout the ancient world young princes and princesses grew up with tutors, or individuals who taught them a wide range of subjects. Stress that the concept of a classroom—and grades—was a later idea. Because even the wealthy members of the ruling class couldn't always afford a year-round tutor, some of these families sent their children to schools in which one teacher would instruct many students. While many of these early schools especially in England were called "public," they were in fact only for those who could afford them. Public schools that were truly open to all did not appear until the early years of the nineteenth century. In the United States, the tradition of public education paid for by the community grew up with the country and remains with us today. Going to school is the law, and it is available to everyone regardless of income or social standing.

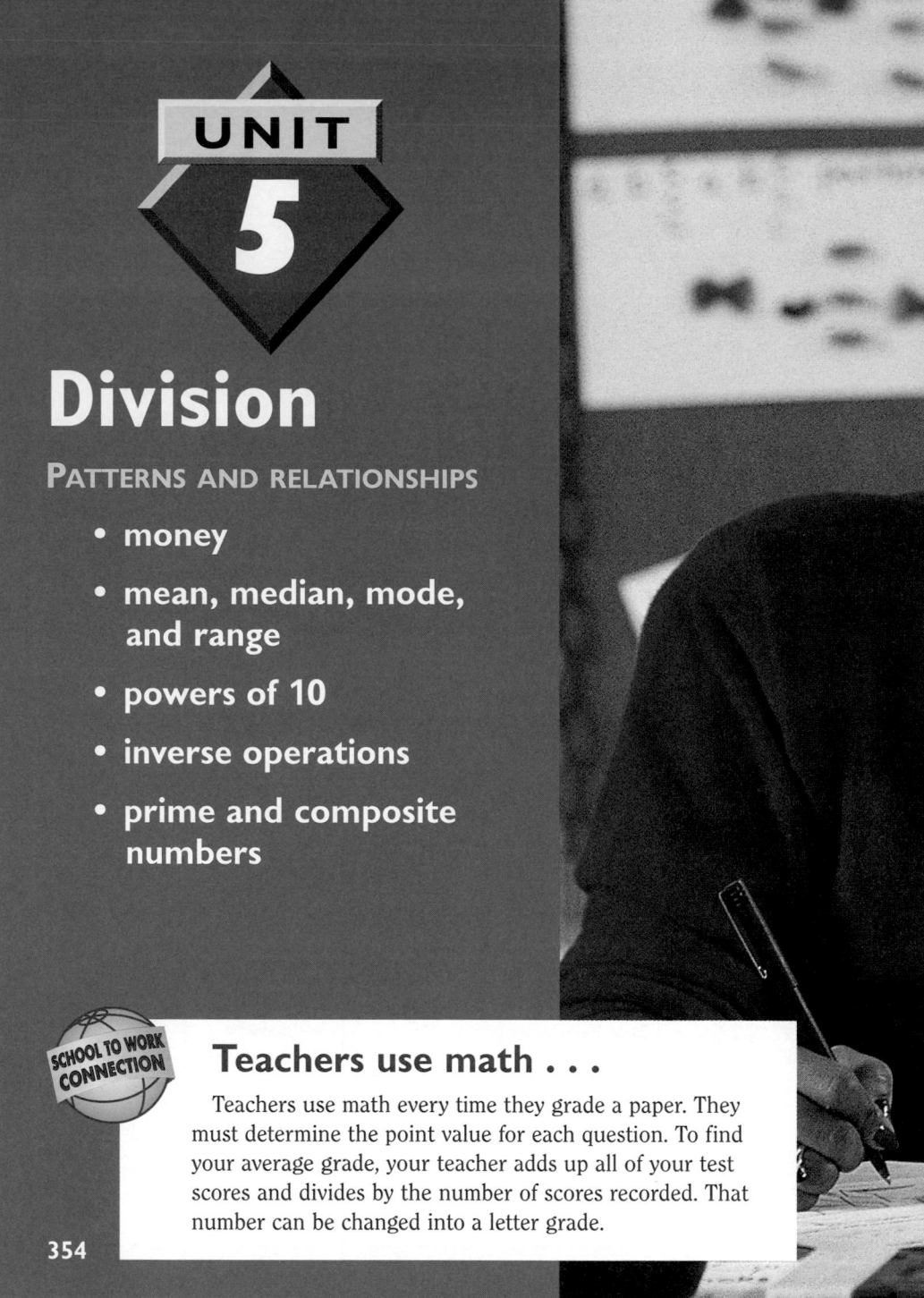

UNIT 5

Division

PATTERNS AND RELATIONSHIPS

- money
- mean, median, mode, and range
- powers of 10
- inverse operations
- prime and composite numbers

Teachers use math . . .

Teachers use math every time they grade a paper. They must determine the point value for each question. To find your average grade, your teacher adds up all of your test scores and divides by the number of scores recorded. That number can be changed into a letter grade.

354

Thinklab™

SRA's *Thinklab™* provides a series of creative and logical problem-solving opportunities for individual students. The problems are designed to appeal to different cognitive abilities.

- Use problems 81–90 with this unit to reinforce perception (extrapolating from and beyond given data).
- Use Problems 91–100 with this unit to reinforce logical analysis (absorbing multiple data, testing hypotheses, and planning a set of operations).

A modern teacher needs to know math not simply to compute averages. Explain that knowing all subjects—science, literature, history, math—is important to a well-rounded education. The idea that a truly educated person should know all subjects was established by a Greek named Aristotle in the 400s B.C. Aristotle taught many subjects, including geometry, literature, writing, and ethics, but over the door of his school he had these words inscribed: “Know thyself.” This advice would later become the cornerstone of the modern college education. While math is a practical skill, it can also be an important building block in a broader education, and an essential skill for a career in education. For a student who wishes to teach one day, math is very practical indeed.

Home Connections You may want to send the Home Connections Blackline Masters letter on pages 48–49 home to introduce this unit.

Cooperate 1

Cooperate 1, published by SRA, provides a series of creative and logical problem-solving opportunities for cooperative groups. The problems are designed to provide practice in problem solving, communication, reasoning, and making connections. *Cooperate 1* presents the following cognitive strategies—perceiving spatial relations, ordering and sequencing, logical deduction, establishing and testing hypotheses, sequential exploration, identifying starting points, attending to detail, organizing information, and screening irrelevant information.

Each Problem Card emphasizes a principal strategy as well as reinforcing other strategies.

- Use Problem Cards 21–24 with this unit to emphasize perceiving spatial relations.
- Use Problem Card 25 with this unit to emphasize logical deduction.

LESSON 104

Student Edition pages 356–361

Dividing by a One-Digit Divisor

LESSON PLANNER

Objectives

- ▶ to introduce a division algorithm for one-digit divisors
- ▶ to demonstrate why the algorithm works

Context of the Lesson This is the first of 13 lessons on division with a one-digit divisor. This lesson develops a long form of the division algorithm. In the next lesson students will learn a shorter form of the algorithm. Lesson 109 presents the standard short form. By the end of this unit students should be proficient in determining when to divide, in using some form of the algorithm to divide whole numbers by one-digit divisors, and in interpreting quotients and remainders.

MANIPULATIVES

envelopes (optional)

play money*

Program Resources

Practice Master 104

Enrichment Master 104

For extra practice: CD-ROM* Lesson 104

Note: This lesson may take more than one day.

1 Warm-Up (5 MINUTES)

Problem of the Day Present this problem: Joey runs one mile every morning. The first morning he ran, it took him 11 minutes. If he improves his time by 5 seconds every day, how quickly will he run the mile three weeks later? (nine minutes and 25 seconds)

Problem-Solving Strategies Ask students who have solved the Problem of the Day to share how they solved it and any strategies they used.

MENTAL MATH Provide practice with basic facts in all four operations. Focus on the inverse relationship between multiplication and division. Write these problems on the chalkboard:

a. 30 ÷ 6 = (5)   5 × 6 = (30)

b. 17 − 9 = (8)   8 + 9 = (17)

c. 4 + 5 = (9)   9 − 5 = (4)

(continued on page 357)

EXPLORE

LESSON 104 — ACT IT OUT

Dividing by a One-Digit Divisor

Seven-Way Split

Rosa and six of her friends were out playing one day when they found an envelope. Inside the envelope was money. There were eight $1000 bills, nine $100 bills, three $10 bills, and six $1 bills.

❶ How much money is that all together? **$8936**

◆ What would you do if you found that much money?

The seven children took the money to the police station and gave it to the person in the lost-and-found department.

After 30 days, nobody had claimed the money. So the police gave the $8936 back to the children. They agreed to share the money evenly.

"How shall we divide the money?" asked Marvin.

"Let's each take a $1000 bill," replied Lloyd.

Each of the seven children took one $1000 bill.

Why teach it this way?

The numbers used in the story are intentionally greater than the numbers students will generally work with in this unit. There are three reasons for this:

1. If the dividend were too low, the characters would not need an algorithm, so the plot would seem artificial.
2. Without a great enough dividend, the pattern repeated in each step might not emerge.
3. By working through a problem with greater numbers, students can realize that the algorithm works with any numbers, not just with simple ones.

*available separately

The children decided to keep a record of what they were doing. Because they wanted the $8936 to be divided into seven equal amounts, they wrote the problem this way:

$7\overline{)8936}$

Each child took $1000. They kept track of this on the top of the record.

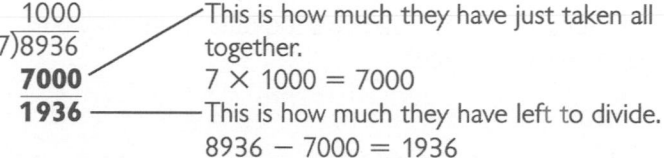

1000 ——— This is how much each child has taken so far.
$7\overline{)8936}$

Now they had used up $7000, leaving $1936. They kept track of this at the bottom of the record.

1000
$7\overline{)8936}$
7000 — This is how much they have just taken all together. $7 \times 1000 = 7000$
1936 ——— This is how much they have left to divide. $8936 - 7000 = 1936$

Now the seven children have one $1000 bill, nine $100 bills, three $10 bills, and six $1 bills. "How shall we divide the rest of the money?" asked Kelli.

"We could each take a $100 bill," said Nasim.

"But what will we do with the $1000 bill?" asked Nora.

Mental Math (continued)

d.	18 ÷ 3 = (6)	3 × 6 = (18)
e.	14 – 8 = (6)	6 + 8 = (14)
f.	4 × 7 = (28)	28 ÷ 4 = (7)
g.	15 – 6 = (9)	9 + 6 = (15)
h.	3 × 8 = (24)	24 ÷ 8 = (3)
i.	8 × 8 = (64)	64 ÷ 8 = (8)
j.	8 × 9 = (72)	72 ÷ 9 = (8)
k.	9 + 8 = (17)	17 – 8 = (9)
l.	8 × 7 = (56)	56 ÷ 8 = (7)

2 Teach

ACT IT OUT **Using the Student Pages** Read this story, which continues through page 361, with the class. It develops an algorithm for dividing a whole number by a one-digit divisor. Stop at each discussion question so students can share ideas and answers. When you reach the point on page 357 where the characters keep track of the division, keep a similar record on the chalkboard. At each step, write out what the figures mean. For example:

1000 ← Amount each child has
$7\overline{)8936}$
7000
1936 ← Money left to be distributed

Make sure students understand each transaction *before* you explain the record-keeping step.

COOPERATIVE LEARNING You may wish to divide the class into groups of seven so that students can act out the story. Each student takes on the role of one of the seven characters. Give each group an **envelope** that has $8936 in **play bills*** so that they can physically model each step of the algorithm. Set up a "bank" in a convenient location for the necessary trades.

*available separately

◆ LESSON 104 Dividing by a One-Digit Divisor

Teach

Using the Student Pages Continue going through the story with students, stopping to discuss each question and to describe the related step of the written algorithm. Model the trades, such as exchanging five \$100 bills for 50 \$10 bills. Be sure students recognize the equivalence of such trades.

ESL

Meeting Individual Needs

Students with limited proficiency in English may have difficulty following this story. Have each student read the story aloud with a partner who is fluent in English. Guide the pairs in summarizing the story to each other as they collaborate on the written steps of the algorithm.

Kelli suggested that they take the extra \$1000 bill to the bank and change it for ten \$100 bills.

2. How many \$100 bills will they have if they do this? **19**

At the bank, they changed the \$1000 bill for ten \$100 bills. Then they had 19 \$100 bills.

"We can each take two \$100 bills," said Jolette.

"Yes, but we'll still have some left over," Rosa said.

3. How many \$100 bills will be left after each child has taken two of them? **5**

The children each took two \$100 bills. Then they put that on their record.

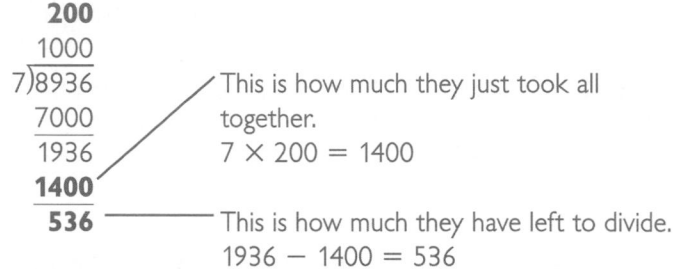

```
   200
  1000
7)8936
  7000
  1936
  1400   This is how much they just took all together. 7 × 200 = 1400
   536   This is how much they have left to divide. 1936 − 1400 = 536
```

4. How much money does each child have now? **\$1200**
5. How many \$100 bills are left in the pile? **5**
6. How much money is left in the pile all together? **\$536**

Literature Connection Read *A Remainder of One* by Elinor J. Pinczes with the class. Have students record the algorithm for each arrangement of bugs that Joe makes.

The children decided that the way to divide the remaining five $100 bills was to exchange them for $10 bills.

7. How many $10 bills should they get for five $100 bills? **50**
8. How many $10 bills will they have all together? **53**
9. How many $10 bills should each child get? **7**
10. How many $10 bills will be left? **4**

Each child took seven $10 bills. Now their record looks like this:

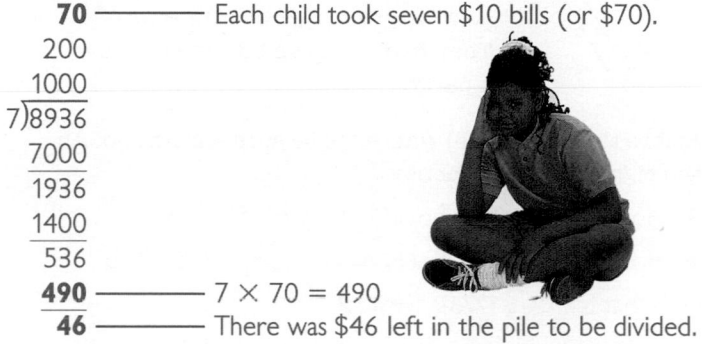

```
     70 ———— Each child took seven $10 bills (or $70).
    200
   1000
7)8936
   7000
   1936
   1400
    536
    490 ———— 7 × 70 = 490
     46 ———— There was $46 left in the pile to be divided.
```

Now there are four $10 bills and six $1 bills.

◆ What would you do? The children traded the four $10 bills for 40 $1 bills, so they had 46 $1 bills in the pile.

11. How many $1 bills can each child take? **6**
12. How many $1 bills will be left? **4**

If a proper foundation that relies appropriately on physical manipulatives and other aspects of the learner's reality is built over a period of years, young children can learn important concepts that might escape their older brothers and sisters who have not had the necessary preparation. The fact that people without appropriate preparation fail to learn something does not, of course, suggest that younger people, with the appropriate foundation, should not be taught the concept . . .

—Stephen S. Willoughby, *Mathematics Education for a Changing World*

Technology Connection You may wish to refer students to the software *Intermediate Math* from Queue (Mac, IBM, for grades 3–9) for further practice with division, metrics, and multidigit multiplication.

◆ LESSON 104 Dividing by a One-Digit Divisor

Teach

Using the Student Pages Complete the story. Then go through the steps of the algorithm on the chalkboard as shown on these pages. As you write, remind students what the characters in the story did at each step. Model each transaction again with **play money***.

GIFTED & TALENTED

Meeting Individual Needs

Gifted and talented students may come up with creative and original ways to divide the $8936 fairly among seven people. Encourage students to share their ideas, even if they differ from the standard algorithm, and to devise ways to record their thinking.

◆ LESSON 104 Dividing by a One-Digit Divisor

Now their record looks like this:

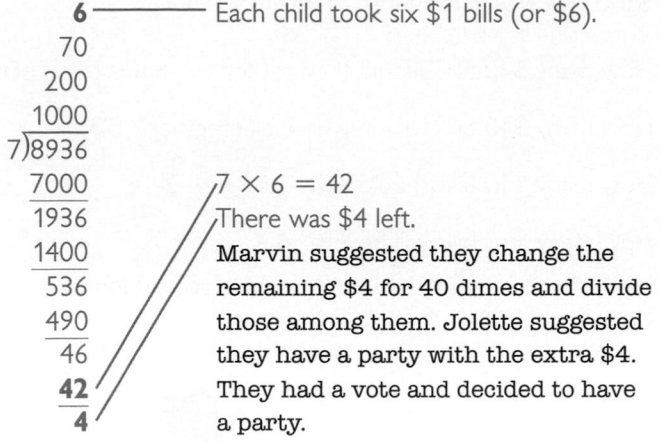

```
     6 ——— Each child took six $1 bills (or $6).
    70
   200
  1000
7)8936
  7000
  1936
  1400
   536
   490
    46
    42
     4
```

7 × 6 = 42

There was $4 left.

Marvin suggested they change the remaining $4 for 40 dimes and divide those among them. Jolette suggested they have a party with the extra $4. They had a vote and decided to have a party.

Before the party, Kelli wanted to be sure she had gotten the right amount of money.

- ◆ How much money should Kelli have? **$1276**
- ◆ How much money should each child have? **$1276**
- ◆ What is 7 × $1276? **$8932**

Why is that $4 less than the total they found, $8936? **There was $4 left after each child took $1276.**

The steps the children took looked like this:

```
Step 1      Step 2      Step 3      Step 4

  1000        1000        1000         200
7)8936      7)8936      7)8936        1000
              7000        7000      7)8936
                          1936        7000
                                      1936
```


RETEACHING

Because this is the first lesson in a sequence on division, reteaching is not essential at this time. Subsequent lessons will provide activities that review this material. You may wish to assign Enrichment Master 104 for this lesson.

*available separately

Step 5
```
    200
   1000
7)8936
   7000
   1936
   1400
```

Step 6
```
    200
   1000
7)8936
   7000
   1936
   1400
    536
```

Step 7
```
     70
    200
   1000
7)8936
   7000
   1936
   1400
    536
```

Step 8
```
     70
    200
   1000
7)8936
   7000
   1936
   1400
    536
    490
```

Step 9
```
     70
    200
   1000
7)8936
   7000
   1936
   1400
    536
    490
     46
```

Step 10
```
      6
     70
    200
   1000
7)8936
   7000
   1936
   1400
    536
    490
     46
```

Step 11
```
      6
     70
    200
   1000
7)8936
   7000
   1936
   1400
    536
    490
     46
     42
```

Step 12
```
      6
     70
    200
   1000
7)8936
   7000
   1936
   1400
    536
    490
     46
     42
      4
```

The answer is 1276, remainder 4.

PRACTICE p. 104

LESSON 104 PRACTICE Name______________________

Divide. Watch for remainders.

❶ 2)96 — 48	❷ 4)288 — 72	❸ 5)645 — 129	❹ 8)728 — 91	❺ 3)244 — 81 R1
❻ 4)512 — 128	❼ 9)189 — 21	❽ 6)936 — 156	❾ 7)0 — 0	❿ 8)92 — 11 R4
⓫ 9)503 — 55 R8	⓬ 5)722 — 144 R2	⓭ 9)112 — 12 R4	⓮ 2)639 — 319 R1	⓯ 4)712 — 178
⓰ 7)216 — 30 R6	⓱ 5)55 — 11	⓲ 5)555 — 111	⓳ 5)556 — 111 R1	⓴ 5)557 — 111 R2
㉑ 2)200 — 100	㉒ 4)200 — 50	㉓ 8)200 — 25	㉔ 8)207 — 25 R7	㉕ 3)75 — 25
㉖ 3)437 — 145 R2	㉗ 7)285 — 40 R5	㉘ 6)756 — 126	㉙ 7)712 — 101 R5	㉚ 8)664 — 83
㉛ 9)333 — 37	㉜ 5)248 — 49 R3	㉝ 2)78 — 39	㉞ 7)420 — 60	㉟ 4)171 — 42 R3

Copyright © SRA/McGraw-Hill. Permission is granted to reproduce this page for classroom use.

104 • *Math Explorations and Applications* Level 4

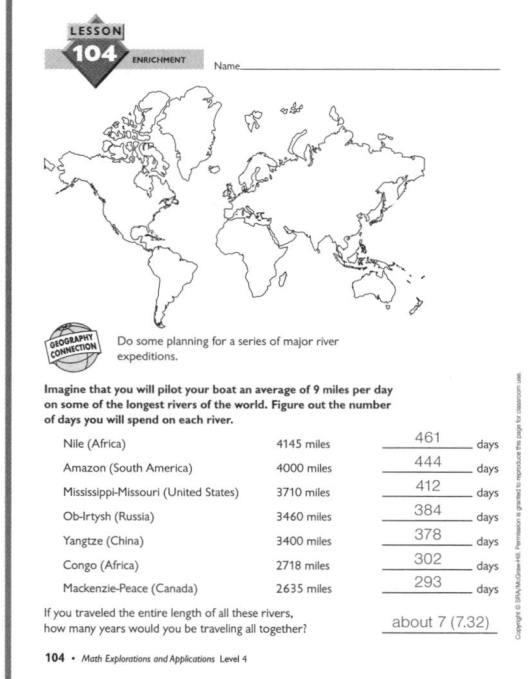

*available separately

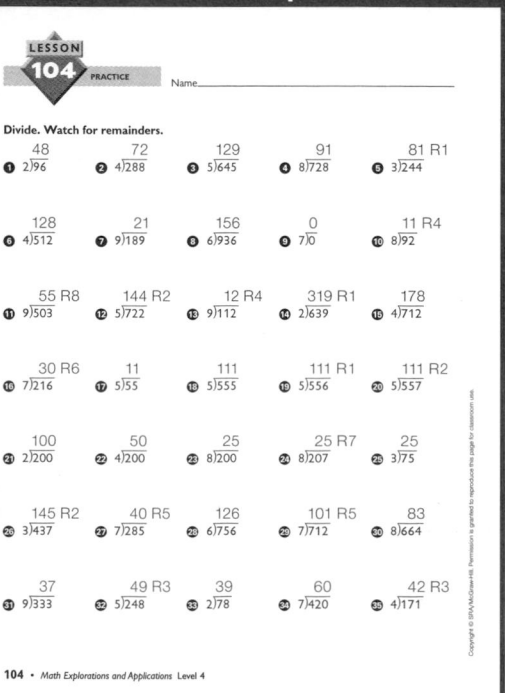

ENRICHMENT p. 104

LESSON 104 ENRICHMENT Name______________________

GEOGRAPHY CONNECTION Do some planning for a series of major river expeditions.

Imagine that you will pilot your boat an average of 9 miles per day on some of the longest rivers of the world. Figure out the number of days you will spend on each river.

Nile (Africa)	4145 miles	461 days
Amazon (South America)	4000 miles	444 days
Mississippi-Missouri (United States)	3710 miles	412 days
Ob-Irtysh (Russia)	3460 miles	384 days
Yangtze (China)	3400 miles	378 days
Congo (Africa)	2718 miles	302 days
Mackenzie-Peace (Canada)	2635 miles	293 days

If you traveled the entire length of all these rivers, how many years would you be traveling all together? about 7 (7.32)

Copyright © SRA/McGraw-Hill. Permission is granted to reproduce this page for classroom use.

104 • *Math Explorations and Applications* Level 4

❸ Wrap-Up (5 MINUTES)

In Closing Ask students if they have ever had to divide money or objects equally among a group of people. Invite volunteers to tell how they did it.

SELF ASSESSMENT Have each student write a brief statement explaining what he or she already knows about division. Then have students set goals for themselves for this unit by explaining what they think they need more practice in or what they would like to learn about division. Have them date their statements and place them in their Math Portfolios as a record of ongoing learning.

Assessment Criteria

Did the student . . .

- ✓ contribute to the story discussion?
- ✓ communicate strategies used to share money equally among seven people?
- ✓ recognize the connection between the story and the written algorithm?

Homework Have students use manipulatives of their choice to model a division problem, such as $7682 ÷ 5 (1536.40), for family members. Have them try to record their steps in the same way you did when reading the story together.

LESSON 105

Student Edition pages 362–363

Keeping Records of Division

LESSON PLANNER

Objective

▶ to develop deeper student understanding of the division algorithm

Context of the Lesson This is the second of 13 lessons on division with a one-digit divisor.

MANIPULATIVES

play money*
calculators*
counters* or checkers (optional)

Program Resources

Reteaching Master
Practice Master 105
Enrichment Master 105
For extra practice: CD-ROM* Lesson 105

1 Warm-Up (5 MINUTES)

Problem of the Day Present students with the following problem, providing **calculators*** if you wish: Miguel wants to divide 97 by 8 on his calculator, but the ÷ key won't work. How can he use his calculator to find the answer? (One way is to enter 97, then subtract 8 over and over until the display shows 0 or a number less than 8, keeping track of how many times 8 is subtracted.)

Problem-Solving Strategies Ask students who have solved the Problem of the Day to share how they solved it and any strategies they used.

MENTAL MATH Provide practice in basic facts. Focus on the inverse relationship between multiplication and division. Write these problems on the chalkboard:

a.	3 × 8 = (24)	24 ÷ 8 = (3)
b.	9 × 7 = (63)	63 ÷ 9 = (7)
c.	6 × 8 = (48)	48 ÷ 8 = (6)
d.	4 + 8 = (12)	12 – 8 = (4)
e.	7 × 6 = (42)	42 ÷ 7 = (6)
f.	9 + 4 = (13)	13 – 4 = (9)
g.	10 × 5 = (50)	50 ÷ 10 = (5)
h.	12 – 7 = (5)	5 + 7 = (12)
i.	4 × 9 = (36)	36 ÷ 9 = (4)
j.	5 + 6 = (11)	11 – 6 = (5)

PROBLEM SOLVING

LESSON 105

Keeping Records of Division

Using play money, work in groups to solve these problems. One person in each group should be the banker to exchange bills. One person should keep the record. Everyone should help solve the problems. Everyone should see that each record is right.

1. Six people want to divide $948 equally. How much should each person get? Will any money be left over? **$158; no**
2. Seven people want to divide $364 equally. How much should each person get? Will any money be left over? **$52; no**
3. Four people want to divide $7433 equally. How much should each person get? How many dollars will be left over? **$1858; $1 left over**
4. Five people want to divide $2707 equally. How much should each person get? How many dollars will be left over? **$541; $2 left over**
5. Nine people want to divide $4536 equally. How much should each person get? How many dollars will be left over? **$504; no money left over**
6. Three people want to share $297 equally. How much money should each person get? Will any money be left over? **$99; no**
7. Eight people want to share $641 equally. How much money should each person get? Will any money be left over? **$80; $1**

Here are the names for the parts of a division problem:

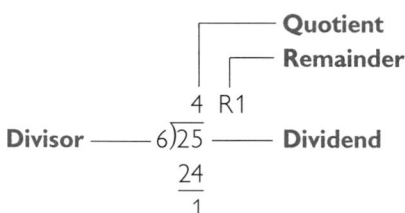

```
                 4 R1   ← Quotient (4), Remainder (R1)
Divisor ——— 6)25 ——— Dividend
               24
                1
```


Literature Connection You might want to read "Divisors" on page 23 of *Mathematics* by Irving Adler to reinforce lesson concepts. Have students use **checkers** or other **counters*** to determine all the divisors of a number that leave no remainder.

RETEACHING p. 33

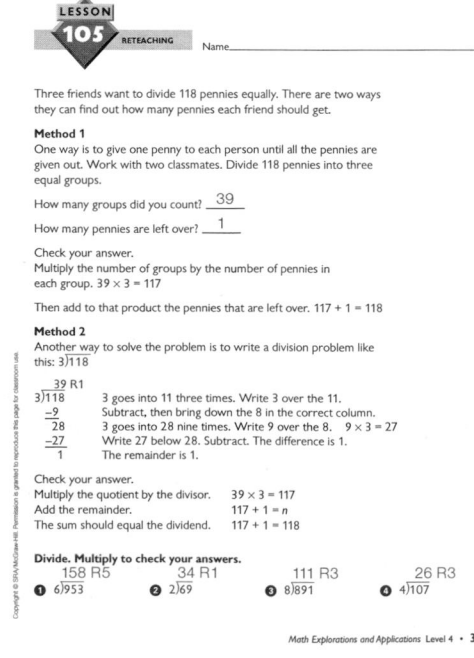

LESSON 105 RETEACHING Name________

Three friends want to divide 118 pennies equally. There are two ways they can find out how many pennies each friend should get.

Method 1
One way is to give one penny to each person until all the pennies are given out. Work with two classmates. Divide 118 pennies into three equal groups.

How many groups did you count? 39

How many pennies are left over? 1

Check your answer.
Multiply the number of groups by the number of pennies in each group. 39 × 3 = 117

Then add to that product the pennies that are left over. 117 + 1 = 118

Method 2
Another way to solve the problem is to write a division problem like this: 3)118

```
  39 R1
3)118     3 goes into 11 three times. Write 3 over the 11.
 -9       Subtract, then bring down the 8 in the correct column.
  28      3 goes into 28 nine times. Write 9 over the 8.   9 × 3 = 27
 -27      Write 27 below 28. Subtract. The difference is 1.
   1      The remainder is 1.
```

Check your answer.
Multiply the quotient by the divisor. 39 × 3 = 117
Add the remainder. 117 + 1 = n
The sum should equal the dividend. 117 + 1 = 118

Divide. Multiply to check your answers.

1. 6)953 — 158 R5
2. 2)69 — 34 R1
3. 8)891 — 111 R3
4. 4)107 — 26 R3

Copyright © SRA/McGraw-Hill. Permission is granted to reproduce this page for classroom use.

*available separately

If you wish, you may keep your records in a shorter form.

Example:

Long Form	Shorter Form: With Zeros	Shorter Form: Without Zeros
1276 Remainder 4	Be careful to put the answers in the correct column.	Subtract and "bring down" only the next digit. Be careful to put the answers in the correct column.
6 70 200 1000 7)8936 7000 1936 1400 536 490 46 42 4	1276 R4 7)8936 7000 1936 1400 536 490 46 42 4	1276 R4 7)8936 7 19 14 53 49 46 42 4

Divide. Keep your records in any of the ways shown on this page. Use money if you like.

8. 5)100 **20**
9. 6)91 **15 R1**
10. 3)513 **171**
11. 2)41,312 **20,656**
12. 3)46 **15 R1**
13. 5)745 **149**
14. 4)804 **201**
15. 9)729 **81**
16. 7)91 **13**
17. 8)416 **52**
18. 2)7046 **3523**
19. 5)52,365 **10,473**

❷ Teach

COOPERATIVE LEARNING · MANIPULATIVES

Using the Student Pages Before students begin to work on page 362, review the division vocabulary at the bottom of the page. Have students work in groups of about four. Group members should use **play money*** and take turns keeping the records, making the transactions, and acting as the banker. The finished record for each problem should look like the example at the bottom of page 362. When students begin recording their own division to solve problems 8–19 on page 363, have them use the shortest form they feel comfortable with. Even though students are working in groups, each student should keep a record of each problem.

❸ Wrap-Up

5 MINUTES

In Closing Write the problem 5463 ÷ 4 on the chalkboard. Have students talk you through the division. Then have them identify the dividend, divisor, quotient, and remainder. (1365 R3)

ALTERNATIVE ASSESSMENT

Informal Assessment Circulate through the class as students work on the division problems on page 363. Notice which form of the algorithm they use, whether they apply the steps correctly, and whether they write the various parts of the algorithm in the right places.

Assessment Criteria

Did the student . . .

- ✓ contribute to solutions of problems in his or her group?
- ✓ communicate strategies used to divide and to record division?
- ✓ record the steps of division using one of the forms of the algorithm?
- ✓ correctly answer at least 75% of the division problems?

Homework Have students look through magazine or newspaper articles for examples of real-world division. Have them bring in clippings to display on a division bulletin board.

PRACTICE p. 105

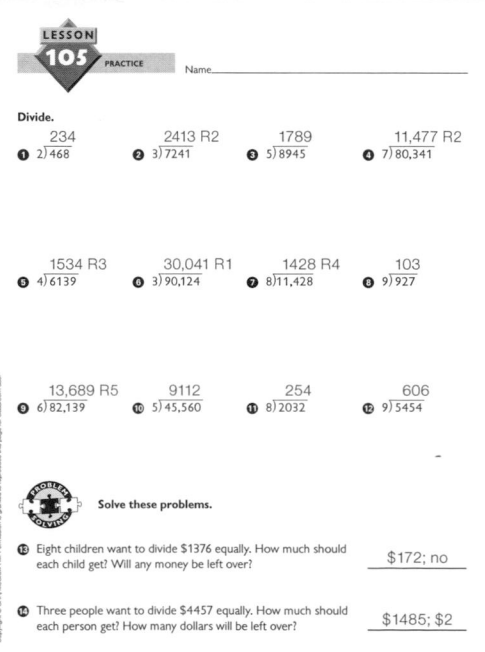

LESSON 105 PRACTICE Name________

Divide.

1. 2)468 234
2. 3)7241 2413 R2
3. 5)8945 1789
4. 7)80,341 11,477 R2
5. 4)6139 1534 R3
6. 3)90,124 30,041 R1
7. 8)11,428 1428 R4
8. 9)927 103
9. 6)82,139 13,689 R5
10. 5)45,560 9112
11. 8)2032 254
12. 9)5454 606

PROBLEM SOLVING **Solve these problems.**

13. Eight children want to divide $1376 equally. How much should each child get? Will any money be left over? $172; no
14. Three people want to divide $4457 equally. How much should each person get? How many dollars will be left over? $1485; $2

Copyright © SRA/McGraw-Hill. Permission is granted to reproduce this page for classroom use.

Math Explorations and Applications Level 4 • **105**

ENRICHMENT p. 105

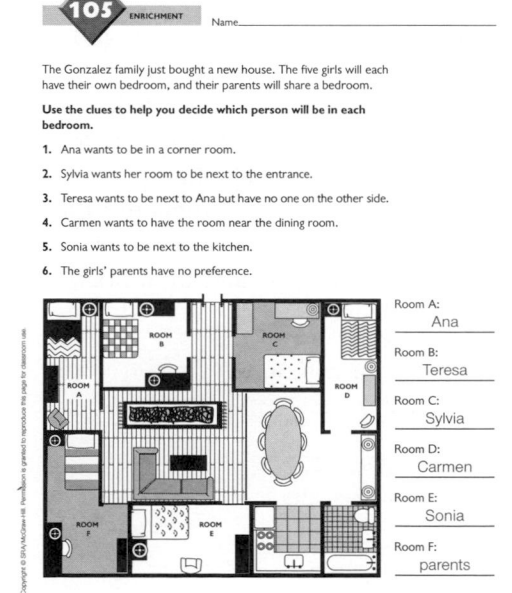

LESSON 105 ENRICHMENT Name________

The Gonzalez family just bought a new house. The five girls will each have their own bedroom, and their parents will share a bedroom.

Use the clues to help you decide which person will be in each bedroom.

1. Ana wants to be in a corner room.
2. Sylvia wants her room to be next to the entrance.
3. Teresa wants to be next to Ana but have no one on the other side.
4. Carmen wants to have the room near the dining room.
5. Sonia wants to be next to the kitchen.
6. The girls' parents have no preference.

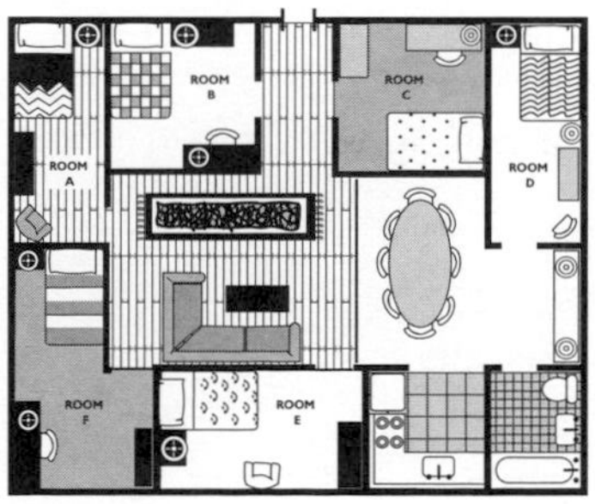

Room A: Ana

Room B: Teresa

Room C: Sylvia

Room D: Carmen

Room E: Sonia

Room F: parents

Copyright © SRA/McGraw-Hill. Permission is granted to reproduce this page for classroom use.

Math Explorations and Applications Level 4 • **105**

*available separately

LESSON 106

Student Edition pages 364–365

Practicing Division

LESSON PLANNER

Objectives

✓ to assess mastery of dividing by one-digit divisors

▶ to review the inverse relationship between multiplication and division and to show how to use multiplication to check division problems

Context of the Lesson This lesson, the third of 13 lessons on division with a one-digit divisor, contains a Mastery Checkpoint for this skill.

MANIPULATIVES

play money* or base-10 blocks* (optional)

flash cards (optional)

Program Resources

Practice Master 106

Enrichment Master 106

Assessment Master

For extra practice:
CD-ROM* Lesson 106

1 Warm-Up

5 MINUTES

Problem of the Day Present this problem: Write a different odd number in each empty box to form a divisor and a quotient that complete the equation with the given dividend. 315 ÷ □ = □ (9, 35 or 5, 63)

Problem-Solving Strategies Ask students who have solved the Problem of the Day to share how they solved it and any strategies they used.

MENTAL MATH On the chalkboard, write these pairs of problems that show the inverse relationship between multiplication and division. Include multidigit problems that students can solve mentally.

a.	5 x 50 = (250)	250 ÷ 5 = (50)
b.	240 x 20 = (4800)	4800 ÷ 20 = (240)
c.	50 x 20 = (1000)	1000 ÷ 50 = (20)

2 Teach

Using the Student Pages Encourage students to use the shortest form of the division algorithm that they are comfortable with when they solve the problems on page 364.

LESSON 106

Practicing Division

Practice division. Use money if you need to. Keep records in the way you like best. When there is a remainder, show it.

1. 3)591 — **197**	2. 4)6128 — **1532**	3. 6)144 — **24**	4. 7)574 — **82**
5. 8)232 — **29**	6. 9)241 — **26 R7**	7. 5)125 — **25**	8. 6)216 — **36**
9. 4)64 — **16**	10. 3)62 — **20 R2**	11. 2)90 — **45**	12. 5)0 — **0**
13. 3)296 — **98 R2**	14. 4)425 — **106 R1**	15. 6)2141 — **356 R5**	16. 5)935 — **187**
17. 4)648 — **162**	18. 8)3426 — **428 R2**	19. 5)614 — **122 R4**	20. 6)472 — **78 R4**
21. 5)153 — **30 R3**	22. 7)381 — **54 R3**	23. 2)547 — **273 R1**	24. 7)8496 — **1213 R5**

Check your answers.

a. Multiply divisor × quotient.
b. Add the remainder.
c. You should get the dividend.

Examples:

7)97 = 13 R6   Check: 13 × 7 = 91   91 + 6 = 97

3)861 = 287   Check: 287 × 3 = 861

7)439 = 62 R5   Check: 62 × 7 = 434   434 + 5 = 439

RETEACHING

MANIPULATIVES Continue to allow students to perform division using **play money*** or **base-10 materials***. Help them to verbalize the steps of division as they record their actions in one of the standard algorithmic forms. Have them use **flash cards**, games, or other drill and practice materials with classmates or at home with family members.

PRACTICE p. 106

LESSON 106 PRACTICE   Name____________________

Find the missing digit.

1. 4)3□75 = 968 R3; 36, 27, 24, 35, 32, 3; □ is 8.	2. □)4634 = 662; 42, 43, 42, 14, 14; □ is 7.	3. 9)74,637 = 8□93; 72, 26, 18, 83, 81, 27, 27; □ is 2.	4. 3)2□57 = 985 R2; 27, 25, 24, 17, 15, 2; □ is 9.
5. 8)36,429 = 4553; 32, 44, 40, 42, 40, 29, 24, □; □ is 5.	6. 6)54,□21 = 9053 R3; 54, 32, 30, 21, 18, 3; □ is 3.	7. 5)□467 = 893 R2; 40, 46, 45, 17, 15, 2; □ is 4.	8. □)17,738 = 2534; 14, 37, 35, 23, 21, 28, 28; □ is 7.

106 • *Math Explorations and Applications* Level 4

Copyright © SRA/McGraw-Hill. Permission is granted to reproduce this page for classroom use.

*available separately

ALGEBRA READINESS

Find the missing digit.

25. 5)145 → 29; 10, 4■5, 45 — **4**
26. 9)928 → 103 R1; 9, 28, 2■7, 1 — **7**
27. 9)929 → 1■3 R2; 9, 29, 27, 2 — **0**
28. 7)309 → 4■ R1; 28, 29, 28, 1 — **4**
29. ■)624 → 104; 6, 24, 24 — **6**
30. 4)721 → 18■ R1; 4, 32, 32, 1 — **0**
31. 8)67■8 → 84 R6; 64, 38, 32, 6 — **8**
32. 9)907 → 10■ R7; 9, 7 — **0**
33. 8)974 → 1■1 R6; 8, 17, 16, 14, 8, 6 — **2**
34. ■)862 → 287 R1; 6, 26, 24, 22, 21, 1 — **3**
35. 8)923 → 115 R■; 8, 12, 8, 43, 40, 3 — **3**
36. 3)800 → 26■ R2; 6, 20, 18, 20, 18, 2 — **6**
37. 5)540 → ■08; 5, 40, 40 — **1**
38. 5)750 → 1■0; 5, 25, 25 — **5**
39. 7)9■0 → 130; 7, 21, 21 — **1**
40. 4)829 → 2■7 R1; 8, 29, 28, 1 — **0**

FANTASTIC FACT

How big can the world's largest turtle get? Pretty big! The shell of a leatherback turtle can grow as large as a king-sized bed.

ALGEBRA READINESS

Before assigning page 365, discuss the format with the class. Students should work through each problem or a part of it until they can figure out the missing digit. Solve one or two with the class, and then have students complete the remaining problems.

3 Wrap-Up

5 MINUTES

In Closing Have students tell how to check whether 51 R5 is the correct answer to 362 ÷ 7.

ANALYZING ANSWERS

For students who have not yet mastered dividing a whole number by a one-digit divisor, the problem may be with basic multiplication, division, or subtraction facts. Provide appropriate review and practice to help students correct their errors.

Mastery Checkpoint 17a

At about this time, most students should demonstrate mastery of dividing a whole number by a one-digit divisor by correctly answering at least 80% of the problems on page 364 or on Assessment Blackline Masters page 44. Results of this assessment may be recorded on the Mastery Checkpoint Chart.

ENRICHMENT p. 106

LESSON 106 ENRICHMENT Name__________

SCIENCE CONNECTION

You are getting ready to lower research instruments and cameras into the deepest parts of the world's oceans.

These include:

Mariana Trench (east of the Philippines)	36,198 ft deep
Puerto Rico Trench (just north of Puerto Rico)	28,374 ft deep
Java Trench (just south of the island of Java)	25,344 ft deep
Eurasia Basin (near the North Pole)	17,880 ft deep

Find these locations on a map. Solve these problems.

1. You can safely lower your instruments by cable at the rate of 8 feet every 30 seconds. How many minutes will it take your instruments to reach the bottom of each trench or basin? (Round any remainders.)
   - Mariana Trench: 4525 half-minutes = 2263 minutes
   - Puerto Rico Trench: 3547 half-minutes = 1774 minutes
   - Java Trench: 3168 half-minutes = 1584 minutes
   - Eurasia Basin: 2235 half-minutes = 1118 minutes
2. Now convert your times to hours. Round to the nearest hour.
   - Mariana Trench: 38 hours; Puerto Rico Trench: 30 hours
   - Java Trench: 26 hours; Eurasia Basin: 19 hours
3. One of the deepest lakes in the world is Lake Tanganyika in Africa (4823 feet deep). Find this lake on a map. How long will it take your instruments to reach the bottom? Convert the time to hours. Round to the nearest hour.
   603 half-minutes = 302 minutes = 5 hours

Copyright © SRA/McGraw-Hill. Permission is granted to reproduce this page for classroom use.

ASSESSMENT p. 44

UNIT 5 **Mastery Checkpoint 17a** Dividing by a one-digit divisor (Lesson 106)

Name__________

The student demonstrates mastery by correctly answering at least 16 of the 20 problems.

Divide. Watch for remainders.

1. 4)756 → 189
2. 3)4269 → 1423
3. 5)210 → 42
4. 6)558 → 93
5. 8)968 → 121
6. 9)306 → 34
7. 8)501 → 62 R5
8. 4)200 → 50
9. 7)315 → 45
10. 5)669 → 133 R4
11. 8)762 → 95 R2
12. 3)291 → 97
13. 5)475 → 95
14. 4)213 → 53 R1
15. 7)912 → 130 R2

Find the missing digit.

16. 5)6[8]3 → 136 R3; −5, 18, −15, 33, −30, 3
17. [6])586 → 97 R4; −54, 46, −42, 4
18. 9)798 → [8]8 R6; −72, 78, −72, 6
19. [7])693 → 99; −63, 63, −63, 0

Solve.

20. Peg has 146 videos that she must put back on the shelves at Play It Again Video Store. If each shelf is only allowed to have nine videos, how many shelves will she be able to fully stock? 16

Copyright © SRA/McGraw-Hill. Permission is granted to reproduce this page for classroom use.

Assessment Criteria

Did the student . . .

- ✓ use the shortest form of the division algorithm with which he or she is comfortable?
- ✓ contribute to the discussion of checking division with multiplication?
- ✓ communicate strategies used to find missing digits in division?
- ✓ correctly answer at least 80% of the division problems?

Homework Have each student create a poster or study guide that presents the steps of the division algorithm and the standard method of checking division. Display the completed works in the classroom.

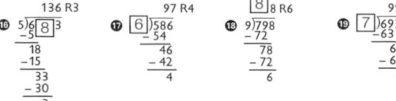

LESSON 107

Student Edition pages 366–369

Division Review: Missing Digits

LESSON PLANNER

Objectives

- ▶ to provide practice with multiplication facts and division with one-digit divisors
- ▶ to provide an intuitive introduction to prime and composite numbers
- ▶ to develop the broad ability to use mathematical common sense

Context of the Lesson This is the fourth of 13 lessons on division with one-digit divisors. Prime and composite numbers will be presented in a more formal manner in Lesson 119. This lesson also contains Part 1 of "Estimating Is Rough," a five-part Thinking Story.

MANIPULATIVES

calculators*

Program Resources

Number Cubes

Practice Master 107

Enrichment Master 107

For career connections:
Careers and Math*

For extra practice:
CD-ROM* Lesson 107
Cumulative Review, page 558

MIXED PRACTICE

LESSON 107

Division Review: Missing Digits

ALGEBRA READINESS

Find the missing digit.

1. 5)676 = 1■5 R1 (**3**); 5, 17, 15, 26, 25, 1
2. 6)824 = 1■7 R2 (**3**); 6, 22, 18, 44, 42, 2
3. 4)537 = 134 R1; 4, 13, 1■ (**2**), 17, 16, 1
4. 3)8■9 (**0**) = 269 R2; 6, 20, 18, 29, 27, 2
5. 9)307 = ■4 R1 (**3**); 27, 37, 36, 1
6. 8)878 = 1■9 R6 (**0**); 8, 78, 72, 6
7. 4)807 = 20■ R3 (**1**); 8, 7, 4, 3
8. 2)207 = 1■3 R1 (**0**); 2, 7, 6, 1
9. 7)763 = 109; 7■ (**7**), 63, 63
10. 9)450 = 50; 4■ (**5**)
11. 3)627 = 209; 6, 2■7 (**2**), 27
12. 7)703 = 100 R3; 7, ■3 (**3**)
13. 7)405 = 5■ R6 (**7**); 35, 55, 49, 6
14. 4)270 = 67 R■ (**2**); 24, 30, 28, 2
15. 5)435 = ■7 (**8**); 40, 35, 35
16. 5)376 = 7■ R1 (**5**); 35, 26, 25, 1

366 • Division

---

1 Warm-Up 5 MINUTES

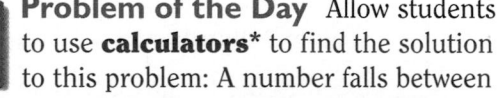

Problem of the Day Allow students to use **calculators*** to find the solution to this problem: A number falls between 100 and 300. The sum of its digits is 12. If you divide the number by 3 or by 5, there is a two-digit quotient and no remainder. But if you divide the number by 2 or by 4, there is a two-digit quotient and a remainder of 1. What is the number? (165)

Problem-Solving Strategies Ask students who have solved the Problem of the Day to share how they solved it and any strategies they used.

Math Connection Reinforce ideas developed in the Thinking Story by providing ongoing estimation activities students can try. You might select a group of students to be an estimation committee for a particular estimate. Allow time for committee members to ask questions and get information from classmates before making their best estimate. Have estimators explain how they arrived at their estimates and describe any strategies they used to help make them. Whenever possible, have students check their estimates. Alternate groups and estimation activities throughout this unit. Some ideas for student estimating activities include: (1) How much chalk will be used in the classroom in a week, a month, or a school year? (2) How many people are in the school building on a particular day? (3) How many cartons of milk are served in the cafeteria on a given day? (4) How many students will be in class tomorrow? (5) How many light bulbs are in all the school's classrooms?

*available separately

COOPERATIVE LEARNING

GAME

Diviso Game

Players: Two or more
Materials: Two 0–5 cubes, two 5–10 cubes
Object: To get a quotient with no remainder
Math Focus: Dividing by one-digit divisors and mental factorization

RULES

1. Roll any two cubes.
2. Make a division problem in this way: Use the product of the numbers rolled as the dividend. Choose another number as the divisor, but do not use either of the numbers rolled, their product, or the numbers 1 or 0.
3. Find the quotient.
4. The player who makes a problem with no remainder earns one point. The first player to earn seven points wins.

SAMPLE GAME

Round One

Tess rolls: 3 2

$3 \times 2 = 6$

She cannot use 3, 2, 6, or 1 as a divisor.
Tess does not score.

Kate rolls: 0 8

$0 \times 8 = 0$

She chooses 7 as the divisor.

$7\overline{)0}$ = 0 Kate earns one point.
Kate wins this round.

Round Two

Tess rolls : 7 10

$7 \times 10 = 70$

She chooses 2 as the divisor.

$2\overline{)70}$ = 35 Tess earns one point.

Kate rolls: 5 4

$5 \times 4 = 20$

She chooses 2 as the divisor.

$2\overline{)20}$ = 10 Kate earns one point.
This round is a tie.

Literature Connection Read Eleanor Coerr's *Sadako and the Thousand Paper Cranes,* or excerpts from it, to the class. Have students use multiplication or division to determine how many paper cranes each person in the class would have to fold to make 1000 cranes.

MENTAL MATH Present division fact problems with and without remainders. Have students show thumbs up if there is a remainder and thumbs down if there is no remainder.

a. 43 ÷ 7 (thumbs up) **b.** 58 ÷ 8 (thumbs up)
c. 28 ÷ 4 (thumbs down) **d.** 50 ÷ 7 (thumbs up)
e. 54 ÷ 9 (thumbs down) **f.** 24 ÷ 6 (thumbs down)
g. 31 ÷ 5 (thumbs up) **h.** 48 ÷ 8 (thumbs down)
i. 83 ÷ 9 (thumbs up) **j.** 90 ÷ 9 (thumbs down)

2 Teach

Using the Student Pages Demonstrate the "Diviso" game for division practice so that those who finish page 366 early can play it. Then have students work on page 366 independently.

GAME The "Diviso" game focuses on dividing by one-digit divisors and mental factorization. Play several sample rounds as the class watches. Identify the divisors that are forbidden by rule 2. Explain how the answer would come out without a remainder if you used one of the forbidden divisors. Have students play in groups of three or four. A copy of this game can also be found on page 22 of the Home Connections Blackline Masters.

SPECIAL NEEDS

Meeting Individual Needs

Regardless of their particular learning styles, some students resist making estimates because they prefer exact answers. Others lack the confidence to make estimates because they have had little experience doing so. Guide these students to recognize the value of estimation by finding various informal situations in which they can make estimates. For instance, you can have them estimate how long it will take to wash the chalkboard, read a story, complete an assignment, walk to the school office and back, and so on. Encourage them to make educated guesses based on other information they know.

◆ LESSON 107 Division Review: Missing Digits

Teach

Using the Thinking Story "Estimating Is Rough (Part 1)" explores making reasonable estimates by observing, selecting pertinent information, and combining this information with general knowledge or common sense.

Answers to Thinking Story Questions:

1. Estimating is a kind of guessing. It is sometimes called "educated guessing," which means guessing that makes good use of what is known. Guessing and estimating are used when an exact answer is not possible or when an approximate answer is good enough, easier to obtain, or makes more sense than a precise answer.
2. Guessing is always possible, even when there is not any clue as to what the answer is. But an estimate requires some clues or knowledge to go on. Generally, the more information used, the more a guess becomes an estimate.
3. Seven years and a day was not an estimate, but an exact figure based on knowing the girl's birthday. Sixty years was not an estimate, but an upper limit. Twenty years would be a reasonable estimate of the age of a university student, so it could be said that Mr. Muddle was estimating in this case, except that he knew that the girl was not a university student.
4. Many clues can help estimate age: size, style of dress, grayness of hair, years in school, ages of brothers and sisters, ages of grandchildren, and so on. In discussing these clues, point out how each can be misleading; for example, people may gray prematurely.
5. Since Mrs. Breezy is Marcus's mother, it might suggest that she is somewhere in the 28–50 age range. A wide range of estimates is acceptable, but it is more important that students pick up evidence and use it to sharpen their estimates.

MATH JOURNAL: In their Math Journals have students develop a character sketch of Mrs. Breezy based on the things she says and does in this story.

◆ LESSON 107 Division Review: Missing Digits

THINKING STORY

Estimating Is Rough

Part 1

"I found a job you might try for," said Mrs. Breezy. "It's a job as chief estimator."

"I'll take it," said Mr. Muddle. "What does an estimator do?"

"An estimator tries to make good guesses about amounts. I'll show you. See that girl out in the hall? How old would you say she is?"

"Seven years and one day," said Mr. Muddle.

"Estimating doesn't mean making an exact guess. You should just say more or less how old you think she is."

"All right," said Mr. Muddle. "My estimate is 60 years old."

"That can't be right," said Mrs. Breezy. "Anyone can see that she is just a young girl."

RETEACHING

No reteaching is recommended at this time. Continue to provide practice on skills introduced in previous lessons, as necessary. You may want to assign Enrichment Master 107 for this lesson.

"You said more or less," Mr. Muddle answered. "I chose less. I'm sure she is less than 60 years old. If I had chosen more then I would have said she is more than one year old."

"That's not the idea," said Mrs. Breezy. "Your estimate should be as close to right as possible. You have to look for evidence and use it to make a good guess."

"I see. It's like being a detective. In that case, I have a new estimate: I estimate that she is 20 years old."

"Now, what would make you think that?" Mrs. Breezy asked.

"Her sweatshirt," said Mr. Muddle. "It has *Harvard University* written on it, and 20 years old should be a good guess for the age of a university student."

"Do you really think a young child like that goes to a university?" Mrs. Breezy asked.

"Not at all," said Mr. Muddle. "Lots of people who don't go to a university wear university sweatshirts. I see them all over."

"Then you shouldn't have based your estimate on her sweatshirt," said Mrs. Breezy. "You should use evidence that you can trust."

"Oh," said Mr. Muddle. "In that case, I will stick with my first estimate." He opened the door and asked the girl, "Are you seven years and one day old?"

"You know I am, Uncle Otto," the girl said. "You and Aunt Emma were at my birthday party yesterday."

. . . to be continued

Work in groups. Discuss your answers and how you figured them out. Then compare your answers with those of other groups. **Answers are in margin.**

1. In what ways is estimating the same as guessing?
2. In what ways is estimating different from guessing?
3. Was Mr. Muddle estimating? If not, what was he doing?
4. What are some clues you would use to estimate a person's age?
5. What would be a good estimate for the age of Mrs. Breezy?

Use the Cumulative Review on page 558 after this lesson.

PRACTICE p. 107

LESSON 107 PRACTICE Name________________

Find the missing digit.

1. 8)418 = 52 R☐; 40; 18; 16; 2 — ☐ is 2.
2. 6)540 = 90; ☐4 — ☐ is 5.
3. 2)17☐ = 8 9 R1; 16; 19; 18; 1 — ☐ is 9.
4. 7)339 = 48 R3; ☐8; 59; 56; 3 — ☐ is 2.
5. 3)914 = 3☐4 R2; 9; 14; 12; 2 — ☐ is 0.
6. 5)504 = 100 R4; 5; ☐ — ☐ is 4.
7. 9)175 = 19 R☐; 9; 85; 81; 4 — ☐ is 4.
8. 6)161 = ☐6 R5; 12; 41; 36; 5 — ☐ is 2.
9. 3)268 = ☐9 R1; 24; 28; 27; 1 — ☐ is 8.
10. 4)540 = 135; 4; 14; 1☐; 20; 20 — ☐ is 2.
11. 8)366 = ☐5 R6; 32; 46; 40; 6 — ☐ is 4.
12. 6)☐20 = 103 R2; 6; 20; 18; 2 — ☐ is 6.

Copyright © SRA/McGraw-Hill. Permission is granted to reproduce this page for classroom use.

Math Explorations and Applications Level 4 • **107**

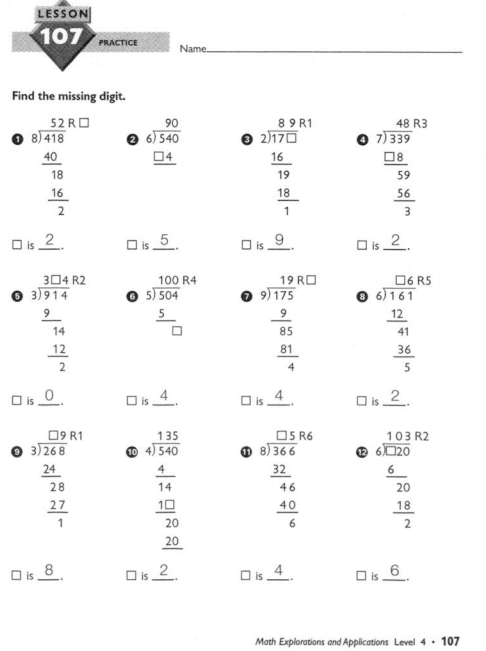

ENRICHMENT p. 107

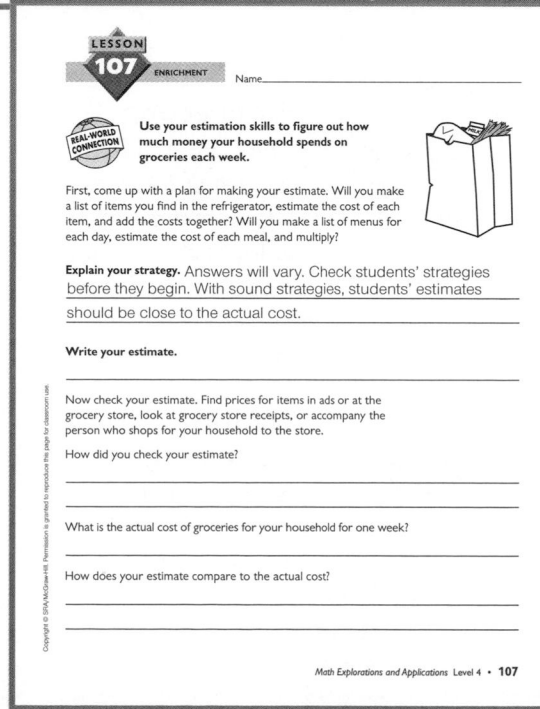

LESSON 107 ENRICHMENT Name________________

REAL-WORLD CONNECTION

Use your estimation skills to figure out how much money your household spends on groceries each week.

First, come up with a plan for making your estimate. Will you make a list of items you find in the refrigerator, estimate the cost of each item, and add the costs together? Will you make a list of menus for each day, estimate the cost of each meal, and multiply?

Explain your strategy. Answers will vary. Check students' strategies before they begin. With sound strategies, students' estimates should be close to the actual cost.

Write your estimate. ________________

Now check your estimate. Find prices for items in ads or at the grocery store, look at grocery store receipts, or accompany the person who shops for your household to the store.

How did you check your estimate? ________________

What is the actual cost of groceries for your household for one week? ________________

How does your estimate compare to the actual cost? ________________

Copyright © SRA/McGraw-Hill. Permission is granted to reproduce this page for classroom use.

Math Explorations and Applications Level 4 • **107**

3 Wrap-Up

5 MINUTES

In Closing Have students give examples of real-life situations in which they made estimates. Invite them to describe the information they used to make reasonable estimates.

ALTERNATIVE ASSESSMENT

Informal Assessment Observe students as they solve the missing-digit problems and play the "Diviso" game. Look for evidence that they know basic multiplication and division facts and that they follow the steps of the general division algorithm to complete page 366. As they play the "Diviso" game, have students explain the reasons for the choices they make in order to evaluate their logical reasoning ability and number sense.

Assessment Criteria

Did the student . . .

- ✓ correctly answer at least 75% of the missing-digit problems?
- ✓ actively participate in playing the "Diviso" game?
- ✓ contribute to the Thinking Story discussion?
- ✓ communicate an understanding of the distinction between guessing and estimating?

Homework Have students estimate three quantities from around their homes, such as the number of socks in a drawer, cans of food on a shelf, or magazines in a basket. Have them record the estimates, then count to find the exact numbers. Ask them to tell what information they used to make their estimates.

LESSON 108

Student Edition pages 370–371

Using Division: Unit Cost

LESSON PLANNER

Objectives

- ▶ to provide practice in dividing by a one-digit divisor
- ▶ to provide practice in using division to find unit costs and determine better buys

Context of the Lesson This is the fifth of 13 lessons on division with one-digit divisors.

MANIPULATIVES

food ads (optional)

play money* (optional)

Program Resources

Number Cubes

Practice Master 108

Enrichment Master 108

For extra practice:
CD-ROM* Lesson 108

1 Warm-Up 5 MINUTES

Problem of the Day Present this problem: Replace each blank with a different digit to form a division problem that checks. □ 71 ÷ 4 = □ 9 □ R3 (771 ÷ 4 = 192 R3)

Problem-Solving Strategies Ask students who have solved the Problem of the Day to share how they solved it and any strategies they used.

MENTAL MATH To emphasize inverse operations, give students pairs of related multidigit multiplication and division problems. Write these problems on the chalkboard:

a.	80 × 30 = (2400)	2400 ÷ 30 = (80)
b.	6 × 50 = (300)	300 ÷ 6 = (50)
c.	7 × 20 = (140)	140 ÷ 20 = (7)
d.	8 × 40 = (320)	320 ÷ 40 = (8)
e.	90 × 20 = (1800)	1800 ÷ 90 = (20)
f.	40 × 80 = (3200)	3200 ÷ 80 = (40)
g.	100 × 90 = (9000)	9000 ÷ 100 = (90)
h.	80 × 60 = (4800)	4800 ÷ 60 = (80)

PROBLEM SOLVING

LESSON 108

Using Division: Unit Cost

REAL-WORLD CONNECTION

Heather wants to buy soup. The store offers two cans of soup for 72¢ or three cans of the same kind of soup for 96¢.

How much does soup cost per can if you buy it in groups of two cans?

Per means "for each." We can find the cost for each can by dividing 72 by 2.

$$\begin{array}{r} 36 \\ 2\overline{)72} \\ \underline{6} \\ 12 \\ \underline{12} \end{array}$$

The soup costs 36¢ per can when you buy it in groups of two cans.

How much does soup cost per can if you buy it in groups of three cans? We can find the cost per can by dividing 96 by 3.

$$\begin{array}{r} 32 \\ 3\overline{)96} \\ \underline{9} \\ 6 \\ \underline{6} \end{array}$$

The soup costs 32¢ per can when you buy it in groups of three.

◆ Which do you think is the better buy? Why? **buying in groups of three; it costs less per can**

Solve these problems.

Luis wants to buy milk. A 4-quart container costs $2.56 (256¢). An 8-quart container of the same kind of milk at a different store costs $4.96 (496¢).

1. How much does milk cost per quart in a 4-quart container? **64¢**
2. How much does milk cost per quart in an 8-quart container? **62¢**
3. Which do you think is the better buy? Why? **the 8-quart container; it costs less per quart**

◆ Could you have found the better buy without dividing?*

*** yes; you could double the cost of the 4-quart container and compare that amount to the cost of the 8-quart container**

370 • Division

Literature Connection With the class, read *The Doorbell Rang* by Pat Hutchins. Have students perform the written algorithm for each situation that occurs when the doorbell rings and the cookies must be divided among a different number of guests.

Real-World Connection By law, many supermarkets must provide the unit cost for items they sell. Have students look at shelf displays in local supermarkets and sketch a unit price label, noting the information given.

RETEACHING

MANIPULATIVES Have students who demonstrate difficulty in finding unit cost use **play money*** to model the division required in each situation presented in the lesson. Have them record their actions in the standard algorithmic form.

*available separately

Yoko wants to buy rice. A 2-kilogram bag costs $1.20. A 5-kilogram bag costs $2.65.

4. How much does rice cost per kilogram in 2-kilogram bags? **60¢**
5. How much does rice cost per kilogram in 5-kilogram bags? **53¢**
6. Which do you think is the better buy? Why? **the 5-kg bag; it costs less per kg**

Solve.

7. Three cans of soup cost 75¢. How much is one can of soup? **25¢**
8. Seven pencils cost 91¢. How much is that per pencil? **13¢**
9. Three quarts of milk cost $1.74 (174¢). How much is that per quart? **58¢**
10. Four apples cost 92¢. How much is that per apple? **23¢**
11. Six oranges cost $1.32 (132¢). How much is that per orange? **22¢**
12. An 8-pound turkey costs $9.50 (950¢). A 9-pound turkey costs $11.40 (1140¢). Which turkey is the better buy? Why? **the 8-pound turkey; it costs less per pound**
13. Three pads of paper cost $1.38 (138¢). How much is that per pad? **46¢**
14. An eight-bottle carton of soda pop costs $3.84 (384¢). How much is that per bottle? **48¢**
15. Nine containers of yogurt cost $5.49 (549¢). How much is that per container of yogurt? **61¢**
16. Ten pencil erasers cost $1.20 (120¢). How much is that per eraser? **12¢**

PRACTICE p. 108

LESSON 108 PRACTICE Name________________

Solve these problems.

Tim wants to buy some popcorn. An 8-ounce bag costs $1.60. A 12-ounce bag costs $1.80.

1. How much does the popcorn cost per ounce in the 8-ounce bag? 20¢
2. How much does the popcorn cost per ounce in the 12-ounce bag? 15¢
3. Which is the better buy? 12-ounce bag

Carol wants to buy some peanuts. She can buy a 3-pound bag for $2.55 or a 5-pound bag for $4.40.

4. How much do the peanuts cost per pound in the 5-pound bag? 88¢
5. How much do the peanuts cost per pound in the 3-pound bag? 85¢
6. Which is the better buy? 3-pound bag
7. Eight erasers cost $1.28. How much is that per eraser? 16¢
8. Five bananas cost $1.10. How much is that per banana? 22¢
9. Six containers of yogurt cost $4.14. How much is that per container? 69¢
10. A box of 12 cookies costs $1.08. How much is that per cookie? 9¢
11. Three tubes of toothpaste cost $6.87. How much is that per tube? $2.29
12. Eight tangerines cost $2.80. How much is that per tangerine? 35¢
13. A four-bottle package of juice costs $1.16. How much is that per bottle? 29¢
14. An 8-ounce package of cheese costs $2.00. A 16-ounce package of cheese costs $3.36. Which is the better buy? 16-ounce package

108 • *Math Explorations and Applications* Level 4

Copyright © SRA/McGraw-Hill. Permission is granted to reproduce this page for classroom use.

ENRICHMENT p. 108

LESSON 108 ENRICHMENT Name________________

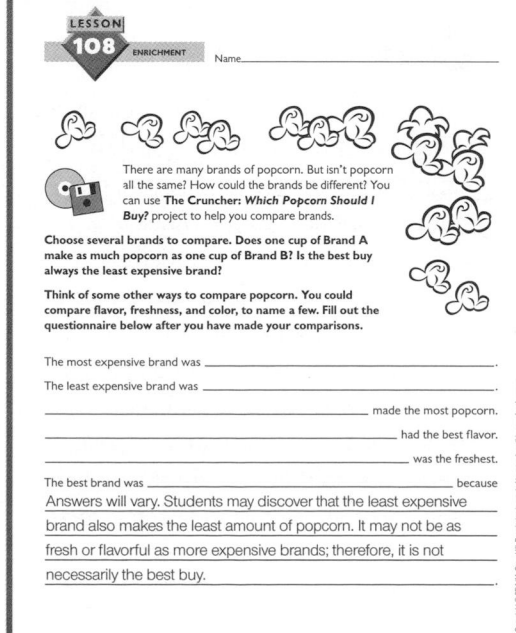

There are many brands of popcorn. But isn't popcorn all the same? How could the brands be different? You can use **The Cruncher: *Which Popcorn Should I Buy?*** project to help you compare brands.

Choose several brands to compare. Does one cup of Brand A make as much popcorn as one cup of Brand B? Is the best buy always the least expensive brand?

Think of some other ways to compare popcorn. You could compare flavor, freshness, and color, to name a few. Fill out the questionnaire below after you have made your comparisons.

The most expensive brand was ________________.

The least expensive brand was ________________.

________________ made the most popcorn.

________________ had the best flavor.

________________ was the freshest.

The best brand was ________________ because Answers will vary. Students may discover that the least expensive brand also makes the least amount of popcorn. It may not be as fresh or flavorful as more expensive brands; therefore, it is not necessarily the best buy.

108 • *Math Explorations and Applications* Level 4

Copyright © SRA/McGraw-Hill. Permission is granted to reproduce this page for classroom use.

2 Teach

Using the Student Pages Go over the examples and discussion questions on page 370 with the class. Talk about the meaning of the term *better buy.* Students may recall the discussion of better buys in Lesson 67. Point out that in the case of the soup, the less expensive item is a better buy only if you can use the extra can of soup. You might want to mention that while other factors such as spoilage, taste, quality, or convenience of a particular store are not relevant in this lesson, they should be considered in real life.

With the class, check the answers for unit costs given in the example. Encourage students to do the same when they work on the remaining problems. After students finish the problems on page 371, discuss them together. Students who finish early may play the "Diviso" game (page 367) in pairs or in small groups for division practice.

3 Wrap-Up

5 MINUTES

In Closing Have students explain the meaning of the terms *unit cost, per,* and *better buy* and explain how to determine unit cost.

ALTERNATIVE ASSESSMENT

MANIPULATIVES

Performance Assessment Provide **store advertisements, newspaper ads,** or **flyers** that describe groups of items for which students can find the unit cost and determine the better buy. Have them present their findings so you can evaluate whether they grasp the concept of unit cost and whether they divided correctly.

Assessment Criteria

Did the student . . .

✓ contribute to the discussion of unit cost?

✓ communicate strategies used to determine the better buy?

✓ correctly answer at least 75% of the word problems?

Homework Have students determine the better buy for a product of their choice and write a brief summary of their findings.

LESSON 109

Student Edition pages 372–373

Dividing by a One-Digit Divisor: Short Form

LESSON PLANNER

Objectives

- ▶ to introduce the "short form" division algorithm
- ▶ to provide practice in dividing and in checking division by multiplying

Context of the Lesson This is the sixth of 13 lessons on division with one-digit divisors.

MANIPULATIVES

none

Program Resources

Practice Master 109

Enrichment Master 109

For extra practice:
CD-ROM* Lesson 109

1 Warm-Up (5 MINUTES)

Problem of the Day Present the following problem, explaining that there are several possible answers: Using the digits 4, 3, 2, and 1, form a division problem that has a two-digit quotient and a remainder. Digits may repeat, and each digit must appear at least once. (One possible solution is 43 ÷ 2 = 21 R1.)

Problem-Solving Strategies Ask students who have solved the Problem of the Day to share how they solved it and any strategies they used.

MENTAL MATH Present students with related pairs of multiplication and division problems. Write these pairs on the chalkboard:

a.	30 × 70 = (2100)	2100 ÷ 30 = (70)
b.	60 × 80 = (4800)	4800 ÷ 80 = (60)
c.	40 × 90 = (3600)	3600 ÷ 90 = (40)
d.	50 × 10 = (500)	500 ÷ 50 = (10)
e.	90 × 60 = (5400)	5400 ÷ 60 = (90)
f.	90 × 90 = (8100)	8100 ÷ 90 = (90)
g.	30 × 90 = (2700)	2700 ÷ 30 = (90)
h.	90 × 50 = (4500)	4500 ÷ 90 = (50)

EXPLORE

LESSON 109

Dividing by a One-Digit Divisor: Short Form

There is a shorter method of keeping division records.

Short Form	Shorter Form	
1 7)8936 7 **19**	**1** 7)8 ¹9 3 6	There is one whole 7 in 8 (write 1 in the answer above the 8). The remainder is 1 (write a small 1 in front of the 9).
1**2** 7)8936 7 19 **14** **53**	1 **2** 7)8 ¹9 ⁵3 6	There are two 7s in 19 (write 2 in the answer above the 9). The remainder is 5 (write a 5 in front of the 3).
12**7** 7)8936 7 19 14 53 **49** **46**	1 2 **7** 7)8 ¹9 ⁵3 ⁴6	There are seven 7s in 53 (write a 7 in the answer above the 3). The remainder is 4 (write a 4 in front of the 6).
127**6 R4** 7)8936 7 19 14 53 49 46 **42** **4**	1 2 7 **6 R4** 7)8 ¹9 ⁵3 ⁴6	There are six 7s in 46 (write a 6 in the answer above the 6). The remainder is 4 (write R4 in the answer).

Why teach it this way?

In this unit students have learned several variations of the division algorithm. After they learn the short form, many students prefer it to the other variations. However, as students become more proficient with division, they should use the algorithmic form with which they feel most comfortable. Have students who use different variations of the algorithm compare their work so they can see that, when used correctly, all the algorithmic forms yield the same quotient.

RETEACHING

Go over the steps of division slowly with students. At each step, ask them the meaning of the numbers they write. Provide support with division facts, if necessary, so that students can focus on the process of the algorithm.

*available separately

Divide. Use whichever method you prefer. Check your answers to the first five problems by multiplying.

1. 7)343 — **49** Check: Does 7 × quotient = 343?
2. 6)174 — **29** Check: Does 6 × quotient = 174?
3. 2)317 — **158 R1** Check: Does (2 × quotient) + **remainder** = 317?
4. 5)812 — **162 R2** Check: Does (5 × quotient) + **remainder** = 812?
5. 9)342 — **38** Check: Does 9 × quotient = 342?

Divide. Use shortcuts when you can.

6. 3)876 **292**	7. 4)512 **128**	8. 4)1000 **250**	9. 8)54 **6 R6**	10. 5)476 **95 R1**
11. 1)42,506 **42,506**	12. 6)372 **62**	13. 3)10 **3 R1**	14. 0)15 **not allowed**	15. 9)289 **32 R1**
16. 3)345 **115**	17. 7)267 **38 R1**	18. 8)849 **106 R1**	19. 4)271 **67 R3**	20. 6)8596 **1432 R4**
21. 5)210 **42**	22. 2)471 **235 R1**	23. 4)1003 **250 R3**	24. 3)4621 **1540 R1**	25. 4)685 **171 R1**
26. 7)496 **70 R6**	27. 6)1479 **246 R3**	28. 8)432 **54**	29. 8)764 **95 R4**	30. 3)456 **152**

- Did you get an answer to problem 14? **no**
- Is there any answer that would work? **no**
- Can it ever be that 0 × a number = 15? **no**

There is no number you can multiply by 0 to get 15. So, no answer could check, unless you decided that the remainder is 15. But the remainder is not supposed to be greater than the divisor. Even if you said the remainder is 15, then any number could be the quotient. But that is not useful. So we make this rule:

Division by 0 is not allowed.

2 Teach

Using the Student Pages Guide students through one or more problems similar to the example on page 372. Highlight the relationship between the shorter and shortest forms of the algorithm. Once students know how to use the shortest form, they should be free to use whichever form they prefer.

Go over problems 1 and 3 on page 373 to make sure that students understand how to check an answer to division by multiplying the divisor by the quotient and adding the remainder, if there is one. Then have students complete the page on their own. Discuss problem 14 with the class by going over the explanation at the bottom of the page.

3 Wrap-Up

5 MINUTES

In Closing Discuss the similarities and differences between the shorter and shortest forms of the division algorithm. Have students demonstrate both forms to solve 435 ÷ 6. (72 R3)

ALTERNATIVE ASSESSMENT

Informal Assessment Circulate throughout the room as students complete the lesson so you can observe them as they work on division and checking division by multiplication. Have students verbalize what they are doing. Point to various numbers in the algorithm and have students explain why they wrote them.

Assessment Criteria

Did the student . . .

- ✓ contribute to the discussion of the shortest form of division?
- ✓ demonstrate understanding of the relationship between the two short forms?
- ✓ correctly use multiplication to check answers to division?
- ✓ correctly answer at least 75% of the division problems on page 373?

Homework Have students play the "Diviso" game with family members for division practice. A copy of this game can also be found on page 22 of the Home Connections Blackline Masters.

PRACTICE p. 109

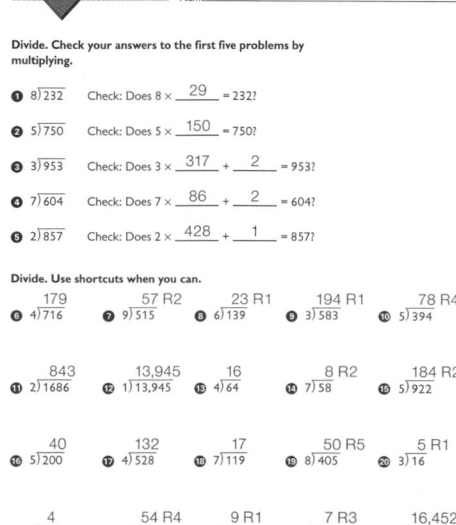

LESSON 109 PRACTICE Name________

Divide. Check your answers to the first five problems by multiplying.

1. 8)232 Check: Does 8 × 29 = 232?
2. 5)750 Check: Does 5 × 150 = 750?
3. 3)953 Check: Does 3 × 317 + 2 = 953?
4. 7)604 Check: Does 7 × 86 + 2 = 604?
5. 2)857 Check: Does 2 × 428 + 1 = 857?

Divide. Use shortcuts when you can.

6. 4)716 179	7. 9)515 57 R2	8. 6)139 23 R1	9. 3)583 194 R1	10. 5)394 78 R4
11. 2)1686 843	12. 1)13,945 13,945	13. 4)64 16	14. 7)58 8 R2	15. 5)922 184 R2
16. 5)200 40	17. 4)528 132	18. 7)119 17	19. 8)405 50 R5	20. 3)16 5 R1
21. 3)12 4	22. 6)328 54 R4	23. 2)19 9 R1	24. 9)66 7 R3	25. 1)16,452 16,452

Copyright © SRA/McGraw-Hill. Permission is granted to reproduce this page for classroom use.

Math Explorations and Applications Level 4 • 109

ENRICHMENT p. 109

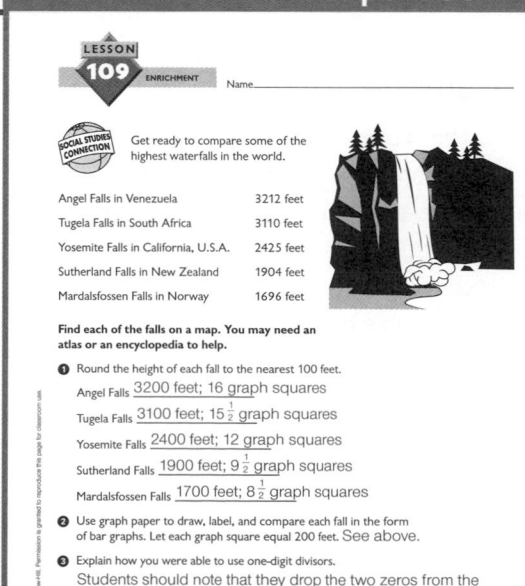

LESSON 109 ENRICHMENT Name________

SOCIAL STUDIES CONNECTION

Get ready to compare some of the highest waterfalls in the world.

Angel Falls in Venezuela	3212 feet
Tugela Falls in South Africa	3110 feet
Yosemite Falls in California, U.S.A.	2425 feet
Sutherland Falls in New Zealand	1904 feet
Mardalsfossen Falls in Norway	1696 feet

Find each of the falls on a map. You may need an atlas or an encyclopedia to help.

1. Round the height of each fall to the nearest 100 feet.
   Angel Falls 3200 feet; 16 graph squares
   Tugela Falls 3100 feet; $15\frac{1}{2}$ graph squares
   Yosemite Falls 2400 feet; 12 graph squares
   Sutherland Falls 1900 feet; $9\frac{1}{2}$ graph squares
   Mardalsfossen Falls 1700 feet; $8\frac{1}{2}$ graph squares
2. Use graph paper to draw, label, and compare each fall in the form of bar graphs. Let each graph square equal 200 feet. See above.
3. Explain how you were able to use one-digit divisors.
   Students should note that they drop the two zeros from the divisor and the dividend to simplify each division problem.

Copyright © SRA/McGraw-Hill. Permission is granted to reproduce this page for classroom use.

Math Explorations and Applications Level 4 • 109

LESSON 110

Student Edition pages 374–377

More Division Practice

LESSON PLANNER

Objectives

- ▶ to provide practice in dividing by one-digit divisors
- ▶ to provide experience in estimating answers to division problems
- ▶ to develop the broad ability to use mathematical common sense

Context of the Lesson This, the seventh of 13 lessons on division with one-digit divisors, contains Part 2 of "Estimating Is Rough," a five-part Thinking Story.

MANIPULATIVES

graph paper

job application forms (optional)

classroom object to be measured

Program Resources

Number Cubes

Practice Master 110

Enrichment Master 110

For career connections: Careers and Math*

For extra practice: CD-ROM* Lesson 110

1 Warm-Up (5 MINUTES)

Problem of the Day Present this problem to the class: Omar is making a calendar for the month of March. How many times will he write the digit 1? (14, not counting any 1s he might write for the year.)

Problem-Solving Strategies Ask students who have solved the Problem of the Day to share how they solved it and any strategies they used.

MIXED PRACTICE

LESSON 110

COOPERATIVE LEARNING

More Division Practice

Four Cube Division Game

Players: Two or more
Materials: Two 0–5 cubes, two 5–10 cubes
Object: To get the least quotient
Math Focus: Dividing by one-digit divisors and place value

RULES

1. Roll all four cubes. If you roll a 10, roll that cube again.
2. Make a division problem using three of the numbers rolled as a three-digit dividend and the other number as the divisor. Zero may not be used as the first number of the dividend and, of course, it cannot be used as the divisor.
3. Find the quotient.
4. The player with the least quotient wins the round. If two players have the same quotient, then the player with the least remainder is the winner.

SAMPLE ROUND

Matthew rolled: 3 4 9 8 He made: $9\overline{)348}$ = 38 R6

Cathy rolled: 2 8 3 5 She made: $8\overline{)235}$ = 29 R3

Max rolled: 1 0 9 5 He made: $9\overline{)105}$ = 11 R6 Max won.

OTHER WAYS TO PLAY THIS GAME

1. The least remainder wins.
2. The least quotient wins, but the remainder must be greater than 5.

374 • Division

Why teach it this way?

The "Four Cube Division" game helps students sharpen their number sense, understand place value, and grasp the relationship among the numbers in a division problem. Students also get valuable experience in estimating.

*available separately

The following 12 division problems have been worked out. There are six wrong answers. Decide which six answers are wrong and which six are correct.

1. $\begin{array}{r}273\\3\overline{)819}\end{array}$ **correct**
2. $\begin{array}{r}28\\3\overline{)624}\end{array}$ **wrong**
3. $\begin{array}{r}12\\7\overline{)714}\end{array}$ **wrong**
4. $\begin{array}{r}99\\3\overline{)297}\end{array}$ **correct**
5. $\begin{array}{r}96\\8\overline{)552}\end{array}$ **wrong**
6. $\begin{array}{r}123\\5\overline{)615}\end{array}$ **correct**
7. $\begin{array}{r}714\\2\overline{)998}\end{array}$ **wrong**
8. $\begin{array}{r}129\\5\overline{)645}\end{array}$ **correct**
9. $\begin{array}{r}399\\2\overline{)998}\end{array}$ **wrong**
10. $\begin{array}{r}223\\9\overline{)1000}\end{array}$ **wrong**
11. $\begin{array}{r}111\\9\overline{)999}\end{array}$ **correct**
12. $\begin{array}{r}147\\2\overline{)294}\end{array}$ **correct**

Six people won a prize of $900. They decided to share the money equally. Each person approximated how much he or she should take.

Decide whether each approximation is reasonable.

13. Max said he thought he ought to get about $500. **no**
14. Emma thought she ought to get about $100. **yes**
15. Abigail thought they each ought to have about $150. **yes**
16. Sam thought each person ought to get about $15. **no**
17. Pete thought each person should get $1500. **no**
18. Jill thought each person should get $105. **yes**

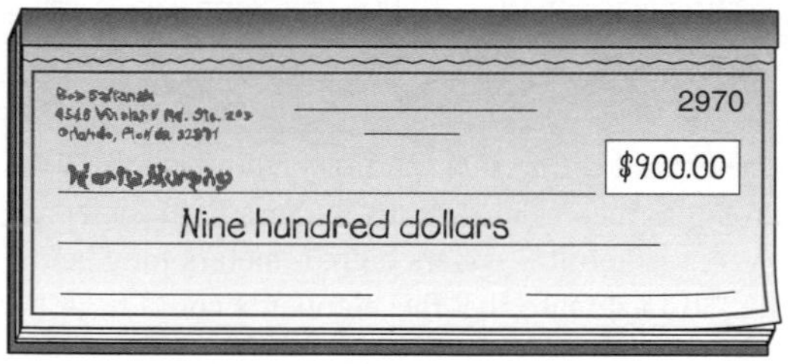

Technology Connection Refer students to the software *Math Blaster: In Search of Spot* or *New Math Blaster Plus* from Davidson (IBM, for grades 1–6) for further practice with multiplication and division skills.

MENTAL MATH Draw the following chart on the chalkboard. Have students estimate whether or not there will be enough gasoline for each trip. They show thumbs up if there is enough gasoline, thumbs down if there is not, and stand if the data are too close to call.

Miles to Travel	Number of Gallons in Tank	Average Number of Miles per Gallon	Is There Enough Gasoline?
300	15	20	(stand)
300	10	25	(thumbs down)
400	15	10	(thumbs down)
400	10	30	(thumbs down)
450	15	30	(stand)

2 Teach

GAME **Using the Student Pages** Introduce the "Four Cube Division" game, which provides practice with division using one-digit divisors and place value. Play two or three rounds at the chalkboard with a group of students. You may wish to have students play the game when they finish their work on page 375.

Have students work in pairs or small groups to complete page 375. Encourage them to discuss the strategies they use to identify the incorrect answers and to check the answers they believe are correct. When you discuss problems 13–18 as a class, invite volunteers to comment on why each approximation is or is not reasonable.

Another kind of application that is real to children, but may not seem entirely real to all adults, is the intelligent playing of certain games. A good mathematics game ordinarily should provide practice in some particular skill, but it also can have good problems imbedded in it so that players can improve their strategies by thinking mathematically.

—Stephen S. Willoughby, *Mathematics Education for a Changing World*

◆ LESSON 110 More Division Practice

Teach

Using the Thinking Story "Estimating Is Rough (Part 2)" explores absurd uses of approximation and precise answers as Mr. Muddle applies for the job of chief estimator. Have students read the story and discuss the questions in groups. Provide **graph paper** students can use to solve problem 2.

Answers to Thinking Story Questions:

1. Giving an approximate address and telephone number is silly, because addresses and phone numbers are not amounts; they are more like names, so estimates and approximations of them are generally of no use. Mr. Muddle's third answer is silly for the opposite reason. No employer would be interested in the exact amount of time he spent on his last job down to the minute; the employer would care only about the number of years or months.
2. The woman figured that since an elephant is about 3 meters high and the room is 3 meters high, an elephant could stand in the room. Five elephants could fit into the room as shown in the diagram.

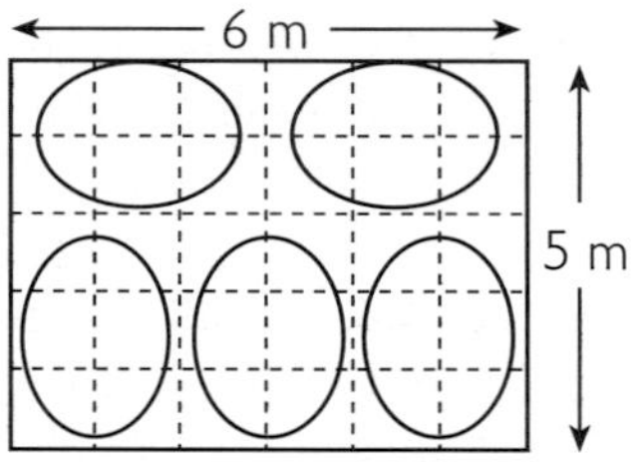

3. Mr. Muddle could have figured that if elephants are nearly 2 meters wide they could not possibly fit through an office door, so no elephants could fit into the room. The answer makes sense, even though it might not be what the boss had in mind.
4. An approximate address would be good enough for estimating distance, as a taxi driver might do, or for finding a place that is easy to spot, such as a stadium or a very large building.

Have students write in their Math Journals what they think the boss might say to Mr. Muddle and the other job applicant about their estimates. Have them select the person they think would be better for the job and give reasons for their choice.

◆ LESSON 110 More Division Practice

THINKING STORY

Estimating Is Rough

Part 2

You may want to refer to the first part of this Thinking Story, *on pages 368–369.*

Mr. Muddle went to try for the job of chief estimator. First he had to fill in a card. It asked for his address. He lived at 577 12th Street. But he wrote:

approximately 600 Tenth Street

The card asked for his telephone number. It was 555-1234, so he wrote:

approximately 6 million

The card asked how long he had worked in his last job. He wrote:

1 year, 2 months, 17 days, 6 hours, and
approximately 30 minutes

After he filled out the card, Mr. Muddle went to talk to the woman who was the boss. Another woman was also trying for the job. "I will give you both a problem," said the boss. "The one who gives the better estimate gets the job. Here is the problem. How many elephants will fit in this room?"

"Let me see," said the woman. "An elephant is about 3 meters high and 3 meters long. It is a bit less than 2 meters wide. This room is about 3 meters high, 6 meters long, and 5 meters wide. So I estimate that five elephants could fit in this room."

Real-World Connection Have students find out what employers look for when they consider someone for a job. Students might interview adults to learn about requirements for their jobs. Students could also pick a job they are familiar with and list qualifications they think someone would need to do it. You might have them examine **job application forms** or invite a career counselor to talk to them about different jobs.

RETEACHING

No specific reteaching is recommended at this time. Continue to provide extra help to students in division and approximation, as needed. You may want to assign Enrichment Master 110 for this lesson.

Mr. Muddle looked carefully around the room, which had two doors and no windows. "Are we talking about whole elephants?" Mr. Muddle asked.

"Whole elephants."

"Then my estimate is zero."

. . . to be continued

Work in groups. Discuss your answers and how you figured them out. Then compare your answers with those of other groups. **Answers are in margin.**

1. What is silly about each of the answers Mr. Muddle wrote on the card?
2. How could five elephants fit in the room? Draw a picture of the room to show where they would be. (Hint: Draw the room so that each square stands for 1 square meter.)
3. What could make Mr. Muddle think that no elephants would fit in the room? (Hint: About how many cars could you get into your classroom?)
4. **Super challenge question:** Can you think of a time when giving an approximate address might be good enough?

3 Wrap-Up (5 MINUTES)

In Closing Have students estimate the height and weight of a classroom **object**, the length of their travel time to school, and the number of students that could stand inside 1 square meter.

Informal Assessment Observe students as they play the "Four Cube Division" game, solve the problems on page 375, and work on the Thinking Story problems. Encourage them to share their thinking so you can assess their solution strategies.

Assessment Criteria

Did the student . . .

- ✓ actively participate in the game?
- ✓ apply approximation strategies to identify incorrect answers and solve word problems?
- ✓ contribute to the Thinking Story discussion?
- ✓ understand the distinction between a good estimate and an absurd one?

Homework Have students play the "Four Cube Division" game with a family member for further practice with division using one-digit divisors. A copy of this game can also be found on page 23 of the Home Connections Blackline Masters.

PRACTICE p. 110

LESSON 110 PRACTICE Name__________

Here are 12 division problems worked out. There are six incorrect answers. Write *correct* or *incorrect* for each problem.

1. 4)2040 = 580 incorrect	2. 5)825 = 165 correct	3. 9)936 = 104 correct	4. 8)504 = 63 correct
5. 6)1236 = 260 incorrect	6. 3)759 = 213 incorrect	7. 2)398 = 199 correct	8. 7)735 = 150 incorrect
9. 8)1608 = 210 incorrect	10. 4)660 = 165 correct	11. 6)762 = 127 correct	12. 3)261 = 97 incorrect

Solve these problems.

13. Nine people decided to share $1620 equally. They approximated how much each person should get. Write *yes* or *no* to show if their approximations are reasonable.
    - **a.** Larry thought each person ought to get about $18. no
    - **b.** Marge thought she should get about $180. yes
    - **c.** Cassandra thought each person should get about $1800. no
14. Four people decide to share $1000 equally. How much should each person get? $250
15. Seven people decide to share $763 equally. How much should each person get? $109

110 • *Math Explorations and Applications* Level 4

Copyright © SRA/McGraw-Hill. Permission is granted to reproduce this page for classroom use.

ENRICHMENT p. 110

LESSON 110 ENRICHMENT Name__________

GEOGRAPHY CONNECTION

Look at a globe. Try to plan an around-the-world land-water trip that will take as little ocean travel as possible. Use a string and the scale of miles on the globe to estimate the miles you will drive and the miles you will travel on a boat.

You will average 40 miles per hour in a car. The boats will average 20 miles per hour. You will average 2 miles per hour on foot.

Trace your route on the map above.

Estimate how long it will take you to travel around the world in hours. ______

Then give your estimate in days. ______

Did mountain ranges and rivers give you problems? How did you deal with them?

Answers will vary. Students may determine that they need to cross mountain ranges on foot or plan their routes around them. Students may decide to use boats to navigate rivers.

110 • *Math Explorations and Applications* Level 4

Copyright © SRA/McGraw-Hill. Permission is granted to reproduce this page for classroom use.

Meeting Individual Needs

GIFTED & TALENTED

Have students work in pairs or small groups to create a list of absurd approximations similar to the ones Mr. Muddle used on his job application. Encourage them to share their approximations with other students.

LESSON 111

Student Edition pages 378–379

Applying Division

LESSON PLANNER

Objectives

- ▶ to provide practice in solving word problems that focus on interpreting answers to multiplication and division, including the meaning of remainders
- ▶ to provide practice in dividing by one-digit divisors

Context of the Lesson This is the eighth of 13 lessons on division with one-digit divisors.

MANIPULATIVES	Program Resources
none	Number Cubes
	Practice Master 111
	Enrichment Master 111
	For extra practice: CD-ROM* Lesson 111

1 Warm-Up 5 MINUTES

Problem of the Day Present the following problem. Groups might act it out to find the solution: In the Warner family, each son has the same number of sisters as he has brothers. Each daughter has twice as many brothers as she has sisters. How many daughters and sons are in the Warner family? (3 daughters, 4 sons)

Problem-Solving Strategies Ask students who have solved the Problem of the Day to share how they solved it and any strategies they used.

MENTAL MATH Provide problems and answers in all four operations. Students show thumbs up for correct or possibly correct answers and thumbs down for obviously wrong answers.

a. 300 + 50 = 1500 (thumbs down)
b. 900 – 400 = 500 (thumbs up)
c. 30 × 40 = 1200 (thumbs up)
d. 50 × 50 = 2500 (thumbs up)
e. 500 ÷ 50 = 100 (thumbs down)
f. 90 – 50 = 30 (thumbs down)
g. 40 + 800 = 940 (thumbs down)
h. 3000 ÷ 100 = 30 (thumbs up)
i. 6 × 500 = 300 (thumbs down)
j. 300 – 75 = 280 (thumbs down)

PROBLEM SOLVING

LESSON 111

Applying Division

Solve these problems. Check that your answers make sense.

1. Mr. Quincy paid $1.05 (105¢) for seven onions. How much did each onion cost? **15¢**
2. Antonio bought nine glass beads for 72¢. How much should ten glass beads cost? **80¢**
3. The grocery store has two cans of cat food on sale for 47¢. How much do you think one can of cat food would cost? **24¢** (Think about this. What would you do if you owned the store?)
4. Greg drove for eight hours. He traveled about 45 miles each hour. About how many miles did he drive? **360**
5. Christy has 27 stickers. She wants to divide the stickers equally among five friends.
   - **a.** How many stickers should she give each friend? **5**
   - **b.** Will there be any stickers left over? **yes**
   - **c.** What should she do with them? **Answers will vary.**
6. Miss Zim needs 45 balloons for a party. Balloons come in packages of eight.
   - **a.** How many packages should she buy? **6**
   - **b.** How many extra balloons will she have? **3**
7. A fabric store has a 156-foot-long piece of pink silk ribbon. How many 6-foot-long pieces of ribbon can be cut from it? **26**

Divide. Use shortcuts when you can.

8. 6)480 **80**	9. 7)523 **74 R5**	10. 5)35 **7**	11. 8)326 **40 R6**	12. 2)632 **316**
13. 9)720 **80**	14. 9)722 **80 R2**	15. 3)426 **142**	16. 8)223 **27 R7**	17. 9)751 **83 R4**
18. 8)222 **27 R6**	19. 8)56 **7**	20. 3)471 **157**	21. 3)472 **157 R1**	22. 3)219 **73**

378 • Division

Real-World Connection Have students investigate the different ways that stores present items for sale. For example, they may price items individually (unit pricing), group them (three for $1), or offer special deals (buy one, get one free). Have students look through grocery stores, department stores, discount stores, or other stores they frequent to list various ways items are presented for sale. Compile a list in class. Analyze the various plans: which are most economical, which are simplest to understand, which move the most products, and so on.

RETEACHING

Students who have difficulty interpreting remainders in division may benefit from learning to analyze the meaning of the remainder as it applies to a particular problem. For instance, for problem 24 on page 379, the quotient 55 R3 does not answer the question of how many minivans to use. Guide students to see that 55 is the number of full vans. The remainder represents three people who still need rides and who have not yet been accounted for. Help them see that in such a case, the remainder means that there must be another van, although it will not be full, to transport the three "remaining" people.

*available separately

Solve these problems.

23. Mr. Taylor has 443 yards of fabric. He can make a complete suit from 8 yards of fabric. How many suits can he make? **55**
24. There are 443 people who will ride to a picnic. Each minivan can take eight people. How many minivans will be needed to take everyone to the picnic? **56**
25. Eight people agree to contribute a total of $443 to a local charity. They decide that each person will contribute an equal amount. How much should each person contribute? **$55.38**
26. Each basketball team must have exactly eight players (five regulars and three substitutes). If 443 people want to play, how many teams will there be? **55 teams; 3 people without a team**
27. What is similar and what is different about your answers to questions 23–26? **Sometimes it is acceptable to drop a remainder; sometimes the remainder must be accounted for.**
28. Monica can do seven difficult mathematics problems in an hour. How many hours will she need to do 21 difficult problems? **3**
29. Marta talked for nine minutes on the telephone. She was charged 657 cents ($6.57) for the call. How much did she pay per minute? **73¢**
30. Omar drove his car 318 miles in six hours. How many miles per hour was that? **53**

FANTASTIC FACT **It takes the human body almost two days to digest one meal.**

PRACTICE p. 111

LESSON 111 PRACTICE Name______________________

Solve these problems.

Mrs. George needs 32 muffins for a class picnic. Muffins come in packages of six.

1. How many packages should she buy? six
2. How many extra muffins will she have? four

Mr. Brown bought six pencils for $1.32.

3. How much did each pencil cost? 22¢
4. How much would 25 pencils cost? $5.50

Tracy baked 40 cookies. She wants to divide the cookies equally among nine children.

5. How many cookies should she give each child? four
6. Will there be any cookies left over? If so, how many? yes, four

There are 235 students going on a field trip. Each van can take seven students.

7. How many vans will be needed to take the students on their field trip? 34

Divide. Use shortcuts when you can.

8. 4)362 — 90 R2
9. 5)123 — 24 R3
10. 9)540 — 60
11. 3)641 — 213 R2
12. 5)302 — 60 R2
13. 3)563 — 187 R2
14. 8)124 — 15 R4
15. 7)249 — 35 R4
16. 4)404 — 101
17. 9)63 — 7

Copyright © SRA/McGraw-Hill. Permission is granted to reproduce this page for classroom use.

Math Explorations and Applications Level 4 • 111

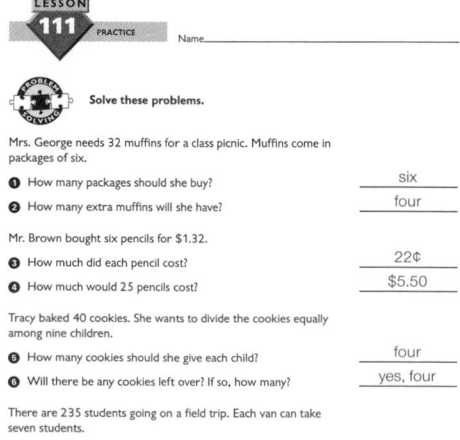

ENRICHMENT p. 111

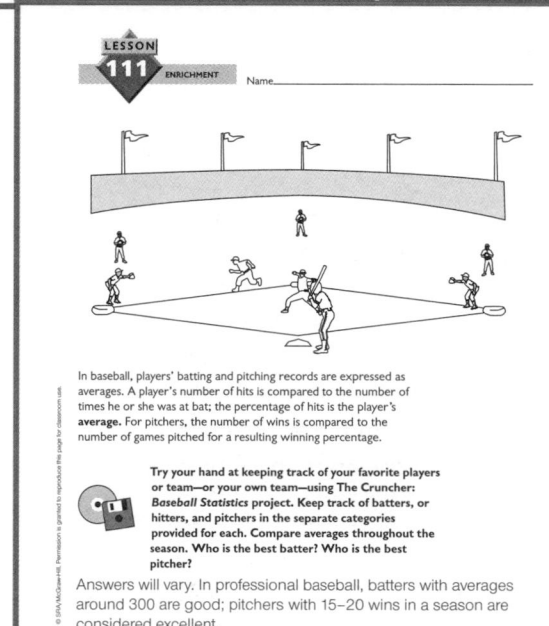

LESSON 111 ENRICHMENT Name______________________

In baseball, players' batting and pitching records are expressed as averages. A player's number of hits is compared to the number of times he or she was at bat; the percentage of hits is the player's **average.** For pitchers, the number of wins is compared to the number of games pitched for a resulting winning percentage.

Try your hand at keeping track of your favorite players or team—or your own team—using The Cruncher: *Baseball Statistics* project. Keep track of batters, or hitters, and pitchers in the separate categories provided for each. Compare averages throughout the season. Who is the best batter? Who is the best pitcher?

Answers will vary. In professional baseball, batters with averages around 300 are good; pitchers with 15–20 wins in a season are considered excellent.

Copyright © SRA/McGraw-Hill. Permission is granted to reproduce this page for classroom use.

Math Explorations and Applications Level 4 • 111

❷ Teach

Using the Student Pages Have students do the problems on pages 378–379 on their own. When students finish, discuss the word problems with the class. In discussing problem 27 on page 379, most students will say that problems 23–26 used the same numbers but in different situations. Although the quotient and remainder were the same in each case, the specifics of the situation determined how to interpret the numbers.

GAME Review the rules for the "Four Cube Division" game (on page 374), which provides practice with dividing by one-digit divisors. Students may play this game after completing pages 378 and 379.

❸ Wrap-Up

5 MINUTES

In Closing Ask students to explain the process for checking answers to division problems.

ALTERNATIVE ASSESSMENT **Performance Assessment** You may wish to use students' work on page 378 or 379 as an informal assessment of their ability to apply and interpret division in problem-solving situations. If so, be sure that students complete the page(s) on their own.

Assessment Criteria

Did the student . . .

✓ demonstrate an understanding of how to interpret answers in division to fit a problem?

✓ use the quotient and/or remainder appropriately for each division situation?

Homework Have students play the "Four Cube Division" game with a family member for further practice in dividing by a one-digit divisor. A copy of this game can also be found on page 23 of the Home Connections Blackline Masters.

LESSON 112

Student Edition pages 380–383

Finding Averages

LESSON PLANNER

Objectives

- ▶ to teach the concept of average (mean) and how to compute it
- ▶ to provide experience in distinguishing correct from incorrect uses of the term *average*
- ▶ to provide another common application of division

Context of the Lesson This is the ninth of 13 lessons on division with one-digit divisors. Averages have been discussed informally in previous grades.

MANIPULATIVES

calculators*
counters*
measuring tools for length*
objects to be measured

Program Resources

Reteaching Master
Practice Master 112
Enrichment Master 112
The Cruncher*
For extra practice:
CD-ROM* Lesson 112
Cumulative Review, page 559

1 Warm-Up

5 MINUTES

Problem of the Day Present the following problem, allowing students to use **calculators*** to find the solution: A hungry caterpillar ate 55 leaves in five days. Each day the caterpillar ate three more leaves than it ate the day before. How many leaves did the caterpillar eat on the first day? (5)

Problem-Solving Strategies Ask students who have solved the Problem of the Day to share how they solved it and any strategies they used.

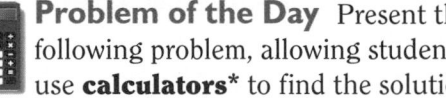

Have students estimate and then use **rulers*** to measure the perimeters and areas of three different rectangular or square objects in the classroom, such as books, posters, windows, or game boards. Use suitable metric or customary units. (Estimates should improve after each object is measured.)

EXPLORE

LESSON 112

Finding Averages

Seven people went out to pick apples. This chart shows how many apples each person picked.

Name	Number of Apples Picked
Marcia	37
Erin	62
Jamie	35
Rita	34
Nico	58
Charles	26
Luis	14

Luis said, "I wish I had as many apples as everybody else."

Rita suggested that they all put their apples together and then take an equal share.

- ◆ How many apples do the seven people have all together? **266**
- ◆ How many would each person get if they put all their apples together and then each took an equal number? **38**
- ◆ Do you think anyone might object to Rita's suggestion? Which people? **yes; Erin and Nico**
- ◆ Which people picked an above-average number of apples? **Erin and Nico**
- ◆ Which people picked a below-average number of apples? **Marcia, Jamie, Rita, Charles, and Luis**
- ◆ Which people picked exactly the average number of apples? **none**

The number 38 is the **average,** or **mean,** of the numbers 37, 62, 35, 34, 58, 26, and 14. The average is a number that can be used to represent a group of numbers. To find one kind of average of a set of numbers, commonly called the mean, add the numbers and divide the sum by the total number of numbers that were added.

380 • Division

Why teach it this way?

The term *average* is used in different ways in different contexts to explore central tendency. The meaning of *average* used in this lesson is also called the arithmetic *mean.* Other measures of central tendency include the *median,* or middlemost number; the *mode,* or most common number; and other means apart from the arithmetic mean, such as geometric mean, harmonic mean, and so on.

*available separately

Find the average of each set of numbers. Use shortcuts when you can.

Example: Find the average of 10, 7, 9, 4, and 10.
Add the numbers. $10 + 7 + 9 + 4 + 10 = 40$
How many numbers were added? five
Divide the sum by how many numbers were added.

$$5\overline{)40}\ \text{→}\ 8$$

The average of 10, 7, 9, 4, and 10 is 8.

1. 3, 4, 5, 6, 7 **5**
2. 4, 2, 8, 16, 0, 5, 12, 17, 25, 11 **10**
3. 13, 14, 15, 16, 17 **15**
4. 44, 44, 44, 44, 44, 44, 44, 44 **44**
5. 30, 40, 50, 60, 70 **50**
6. 27, 103, 59, 68, 112, 96, 84, 11 **70**
7. 7, 12, 63, 15, 28 **25**
8. 125, 39, 247, 362, 189, 154 **186**
9. 82, 57, 49, 63, 85, 42 **63**
10. 2843, 2844, 2845, 2846, 2847 **2845**
11. 25, 64, 27, 39, 15 **34**
12. 121, 174, 156, 29 **120**
13. 45, 16, 18, 93, 21, 5 **33**
14. 1, 15, 61, 28, 39, 12, 12 **24**

Solve these problems.

15. Neal bowled three games. His scores were 143, 129, and 151. What was his average score for the three games? **141**
16. Alma bowled three games. Her scores were 187, 202, and 192. About what was her average score for the three games? **194**
17. Maya drove 335 miles in seven hours. What was the average number of miles she drove each hour? (We call this the average speed.) **about 48**
18. Carolyn sells hot dogs at the ballpark. She sold 192 on Monday, 160 on Tuesday, 233 on Friday, 220 on Saturday, and 260 on Sunday. There were no games on Wednesday and Thursday. For this week, what was the average number of hot dogs Carolyn sold during a day's work? **213**

2 Teach

Using the Student Pages Go through the story on page 380 with students. Let them suggest solutions to Luis's wish. Encourage them to demonstrate their solutions and the solution Rita proposes. Provide **counters*** so students can model the number of apples picked and manipulate them to get a feeling for the concept of average. Students can use a blank **Cruncher*** spreadsheet to create a table that will calculate the average given a set of numbers. You may want to discuss the term *range* with students, which is the difference between the greatest and least values in a set of numbers.

Go over the material at the top of page 381 to review the steps students follow to find the average of a set of numbers. Then have them complete the page on their own. You may wish to preview problem 17. Point out that the sum has already been determined, so students need only to divide to calculate average speed.

Why teach it at this time?

In this unit students calculate and interpret averages in various contexts and practice division. Throughout this and later grades, students will work with averages in different contexts, such as average speed, average height, average score, and so on. This lesson will help students gradually develop a solid understanding of the meaning of *average* and the ability to work with averages. To this end, the problems on page 382 provide the basis for a group discussion of the meaning of *average* and ways to use averages sensibly.

*available separately

Language Arts Connection Spend some time discussing the word *average.* Ask students to recall ways they have heard or used the word. Some examples include "We're an *average* family," "We get an *average* of 30 minutes of math homework per night," and "Her batting *average* is the best on the team." Have students explain what they think *average* means. Responses may include: something that is as much like others in its group as possible, a middle number, or the number you get if you even out all numbers so they are the same. Brainstorm other words with similar or related meanings, such as *typical, representative, usual amount,* and *normal.*

◆ LESSON 112 Finding Averages

Teach

Using the Student Pages Use page 382 for class discussion. The goal of the discussion is to help students recognize that there is more to using averages than adding and dividing. Encourage students to give and defend their opinions. Provide adequate time to discuss each situation and identify why it does or does not make sense.

Answers for page 382:

21. Doesn't make sense; an individual doesn't have an average age.
22. This makes sense because there can be an average age for a group of people.
23. This makes sense even though it is not possible to have half a child. This is a good application of averages.
25. This makes sense; the corn grew a total of 64 cm in one month, so in half that time it may have grown 32 cm. 32 cm + 9 cm = 41 cm.

Have students work in pairs to solve the problems on page 383. Encourage partners to discuss their thinking and prepare to share their ideas in a whole-class discussion.

PRACTICE

◆ LESSON 112 Finding Averages

What do you think about each statement? Which make sense? Which statements don't make sense? Explain your reasons.

19. Kenny used to live at 600 Elm Street. Now he lives at 200 Elm Street. On the average he has lived at 400 Elm Street. **It doesn't make sense to speak of addresses in terms of averages.**

20. Adela and Vincent were in the running for the spelling award. Adela's test scores were 96, 94, 98, and 96. Vincent's scores were 92, 94, 100, and 90. Adela won the award because she had the higher average, even though Vincent had the highest single score. **It would make sense to use this method for determining a winner.**

21. Hana is 14 years old. She used to be 6 years old. Her average age is 10. **See margin.**

22. In the United States population, the average age is about 33 years old. **See margin.**

23. One hundred years ago the average number of children in a family was about three. Now the average number of children in a family is about one and one half. So families have fewer people now than they did 100 years ago. **See margin.**

24. Alan's average bowling score for his first nine games is 100. He bowled a 200 on his tenth game, so his average score for the ten games is 150.

24 This does not make sense. He scored 100 far more than he scored 200, so his average would be closer to 100.

25. The corn in Rudolfo's corn field was 9 centimeters tall at the end of June. It was 73 centimeters tall at the end of July. So Rudolfo said his corn was 41 centimeters tall in the middle of July. **See margin.**

26. Gina was 140 centimeters tall on her 10th birthday. On her 14th birthday she was 180 centimeters tall. She grew an average of 10 centimeters a year from age 10 to age 14. **This makes sense; average growth per year can be calculated.**

Literature Connection Read pertinent excerpts from *Averages* by Jean Srivastava with the class to expand their understanding of the meaning of *average.*

RETEACHING p. 34

LESSON 112 RETEACHING Name__________

An **average** gives you a general idea about a group of numbers.

In other words, an average tells you the number you would get if you even out all the numbers in a group so that they are the same.

To find an average, follow these steps:

Step 1 Add all the numbers.

Step 2 Count how many numbers you added.

Step 3 Divide the sum by how many numbers you counted.

Example:
Read the following statement.

Susan practiced the piano seven hours last week. She practiced an average of one hour a day.

This statement gives you a good idea of how long Susan practiced per day without knowing exactly how long she practiced each day of the week. The chart shows the actual hours Susan practiced each day last week.

Day	Hours of Practice
Sunday	0
Monday	1
Tuesday	0
Wednesday	2
Thursday	1
Friday	1
Saturday	2
Weekly average: 1 hour per day	

0 + 1 + 0 + 2 + 1 + 1 + 2 = 7

$7\overline{)7}$ = 1 — number of days: 7; weekly average: 1; sum of numbers counted: 7

Find the average of each set of numbers.

1. 6, 12, 18, 36 __18__
2. 200, 400, 200, 400 __300__
3. 5, 6, 7, 8, 9 __7__
4. 130, 23, 122, 121 __99__
5. 55, 78, 22, 81, 99 __67__
6. 132, 23, 34 __63__

34 • *Math Explorations and Applications* Level 4

Copyright © SRA/McGraw-Hill. Permission is granted to reproduce this page for classroom use.

Sara made a chart to show her scores on her spelling tests. But her dog, Chomps, got the chart and chewed part of it. Here's the chart after Chomps was through with it.

Answer these questions.

27. What was Sara's grade on September 13? **81**
28. On what date did Sara get a grade of 95? **September 27**
29. On what date do you think Sara got a grade of 85? **probably on September 16**
30. On what days of the week do you think Sara's teacher gives spelling tests? **probably Monday, Wednesday, and Friday**

Mark helped at a farm on weekends. He sold tomatoes for 59 cents per pound. People often asked to buy tomatoes by the pound, so he made the following chart to help him estimate the number of tomatoes per pound. To make the chart, Mark put tomatoes on the scale, one at a time, and recorded their weight as a whole number of pounds. If the scale went over a whole pound, he still recorded the weight as a whole number.

Pounds	1	2	3	4	5	6	7	8	9	10
Number of Tomatoes	4	7	10	14	17	20	24	27	30	34

Answer these questions.

31. About how many tomatoes are in 1 pound? **4**
32. About how many tomatoes are in 10 pounds? **34**
33. Compare your answers to questions 31 and 32. Discuss the possible reasons why your answers might not agree with each other. **Answers are not precise because we can only approximate the weight of each tomato.**

Use the Cumulative Review on page 559 after this lesson.

PRACTICE p. 112

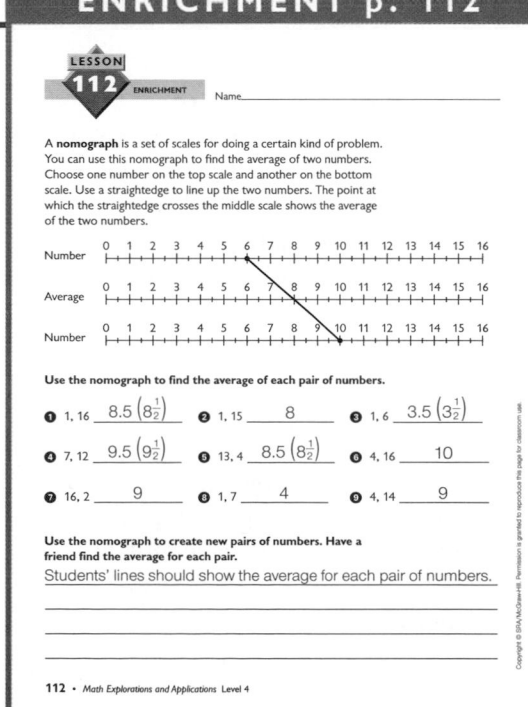

LESSON 112 PRACTICE Name______________________

Find the average of each set of numbers. Use shortcuts when you can.

1. 4, 5, 6, 7, 8 __6__
2. 19, 20, 21, 22, 23 __21__
3. 15, 20, 25, 30, 35 __25__
4. 12, 15, 21, 19, 10, 7 __14__
5. 66, 66, 66, 66, 66, 66, 66 __66__
6. 1, 2, 3, 4, 5, 6, 7, 8, 9, 5 __5__
7. 42, 61, 88, 24, 35 __50__
8. 4634, 4635, 4636, 4637, 4638 __4636__
9. 37, 47, 57, 67, 77, 87 __62__
10. 25, 49, 73, 37, 61 __49__
11. 340, 360, 400, 380, 420 __380__
12. 3912, 3914, 3918, 3920, 3922, 3916 __3917__

Solve these problems.

13. Rita bowled three games. Her scores were 182, 173, and 209.
    a. What was her average score for the three games? __188__
    b. If Rita bowled a fourth game and scored 188, what would her average score be for the four games? __188__
14. Molly took four math tests. Her grades were 95, 83, 74, and 88.
    a. What was her average grade for the four tests? __85__
    b. If Molly took a fifth test and received a grade of 85, what would her average grade for the five tests be? __85__

112 • *Math Explorations and Applications* Level 4

Copyright © SRA/McGraw-Hill. Permission is granted to reproduce this page for classroom use.

ENRICHMENT p. 112

LESSON 112 ENRICHMENT Name______________________

A **nomograph** is a set of scales for doing a certain kind of problem. You can use this nomograph to find the average of two numbers. Choose one number on the top scale and another on the bottom scale. Use a straightedge to line up the two numbers. The point at which the straightedge crosses the middle scale shows the average of the two numbers.

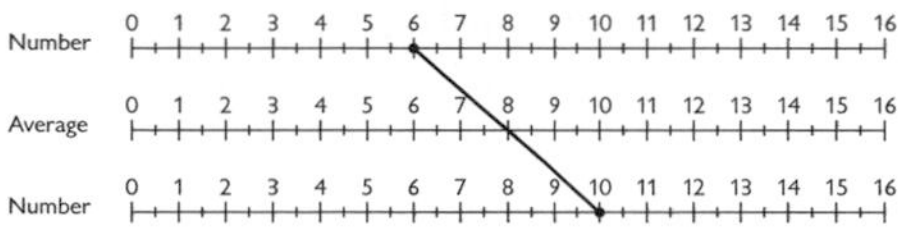

Use the nomograph to find the average of each pair of numbers.

1. 1, 16 __8.5 ($8\frac{1}{2}$)__
2. 1, 15 __8__
3. 1, 6 __3.5 ($3\frac{1}{2}$)__
4. 7, 12 __9.5 ($9\frac{1}{2}$)__
5. 13, 4 __8.5 ($8\frac{1}{2}$)__
6. 4, 16 __10__
7. 16, 2 __9__
8. 1, 7 __4__
9. 4, 14 __9__

Use the nomograph to create new pairs of numbers. Have a friend find the average for each pair.

Students' lines should show the average for each pair of numbers.

112 • *Math Explorations and Applications* Level 4

Copyright © SRA/McGraw-Hill. Permission is granted to reproduce this page for classroom use.

3 Wrap-Up (5 MINUTES)

In Closing Have students give examples of situations in which they might want to find the average of a set of numbers. Discuss how averages are used in school or in the community.

ALTERNATIVE ASSESSMENT

Portfolio Assessment Have each student write an explanation of the meaning of *average* in a mathematical sense. Have them give the steps to follow to find the average of a set of numbers. Students can add their statements to their Math Portfolios as evidence of ongoing learning.

Assessment Criteria

Did the student . . .

✓ contribute to the discussion of the meaning and sensible use of *average?*

✓ demonstrate how to calculate the average of a set of numbers?

✓ accurately solve problems involving averages?

Homework Have students select three books or magazines they have recently read and calculate their average length in terms of number of pages.

LESSON 113

Student Edition pages 384–385

Mean, Median, and Mode

LESSON PLANNER

Objectives

- ▶ to introduce three measures of central tendency: mean, median, and mode
- ▶ to provide practice computing and thinking about means, medians, and modes

Context of the Lesson This is the tenth of 13 lessons on division with one-digit divisors. It extends the work with averages from the previous lesson by introducing two other measures of central tendency.

MANIPULATIVES

recording of popular song (optional)

Program Resources

Reteaching Master

Practice Master 113

Enrichment Master 113

For extra practice:
CD-ROM* Lesson 113

1 Warm-Up

5 MINUTES

Problem of the Day Present the following problem: Joe and Flo were returning books to the library. Flo said, "If you give me one of your books, I'll have twice as many books as you. But if I give you one of my books, we'll both have the same number of books." How many books did Joe and Flo have? (Joe had 5 books, Flo had 7.)

Problem-Solving Strategies Ask students who have solved the Problem of the Day to share how they solved it and any strategies they used.

MENTAL MATH Provide practice in addition and subtraction as inverse operations. Emphasize speedy response.

a. 40 + 50 = (90); 90 − 50 = (40)
b. 35 + 35 = (70); 70 − 35 = (35)
c. 84 + 84 = (168); 168 − 84 = (84)
d. 377 + 200 = (577); 577 − 377 = (200)
e. 123 + 321 = (444); 444 − 321 = (123)
f. 425 + 425 = (850); 850 − 425 = (425)
g. 9000 + 7000 = (16,000); 16,000 − 7,000 = (9000)
h. 1562 + 3000 = (4562); 4562 − 3000 = (1562)
i. 606 + 707 = (1313); 1313 − 606 = (707)
j. 44,000 + 35,000 = (79,000); 79,000 − 35,000 = (44,000)

EXPLORE

LESSON 113

Mean, Median, and Mode

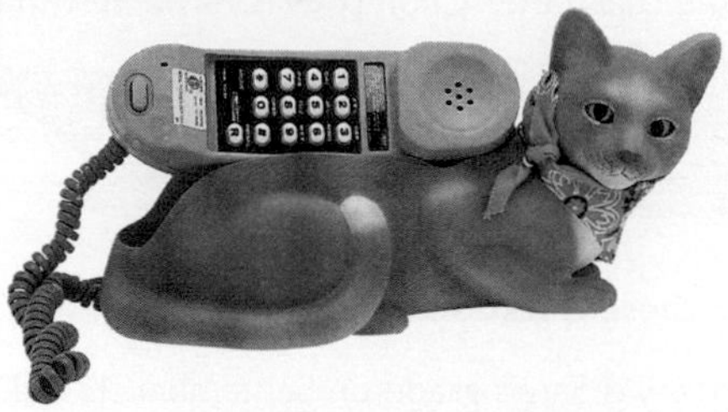

The **mean** is often used as the most representative number for a group of numbers. But sometimes, people think a better choice is the number that appears most often. That number is called the **mode.**

Another number often used to describe a set of numbers is the **median.** The median is the middle number of a set of numbers placed in order from least to greatest. Half the numbers are greater than the median. Half are less than the median.

Yolanda kept track of how many telephone calls she made each day for nine days. These are the numbers: 2, 3, 2, 15, 3, 5, 3, 0, 3

What number do you think best describes how many calls Yolanda usually makes each day? Discuss this with other members of your class. Do you all agree?

Answer these questions.

1. What is the most common number of calls Yolanda made in one day? **3**
2. Yolanda put the number of calls in order from fewest to most. If she counts up to the middle number, what will it be? **3**
3. What is the mode of the number of times per day Yolanda made telephone calls? **3**
4. What is the median of the number of times per day Yolanda made telephone calls? **3**
5. What is the median of the following set of numbers? **6**

   2, 4, 5, 7, 8, 9

Music Connection Have students conduct an investigation of the average length of popular **songs**. Students can work individually or in small groups. Have them list several songs they like. When they hear the songs, they should time them to find their length in seconds, then use the data to find the average length of the songs. Follow up by having students evaluate whether most songs they listen to are of average length, above-average length, or less-than-average length.

RETEACHING p. 35

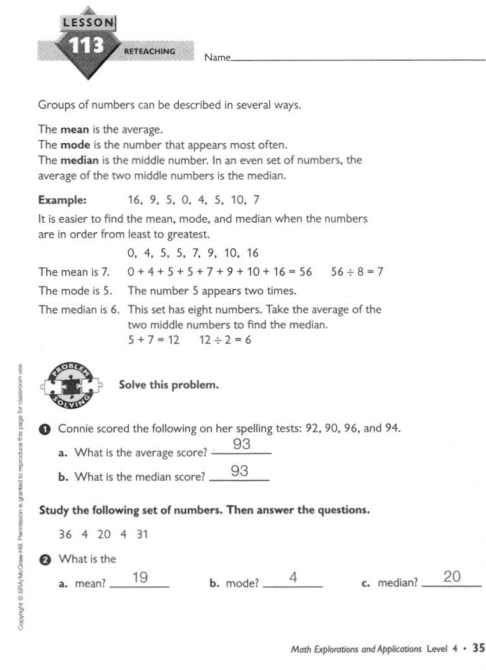

LESSON 113 RETEACHING Name______

Groups of numbers can be described in several ways.

The **mean** is the average.
The **mode** is the number that appears most often.
The **median** is the middle number. In an even set of numbers, the average of the two middle numbers is the median.

Example: 16, 9, 5, 0, 4, 5, 10, 7

It is easier to find the mean, mode, and median when the numbers are in order from least to greatest.

0, 4, 5, 5, 7, 9, 10, 16

The mean is 7. 0 + 4 + 5 + 5 + 7 + 9 + 10 + 16 = 56 56 ÷ 8 = 7

The mode is 5. The number 5 appears two times.

The median is 6. This set has eight numbers. Take the average of the two middle numbers to find the median.
5 + 7 = 12 12 ÷ 2 = 6

Solve this problem.

1. Connie scored the following on her spelling tests: 92, 90, 96, and 94.
   a. What is the average score? 93
   b. What is the median score? 93

Study the following set of numbers. Then answer the questions.

36 4 20 4 31

2. What is the
   a. mean? 19 b. mode? 4 c. median? 20

Copyright © SRA/McGraw-Hill. Permission is granted to reproduce this page for classroom use.

*available separately

When there is an even number of numbers in a set, as in problem 5, we usually use the average of the two middle numbers as the median. In this case, the median would be 6.

Sometimes a set of data will have more than one mode. In that case, report both modes. Are modes and medians easier to find when the numbers are in order from least to greatest? You may choose to reorder data before trying to find the mean, median, and mode.

For each of the following sets of numbers, write the mean, the median, and the mode. Use a calculator if you wish.

6. 1, 2, 2, 3, 3, 3, 4, 4, 4, 4, 5, 5, 5, 5, 5, 6, 6, 6, 6, 7, 7, 7, 8, 8, 9 **5; 5; 5**
7. 2, 4, 5, 7, 7, 8, 11 **6.29; 7; 7**
8. 12, 4, 9, 0, 8, 4, 13, 4, 6, 8, 5, 8 **6.75; 7; 8 and 4**
9. 7, 12, 3, 8, 4, 5, 7, 6, 0 **5.78; 6; 7**

The Fabulous Phone Company has nine employees, including the owner. Their yearly salaries are as follows.

$10,000; $10,000; $10,000; $10,000; $12,000; $13,000; $14,000; $15,000; $50,000

Answer these questions.

10. What is the average, or mean, salary of the employees? **$16,000**
11. What is the median salary of the employees? **$12,000**
12. What is the mode of the salaries of the employees? **$10,000**
13. Of the three numbers, the mean, the median, or the mode, which do you think best represents the salaries of the Fabulous Phone Company employees? **Either the median or the mode; accept reasonable answers.**

2 Teach

Using the Student Pages Review the term *mean*. Then tell students that there are other ways to select one number to represent a set of numbers. Discuss the material on page 384 with the class. Help students understand the meanings of and distinctions among *mean, median,* and *mode.* Then have them complete page 385 on their own or in pairs. Discuss the answers when everyone finishes. For question 13, students may defend any measure as the best; accept any answers students can justify.

3 Wrap-Up

5 MINUTES

In Closing Have students find the mean, median, and mode for this set of numbers: 9, 14, 10, 11, 12, 9, 18. (12, 11, 9)

SELF ASSESSMENT

Have students write a brief statement in which they describe their understanding of *mean, median,* and *mode* and explain the distinctions among them.

Assessment Criteria

Did the student . . .

- ✓ contribute to the discussion of mean, median, and mode?
- ✓ explain how to find the mean, median, and mode for sets of numbers?
- ✓ correctly complete the problems on page 385?
- ✓ write a comprehensible statement about mean, median, and mode?

Homework Assign Practice Master 113 or Enrichment Master 113 for further practice with mean, median, and mode.

PRACTICE p. 113

LESSON 113 PRACTICE Name________

For each of the following sets of numbers, find the mean, the median, and the mode.

1. 10, 3, 17, 8, 12, 3, 9, 4 8.25, 8.5, 3
2. 14, 10, 10, 11, 12, 11, 12, 12, 14, 13, 14, 13, 13, 12 12.2, 12, 12
3. 83, 54, 72, 64, 90, 56, 83 71.7, 72, 83
4. 9, 8, 3, 0, 8, 4, 10, 7, 5, 4, 8, 2 5.7, 6, 8

The heights of 14 students, in centimeters, was recorded. The heights are:
121, 120, 121, 126, 130, 134, 160, 147, 142, 152, 150, 128, 140, 124

5. What is the average height of the students? 135.4
6. What is the median height of the students? 132
7. What is the mode of the heights of the students? 121

Two math classes took the same test. The scores are as follows:
Class 1: 93, 93, 76, 93, 87, 86, 86, 81, 86, 80, 80, 79, 76, 75, 72, 62, 60, 60, 57, 58
Class 2: 95, 92, 92, 92, 66, 67, 75, 68, 77, 77, 82, 79, 84, 83, 87, 87, 90, 85, 85, 90

8. What is the mean of the scores for Class 1? 77
9. What is the median of the scores for Class 1? 79.5
10. What is the mode of the scores for Class 1? 86 and 93
11. What is the mean of the scores for Class 2? 82.7
12. What is the median of the scores for Class 2? 84.5
13. What is the mode of the scores for Class 2? 92
14. Which class did better on the test? Explain your answer. Class 2; the mean was higher.

Copyright © SRA/McGraw-Hill. Permission is granted to reproduce this page for classroom use.

Math Explorations and Applications Level 4 • 113

ENRICHMENT p. 113

LESSON 113 ENRICHMENT Name________

Your pulse rate changes as your level of activity changes.

You can use **The Cruncher: *Pulse Rate After Exercise*** project to figure out the average pulse rate for different activities. Then use the graphs to compare pulse rates.

Try comparing your own pulse rate and the pulse rates of your friends or family members after various activities, such as walking in place, running in place, and jumping rope.

What is the mean pulse rate for each activity? What is the mode? What is the range?
Answers will vary.

What is the best method of comparing pulse rates? Why do you think so?
Answers will vary. When comparing pulse rates, students should take age into consideration. The pulse rate of a ten-year-old will be different from that of an adult.

Copyright © SRA/McGraw-Hill. Permission is granted to reproduce this page for classroom use.

Math Explorations and Applications Level 4 • 113

UNIT 5

Student Edition pages 386–389

Mid-Unit Review

The Mid-Unit Review pinpoints troublesome skill areas for students, allowing time for additional practice and reteaching before the unit ends. If students did not do well on the Mid-Unit Review and have completed additional practice, you may want to use the Mid-Unit Review provided on Assessment Blackline Masters page 45.

Using the Student Pages Have students complete problems 1–60 on pages 386–389 on their own. Have **calculators*** available for page 389. You might treat this review as a formal assessment of students' skills and have students complete this review as a timed test. See suggestions on page 51.

Mid-Unit Review

Use the method you like best to solve these division problems. Use play money if you need to. Watch for remainders.

1. 4)100 **25**
2. 3)73 **24 R1**
3. 7)84 **12**
4. 9)92 **10 R2**
5. 2)453 **226 R1**
6. 5)80 **16**
7. 7)439 **62 R5**
8. 3)761 **253 R2**
9. 4)856 **214**
10. 2)747 **373 R1**
11. 4)500 **125**
12. 3)1572 **524**
13. 5)3542 **708 R2**
14. 6)606 **101**
15. 8)248 **31**
16. 5)54,320 **10,864**

Find the missing digit.

17. 5)182 = 36 R■ **2**; 15, 32, 30, 2
18. 6)743 = 12■ R5 **3**; 6, 14, 12, 23, 18, 5
19. ■)546 = 273 **2**; 4, 14, 14, 6, 6
20. 9)381 = 4■ R3 **2**; 36, 21, 18, 3
21. 5)789 = 1■7 R4 **5**; 5, 28, 25, 39, 35, 4
22. 4)947 = ■36 R3 **2**; 8, 14, 12, 27, 24, 3
23. 8)583 = 72 R7; 56, 2■3 **2**, 16, 7
24. 3)804 = 268; 6, 20, 1■ **8**, 24, 24

*available separately

Solve these problems.

25 Felix wants to buy some cider. A 4-cup carton costs $1.44 (144¢). An 8-cup carton of the same kind of cider costs $2.72 (272¢).

a. How much does cider cost per cup in a 4-cup carton? **36¢**

b. How much does cider cost per cup in an 8-cup carton? **34¢**

c. Which do you think is the better buy? Why? **The 8-cup carton is a better buy as long as the extra 4 cups don't go to waste.**

26 Six limes cost 96¢. How much does one lime cost? **16¢**

27 Three stickers cost 75¢. How much is that per sticker? **25¢**

28 Four cans of tuna cost $4.68 (468¢). How much is that per can? **$1.17**

29 Two wallets cost $26. How much does one wallet cost? **$13**

30 An 8-ounce jar of pickles costs $1.84 (184¢). How much is that per ounce? **23¢**

31 A 5-pound bag of frozen corn costs $2.15 (215¢). A 7-pound bag of frozen corn costs $3.22 (322¢). Which bag is the better buy? Why? **The better value depends on how much corn you need. The 5-pound bag is cheaper per pound (43¢); however, if you need at least 7 pounds of corn but less than 10 pounds, then the 7-pound bag is a better buy (46¢).**

32 Nine boxes of spaghetti cost $8.73 (873¢). How much is that per box? **97¢**

Divide. Use whichever method you like best. Check your answers by multiplying.

33 $6\overline{)234}$ Check: Does 6 × **quotient** = 234? **39; yes**

34 $5\overline{)385}$ Check: Does 5 × **quotient** = 385? **77; yes**

35 $7\overline{)290}$ Check: Does (7 × **quotient**) + **remainder** = 290? **41 R3; yes**

36 $3\overline{)227}$ Check: Does (3 × **quotient**) + **remainder** = 227? **75 R2; yes**

Divide. Use shortcuts when you can.

37 $4\overline{)987}$ **246 R3**

38 $5\overline{)4000}$ **800**

39 $8\overline{)649}$ **81 R1**

40 $1\overline{)54,326}$ **54,326**

Home Connections You may want to send home the Home Connections Blackline Masters letter on pages 50–51 to provide additional activities that families can complete together. These activities apply the skills presented in this unit.

ALTERNATIVE ASSESSMENT

Portfolio Assessment The Portfolio Assessment task provided on Assessment Blackline Masters page 97 can be used at this time to evaluate students' proficiency with finding averages.

ALTERNATIVE ASSESSMENT

Performance Assessment Performance Assessment Task 1, provided on Assessment Blackline Masters pages 83–84, can be used at this time to evaluate students' proficiency with division. You may want to administer this assessment to individual students or small groups of students.

Unit Project This would be a good time to assign "The Broad-Jump Contest" project on pages 428 and 429. Students can begin working on the project in cooperative groups in their free time as they work through the unit. The Unit Project is a good opportunity for students to work with data that can be interpreted in more than one way and to design a "fair" contest.

◆ UNIT 5 Mid-Unit Review

Solve.

41. Andrew paid $3.15 (315¢) for seven magnets. How much did each magnet cost? **45¢**

42. Rosa got four tacos for $3.80. How much should ten tacos cost? **$9.50**

43. Melido called his aunt in Peru. They talked on the phone for seven minutes. Melido was charged $4.76 for the call. How much did he pay per minute? **68¢**

44. Michael needs 65 candles for his grandmother's birthday cake. Candles come in packages of ten.
    - **a.** How many packages should he buy? **7**
    - **b.** How many extra candles will he have? **5**

45. Mrs. Grant drove for six hours. She traveled about 54 miles each hour. About how many miles did she drive? **324**

46. There are 385 people who will ride in minivans for a school trip. Each minivan can take nine people. How many minivans are needed to take everyone on the trip? **43**

47. Each relay team needs exactly seven runners. How many teams can be formed if 91 runners want to race? **13**

Find the average of each set of numbers.

48. 5, 6, 7, 8, 9 **7**

49. 12, 10, 18, 14, 27, 15 **16**

50. 10, 20, 30, 40, 50 **30**

51. 32, 32, 32, 32, 32, 32, 32 **32**

52. 123, 234, 345, 456, 567 **345**

53. 28, 60, 15, 7, 12, 10 **22**

Solve.

54. Lauren bowled three games. Her scores were 136, 98, and 117. What was her average score for the three games? **117**

55. Joshua drove 423 miles in eight hours. What was the average number of miles per hour (or average speed) he drove? **about 53 miles per hour**

For each of the following sets of numbers, write the mean, the median, and the mode. Use a calculator if you wish.

56. 1, 2, 3, 4, 6, 6, 8, 10 **5; 5; 6**

57. 3, 7, 12, 4, 10, 5, 0, 6, 7 **6; 6; 7**

58. 2, 2, 3, 3, 3, 4, 4, 4, 4, 5, 5, 5, 5, 5, 6, 6, 6, 6, 6, 6 **4.5; 5; 6**

Solve.

59. Matt kept track of how many pieces of mail he got each day for seven days. He recorded these numbers: 5, 7, 4, 6, 8, 4, and 1. Find the mean, median, and mode. **5; 5; 4**

60. Emily recorded the number of goals she scored in her nine soccer games. Emily recorded 3, 4, 3, 4, 6, 1, 3, 1, and 2. Find the mean, median, and mode. **3; 3; 3**

ASSESSMENT p. 45

UNIT 5

Mid-Unit Review (Use after Lesson 113.)

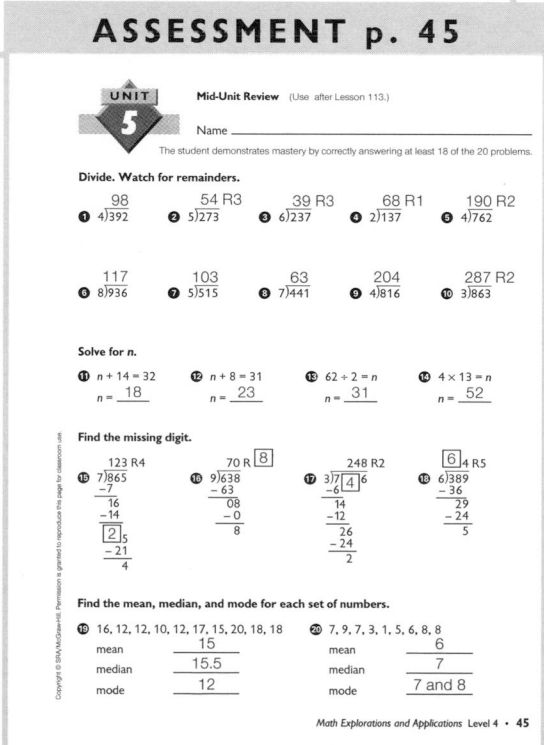

Name ____________________

The student demonstrates mastery by correctly answering at least 18 of the 20 problems.

Divide. Watch for remainders.

1. $4\overline{)392}$ 98
2. $5\overline{)273}$ 54 R3
3. $6\overline{)237}$ 39 R3
4. $2\overline{)137}$ 68 R1
5. $4\overline{)762}$ 190 R2
6. $8\overline{)936}$ 117
7. $5\overline{)515}$ 103
8. $7\overline{)441}$ 63
9. $4\overline{)816}$ 204
10. $3\overline{)863}$ 287 R2

Solve for *n*.

11. $n + 14 = 32$ $n =$ 18
12. $n + 8 = 31$ $n =$ 23
13. $62 \div 2 = n$ $n =$ 31
14. $4 \times 13 = n$ $n =$ 52

Find the missing digit.

15. $7\overline{)865}$ = 123 R4; −7, 16, −14, [2]5, −21, 4
16. $9\overline{)638}$ = 70 R [8]; −63, 08, −0, 8
17. $3\overline{)7[4]6}$ = 248 R2; −6, 14, −12, 26, −24, 2
18. $6\overline{)389}$ = [6]4 R5; −36, 29, −24, 5

Find the mean, median, and mode for each set of numbers.

19. 16, 12, 12, 10, 12, 17, 15, 20, 18, 18
    mean 15
    median 15.5
    mode 12

20. 7, 9, 7, 3, 1, 5, 6, 8, 8
    mean 6
    median 7
    mode 7 and 8

Copyright © SRA/McGraw-Hill. Permission is granted to reproduce this page for classroom use.

LESSON 114

Student Edition pages 390–391

Division Patterns

LESSON PLANNER

Objectives

✓ to assess students' mastery of dividing by one-digit divisors

▶ to provide practice in dividing with one-digit divisors

Context of the Lesson This lesson, the 11th of 13 lessons on division with one-digit divisors, contains another Mastery Checkpoint on division with one-digit divisors.

MANIPULATIVES

none

Program Resources

Practice Master 114

Enrichment Master 114

Assessment Master

For extra practice:
CD-ROM* Lesson 114

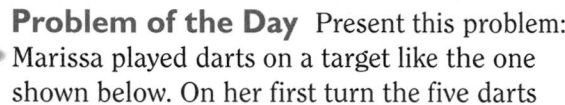

1 Warm-Up

5 MINUTES

Problem of the Day Present this problem: Marissa played darts on a target like the one shown below. On her first turn the five darts earned a total of 34 points. On her next turn she earned the same total but in a different way. Where did Marissa's darts land on each turn? (four 8s and one 2 on one turn, three 8s and two 5s on the other turn)

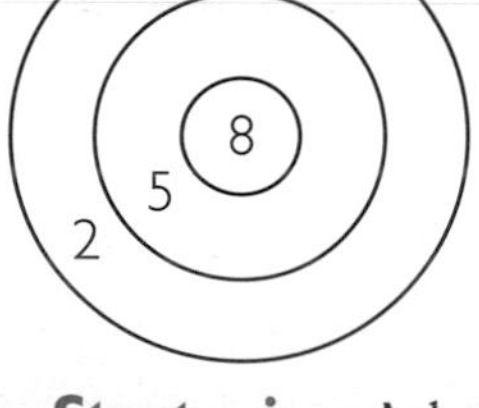

Problem-Solving Strategies Ask students who have solved the Problem of the Day to share how they solved it and any strategies they used.

MENTAL MATH Provide practice with multiplication and division as inverse operations. Write these problems on the chalkboard:

a.	3 × 30 = (90)	90 ÷ 30 = (3)
b.	8 × 90 = (720)	720 ÷ 90 = (8)
c.	300 × 6 = (1800)	1800 ÷ 300 = (6)
d.	60 × 40 = (2400)	2400 ÷ 40 = (60)
e.	75 × 10 = (750)	750 ÷ 75 = (10)
f.	70 × 90 = (6300)	6300 ÷ 70 = (90)

MIXED PRACTICE

LESSON 114

Division Patterns

When you solve similar problems, you may notice patterns that can help you find answers quickly. Look for patterns. Think about how to use the patterns to find the answers.

Divide. Remember to write any remainders. Watch your numbering.

1. 3)10 **3 R1**	15. 8)1000 **125**	29. 5)2520 **504**
2. 3)100 **33 R1**	16. 8)2000 **250**	30. 6)2520 **420**
3. 3)1000 **333 R1**	17. 9)1000 **111 R1**	31. 7)2520 **360**
4. 2)10 **5**	18. 9)2000 **222 R2**	32. 8)2520 **315**
5. 2)100 **50**	19. 9)3000 **333 R3**	33. 9)2520 **280**
6. 2)1000 **500**	20. 2)246 **123**	34. 2)210 **105**
7. 4)100 **25**	21. 3)785 **261 R2**	35. 3)210 **70**
8. 4)1000 **250**	22. 4)1256 **314**	36. 5)210 **42**
9. 4)10,000 **2,500**	23. 5)847 **169 R2**	37. 7)210 **30**
10. 5)10 **2**	24. 7)9482 **1354 R4**	38. 8)210 **26 R2**
11. 5)100 **20**	25. 1)2520 **2520**	39. 7)1,000,000 **142,857 R1**
12. 5)1000 **200**	26. 2)2520 **1260**	40. 7)2,000,000 **285,714 R2**
13. 6)1000 **166 R4**	27. 3)2520 **840**	41. 7)3,000,000 **428,571 R3**
14. 6)100 **16 R4**	28. 4)2520 **630**	42. 7)4,000,000 **571,428 R4**

RETEACHING

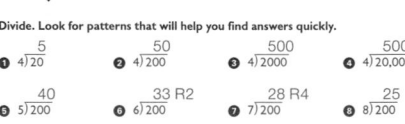

COOPERATIVE LEARNING Have students solve division problems in pairs. Each student does the algorithm as his or her partner watches. If the partner detects an error, have the two correct it together before they switch roles.

PRACTICE p. 114

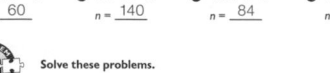

LESSON 114 PRACTICE Name__________

Divide. Look for patterns that will help you find answers quickly.

1. 4)20 5	2. 4)200 50	3. 4)2000 500	4. 4)20,000 5000
5. 5)200 40	6. 6)200 33 R2	7. 7)200 28 R4	8. 8)200 25
9. 2)148 74	10. 3)384 128	11. 4)1636 409	12. 5)926 185 R1

Divide to solve for *n*.

13. 700 ÷ 7 = n n = 100	14. 360 ÷ 3 = n n = 120	15. 48 ÷ 6 = n n = 8	16. 3753 ÷ 9 = n n = 417
17. 420 ÷ 7 = n n = 60	18. 420 ÷ 3 = n n = 140	19. 420 ÷ 5 = n n = 84	20. 1398 ÷ 6 = n n = 233

PROBLEM SOLVING **Solve these problems.**

Sam wants to give a whistle to each of the 17 people coming to his birthday party. The whistles come in packages of six.

21. How many packages does he need to buy? three
22. How many extra whistles will he have? one

Mrs. Simms cut a pan of brownies into 24 servings. She wishes to serve nine friends.

23. How many brownies should she serve each friend? two
24. How many brownies will be left over? six

114 • *Math Explorations and Applications* Level 4

Copyright © SRA/McGraw-Hill. Permission is granted to reproduce this page for classroom use.

*available separately

Divide to solve for *n*. Watch your numbering.

43. 900 ÷ 9 = *n* **100**
44. 210 ÷ 7 = *n* **30**
45. 200 ÷ 8 = *n* **25**
46. 100 ÷ 4 = *n* **25**
47. 72 ÷ 9 = *n* **8**
48. 360 ÷ 6 = *n* **60**
49. 360 ÷ 4 = *n* **90**
50. 360 ÷ 9 = *n* **40**
51. 360 ÷ 8 = *n* **45**
52. 360 ÷ 5 = *n* **72**
53. 350 ÷ 7 = *n* **50**
54. 80 ÷ 5 = *n* **16**
55. 900 ÷ 6 = *n* **150**
56. 2871 ÷ 9 = *n* **319**
57. 1024 ÷ 8 = *n* **128**

PROBLEM SOLVING

Solve these problems.

58. Angie is making earrings. She needs three beads for each wire. She has 97 beads.
    - **a.** How many earrings can Angie make? **32**
    - **b.** If there are two earrings in a set, how many sets of earrings can Angie make? **16**
    - **c.** How many beads will be left over? **1**
59. Winter Elementary's secretary ordered 141 notebooks to be divided exactly among six classrooms. How many notebooks were given to each classroom? How many notebooks were left over? **23; 3**
60. Ruby wants to give an eraser to each of the 28 people coming to her party. The erasers she wants come in packages of eight.
    - **a.** How many packages does she need to buy? **4**
    - **b.** How many extra erasers will she have? **4**

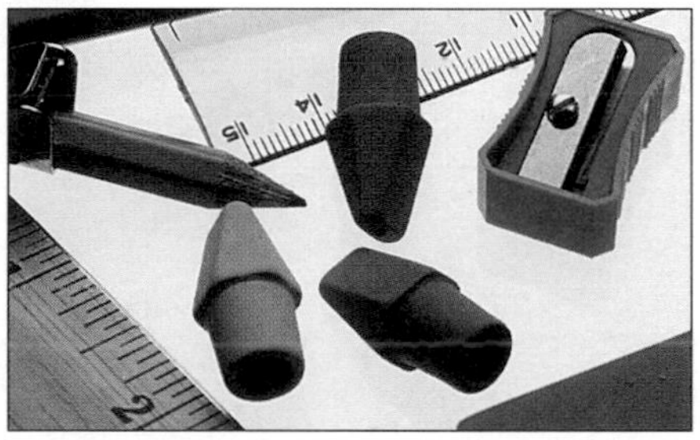

❷ Teach

Using the Student Pages Have students work independently to solve the problems on pages 390–391. Students may use any algorithmic form with which they feel comfortable. Students should see the division patterns on page 390 and solve these problems quickly.

❸ Wrap-Up

5 MINUTES

In Closing Have students explain how they can solve for *n* in the problem 320 ÷ 4 = *n* and how they can check their answer. (Divide 320 by 4 to get 80, then multiply 4 by 80 for an answer of 320 to check the division.)

ANALYZING ANSWERS

Go over answers carefully to determine why students made mistakes. If the errors occurred from misapplication of the algorithm, provide extra help for these students or suggest that they use a different variation of the algorithm. If the errors resulted from basic fact errors, have students redo the problems. Errors in subtraction may require review of the subtraction algorithm.

Mastery Checkpoint 17b

At this time most students should demonstrate mastery of division with one-digit divisors using short forms. Although this skill was assessed in Lesson 106, students have now learned a shorter method. Students should correctly answer 80% of the problems on pages 390–391 or on Assessment Blackline Masters page 46. Results of this assessment may be recorded on the Mastery Checkpoint Chart.

ENRICHMENT p. 114

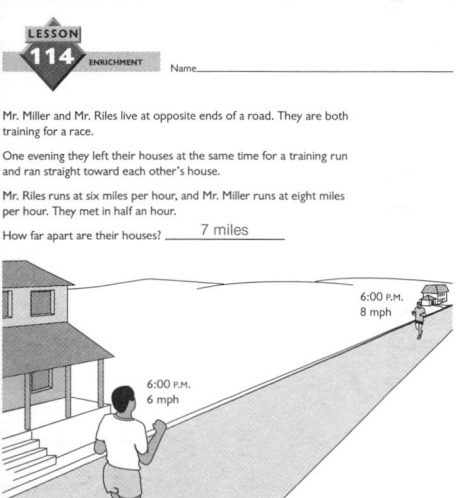

LESSON 114 ENRICHMENT Name__________

Mr. Miller and Mr. Riles live at opposite ends of a road. They are both training for a race.

One evening they left their houses at the same time for a training run and ran straight toward each other's house.

Mr. Riles runs at six miles per hour, and Mr. Miller runs at eight miles per hour. They met in half an hour.

How far apart are their houses? 7 miles

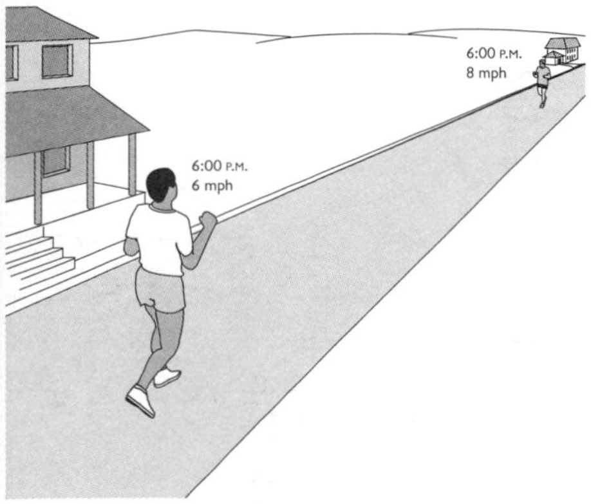

Copyright © SRA/McGraw-Hill. Permission is granted to reproduce this page for classroom use.

114 • *Math Explorations and Applications* Level 4

ASSESSMENT p. 46

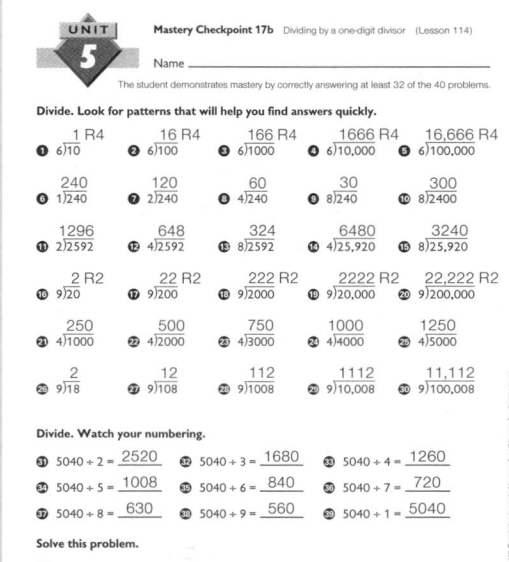

UNIT 5 **Mastery Checkpoint 17b** Dividing by a one-digit divisor (Lesson 114)

Name__________

The student demonstrates mastery by correctly answering at least 32 of the 40 problems.

Divide. Look for patterns that will help you find answers quickly.

1. 6)10 1 R4	2. 6)100 16 R4	3. 6)1000 166 R4	4. 6)10,000 1666 R4	5. 6)100,000 16,666 R4
6. 1)240 240	7. 2)240 120	8. 4)240 60	9. 8)240 30	10. 8)2400 300
11. 2)2592 1296	12. 4)2592 648	13. 8)2592 324	14. 4)25,920 6480	15. 8)25,920 3240
16. 9)20 2 R2	17. 9)200 22 R2	18. 9)2000 222 R2	19. 9)20,000 2222 R2	20. 9)200,000 22,222 R2
21. 4)1000 250	22. 4)2000 500	23. 4)3000 750	24. 4)4000 1000	25. 4)5000 1250
26. 9)18 2	27. 9)108 12	28. 9)1008 112	29. 9)10,008 1112	30. 9)100,008 11,112

Divide. Watch your numbering.

31. 5040 ÷ 2 = 2520
32. 5040 ÷ 3 = 1680
33. 5040 ÷ 4 = 1260
34. 5040 ÷ 5 = 1008
35. 5040 ÷ 6 = 840
36. 5040 ÷ 7 = 720
37. 5040 ÷ 8 = 630
38. 5040 ÷ 9 = 560
39. 5040 ÷ 1 = 5040

Solve this problem.

40. Jenny gave a notepad to each of her 35 friends. Notepads come in packages of five.
    - **a.** How many packages must she buy? 7
    - **b.** Will she have any left? no

Copyright © SRA/McGraw-Hill. Permission is granted to reproduce this page for classroom use.

46 • *Math Explorations and Applications* Level 4

Assessment Criteria

Did the student . . .

- ✓ correctly answer 80% of the problems on pages 390–391?
- ✓ explain how to solve for *n*?

Homework Have students play the "Four Cube Division" game on page 374 with a family member for further practice with dividing by a one-digit divisor. A copy of this game can also be found on page 23 of the Home Connections Blackline Masters.

LESSON 115

Student Edition pages 392–395

Using Division

LESSON PLANNER

Objectives

- ▶ to provide practice solving word problems, some of which require division
- ▶ to help students make and develop the meaning of predictions based on average
- ▶ to review converting units of liquid measure

Context of the Lesson This is the 12th of 13 lessons on division with one-digit divisors.

MANIPULATIVES	Program Resources
calculators*	Number Cubes
cup, pint, quart, gallon, and liter containers*	Practice Master 115
	Enrichment Master 115
	For extra practice: CD-ROM* Lesson 115

1 Warm-Up

5 MINUTES

Problem of the Day Present the following problem: Dorrie spent $4.00 to buy two magazines. One magazine cost 50¢ less than the other. How much did each magazine cost? ($1.75 and $2.25)

Problem-Solving Strategies Ask students who have solved the Problem of the Day to share how they solved it and any strategies they used.

MENTAL MATH Provide students with addition, subtraction, multiplication, and division problems. Have them show thumbs up for correct or possibly correct answers and thumbs down for obviously wrong answers.

a. 400 × 3 = 20 (thumbs down)

b. 850 − 440 = 410 (thumbs up)

c. 900 ÷ 30 = 200 (thumbs down)

d. 460 + 460 = 1120 (thumbs down)

e. 543 × 35 = 54,000 (thumbs down)

f. 745 + 840 = 1585 (thumbs up)

g. 922 − 420 = 502 (thumbs up)

h. 780 × 100 = 7800 (thumbs down)

i. 402 × 55 = 36,075 (thumbs down)

j. 877 − 398 = 211 (thumbs down)

PROBLEM SOLVING

LESSON 115

Using Division

Solve these problems. Check that your answers make sense and that they fit the situations.

1. Nine people took a 40-word spelling test. Their scores were 39, 38, 30, 39, 26, 31, 35, 7, and 34.
   - **a.** What was the average score? **31**
   - **b.** How many people had above-average scores? **5**
   - **c.** How many people had below-average scores? **3**
   - **d.** How many people had exactly average scores? **1**
2. Seven people took a 30-problem math quiz. Their scores were 21, 29, 30, 20, 17, 14, and 11.
   - **a.** About what was the average score? **about 20**
   - **b.** How many people had above-average scores? **3**
   - **c.** How many people had below-average scores? **4**
   - **d.** How many people scored within one point of the average score? **2**

3. Mr. Epstein knows that his living room rug is rectangular and that its area is 42 square meters.
   - **a.** He knows it is 6 meters wide, but he cannot remember how long it is. How long is the rug? **7 m**
   - **b.** If the local cleaner charges $2.53 (253¢) for each square meter of rug cleaned, how much will it cost Mr. Epstein to have his rug cleaned? **$106.26 (10,626¢)**

392 • Division

Literature Connection

Select suitable math puzzles and enrichment activities from *The Sneaky Square + 113 Other Math Activities for Kids* by Richard Sharp and Seymour Metzner to present to individuals, small groups, or the entire class.

*available separately

4. Ms. McConnell heard that cabbages at her favorite store weigh about 1 kilogram (1000 grams). She bought nine cabbages and weighed them to see if they weighed 1 kilogram each. Their weights were 932 grams, 961 grams, 982 grams, 989 grams, 994 grams, 996 grams, 1008 grams, 1087 grams, and 1096 grams.
   - **a.** How many of the nine cabbages weighed more than 1 kilogram? **3**
   - **b.** What was the average weight of the nine cabbages? **1005 g**
   - **c.** Would it have cost Ms. McConnell less to buy the cabbages for 65¢ per cabbage or for 65¢ per kilogram? **65¢ per cabbage**

5. When Roland bowls, he bowls a series of three games. The last seven times he bowled, his total scores for three games were 561, 570, 572, 568, 430, 564, and 571.
   - **a.** For the last seven times he bowled, could Roland's average score for a series of three games be 400? Could it be 430? Could it be 600? Could it be 572? **no; no; no; no**
   - **b.** Make your best estimate of Roland's average score. Then calculate the average to see how close you were. **The average is 548.**
   - **c.** About what do you think Roland's score will be the next time he bowls? **about 570**

6. The temperature in Sunnydale has varied greatly over the past 14 days. The high temperatures for each day were 97°F, 75°F, 70°F, 99°F, 73°F, 80°F, 63°F, 70°F, 68°F, 79°F, 77°F, 79°F, 79°F, and 77°F.
   - **a.** What was the average high temperature in this 14-day period? **77.6°F**
   - **b.** Over the past 100 years, the average daily high temperature in Sunnydale for this 14-day period was 73°F. Would you say that this same period this year is warmer than usual, cooler than usual, or about average? **warmer than usual**

2 Teach

Using the Student Pages Review the rules for the "Diviso" game (page 367) or the "Four Cube Division" game (page 374), both of which provide practice with dividing by one-digit divisors. Students may play either game when they have completed pages 392–395.

Have students work on problems 1–3 in small groups or individually. Discuss answers with the whole class when everyone finishes. In problem 2, students should see that the average is between 20 and 21, so a score of 20 would be below average. Next, go over the rest of the problems on page 393 with the class. When discussing Roland's next bowling score, you might ask whether 570 is a better guess than Roland's average of 548. It may be, considering the consistency of a bowler who had only one of seven scores that was significantly different from the rest.

> ***If practice is essential, we should try to provide practice that the learners will enjoy so they will continue practicing. Some children do enjoy practicing with flash cards or electronic equivalents of flash cards, and there is no harm in letting them practice with such devices if they enjoy it. But a well-devised game can often provide a great deal more than just enjoyable practice.***
>
> –Stephen S. Willoughby,
> Mathematics Education for a Changing World

Technology Connection Students can engage in teamwork as they solve problems relating to averaging, unit conversions, and graphing presented in the video *The Wonderful Problems of Fizz & Martina, Volume 3: Fizz and Martina Do Hollywood* from Tom Snyder Productions (VHS, for grades 3–6).

◆ LESSON 115 Using Division

Teach

Using the Student Pages Have students work on page 394 independently. When students finish, discuss the answers to exercises 33 and 36 to reinforce the concept that division by 0 is not allowed. Have students complete page 395 independently. You might display an assortment of **containers*** to review the relative size of the liquid measures.

GIFTED & TALENTED — Meeting Individual Needs

Have students investigate averages in school or in your community. For instance, they might determine the average class size in your school, the average number of pets students have, the average number of rooms in homes or apartments in their neighborhood, and so on. Have students pick a question to investigate, create a plan for collecting data, perform the necessary calculations to determine the average, and, when applicable, evaluate the number of people surveyed who fit the average and who fall above and below it.

◆ LESSON 115 Using Division

Keep in shape by practicing all four operations. Remember to check that your answers make sense.

Solve for *n*. Watch your numbering.

7. $36 + 9 = n$ **45**
8. $36 - 9 = n$ **27**
9. $36 \times 9 = n$ **324**
10. $36 \div 9 = n$ **4**
11. $36 + 6 = n$ **42**
12. $36 - 6 = n$ **30**
13. $36 \times 6 = n$ **216**
14. $36 \div 6 = n$ **6**
15. $n = 42 \times 7$ **294**
16. $n = 42 - 7$ **35**
17. $n = 42 \div 7$ **6**
18. $n = 42 + 7$ **49**
19. $n = 243 + 512$ **755**
20. $n = 648 - 471$ **177**
21. $286 \times 8 = n$ **2288**
22. $n = 512 \div 4$ **128**
23. $407 \times 58 = n$ **23,606**
24. $n = 63 \times 57$ **3591**
25. $n = 1000 \div 8$ **125**
26. $73 \times 89 = n$ **6497**
27. $2 \times 2 = n$ **4**
28. $2 + 2 = n$ **4**
29. $0 \times 5783 = n$ **0**
30. $n = 5783 + 0$ **5783**
31. $0 \times 5 = n$ **0**
32. $n = 0 \div 5$ **0**
33. $n = 5 \div 0$ **not allowed**
34. $0 \div 9 = n$ **0**
35. $9 \times 0 = n$ **0**
36. $9 \div 0 = n$ **not allowed**
37. $7 \times 8 = n$ **56**
38. $56 \div 7 = n$ **8**
39. $n = 42 \div 6$ **7**
40. $n = 83 + 249$ **332**
41. $n = 1000 - 783$ **21**
42. $n = 426 + 574$ **1000**

Watch the signs.

43. 8562 + 9408 = **17,970**
44. 52,071 − 3,468 = **48,603**
45. 832 × 706 = **587,392**
46. 647 + 352 = **999**
47. 5407 + 4593 = **10,000**
48. 10,000 − 7,654 = **2,346**
49. 10,000 − 3,819 = **6,181**
50. 301 × 299 = **89,999**
51. 250 + 250 = **500**
52. 70 × 30 = **2100**
53. 1000 − 998 = **2**
54. 600 × 40 = **24,000**

Divide.

55. 9)54 **6**
56. 7)497 **71**
57. 6)2844 **474**
58. 8)26,648 **3,331**

394 • Division

RETEACHING

Allow students to use **calculators*** to compute averages. Ask them to verbalize the steps to follow and to tell how they know that the answer makes sense.

*available separately

Remember: 8 fluid ounces = 1 cup
2 cups = 1 pint
8 pints = 1 gallon
4 quarts = 1 gallon

Answer these questions.

59. How many fluid ounces are there in 5 cups? **40**
60. How many cups are there in 40 fluid ounces? **5**
61. How many cups are there in 72 fluid ounces? **9**
62. How many gallons are there in 72 pints? **9**
63. How many gallons are there in 72 quarts? **18**
64. A doctor recommended that his patient drink at least 16 cups of water every day. How many pints is that? How many quarts is that? How many gallons is that? How many fluid ounces is that? **8; 4; 1; 128**

Remember: 1000 milliliters = 1 liter

Answer these questions.

65. How many milliliters are there in 5 liters? **5000**
66. How many liters are there in 5000 milliliters? **5**
67. How many liters are there in 12,000 milliliters? **12**
68. The doctor recommended that another patient drink at least 4000 milliliters of water each day. How many liters is that? **4**

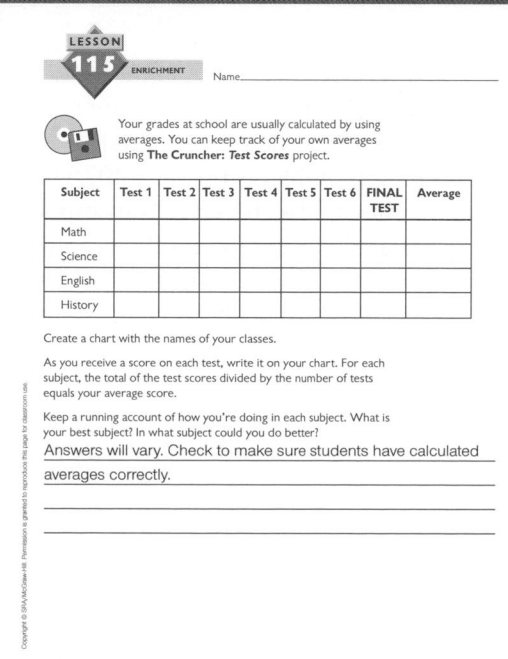

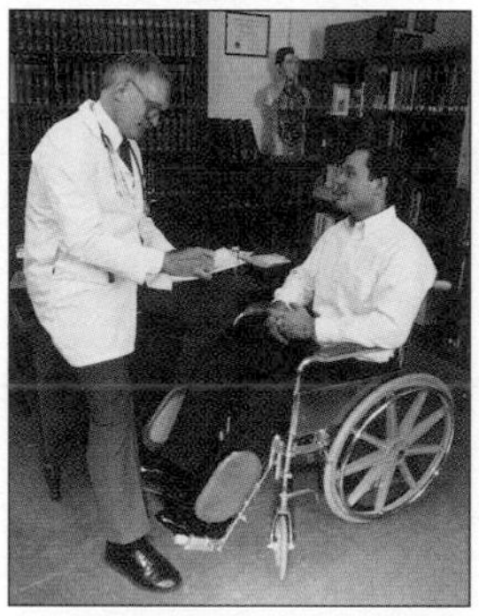

3 Wrap-Up

5 MINUTES

In Closing Ask students what they think the average temperature is for your area at this time of year. Discuss how to verify this information.

ANALYZING ANSWERS

If students make errors in finding averages, determine whether the error is in addition, division, or interpreting the results. Provide extra practice in the appropriate skills.

ALTERNATIVE ASSESSMENT

Performance Assessment You may wish to use students' work on page 394 as an assessment of their recall of basic number facts and mixed review of multidigit arithmetic. If so, be sure students work independently.

Assessment Criteria

Did the student . . .

- ✓ contribute to the discussion of averages?
- ✓ communicate strategies used to solve word problems?
- ✓ explain how to solve for *n*?
- ✓ correctly answer at least 75% of the computation problems?

Homework Have students count the number of pairs of shoes each family member has. They should include slippers, boots, sports footwear, and so on. Have them determine the average number of pairs of shoes for people in their families, and evaluate each family member's shoe collection as average, above average, or below average.

PRACTICE p. 115

LESSON 115 PRACTICE Name________

Remember: 8 fluid ounces = 1 cup; 2 cups = 1 pint; 8 pints = 1 gallon; 4 quarts = 1 gallon.

1. How many gallons are there in 64 pints? 8
2. How many cups are there in 64 fluid ounces? 8
3. How many fluid ounces are there in 10 cups? 80
4. How many pints are there in 5 gallons? 40

Remember: 1000 milliliters = 1 liter.

5. How many milliliters are there in 7 liters? 7000
6. How many liters are there in 10,000 milliliters? 10

Solve. Watch the signs.

7. 205 × 125 = 25,625
8. 642 + 978 = 1620
9. 5183 − 625 = 4558
10. 10,000 − 5267 = 4733
11. 300 × 50 = 15,000
12. 1823 + 6389 = 8212
13. 650 + 450 = 1100
14. 1000 − 489 = 511
15. 80 × 70 = 5600
16. 703 × 319 = 224,257

Solve for *n*.

17. $8 \times 6 = n$ — $n =$ 48
18. $0 \div 5 = n$ — $n =$ 0
19. $n = 24 - 6$ — $n =$ 18
20. $n = 6 \times 4$ — $n =$ 24
21. $38 \times 12 = n$ — $n =$ 456
22. $3 \times 0 = n$ — $n =$ 0
23. $n = 588 \div 7$ — $n =$ 84
24. $500 - 234 = n$ — $n =$ 266
25. $n = 336 + 164$ — $n =$ 500
26. $381 \div 3 = n$ — $n =$ 127

Copyright © SRA/McGraw-Hill. Permission is granted to reproduce this page for classroom use.

Math Explorations and Applications Level 4 • 115

ENRICHMENT p. 115

LESSON 115 ENRICHMENT Name________

Your grades at school are usually calculated by using averages. You can keep track of your own averages using **The Cruncher: *Test Scores*** project.

Subject	Test 1	Test 2	Test 3	Test 4	Test 5	Test 6	FINAL TEST	Average
Math								
Science								
English								
History								

Create a chart with the names of your classes.

As you receive a score on each test, write it on your chart. For each subject, the total of the test scores divided by the number of tests equals your average score.

Keep a running account of how you're doing in each subject. What is your best subject? In what subject could you do better?

Answers will vary. Check to make sure students have calculated averages correctly.

Copyright © SRA/McGraw-Hill. Permission is granted to reproduce this page for classroom use.

Math Explorations and Applications Level 4 • 115

LESSON 116

Student Edition pages 396–399

Practicing Division: Missing Digits

LESSON PLANNER

Objectives

- to provide practice in dividing by one-digit divisors
- to provide practice in solving geometry problems by graphing ordered pairs
- to help students develop the broad ability to use mathematical common sense

Context of the Lesson This is the last of 13 lessons on division with one-digit divisors. This lesson also contains Part 3 of "Estimating Is Rough," a five-part Thinking Story.

MANIPULATIVES

graph paper

ruler* or straightedge

Program Resources

Practice Master 116

Enrichment Master 116

For career connections: Careers and Math*

For extra practice: CD-ROM* Lesson 116 Cumulative Review, page 560

1 Warm-Up (5 MINUTES)

Problem of the Day Present this problem and tell students that there is more than one answer: Replace the letters with digits to make the division problem work. If a letter appears more than once, replace it with the same digit each time. *TAP* ÷ *A* = *UP* (one possible answer: 150 ÷ 5 = 30)

Problem-Solving Strategies Ask students who have solved the Problem of the Day to share how they solved it and any strategies they used.

MENTAL MATH Give division fact problems with and without remainders. Have students show thumbs up if there is a remainder and thumbs down if there is no remainder.

a. 17 ÷ 3 (thumbs up) **b.** 5 ÷ 1 (thumbs down)

c. 38 ÷ 6 (thumbs up) **d.** 6 ÷ 3 (thumbs down)

e. 56 ÷ 6 (thumbs up) **f.** 78 ÷ 9 (thumbs up)

g. 27 ÷ 3 (thumbs down) **h.** 25 ÷ 6 (thumbs up)

i. 18 ÷ 4 (thumbs up) **j.** 20 ÷ 2 (thumbs down)

MIXED PRACTICE

LESSON 116

Practicing Division: Missing Digits

ALGEBRA READINESS

Find the missing digits. Check your answers.

1. **0** / 1■8 R3 / 5)543 / 5 / 43 / 40 / 3
2. 62 R3 / 7)437 / 42 / **1**■7 / 14 / 3
3. **7** / 74 R■ / 8)599 / 56 / 39 / 32 / 7
4. 23 R2 / 9)209 / 18 / 29 / 27 / ■**2**
5. **2** / 40 R■ / 8)322 / 32 / 2
6. **0** / 10■ R5 / 8)805 / 8 / 5
7. **7** / ■8 / 8)624 / 56 / 64 / 64
8. **0** / 1■6 / 6)636 / 6 / 36 / 36
9. 119 / 8)952 / 8 / 1■**5** / 8 / 72 / 72
10. **8** / 4■2 / 2)964 / 8 / 16 / 16 / 4 / 4
11. **8** / 1■3 / 4)732 / 4 / 33 / 32 / 12 / 12
12. **6** / 2■9 / 3)807 / 6 / 20 / 18 / 27 / 27
13. 167 / 3)501 / 3 / 20 / 1■**8** / 21 / 21
14. 127 / 6)■62 / 6 **7** / 16 / 12 / 42 / 42
15. 118 / 7)826 / **7**■ / 12 / 7 / 56 / 56
16. 163 / **2** ■)326 / 2 / 12 / 12 / 6 / 6

COOPERATIVE LEARNING You might have students work in pairs to solve the function and graphing problems on page 397. One student can list the set of four ordered pairs as the other makes the graph and plots the points. Have them switch roles for each problem.

*available separately

You have learned to make graphs of ordered pairs from function rules. For example, find four ordered pairs that fit the following situation. The first number in an ordered pair is the length of a side of a square. The second number is the perimeter of the square.

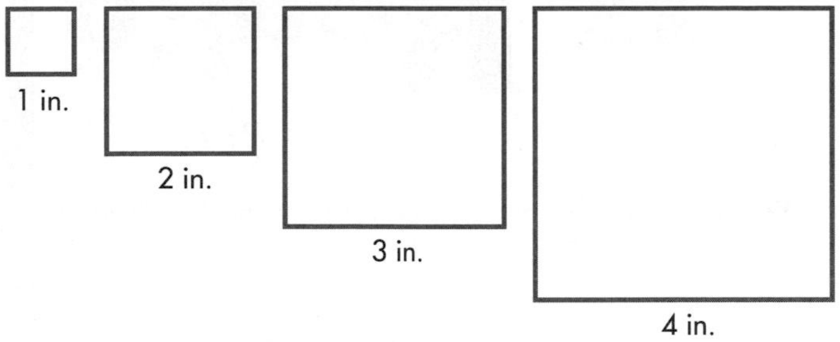

Answer these questions.

17. If the side is 1 inch long, what is the perimeter? The ordered pair is (1, 4). **4**

18. Find the perimeter and ordered pairs for the other three squares. Graph the ordered pairs. Will one line go through all four points? **For example: (0, 0), (2, 8), (3, 12); yes**

For each of the following rules find four ordered pairs. Then graph the four points corresponding to those ordered pairs. Try to draw a line through the four points.

19. The first number is the length of a side of an equilateral triangle. The second number is the perimeter of the triangle. **$y = 3x$; For example: (0, 0), (1, 3), (2, 6), (5, 15)**

20. The first number is the number of yards in a particular distance. The second number is the number of feet in that same distance. **$y = 3x$; For example: (0, 0), (1, 3), (2, 6), (8, 24)**

21. The first number is the length of a side of a square in inches. The second number is the area of that square in square inches. **$y = x^2$; For example: (0, 0), (1, 1), (2, 4), (4, 16)**

2 Teach

Using the Student Pages

Have students complete page 396 independently. By now they should be familiar with the format. Remind them to verify that their answers fit the problems. The problems on page 397 review functions and graphing ordered pairs. Solve problems 17 and 18 with the class to review these concepts. Tell students to determine the four ordered pairs for each function before they make the corresponding graph so they will know what scale to use. Have **graph paper** and **rulers*** available.

Meeting Individual Needs

SPECIAL NEEDS

Students who live in rural or urban communities may not be familiar with house numbering or street naming systems like those Mr. Muddle is studying. Explain that the numbers probably decrease from 1500 East Elm Street to 0 at the point where East Elm Street becomes West Elm Street and then increase to 2600. Ask students what they notice about their own community's naming and numbering.

Technology Connection Refer students to the software *Mystery Math Island* from Lawrence Productions (Mac, IBM, for grades 3–8) for practice with geometry, measurement, data, number sense, operations, patterns, and problem solving.

*available separately

◆ LESSON 116 Practicing Division: Missing Digits

Teach

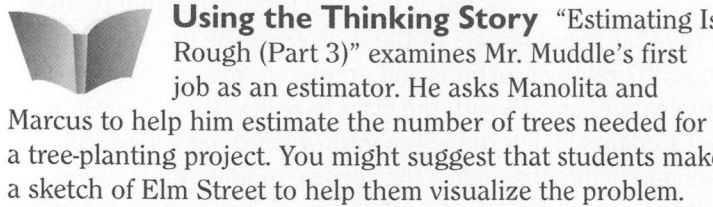

Using the Thinking Story "Estimating Is Rough (Part 3)" examines Mr. Muddle's first job as an estimator. He asks Manolita and Marcus to help him estimate the number of trees needed for a tree-planting project. You might suggest that students make a sketch of Elm Street to help them visualize the problem.

Answers to Thinking Story Questions:

1. Manolita probably counted steps and multiplied by her stride length. To estimate how many steps she took, students could measure their strides and find the average. A reasonable stride length for a nine-year-old is 2 to $2\frac{1}{2}$ feet, which would mean that Manolita took 240–300 steps to cover 600 feet.
2. Nine times 600 is greater than 5280. Even if 600 feet is an overestimate, a good estimator would allow for the width of the cross streets, which would add another 40–60 feet.
3. House numbers would have to change by 100 for each block, or else there would have to be 100 houses to a block. Either of these cases might be true, but Mr. Muddle and his friends should have checked.
4. Possibilities include driving a car from one end to the other and checking the odometer; measuring the distance on a map that includes a mileage scale; or walking part of the distance wearing a pedometer, then multiplying to complete the estimate.
5. Ten trees to the mile would mean only about one tree in each block, which wouldn't be enough trees to make Elm Street shady.
6. Marcus estimated that there were 4100 houses on Elm Street based on the house numbers ranging from 1500 East to 2600 West. Mr. Muddle probably just added the two numbers without having any reason for doing so.

MATH JOURNAL Have students explain in their Math Journals what they might have done to make an estimate of the number of trees needed for the Elm Street project.

◆ LESSON 116 Practicing Division: Missing Digits

THINKING STORY

Estimating Is Rough

Part 3

You may want to refer to previous parts of this Thinking Story, on pages 368–369 and 376–377.

Mr. Muddle's first job as an estimator took him to City Hall. "Do you remember when Elm Street had big elm trees growing all along it?" the commissioner asked.

"Not exactly," said Mr. Muddle. "But I do remember it used to be very shady walking down Elm Street, and now it isn't shady anymore."

"That's because Dutch elm disease came through and all the elm trees died. We'd like to plant new trees so that Elm Street will be shady again someday. We want to plant trees the whole length of the street, from 1500 East Elm Street to 2600 West Elm Street. So I need an estimate of how many trees we will have to buy."

"I'd say 4100 trees," said Mr. Muddle, "but my first estimates are not always good. So I want to take time and make a really good estimate."

Mr. Muddle called on his friends Manolita and Marcus to help him estimate. "First we need to find out the distance from 1500 East Elm Street to 2600 West Elm Street," he said. Marcus had a 12-inch ruler and started measuring the length of one block along Elm Street.

"I have a quicker way," said Manolita. She walked from one end of the block to the other, counting softly to herself as she walked. When she got to the end of the block she shouted, "This block is about 600 feet long."

"That means there are about eight blocks in a mile," said Marcus.

"So Elm Street must be about 5 miles long," Manolita said.

"It's amazing the things they teach children in school these days!" Mr. Muddle said. He hurried back to City Hall and told the

RETEACHING

No reteaching is suggested for this lesson. Continue any extra help or reteaching you began in previous lessons, as needed. You may want to assign Enrichment Master 116 for this lesson.

commissioner, "Elm Street is about 5 miles long. Ten trees to a mile sounds about right, so my estimate is that you'll need 50 trees."

"That doesn't sound like nearly enough," the commissioner said. "We'd like to have a tree in front of every house."

Mr. Muddle went with his friends back to Elm Street and told them to start counting houses. Manolita counted the houses on the south side of the street. They were numbered 801, 803, 805, and so on. Marcus counted the houses on the north side of the street: 800, 802, 804, and so on. Suddenly he said, "I think I have a good estimate. There are about 4100 houses on Elm Street."

Mr. Muddle told the commissioner that his first estimate was a good one after all. "You'll need about 4100 trees."

A few months later Mr. Muddle met the commissioner walking down Elm Street admiring the new trees. "Your estimate was very close," the commissioner told him. "We had a couple of hundred trees more than we needed, but we found other places to plant them. Good work!"

. . . to be continued

Work in groups. Discuss your answers and how you figured them out. Then compare your answers with those of other groups. Answers are in margin.

1. How do you think Manolita estimated the length of the block? Estimate how many steps she would have taken.
2. If a block is 600 feet long, why is eight blocks to the mile a better estimate than nine blocks to the mile? (There are 5280 feet in a mile.)
3. Is 5 miles a good estimate for the length of Elm Street? What would have to be true for this to be a good estimate?
4. What are other ways to estimate the length of Elm Street?
5. How could you tell that 50 trees was too low an estimate?
6. Explain Marcus's estimate of 4100 trees. Did Marcus arrive at the number 4100 the same way Mr. Muddle did?

Use the Cumulative Review on page 560 after this lesson.

PRACTICE p. 116

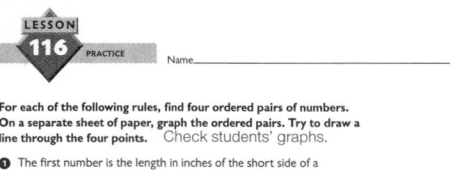

LESSON 116 PRACTICE Name________________

For each of the following rules, find four ordered pairs of numbers. On a separate sheet of paper, graph the ordered pairs. Try to draw a line through the four points. Check students' graphs.

1. The first number is the length in inches of the short side of a rectangle whose long side is four times as long. The second number is the perimeter in inches of the rectangle. (1, 10), (2, 20), (3, 30), (4, 40)
2. The first number is the length in inches of the short side of a rectangle whose long side is four times as long. The second number is the area in square inches of the rectangle. (1, 4), (2, 16), (3, 36), (4, 64)

Find the missing digit.

3. 6)□52 = 142; 6, 25, 24, 12, 12. □ is 8.
4. 4)946 = 236 R2; □, 14, 12, 26, 24, 2. □ is 8.
5. 3)951 = 3□7; 9, 5, 3, 21. □ is 1.
6. 5)344 = 6□ R4; 30, 44, 40, 4. □ is 8.
7. 8)842 = 10□ R2; 8, 42, 40, 2. □ is 5.
8. □)717 = 239; 6, 11, 9, 27, 27. □ is 3.
9. 7)904 = 1□9 R1; 7, 20, 14, 64, 63, 1. □ is 2.
10. 9)687 = □6 R3; 63, 57, 54, 3. □ is 7.

Copyright © SRA/McGraw-Hill. Permission is granted to reproduce this page for classroom use.

ENRICHMENT p. 116

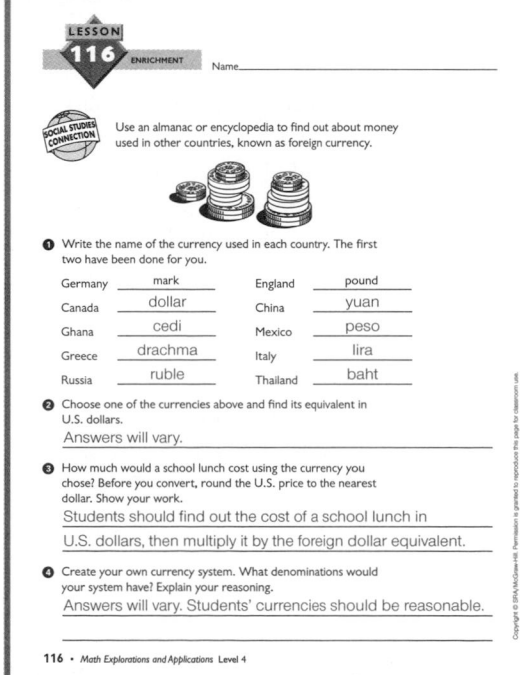

LESSON 116 ENRICHMENT Name________________

SOCIAL STUDIES CONNECTION Use an almanac or encyclopedia to find out about money used in other countries, known as foreign currency.

1. Write the name of the currency used in each country. The first two have been done for you.

Germany	mark	England	pound
Canada	dollar	China	yuan
Ghana	cedi	Mexico	peso
Greece	drachma	Italy	lira
Russia	ruble	Thailand	baht

2. Choose one of the currencies above and find its equivalent in U.S. dollars.
   Answers will vary.
3. How much would a school lunch cost using the currency you chose? Before you convert, round the U.S. price to the nearest dollar. Show your work.
   Students should find out the cost of a school lunch in U.S. dollars, then multiply it by the foreign dollar equivalent.
4. Create your own currency system. What denominations would your system have? Explain your reasoning.
   Answers will vary. Students' currencies should be reasonable.

Copyright © SRA/McGraw-Hill. Permission is granted to reproduce this page for classroom use.

3 Wrap-Up 5 MINUTES

In Closing Ask students how they would go about estimating the number of trees to plant in order to form a shady border around the schoolyard.

ALTERNATIVE ASSESSMENT

Performance Assessment Present an estimation problem students can solve in pairs or small groups. Have them apply their estimating, arithmetic, and problem-solving skills to make a reasonable estimate and prepare to defend it. Activities might include estimating the number of math books needed for a stack that reaches the ceiling, the number of reflectors needed to put one every 10 feet along the school driveway, the number of cars that could park in a vacant lot or open field, or the number of desks you could store in the classroom if they were all pushed together.

Assessment Criteria

Did the student . . .

- ✓ correctly find the missing digits in at least 75% of the problems on page 396?
- ✓ determine number pairs to fit each function rule?
- ✓ create accurate graphs of the function problems on page 397?
- ✓ contribute to the Thinking Story discussion?'

Homework Assign Practice Master 116 for further practice with division.

LESSON 117

Student Edition pages 400–403

Multiply and Divide

LESSON PLANNER

Objectives

- to review the inverse relationship of multiplication and division and to show how to use that relationship to solve division problems
- to review functions and graphing
- to demonstrate how to use a graph of a multiplication function to solve related division problems

Context of the Lesson This is the first of two lessons that review the inverse relationship between multiplication and division. This relationship was taught in Unit 3 and has been the focus of many Mental Math exercises. These two lessons show students a way to solve multidigit divisor problems by estimating and multiplying. They will also help broaden students' understanding of division.

MANIPULATIVES

counters*

paints, crayons, and white paper (optional)

colored paper (optional)

Program Resources

Reteaching Master

Practice Master 117

Enrichment Master 117

For extra practice:
CD-ROM* Lesson 117

1 Warm-Up

5 MINUTES

Problem of the Day Present the following problem, encouraging students to use **counters*** to act it out: Alana shared some peanuts with her friends. First she gave Rashid six peanuts. Then she gave Beth half of the peanuts she had left. Next, Damon got half the peanuts that were left, plus one more. Alana ate the last six peanuts herself. How many peanuts did Alana start with? ((6 + 7 + 1) x 2 + 6 = 34)

Problem-Solving Strategies Ask students who have solved the Problem of the Day to share how they solved it and any strategies they used.

MENTAL MATH Students can practice using corresponding pairs of multidigit multiplication and division problems. Write these problems on the chalkboard:

a. 9 x 20 = (180) 180 ÷ 9 = (20)

b. 8 x 30 = (240) 240 ÷ 30 = (8)

(continued on page 401)

EXPLORE

LESSON 117

Multiply and Divide

ACT IT OUT

Oodles of Gooples

Landon dreamed about a trip to Lotsamonia. He went there with his friends Mindy, Tyler, Keesha, Tony, and Jordan.

They landed near a hamburger stand, which reminded them how hungry they were.

"How much are your hamburgers?" Landon asked the man behind the counter.

"23 gooples," he said.

"Gooples!" said Landon. "What are those?"

"A goople is our unit of money in Lotsamonia," the man explained.

"We have dollars and cents," said Landon.

"Well, then," said the man, "go exchange them for gooples."

Off they went to the Bank of Lotsamonia, where they found out that 23 gooples are worth exactly $1.

"How many gooples can I get for $3?" Jordan asked.

◆ Do you know the answer to that question? **69 gooples**

"I gave the teller $27," said Keesha, "and he gave me 621 gooples. Does that make sense?"

400 • Division

Art Connection Have students create color-coded equations that blend inverse relationships (addition and subtraction or multiplication and division) with the concept of mixing colors. Provide **paints, crayons,** and **white paper** for students to create colorful examples of these relationships. Ask them to think of colors that result from combining two other colors. For example, purple is created by mixing red and blue. Then have students determine how the colors in these blending "equations" correspond to the elements of the multiplication and division algorithms. For example, they can use factors of yellow and blue to yield a green product. Or, they can divide an orange dividend by a yellow divisor to get a red quotient.

*available separately

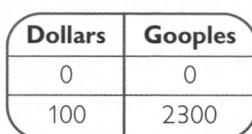

"I have an idea," said Tony. "Let's make a graph so we can check whether we are getting about the right number of gooples for our dollars."

"OK," they all agreed.

First they made a chart using some numbers that were easy to multiply.

Dollars	Gooples
0	0
100	2300

Next, Landon and his friends made a graph of the ordered pairs on the chart: (0, 0) and (100, 2300). They drew a straight line through the points.

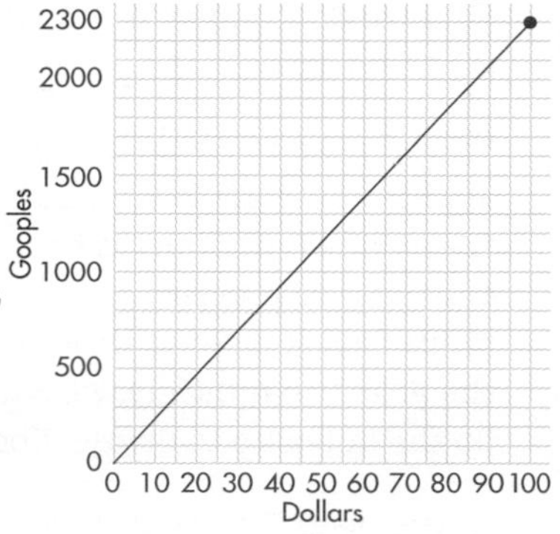

"I have $65," said Jordan. "About how many gooples will I get?"

"Simple," said Tony, "find 65 on the sideways axis, go straight up to the line, then go across to the up-and-down axis."

Jordan watched Tony put his finger on 65, then move it up and over. He said, "My 65 dollars are worth about 1500 gooples."

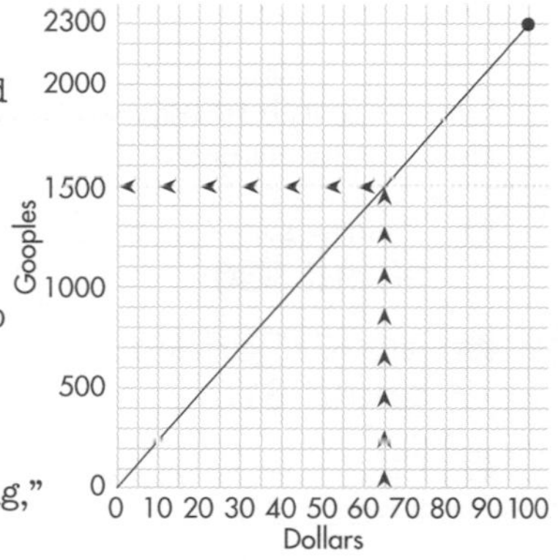

They all exchanged their dollars for gooples and used the graph to check their amounts.

"Now we can get some hamburgers and then go shopping," said Landon. And off they went.

Technology Connection On the Internet, visit the NASA Home Page (http://www.gsfc.nasa.gov) for a look at graphics and projects to enhance math lessons.

Mental Math (continued)

c.	3 x 50 = (150)	150 ÷ 50 = (3)
d.	40 x 80 = (3200)	3200 ÷ 80 = (40)
e.	70 x 60 = (4200)	4200 ÷ 60 = (70)
f.	90 x 60 = (5400)	5400 ÷ 90 = (60)
g.	80 x 70 = (5600)	5600 ÷ 80 = (70)
h.	25 x 100 = (2500)	2500 ÷ 25 = (100)
i.	70 x 70 = (4900)	4900 ÷ 70 = (70)
j.	50 x 70 = (3500)	3500 ÷ 70 = (50)

2 Teach

ACT IT OUT

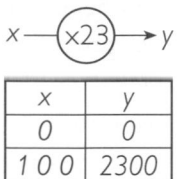

Using the Student Pages This story, which continues through page 402, shows how to use a graph of the multiplication function x23 to approximate quotients for dividing by 23. Read through the story with the class. Pause to let students discuss and answer the questions. Make sure students see that they convert dollars to gooples by multiplying the number of dollars by 23.

When you discuss the chart on page 401, point out that it is like a function machine chart for the x23 function rule. In Unit 3 students made and completed such charts in this form:

x —(x23)→ y

x	y
0	0
100	2300

If possible, draw a grid like the one on page 401 on the chalkboard or display one on an overhead projector. Have students plot the two points (0, 0) and (100, 2300). Remind students that any ordered pair on the dollar-goople chart will fall on the line that connects the two points. As you get to the part of the story when Tony uses the graph to find that $65 equals about 1500 gooples, demonstrate the procedure he used as indicated by the arrows on the graph on page 401. Check that students understand how to use the graph to convert dollars to gooples. For example, ask "How does the graph show that it makes sense for Keesha to get 621 gooples for her $27?" and "If Jordan had $45, about how many gooples could he get?" (about 1000) Emphasize that a small graph like the one in the book will provide only approximate answers.

◆ LESSON 117 Multiply and Divide

Teach

ACT IT OUT

Using the Student Pages As you read page 402, demonstrate how Tony reads the graph "backwards" to divide. Model moving your finger up and across as you ask, "How many googles is $65 worth?" (about 1500) As you retrace your finger's path across and down ask, "How many dollars is 1500 googles worth?" (about $65) Emphasize again that a small graph like this provides only approximate answers. Then do the first one or two problems with the class before having students complete the rest on their own.

For page 403, go over the inverse, or opposite, function machines, reminding students that they worked with inverse function machines in Unit 3. Then have students complete page 403 on their own. Students should realize that because the problems are paired, they will not have to divide by two-digit numbers in order to solve problems 7–24. Some students may recognize that they need not multiply if they apply the inverse relationship of multiplication and division.

LEARNING STYLES · MANIPULATIVES

Meeting Individual Needs Students who are visual or kinesthetic learners may benefit from using colors to highlight the inverse relationship between multiplication and division. Use three colors of **paper squares** to present a multiplication problem, such as 20 x 25 = 500. Write one factor on a yellow square, another factor on a blue square, and the product on a green square. Then have students rearrange the same three squares to form a different multiplication equation (25 x 20 = 500), and then two division equations (500 ÷ 20 = 25 and 500 ÷ 25 = 20).

◆ LESSON 117 Multiply and Divide

ACT IT OUT

Tyler saw a radio that he wanted to buy. Then he saw the price.

"It costs 1000 gooples," he said. "That's too much money."

"It's not as much as it sounds," Tony said. "You have to divide 1000 by 23 to find out how much that is in dollars."

"But we don't know how to divide by big numbers like 23," said Tyler.

"We can use our graph to get an approximate answer," said Tony. "Remember, dividing is the opposite, or inverse, of multiplication. So, if we can use the graph to multiply, we can just do the opposite to divide. Look."

"I see," said Tyler. "1000 gooples are worth a little less than $45."

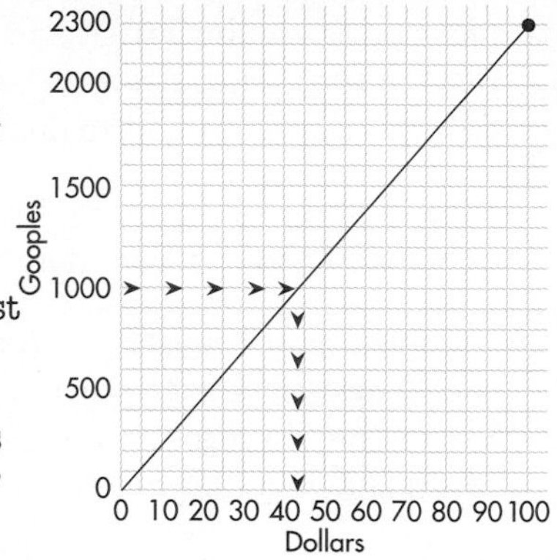

Use the graph to approximate how many dollars each of these items costs.

1. Running suit—649 gooples **about $30**
2. Baseball glove—415 gooples **about $20**
3. Shirt—225 gooples **about $10**
4. Bicycle—1820 gooples **about $80**
5. Calculator—110 gooples **about $5**
6. CD player—803 gooples **about $35**

Literature Connection With students, read *Math Curse* by Jon Scieska, which presents a humorous account of the math problems a student encounters in a day at school.

RETEACHING p. 36

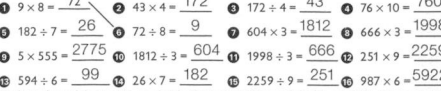

LESSON 117 RETEACHING Name____________

Knowing your multiplication facts can help you divide.

These counters show the multiplication fact 4 × 3 = 12.

There are three rows of counters with four counters in each row.

These groups of counters show the division fact 12 ÷ 3 = 4.

12 counters can be divided into three groups of counters with four counters in each group.

As you can see, these two facts are related. To check that 12 ÷ 3 = 4, you would multiply the quotient by the divisor (4 × 3) to find the dividend (12).

Follow the examples above and draw the multiplication fact 9 × 4 = 36 and the division fact 36 ÷ 9 = 4.

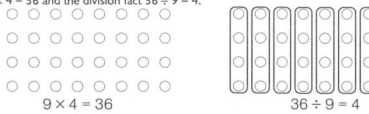

9 × 4 = 36 36 ÷ 9 = 4

Use counters to solve these problems. Draw lines between the problems that are related. The first one is done for you.

1. 9 × 8 = 72
2. 43 × 4 = 172
3. 172 ÷ 4 = 43
4. 76 × 10 = 760
5. 182 ÷ 7 = 26
6. 72 ÷ 8 = 9
7. 604 × 3 = 1812
8. 666 × 3 = 1998
9. 5 × 555 = 2775
10. 1812 ÷ 3 = 604
11. 1998 ÷ 3 = 666
12. 251 × 9 = 2259
13. 594 ÷ 6 = 99
14. 26 × 7 = 182
15. 2259 ÷ 9 = 251
16. 987 × 6 = 5922

Related problems: 5 and 14; 2 and 3; 10 and 7; 11 and 8; 15 and 12.

36 • *Math Explorations and Applications* Level 4

Copyright © SRA/McGraw-Hill. Permission is granted to reproduce this page for classroom use.

Remember:

35 → in | ×23 | out → 805

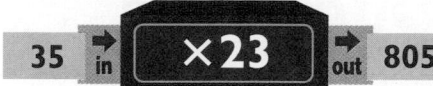

If you put 35 into a ×23 machine, 805 will come out.

A ÷23 machine does the opposite. If you put in 805, then 35 will come out.

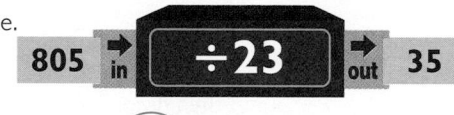

805 → in | ÷23 | out → 35

35 —(×23)→ 805   805 ←(÷23)— 35

In each problem, find the value of *x* or *y*. The answers to the problems on the left will help you solve the problems on the right.

ALGEBRA READINESS

7. 20 —(×25)→ *y* **500**   8. *x* ←(÷25)— 500 **20**
9. 13 —(×75)→ *y* **975**   10. *x* ←(÷75)— 975 **13**
11. 92 —(×10)→ *y* **920**   12. *x* ←(÷10)— 920 **92**
13. 63 —(×12)→ *y* **756**   14. *x* ←(÷12)— 756 **63**
15. 3 —(×752)→ *y* **2256**   16. *x* ←(÷752)— 2256 **3**
17. 6 —(×375)→ *y* **2250**   18. *x* ←(÷375)— 2250 **6**
19. 18 —(×452)→ *y* **8136**   20. *x* ←(÷452)— 8136 **18**
21. 75 —(×260)→ *y* **19,500**   22. *x* ←(÷260)— 19,500 **75**
23. 54 —(×145)→ *y* **7830**   24. *x* ←(÷145)— 7830 **54**

③ Wrap-Up (5 MINUTES)

In Closing Have students demonstrate how to use the graph of a multiplication function to divide.

ALTERNATIVE ASSESSMENT

Informal Assessment Observe students as they work on this lesson. Ask them to show how to use the graph to find the answer to a division problem that is related to the multiplication function ×23. Then have students verbalize how they used the pairs of problems on page 403 to find the values of *x* and *y*.

Assessment Criteria

Did the student . . .

- ✓ contribute to the discussion of the story?
- ✓ communicate how to use the graph of a multiplication function to divide?
- ✓ explain how to use inverse operations to solve for *x* and *y*?

Homework For further reinforcement of using inverse operations, assign Practice Master 117.

PRACTICE p. 117

LESSON 117 PRACTICE   Name______

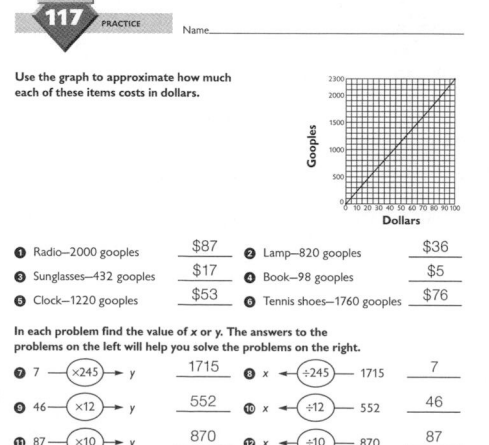

Use the graph to approximate how much each of these items costs in dollars.

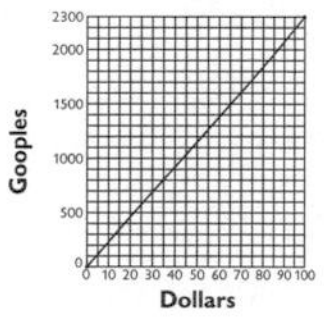

1. Radio—2000 gooples $87   2. Lamp—820 gooples $36
3. Sunglasses—432 gooples $17   4. Book—98 gooples $5
5. Clock—1220 gooples $53   6. Tennis shoes—1760 gooples $76

In each problem find the value of *x* or *y*. The answers to the problems on the left will help you solve the problems on the right.

7. 7 —(×245)→ *y* 1715   8. *x* ←(÷245)— 1715 7
9. 46 —(×12)→ *y* 552   10. *x* ←(÷12)— 552 46
11. 87 —(×10)→ *y* 870   12. *x* ←(÷10)— 870 87
13. 19 —(×81)→ *y* 1539   14. *x* ←(÷81)— 1539 19
15. 30 —(×65)→ *y* 1950   16. *x* ←(÷65)— 1950 30
17. 52 —(×31)→ *y* 1612   18. *x* ←(÷31)— 1612 52
19. 4 —(×63)→ *y* 252   20. *x* ←(÷63)— 252 4

Copyright © SRA/McGraw-Hill. Permission is granted to reproduce this page for classroom use.

Math Explorations and Applications Level 4 • 117

ENRICHMENT p. 117

LESSON 117 ENRICHMENT   Name______

Take some coins from your pocket or piggy bank and look at the date on them. The date tells when they were made, or minted. Were they minted in the same year or within a few years of one another? What's the oldest coin you have? What's the newest?

You can keep track of coins by the year they were minted using **The Cruncher: *Money, Money*** project. Get several rolls of pennies from a bank, look at the date each penny was minted, and enter the information into **The Cruncher** spreadsheet.

Once your information is entered, use **The Cruncher** to make a bar graph that shows information about your coins.

1. In what year were the most coins minted? Answers will vary depending
2. How many coins were minted in that year? on the number of students'
3. In what year were the fewest coins minted? coins and their dates.
4. How many coins were minted in that year? ______
5. What is the total value of your coins? ______

Copyright © SRA/McGraw-Hill. Permission is granted to reproduce this page for classroom use.

Math Explorations and Applications Level 4 • 117

SPECIAL NEEDS

Meeting Individual Needs

Some students may not understand why they should know that 975 ÷ 13 = 75 and 975 ÷ 75 = 13 without performing any computations if they know that 13 x 75 = 975. Until students are confident of the inverse relationship, work with lesser numbers, such as 8 ÷ 4 = 2 because 4 x 2 = 8. Also, you can relate this inverse relationship to the way students check quotients.

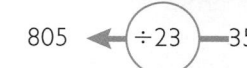

LESSON 118

Student Edition pages 404–405

Multiplying to Find Quotients

LESSON PLANNER

Objectives

- ▶ to continue reviewing the inverse relationship between multiplication and division
- ▶ to provide practice for applying the inverse relationship between multiplication and division to solve division problems

Context of the Lesson This is the second of two lessons on the inverse relationship between multiplication and division. This topic leads into the work in the next lesson on prime and composite numbers.

MANIPULATIVES

calculators* (optional)

Program Resources

Practice Master 118

Enrichment Master 118

For extra practice: CD-ROM* Lesson 118

1 Warm-Up 5 MINUTES

Problem of the Day Present this problem, which has several possible answers: All the telephone numbers in Dee's neighborhood start with 6. The first three digits in Dee's number have the same sum as the last four digits. If there are no odd numbers in Dee's phone number, what could her phone number be? (One answer is 624-4404.)

Problem-Solving Strategies Ask students who have solved the Problem of the Day to share how they solved it and any strategies they used.

MENTAL MATH Provide practice working with pairs of related multidigit multiplication and division problems. Write these problems on the chalkboard:

a.	7 x 70 = (490)	490 ÷ 7 = (70)
b.	90 x 60 = (5400)	5400 ÷ 60 = (90)
c.	80 x 10 = (800)	800 ÷ 80 = (10)
d.	60 x 70 = (4200)	4200 ÷ 60 = (70)
e.	60 x 80 = (4800)	4800 ÷ 60 = (80)
f.	20 x 60 = (1200)	1200 ÷ 60 = (20)
g.	30 x 30 = (900)	900 ÷ 30 = (30)
h.	9 x 900 = (8100)	8100 ÷ 900 = (90)
i.	200 x 20 = (4000)	4000 ÷ 20 = (200)

MIXED PRACTICE

LESSON 118

Multiplying to Find Quotients

You can use multiplication to find or check answers to division problems.

Remember:

Multiplication is the inverse of division. So if you multiply by 7 and then divide by 7, you get back the number you started with.

Example A: Start with 8 and multiply by 7.

7 × 8 = 56

56 ÷ 7 = 8

Example B:

```
  283
×  28
 2264
 566
 7924
```

Start with 283 and multiply by 28.

28 × 283 = 7924

```
     283
28)7924
```

7924 ÷ 28 = 283

Solve these problems without dividing or subtracting. Use the information in the box to help you.

1. 25)625 **25**
2. 250)1000 **4**
3. 125)1000 **8**
4. 52)2496 **48**
5. 4)1000 **250**
6. 79)6399 **81**
7. 8)1000 **125**
8. 81)6399 **79**
9. 48)2496 **52**
10. 843)22,761 **27**
11. 13,129 − 7,846 = **5,283**
12. 13,129 − 5,283 = **7,846**

5283 + 7846 = 13,129
8 × 125 = 1000
4 × 250 = 1000
52 × 48 = 2496
25 × 25 = 625
843 × 27 = 22,761
81 × 79 = 6399

Why teach it this way?

Students will learn the algorithm for dividing by two-digit divisors in Level 5. For now, they can use their understanding of the inverse relationship between multiplication and division to find quotients through multiplication. This approach combines the techniques of approximation and computation.

RETEACHING

Have students use only the multiplication function of the **calculator*** to find the quotients for the problems on page 405. This approach lets students apply their understanding of approximation and inverse operations to solve division problems without getting slowed down by too much computation.

*available separately

For each problem, several answers are given but only one is correct. Choose the correct answer without dividing.

Example: 25)175 **a.** 4 **b.** 6 **c.** 7 **d.** 10 **e.** 11

25	25	25
× 4	× 6	× 7
100	150	175

7 × 25 = 175. So 175 ÷ 25 must be 7. The correct answer is **c.**

13	12)96	a. 7	(b.) 8	c. 9	d. 10	e. 11
14	15)225	a. 5	b. 8	c. 0	d. 13	(e.) 15
15	24)96	(a.) 4	b. 5	c. 6	d. 7	e. 8
16	250)1000	a. 3	(b.) 4	c. 5	d. 6	e. 7
17	12)144	a. 8	b. 9	c. 10	(d.) 12	e. 14
18	15)75	(a.) 5	b. 6	c. 7	d. 8	e. 10
19	11)154	a. 12	(b.) 14	c. 16	d. 20	e. 24
20	17)357	a. 19	b. 20	(c.) 21	d. 22	e. 23
21	22)242	a. 9	(b.) 11	c. 13	d. 15	e. 17
22	16)96	a. 5	(b.) 6	c. 8	d. 14	e. 16
23	13)169	a. 2	b. 5	c. 7	d. 9	(e.) 13
24	150)600	(a.) 4	b. 5	c. 6	d. 7	e. 8
25	12)108	a. 7	b. 8	(c.) 9	d. 10	e. 11
26	14)182	a. 11	b. 12	(c.) 13	d. 14	e. 15
27	19)247	a. 2	b. 3	c. 5	(d.) 13	e. 17
28	18)324	a. 15	b. 16	(c.) 18	d. 19	e. 20
29	14)168	a. 11	(b.) 12	c. 13	d. 14	e. 15

❷ Teach

Using the Student Pages Discuss the top section of page 404. Then ask students whether anyone sees a product in the box that would help to solve problem 1. Students should know that because 25 x 25 = 625, the quotient for problem 1 should be 25. Repeat this procedure for problem 2. To prepare students for problems 11 and 12, ask what other two operations are the opposite or inverse of each other. (addition and subtraction) Have students complete the problems on page 404 on their own.

COOPERATIVE LEARNING Go over the examples at the top of page 405. Ask students which of the five choices they would have tried first. Then have students complete the rest of the page independently, in pairs, or in trios. Group members can share their reasoning for choosing a particular quotient, or they can share the task of multiplying to find the quotient.

❸ Wrap-Up

5 MINUTES

In Closing Have students explain how they can use an inverse operation to solve 960 ÷ 16 if they know that 16 x 60 = 960.

ALTERNATIVE ASSESSMENT

Performance Assessment Observe students as they complete the problems on page 405. Ask them to explain how they narrowed their choices to select the correct answers without actually dividing.

Assessment Criteria

Did the student . . .

- ✓ contribute to the discussion of inverse relationships?
- ✓ communicate strategies used to determine the correct quotient without dividing?
- ✓ correctly answer at least 75% of the problems on pages 404–405?

Homework Provide a set of five multiplication equations such as the ones given in the box on page 404. Have students create and solve ten division problems based on that information.

PRACTICE p. 118

LESSON 118 PRACTICE Name________________

For each problem several answers are given, but only one is correct. Choose the correct answer without dividing. Then ring the letter for that answer.

1	11)88	a. 6	b. 7	c. 9	d. 10	(e.) 8
2	10)120	a. 8	(b.) 12	c. 10	d. 14	e. 4
3	50)500	a. 5	(b.) 10	c. 15	d. 20	e. 25
4	25)625	a. 15	b. 35	c. 75	d. 100	(e.) 25
5	12)360	(a.) 30	b. 50	c. 70	d. 90	e. 110
6	12)84	(a.) 7	b. 8	c. 9	d. 10	e. 11
7	14)196	a. 12	b. 16	(c.) 14	d. 20	e. 18
8	15)180	a. 9	b. 11	c. 15	d. 14	(e.) 12
9	18)198	(a.) 11	b. 14	c. 17	d. 20	e. 23
10	30)3000	a. 50	b. 75	(c.) 100	d. 150	e. 200
11	21)63	a. 2	(b.) 3	c. 4	d. 5	e. 6
12	30)120	a. 1	b. 2	c. 3	(d.) 4	e. 5
13	13)182	a. 11	(b.) 14	c. 17	d. 19	e. 24
14	19)209	a. 7	b. 9	(c.) 11	d. 13	e. 15
15	12)180	(a.) 15	b. 18	c. 20	d. 22	e. 25
16	25)200	a. 4	b. 5	c. 6	d. 7	(e.) 8
17	70)630	a. 6	b. 7	c. 8	(d.) 9	e. 10
18	12)144	a. 10	(b.) 12	c. 14	d. 16	e. 18
19	11)121	a. 7	b. 9	(c.) 11	d. 13	e. 15
20	90)360	a. 12	b. 10	c. 8	d. 6	(e.) 4

118 • *Math Explorations and Applications* Level 4

Copyright © SRA/McGraw-Hill. Permission is granted to reproduce this page for classroom use.

ENRICHMENT p. 118

LESSON 118 ENRICHMENT Name________________

The U.S. House of Representatives has 435 members. Each state has at least one representative, but the total number from each state is based on the state's population. The chart below shows the population for each of the six New England states, according to the 1990 census. The actual number of representatives from the state with the smallest population is given. From these figures make your best estimate of the number of representatives from each state. Remember, the total number must be 23.

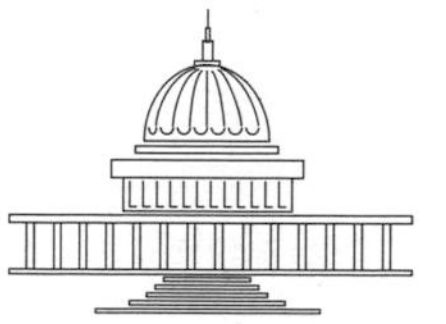

Check your estimates by looking at a reference book.

State	Population	Estimated Number of Representatives	Actual Number of Representatives
Maine	1,127,928	Answers will vary.	2
New Hampshire	1,109,252		2
Vermont	562,758		1
Massachusetts	6,016,425		10
Rhode Island	1,003,464		2
Connecticut	3,287,116		6
Total	13,106,943		23

118 • *Math Explorations and Applications* Level 4

Copyright © SRA/McGraw-Hill. Permission is granted to reproduce this page for classroom use.

LESSON 119

Student Edition pages 406–407

Prime and Composite Numbers

LESSON PLANNER

Objective

- to introduce the concepts of factors, prime numbers, and composite numbers

Context of the Lesson This lesson offers a conceptual application of the relationship between multiplication and division and of rectangular arrays as a concrete illustration of factors.

MANIPULATIVES

United States flag (real or illustration)

Program Resources

Practice Master 119

Enrichment Master 119

For extra practice:
CD-ROM* Lesson 119

1 Warm-Up (5 MINUTES)

Problem of the Day Present this problem: Ms. Lev's class is putting on a play and needs to set up 48 chairs for guests. They want to make at least two rows, but no more than eight, with the same number of chairs in each row. Find all possible ways they can arrange the chairs. (two rows of 24 chairs, three rows of 16, four rows of 12, six rows of 8, eight rows of 6)

Problem-Solving Strategies Ask students who have solved the Problem of the Day to share how they solved it and any strategies they used.

MENTAL MATH Present the following problems orally:

a. 15 – 10 + 4 – 1 = (8)	**b.** 14 + 7 ÷ 3 + 3 = (10)
c. 6 + 16 + 20 ÷ 6 = (7)	**d.** 18 – 9 – 3 + 2 = (8)
e. 81 ÷ 9 – 1 ÷ 2 = (4)	**f.** 3 + 2 x 6 – 1 = (29)
g. 6 x 8 ÷ 6 x 2 = (16)	**h.** 5 x 9 + 5 – 10 = (40)
i. 72 ÷ 9 x 6 ÷ 8 = (6)	**j.** 2 x 2 x 2 x 2 = (16)

EXPLORE

LESSON 119

Prime and Composite Numbers

SOCIAL STUDIES CONNECTION

Our flag has had 50 stars only since 1960. A previous flag had 48 stars and was the United States flag longer than any other. The stars were arranged in six rows of eight.

From 1818 to 1836 the United States flag had 20 stars.

◆ How do you think the stars were arranged? **For example: ten rows of two, five rows of four, four rows of five (this was the actual arrangement)**

For many numbers of stars it is possible to arrange them in different rectangles. For some numbers, the only possible rectangles would have one row (or one column). The possible rectangles that can be made with 20 stars are:

1 by 20   2 by 10   4 by 5

You could make three more by turning these rectangles to show 20 by 1, 10 by 2, and 5 by 4.

Solve these problems.

1. List all possible rectangles that could be made with
   a. one star **1 × 1**
   b. two stars **1 × 2, 2 × 1**
   c. three stars **1 × 3, 3 × 1**
   d. four stars **1 × 4, 4 × 1, 2 × 2**
   e. five stars **1 × 5, 5 × 1**
   f. six stars **1 × 6, 6 × 1, 2 × 3, 3 × 2**
2. How many rectangles did you list for one star? Do you think there are any other numbers besides 1 for which there is only one rectangle? **1; no**
3. How many rectangles did you list for two, three, and five stars? Do you think there are other numbers for which there are only two rectangles? **2 each; yes**
4. List three other numbers for which there are only two rectangles. **For example: 7, 29, 53**

Why teach it this way?

To help students better understand the concept, we define prime and composite numbers concretely in terms of rectangles, rather than in the more abstract terms of factors or divisibility. However, the formal definition of *prime number* is "a whole number that is divisible only by itself and 1;" all others (except 1) are composite numbers.

Literature Connection Invite students to complete the "Prime Numbers" activity, found on page 22 of *Mathematics* by Irving Adler.

RETEACHING

No reteaching is needed at this time. Prime numbers, composite numbers, and factorization are taught again in Levels 5 and 6 of this program. You might want to assign Enrichment Master 119 for this lesson.

*available separately

Solve these problems.

Prime numbers have exactly two rectangles.

Composite numbers have more than two rectangles.

5. List five prime numbers. **For example: 5, 17, 31, 43, 61**
6. List five composite numbers. **For example: 4, 6, 24, 32, 40**
7. Is the number 1 prime or composite? **neither**

Remember, a factor of a number is any number that divides it without a remainder. For example, the factors of 36 are 1, 2, 3, 4, 6, 9, 12, 18, and 36. You can divide 36 by any of these numbers and there will be no remainder.

8. List the factors of the following numbers.
   a. 1 **1** **b.** 2 **1, 2** **c.** 3 **1, 3** **d.** 4 **1, 2, 4** **e.** 5 **1, 5** **f.** 6 **1, 2, 3, 6**
9. How many factors does 1 have? **1**
10. How many factors do each of the following numbers have?
    a. 2 **2** **b.** 3 **2** **c.** 5 **2**
11. How many factors does 4 have? **3**
12. List all numbers that you think have just one factor.
    1 is the only number with one factor
13. List four numbers that have exactly two factors. **For example: 2, 3, 5, 7**
14. List six numbers that have more than two factors. **For example: 4, 6, 8, 9, 10, 12**
15. How many factors do prime numbers have? **2**
16. How many factors do composite numbers have? **more than 2**
17. Why might (6 × 5) + (5 × 4) remind someone of the flag of the United States? **The flag has five rows of six stars (6 × 5) and four rows of five stars (5 × 4).**

MATH JOURNAL

In your Math Journal list all the prime numbers less than 100. **2, 3, 5, 7, 11, 13,17, 19, 23, 29, 31, 37, 41, 43, 47, 53, 59, 61, 67, 71, 73, 79, 83, 89, 97**

2 Teach

Using the Student Pages Go over page 406 with the class. In discussing possible rectangular arrays for 20 stars, point out that, for example, 4 × 5 and 5 × 4 are the same rectangle: one is a rotated version of the other. Once students understand the terminology of the lesson, proceed to page 407. Have students complete problem 9 on their own. Then discuss the answers with the class. Point out that, according to the definitions given on the page, the number 1 is neither prime nor composite. All other counting numbers are either prime or composite. Briefly discuss the meaning of the word *factor* as given on page 407. Then have students complete problems 10–17 independently. Display a current **United States flag** or an illustration of one to help with problem 17.

3 Wrap-Up

5 MINUTES

In Closing Have students describe the difference between a prime number and a composite number and give an example of each.

ALTERNATIVE ASSESSMENT

Portfolio Assessment Have each student write a brief statement that explains, in his or her own words, prime and composite numbers. Encourage students to draw rectangles to support their answers. Have students date and add their statements to their Math Portfolios as evidence of ongoing learning.

Assessment Criteria

Did the student . . .

- ✓ contribute to the discussion of prime and composite numbers and factors?
- ✓ illustrate composite numbers with two or more rectangles?
- ✓ find examples of prime and composite numbers?

Homework Have students draw rectangles to represent all the different factors for each of the numbers 2 through 12 and identify which are prime numbers and which are composite numbers.

PRACTICE p. 119

LESSON 119 PRACTICE Name__________

Write the factors of each of the following numbers.

1. 24 1, 2, 3, 4, 6, 8, 12, 24
2. 10 1, 2, 5, 10
3. 12 1, 2, 3, 4, 6, 12
4. 7 1, 7
5. 32 1, 2, 4, 8, 16, 32
6. 23 1, 23
7. 8 1, 2, 4, 8
8. 15 1, 3, 5, 15
9. 20 1, 2, 4, 5, 10, 20
10. 19 1, 19

How many factors does each of the following numbers have?

11. 13 2
12. 18 6
13. 21 4
14. 9 3
15. 11 2
16. 16 5
17. 5 2
18. 22 4
19. 25 3
20. 30 8

Answer these questions. Remember: Prime numbers have exactly two factors. Composite numbers have more than two factors.

21. List three prime numbers. Sample answer: 3, 5, 7
22. List three composite numbers. Sample answer: 4, 6, 8

Determine whether the following numbers are prime or composite.

23. 42 composite
24. 19 prime
25. 14 composite
26. 27 composite
27. 29 prime
28. 28 composite
29. 46 composite
30. 50 composite

Copyright © SRA/McGraw-Hill. Permission is granted to reproduce this page for classroom use.

ENRICHMENT p. 119

LESSON 119 ENRICHMENT Name__________

Read these problems and answer the questions.

1. Write ten or more prime numbers below. How do you know they are prime numbers?
   Possible answer: A prime number has only two factors, itself and 1.
   Possible list of prime numbers:
   a. 2 b. 5
   c. 11 d. 17
   e. 23 f. 3
   g. 7 h. 13
   i. 19 j. 19
2. Add ten different pairs of these numbers. Are the sums you find prime or composite? Show your work.
   Possible problems:

Prime sums:	Composite sums:
2 + 3 = 5	3 + 7 = 10
2 + 5 = 7	29 + 5 = 34
2 + 11 = 13	11 + 17 = 28
2 + 17 = 19	13 + 23 = 36
2 + 29 = 31	17 + 5 = 22

3. Subtract ten different pairs of prime numbers. Use the list you created above or think of other prime numbers. Are the answers prime or composite? Show your work.
   Possible problems:

Prime answers:	Composite answers:
5 − 3 = 2	23 − 2 = 21
31 − 29 = 2	19 − 3 = 16
19 − 2 = 17	29 − 7 = 22
7 − 5 = 2	13 − 5 = 8
13 − 2 = 11	11 − 5 = 6

Copyright © SRA/McGraw-Hill. Permission is granted to reproduce this page for classroom use.

LESSON 120

Student Edition pages 408–411

Using a Bar Graph

LESSON PLANNER

Objectives

- to provide practice in reading a bar graph and in solving problems based on it
- to provide practice in dividing with one-digit divisors
- to help students develop the broad ability to use mathematical common sense

Context of the Lesson This lesson and the rest of the lessons in this unit provide practice with and applications of division and other operations. This lesson also contains Part 4 of "Estimating Is Rough," a five-part Thinking Story.

MANIPULATIVES

calendar (optional)
graph paper (optional)
interlocking cubes* (optional)
play money* (optional)

Program Resources

"Harder Snake" Game Mat
Practice Master 120
Enrichment Master 120
The Cruncher*
For career connections: Careers and Math*
For additional math integration: Math Throughout the Day*
For extra practice: CD-ROM* Lesson 120

1 Warm-Up

5 MINUTES

Problem of the Day Present this problem to students: Larry, Marco, Shari, and Tess were playing a card game. They formed partners. The boys were not partners. People whose names rhymed were not partners. Who were the partners? (Larry and Tess, Shari and Marco)

Problem-Solving Strategies Ask students who have solved the Problem of the Day to share how they solved it and any strategies they used.

MENTAL MATH Present the following problems to provide practice in all four operations. Have students indicate thumbs up if the answer falls within the bounds 2000–3000 and thumbs down if it does not.

a. 100 × 201 (thumbs down)

b. 1500 + 600 (thumbs up)

(continued on page 409)

MIXED PRACTICE

LESSON 120

Using a Bar Graph

Alex earns $8.00 an hour working at the Splish-Splash Car Wash. The bar graph shows the total amount of money he earned each day last week.

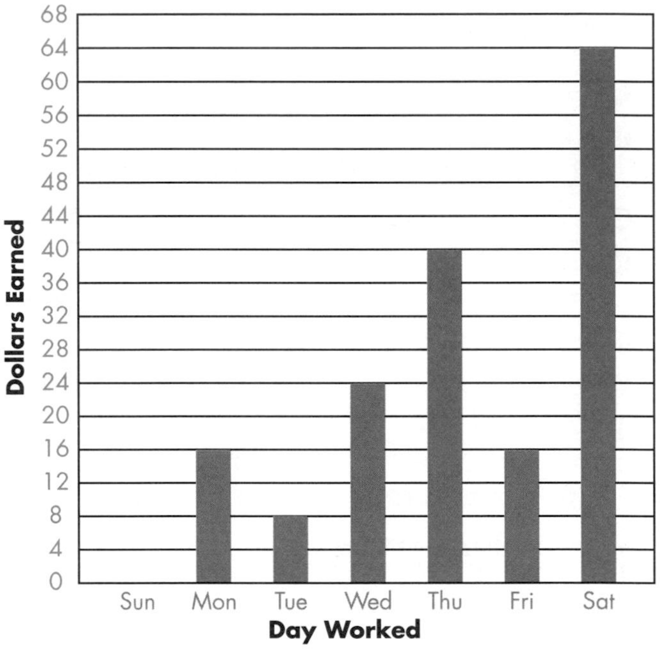

Language Arts Connection Have students write and present additional questions classmates can answer from the graph on page 408. For example: On which day or days did Alex not work? (Sunday) How much more money did Alex earn on Thursday than on Friday? ($24) How many more hours did he work that day? (three)

*available separately

Use the graph to answer these questions.

1. How much money did Alex earn on Monday? **$16**
2. How much money did he earn on Tuesday? **$8**
3. How much money did he earn on Friday? **$16**
4. How many hours did Alex work on Wednesday? (Remember, he earns $8 an hour.) **3**
5. How many hours did he work on Saturday? **8**
6. How many hours did Alex work on Tuesday? **1**
7. On which day did he earn the most money? **Saturday**
8. How much money did Alex earn during the entire week? **$168**
9. What was the average amount of money he made per day for the six days he worked? **$28**
10. If he had earned $4 an hour, how much would Alex have earned during the entire week? **$84**

Divide.

11. 8)410 **51 R2**	12. 6)236 **39 R2**	13. 5)500 **100**	14. 3)271 **90 R1**	15. 9)810 **90**
16. 4)237 **59 R1**	17. 3)229 **76 R1**	18. 4)804 **201**	19. 6)732 **122**	20. 7)210 **30**
21. 9)63 **7**	22. 8)539 **67 R3**	23. 2)107 **53 R1**	24. 7)622 **88 R6**	25. 8)48 **6**
26. 3)408 **136**	27. 4)792 **198**	28. 6)360 **60**	29. 9)72 **8**	30. 6)201 **33 R3**
31. 3)273 **91**	32. 8)32 **4**	33. 9)706 **78 R4**	34. 6)240 **40**	35. 8)324 **40 R4**
36. 2)970 **485**	37. 6)437 **72 R5**	38. 8)342 **42 R6**	39. 9)108 **12**	40. 4)960 **240**

Solve.

41. Ray traveled 300 miles in his car in six hours. How many miles per hour is that? **50**

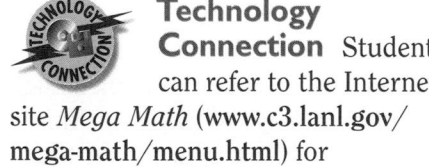

Technology Connection Students can refer to the Internet site *Mega Math* (www.c3.lanl.gov/mega-math/menu.html) for challenging math lessons.

Mental Math (continued)

c. 300 ÷ 3 (thumbs down)
d. 40 x 50 (thumbs up)
e. 2900 + 50 (thumbs up)
f. 4300 – 2100 (thumbs up)

2 Teach

Using the Student Pages Before students begin working on these pages, demonstrate the "Harder Snake" Game Mat so that students can play it as they finish. This game provides practice with solving missing term problems using multiplication and division.

To help focus students on the data given in the bar graph on page 408, present some preliminary questions. For example, ask, "How much money did Alex earn on Thursday?" ($40) Some students may want to use a blank **Cruncher*** spreadsheet to create a table and bar graph to see the results visually. After students complete the problems related to the bar graph, they should do exercises 11–41 on page 409, which provides practice in dividing by a one-digit divisor.

AT RISK **Meeting Individual Needs**
Most students, regardless of their interests, do something each day that they can record on a bar graph. Possible activities include sleeping, doing chores, playing sports, playing music, surfing the Internet, or caring for a pet. Have students identify an activity and keep track of the time they spend doing it each day for a week. Provide **graph paper** and have them show their results in a bar graph.

*available separately

◆ LESSON 120 Using a Bar Graph

Teach

Using the Thinking Story "Estimating Is Rough (Part 4)" centers on conducting a marketing survey. Mr. Muddle asks inappropriate questions and makes false assumptions based on the responses he gets.

Answers to Thinking Story Questions:

1. About half the customers Mr. Muddle interviewed had big roasting pans (41 had pans and 42 did not). From this sample Mr. Muddle figured that one half of all customers would have roasting pans and that everyone with a pan would buy a turkey. So he took one half of the total number of customers and got 1000.
2. No. Just because people have roasting pans does not mean they will buy a turkey. Some people who do not have roasting pans may buy a pan, cook a turkey in something else, or borrow a roasting pan. Also, Mr. Muddle may have asked different people in the same household whether they had pans. They may all have said yes, but they would not all buy turkeys.
3. He probably took all the people he thought had roasting pans (1000) and subtracted the number of people who bought Thanksgiving turkeys. He probably figured that the people who bought Thanksgiving turkeys would not buy turkeys for Christmas.
4. No. People may buy a turkey for Thanksgiving and another one for Christmas. Mr. Muddle still has not figured out why 1000 was a poor estimate in the first place.
5. Customers could be asked whether they plan to buy a turkey instead of whether they have a roasting pan, or the grocer could be asked how many turkeys he ordered and sold last Christmas.

MATH JOURNAL

Have students list in their Math Journals seasonal items that store owners make available for their customers. For each item, have students suggest methods the store owner might use to figure out how many or how much to order.

GAME

Introducing the "Harder Snake" Game Mat Students play this game in the same way as the "Snake" Game Mat, which was introduced in Lesson 53. This Game Mat focuses on solving missing-term problems, mental arithmetic, and mathematical reasoning. Be sure students realize that only multiplication and division rules are allowed. The "Snake" Game Mat allowed only addition and subtraction. Complete directions are on the Game Mat. A copy of this Game Mat can also be found on page 604 of this Teacher's Guide.

◆ LESSON 120 Using a Bar Graph

THINKING STORY

Estimating Is Rough

Part 4

You may wish to refer to previous parts of this Thinking Story, on pages 368–369, 376–377, and 398–399.

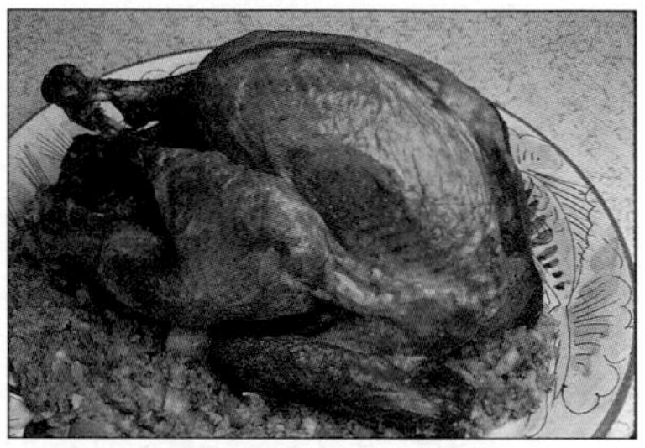

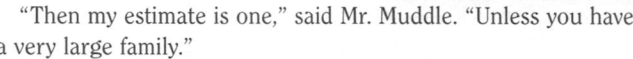

"I need your help, Mr. Muddle," said the grocer. "Could you help me figure out how many turkeys to order for Christmas?"

"Is your store open on Christmas Day?"

"No," said the grocer.

"Then my estimate is one," said Mr. Muddle. "Unless you have a very large family."

"I have a small family," said the grocer. "But I have lots of customers. Some of them buy turkeys for Christmas. I'd like you to estimate how many."

Mr. Muddle stopped a shopper. "Pardon me, sir. Do you plan to buy a turkey for Christmas?"

"I don't think so," said the shopper. "We don't have a big roasting pan."

Mr. Muddle asked more shoppers. But he changed the question. He found that 41 had big roasting pans and 42 didn't. Then he asked the grocer, "How many customers do you have all together?"

LITERATURE CONNECTION

Literature Connection Students can use three different bar graphs to get information on pages 129–136 in *Math for Every Kid* by Janice Van Cleave.

RETEACHING

MANIPULATIVES

Students who have trouble determining the number of hours Alex worked based on the amount of money he earned might use **play money*** to help solve this kind of problem. They can divide his total earnings for each day by $8 to find out how many hours he worked.

*available separately

"About 2000."

"Then I estimate you will need 1000 turkeys."

"But . . . but I've never sold that many! I sold only 600 at Thanksgiving."

"I forgot Thanksgiving," said Mr. Muddle. "You have 1000 people buying turkeys. You sold 600 turkeys at Thanksgiving. That means you will sell 400 at Christmas. Order 400 turkeys and 600 ducks. That way everyone with a roasting pan will have something to roast."

. . . to be continued

Work in groups. Discuss your answers and how you figured them out. Then compare your answers with those of other groups. **Answers are in margin.**

1. How did Mr. Muddle get his first estimate of 1000 turkeys?
2. Were his reasons very good for estimating 1000? Why or why not?
3. How did Mr. Muddle get his second estimate of 400?
4. Were his reasons very good for estimating 400 turkeys? Why or why not?
5. **Super challenge question:** If you were asking the questions instead of Mr. Muddle, what questions would you have asked to figure out how many turkeys to order?

3 Wrap-Up (5 MINUTES)

In Closing Ask students what other data they could obtain from the bar graph on page 408.

SELF ASSESSMENT Have students write a brief statement that evaluates their own performance on the questions related to the bar graph on page 408 and on the division exercises on page 409. Encourage them to identify what kinds of problems they are good at and why, as well as aspects in which they may require additional practice.

Assessment Criteria

Did the student . . .

✓ demonstrate an ability to read and interpret data from a bar graph?

✓ correctly answer at least 75% of the division problems?

✓ contribute to the Thinking Story discussion?

✓ communicate strategies used to analyze Mr. Muddle's responses?

Homework Have students record the amount of time they watch television each day for one week and show the results on a bar graph.

LEARNING STYLES • MANIPULATIVES

Meeting Individual Needs

Concrete or hands-on learners may solve the problems about the bar graph more successfully if they use manipulatives, such as **interlocking cubes***, to make a model of the graph. Or they might affix **play money*** to the days of a large **calendar** to show how much Alex earned each day.

PRACTICE p. 120

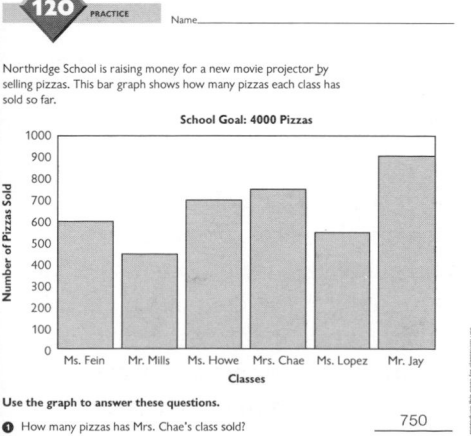

LESSON 120 PRACTICE Name____________________

Northridge School is raising money for a new movie projector by selling pizzas. This bar graph shows how many pizzas each class has sold so far.

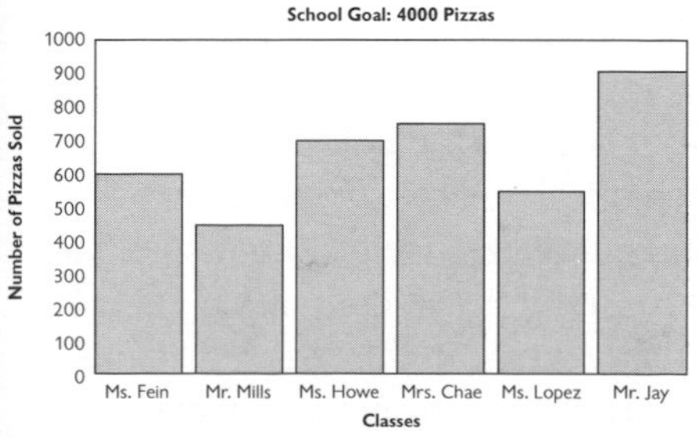

Use the graph to answer these questions.

1. How many pizzas has Mrs. Chae's class sold? 750
2. Which class has sold the most pizzas so far? Mr. Jay's
3. How many pizzas has that class sold? 900
4. Which class has sold the fewest pizzas so far? Mr. Mills's
5. How many pizzas has that class sold? 450
6. How many pizzas have been sold all together? 3950
7. How many more pizzas must be sold for the school to meet its goal? 50

120 • *Math Explorations and Applications* Level 4

Copyright © SRA/McGraw-Hill. Permission is granted to reproduce this page for classroom use.

ENRICHMENT p. 120

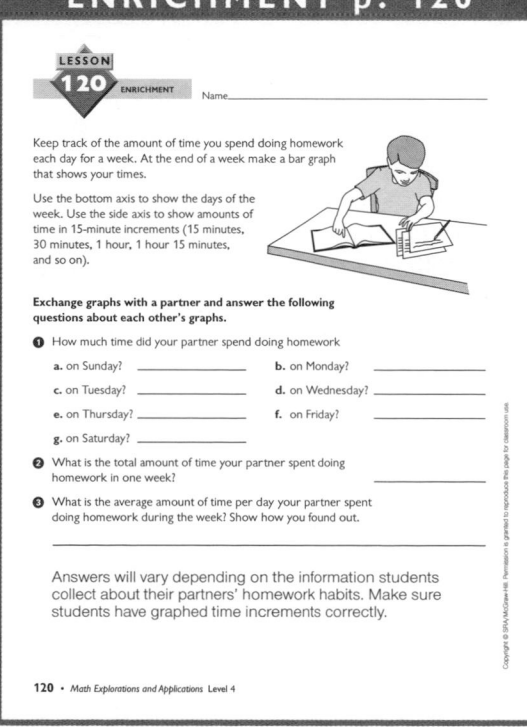

LESSON 120 ENRICHMENT Name____________________

Keep track of the amount of time you spend doing homework each day for a week. At the end of a week make a bar graph that shows your times.

Use the bottom axis to show the days of the week. Use the side axis to show amounts of time in 15-minute increments (15 minutes, 30 minutes, 1 hour, 1 hour 15 minutes, and so on).

Exchange graphs with a partner and answer the following questions about each other's graphs.

1. How much time did your partner spend doing homework
   - **a.** on Sunday? ______ **b.** on Monday? ______
   - **c.** on Tuesday? ______ **d.** on Wednesday? ______
   - **e.** on Thursday? ______ **f.** on Friday? ______
   - **g.** on Saturday? ______
2. What is the total amount of time your partner spent doing homework in one week? ______
3. What is the average amount of time per day your partner spent doing homework during the week? Show how you found out.

Answers will vary depending on the information students collect about their partners' homework habits. Make sure students have graphed time increments correctly.

120 • *Math Explorations and Applications* Level 4

Copyright © SRA/McGraw-Hill. Permission is granted to reproduce this page for classroom use.

*available separately

LESSON 121

Student Edition pages 412–413

More Division Review

LESSON PLANNER

Objectives

- to provide practice in reading a telephone bill and solving problems based on it
- to provide practice in finding unit cost
- to provide practice with division

Context of the Lesson This lesson and the rest of the lessons in the unit provide practice with, and application of, division and other operations.

MANIPULATIVES

flash cards (optional)

map (optional)

Program Resources

Practice Master 121

Enrichment Master 121

The Cruncher: Mystery Population*

For extra practice:
CD-ROM* Lesson 121

1 Warm-Up 5 MINUTES

Problem of the Day Present this problem to students: Kristina makes a beaded necklace with this repeating pattern: red bead, green bead, yellow bead, yellow bead, green bead, yellow bead. The finished necklace will have 174 beads. How many of each color will she use? (29 red, 58 green, 87 yellow.)

Problem-Solving Strategies Ask students who have solved the Problem of the Day to share how they solved it and any strategies they used.

MENTAL MATH Present students with the following problems involving all four operations with multidigit numbers to solve mentally:

a. 240 ÷ 30 = (8) **b.** 25 × 200 = (5000)

c. 350 − 45 = (305) **d.** 800 + 78 = (878)

e. 40 × 25 = (1000) **f.** 280 ÷ 4 = (70)

2 Teach

Using the Student Pages Because the telephone bill on page 412 gives no data about discounts or special rates at certain times of day, students can assume that it always costs the same amount per minute to call the same town.

PRACTICE

LESSON 121

More Division Review

Knowledge of math is helpful in understanding bills.

Mr. Cooper received this telephone bill in the mail.

REAL-WORLD CONNECTION

RINGVILLE TELEPHONE COMPANY
Monthly Statement for October

James Cooper
577 12th St.
Ringville

Telephone Number 555-5505

Date	Calls to	Number of Minutes	Price
Oct. 10	Midway	5	$1.25
Oct. 13	Midway	10	$2.50
Oct. 24	Horton	10	$0.80
Oct. 25	Cordville	3	$6.00
Oct. 27	Troy	2	$8.30
Oct. 29	Tone's Ferry	15	$1.50
Oct. 30	Midway	8	$3.00

Ringville Telephone Company rate information: All calls to other cities are charged by the minute. The farther a city is from Ringville, the higher the rate will be.

Answer the following questions.

1. How much per minute does it cost to call
   a. Midway? **25¢** **b.** Cordville? **$2.00** **c.** Tone's Ferry? **10¢**
   d. Horton? **8¢** **e.** Troy? **$4.15**
2. Which city is farther from Ringville—Horton or Midway? **Midway**
3. For one of his phone calls, Mr. Cooper was charged the wrong rate. Help him find the error. How much will Mr. Cooper save if he finds the error? **Oct. 30 call to Midway should be $2.00; he will save $1.00.**
4. Order the cities Mr. Cooper called, from the nearest to the farthest from Ringville. **Horton, Tone's Ferry, Midway, Cordville, Troy**
5. For how many minutes did Mr. Cooper use the telephone in October on calls that he made to other cities? **53**

LITERATURE CONNECTION

Literature Connection Invite students to read *Making Cents: Every Kid's Guide to Money* by Elizabeth Wilkinson. Have students determine the rate of earnings for one of the money-making ideas presented in this book.

RETEACHING

MANIPULATIVES Watch for students who still have trouble with the multiplication and division facts. You might want to have students practice with family members, a teacher's aide, a classmate, or on their own using **flash cards,** games, mechanical devices, speed tests, or **manipulatives.** Help students who are confused by the phone bill on page 412 by using a **map** to discuss how cities that are farther away usually cost more to call than cities that are nearer.

*available separately

Divide. Watch for remainders.

6. 3)42 **14**	7. 2)100 **50**	8. 7)8575 **1225**	9. 10)100 **10**
10. 3)20 **6 R2**	11. 8)1000 **125**	12. 7)98 **14**	13. 5)63,407 **12,681 R2**
14. 9)9 **1**	15. 9)80 **8 R8**	16. 4)100 **25**	17. 1)73,596 **73,596**
18. 5)125 **25**	19. 1)100 **100**	20. 6)44 **7 R2**	21. 6)35,172 **5,862**
22. 4)1298 **324 R2**	23. 7)507 **72 R3**	24. 9)0 **0**	25. 8)500 **62 R4**

PROBLEM SOLVING

Solve.

26. Last week Kirsten jogged every day. She didn't jog the same distance each day. These are the distances she jogged during the week: 9 miles, 11 miles, 12 miles, 9 miles, 10 miles, 12 miles, and 5 miles.
   - **a.** What is the average distance Kirsten jogged each day? **9.71 miles**
   - **b.** Did she jog the average distance on any day? **no**
   - **c.** On how many days did she run more than the average distance? **4**
   - **d.** On how many days did Kirsten run less than the average distance? **3**

27. A thermos holds 64 ounces of water. How many 4-ounce glasses can be filled from the thermos? **16**

Ask preliminary questions, such as the following, to help students understand the telephone bill:

- To what town did Mr. Cooper make a call on October 10? (Midway)
- How many minutes did that call last? (5 minutes)
- How much was Mr. Cooper charged for that call? ($1.25)
- How much per minute does it cost to call Midway? ($0.25)

Once students show an understanding of Mr. Cooper's telephone bill, have them solve problems 1–5 on their own. Discuss the answers as a class. For problem 3 on page 412, the assumption is based on two other calls to Midway, which were charged at a rate of $0.25 per minute. Discuss any other possibilities students may suggest. Students can use **The Cruncher*** spreadsheet to help them compare data. When they finish, students can solve the problems on page 413 independently.

3 Wrap-Up

5 MINUTES

In Closing Have students explain how they can use division to verify the charges on a telephone bill like the one Mr. Cooper received.

SELF ASSESSMENT

Have students evaluate how well they answered problems 6–27 on page 413. Ask them to tell what aspects of division they find easiest and what aspects they find most challenging.

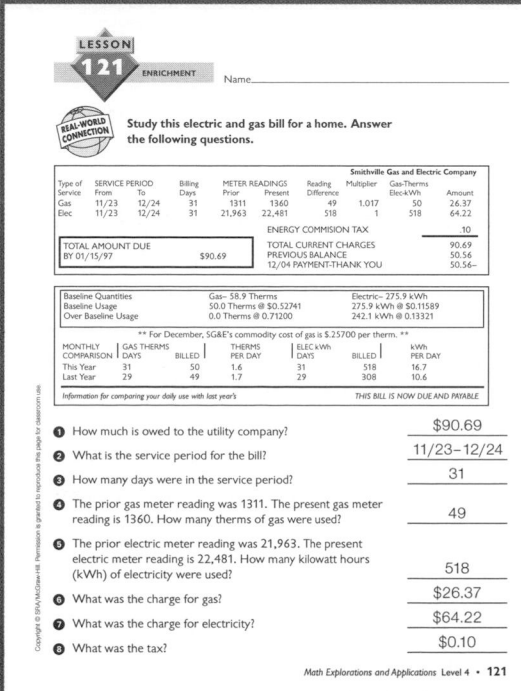

Assessment Criteria

Did the student . . .

- ✓ contribute to the discussion of the telephone bill?
- ✓ communicate strategies used to solve the problems?
- ✓ correctly answer at least 75% of the computation problems on page 413?

Homework Have students determine the per-minute rate for long distance calls that appear on a recent telephone bill.

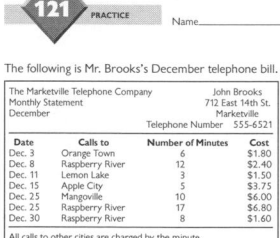

PRACTICE p. 121

LESSON 121 PRACTICE Name________________

The following is Mr. Brooks's December telephone bill.

The Marketville Telephone Company
Monthly Statement
December

John Brooks
712 East 14th St.
Marketville
Telephone Number 555-6521

Date	Calls to	Number of Minutes	Cost
Dec. 3	Orange Town	6	$1.80
Dec. 8	Raspberry River	12	$2.40
Dec. 11	Lemon Lake	3	$1.50
Dec. 15	Apple City	5	$3.75
Dec. 25	Mangoville	10	$6.00
Dec. 25	Raspberry River	17	$6.80
Dec. 30	Raspberry River	8	$1.60

All calls to other cities are charged by the minute.
The farther a city is from Marketville, the higher the rate.

Answer these questions.
How much does it cost per minute to call each of the following places?

1. Orange Town 30¢
2. Raspberry River 20¢
3. Lemon Lake 50¢
4. Apple City 75¢
5. Mangoville 60¢
6. Which city is farther from Marketville–Mangoville or Lemon Lake? Mangoville
7. There is an error in one of the charges on Mr. Brooks's bill. How much will Mr. Brooks save if he finds the error? $3.40
8. Order the cities Mr. Brooks called, from farthest from to nearest to Marketville. Apple City, Mangoville, Lemon Lake, Orange Town, Raspberry River
9. For how many minutes did Mr. Brooks use the telephone in December on calls to other cities? 61
10. After the error was corrected, what was the total cost of Mr. Brooks's December telephone bill? $20.45

Copyright © SRA/McGraw-Hill. Permission is granted to reproduce this page for classroom use.

ENRICHMENT p. 121

LESSON 121 ENRICHMENT Name________________

REAL-WORLD CONNECTION

Study this electric and gas bill for a home. Answer the following questions.

Smithville Gas and Electric Company

Type of Service	Service Period From	Service Period To	Billing Days	Meter Readings Prior	Meter Readings Present	Reading Difference	Multiplier	Gas-Therms Elec-kWh	Amount
Gas	11/23	12/24	31	1311	1360	49	1.017	50	26.37
Elec	11/23	12/24	31	21,963	22,481	518	1	518	64.22

TOTAL AMOUNT DUE BY 01/15/97 $90.69

ENERGY COMMISION TAX	.10
TOTAL CURRENT CHARGES	90.69
PREVIOUS BALANCE	50.56
12/04 PAYMENT-THANK YOU	50.56–

Baseline Quantities	Gas– 58.9 Therms	Electric– 275.9 kWh
Baseline Usage	50.0 Therms @ $0.52741	275.9 kWh @ $0.11589
Over Baseline Usage	0.0 Therms @ 0.71200	242.1 kWh @ 0.13321

** For December, SG&E's commodity cost of gas is $.25700 per therm. **

MONTHLY COMPARISON	GAS THERMS DAYS	BILLED	THERMS PER DAY	ELEC kWh DAYS	BILLED	kWh PER DAY
This Year	31	50	1.6	31	518	16.7
Last Year	29	49	1.7	29	308	10.6

Information for comparing your daily use with last year's *THIS BILL IS NOW DUE AND PAYABLE*

1. How much is owed to the utility company? $90.69
2. What is the service period for the bill? 11/23–12/24
3. How many days were in the service period? 31
4. The prior gas meter reading was 1311. The present gas meter reading is 1360. How many therms of gas were used? 49
5. The prior electric meter reading was 21,963. The present electric meter reading is 22,481. How many kilowatt hours (kWh) of electricity were used? 518
6. What was the charge for gas? $26.37
7. What was the charge for electricity? $64.22
8. What was the tax? $0.10

Copyright © SRA/McGraw-Hill. Permission is granted to reproduce this page for classroom use.

*available separately

LESSON 122

Student Edition pages 414–415

Division Applications

LESSON PLANNER

Objectives

- to provide practice in solving word problems, some of which require division
- to provide practice in approximating answers to division problems, using the inverse operation of multiplication

Context of the Lesson This lesson continues to expand students' understanding of the appropriate use of division and other operations to solve problems.

MANIPULATIVES

map or atlas (optional)

Program Resources

"Harder Snake" Game Mat

Number Cubes

Practice Master 122

Enrichment Master 122

For additional math integration:
Math Throughout the Day*

For extra practice:
CD-ROM* Lesson 122
Cumulative Review, page 561

1 Warm-Up (5 MINUTES)

Problem of the Day Present this problem to students, warning them that the answer involves a trick. Austin has 27 rabbits. How can he put them in four cages so that he has an odd number of rabbits in each cage? (Put nine rabbits in each of three cages, put the three cages inside one large cage.)

Problem-Solving Strategies Ask students who have solved the Problem of the Day to share how they solved it and any strategies they used.

MENTAL MATH Provide these problems involving all four operations and multidigit numbers:

a. 8 x 3 = (24) b. 24 ÷ 8 = (3)

c. 8 + 3 = (11) d. 11 – 3 = (8)

e. 2400 ÷ 30 = (80) f. 240 ÷ 80 = (3)

PROBLEM SOLVING

LESSON 122

Division Applications

Solve these problems. Check that your answers make sense.

1. Claire and her three friends wanted to share 36 pretzels equally. How many should each person get? **9**
2. Dr. Lin drove 250 kilometers in three hours. About what was her average speed? **83 km per hour**
3. Mrs. Vega drove for seven hours. She drove 90 kilometers the first hour, 85 kilometers the second hour, 50 kilometers the third hour, 50 kilometers the fourth hour, 85 kilometers the fifth hour, 85 kilometers the sixth hour, and 80 kilometers the seventh hour. About what was her average speed? **75 km per hour**
4. Sita can buy six cans of cola for $2.04. What is the cost for each can of cola? **34¢**
5. Gregory can buy an eight-pack of cola for $3.12 (or 312¢). What is the cost for each bottle of cola if he buys it in an eight-pack? **39¢**
6. Mr. Nolan drove 510 kilometers in six hours. What was his average speed? **85 km per hour**
7. Hari bought nine goldfish that cost 89¢ each. The tax was 48¢. He gave the storekeeper a $10 bill. How much change should he get back? **$1.51**
8. Judith bought nine cans of lemonade. The storekeeper charged her $5.85 (585¢) for the nine cans. How much did each can of lemonade cost? **65¢**
9. Kimberly and Jorge left Seneca at the same time. Kimberly drove 532 kilometers and Jorge drove 510 kilometers. How far apart were they? **can't tell**
10. Mr. Kwan drove 530 miles one day and 610 miles the next. His total trip was to be about 1500 miles. About how far did he still have to go? **360 km**

Literature Connection Have students read the true story "Five Fruit Jars" on pages 49–50 of *Gold and Silver, Silver and Gold* by Alvin Schwartz. Have them determine how much money each of the boys would have gotten if they had divided the treasure evenly before subtracting costs.

Geography Connection Have students use a **map** or **atlas** to create word problems that involve real distances, rates of speed, travel times, and so on. Allow students to estimate, if necessary. Have them provide solutions to the problems they create.

RETEACHING

Have students think carefully about the operation that is needed to solve the word problems.

*available separately

For each problem, several answers are given but only one is correct. Choose the correct answer. Use shortcuts when you can.

11	1)350	a. 27	b. 35	c. 270	(d.) 350	e. 400
12	10)350	a. 27	(b.) 35	c. 270	d. 350	e. 400
13	15)60	a. 2	b. 3	(c.) 4	d. 5	e. 6
14	2)10	a. 2	b. 3	c. 4	(d.) 5	e. 6
15	20)100	a. 2	b. 3	c. 4	(d.) 5	e. 6
16	3)100	a. 3 R1	b. 30 R1	(c.) 33 R1	d. 3 R2	e. 33 R2
17	33)100	(a.) 3 R1	b. 30 R1	c. 33 R1	d. 3 R2	e. 33 R2
18	10)2300	a. 2300	b. 4600	c. 46	(d.) 230	e. 23
19	100)2300	a. 2300	b. 4600	c. 46	d. 230	(e.) 23
20	100)23,000	a. 2300	b. 4600	c. 46	(d.) 230	e. 23
21	7)67	a. 9 R2	b. 9 R3	(c.) 9 R4	d. 8 R5	e. 7 R6
22	18)90	a. 3	b. 4	(c.) 5	d. 6	e. 7
23	11)132	(a.) 12	b. 14	c. 16	d. 18	e. 20
24	5)75	a. 13	b. 14	(c.) 15	d. 16	e. 17
25	50)750	(a.) 15	b. 150	c. 30	d. 35	e. 50
26	50)75,000	a. 150	b. 175	c. 600	(d.) 1500	e. 3000
27	13)195	a. 14	(b.) 15	c. 17	d. 19	e. 23
28	4)84	a. 17	b. 18	c. 20	(d.) 21	e. 22
29	40)8400	(a.) 210	b. 220	c. 420	d. 620	e. 820
30	40)84,000	a. 420	b. 21,000	c. 187	d. 210	(e.) 2100

Use the Cumulative Review on page 561 after this lesson.

PRACTICE p. 122

LESSON 122 PRACTICE Name________

Solve these problems.

1. Vanessa bought seven cans of fruit. She was charged $2.73. How much did each can of fruit cost? 39¢
2. Jorge's family has six people. They want to share four large pizzas equally. Each large pizza is cut into 12 slices. How many slices will each family member get? 8
3. Mrs. Scott drove 455 kilometers in seven hours. What was her average speed? 65 km/hr
4. Mr. Thomas drove 265 kilometers in four hours. About what was his average speed? 66 km/hr
5. Will can buy eight doughnuts for $1.28. What is the cost per doughnut? 16¢
6. Kim bought five apples that cost 26¢ each. The tax was 17¢. She paid with a $5 bill. How much change should she get back? $3.53
7. The fourth-grade class needed to raise $1800 for a class trip. The students earned $420 from a popcorn sale and $750 from a fruit sale. How much did they still need? $630
8. Mark ran every day for seven days. He ran the following distances on those days: 12 kilometers, 15 kilometers, 8 kilometers, 14 kilometers, 6 kilometers, 12 kilometers, 10 kilometers. What is the average distance Mark ran each day? 11 km

For each problem several answers are given, but only one is correct. Choose the correct answer without dividing.

9	17)102	a. 3	b. 4	c. 5	(d.) 6	e. 7
10	100)740,000	a. 740	b. 148	(c.) 7400	d. 1480	e. 74
11	9)85	a. 9 R5	b. 9 R3	(c.) 9 R4	d. 8 R5	e. 8 R6

122 • *Math Explorations and Applications* Level 4

Copyright © SRA/McGraw-Hill. Permission is granted to reproduce this page for classroom use.

ENRICHMENT p. 122

LESSON 122 ENRICHMENT Name________

Suppose you have a wooden cube that has been painted blue. The cube measures 3 inches in height, 3 inches in width, and 3 inches in length.

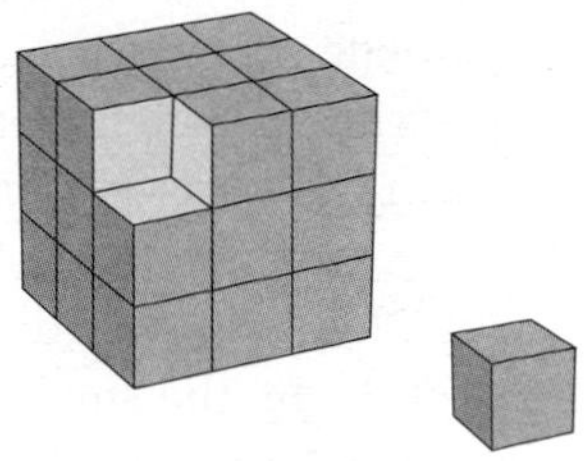

Use the cube to answer these questions.

1. If you were to break your cube apart into 1-inch cubes, how many of the 1-inch cubes would have three sides painted blue? 8
2. How many cubes would have the following sides painted blue?
   a. No sides 1 cube
   b. One side 6 cubes
   c. Two sides 12 cubes
   d. Four sides 0 cubes
   e. Five sides 0 cubes
   f. Six sides 0 cubes

122 • *Math Explorations and Applications* Level 4

Copyright © SRA/McGraw-Hill. Permission is granted to reproduce this page for classroom use.

2 Teach

Using the Student Pages Have students work independently on page 414. As students begin page 415, encourage them to look for patterns and relationships among the numbers. Students who finish early can play "Cubo," the "Diviso" game, the "Four Cube Division" game, or the "Harder Snake" Game Mat in pairs or small groups for multiplication and division practice.

3 Wrap-Up

5 MINUTES

In Closing Have students explain how they knew when the problems on pages 414 and 415 required division.

ANALYZING ANSWERS · MANIPULATIVES

For the word problems on page 414, determine whether errors resulted from computation mistakes or from choosing the wrong operation. If the errors were computational in nature, have students make the necessary corrections. If the errors stemmed from using the wrong operation, have students act out or model the problem with **manipulatives.**

ALTERNATIVE ASSESSMENT

Informal Assessment Observe students as they work through the problems in this lesson. Have them explain how they chose the correct operation to solve the problems on page 414 and how they determined the best choice without dividing on page 415.

Assessment Criteria

Did the student . . .

✓ choose the correct operation to solve the word problems?

✓ accurately calculate answers to the word problems?

✓ explain how to select the correct quotient without dividing?

✓ correctly answer at least 75% of the computation problems on page 415?

Homework Have students create and solve five word problems: two involving division, and one each involving multiplication, addition, or subtraction.

LESSON 123

Student Edition pages 416–419

Division Revisited: Missing Digits

LESSON PLANNER

Objectives

- to provide practice dividing with one-digit divisors
- to provide practice with basic facts and multidigit arithmetic
- to help students develop the broad ability to use mathematical common sense

Context of the Lesson This lesson includes Part 5 of "Estimating Is Rough," a five-part Thinking Story. The next lesson begins the end-of-unit sequence of review, practice, and testing.

MANIPULATIVES

calculators* (optional)

carton of eggs (optional)

scale* (optional)

Program Resources

Number Wheels

Practice Master 123

Enrichment Master 123

For career connections: Careers and Math*

For extra practice: CD-ROM* Lesson 123

1 Warm-Up (5 minutes)

Problem of the Day Present this problem to students: Barry, Gary, and Larry are brothers. If you add their ages, the sum is 53. What will the sum of their ages be ten years from now? (83)

Problem-Solving Strategies Ask students who have solved the Problem of the Day to share how they solved it and any strategies they used.

MENTAL MATH Provide fast-paced practice with basic number facts in all four operations. Some missing-term problems are included in all four operations. Have students use their Number Wheels to quickly show the answer.

a. 80 ÷ 8 = (10)	**b.** 10 + 10 = (20)
c. 9 ÷ *n* = 3 (3)	**d.** 12 – *n* = 6 (6)
e. 3 × 8 = (24)	**f.** 6 × *n* = 6 (1)
g. 8 + 4 = (12)	**h.** 13 – 8 = (5)

(continued on page 417)

PRACTICE

LESSON 123

Division Revisited: Missing Digits

ALGEBRA READINESS

Find the missing digits.

1. 6)630 = 1■5 **(0)**; 6; 30; 30
2. 5)550 = 110; 5■ **(5)**; 5; 5
3. 3)624 = 2■8 **(0)**; 6; 24; 24
4. 7)84■ **(0)** = 120; 7; 14; 14
5. 8)■42 **(6)** = 80 R2; 64; 2
6. 7)4■0 **(9)** = 70; 49
7. 9)810 = 90; ■1 **(8)**
8. 9)810 = ■0 **(9)**; 81
9. 6)766 = 12■ **(7)** R4; 6; 16; 12; 46; 42; 4
10. 4)926 = 231 R2; 8; ■2 **(1)**; 12; 6; 4; 2
11. 8)923 = 115 R■ **(3)**; 8; 12; 8; 43; 40; 3
12. 8)907 = 113 R3; 8; 10; ■ **(8)**; 27; 24; 3
13. 5)391 = 7■ **(8)** R1; 35; 41; 40; 1
14. 8)627 = 78 R■ **(3)**; 56; 67; 64; 3
15. 8)379 = 47 R3; 32; ■9 **(5)**; 56; 3
16. 5)666 = 133 R■ **(1)**; 5; 16; 15; 16; 15; 1

416 • Division

Science Connection Have students do research to learn more about eggs. They can investigate the relative sizes of the eggs of various birds, such as chickens, ducks, turkeys, geese, and quail. Or, they can use reference materials to look for "egg records," such as the largest egg, the smallest egg, the heaviest egg, or the oldest egg. Encourage students to present their data in tables or charts, or to determine average, range, or other comparative measures.

*available separately

Solve for *n*. Watch the signs.

17 $n = 16 \div 8$ **2**	18 $19 + n = 58$ **39**	19 $n = 81 \div 9$ **9**
20 $16 + 8 = n$ **24**	21 $9 \times 7 = n$ **63**	22 $n + 28 = 77$ **49**
23 $n = 5 \times 9$ **45**	24 $36 - n = 27$ **9**	25 $33 = 41 - n$ **8**
26 $49 \div n = 7$ **7**	27 $n \div 7 = 5$ **35**	28 $7 \times 8 = n$ **56**
29 $37 - 19 = n$ **18**	30 $6 \times 9 = n$ **54**	31 $27 \div n = 9$ **3**

Multiply.

32 9×100 **900**	33 14×1000 **14,000**	34 8×10 **80**
35 10×23 **230**	36 $10{,}000 \times 37$ **370,000**	37 80×100 **8000**
38 $100 \times 10{,}000$ **1,000,000**	39 $10{,}000 \times 370$ **3,700,000**	40 800×1000 **800,000**
41 $100 \times 10{,}001$ **1,000,100**	42 $10{,}001 \times 370$ **3,700,370**	43 $8000 \times 1{,}000{,}000$ **8,000,000,000**
44 90×100 **9000**	45 900×100 **90,000**	46 500×700 **350,000**

Watch the signs. Use shortcuts when you can.

47 3×9 **27**	48 $81 + 17$ **98**	49 $91 \div 7$ **13**
50 $90 \div 2$ **45**	51 9×7 **63**	52 $39 + 22$ **61**
53 $16 + 7$ **23**	54 $35 - 29$ **6**	55 $87 - 69$ **18**
56 $33 - 15$ **18**	57 12×13 **156**	58 7×6 **42**
59 $28 \div 7$ **4**	60 $16 + 17$ **33**	61 $47 + 74$ **121**

Divide. Use shortcuts when you can.

62 $8\overline{)56}$ **7**	63 $4\overline{)404}$ **101**	64 $3\overline{)30{,}000}$ **10,000**
65 $3\overline{)120}$ **40**	66 $5\overline{)450}$ **90**	67 $4\overline{)40{,}000}$ **10,000**
68 $7\overline{)4900}$ **700**	69 $6\overline{)4200}$ **700**	70 $4\overline{)80{,}000}$ **20,000**
71 $9\overline{)63}$ **7**	72 $4\overline{)3200}$ **800**	73 $4\overline{)160{,}000}$ **40,000**
74 $2\overline{)8006}$ **4003**	75 $7\overline{)6300}$ **900**	76 $1\overline{)3{,}987{,}263}$ **3,987,263**

Mental Math (continued)

i. $10 - n = 9$ (1)	**j.** $8 \times 7 =$ (56)
k. $12 - 8 =$ (4)	**l.** $8 + n = 15$ (7)
m. $7 \times 9 =$ (63)	**n.** $12 + 2 =$ (14)

2 Teach

Using the Student Pages Have students work independently on these two pages. Remind them about the rules for multiplying multiples of 10. As soon as they finish, they can play math games of their choice in pairs or small groups.

> ***Rather than giving up on those children who have serious difficulties or are different from typical successful mathematics students in other ways, we must do a better job of helping them. We must be alert to differences among children whenever they occur. We must have high expectations for all children, and we must give them the necessary help to live up to those high expectations. All children can and should learn mathematics.***
>
> —Stephen S. Willoughby, *Mathematics Education for a Changing World*

Technology Connection Refer students to the software *New Math Blaster Plus* from Davidson (IBM, for grades 1–6) for further practice with basic computation (addition, subtraction, multiplication and division), number patterns, estimation, fractions, decimals, and percents.

◆ LESSON 123 Division Revisited: Missing Digits

Teach

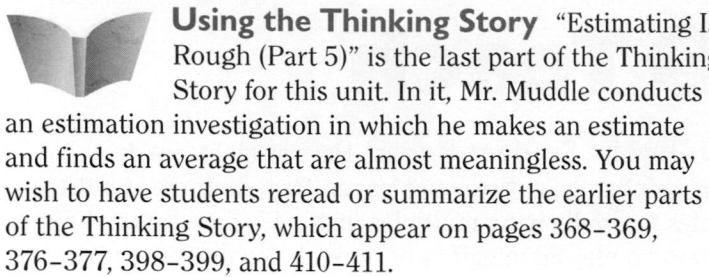

Using the Thinking Story "Estimating Is Rough (Part 5)" is the last part of the Thinking Story for this unit. In it, Mr. Muddle conducts an estimation investigation in which he makes an estimate and finds an average that are almost meaningless. You may wish to have students reread or summarize the earlier parts of the Thinking Story, which appear on pages 368–369, 376–377, 398–399, and 410–411.

Answers to Thinking Story Questions:

1. A good response would explain that the question does not call for an estimate.
2. By definition, *dozen* means "12." A carton of a dozen eggs may not contain twelve usable eggs—some might be broken or missing. Assuming the carton is full and undamaged, students can be sure there will always be 12 eggs in a dozen.
3. Except for a rounding error, students should get 12. Students can get an idea of why this is true by experimenting with various weights. They can write down any 12 numbers, find their average, and divide the sum of the 12 numbers by the average. Students may recognize that the result has to be 12.
4. He failed to account for the weight of the carton.

MATH JOURNAL Have students summarize in their Math Journals the estimation tasks Mr. Muddle attempted throughout the five parts of this Thinking Story. Have them tell which of his assignments they enjoyed most and why.

◆ LESSON 123 Division Revisited: Missing Digits

THINKING STORY

Estimating Is Rough

Part 5

You may wish to review earlier parts of this Thinking Story, on pages 368–369, 376–377, 398–399, and 410–411.

The grocer and some other people went to see Mr. Muddle's boss. "We don't think Mr. Muddle knows how to estimate," said the grocer. "He comes up with answers in nutty ways."

"But his estimates are good," said the boss. "He was very close in his estimate of how many trees to plant on Elm Street."

"He must be lucky, then," said the grocer, "or else he had some help. I'll bet he would have trouble estimating how many eggs are in a dozen!"

"We'll see about that," said the boss. She called in Mr. Muddle and told him to estimate how many eggs are in a dozen.

"That will take some work," said Mr. Muddle. "I'll try to have the estimate for you by tomorrow."

Mr. Muddle thought about how he would make the estimate. "I wish they had just asked me exactly how many eggs are in a dozen," he said. "I could have told them that. Estimating is rough, but I'll think of a way."

He went to the grocery store and bought five dozen eggs, because he knew that you need a good sample to make an estimate. Then he weighed each carton of eggs.

LEARNING STYLES · MANIPULATIVES

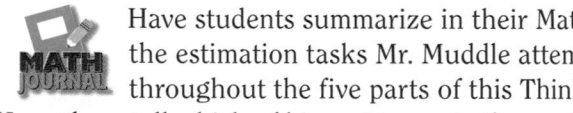

Meeting Individual Needs Kinesthetic, logical, mathematical, and interpersonal learners may benefit from replicating Mr. Muddle's estimation investigation to better understand his reasoning. Provide a **carton of eggs,** a **metric scale*,** and a **calculator*** so students can act out the story in small groups as they read along.

LITERATURE CONNECTION

Literature Connection Invite pairs or small groups of students to select a trick or experiment from *The I Hate Mathematics! Book* by Marilyn Burns and perform it for classmates.

RETEACHING

No reteaching is recommended at this time. Continue to provide extra help based on previous lessons, as needed. You may want to assign Enrichment Master 123 for this lesson.

*available separately

These are the weights that he got:

700 grams   652 grams
664 grams   736 grams
760 grams

"So," said Mr. Muddle, "an average dozen eggs weighs about 702 grams."

Then he weighed one egg from each carton. These are the weights he got:

55 grams   51 grams
52 grams   58 grams
60 grams

"So an average egg weighs about 55 grams," he said. Using his calculator, he divided 702 by 55. The result was 12.763636.

The next day Mr. Muddle told his boss, "I have my estimate. A dozen is about 13 eggs."

"That is close," said the boss. "But I thought you would know there are exactly 12 eggs in a dozen."

"Of course I do," said Mr. Muddle, "but you didn't ask me that. You asked me to estimate."

. . . the end

Work in groups. Discuss your answers and how you figured them out. Then compare your answers with those of other groups. **Answers are in margins.**

1. What would you have done if your boss had asked you to estimate how many eggs are in a dozen?
2. Can you be sure that there will always be 12 eggs in a dozen? Why or why not?
3. If you weigh a dozen eggs and divide by the average weight of an egg, what number should you get?
4. Why did Mr. Muddle end up with an estimate of 13 eggs in a dozen?

PRACTICE p. 123

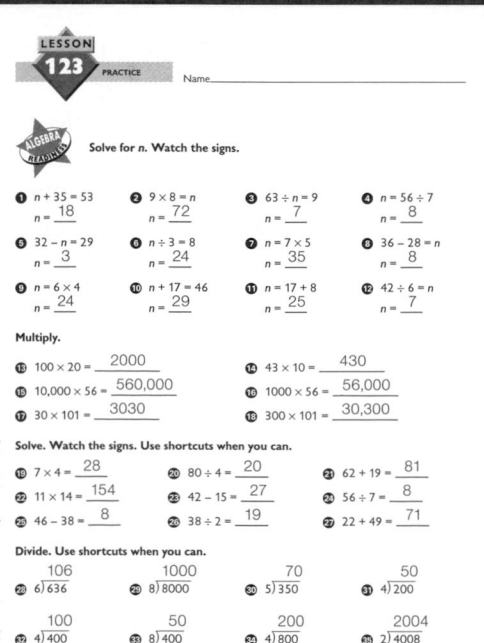

LESSON 123 PRACTICE   Name______

ALGEBRA READINESS **Solve for *n*. Watch the signs.**

1. $n + 35 = 53$; $n =$ 18	2. $9 \times 8 = n$; $n =$ 72	3. $63 \div n = 9$; $n =$ 7	4. $n = 56 \div 7$; $n =$ 8
5. $32 - n = 29$; $n =$ 3	6. $n \div 3 = 8$; $n =$ 24	7. $n = 7 \times 5$; $n =$ 35	8. $36 - 28 = n$; $n =$ 8
9. $n = 6 \times 4$; $n =$ 24	10. $n + 17 = 46$; $n =$ 29	11. $n = 17 + 8$; $n =$ 25	12. $42 \div 6 = n$; $n =$ 7

Multiply.

13. $100 \times 20 =$ 2000
14. $43 \times 10 =$ 430
15. $10{,}000 \times 56 =$ 560,000
16. $1000 \times 56 =$ 56,000
17. $30 \times 101 =$ 3030
18. $300 \times 101 =$ 30,300

Solve. Watch the signs. Use shortcuts when you can.

19. $7 \times 4 =$ 28
20. $80 \div 4 =$ 20
21. $62 + 19 =$ 81
22. $11 \times 14 =$ 154
23. $42 - 15 =$ 27
24. $56 \div 7 =$ 8
25. $46 - 38 =$ 8
26. $38 \div 2 =$ 19
27. $22 + 49 =$ 71

Divide. Use shortcuts when you can.

28. $6\overline{)636}$ 106
29. $8\overline{)8000}$ 1000
30. $5\overline{)350}$ 70
31. $4\overline{)200}$ 50
32. $4\overline{)400}$ 100
33. $8\overline{)400}$ 50
34. $4\overline{)800}$ 200
35. $2\overline{)4008}$ 2004

Copyright © SRA/McGraw-Hill. Permission is granted to reproduce this page for classroom use.

ENRICHMENT p. 123

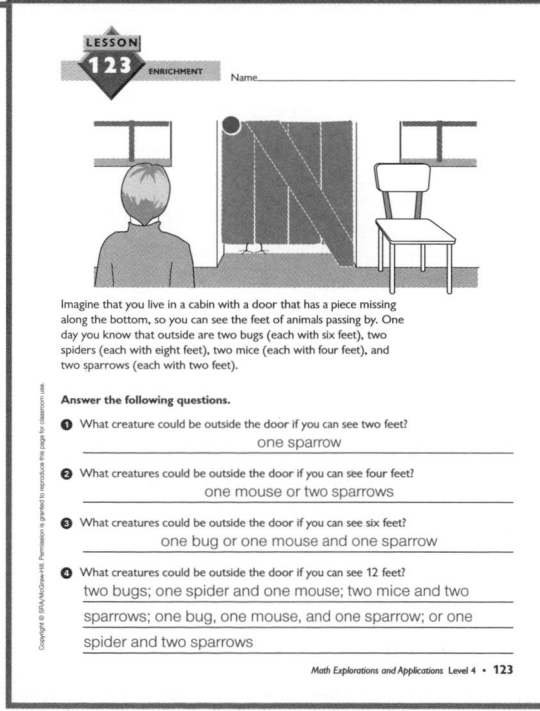

LESSON 123 ENRICHMENT   Name______

Imagine that you live in a cabin with a door that has a piece missing along the bottom, so you can see the feet of animals passing by. One day you know that outside are two bugs (each with six feet), two spiders (each with eight feet), two mice (each with four feet), and two sparrows (each with two feet).

Answer the following questions.

1. What creature could be outside the door if you can see two feet? one sparrow
2. What creatures could be outside the door if you can see four feet? one mouse or two sparrows
3. What creatures could be outside the door if you can see six feet? one bug or one mouse and one sparrow
4. What creatures could be outside the door if you can see 12 feet? two bugs; one spider and one mouse; two mice and two sparrows; one bug, one mouse, and one sparrow; or one spider and two sparrows

Copyright © SRA/McGraw-Hill. Permission is granted to reproduce this page for classroom use.

3 Wrap-Up (5 MINUTES)

In Closing Ask students to explain whether or not it makes sense to estimate how many socks are in a pair or how many years are in a decade. Have them justify their responses.

ALTERNATIVE ASSESSMENT **Informal Assessment** Observe students as they solve the problems on pages 416–417. Ask them to verbalize their thinking as they proceed so you can follow their methods. You may wish to use their performance on these pages as an informal assessment of achievement in basic number facts and multidigit arithmetic, especially multiplication and division.

Assessment Criteria

Did the student . . .

- ✓ explain how to solve for *n*?
- ✓ correctly answer at least 75% of the mixed computation problems on pages 416–417?
- ✓ contribute to the Thinking Story discussion?
- ✓ communicate an understanding of reasonable situations in which to estimate?

Homework Have students estimate the number of drinking glasses they have at home, then count to find the actual number. Use students' data to determine a class average.

Student Edition pages 420–421

LESSON 124 Unit 5 Review

Using the Student Pages Use this Unit 5 Review as a preliminary unit test to indicate areas in which each student is having difficulty or in which the entire class may need help. If students do well on the Unit 5 Review, you may wish to skip directly to the next unit. If not, you may spend a day or so helping students overcome their individual difficulties before they take the Unit Test.

Next to each set of problems is a list of the lessons in the unit covered in those problems. Students can refer to a specific lesson for additional instruction if they need help. You can also use this information to make additional assignments based on the previous lesson concepts.

Problems 1–8 Students who miss more than one of these division problems should be checked individually. The "Diviso" game on page 367 provides practice with dividing by one-digit divisors and mental factorization. The "Four Cube Division" game on page 374, which reinforces the skill of dividing by one-digit divisors and using place value, also provides extra practice.

Problems 9–13 If students miss more than one of these division problems involving approximation, check to see that they understand how to check a division problem by multiplication. Use **play money*** or **base-10 blocks*** to reteach those who need help with the checking procedure.

Problems 14–22 If students miss more than two of these arithmetic and missing-term problems, try to see if there is a pattern to their errors. Explain to students that the answer that can be substituted for *n* will make the equation a true statement.

Problems 23–26 If students miss more than one of these finding-averages problems, check to see whether the problem is with forgetting the steps of the procedure or with the arithmetic. Reteach as necessary, focusing on the arithmetic steps.

Problems 27–30 Provide extra reteaching in finding factors as needed. Refer to Lesson 119 for this review.

ASSESSMENT

LESSON 124 Unit 5 Review

Divide. Watch for remainders.

Lessons 104, 105, 109

1. 3)26 **8 R2**
2. 3)999 **333**
3. 7)782 **111 R5**
4. 6)2964 **494**
5. 8)300 **37 R4**
6. 4)10,000 **2,500**
7. 5)386 **77 R1**
8. 3)2721 **907**

For each problem, several answers are given, but only one is correct. Choose the correct answer.

Lessons 118, 122

9. 17)51 — a. 2 — (b.) 3 — c. 4 — d. 5 — e. 6
10. 39)468 — a. 2 — b. 4 — (c.) 12 — d. 50 — e. 100
11. 25)625 — a. 10 — b. 15 — c. 17 — d. 20 — (e.) 25
12. 11)1342 — a. 12 — b. 120 — c. 121 — (d.) 122 — e. 1202
13. 37)518 — a. 11 — b. 12 — (c.) 14 — d. 24 — e. 34

ALGEBRA READINESS

Solve for *n*.

Lessons 115, 123

14. $n = 13 - 7$ **6**
15. $n + 18 = 25$ **7**
16. $32 \div 8 = n$ **4**
17. $7 + 13 = n$ **20**
18. $37 - n = 16$ **21**
19. $4 \times 80 = n$ **320**
20. $7 \times 13 = n$ **91**
21. $n \div 6 = 6$ **36**
22. $4 = n \div 80$ **320**

Find the average of each set of numbers.

Lessons 112, 113

23. 7, 10, 5, 0, 8 **6**
24. 70, 100, 50, 0, 80 **60**
25. 1000, 2000, 3000, 4000, 5000, 6000 **3500**
26. Hallie took five spelling tests this month. Her scores were 91, 82, 100, 85, and 92. What was her average score for the five tests? **90**

List the factors of the following numbers.

Lesson 119

27. 15 **1, 3, 5, 15**
28. 12 **1, 2, 3, 4, 6, 12**
29. 11 **1, 11**
30. 16 **1, 2, 4, 8, 16**

420 • Division

RETEACHING

Students who have difficulty with this Unit Review should have further opportunity to review and to practice the skills before they proceed on with the next unit. For each set of problems there are specific suggestions for reteaching. These suggestions can be found in the margins.

*available separately

Solve these problems.

Lessons 108, 111–113, 115, 122

31. Mr. Mora drove 792 kilometers in nine hours. What was his average speed? **88 km per hour**
32. Daniel mows lawns and gets paid $5 for each hour he works. He worked four hours on Saturday and three hours on Sunday. How much did he earn for the two days? **$35**
33. Shannon has $3. Does she have enough money to buy six notepads that cost 79¢ each? **no**
34. Robbie wants to skate 50 kilometers this week. He skated 7 kilometers each day from Monday to Saturday. How many kilometers must he skate on Sunday to reach his goal? **8**
35. Lola is setting up chairs for a show. She sets up nine rows with seven chairs in each row and one row of eight chairs. How many people can be seated for the show? **71**
36. Terry is growing a bean plant. On Monday the plant was 8 centimeters tall. On Friday the plant was 16 centimeters tall. How much did the plant grow between Monday and Friday? **8 cm**
37. Janelle works part-time at a grocery store. The hours she worked for each of the past seven weeks were 18, 23, 11, 16, 25, 17, and 16. About what is the average number of hours she works in a week? **18**

Jason takes care of a dolphin named Finny at an aquarium. He feeds Finny 3 kilograms of fish a day.

38. How much fish does Finny eat in a week? **21 kg**
39. A kilogram of fish costs $5.71. How much does it cost the aquarium to feed Finny each week? **$119.91**
40. Gretchen has $40 to spend on her sister's birthday present. Does she have enough money to buy two sweaters that cost $21 each? **no**

Problems 31–40 Provide extra teaching to students who miss more than two of these word problems. Students may use drawings to help them solve the problems.

ALTERNATIVE ASSESSMENT

Portfolio Assessment If you have not already completed the Portfolio Assessment task provided on Assessment Blackline Masters page 97, it can be used at this time to evaluate students' proficiency with finding averages.

ALTERNATIVE ASSESSMENT

Performance Assessment Performance Assessment Task 2, provided on Assessment Blackline Masters pages 85–86, can be used at this time to evaluate students' proficiency with converting metric and customary units and division. You may want to administer this assessment to individual students or small groups of students.

Unit Project If you have not already assigned "The Broad-Jump Contest" project on pages 428 and 429, you may want to do so at this time. This project is a good opportunity for students to work with data that can be interpreted in more than one way and to design a "fair" contest.

PRACTICE p. 124

LESSON 124 PRACTICE Name________

Divide. Watch for remainders.

1. $4\overline{)75}$ 18 R3
2. $6\overline{)2088}$ 348
3. $8\overline{)125}$ 15 R5
4. $9\overline{)1809}$ 201
5. $6\overline{)1000}$ 166 R4
6. $3\overline{)6147}$ 2049
7. $8\overline{)20{,}000}$ 2500
8. $4\overline{)603}$ 150 R3
9. $7\overline{)441}$ 63
10. $5\overline{)910}$ 182

Solve for *n*. Watch the signs.

11. $n = 360 \div 4$ $n =$ 90
12. $n + 23 = 52$ $n =$ 29
13. $n = 12 \times 8$ $n =$ 96
14. $8 + 13 = n$ $n =$ 21
15. $n = 20 \times 6$ $n =$ 120
16. $16 + n = 23$ $n =$ 7

Find the mean, median, and mode of each set of numbers.

17. 14, 9, 2, 7, 9, 13 — 9; 9; 9
18. 140, 90, 20, 70, 90, 130 — 90; 90; 90

Solve these problems.

19. Marchita has $5. Does she have enough money to buy 12 cookies at 32¢ each? — yes
20. Karen can buy six bags of popcorn for $4.50. How much does each bag of popcorn cost? — 75¢
21. Ken baby-sits after school each day. He earned $6 on Monday, $8 on Tuesday, $8 on Wednesday, $12 on Thursday, and $4 on Friday. What is the average amount he earned per day? — $7.60
22. Nancy drinks four glasses of milk a day. How many glasses of milk does she drink in a week? — 28
23. Alonzo drove 342 kilometers in six hours. What was his average speed? — 57 kilometers per hour

Copyright © SRA/McGraw-Hill. Permission is granted to reproduce this page for classroom use.

124 • *Math Explorations and Applications* Level 4

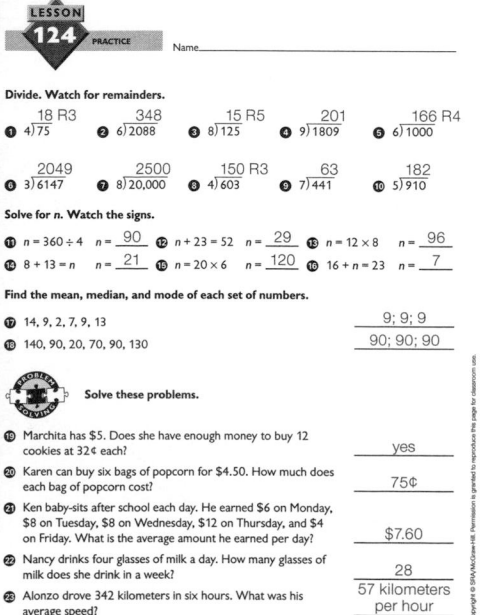

ENRICHMENT p. 124

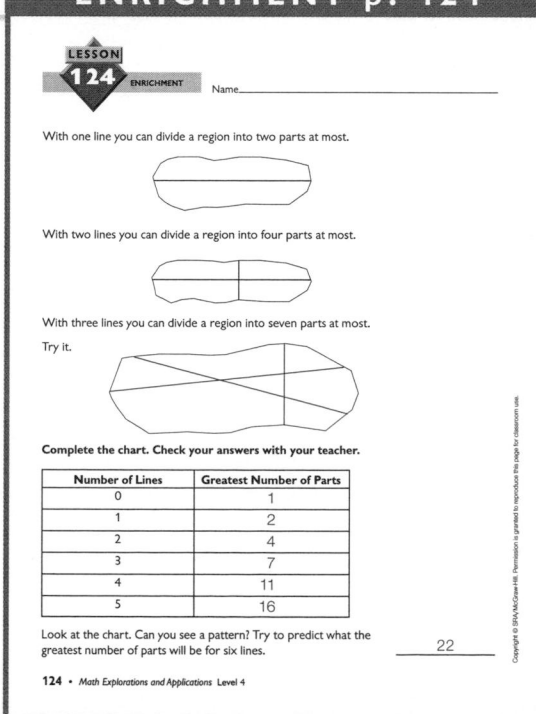

LESSON 124 ENRICHMENT Name________

With one line you can divide a region into two parts at most.

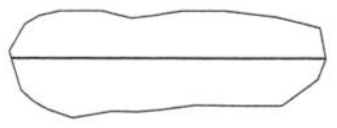

With two lines you can divide a region into four parts at most.

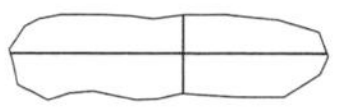

With three lines you can divide a region into seven parts at most.

Try it.

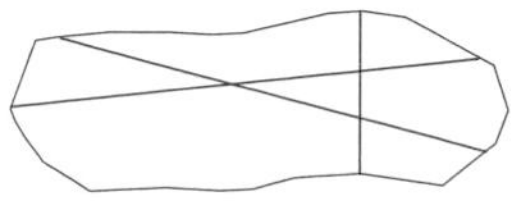

Complete the chart. Check your answers with your teacher.

Number of Lines	Greatest Number of Parts
0	1
1	2
2	4
3	7
4	11
5	16

Look at the chart. Can you see a pattern? Try to predict what the greatest number of parts will be for six lines. — 22

Copyright © SRA/McGraw-Hill. Permission is granted to reproduce this page for classroom use.

124 • *Math Explorations and Applications* Level 4

LESSON 125

Student Edition pages 422–425

Unit 5 Practice

Using the Student Pages The purpose of these pages is to provide additional practice for those students who demonstrated a need for it on the Unit 5 Review. You may wish to assign only the specific exercises in this Unit 5 Practice in which students need further reinforcement. Listed in the margin beside each instruction line are the lessons covered in the unit so that you or the students can refer to the specific lesson for additional review and instruction.

GAME Students who do not require additional practice on specific concepts may enjoy playing any of the games you have played so far, such as the "Diviso" game on page 367. This game provides practice with dividing by one-digit divisors and mental factorization. These students may also help by practicing flash card drills and playing appropriate games with students who need remedial practice or by actually teaching certain procedures to other students.

You may want to use the Cumulative Review on page 562 after this lesson.

MIXED PRACTICE

LESSON 125

Unit 5 Practice

Lessons 104, 105, 109 **Divide. Watch for remainders.**

1. 3)72 **24**	2. 6)922 **153 R4**	3. 3)805 **268 R1**	4. 7)625 **89 R2**
5. 5)75 **15**	6. 2)713 **356 R1**	7. 4)209 **52 R1**	8. 4)280 **70**
9. 5)325 **65**	10. 7)600 **85 R5**	11. 9)263 **29 R2**	12. 3)725 **241 R2**
13. 3)74 **24 R2**	14. 8)735 **91 R7**	15. 5)211 **42 R1**	16. 6)2345 **390 R5**
17. 4)62 **15 R2**	18. 2)1063 **531 R1**	19. 2)603 **301 R1**	20. 6)1005 **167 R3**

Lessons 118, 122 **Choose the correct answer for each problem.**

21. 10)400 — **a.** 4 **b.** 20 **c.** 30 **(d.)** 40 **e.** 50
22. 100)6000 — **a.** 6 **b.** 30 **(c.)** 60 **d.** 300 **e.** 600
23. 12)63 — **a.** 5 R2 **b.** 5 **(c.)** 5 R3 **d.** 5 R4 **e.** 5 R1
24. 18)108 — **a.** 5 **(b.)** 6 **c.** 7 **d.** 8 **e.** 9

Lessons 106, 107, 116, 123 **Find the missing digit.**

25. 5)260 = 5■; 25; 10 — **2**
26. 3)1217 = 4■5 R2; 12; 17; 15; 2 — **0**
27. 7)4■0 = 70; 49 — **9**
28. 5)550 = 1■0; 5; 5; 5 — **1**

ALGEBRA READINESS

Lessons 115, 123 **Solve for *n*. Watch the signs.**

29. $n + 5 = 8$ **3**
30. $5 \times n = 35$ **7**
31. $3 \times n = 9$ **3**
32. $16 \div n = 8$ **2**
33. $n \div 4 = 6$ **24**
34. $243 \div 9 = n$ **27**
35. $47 - n = 28$ **19**
36. $2 \times 2 = n$ **4**
37. $n = 64 \times 32$ **2048**

Lesson 115 **Solve.**

38. How many milliliters are there in 10 liters? **10,000**
39. How many liters are there in 4000 milliliters? **4**
40. How many cups are there in 64 fluid ounces? **8**

Lessons 112, 113 **Find the average for each set of numbers.**

41. 10, 10, 10, 10, 10 **10**
42. 8, 9, 10, 11, 12 **10**
43. 18, 19, 20, 21, 22 **20**
44. 10, 20, 30, 40, 50, 60 **35**
45. 6, 8, 9, 8, 14 **9**
46. 8, 10, 11, 10, 16 **11**

PROBLEM SOLVING

Lessons 108, 111–113, 115, 122

Solve.

47. Nick drove 650 kilometers in ten hours. Mallory drove 495 kilometers in seven hours.
    a. What was Nick's average speed? **65 km per hour**
    b. What was Mallory's average speed? **about 70 km per hour**
    c. How much farther did Nick drive than Mallory? **155 km**

48. Angelo weighed 50 kilograms at the beginning of September. He gained 3 kilograms during September. Then he lost 5 kilograms during October. How much did Angelo weigh at the end of October? **48 kg**

49. When Juli was two years old, she was 75 centimeters tall. During the next 18 years, her height doubled. How tall was she at the age of 20? **150 cm**

50. Penny bought two pads of paper that cost 38¢ each. She was charged 80¢ for the two pads, including tax.
    a. How much was the tax? **4¢**
    b. If Penny paid with a $1 bill, how much change should she have gotten? **20¢**

51. Tim and Paul put their dogs on a scale at the same time. Together, the dogs weighed 42 pounds. What was their average weight? **21 pounds**

◆ LESSON 125 Unit 5 Practice

Students may use a blank **Cruncher*** spreadsheet to create a table that shows the rate of earning for different amounts of hours.

◆ LESSON 125 Unit 5 Practice

Lessons 108, 111, 112, 115, 122 Carmen wants to earn money to buy a VCR that costs $440. She made a chart to show how many hours she would have to work to earn the money.

Help Carmen complete the chart. Then answer the questions.

52 Use a computer or other means to draw the chart and complete it.

If I Make This Much per Hour	In 40 Hours I Will Make	In 60 Hours I Will Make	In 100 Hours I Will Make
$3.50 (350¢)	$140.00	**$210.00**	**$350.00**
$4.50 (450¢)	$180.00	**$270.00**	**$450.00**
$5.00 (500¢)	$200.00	**$300.00**	**$500.00**
$5.50 (550¢)	$220.00	**$330.00**	**$550.00**

53 Will Carmen earn enough money for the VCR if she works for 60 hours at $5.50 per hour? **no**

54 Will she earn enough if she works for 100 hours at $3.50 per hour? **no**

55 Will she earn enough if she works for 100 hours at $4.50 per hour? **yes**

56 **Challenge:** How many hours must Carmen work to buy the VCR if she earns

a. $3.50 per hour? **126** **b.** $4.50 per hour? **98**
c. $5.00 per hour? **88** **d.** $5.50 per hour? **80**

Answer the questions based on the following set of numbers.

2, 7, 7, 6, 7, 4, 2, 1

Lesson 113 57 What is the mode? **7** 58 What is the median? **5**

RETEACHING

Students who have difficulty with this Unit Practice should have further opportunity to review and to practice the skills before they proceed on with the next unit. Beside each set of problems is a reference to the lesson or lessons from which the problems were taken. You may want to review the individual lessons with students who are having difficulty with them.

*available separately

Solve these problems.

Lessons 108, 111–113, 115, 122

Mr. Ramirez has a solid fence that is 100 meters long and 2 meters high. He wants to paint both sides of the fence. He has the following recipe for making his own whitewash.

Whitewash (for 200 square meters)	
Table salt	2 pounds
Water	1 gallon
Hydrated lime	6 pounds
Dissolve the salt in the water.	
Then add the lime slowly as you stir.	

59 How much of each will Mr. Ramirez need?

a. Table salt **4 pounds**

b. Water **2 gallons**

c. Hydrated lime **12 pounds**

60 Mr. Ramirez went to the store and found out that table salt costs \$1.30 per pound and hydrated lime costs \$1.80 per pound. How much money will he have to spend for both of these items to make enough whitewash for his fence? **\$26.80**

Use the Cumulative Review on page 562 after this lesson.

Students may use a blank **Cruncher*** spreadsheet to create a table that calculates the amount of materials needed to cover a given surface area.

PRACTICE p. 125

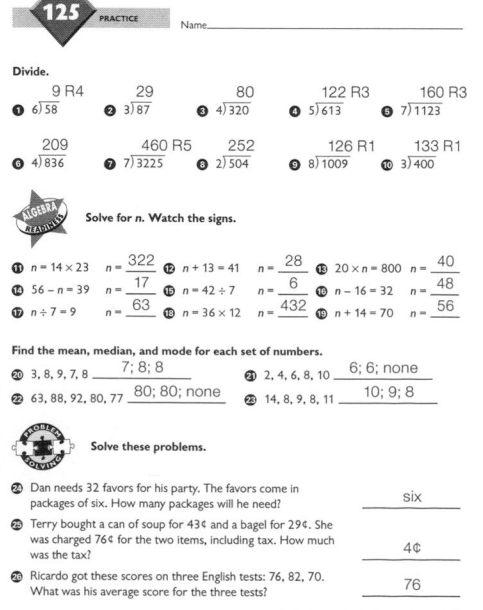

LESSON 125 PRACTICE Name__________

Divide.

1. 6)58 — 9 R4
2. 3)87 — 29
3. 4)320 — 80
4. 5)613 — 122 R3
5. 7)1123 — 160 R3
6. 4)836 — 209
7. 7)3225 — 460 R5
8. 2)504 — 252
9. 8)1009 — 126 R1
10. 3)400 — 133 R1

ALGEBRA READINESS **Solve for *n*. Watch the signs.**

11. $n = 14 \times 23$ $n =$ 322
12. $n + 13 = 41$ $n =$ 28
13. $20 \times n = 800$ $n =$ 40
14. $56 - n = 39$ $n =$ 17
15. $n = 42 \div 7$ $n =$ 6
16. $n - 16 = 32$ $n =$ 48
17. $n \div 7 = 9$ $n =$ 63
18. $n = 36 \times 12$ $n =$ 432
19. $n + 14 = 70$ $n =$ 56

Find the mean, median, and mode for each set of numbers.

20. 3, 8, 9, 7, 8 — 7; 8; 8
21. 2, 4, 6, 8, 10 — 6; 6; none
22. 63, 88, 92, 80, 77 — 80; 80; none
23. 14, 8, 9, 8, 11 — 10; 9; 8

PROBLEM SOLVING **Solve these problems.**

24. Dan needs 32 favors for his party. The favors come in packages of six. How many packages will he need? — six
25. Terry bought a can of soup for 43¢ and a bagel for 29¢. She was charged 76¢ for the two items, including tax. How much was the tax? — 4¢
26. Ricardo got these scores on three English tests: 76, 82, 70. What was his average score for the three tests? — 76

Copyright © SRA/McGraw-Hill. Permission is granted to reproduce this page for classroom use.

Math Explorations and Applications Level 4 • 125

ENRICHMENT p. 125

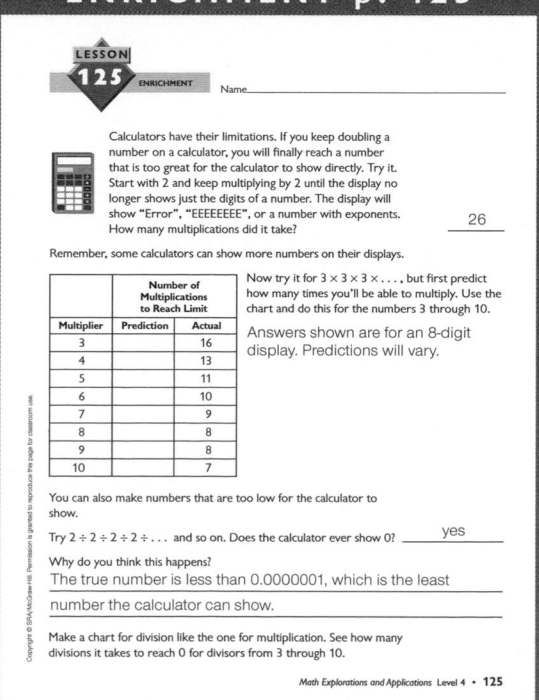

LESSON 125 ENRICHMENT Name__________

Calculators have their limitations. If you keep doubling a number on a calculator, you will finally reach a number that is too great for the calculator to show directly. Try it. Start with 2 and keep multiplying by 2 until the display no longer shows just the digits of a number. The display will show "Error", "EEEEEEEE", or a number with exponents. How many multiplications did it take? 26

Remember, some calculators can show more numbers on their displays.

	Number of Multiplications to Reach Limit	
Multiplier	**Prediction**	**Actual**
3		16
4		13
5		11
6		10
7		9
8		8
9		8
10		7

Now try it for $3 \times 3 \times 3 \times \ldots$, but first predict how many times you'll be able to multiply. Use the chart and do this for the numbers 3 through 10.

Answers shown are for an 8-digit display. Predictions will vary.

You can also make numbers that are too low for the calculator to show.

Try $2 \div 2 \div 2 \div 2 \div \ldots$ and so on. Does the calculator ever show 0? yes

Why do you think this happens?

The true number is less than 0.0000001, which is the least number the calculator can show.

Make a chart for division like the one for multiplication. See how many divisions it takes to reach 0 for divisors from 3 through 10.

Copyright © SRA/McGraw-Hill. Permission is granted to reproduce this page for classroom use.

Math Explorations and Applications Level 4 • 125

*available separately

UNIT 5

Student Edition pages 426–427

Unit Test

Using the Student Pages The Unit 5 Test on Student Edition pages 426 and 427 provides an opportunity to formally evaluate your students' proficiency with concepts developed in this unit. It is similar in content and format to the Unit 5 Review. Students who did well on the Unit 5 Review may not need to take this test. Students who did not do well on the Unit 5 Review should be provided with additional practice opportunities, such as the Unit 5 Practice pages, before taking the Unit 5 Test. For further evaluation, you may wish to have these students also take the Unit 5 Test in standardized format, provided on Assessment Blackline Masters pages 141–148 or the Unit 5 Test on Assessment Blackline Masters pages 47–50.

UNIT 5 **ASSESSMENT**

Unit Test

Divide. Watch for remainders.

1. 7)42 **6**
2. 3)82 **27 R1**
3. 8)100 **12 R4**
4. 5)168 **33 R3**
5. 5)317 **63 R2**
6. 9)99 **11**
7. 4)13,476 **3,369**
8. 6)274 **45 R4**
9. 6)312 **52**
10. 2)76 **38**
11. 7)147 **21**
12. 9)385 **42 R7**

Choose the correct answer for each problem.

13. 12)36 — (**a.**) 3 **b.** 4 **c.** 5 **d.** 6 **e.** 7
14. 15)105 — **a.** 3 **b.** 4 **c.** 5 **d.** 6 (**e.**) 7
15. 24)144 — **a.** 3 **b.** 4 **c.** 5 (**d.**) 6 **e.** 7

ALGEBRA READINESS

Solve for *n*.

16. $n = 15 + 3$ **18**
17. $42 + 7 = n$ **49**
18. $13 + n = 17$ **4**
19. $n = 15 - 3$ **12**
20. $24 = n \times 8$ **3**
21. $n - 7 = 15$ **22**
22. $42 \div 7 = n$ **6**
23. $24 = n \div 8$ **192**
24. $6 \times 7 = n$ **42**

Find the average for each set of numbers.

25. 8, 9, 10, 11, 12 **10**
26. 80, 90, 100, 110, 120 **100**
27. 5, 23, 12, 11, 15, 16, 9 **13**
28. 7, 9, 11, 124, 15 **about 33**

Answer the questions using the following set of numbers.

1, 1, 3, 1, 2, 4, 6

29. What is the mode? **1**
30. What is the median? **2**

PROBLEM SOLVING

Solve these problems.

31. Ellie bowled three games and got scores of 145, 132, and 129. Could her average score be 129? **no**
32. Dan got these scores on four math tests: 92, 84, 79, and 89. What was his average score for the four tests? **86**

426 • Division

33. Annie has $1 and wants to buy three postcards that cost 29¢ each. Does she have enough money? **yes**

34. Reggie gets paid a certain amount for each hour he works. Today he worked six hours and earned $36. How much money does he earn in an hour? **$6**

35. Mr. Byrd needs 45 hamburger rolls for a cookout. The rolls come in packages of eight. How many packages does he need? **6**

36. How many gallons are there in 36 quarts? **9**

37. How many milliliters are there in 6 liters? **6000**

38. Laura bought a pen for 39¢ and a ruler for 49¢. The storekeeper charged her 93¢ for the two items, including tax. How much was the tax? **5¢**

39. Cheryl's puppy weighed 4 pounds last month and 5 pounds today. How much weight did the puppy gain during the month? **1 pound**

40. Cal is painting his garage. The area of one wall is 43 square meters. One can of paint covers 8 square meters. How many cans of paint does Cal need to paint this side of his garage? **6**

ASSESSMENT p. 47

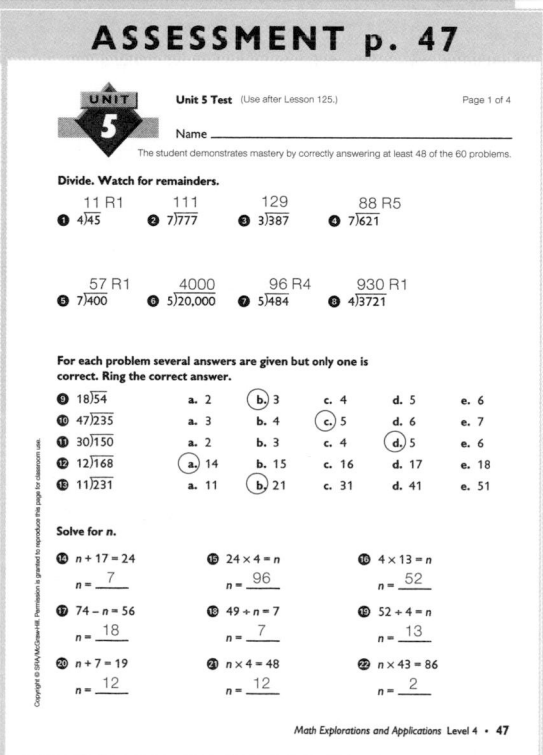

UNIT 5 **Unit 5 Test** (Use after Lesson 125.) Page 1 of 4

Name ____________________

The student demonstrates mastery by correctly answering at least 48 of the 60 problems.

Divide. Watch for remainders.

1. $4\overline{)45}$ 11 R1
2. $7\overline{)777}$ 111
3. $3\overline{)387}$ 129
4. $7\overline{)621}$ 88 R5
5. $7\overline{)400}$ 57 R1
6. $5\overline{)20,000}$ 4000
7. $5\overline{)484}$ 96 R4
8. $4\overline{)3721}$ 930 R1

For each problem several answers are given but only one is correct. Ring the correct answer.

9. $18\overline{)54}$	a. 2	(b.) 3	c. 4	d. 5	e. 6
10. $47\overline{)235}$	a. 3	b. 4	(c.) 5	d. 6	e. 7
11. $30\overline{)150}$	a. 2	b. 3	c. 4	(d.) 5	e. 6
12. $12\overline{)168}$	(a.) 14	b. 15	c. 16	d. 17	e. 18
13. $11\overline{)231}$	a. 11	(b.) 21	c. 31	d. 41	e. 51

Solve for *n*.

14. $n + 17 = 24$ $n =$ 7
15. $24 \times 4 = n$ $n =$ 96
16. $4 \times 13 = n$ $n =$ 52
17. $74 - n = 56$ $n =$ 18
18. $49 \div n = 7$ $n =$ 7
19. $52 \div 4 = n$ $n =$ 13
20. $n + 7 = 19$ $n =$ 12
21. $n \times 4 = 48$ $n =$ 12
22. $n \times 43 = 86$ $n =$ 2

Copyright © SRA/McGraw-Hill. Permission is granted to reproduce this page for classroom use.

UNIT 5

Student Edition pages 428–429

Wrap-Up

PRESENTING THE PROJECT

Project Objectives

- ▶ to provide experience working with data that can be interpreted in more than one way
- ▶ to provide experience in designing a “fair” contest

To begin the project, discuss the text on page 428. Help students see that it is possible to pick a winner with only one jump, but that the winner is not necessarily the best jumper. Could Bill, for example, have tripped? Perhaps he could have won.

Although you might want to allow unstructured discussion, a structured method of solving this problem is to have students use a **calculator*, The Cruncher*** spreadsheet, or paper and pencil and make a chart showing the following:

Name	Best Jump	Average of two best jumps (cm)	Average of three jumps (cm)
Mary	182	177.5	174
Justin	121	119.5	116
Elise	156	152	140.7
Clark	188	186	176
Hannah	186	184.5	183.7
Lisette	122	118.5	114.7
Bill	190	185.5	137.7
Matt	137	129.5	126

From these data, we can see that . . .

- ▶ Bill is the winner if we count the best jump.
- ▶ Clark is the winner if we count the average of the two best jumps.
- ▶ Hannah is the winner if we count the average of the three best jumps.
- ▶ Some students might argue that Hannah is the most consistent as well.

So who is the best jumper? We cannot tell. We can only tell who the winner is based on the rules we decide to use in the beginning.

UNIT 5 WRAP-UP

PROJECT

COOPERATIVE LEARNING

The Broad-Jump Contest

Mary and her track team, the Lancers, competed in a broad-jump contest. They each made one jump. They recorded the results in the chart below.

NAME	DISTANCE JUMPED (IN CENTIMETERS)
Mary	170
Justin	115
Elise	121
Clark	181
Hannah	182
Lisette	110
Bill	30
Matt	100

❶ No; we only know that she jumped the farthest in this round.

❷ Have each person jump several times and figure an average distance per person.

Hannah was declared the winner of the group.

❶ Can you be sure that Hannah is the best broad-jumper?

❷ What is another way to have a fair contest?

*available separately

The Lancers realized that one jump was not enough.
They changed the contest to allow each athlete to jump three times.

Here are the results of the new contest.

NAME	DISTANCE JUMPED (IN CENTIMETERS)		
	FIRST JUMP	SECOND JUMP	THIRD JUMP
Mary	167	173	182
Justin	121	118	109
Elise	118	148	156
Clark	184	156	188
Hannah	182	183	186
Lisette	115	107	122
Bill	181	190	42
Matt	122	119	137

Answer these questions.

3. Which Lancers improved their score after every jump? **Mary, Elise, and Hannah**
4. Which Lancers scored higher on their second jump than on their first jump? **Mary, Elise, Hannah, and Bill**
5. Who had the lowest score on the first jump? The second? The third? **Lisette; Lisette; Bill**

COOPERATIVE LEARNING **Work in small groups. Who do you think should be declared the winner? Write the reasons why you believe your choice is fair.**

Design your own contest. Discuss ways to make it fair.

What Is a Math Project? If this is the first time you have used math projects in your classroom, you may want to refer to pages 96–97 in this Teacher's Guide for more detailed information about effectively implementing and assessing projects.

Homework Working alone or in small groups, ask students to design a race or other contest. Among areas they should consider are:

- What will they measure?
- How many trials will be allowed?
- How will the winner be determined?

Wrapping Up the Project Allow students to present their proposed contests and explain why they think their contests are fair.

Assessing the Project Note students who become uneasy or frustrated because there is no single correct answer to determine the best jumper. Help these students realize that there is often more than one way to solve a problem in mathematics.

COOPERATIVE LEARNING **Minds on Math** SRA's *Minds on Math* is a series of units covering Problem Solving, Data Collection, Number Sense, Measurement, Money, and Geometry and Spatial Relations. Each unit provides a series of open-ended projects for individuals or small groups. These projects develop problem-solving and critical-thinking skills, utilize real-world materials, emphasize language, and integrate cross-curricular connections. Use projects from collecting data to practice collecting, recording, and organizing data.

Why teach it at this time?

Although this project can be done at any time, the data analysis makes extensive use of division, the main topic of this unit.

UNIT 6 Fractions and Decimals

APPLICATIONS IN MEASUREMENT

OVERVIEW

This unit begins with a review of fractions of areas and fractions of sets. Students find fractions of whole numbers and relate fractions to probability concepts. They also find equivalent fractions and mixed numbers, and relate fractions to customary units of length: inches, feet, and yards. The measurement units are used to help students add and subtract fractions with like and unlike denominators. Students then relate decimals and fractions and learn to compare and round decimals. They learn to multiply and divide decimals by powers of 10 and to apply that skill to converting metric units of length. Students add and subtract decimals to solve word problems. They also multiply decimals and whole numbers and use measures of weight and volume.

Integrated Topics in This Unit Include:

- reviewing fractional notation
- finding simple probabilities
- finding equivalent fractions
- comparing fractions
- writing mixed numbers and improper fractions
- adding and subtracting fractions and mixed numbers
- relating decimals and fractions
- ordering and comparing decimals
- rounding decimals
- multiplying and dividing decimals by powers of 10
- multiplying decimals by whole numbers
- using decimals in weights and volumes

MULTIPLYING AND DIVIDING DECIMALS BY POWERS OF 10

USING DECIMALS IN WEIGHT AND VOLUME

> **"***Fractions and decimals represent a significant extension of children's knowledge about numbers. When children possess a sound understanding of fraction and decimal concepts, they can use this knowledge to describe real-world phenomena and apply it to problems involving measurement, probability, and statistics.***"**
>
> *—NCTM Curriculum and Evaluation Standards for School Mathematics*

GAMES

Motivating Mixed Practice

Games provide **basic math skills** practice in cooperative groups. Playing the games also helps students develop **mathematical reasoning**.

Fractions of 60	Lesson 127	page 435
Anything but 10	Lesson 130	page 441
Fracto 1 and 2 Game Mats	Lesson 131	page 443
Fracto 1 Game Mat	Lesson 132	page 446
Fracto 1 and 2 Game Mats	Lesson 133	page 450
Fracto 1 and 2 Game Mats	Lesson 135	page 455
Roll a Decimal	Lesson 140	page 474
Find the Distance 1 and 2 Game Mats	Lesson 146	page 494
Harder Roll a Decimal	Lesson 148	page 501
Checkbook and Harder Checkbook Game Mats	Lesson 149	page 504
Metric Unit Game Mat	Lesson 153	page 517
Fracto 1 and 2 Game Mats	Lesson 154	page 519
Fractions of 60	Lesson 154	page 519

THINKING STORY

Integrated Problem Solving

Thinking Stories provide opportunities for students to work in **cooperative groups** and develop **logical reasoning** while they integrate **reading skills** with mathematics.

Iron and Gold

Part 1	Lesson 141	pages 478–479
Part 2	Lesson 144	pages 488–489
Part 3	Lesson 149	pages 504–505
Part 4	Lesson 151	pages 512–513
Part 5	Lesson 154	pages 520–521

Story Summary "Iron and Gold" focuses on probability and continues the saga of the four children who have found the royal treasure on Mugg Island. The children are offered rewards, but they must choose among three bags of mixed coins—some iron, some gold—without knowing which bag has the most gold. In the last part of the story, the children are blindfolded and asked to choose one stone from one of several jars containing rubies and glass. Students refine their understanding of probability and estimation as they evaluate the children's decisions.

PROJECT

Making Connections

The Unit 6 Project makes real-world connections. Students work in **cooperative groups** to problem solve and to communicate their findings.

The project presented in the Unit 6 Wrap-Up asks students to study the fictional Fairlawn School's plan to raise money to purchase a computer. Then they are asked to evaluate whether a computer or other equipment would be a benefit to their education and to develop a plan to raise the necessary money. This project can be started at any time throughout the unit during students' free time.

Fractions and Decimals Lesson Plans

LESSON		PACING	PRIMARY OBJECTIVES	FEATURE	RESOURCES	NCTM STANDARDS
126	Writing Appropriate Fractions 432–433	1 day	to review fractions of areas		Reteaching Master Practice Master 126 Enrichment Master 126	4, 12
127	Fractions of Whole Numbers 434–435	1 day	to review fractions and fraction notation	Game	Reteaching Master Practice Master 127 Enrichment Master 127	12
128	Probability 436–437	1 day	to review the concept of probability		Reteaching Strategy Practice Master 128 Enrichment Master 128	11
129	Fractions and Probability 438–439	1 day	to associate numbers with probability and to encourage thinking about probability concepts		Reteaching Strategy Practice Master 129 Enrichment Master 129	1, 2, 3, 4, 11, 12
130	Applying Fractions 440–441	1 day	✓ to assess students' understanding of fractions	Game	Reteaching Strategy Practice Master 130 Enrichment Master 130 Assessment Master	11, 12
131	Equivalent Fractions: Probability 442–443	1 day	to provide practice in solving simple probability problems	Game	Reteaching Strategy Practice Master 131 Enrichment Master 131	4, 9, 11, 12
132	Equivalent Fractions 444–447	1 day	✓ to assess students' ability to understand fractions of numbers	Game	Reteaching Master Practice Master 132 Enrichment Master 132 Assessment Master	1, 2, 3, 4, 12
133	Mixed Numbers 448–451	1 day	to provide practice in writing mixed numbers and improper fractions	Game	Reteaching Master Practice Master 133 Enrichment Master 133	12
134	Inches, Feet, and Yards 452–453	1 day	to provide practice in measuring objects using customary units		Reteaching Strategy Practice Master 134 Enrichment Master 134	10, 12
135	Adding and Subtracting Fractions of Inches 454–455	1 day	to introduce and to provide practice with addition and subtraction of simple fractions and mixed numbers	Game	Reteaching Strategy Practice Master 135 Enrichment Master 135	1, 2, 3, 4, 12
136	Adding and Subtracting Fractions 456–457	1 day	to add and subtract fractions with unlike denominators		Reteaching Master Practice Master 136 Enrichment Master 136	12
137	Adding and Subtracting Mixed Numbers and Improper Fractions 458–459	1 day	to add and subtract mixed numbers with unlike denominators		Reteaching Master Practice Master 137 Enrichment Master 137	12
	Mid-Unit Review 460–463	1 day			Assessment Masters	
138	Parts of a Whole 464–467	1 day	to reintroduce the meaning of and standard notation for decimals		Reteaching Master Practice Master 138 Enrichment Master 138	4, 12
139	Decimals and Fractions 468–471	1 day	to develop students' understanding of the relationship among tenths, hundredths, and thousandths		Reteaching Strategy Practice Master 139 Enrichment Master 139	4, 12
140	Ordering Decimals 472–475	1 day	to show how to annex 0s to compare decimals with different numbers of digits to the right of the decimal point	Game	Reteaching Master Practice Master 140 Enrichment Master 140	12
141	Comparing Decimals Review 476–479	1 day	✓ to assess students' understanding of the relative magnitude of decimals	Thinking Story	Reteaching Strategy Practice Master 141 Enrichment Master 141 Assessment Master	1, 2, 3, 4, 12
142	Rounding Decimals 480–481	1 day	to provide practice rounding numbers to a specified degree of precision		Reteaching Master Practice Master 142 Enrichment Master 142	1, 2, 3, 4, 5, 12

	LESSON	PACING	PRIMARY OBJECTIVES	FEATURE	RESOURCES	NCTM STANDARDS
143	Decimals: Multiplying and Dividing by Powers of 10 482–485	1 day	to introduce procedures for multiplying and dividing decimals by 10, 100, and 1000		Reteaching Master Practice Master 143 Enrichment Master 143	4, 8, 10, 12
144	Approximating Errors Using Decimals 486–489	1 day	✓ to provide practice in and assess mastery of multiplying and dividing decimals by powers of 10	Thinking Story	Reteaching Strategy Practice Master 144 Enrichment Master 144 Assessment Master	1, 2, 3, 4, 5, 8, 12
145	Metric Units: Multiply and Divide by Powers of 10 490–491	1 day	to introduce the relationships among metric units of length		Reteaching Master Practice Master 145 Enrichment Master 145	1, 2, 3, 4, 10, 12
146	Metric Measurements of Length 492–495	2 days	to demonstrate how to express metric measures as decimals with one unit	Game	Reteaching Strategy Practice Master 146 Enrichment Master 146	1, 2, 3, 4, 9, 10, 12
147	Adding and Subtracting Decimals 496–499	1 day	✓ to assess mastery of adding and subtracting decimals using monetary amounts		Reteaching Master Practice Master 147 Enrichment Master 147 Assessment Master	1, 2, 3, 4, 8, 12
148	Addition and Subtraction of Decimals: Applications 500–501	1 day	to provide practice in adding and subtracting decimals	Game	Reteaching Strategy Practice Master 148 Enrichment Master 148	1, 2, 3, 4, 8, 12
149	Adding and Subtracting Decimals: Balancing a Checkbook.... 502–505	1 day	to provide realistic problems and practice in adding and subtracting money amounts	Thinking Story Game	Reteaching Strategy Practice Master 149 Enrichment Master 149	1, 2, 3, 4, 8, 12
150	Multiplying a Decimal by a Whole Number 506–509	1 day	to provide practice multiplying a decimal by a whole number		Reteaching Master Practice Master 150 Enrichment Master 150	8, 12
151	Practicing Multiplication of Decimals and Whole Numbers 510–513	1 day	to provide practice with applying function rules and graphing to decimals and fractions	Thinking Story	Reteaching Strategy Practice Master 151 Enrichment Master 151	1, 2, 3, 4, 5, 8, 12, 13
152	Using Decimals: Weight and Volume 514–515	1 day	✓ to assess understanding of measuring and converting metric units		Reteaching Strategy Practice Master 152 Enrichment Master 152 Assessment Master	4, 10, 11
153	Cubic Centimeters 516–517	1 day	to review volume as measured in cubic units	Game	Reteaching Strategy Practice Master 153 Enrichment Master 153	1, 2, 3, 4, 10
154	Keep in Shape: Fractions and Decimals 518–521	1 day	✓ to assess students' proficiency in adding and subtracting simple fractions	Thinking Story Game	Reteaching Strategy Practice Master 154 Enrichment Master 154 Assessment Masters	1, 2, 3, 4, 8, 12
155	Unit 6 Review 522–525		to review fractions/decimals		Practice Master 155 Enrichment Master 155	
156	Unit 6 Practice 526–529		to practice fractions/decimals		Practice Master 156 Enrichment Master 156	
	Unit 6 Test 530–531		to review fractions/decimals		Assessment Masters	
	Unit 6 Wrap-Up .... 532–533 Fairlawn School Buys a Computer			Project		

UNIT CONNECTIONS

INTERVENTION STRATEGIES

In this Teacher's Guide there will be specific strategies suggested for students with individual needs. These strategies appear with icons under the headings ESL, Gifted and Talented, Special Needs, Learning Styles, and At Risk. Following are the icons to look for and the types of strategies that accompany them:

ESL

English as a Second Language

These strategies, designed for students who do not speak the English language fluently, suggest meaningful ways to present the lesson concepts and vocabulary.

GIFTED & TALENTED

Gifted and Talented

These strategies are designed to enrich and extend the lessons and offer further challenges to students who have easily mastered the concepts already presented.

SPECIAL NEEDS

Special Needs

Students who are physically challenged or who have learning disabilities may require alternative ways to complete activities, record answers, use manipulatives, and so on. The strategies labeled with this icon offer appropriate methods of teaching lesson concepts to these students.

LEARNING STYLES

Learning Styles

Each student has his or her individual approach to learning. The strategies labeled with this icon suggest ways to present lesson concepts so that various learning modalities–such as tactile/kinesthetic, visual, and auditory–can be addressed.

AT RISK

At Risk

These strategies highlight the relevancy of the skills presented by making the connection between school and real life. They are directed toward students who appear to be at risk of dropping out of school before graduation.

TECHNOLOGY CONNECTIONS

The following materials, designed to reinforce and extend lesson concepts, are referred to throughout this Teacher's Guide. It might be helpful to either order the software and videos or check them out of the school media center or community library.

TECHNOLOGY CONNECTION

Look for this **Technology Connection** *icon.*

- *Fraction Attraction,* from Sunburst Communications; Mac, IBM, for grades 3-8 (software)
- *Fraction Munchers,* from MECC; Mac, for grades 3-12 (software)
- *Math Power Series: Balancing Act,* from Ventura Educational Systems; Mac, for grades K-8 (software)
- *Math Shop Spotlight: Fractions & Decimals,* from Scholastic; Mac, IBM, for grades 4-8 (software)
- *Math Skills Collection,* from Hartley; Mac, IBM, for grades 4-6 (software)
- *Math Keys: Unlocking Fractions and Decimals,* from MECC; Mac, IBM, for grades 3-6 (software)
- *Whole Numbers, Decimals, and Fractions/Decimals: Multiplication and Division,* from Gamco; Mac, IBM, for grades 3-10 (software)
- *Math Football: Fractions* or *Touchdown Math: Fractions,* from Gamco; IBM, Mac, for grades 4-12 (software)

CROSS-CURRICULAR CONNECTIONS

This Teacher's Guide offers specific suggestions on ways to connect the math concepts presented in this unit with other subjects that students are studying. Students can connect math concepts with topics they already know about, and they can find examples of math in other subjects and in real-world situations. These strategies are given at the point of use.

Look for these icons:

- Geography
- Health
- Social Studies
- Music
- Science
- Math
- Art
- Physical Education
- Language Arts
- Careers

LITERATURE CONNECTIONS

The following books are referenced throughout this Teacher's Guide at the points where they can be used to introduce, reinforce, or extend specific lesson concepts. You may want to locate these books in your school or community library.

Look for this **Literature Connection** *icon.*

- *Fraction Action* by Loreen Leedy. Holiday Books, 1994.
- *Do You Wanna Bet?* by Jean Cushman. Clarion Books, 1991.
- *Hours, Days, and Years (Ripley's Believe It or Not!)* Capstone Press, Inc. Capstone Press, 1991.
- *Thundercake* by Patricia Polacco. Philomel Books, 1990.
- *Measuring Up* by Sandra Markle. Atheneum Books for Young Readers, 1995.
- *Money* by Joe Cribb. Knopf, 1990.
- *Math for Smarty Pants* by Marilyn Burns. Little, Brown, 1982.
- *Is a Blue Whale the Biggest Thing There Is?* by Robert E. Wells. A. Whitman, 1993.
- *Measure* by Ivan Bulloch. Thomson Learning, 1994.
- *Penelope Gets Wheels* by Esther Allen Peterson. Crown Publishers, 1982.
- *Jobs for Kids* by Carol Barkin and Elizabeth James. Lothrop, Lee & Shepard Books, 1990.
- *Benjamin's 365 Birthdays* by Judi Barrett. Atheneum, 1992.
- *Kid Power* by Susan Beth Pfeffer. F. Watts, 1977.

ASSESSMENT OPPORTUNITIES AT-A-GLANCE

LESSON	PORTFOLIO	PERFORMANCE	FORMAL	SELF	INFORMAL	CUMULATIVE REVIEWS	MULTIPLE-CHOICE	MASTERY CHECKPOINTS	ANALYZING ANSWERS
126					✓				
127					✓				
128	✓								
129	✓								
130			✓					✓	
131					✓	✓			
132			✓					✓	
133				✓					
134		✓							
135				✓					
136					✓	✓			
137					✓				
Mid-Unit Review	✓	✓	✓						
138					✓				
139					✓				
140				✓		✓			
141			✓					✓	✓
142					✓				
143					✓				
144			✓			✓		✓	
145		✓							✓
146		✓							
147			✓					✓	✓
148					✓	✓			
149	✓								
150		✓							✓
151					✓				
152			✓					✓	
153				✓		✓			
154			✓					✓	
155	✓	✓	✓						
156						✓			
Unit Test			✓				✓		

ASSESSMENT OPTIONS

PORTFOLIO ASSESSMENT

Throughout this Teacher's Guide are suggestions for activities in which students draw pictures, make graphs, and write about mathematics. Keep students' work to assess growth of understanding as the year progresses.

Lessons 128, 129, Mid-Unit Review, 149, and 155

PERFORMANCE ASSESSMENT

Performance Assessment items focus on evaluating how students think and work as they solve problems. Opportunities for performance assessment can be found throughout the unit. Rubrics and guides for grading can be found in the front of the Assessment Blackline Masters.

Lessons 134, Mid-Unit Review, 145, 146, 150, and 155

FORMAL ASSESSMENT

A Mid-Unit Review, Unit Review, and Unit Test help assess students' understanding of concepts and skills and problem-solving ability. The *Math Explorations and Applications* CD-ROM Test Generator can create additional unit tests at three ability levels. Also, Mastery Checkpoints are provided periodically throughout the unit.

Lessons 130, 132, Mid-Unit Review, 141, 144, 147, 152, 154, 155, and Unit Test

SELF ASSESSMENT

Throughout the program students are given the opportunity to check their own math skills.

Lessons 133, 135, 140, and 153

INFORMAL ASSESSMENT

A variety of assessment suggestions is provided throughout the unit, including interviews, oral questions or presentations, and debates. Also, each lesson includes Assessment Criteria, a list of questions about each student's progress, understanding, and participation.

Lessons 126, 127, 131, 136, 137, 138, 139, 142, 143, 148, and 151

CUMULATIVE REVIEW

Cumulative Reviews, covering material presented thus far in the year, are provided in the unit for use as either assessment or practice.

Lessons 131, 136, 140, 144, 148, 153, and 156

MULTIPLE-CHOICE TESTS (STANDARDIZED FORMAT)

Each unit provides a Unit Test in standardized format, giving students many opportunities to practice taking tests in this format.

MASTERY CHECKPOINTS

Mastery Checkpoints are provided throughout the unit to assess student proficiency in specific skills. Checkpoints reference appropriate Assessment Blackline Masters and other assessment options. Results of these evaluations can be recorded on the Mastery Checkpoint Chart.

Lessons 130, 132, 141, 144, 147, 152, and 154

ANALYZING ANSWERS

Analyzing Answers items suggest possible sources of student error and offer teaching strategies for addressing difficulties.

Lessons 141, 145, 147, and 150

Look for these icons:

ALTERNATIVE ASSESSMENT

ANALYZING ANSWERS

SELF ASSESSMENT

> ***"The primary question to be answered by teachers is, How is each student progressing in relation to the goals we have set and agreed on?"***
>
> *–NCTM Assessment Standards*

MASTERY CHECKPOINTS

WHAT TO EXPECT FROM STUDENTS AS THEY COMPLETE THIS UNIT

⑱ UNDERSTANDING FRACTIONS—LESSON 130

At this time most students should understand fractional notation and be able to use fractions intelligently. Students should correctly answer at least 80% of the problems on page 440. You may wish to record the results of this assessment on the Mastery Checkpoint Chart. You may also wish to assign Assessment Blackline Masters page 51 to determine mastery.

⑲ FRACTIONS OF WHOLE NUMBERS—LESSON 132

At about this time most students should demonstrate proficiency in finding simple fractions of whole numbers. You can assess this ability from students' performance during the Mental Math drill in Lesson 132. You may also wish to assign Assessment Blackline Masters page 52 to determine mastery. Record the results of this assessment on the Mastery Checkpoint Chart.

⑳ RELATIVE MAGNITUDE OF DECIMAL—LESSON 141

At this time most students should demonstrate mastery of the relative magnitude of decimals by correctly answering 80% of the problems on page 476 or a similar page. You may also wish to assign Assessment Blackline Masters page 53 to determine mastery. Record the results of this assessment on the Mastery Checkpoint Chart.

㉑ MULTIPLYING AND DIVIDING DECIMALS BY POWERS OF 10—LESSON 144

By this time most students should be proficient with multiplying and dividing decimals by powers of 10. You can assess this ability by using page 487 or a similar page. To demonstrate mastery students should correctly answer at least 80% of the problems on the page. You may also wish to assign Assessment Blackline Masters page 56 to determine mastery. Record the results of this assessment on the Mastery Checkpoint Chart.

㉒ ADDING AND SUBTRACTING DECIMALS—LESSON 147

At about this time most students should demonstrate mastery of addition and subtraction of decimals by correctly answering at least 80% of the problems on page 497 and by using correct procedures in at least ten of the word problems on pages 498–499. You may also wish to assign Assessment Blackline Masters page 57 to determine mastery. Results of this assessment may be recorded on the Mastery Checkpoint Chart.

㉓ MEASURING WITH AND CONVERTING METRIC UNITS—LESSON 152

Students should demonstrate mastery of measuring with and converting to metric units by correctly answering at least 80% of the problems on page 514 or on Assessment Blackline Masters page 58. Results may be recorded on the Mastery Checkpoint Chart.

㉔ ADDING AND SUBTRACTING SIMPLE FRACTIONS—LESSON 154

By this time most students should be able to add and subtract simple fractions. Students should correctly answer at least 80% of the problems on page 518. You may also wish to assign Assessment Blackline Masters pages 59–60 to determine mastery. Record the results of this assessment on the Mastery Checkpoint Chart.

UNIT 6

PROGRAM RESOURCES

THESE ADDITIONAL COMPONENTS OF *MATH EXPLORATIONS AND APPLICATIONS* CAN BE PURCHASED SEPARATELY FROM SRA/MCGRAW-HILL.

LESSON	BASIC MANIPULATIVE KIT	GAME MAT PACKAGE	TEACHER MANIPULATIVE KIT	INTERMEDIATE MANIPULATIVE KIT	INTERMEDIATE OVERHEAD MANIPULATIVE KIT	*THE CRUNCHER* SOFTWARE	*MATH EXPLORATIONS AND APPLICATIONS* CD-ROM
126				counters, interlocking cubes	counters, fraction tiles		Lesson 126
127	Number Cubes						Lesson 127
128	Number Cubes	play money		counters, spinners	coins, counters, spinners		Lesson 128
129	Number Cubes						Lesson 129
130	Number Cubes	Fracto 1 and 2 games					Lesson 130
131	Number Cubes	Fracto 1 and 2 games play money		angle rulers	bills, coins		Lesson 131
132		Fracto 1 game		counters	counters		Lesson 132
133		Fracto 1 and 2 games		counters	counters		Lesson 133
134				angle rulers, tape measures			Lesson 134
135		Fracto 1 and 2 games	scale				Lesson 135
136				fraction tower cubes			Lesson 136
137							Lesson 137
138		play money	place-value pad		bills, coins		Lesson 138
139		play money	scale	base-10 blocks	bills, coins		Lesson 139
140	Number Cubes		place-value pad				Lesson 140
141		play money		base-10 blocks	bills, coins		Lesson 141
142							Lesson 142
143	Number Wheels					spreadsheet	Lesson 143
144		play money		base-10 blocks, counters	bills, coins, counters		Lesson 144
145				base-10 blocks, angle ruler			Lesson 145
146		Find the Distance 1 and Find the Distance 2 games		angle rulers		spreadsheet	Lesson 146
147		play money			bills, coins	spreadsheet	Lesson 147
148	Number Cubes						Lesson 148
149		Checkbook and Harder Checkbook games play money			bills, coins		Lesson 149
150							Lesson 150
151		play money			bills, coins		Lesson 151
152	Number Wheels			balance			Lesson 152
153		Metric Unit game play money		angle rulers, tape measure	bills, coins		Lesson 153
154	Number Cubes, Number Wheels	Fracto 1 and 2 games, play money		fraction tower cubes	counters bills, coins		Lesson 154
155		play money		angle rulers	bills, coins		Lesson 155
156						spreadsheet	Lesson 156

UNIT 6

Student Edition pages 430–431

Fractions and Decimals

INTRODUCING THE UNIT

Using the Student Pages Begin your discussion of the opening unit photo by asking students, "What does a zookeeper or naturalist measure?" Then read aloud the paragraph on the student page that highlights zookeeping (or caring for animals) as a career. This helps make the connection between school and work and encourages students to explore how math is used in the real world.

ACTIVITY Ask students to do some research in an **encyclopedia** about their favorite animal. Have them find out how much the animal weighs at birth and how long it is. Challenge them to discover what their animal's mature weight and length will be.

FYI The earliest recorded zoo was kept by Queen Hatshepsut of Egypt around 1500 B.C. Five hundred years later the Chinese emperor Wen Wang built the Garden of Intelligence—a vast zoo covering more than 500 acres. Between 1000 and 400 B.C., rulers of North Africa, India, and China created many small zoos as a display of wealth and power. By the 200s B.C., however, ancient Greece was building public zoos that were mainly for study. Visiting the local zoo and learning about plants and animals from other places was considered an important part of a well-rounded education. Zoos disappeared in Europe's Middle Ages but continued in other parts of the world. When Cortez first met with the Aztecs of Central America in 1519, their capital city had a flourishing zoo. With a renewed interest in science in the 1700s, zoos came back into fashion in Europe. By the nineteenth century a zoo was considered essential for a major city. New York City got its first zoo in 1864, and other American cities quickly followed suit. Today zoos and aquariums are usually used both for research and public entertainment.

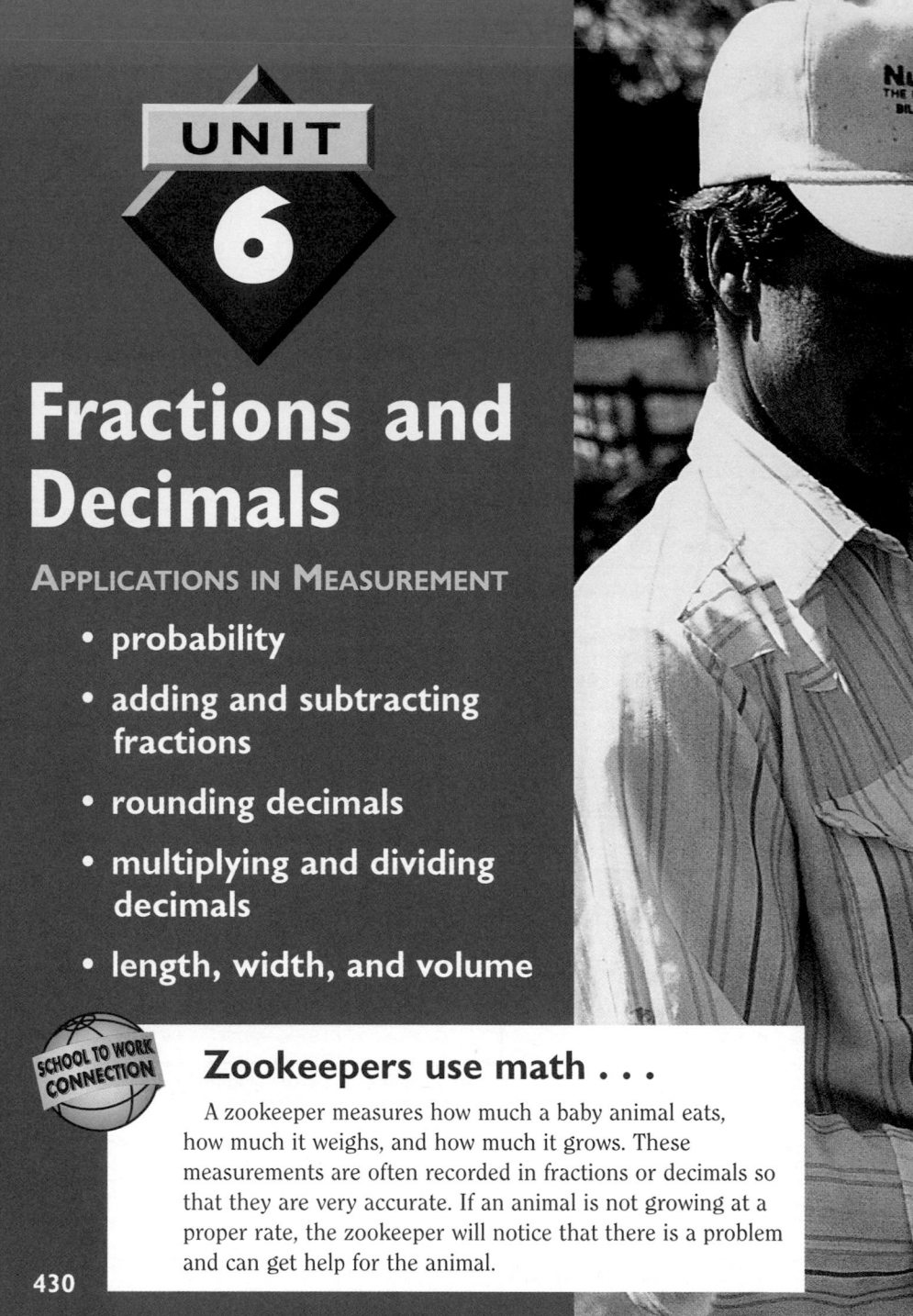

UNIT 6

Fractions and Decimals

APPLICATIONS IN MEASUREMENT

- probability
- adding and subtracting fractions
- rounding decimals
- multiplying and dividing decimals
- length, width, and volume

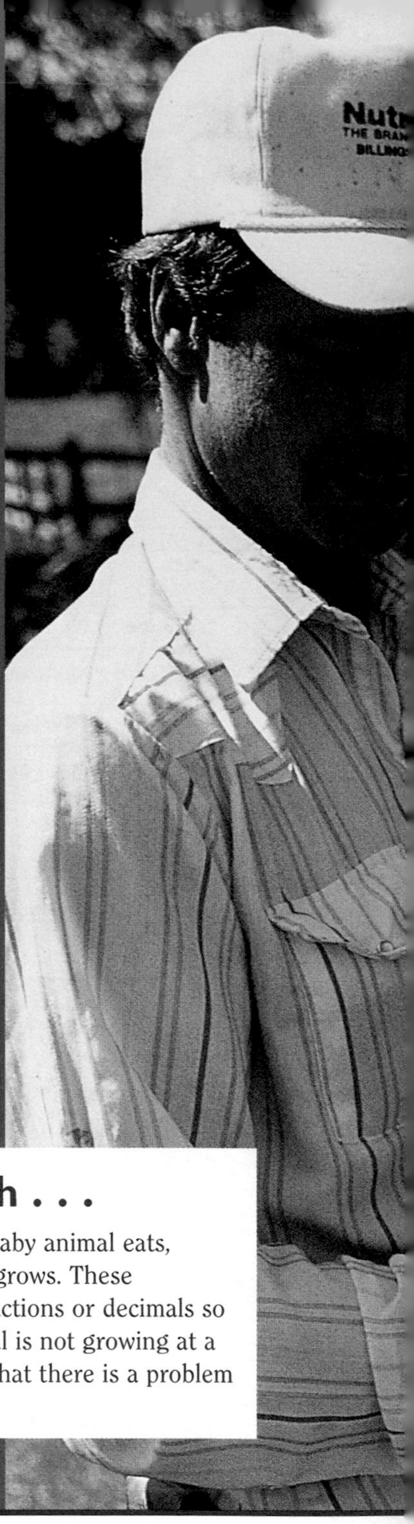

Zookeepers use math . . .

A zookeeper measures how much a baby animal eats, how much it weighs, and how much it grows. These measurements are often recorded in fractions or decimals so that they are very accurate. If an animal is not growing at a proper rate, the zookeeper will notice that there is a problem and can get help for the animal.

430

Thinklab™

SRA's *Thinklab*™ provides a series of creative and logical problem-solving opportunities for individual students. The problems are designed to appeal to different cognitive abilities.

- Use Problems 101–110 with this unit to reinforce creative insight (developing abstract relationships from given data).
- Use Problems 111–125 with this unit to reinforce logical analysis (absorbing multiple data, testing hypotheses, and planning a set of operations).

There are many jobs in a zoo or wildlife refuge. A zookeeper is usually responsible for the raising and feeding of animals, while a zoo biologist might spend all his or her time in the field studying the behavior of animals in the wild. The information a zoo biologist gains is used by zoos to help ensure that species can be kept alive in captivity. This is especially important when a breed of animal may become extinct—like Przewalski's Horse, which is no longer found in the wild but exists in healthy numbers in zoos. While most zoo jobs require advanced degrees, volunteering for a zoo requires no degree and can be an excellent way to learn more about such a career. Math will come into play in even the simplest tasks in a zoo, from deciding how much to feed to a gorilla to measuring and weighing baby chicks.

Home Connections You may want to send home the Home Connections Blackline Masters letter on pages 52–53 to introduce this unit.

Cooperate 1

Cooperate 1, published by SRA, provides a series of creative and logical problem-solving opportunities for cooperative groups. The problems are designed to provide practice in problem solving, communication, reasoning, and making connections. *Cooperate 1* presents the following cognitive strategies—perceiving spatial relations, ordering and sequencing, logical deduction, establishing and testing hypotheses, sequential exploration, identifying starting points, attending to detail, organizing information, and screening irrelevant information.

Each Problem Card emphasizes a principal strategy as well as reinforcing other strategies.

- Use Problem Card 26 with this unit to emphasize logical deduction.
- Use Problem Cards 27–28 with this unit to emphasize perceiving spatial relations.
- Use Problem Cards 29–30 with this unit to emphasize attending to detail.

LESSON 126

Student Edition pages 432–433

Writing Appropriate Fractions

LESSON PLANNER

Objectives

- ▶ to review fractions of areas
- ▶ to review fractions of sets

Context of the Lesson This is the first of 12 lessons on understanding and using fractions and mixed numbers. Students have worked with fractions since Level 1 and they reviewed fractions in Unit 1.

MANIPULATIVES

counters* or beads

geoboards and rubber bands (optional)

fraction tiles* (optional)

interlocking cubes* (optional)

Program Resources

Reteaching Master

Practice Master 126

Enrichment Master 126

For extra practice:
CD-ROM* Lesson 126

1 Warm-Up

5 MINUTES

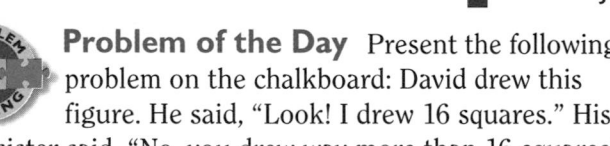

Problem of the Day Present the following problem on the chalkboard: David drew this figure. He said, "Look! I drew 16 squares." His older sister said, "No, you drew way more than 16 squares!" How many squares are in David's drawing? (30)

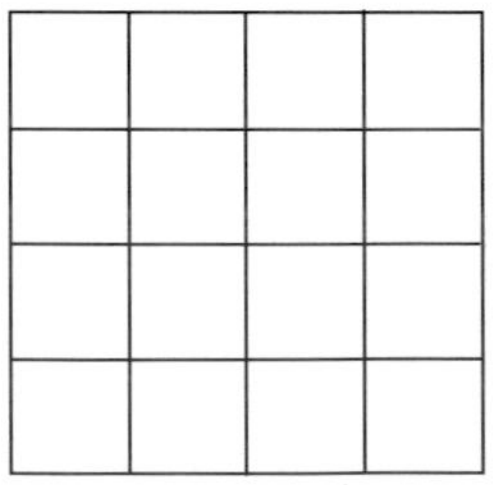

Problem-Solving Strategies Ask students who have solved the Problem of the Day to share how they solved it and any strategies they used.

MENTAL MATH Provide fractions-of-number problems based on money. Encourage quick responses.

a. How many cents are in $\frac{1}{2}$ of a dollar? (50)

b. How many cents are in $\frac{1}{2}$ of a dime? (5)

c. How many cents are in $\frac{1}{4}$ of a dollar? (25)

(continued on page 433)

PRACTICE

LESSON 126

Writing Appropriate Fractions

Answer the question using the figures below.

What fraction of each of the following figures has been shaded?

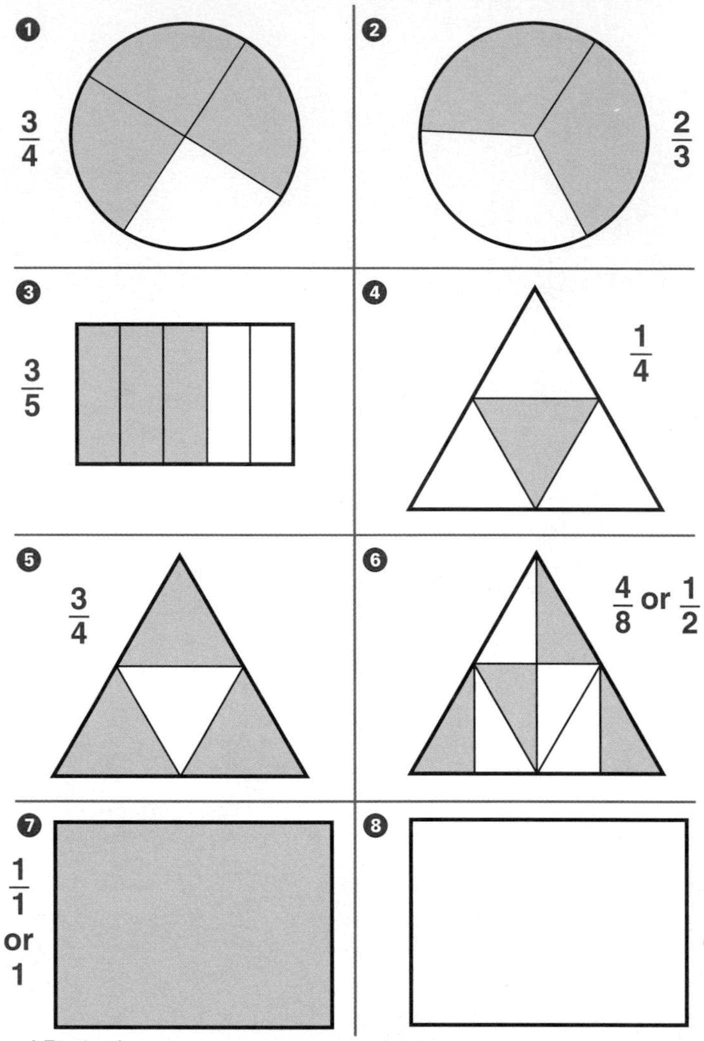

LEARNING STYLES · MANIPULATIVES

Meeting Individual Needs

Students who are visual, artistic, or spatial learners may benefit from exploring fractions with manipulative materials. Provide paper they can fold; **geoboards** and **rubber bands; fraction tiles***; or sets of objects in different colors, such as **interlocking cubes*, counters***, or **beads,** so students can manipulate fractional amounts.

RETEACHING p. 37

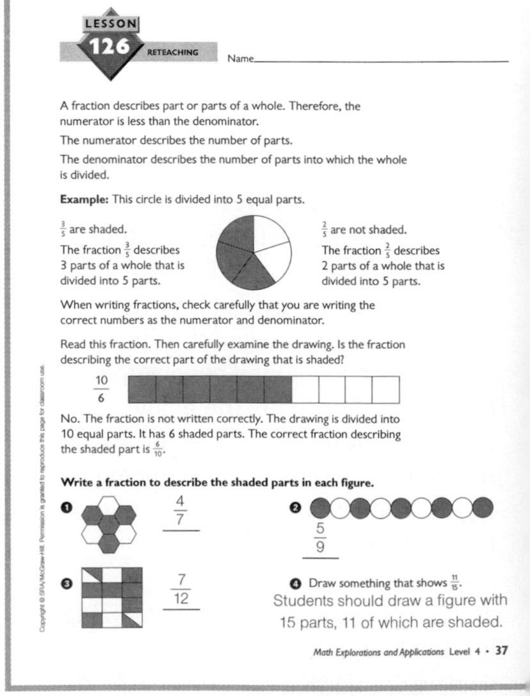

LESSON 126 RETEACHING Name______

A fraction describes part or parts of a whole. Therefore, the numerator is less than the denominator.

The numerator describes the number of parts.

The denominator describes the number of parts into which the whole is divided.

Example: This circle is divided into 5 equal parts.

$\frac{3}{5}$ are shaded.

The fraction $\frac{3}{5}$ describes 3 parts of a whole that is divided into 5 parts.

$\frac{2}{5}$ are not shaded.

The fraction $\frac{2}{5}$ describes 2 parts of a whole that is divided into 5 parts.

When writing fractions, check carefully that you are writing the correct numbers as the numerator and denominator.

Read this fraction. Then carefully examine the drawing. Is the fraction describing the correct part of the drawing that is shaded?

$\frac{10}{6}$

No. The fraction is not written correctly. The drawing is divided into 10 equal parts. It has 6 shaded parts. The correct fraction describing the shaded part is $\frac{6}{10}$.

Write a fraction to describe the shaded parts in each figure.

1 $\frac{4}{7}$

2 $\frac{5}{9}$

3 $\frac{7}{12}$

4 Draw something that shows $\frac{11}{15}$. Students should draw a figure with 15 parts, 11 of which are shaded.

Copyright © SRA/McGraw-Hill. Permission is granted to reproduce this page for classroom use.

*available separately

Answer the question using the pictures below.

What fraction of each of the following sets has a ring around it?

9. $\frac{3}{4}$

10. $\frac{5}{6}$
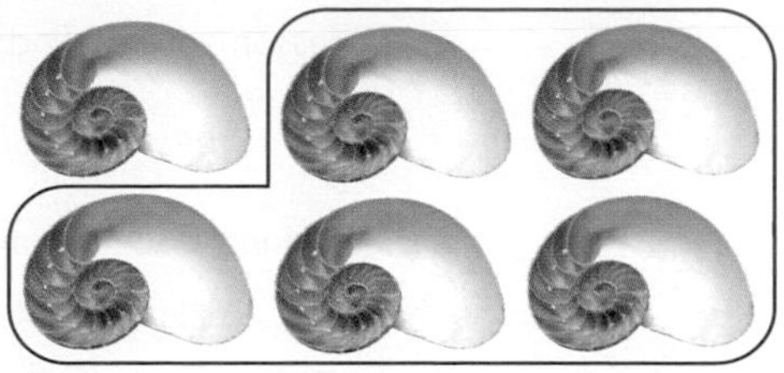

11. $\frac{5}{10}$ or $\frac{1}{2}$

12. $\frac{2}{7}$
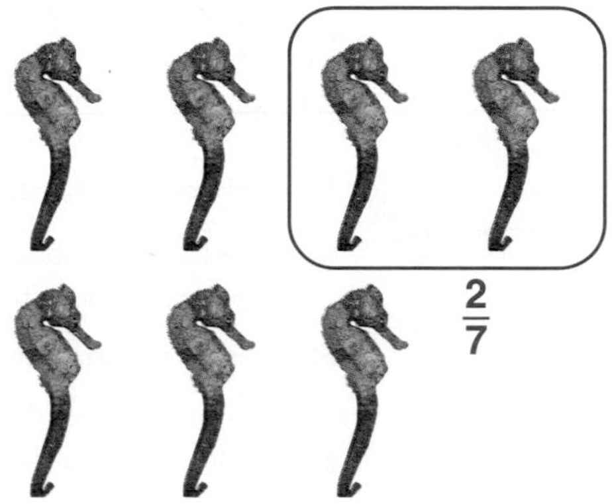

13. $\frac{5}{5}$ or 1

14. $\frac{0}{5}$ or 0
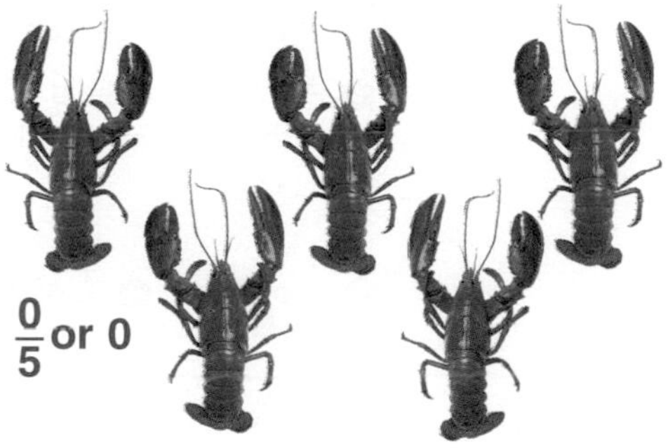

PRACTICE p. 126

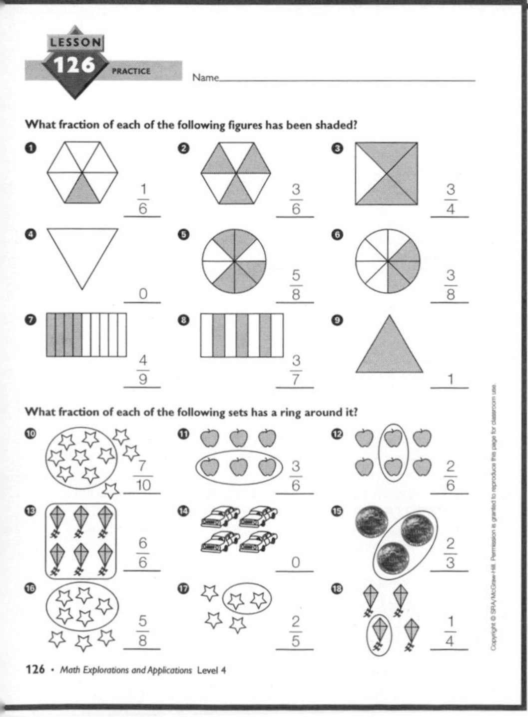
LESSON 126 PRACTICE Name__________

What fraction of each of the following figures has been shaded?

1. $\frac{1}{6}$ 2. $\frac{3}{6}$ 3. $\frac{3}{4}$
4. 0 5. $\frac{5}{8}$ 6. $\frac{3}{8}$
7. $\frac{4}{9}$ 8. $\frac{3}{7}$ 9. 1

What fraction of each of the following sets has a ring around it?

10. $\frac{7}{10}$ 11. $\frac{3}{6}$ 12. $\frac{2}{6}$
13. $\frac{6}{6}$ 14. 0 15. $\frac{2}{3}$
16. $\frac{5}{8}$ 17. $\frac{2}{5}$ 18. $\frac{1}{4}$

126 • Math Explorations and Applications Level 4

ENRICHMENT p. 126

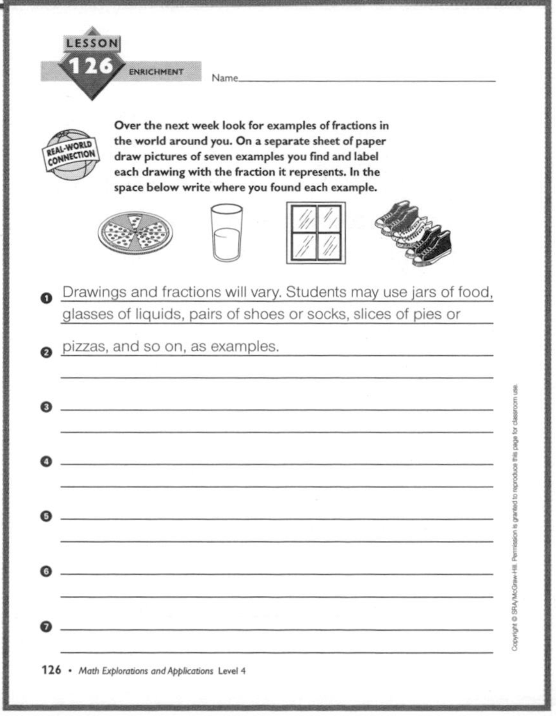
LESSON 126 ENRICHMENT Name__________

REAL-WORLD CONNECTION

Over the next week look for examples of fractions in the world around you. On a separate sheet of paper draw pictures of seven examples you find and label each drawing with the fraction it represents. In the space below write where you found each example.

1. Drawings and fractions will vary. Students may use jars of food, glasses of liquids, pairs of shoes or socks, slices of pies or
2. pizzas, and so on, as examples.
3. __________
4. __________
5. __________
6. __________
7. __________

126 • Math Explorations and Applications Level 4

*available separately

Mental Math (continued)

d. How many cents are in $\frac{1}{10}$ of a dime? (1)

e. How many cents are in $\frac{1}{10}$ of a dollar? (10)

2 Teach

Using the Student Pages Review with the class the meaning of fraction notation. Guide students to recall that the denominator, or "downstairs" number, tells how many equal parts there are in the whole, and the numerator, or "upstairs" number, tells how many of those equal parts to consider. For example, to serve $\frac{3}{4}$ of a pie, divide the pie into four equal parts, each of which is called $\frac{1}{4}$, and serve three of those parts, or $\frac{3}{4}$ of the pie. You may want to use **counters*** to make sets in which students describe the fractional part that is a certain color. For example, display three red and five blue counters. Ask how many counters are in the set (8). Then ask what fraction of the set is red ($\frac{3}{8}$) and blue ($\frac{5}{8}$). Ask what fraction of the set is yellow ($\frac{0}{8}$). Then have students complete these pages on their own.

3 Wrap-Up

5 MINUTES

In Closing Have students summarize the meaning of the fraction $\frac{3}{4}$ and draw pictures to support their explanations.

Informal Assessment Observe students as they work on this lesson. Encourage them to verbalize their thinking about fractions and to explain the meaning of each term in a fraction. Also have them use fractions to describe what they see by asking questions such as "What fraction of our windows is open?" or "What fraction of our class is boys?"

Assessment Criteria

Did the student . . .

✓ contribute to the discussion of fractions?

✓ communicate strategies used to identify fractions?

✓ correctly answer at least 75% of the problems on pages 432 and 433?

Homework Have students use fractions to describe at least five regions or sets in their families or homes. For example, one might say that $\frac{1}{2}$ of his family are females, and another might say $\frac{2}{3}$ of her pets are fish.

LESSON 127

Student Edition pages 434–435

Fractions of Whole Numbers

LESSON PLANNER

Objectives

- to review the meaning of fractions and fraction notation
- to provide practice in finding fractions of whole numbers

Context of the Lesson This is the second of 12 lessons on understanding and using fractions and mixed numbers.

MANIPULATIVES

none

Program Resources

Number Cubes (0–5)
Reteaching Master
Practice Master 127
Enrichment Master 127
For extra practice:
CD-ROM* Lesson 127

1 Warm-Up

5 MINUTES

Problem of the Day Present this problem: Tonya and Emmitt buy a meatball sandwich to share. The clerk cuts it in half for them before she wraps it. "I want the bigger half," says Emmitt. "Impossible!" answers Tonya. What does Tonya mean? (If an object is cut in half, that means it is in two equal parts; neither half is bigger than the other.)

Problem-Solving Strategies Ask students who have solved the Problem of the Day to share how they solved it and any strategies they used.

MENTAL MATH Give students fractions-of-number problems based on telling time:

a. How many minutes are in $\frac{1}{3}$ hour? (20)
b. What is $\frac{1}{3}$ of 60? (20)
c. How many minutes are in $\frac{2}{3}$ hour? (40)
d. What is $\frac{2}{3}$ of 60? (40)
e. How many minutes are in $\frac{1}{12}$ hour? (5)
f. What is $\frac{1}{12}$ of 60? (5)

MIXED PRACTICE

LESSON 127

Fractions of Whole Numbers

In this lesson you will find the fraction of a number.

$\frac{2}{3}$ of 24 = ?

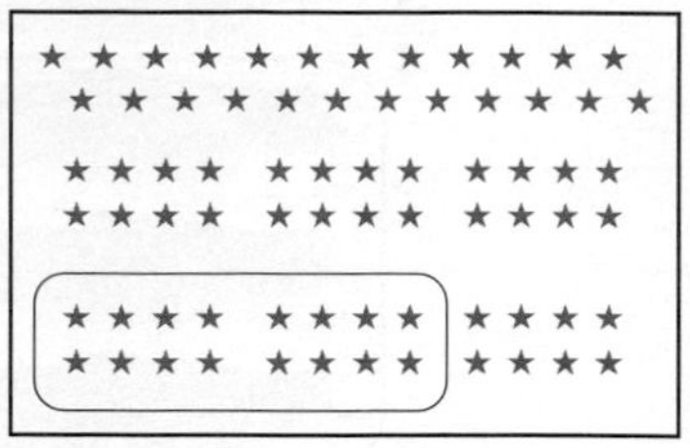

Divide 24 into 3 equal parts. $3\overline{)24}$ → 8

Then take 2 parts. $2 \times 8 = 16$

So $\frac{2}{3}$ of 24 is 16.

Remember: The bottom part (**denominator**) of a fraction tells how many equal parts to divide something into. The top part (**numerator**) of a fraction tells how many of those parts to take.

2—numerator
3—denominator

Solve these problems.

1. Paige has gone about $\frac{1}{4}$ of the way to Seattle, which is 120 miles away. About how many miles has she traveled? **30**
2. Grant is reading a magazine that is 75 pages long. He has read 55 pages. Has he read more than $\frac{2}{3}$ of the magazine? **yes**
3. A video that usually sells for $24 is on sale for $\frac{1}{3}$ off.
   a. How much is $\frac{1}{3}$ of 24? **8**
   b. What is the sale price of the video? **$16.00**
4. A jar that can hold 300 milliliters of water is about $\frac{2}{3}$ full. About how many milliliters of water are in the jar? **200 mL**

Solve.

5. $\frac{1}{2}$ of 12 **6**
6. $\frac{1}{4}$ of 20 **5**
7. $\frac{1}{5}$ of 100 **20**
8. $\frac{3}{10}$ of 100 **30**
9. $\frac{2}{3}$ of 24 **16**
10. $\frac{1}{3}$ of 9 **3**
11. $\frac{1}{2}$ of 20 **10**
12. $\frac{3}{5}$ of 100 **60**
13. $\frac{3}{10}$ of 50 **15**
14. $\frac{1}{8}$ of 24 **3**
15. $\frac{2}{3}$ of 9 **6**
16. $\frac{3}{4}$ of 20 **15**
17. $\frac{1}{6}$ of 36 **6**
18. $\frac{2}{3}$ of 30 **20**
19. $\frac{3}{8}$ of 24 **9**

434 • Fractions and Decimals

Literature Connection Read *Fraction Action* by Loreen Leedy to the class. Encourage students to solve the problems that involve fractions.

RETEACHING p. 38

LESSON 127 RETEACHING Name______________

Melissa has 30 new marbles. She wants to share them equally with 5 friends.

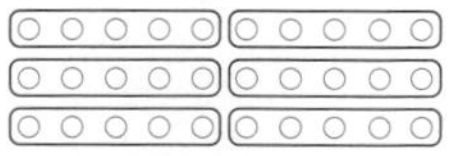

This can be described by the number sentence 30 ÷ 6 = 5.

She could divide the marbles into 6 equal groups. Each group would have 5 marbles. Each group of 5 marbles can be described as being $\frac{1}{6}$ of 30. That means that Melissa and each friend would get 5 marbles, or $\frac{1}{6}$ of the marbles.

A fraction describes part of a whole.

1 ← This is the numerator.
6 ← This is the denominator.

The denominator tells how many equal parts to divide something into. The numerator tells how many of those parts to take.

Example 1: Compare $\frac{1}{6}$ of 30 to $\frac{1}{6}$ of 36. Use counters.

Step 1 The denominator tells you to divide 36 into 6 equal groups. Each group should have 6 counters. 36 ÷ 6 = 6

Step 2 The numerator tells you that you are interested in 1 of these groups.

Step 3 One of these groups equals 6 (1 × 6 = 6). Therefore, $\frac{1}{6}$ of 36 = 6.

Example 2: Show that $\frac{5}{6}$ of 36 is 30.

Step 1 You know that 36 can be divided into 6 equal groups of 6. 36 ÷ 6 = 6

Step 2 The numerator tells you that you are interested in 5 of these groups.

Step 3 Five of these groups equals 30 (5 × 6 = 30). Therefore, $\frac{5}{6}$ of 36 = 30.

Use counters to help you solve these problems.

1. $\frac{1}{2}$ of 50 25
2. $\frac{7}{10}$ of 100 70
3. $\frac{2}{3}$ of 36 24
4. $\frac{3}{5}$ of 250 150
5. $\frac{3}{8}$ of 32 12
6. $\frac{5}{9}$ of 63 35
7. $\frac{1}{2}$ of 1000 500
8. $\frac{4}{7}$ of 49 28

38 • *Math Explorations and Applications* Level 4

Copyright © SRA/McGraw-Hill. Permission is granted to reproduce this page for classroom use.

*available separately

COOPERATIVE LEARNING

Fractions of 60 Game

GAME

Players:	**Two or more**
Materials:	**Two 0–5 cubes**
Object:	**To score a total of 150 or more**
Math Focus:	**Finding fractions of a number and adding**

RULES

1. Roll both cubes. Combine the numbers rolled to make a fraction no greater than 1.
2. Find that fraction of 60 and write the answer.
3. Add the answer to your last score.
4. If you roll one 0, your score for that turn is 0. If you roll two 0s together, roll both cubes again.
5. The first player whose score totals 150 or more is the winner.

If you rolled:	You would take:	Your answer would be:
2 3	$\frac{2}{3}$ of 60	40
0 4	$\frac{0}{4}$ of 60	0
2 2	$\frac{2}{2}$ of 60	60

OTHER WAYS TO PLAY THIS GAME

1. Try to score a different total.
2. Change the game to "Fractions of 120."

MATH JOURNAL

In your Math Journal explain your strategy for playing this game.

PRACTICE p. 127

LESSON 127 PRACTICE Name__________

Solve.

1. $\frac{1}{3}$ of 24 = 8
2. $\frac{1}{2}$ of 24 = 12
3. $\frac{3}{4}$ of 24 = 18
4. $\frac{5}{6}$ of 24 = 20
5. $\frac{1}{6}$ of 18 = 3
6. $\frac{2}{3}$ of 18 = 12
7. $\frac{1}{4}$ of 60 = 15
8. $\frac{3}{10}$ of 60 = 18
9. $\frac{1}{3}$ of 60 = 20
10. $\frac{1}{9}$ of 36 = 4
11. $\frac{2}{9}$ of 36 = 8
12. $\frac{3}{8}$ of 16 = 6
13. $\frac{1}{4}$ of 16 = 4
14. $\frac{1}{5}$ of 30 = 6
15. $\frac{2}{3}$ of 30 = 20

PROBLEM SOLVING **Solve these problems.**

16. A coat that sells for $48 is on sale for $\frac{1}{4}$ off.
    a. How much is $\frac{1}{4}$ of 48? 12
    b. What is the sale price of the coat? $36

Remember: 8 ounces = 1 cup.

17. A 4-cup container of milk is $\frac{1}{8}$ full. How many ounces are in the container? 4
18. Sally is typing her English paper. Her paper is 200 words long. She has typed 80 words so far. Has she typed more than $\frac{3}{8}$ of the paper? yes
19. Mrs. King's fourth-grade class has 30 students. Girls make up $\frac{2}{5}$ of the students. How many girls are in Mrs. King's fourth-grade class? 12

Copyright © SRA/McGraw-Hill. Permission is granted to reproduce this page for classroom use.

ENRICHMENT p. 127

LESSON 127 ENRICHMENT Name__________

REAL-WORLD CONNECTION How much is a $40 sweater when it is on sale for $\frac{1}{4}$ off? $30

Look for examples of fractions in ads. Write or glue five examples here. Write the regular price, the fraction that will be taken off, and the sale price. Show how you figured out each sale price.

Answers will vary depending on the items students choose but should reflect the correct fraction off the regular price.

1. Regular price ________ ________ off Sale price ________
2. Regular price ________ ________ off Sale price ________
3. Regular price ________ ________ off Sale price ________
4. Regular price ________ ________ off Sale price ________
5. Regular price ________ ________ off Sale price ________

Copyright © SRA/McGraw-Hill. Permission is granted to reproduce this page for classroom use.

❷ Teach

Using the Student Pages Demonstrate the "Fractions of 60" game so students can play it as they finish their work on page 434. This game focuses on finding fractions of whole numbers.

Briefly review the material at the top of page 434. Have students complete problems 1–19 on their own. Discuss them afterward, asking students to explain their solutions.

GAME The "Fractions of 60" game provides practice in finding fractions of a number and addition. Have students play in pairs or small groups. Encourage them to try variations 1 and 2 after playing the regular version several times.

❸ Wrap-Up

5 MINUTES

In Closing Have students explain the meaning of the denominator of a fraction and tell how to use this information to find $\frac{2}{3}$ of 15. (10)

ALTERNATIVE ASSESSMENT **Informal Assessment** Observe students as they work on page 434. Be sure they understand that the denominator of a fraction indicates the number of equal parts to divide the set or object into. Encourage students to verbalize the process they use to solve problems 1–19.

Assessment Criteria

Did the student . . .

✓ communicate the meaning of the numerator and denominator of a fraction?

✓ explain how to find a fractional part of a whole number?

✓ correctly answer at least 75% of the computation problems on page 434?

✓ actively participate in playing the "Fractions of 60" game?

Homework Have students play the "Fractions of 60" game with family members to reinforce the skill of finding a fraction of a whole number. A copy of this game can also be found on page 27 of the Home Connections Blackline Masters.

LESSON 128

Student Edition pages 436–437

Probability

LESSON PLANNER

Objectives

- ▶ to review the concept of probability
- ▶ to provide an explanation of how to calculate simple probabilities

Context of the Lesson This is the third of 12 lessons on understanding and using fractions and mixed numbers.

MANIPULATIVES

coins*

counters* in assorted colors, shapes, or sizes

overhead projector

spinners* (optional)

Program Resources

Number Cubes

Practice Master 128

Enrichment Master 128

For extra practice:
CD-ROM* Lesson 128

1 Warm-Up

5 MINUTES

Problem of the Day Present the following problem: Six boys are playing a guessing game. One boy must find a bead hidden in one of the other boys' closed fists. Five boys each hold out two closed fists so the boy can guess. Which is easier–to pick the right boy or the right fist? Explain. (It is easier to pick the right boy because the boy who is choosing has 1 chance in 5 to be right; to pick the right fist, the odds are 1 in 10.)

Problem-Solving Strategies Ask students who have solved the Problem of the Day to share how they solved it and any strategies they used.

MENTAL MATH

Provide practice naming fractions of a set. Use an **overhead projector.** Display five different sets of **counters*,** each of which is distinguished by a fractional part in a different color, size, or shape. (Be sure that the counters are transparent enough to show the colors.) Have students name the fractional part as you describe it. For example, ask "What fraction of the set is red [blue, square, triangles, etc.]?"

EXPLORE

LESSON 128

Probability

A **probability** is a number that tells what fraction of the time something is expected to happen.

- ◆ If you flip a coin, what is the probability that it will land heads up? $\frac{1}{2}$
- ◆ What is the probability that a coin will land tails up? $\frac{1}{2}$
- ◆ What is the probability that a coin will land on its edge? **0**

Even though the coin might land on its edge, this event is so unlikely that we don't usually consider it. So we expect that about half the time the coin will land heads up and the other half of the time the coin will land tails up. Nothing else is likely to happen.

If something cannot possibly happen, the probability is 0. If something is certain to happen, the probability is 1.

Answer these questions.

1. If you guess an answer on a true-false test, what do you think is the probability that you'll get the right answer? $\frac{1}{2}$
2. If you roll a 0–5 cube, what is the probability that you will roll a 7? **0**
3. If you roll a 0–5 cube, what is the probability that you will roll a number less than 7? **1**
4. If you roll a 0–5 cube, what is the probability that you will roll an even number? $\frac{3}{6}$ **or** $\frac{1}{2}$
5. If you roll a 0–5 cube, what is the probability that you will roll an odd number? $\frac{3}{6}$ **or** $\frac{1}{2}$
6. Suppose you put four red chips and six white chips in a hat. You draw one of them out without looking. What is the probability that the chip you draw will be red? $\frac{4}{10}$ **or** $\frac{2}{5}$

Language Arts Connection Have students brainstorm various words that are related to probability, such as *likely, certain, uncertain, unlikely, possibly, probable, probably, likelihood,* and so on. Challenge students to make a list of statements that use the words they list. For example, they might say that it is *certain* that the sun will set later, or it is *unlikely* that lobster will be served for lunch in the school cafeteria.

RETEACHING

Have students conduct hands-on experiments with **coins,** Number Cubes, **spinners*,** and other materials so they can better understand the meaning of probability. Students can predict the probability of a certain outcome and then test their predictions, using the discussion on page 436 as a reference.

*available separately

For each of the following spinners, give the probability that the pointer will stop on red.

7 $\frac{3}{4}$

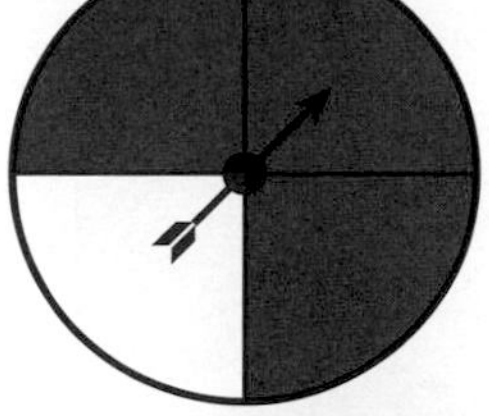

8 $\frac{2}{3}$

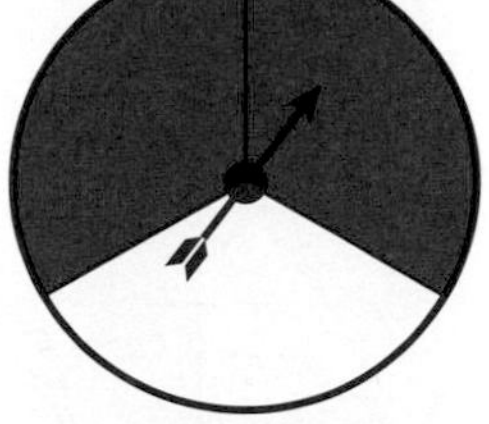

9 $\frac{1}{2}$

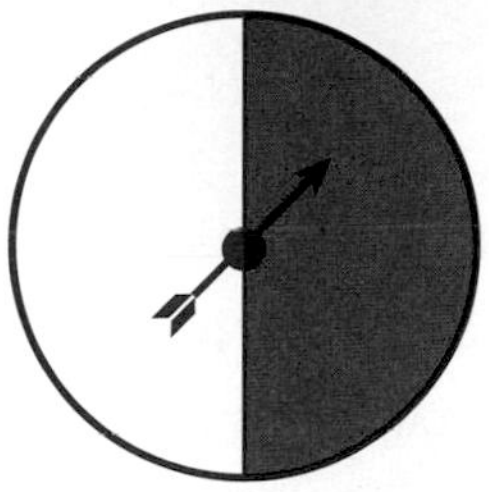

10 $\frac{4}{5}$

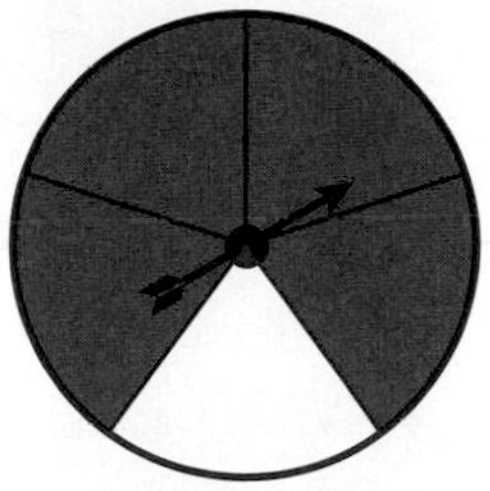

11 0

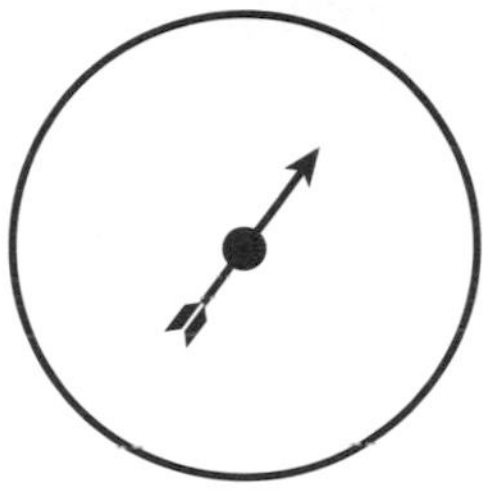

12 1

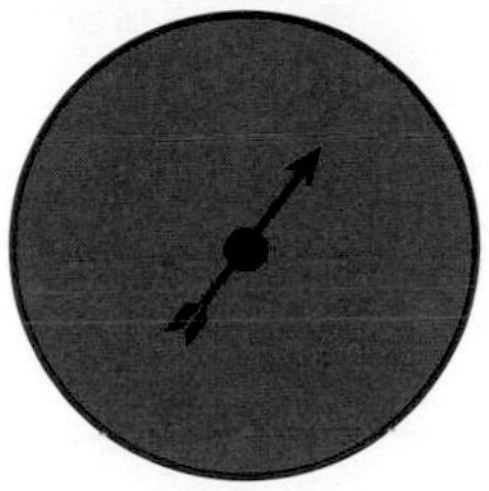

13 $\frac{1}{6}$

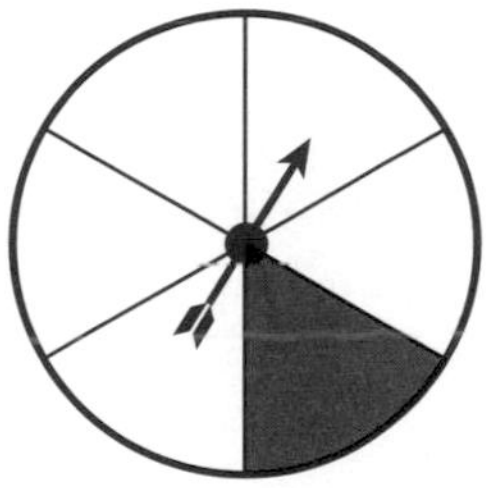

14 $\frac{1}{3}$

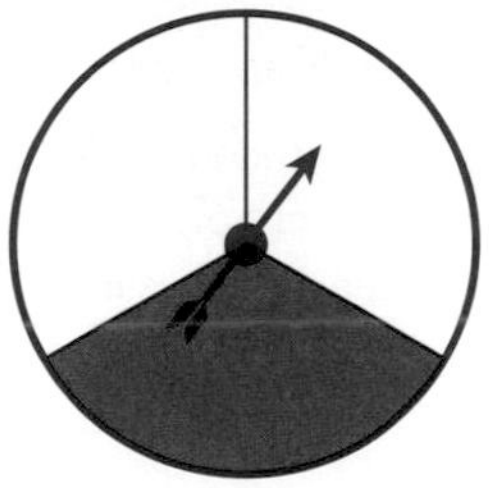

❷ Teach

Using the Student Pages Discuss the materials presented on page 436. Allow students to toss **coins***, roll Number Cubes, or otherwise model the situations described on the page to support the points you make in your discussion. You might also explain that people make assumptions that may not be entirely true, but are *probably* true. Mathematicians describe the probability of flipping heads as one half, even if the coin actually comes up heads more or less than half the time. Have students complete the pages individually. Discuss the answers together.

❸ Wrap-Up

5 MINUTES

In Closing Have students explain the meaning of a probability of $\frac{3}{5}$.

ALTERNATIVE ASSESSMENT

Portfolio Assessment Have students write a brief paragraph in which they explain the concept of probability. Ask them to discuss the difference between a probable and a definite outcome. Have students include their paragraphs in their Math Portfolios.

Assessment Criteria

Did the student . . .

- ✓ contribute to the discussion of probability?
- ✓ explain how to determine the probability of an event occurring?
- ✓ correctly answer at least 75% of the problems in the lesson?

Homework Have students conduct a probability experiment that involves a coin. For instance, they might predict how many times a coin will land on heads if it is flipped 50 times. Students conduct the experiment, keep track of the results, and compare results with their predictions.

PRACTICE p. 128

LESSON 128 PRACTICE Name__________

Answer these questions.

A probability is a number that tells what fraction of the time something is expected to happen.

1. If you roll a cube numbered 0–5, what do you think is the probability that the number showing will be a 4? $\frac{1}{6}$
2. If you roll a cube numbered 0–5, what do you think is the probability that the number showing will be a 0? $\frac{1}{6}$
3. If you roll a cube numbered 0–5, what do you think is the probability that the number showing will be even? $\frac{3}{6}$ or $\frac{1}{2}$
4. If you roll a cube numbered 0–5, what do you think is the probability that the number showing will be less than 3? $\frac{3}{6}$ or $\frac{1}{2}$
5. If you roll a cube numbered 0–5, what do you think is the probability that the number showing will be greater than 2? $\frac{3}{6}$ or $\frac{1}{2}$
6. If you roll a cube numbered 0–5, what do you think is the probability that the number showing will be less than 6? 1

Suppose you have a jar of 100 jelly beans. Of those, 30 are red, 45 are green, 15 are white, and 10 are yellow.

7. If you take a jelly bean from the jar without looking, what do you think is the probability that the jelly bean you choose will be green? $\frac{45}{100}$
8. If you take a jelly bean from the jar without looking, what do you think is the probability that the jelly bean you choose will be white? $\frac{15}{100}$
9. If you take a jelly bean from the jar without looking, what do you think is the probability that the jelly bean you choose will be orange? 0
10. If you take a jelly bean from the jar without looking, what do you think is the probability that the jelly bean you choose will be red or yellow? $\frac{40}{100}$

Copyright © SRA/McGraw-Hill. Permission is granted to reproduce this page for classroom use.

128 • *Math Explorations and Applications* Level 4

ENRICHMENT p. 128

LESSON 128 ENRICHMENT Name__________

Try your own experiment with probability, using the spinner shown.

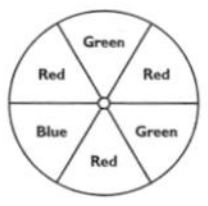

To spin, place the tip of a pencil inside a paper clip, put the tip of the pencil in the center of the spinner, and flick the paper clip with your index finger. The color on which the paper clip stops is your result.

1. Predict how many times the spinner will land on red if you spin 40 times.
   There is a $\frac{3}{6}$, or 50%, chance of landing on red; therefore, the spinner will land on red about 20 times.
2. Now spin the spinner 40 times. Use tally marks to record each result.
   Red Green Blue
   Results will vary.

3. How did your prediction compare to your results?
   Answers will vary.
4. What do you think the results would be if you were to spin the spinner 40 more times? Write your prediction.
   Predictions will vary, but students should see that results would be similar to spinning the first 40 times.
5. Spin the spinner 40 more times. Record the results.
   Red Green Blue
   Results will vary.
6. What conclusions can you make?
   Conclusions will vary. Students should see that the greater the area of a certain color on a spinner, the greater their chance is of stopping on it.

Copyright © SRA/McGraw-Hill. Permission is granted to reproduce this page for classroom use.

128 • *Math Explorations and Applications* Level 4

*available separately

LESSON 129

Student Edition pages 438–439

Fractions and Probability

LESSON PLANNER

Objectives

- ▶ to introduce the idea of associating numbers with probability and to encourage thinking about probability concepts
- ▶ to provide practice with using fractions in common applications

Context of the Lesson This is the fourth of 12 lessons on understanding and using fractions and mixed numbers. Students have worked informally with probability since Level 1. In this lesson probability concepts are formally introduced. Probability concepts will be developed further in Levels 5 and 6.

MANIPULATIVES	Program Resources
none	Number Cubes (0–5)
	Practice Master 129
	Enrichment Master 129
	For extra practice: CD-ROM* Lesson 129

1 Warm-Up

5 MINUTES

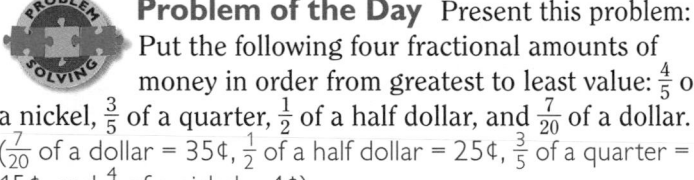

Problem of the Day Present this problem: Put the following four fractional amounts of money in order from greatest to least value: $\frac{4}{5}$ of a nickel, $\frac{3}{5}$ of a quarter, $\frac{1}{2}$ of a half dollar, and $\frac{7}{20}$ of a dollar. ($\frac{7}{20}$ of a dollar = 35¢, $\frac{1}{2}$ of a half dollar = 25¢, $\frac{3}{5}$ of a quarter = 15¢, and $\frac{4}{5}$ of a nickel = 4¢)

Problem-Solving Strategies Ask students who have solved the Problem of the Day to share how they solved it and any strategies they used.

MENTAL MATH Present fraction problems related to money:

a. How many cents are in a dollar? (100)

b. How many cents are in a quarter? (25)

c. What is $\frac{1}{4}$ of 100? (25)

d. How many cents are in a dime? (10)

e. What is $\frac{1}{10}$ of 100? (10)

f. How many cents are in a nickel? (5)

g. What is $\frac{1}{20}$ of 100? (5)

h. How many cents are in $5.00? (500)

PRACTICE

LESSON 129

Fractions and Probability

Jimmy and Naomi are rolling a 0–5 cube. Jimmy wins if a 0 is rolled. Naomi wins if a 1, 2, 3, 4, or 5 is rolled.

- ◆ Who do you think will win more often? **Naomi**
- ◆ What fraction of the time do you think Jimmy will win? $\frac{1}{6}$
- ◆ If they roll the cube 6 times, how many times would you expect Jimmy to win? What is $\frac{1}{6}$ of 6? **once; 1**
- ◆ Would you be surprised if Jimmy did not win exactly 1 time out of 6 tries? **no**

Jimmy's probability of winning is $\frac{1}{6}$.

- ◆ What is Naomi's probability of winning? $\frac{5}{6}$

Here's an experiment Jimmy did with his class.

Each student rolled a 0–5 cube six times. Each person kept track of how many times he or she rolled 0 in the six tries. Then Jimmy made a chart to show how many people didn't roll a 0 at all, how many rolled one 0, and so on.

Why teach it at this time?

In this lesson students should begin to see that predicting the outcome of only one chance event is generally impossible. However, it is reasonable to predict the approximate outcomes of a large number of repeated events. This lesson also helps students to see probability as a useful application of fractions.

Literature Connection Read aloud sections of *Do You Wanna Bet?* by Jean Cushman. Discuss how probability is used in games and how to create games whose rules are fair for all players.

RETEACHING

No reteaching is recommended at this time. You might want to assign Enrichment Master 129.

*available separately

Number of Times 0 Was Rolled in Six Tries	Number of People
0	10
1	12
2	6
3	2
4	0
5	0
6	0

- How many people took part in Jimmy's experiment? **30**
- How many people in the class rolled a 0

  a. 1 out of 6 times? **12** **b.** 2 out of 6 times? **6** **c.** 3 out of 6 times? **2**

  d. 4 out of 6 times? **0** **e.** 5 out of 6 times? **0** **f.** 0 out of 6 times? **10**

Try an experiment like Jimmy's in your class, but use a 5–10 cube instead. Each person should roll the cube six times and write down how many times he or she rolls an 8. Then put the results in a chart like Jimmy's.

Answer these questions.

1. Does your chart look exactly like Jimmy's? **It will not.**
2. In what ways is your chart similar to Jimmy's? **The distribution will be similar.**
3. How many people in Jimmy's class rolled a 0 either 4, 5, or 6 times? **none**
4. How many people in your class rolled an 8 either 4, 5, or 6 times? **The answer will be a low number.**
5. More than $\frac{2}{3}$ of the people in Jimmy's class rolled a 0 either 0 times or 1 time. Did most of the people in your class roll an 8 either 0 times or 1 time? **The answer will probably be yes.**

PRACTICE p. 129

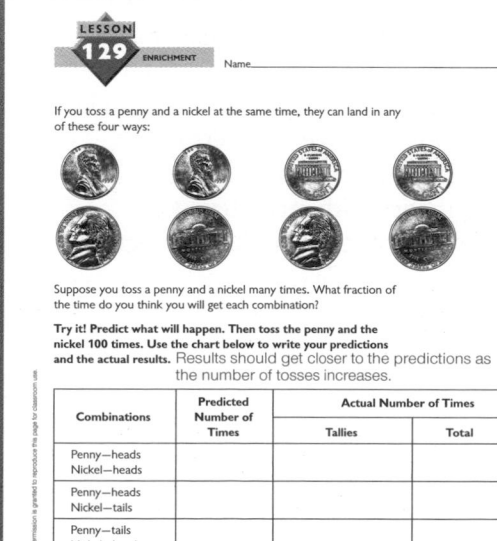

LESSON 129 PRACTICE Name__________

Max and Tess are spinning a spinner that has the colors red, white, yellow, blue, green, and black. Max wins if the color red or green is spun. Tess wins if white, yellow, blue, or green is spun.

1. Who do you think will win more often? Tess
2. What fraction of the time do you think Tess will win? $\frac{4}{6}$
3. If they spin the spinner 6 times, how many times would you expect Tess to win? 4
4. What is $\frac{4}{6}$ of 6? 4
5. Tess's probability of winning is $\frac{4}{6}$. What is Max's probability of winning? $\frac{2}{6}$

Here is an experiment Tess did with her class. Each student spun the 6 colored spinners 6 times. Each student kept track of how many times he or she spun the color blue in the 6 spins. Tess made a chart to show how many of the students did not spin blue at all, how many spun blue one time, and so on.

Number of Times Blue Was Spun in 6 Tries	Number of Students
0	8
1	11
2	3
3	2
4	1
5	0
6	0

6. How many students took part in Tess's experiment? 25
7. How many students in the class spun blue
   - **a.** 1 out of 6 times? 11
   - **b.** 2 out of 6 times? 3
   - **c.** 3 out of 6 times? 2
   - **d.** 4 out of 6 times? 1
   - **e.** 5 out of 6 times? 0
   - **f.** 6 out of 6 times? 0
   - **g.** 0 out of 6 times? 8

Copyright © SRA/McGraw-Hill. Permission is granted to reproduce this page for classroom use.

ENRICHMENT p. 129

LESSON 129 ENRICHMENT Name__________

If you toss a penny and a nickel at the same time, they can land in any of these four ways:

Suppose you toss a penny and a nickel many times. What fraction of the time do you think you will get each combination?

Try it! Predict what will happen. Then toss the penny and the nickel 100 times. Use the chart below to write your predictions and the actual results. Results should get closer to the predictions as the number of tosses increases.

Combinations	Predicted Number of Times	Actual Number of Times	
		Tallies	Total
Penny—heads Nickel—heads			
Penny—heads Nickel—tails			
Penny—tails Nickel—heads			
Penny—tails Nickel—tails			

Copyright © SRA/McGraw-Hill. Permission is granted to reproduce this page for classroom use.

2 Teach

Using the Student Pages Discuss the questions on page 438 with the class. In discussing the fourth question, point out that although Jimmy can expect to win about once in six tries, he should not be surprised if, on a particular round of six throws, he rolls no 0s at all.

MANIPULATIVES Go over the story at the bottom of page 438 with the class. Demonstrate Jimmy's experiment to ensure that students understand that each student in Jimmy's class rolled a cube six times. Discuss Jimmy's chart on page 439. Next, have each student roll a 5–10 cube exactly six times and record the number of 8s he or she rolls. Then make a class chart of their results on the chalkboard. Identify similarities and differences between Jimmy's chart and the class chart. Finally, have students solve problems 1–5 on their own and discuss the answers with the class.

3 Wrap-Up

5 MINUTES

In Closing Have students explain what it means for an event to have a probability of 1 or of 0.

ALTERNATIVE ASSESSMENT **Portfolio Assessment** Have students name one or more events with a probability of 0, with a probability of 1, and with a probability of $\frac{1}{2}$. Students should record the events in their Math Portfolios as evidence of ongoing learning.

Assessment Criteria

Did the student . . .

- ✓ contribute to the discussion of probability?
- ✓ communicate an understanding of the probability experiment?
- ✓ participate in the class experiment and contribute to the class chart of results?

Homework Have students create and perform a simple probability experiment at home with family members and record the results in a chart. They might flip a coin or spin a spinner from a game.

LESSON 130

Student Edition pages 440–441

Applying Fractions

LESSON PLANNER

Objectives

✓ to assess students' understanding of fractions

▶ to provide an opportunity to apply probability concepts to a real situation

▶ to provide practice with mental addition

▶ to provide an informal introduction to equivalent fractions

Context of the Lesson This lesson, the fifth of 12 lessons on using fractions and mixed numbers, contains a Mastery Checkpoint on understanding fractions.

MANIPULATIVES
none

Program Resources
"Fracto 1" and "Fracto 2" Game Mats (optional)
Number Cubes
Practice Master 130
Enrichment Master 130
Assessment Master
For extra practice:
CD-ROM* Lesson 130

1 Warm-Up

5 MINUTES

Problem of the Day Present this problem: If you take a △ off each side of the balance, which is heavier, □ or △? How can you tell?

(□ is heavier.)

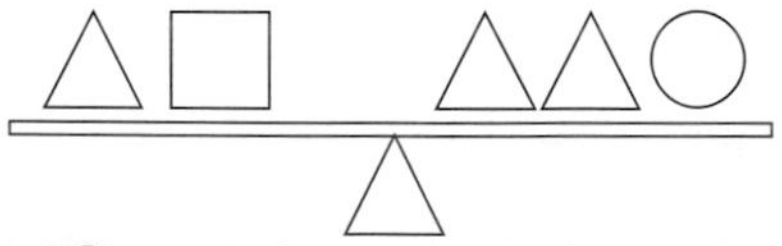

Problem-Solving Strategies Ask students who have solved the Problem of the Day to share how they solved it and any strategies they used.

MENTAL MATH Provide students practice in comparing fractions of the same whole number. Students show thumbs up if the fractions are equivalent or thumbs down if not. Write these problems on the chalkboard:

a. $\frac{1}{4}$ of 60, $\frac{1}{2}$ of 60 (thumbs down)

b. $\frac{5}{10}$ of 60, $\frac{6}{12}$ of 60 (thumbs up)

c. $\frac{4}{6}$ of 60, $\frac{2}{3}$ of 60 (thumbs up)

MIXED PRACTICE

LESSON 130

Applying Fractions

Use your understanding of finding fractions of numbers to solve these problems.

1. The city council can vote only if at least $\frac{5}{6}$ of its members are present. The city council has 18 members. How many members must be present for a vote to take place? **at least 15**
2. About $\frac{1}{7}$ of the total population is left-handed. There are 21 students in Ellen's class.
   a. About how many students in her class might be left-handed? **3 is a reasonable estimate.**
   b. Would you be surprised if your answer was not exactly right? **no**
3. Winston has nine cousins, and $\frac{2}{3}$ of them are boys. How many of his cousins are girls? **3**
4. Tasha can save $\frac{1}{4}$ of the cost of a chemistry set if she waits until it goes on sale. How much will a $28 chemistry set cost on sale? **$21.00**
5. Chip's doctor said that $\frac{3}{5}$ of all schoolchildren get two colds every winter.
   a. How many students in a class of 30 might Chip expect to have two colds this winter? **18**
   b. Could Chip be sure of exactly how many classmates would have two colds? **no**

Solve. Watch your numbering.

6. What is $\frac{2}{3}$ of 30? **20**
7. What is $\frac{3}{3}$ of 30? **30**
8. What is $\frac{0}{3}$ of 30? **0**
9. What is $\frac{1}{6}$ of 30? **5**
10. What is $\frac{3}{6}$ of 30? **15**
11. What is $\frac{4}{6}$ of 30? **20**
12. What is $\frac{5}{6}$ of 30? **25**
13. What is $\frac{6}{6}$ of 30? **30**

◆ Compare your answers to problems 6 and 11. Why are they the same? **$\frac{2}{3}$ and $\frac{4}{6}$ are equivalent fractions**

RETEACHING

GAME Have students play the "Fractions of 60" game (page 435) for practice with finding fractions of whole numbers or the "Fracto 1" and "Fracto 2" Game Mats for practice with recognizing the fractional areas of circles and rectangles.

PRACTICE p. 130

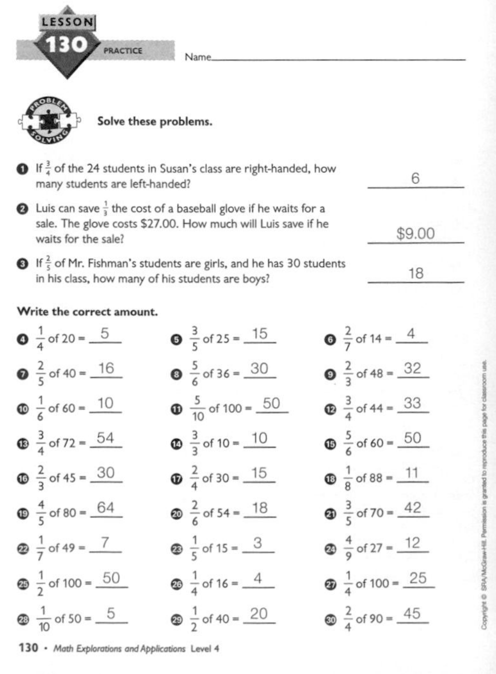

LESSON 130 PRACTICE

Name__________

Solve these problems.

1. If $\frac{3}{4}$ of the 24 students in Susan's class are right-handed, how many students are left-handed? 6
2. Luis can save $\frac{1}{3}$ the cost of a baseball glove if he waits for a sale. The glove costs $27.00. How much will Luis save if he waits for the sale? $9.00
3. If $\frac{2}{5}$ of Mr. Fishman's students are girls, and he has 30 students in his class, how many of his students are boys? 18

Write the correct amount.

4. $\frac{1}{4}$ of 20 = 5	5. $\frac{3}{5}$ of 25 = 15	6. $\frac{2}{7}$ of 14 = 4
7. $\frac{2}{5}$ of 40 = 16	8. $\frac{5}{6}$ of 36 = 30	9. $\frac{2}{3}$ of 48 = 32
10. $\frac{1}{6}$ of 60 = 10	11. $\frac{5}{10}$ of 100 = 50	12. $\frac{3}{4}$ of 44 = 33
13. $\frac{3}{4}$ of 72 = 54	14. $\frac{3}{3}$ of 10 = 10	15. $\frac{5}{6}$ of 60 = 50
16. $\frac{2}{3}$ of 45 = 30	17. $\frac{2}{4}$ of 30 = 15	18. $\frac{1}{8}$ of 88 = 11
19. $\frac{4}{5}$ of 80 = 64	20. $\frac{2}{6}$ of 54 = 18	21. $\frac{3}{5}$ of 70 = 42
22. $\frac{1}{7}$ of 49 = 7	23. $\frac{1}{5}$ of 15 = 3	24. $\frac{4}{9}$ of 27 = 12
25. $\frac{1}{2}$ of 100 = 50	26. $\frac{1}{4}$ of 16 = 4	27. $\frac{1}{4}$ of 100 = 25
28. $\frac{1}{10}$ of 50 = 5	29. $\frac{1}{2}$ of 40 = 20	30. $\frac{2}{4}$ of 90 = 45

130 • *Math Explorations and Applications* Level 4

Copyright © SRA/McGraw-Hill. Permission is granted to reproduce this page for classroom use.

*available separately

Anything but 10 Game

COOPERATIVE LEARNING

GAME

Players:	Two or more
Materials:	One 0–5 cube, one 5–10 cube
Object:	To score a total of 100 or more
Math Focus:	Addition and mathematical reasoning

RULES

1. Roll both cubes. Find the sum of the two numbers rolled.
2. If the sum is not 10, you get the number of points rolled. Keep your turn and roll again, or stop and add those points to your score.
3. On each turn you may have as many rolls as you like until you either roll a sum of 10 or choose to stop.
4. When you roll a sum of 10, you lose your turn and you lose any other points you may have had on that turn.
5. The first player to score 100 or over is the winner.

SAMPLE GAME

Round	Janice Rolls:	Sum	Score	Austin Rolls:	Sum	Score
1	7 5	12		9 4	13	
	5 4	9		6 2	8	21
	10 5	15	36	Stops		
	Stops					
2	8 3	11		10 4	14	
	7 0	7		8 3	11	
	6 4	10	36	7 1	8	54
	Loses turn			Stops		

After two rounds, Austin is ahead.

② Teach

Using the Student Pages Before students begin work on page 440, demonstrate the "Anything but 10" game on page 441 so that students can play it when they complete page 440. This game focuses on addition facts. Have students work on page 440 independently. Then discuss the problems and the two discussion questions with the class.

GAME The "Anything but 10" game reinforces addition and mathematical reasoning. Encourage students to come up with their own strategies and intuitive concepts of probability. Once students understand the rules, have them play in pairs or small groups.

③ Wrap-Up

5 MINUTES

In Closing Have students explain and demonstrate why $\frac{2}{3}$ of 18 is the same as $\frac{4}{6}$ of 18.

Mastery Checkpoint 18

At this time most students should understand fraction notation and be able to use fractions intelligently. Students should correctly answer at least 80% of the problems on page 440. You may wish to record the results of this assessment on the Mastery Checkpoint Chart. You may also wish to assign Assessment Blackline Masters page 51 to determine mastery.

Assessment Criteria

Did the student . . .

- ✓ communicate the strategies used to find fractions of numbers to solve problems?
- ✓ actively participate in the "Anything but 10" game?
- ✓ correctly answer at least 80% of the problems on page 440?

Homework Have students play the "Anything but 10" game with family members to practice addition. A copy of this game can also be found on page 27 of the Home Connections Blackline Masters.

ENRICHMENT p. 130

LESSON 130 ENRICHMENT Name________________

Find out more about your classmates by conducting a survey. Think of a question you would like to ask each of them. Would you like to know how old they are? How many siblings do they have? What are their favorite winter sports? What kind of pets do they have?

For example, if you surveyed 30 classmates about their pets, their responses might look like this:

Dog	Cat	Bird	Ferret	None
卌 卌	卌 卌 ||||	|||	|	||

Now take a look at your results. Use fractions to write a summary of what you found out.

Your summary would look like this:

$\frac{10}{30}$ have dogs
$\frac{14}{30}$ have cats
$\frac{3}{30}$ have birds
$\frac{1}{30}$ has a ferret
$\frac{2}{30}$ have no pets

Choose a question to ask. Ask your classmates and record their answers. You may want to write possible responses on a sheet of paper and put tally marks beneath each heading, adding headings as needed. Organize your information in a chart using fractions.

Answers will vary depending on the questions students ask, the number of students surveyed, and the numbers and types of responses received.

Copyright © SRA/McGraw-Hill. Permission is granted to reproduce this page for classroom use.

130 • *Math Explorations and Applications* Level 4

ASSESSMENT p. 51

UNIT 6 **Mastery Checkpoint 18** Understanding fractions (Lesson 130)

Name________________

The student demonstrates mastery by correctly answering at least 4 of the 5 problems.

Solve these problems.

1. There are 30 students in Joli's math class. Of these students, $\frac{3}{5}$ are boys.
   a. How many of the students are boys? 18
   b. How many of the students are girls? 12
2. Bob has a recipe for soup that serves eight people. For dinner tonight he needs to make only $\frac{1}{2}$ the recipe.
   a. About how many people will probably be there for dinner tonight? 4 is a reasonable guess
   b. Would you be surprised if there were fewer than four? not really
3. Ana has medical insurance that pays for $\frac{2}{3}$ of her medical bills. Last year her medical expenses were $300. How much did she have to pay? $100
4. Ellen's teacher was happy because $\frac{5}{6}$ of the class got a score higher than 90 on the math test. There are 30 students in Ellen's class. How many students got a score over 90? 25
5. Monty spends $\frac{1}{4}$ of each weekday in school. There are 24 hours in a day. How many hours a weekday does Monty spend in school? 6

Copyright © SRA/McGraw-Hill. Permission is granted to reproduce this page for classroom use.

Math Explorations and Applications Level 4 • 51

LESSON 131

Student Edition pages 442–443

Equivalent Fractions: Probability

LESSON PLANNER

Objectives

- to provide practice in solving simple probability problems
- to provide practice in finding fractions of whole numbers
- to demonstrate that there are many ways to shade a fractional part of a geometric figure

Context of the Lesson This is the sixth of 12 lessons on understanding fractions and mixed numbers.

MANIPULATIVES

graph paper
play coins*
rulers*

Program Resources

"Fracto 1" and "Fracto 2" Game Mats
Number Cubes
Practice Master 131
Enrichment Master 131
For additional math integration: Math Throughout the Day*
For extra practice: CD-ROM* Lesson 131
Cumulative Review, page 563

1 Warm-Up 5 MINUTES

Problem of the Day Write this problem on the chalkboard: Before lunch David set out a row of six glasses. The first three were full of juice, and the next three were empty. How could David move just one glass so that every full glass would be next to an empty one? (He could pour juice from the second glass into the fifth glass and return the second glass to its original spot.)

Problem-Solving Strategies Ask students who have solved the Problem of the Day to share how they solved it and any strategies they used.

MENTAL MATH Write these problems on the chalkboard. Students show thumbs up if the two fractions are equivalent and thumbs down if they are not.

a. $\frac{1}{8}$ of 60, $\frac{2}{16}$ of 60 (up) **b.** $\frac{2}{10}$ of 60, $\frac{1}{5}$ of 60 (up)

c. $\frac{1}{8}$ of 60, $\frac{1}{4}$ of 60 (down) **d.** $\frac{6}{8}$ of 60, $\frac{3}{4}$ of 60 (up)

LESSON 131

Equivalent Fractions: Probability

Solve these problems.

Andre and Emma are rolling a 0–5 cube. When it shows 0 or 1, Andre wins. When it shows 2, 3, 4, or 5, Emma wins.

1. What is the probability that Andre will win? $\frac{2}{6}$ **or** $\frac{1}{3}$
2. What is the probability that Emma will win? $\frac{4}{6}$ **or** $\frac{2}{3}$
3. Suppose Andre and Emma play their game 120 times.
   - **a.** About how many times would you expect Andre to win? **40**
   - **b.** About how many times would you expect Emma to win? **80**
   - **c.** Would you be surprised if Andre did not win exactly 40 times? **no**

They change their game so that Emma wins if the cube shows 5, 4, or 3. Andre wins if it shows 2, 1, or 0.

4. What is the probability that Emma will win? $\frac{3}{6}$ **or** $\frac{1}{2}$
5. What is the probability that Andre will win? $\frac{3}{6}$ **or** $\frac{1}{2}$
6. Suppose they play the new game 120 times.
   - **a.** About how many times would you expect Emma to win? **60**
   - **b.** About how many times would you expect Andre to win? **60**
   - **c.** Would you be surprised if Emma did not win exactly 60 times? **no**

Skyler and Mackenzie flip a coin. Skyler will win if it lands heads up. Mackenzie will win if it lands tails up.

7. What is the probability that Skyler will win? $\frac{1}{2}$
8. If they play 120 times, about how many games would you expect Skyler to win? **60**
9. Compare your answers for problems 6 and 8. (Compare $\frac{3}{6}$ of 120 and $\frac{1}{2}$ of 120.) **They are equivalent.**
10. Which probability is greater, $\frac{3}{6}$ or $\frac{1}{2}$? **They are the same.**

Literature Connection Read some catchy tidbits from *Hours, Days, and Years (Ripley's Believe It or Not!)*. This book provides quirky facts about clocks and time. Have students compare fractional parts of an hour, day, or year and express them in other ways, such as 12 hours equal one half day.

RETEACHING

MANIPULATIVES Students who have trouble with probability concepts may benefit from acting out the ten problems on page 442. They can use 0–5 Number Cubes and a **coin.*** Be sure to help them understand any discrepancy between the theoretical probability and the actual outcomes.

*available separately

11 What is the probability of landing on red if you
a. spin spinner A? $\frac{1}{2}$ b. spin spinner B? $\frac{3}{6}$ or $\frac{1}{2}$

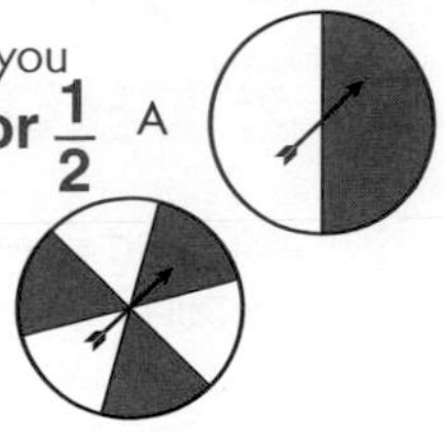

12 Which spinner gives you a better chance of landing on red?
They give you the same chance.

What fraction of the circle is shaded?

13 $\frac{1}{2}$ 14 $\frac{1}{4}$ 15 $\frac{1}{2}$ 16 $\frac{2}{4}$ or $\frac{1}{2}$

17 Which is greater, $\frac{1}{4}$ of the circle or $\frac{1}{2}$ of the circle? $\frac{1}{2}$

18 Which is greater, $\frac{3}{4}$ of the circle or $\frac{1}{2}$ of the circle? $\frac{3}{4}$

What fraction of the rectangle is shaded?

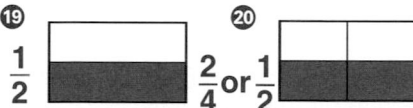

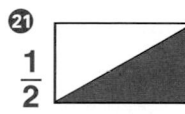

19 $\frac{1}{2}$ 20 $\frac{2}{4}$ or $\frac{1}{2}$ 21 $\frac{1}{2}$

Draw five rectangles that are each 4 centimeters long and 3 centimeters wide.

22 What is the area of each rectangle you drew? **12 sq. cm**

Shade $\frac{1}{2}$ of each rectangle in a different way.

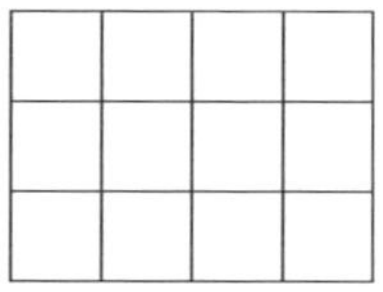

23 What is the area of the shaded part of each rectangle? **6 sq. cm**

Use the Cumulative Review on page 563 after this lesson.

Draw three more rectangles that are each 4 centimeters long and 3 centimeters wide. Shade $\frac{2}{4}$ of each rectangle in a different way.

24 What is the area of the shaded part of each rectangle? **6 sq. cm**

25 Why do you think the answers to questions 23 and 24 are the same? **Because $\frac{1}{2}$ and $\frac{2}{4}$ are equivalent fractions.**

PRACTICE p. 131

LESSON 131 PRACTICE Name______

What fraction of the rectangle is shaded?

1 $\frac{2}{6}$ or $\frac{1}{3}$ 2 $\frac{1}{3}$ 3 $\frac{4}{12}$ or $\frac{1}{3}$

What fraction of the circle is shaded?

4 $\frac{2}{4}$ or $\frac{1}{2}$ 5 $\frac{2}{4}$ or $\frac{1}{2}$ 6 $\frac{2}{8}$ or $\frac{1}{4}$ 7 $\frac{4}{8}$ or $\frac{1}{2}$

Ring the greater fraction.

8 $\frac{1}{4}$ or ($\frac{3}{8}$) 9 ($\frac{5}{8}$) or $\frac{1}{2}$ 10 $\frac{3}{4}$ or ($\frac{7}{8}$)

Solve these problems.

Grant and Iris are spinning a spinner that has the colors red, white, yellow, blue, green, and black. Iris wins if the color blue, red, black, or white is spun. Grant wins if yellow or green is spun.

11 What is the probability that Iris will win? $\frac{4}{6}$ or $\frac{2}{3}$

12 What is the probability that Grant will win? $\frac{2}{6}$ or $\frac{1}{3}$

Copyright © SRA/McGraw-Hill. Permission is granted to reproduce this page for classroom use.

Math Explorations and Applications Level 4 • 131

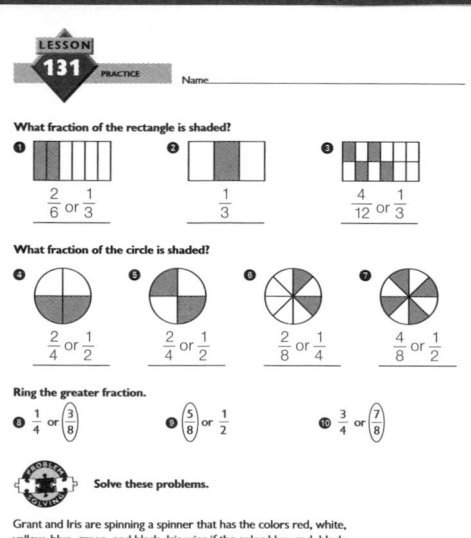

ENRICHMENT p. 131

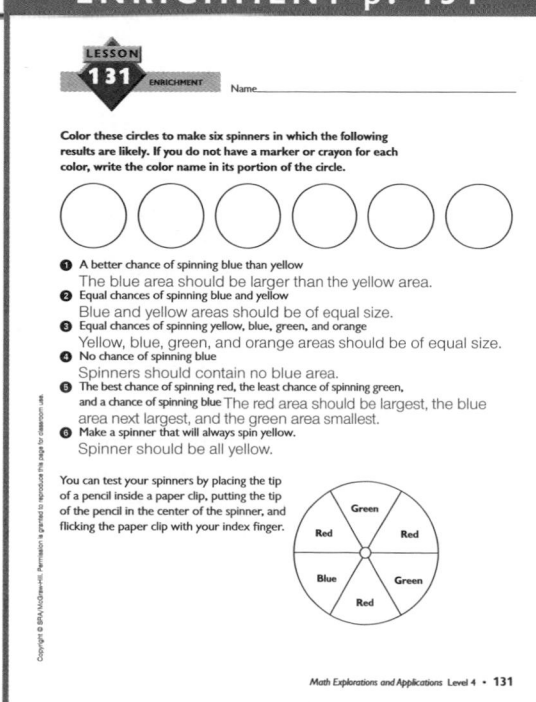

LESSON 131 ENRICHMENT Name______

Color these circles to make six spinners in which the following results are likely. If you do not have a marker or crayon for each color, write the color name in its portion of the circle.

1 A better chance of spinning blue than yellow
The blue area should be larger than the yellow area.
2 Equal chances of spinning blue and yellow
Blue and yellow areas should be of equal size.
3 Equal chances of spinning yellow, blue, green, and orange
Yellow, blue, green, and orange areas should be of equal size.
4 No chance of spinning blue
Spinners should contain no blue area.
5 The best chance of spinning red, the least chance of spinning green, and a chance of spinning blue The red area should be largest, the blue area next largest, and the green area smallest.
6 Make a spinner that will always spin yellow.
Spinner should be all yellow.

You can test your spinners by placing the tip of a pencil inside a paper clip, putting the tip of the pencil in the center of the spinner, and flicking the paper clip with your index finger.

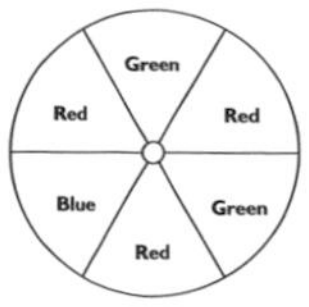

Copyright © SRA/McGraw-Hill. Permission is granted to reproduce this page for classroom use.

Math Explorations and Applications Level 4 • 131

*available separately

2 Teach

Using the Student Pages Briefly review the "Fracto" Game Mats so students can play them as they finish page 443. The games focus on recognizing fractional areas of circles and rectangles.

Then have students solve the problems on pages 442 and 443 on their own. Encourage them to use **graph paper** to solve problems 22–25 on page 443. The shaded portions for the figures drawn need not be contiguous. Discuss both pages after the class has finished. Have **rulers*** available.

Using the "Fracto 1" and "Fracto 2" Game Mats These Game Mats were introduced in Lesson 20. They provide practice in recognizing fractional areas of circles and rectangles. Encourage students to play in pairs. Directions can be found on the Game Mats. A copy of these Game Mats can also be found on pages 592–593 of this Teacher's Guide.

3 Wrap-Up

5 MINUTES

In Closing Have students design two spinners: one that has a probability of $\frac{1}{4}$ for landing on any section, and another that has a probability of $\frac{1}{3}$ for landing on any section.

Informal Assessment Encourage students to explain their reasoning as they work through this lesson. You may want to display the various solutions students find for problems 23–25.

Assessment Criteria

Did the student . . .

- ✓ contribute to the discussion of probability?
- ✓ accurately compare fractions?
- ✓ demonstrate understanding of the concept of equivalent fractions?

Homework Have students draw five 3 x 5 rectangles on graph paper and shade $\frac{1}{5}$ of each rectangle in a different way.

LESSON 132

Student Edition pages 444–447

Equivalent Fractions

LESSON PLANNER

Objectives

✓ to assess students' ability to understand fractions of numbers

▶ to review the concept of and provide practice in finding equivalent fractions

▶ to introduce the use of equivalent fractions to compare fractions with unlike denominators

▶ to provide practice solving word problems

Context of the Lesson This, the seventh of 12 lessons on understanding and using fractions and mixed numbers, contains Mastery Checkpoint 19 for assessing mastery of fractions.

MANIPULATIVES

white paper

graph paper (optional)

egg carton (optional)

counters* (optional)

Program Resources

"Fracto 1" Game Mat

Reteaching Master

Practice Master 132

Enrichment Master 132

Assessment Master

For additional math integration: Math Throughout the Day*

For extra practice: CD-ROM* Lesson 132

1 Warm-Up

5 MINUTES

Problem of the Day Present the following problem to students: Each fall, the softball league holds its annual championship playoff tournament. This year, 32 teams are competing. According to the rules, a team is out after one loss. How many games will be played to find the tournament champion? (31)

Problem-Solving Strategies Ask students who have solved the Problem of the Day to share how they solved it and any strategies they used.

MENTAL MATH Provide fraction-of-number problems with common fractions and simple whole numbers. Encourage students to answer quickly.

a. $\frac{1}{2}$ of 50 is (25) **b.** $\frac{2}{3}$ of 60 is (40)

c. $\frac{1}{10}$ of 70 is (7) **d.** $\frac{1}{5}$ of 25 is (5)

(continued on page 445)

EXPLORE

LESSON 132

Equivalent Fractions

Mark and Chet bought a pizza. It was cut into eight equal pieces. Mark ate two of the pieces. Chet said, "You ate two eighths of the pizza." Mark said, "No, I didn't. I ate only one fourth of the pizza."

◆ Who is right? **They both are right.**

There are many different ways to write a fraction. In this example both Mark and Chet are right. Mark ate 2 of the 8 equal pieces, so he ate $\frac{2}{8}$ of the pizza. But if the pizza had been cut into only 4 equal pieces, he could have eaten just 1 piece and still have eaten the same amount. He would have eaten $\frac{1}{4}$ of the pizza.

Answer these questions.

1. If the pizza had been cut into 12 equal pieces, how many would Mark have had to eat to equal $\frac{1}{4}$ of the pizza? **3**
2. If the pizza had been cut into 40 equal pieces, how many would Mark have had to eat to equal $\frac{1}{4}$ of the pizza? **10**

You might not think that 10 tiny pieces, each $\frac{1}{40}$ of the pizza, are as satisfying as $\frac{2}{8}$ of the pizza. Still, the two fractions are equal. We say that $\frac{1}{4}$, $\frac{2}{8}$, $\frac{3}{12}$, and $\frac{10}{40}$ are all **equivalent fractions.** We show this by writing = between them:

$$\frac{1}{4} = \frac{2}{8} = \frac{3}{12} = \frac{10}{40}$$

Solve.

3. Write a fraction with a denominator of 20 that is equivalent to $\frac{3}{4}$. $\mathbf{\frac{15}{20}}$
4. Write a fraction with a denominator of 60 that is equivalent to $\frac{5}{12}$. $\mathbf{\frac{25}{60}}$

444 • Fractions and Decimals

Art Connection Have students create visual examples of equivalent fractions by folding **paper** or by coloring parts of **graph paper**. For example, they can fold a sheet of paper into eighths and highlight the various creases to show that $\frac{2}{8} = \frac{1}{4}$ or $\frac{4}{8} = \frac{1}{2}$, and so on. Or, they can use a 4 x 4 piece of graph paper to show that $\frac{4}{16} = \frac{1}{4}$, that $\frac{8}{16} = \frac{1}{2}$, and so on. Encourage creative representations of mathematical statements of equivalence.

*available separately

When comparing two fractions it is helpful to have fractions with the same denominator. You can always use the product of the two denominators as the new denominator for both fractions.

Example: $\frac{3}{4}$ ● $\frac{1}{3}$ = $\frac{9}{12}$ ● $\frac{4}{12}$

We know that $\frac{9}{12}$ is greater than $\frac{4}{12}$, so $\frac{9}{12} > \frac{4}{12}$. Often you can find a lesser denominator that will work.

Convert each fraction to one that is equivalent but has a denominator of 12.

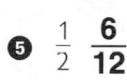

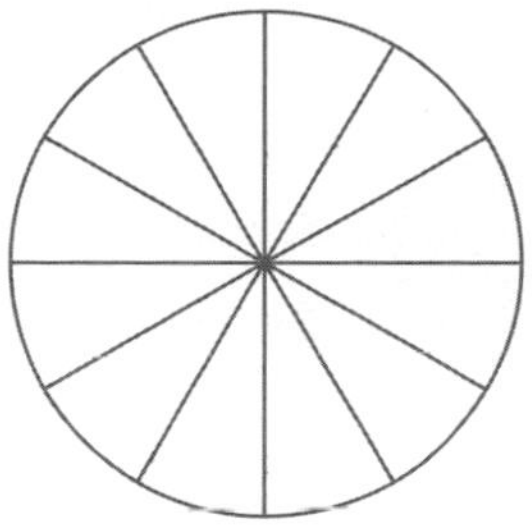

5. $\frac{1}{2}$ **$\frac{6}{12}$**
6. $\frac{3}{4}$ **$\frac{9}{12}$**
7. $\frac{4}{6}$ **$\frac{8}{12}$**
8. $\frac{1}{3}$ **$\frac{4}{12}$**
9. $\frac{5}{6}$ **$\frac{10}{12}$**
10. $\frac{3}{6}$ **$\frac{6}{12}$**
11. $\frac{1}{4}$ **$\frac{3}{12}$**
12. $\frac{3}{6}$ **$\frac{6}{12}$**
13. $\frac{2}{6}$ **$\frac{4}{12}$**
14. $\frac{1}{6}$ **$\frac{2}{12}$**
15. $\frac{2}{4}$ **$\frac{6}{12}$**
16. $\frac{3}{6}$ **$\frac{6}{12}$**
17. $\frac{2}{3}$ **$\frac{8}{12}$**
18. $\frac{2}{8}$ **$\frac{3}{12}$**
19. $\frac{4}{6}$ **$\frac{8}{12}$**

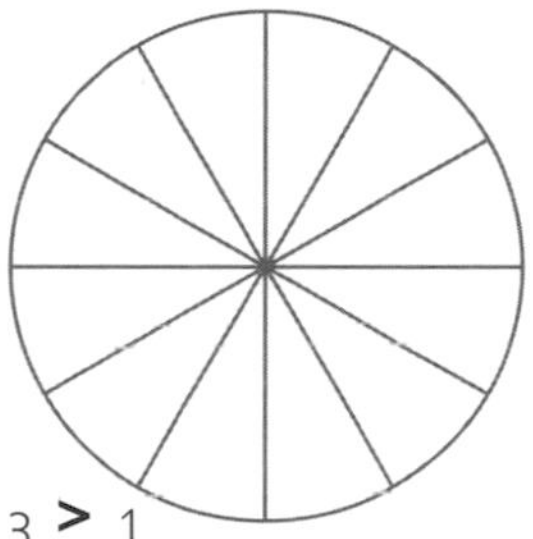

Show which fraction of the circle is larger or whether they are the same. Replace ● with <, >, or =.

20. $\frac{1}{6}$ ● $\frac{1}{4}$ **<**
21. $\frac{5}{6}$ ● $\frac{2}{4}$ **>**
22. $\frac{1}{2}$ ● $\frac{6}{12}$ **=**
23. $\frac{3}{4}$ ● $\frac{1}{2}$ **>**
24. $\frac{2}{4}$ ● $\frac{1}{2}$ **=**
25. $\frac{6}{12}$ ● $\frac{2}{4}$ **=**
26. $\frac{7}{12}$ ● $\frac{1}{4}$ **>**
27. $\frac{5}{12}$ ● $\frac{1}{2}$ **<**
28. $\frac{2}{4}$ ● $\frac{3}{4}$ **<**
29. $\frac{1}{3}$ ● $\frac{5}{6}$ **<**
30. $\frac{4}{8}$ ● $\frac{2}{3}$ **<**
31. $\frac{6}{9}$ ● $\frac{2}{4}$ **>**
32. $\frac{2}{12}$ ● $\frac{1}{3}$ **<**
33. $\frac{6}{7}$ ● $\frac{3}{4}$ **>**
34. $\frac{8}{9}$ ● $\frac{2}{3}$ **>**
35. $\frac{3}{6}$ ● $\frac{1}{2}$ **=**

Technology Connection Refer students to the software *Fraction Attraction* from Sunburst Communications (Mac, IBM, for grades 3–8) for practice with ordering, equivalence, relative size, multiple representations, and location of fractions on a number line.

Mental Math (continued)

e. $\frac{1}{4}$ of 16 is (4)
f. $\frac{2}{5}$ of 40 is (16)
g. $\frac{5}{6}$ of 30 is (25)
h. $\frac{3}{8}$ of 24 is (9)
i. $\frac{1}{6}$ of 36 is (6)
j. $\frac{7}{10}$ of 100 is (70)
k. $\frac{1}{3}$ of 99 is (33)
l. $\frac{1}{8}$ of 32 is (4)
m. $\frac{3}{4}$ of 20 is (15)
n. $\frac{2}{9}$ of 18 is (4)

2 Teach

Using the Student Pages You may wish to review the rules for the "Fracto 1" Game Mat so that students can play as they finish their work on pages 445–447. This game provides practice with finding fractional areas of circles.

Discuss problems 1–4 on page 444 and the material at the top of page 445 with the class. Briefly review the relation signs: <, >, and =. Then have students complete the rest of the problems on these pages on their own or in small groups. The illustrations of the circles divided into 12ths may help students do the comparisons.

LEARNING STYLES

Meeting Individual Needs

Students who are logical or abstract learners may be able to describe a procedure for finding equivalent fractions and explain why the procedure works. Have them write down the steps to this procedure and share them with classmates. For example, students might say to multiply the top and bottom number by the same factor. If you double the numerator, you have to double the denominator also to keep the fraction equal.

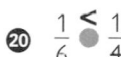

◆ LESSON 132 Equivalent Fractions

Teach

Using the Student Pages Have students complete page 446 independently. When students finish, they should go on to page 447.

The solutions to the problems on page 447 require a variety of computational and reasoning skills. Alert students to read the problems carefully and think about each situation. Discuss the problems together after students have finished, especially problems 56 and 60, which do not provide enough information. Ask students what other data are needed. In problem 56, for example, you need to know how many cards Eve has or how many cards Eve and Spencer have together to determine how many cards Spencer has. In problem 60, you need to know how many boys or girls are in the class to determine how many children there are in all.

Using the "Fracto 1" Game Mat Have students play "Fracto 1" to practice working with equivalent fractions. The focus of this game is recognizing fractional areas of a circle and recognizing which fractional areas combine to make more than half the area of a circle. Complete instructions can be found on the Game Mat.

SPECIAL NEEDS

Meeting Individual Needs

Some students need many hands-on experiences with equivalent fractions before they grasp the concept. You can use an empty **egg carton** and **counters*** to model equivalent fractions. For example, fill 6 of the 12 cups of the egg carton and have students tell the fraction of the carton that is filled. ($\frac{6}{12}$ or $\frac{1}{2}$) Help students visualize how $\frac{6}{12}$ and $\frac{1}{2}$ are equivalent fractions. Repeat with other examples of equivalent fractions in the egg carton.

◆ LESSON 132 Equivalent Fractions

Replace ● with <, >, or =.

36. $\frac{1}{4}$ ● $\frac{4}{12}$ **<**
37. $\frac{7}{8}$ ● $\frac{3}{4}$ **>**
38. $\frac{2}{3}$ ● $\frac{1}{2}$ **>**
39. $\frac{1}{6}$ ● $\frac{1}{12}$ **>**
40. $\frac{5}{6}$ ● $\frac{10}{12}$ **=**
41. $\frac{2}{3}$ ● $\frac{2}{6}$ **>**
42. $\frac{1}{2}$ ● $\frac{3}{8}$ **>**
43. $\frac{5}{8}$ ● $\frac{1}{2}$ **>**
44. $\frac{3}{6}$ ● $\frac{1}{2}$ **=**
45. $\frac{3}{4}$ ● $\frac{9}{12}$ **=**

Solve.

46. Which is bigger, $\frac{1}{2}$ of the big pie or $\frac{1}{2}$ of the small pie? **$\frac{1}{2}$ of the big pie**
47. Mrs. Packard had $36. She spent $\frac{1}{3}$ of the money on a pair of earrings. How much did the earrings cost? **$12**
48. Ricky read $\frac{2}{3}$ of a 250-page book, and Ramona read $\frac{2}{3}$ of a 150-page book.
    a. Who read more pages? **Ricky**
    b. Who read more words? **can't tell**
49. There are 16 tomato plants in a tray. Jenna planted $\frac{3}{4}$ of them. How many did she plant? **12**
50. Linda mowed $\frac{1}{2}$ of her yard. Jeremy mowed $\frac{2}{3}$ of his yard, which is the same size as Linda's. Who mowed more? **Jeremy**
51. Rachel and Jeremy want to share a pizza that has been sliced into 12 pieces. If Rachel eats five pieces, will she have eaten more or less than $\frac{1}{2}$ of the pizza? **less than $\frac{1}{2}$**

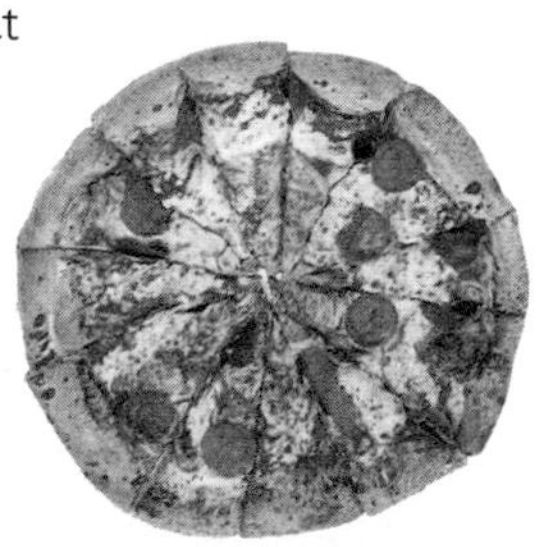

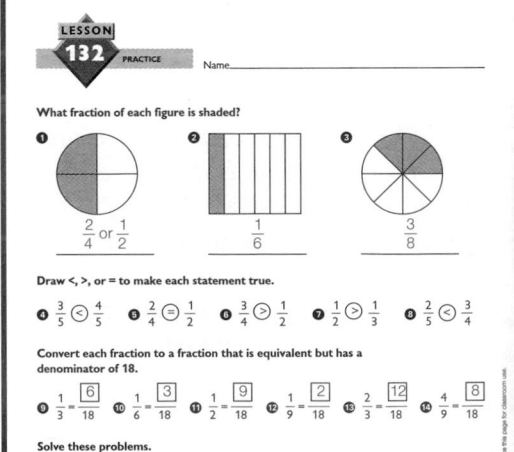

446 • Fractions and Decimals

RETEACHING p. 39

LESSON 132 RETEACHING Name________________

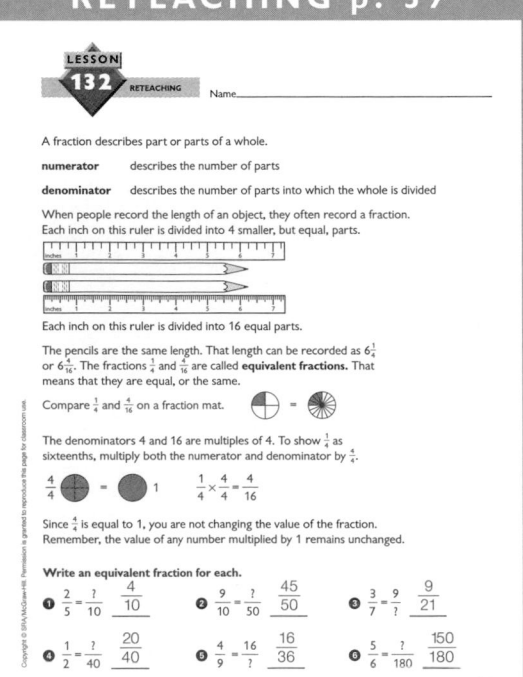

A fraction describes part or parts of a whole.

numerator describes the number of parts

denominator describes the number of parts into which the whole is divided

When people record the length of an object, they often record a fraction. Each inch on this ruler is divided into 4 smaller, but equal, parts.

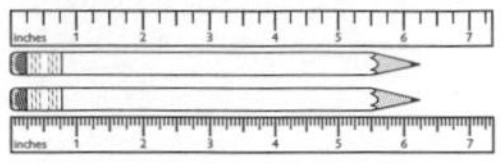

Each inch on this ruler is divided into 16 equal parts.

The pencils are the same length. That length can be recorded as $6\frac{1}{4}$ or $6\frac{4}{16}$. The fractions $\frac{1}{4}$ and $\frac{4}{16}$ are called **equivalent fractions.** That means that they are equal, or the same.

Compare $\frac{1}{4}$ and $\frac{4}{16}$ on a fraction mat.

The denominators 4 and 16 are multiples of 4. To show $\frac{1}{4}$ as sixteenths, multiply both the numerator and denominator by $\frac{4}{4}$.

$\frac{1}{4} \times \frac{4}{4} = \frac{4}{16}$

Since $\frac{4}{4}$ is equal to 1, you are not changing the value of the fraction. Remember, the value of any number multiplied by 1 remains unchanged.

Write an equivalent fraction for each.

1. $\frac{2}{5} = \frac{?}{10}$ $\frac{4}{10}$
2. $\frac{9}{10} = \frac{?}{50}$ $\frac{45}{50}$
3. $\frac{3}{7} = \frac{9}{?}$ $\frac{9}{21}$
4. $\frac{1}{2} = \frac{?}{40}$ $\frac{20}{40}$
5. $\frac{4}{9} = \frac{16}{?}$ $\frac{16}{36}$
6. $\frac{5}{6} = \frac{?}{180}$ $\frac{150}{180}$

Copyright © SRA/McGraw-Hill. Permission is granted to reproduce this page for classroom use.

Math Explorations and Applications Level 4 • 39

PRACTICE p. 132

LESSON 132 PRACTICE Name________________

What fraction of each figure is shaded?

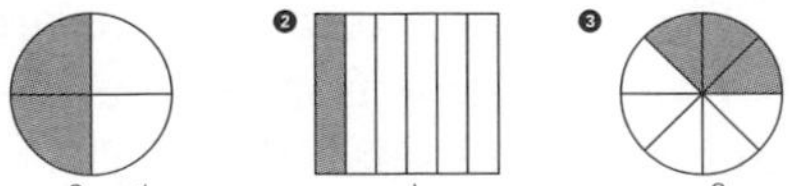

1. $\frac{2}{4}$ or $\frac{1}{2}$
2. $\frac{1}{6}$
3. $\frac{3}{8}$

Draw <, >, or = to make each statement true.

4. $\frac{3}{5}$ (<) $\frac{4}{5}$
5. $\frac{2}{4}$ (=) $\frac{1}{2}$
6. $\frac{3}{4}$ (>) $\frac{1}{2}$
7. $\frac{1}{2}$ (>) $\frac{1}{3}$
8. $\frac{2}{5}$ (<) $\frac{3}{4}$

Convert each fraction to a fraction that is equivalent but has a denominator of 18.

9. $\frac{1}{3} = \frac{6}{18}$
10. $\frac{1}{6} = \frac{3}{18}$
11. $\frac{1}{2} = \frac{9}{18}$
12. $\frac{1}{9} = \frac{2}{18}$
13. $\frac{2}{3} = \frac{12}{18}$
14. $\frac{4}{9} = \frac{8}{18}$

Solve these problems.

15. Maxine baked 20 cookies. Rory ate seven cookies. Did Rory eat more or less than $\frac{2}{5}$ of the cookies? less
16. Mark earns $9 each week. How much does he earn in one year? $468
17. A movie lasts 1 hour and 20 minutes. If the movie begins at 3:10 P.M., what time will it end? 4:30 P.M.
18. Samantha typed $\frac{3}{5}$ of a 200-word essay for history. Greg typed $\frac{1}{4}$ of a 300-word essay for history.
    a. Who typed more words? Samantha
    b. How many more words? 45

132 • *Math Explorations and Applications* Level 4

Copyright © SRA/McGraw-Hill. Permission is granted to reproduce this page for classroom use.

*available separately

52 Eli can save $4 each week. How much can he save in one year (52 weeks)? **$208**

53 Tiffany can save $6 each week. How much can she save in one year? **$312**

54 Lance has $10.00. He wants to buy a belt for $8.57 and a comic book for $2.00. Does he have enough money? **no**

55 Noelle has 35 meters of fencing. If she builds a garden with an area of 36 square meters, is it possible that she has enough fencing to enclose it? **yes**

56 Spencer has a stack of baseball cards. Eve has a stack four times as high as Spencer's. How many baseball cards does Spencer have? **can't tell**

57 Brent's garden is shaped like a rectangle. It is 10 meters long and 8 meters wide. Denise's garden is shaped like a square. Each side measures 9 meters.

a. Whose garden has the larger area? **Denise's**

b. How much larger? **1 sq. m**

58 Dean earns $5.75 per hour. He works 40 hours each week. How much money does he earn in one year (52 weeks)? **$11,960**

59 A play lasts 2 hours and 35 minutes. If the play starts at 8:15 P.M., what time will it end? **10:50 P.M.**

60 Half the children in Jordan's class are girls. How many children are in his class? **can't tell**

61 Virginia has $239.40 in her checking account. She deposits $148.00 and then writes a check for $239.40. How much money is left in her account? **$148**

3 Wrap-Up

5 MINUTES

In Closing Ask students how to find a fraction that is equivalent to $\frac{2}{3}$ but has a different denominator.

Mastery Checkpoint 19

At about this time most students should demonstrate proficiency in finding simple fractions of whole numbers. You can assess this ability from students' performances during the Mental Math drill. You may also wish to assign Assessment Blackline Masters page 52 to determine mastery. The results of this assessment may be recorded on the Mastery Checkpoint Chart.

Assessment Criteria

Did the student . . .

- ✓ demonstrate ability in finding simple fractions of whole numbers?
- ✓ contribute to the discussion of equivalent fractions?
- ✓ use equivalent fractions to compare fractions with unlike denominators?
- ✓ accurately solve a variety of word problems?
- ✓ correctly answer at least 80% of the computation problems?

Homework Have students play the "Fractions of 60" game for practice with finding fractions of whole numbers. A copy of this game can also be found on page 26 of the Home Connections Blackline Masters.

ENRICHMENT p. 132

LESSON 132 ENRICHMENT Name________

Draw a line that divides the rectangle below into two equal parts. Shade one of the parts.

1 Write a fraction for the shaded part. $\frac{1}{2}$

2 Now draw lines to divide the rectangle into four equal parts. Write a fraction for the shaded part. $\frac{2}{4}$

3 Now draw lines to divide the rectangle into eight equal parts. Write a fraction for the shaded part. $\frac{4}{8}$

4 Now draw lines to divide the rectangle into 16 equal parts. Write a fraction for the shaded part. $\frac{8}{16}$

5 What can you say about the fractions you wrote for problems 2–4? They are all equivalent to $\frac{1}{2}$.

6 Do you see any pattern in the fractions you wrote? The numerators and denominators double each time.

Predict what the next equivalent fraction will be. $\frac{16}{32}$

Copyright © SRA/McGraw-Hill. Permission is granted to reproduce this page for classroom use.

132 • *Math Explorations and Applications* Level 4

ASSESSMENT p. 52

UNIT 6 **Mastery Checkpoint 19** Fractions of numbers (Lesson 132)

Name________

The student demonstrates mastery by correctly answering at least 12 of the 15 problems.

Solve these problems.

1 Ms. Fong has driven about $\frac{1}{5}$ of the way from Booneville to Harristown. The towns are about 150 kilometers apart. About how many kilometers has Ms. Fong driven? 30

2 Wendy has finished 14 of the 18 problems she had for math homework. Has she finished more than $\frac{2}{3}$ of her math homework? yes

3 A calculator that usually costs $14 is on sale for $\frac{1}{2}$ off.

a. How much is $\frac{1}{2}$ of $14? $7

b. What is the sale price of the calculator? $7

Write the equivalent fraction with a denominator of 20.

4 $\frac{3}{4} = \frac{15}{20}$ 5 $\frac{2}{5} = \frac{8}{20}$ 6 $\frac{6}{10} = \frac{12}{20}$

Write the equivalent fraction with a denominator of 16.

7 $\frac{1}{4} = \frac{4}{16}$ 8 $\frac{3}{8} = \frac{6}{16}$ 9 $\frac{1}{2} = \frac{8}{16}$

Write the equivalent fraction with a denominator of 12.

10 $\frac{3}{6} = \frac{6}{12}$ 11 $\frac{3}{4} = \frac{9}{12}$ 12 $\frac{2}{3} = \frac{8}{12}$

Solve.

13 What fraction with a denominator of 10 equals $\frac{3}{5}$? $\frac{6}{10}$

14 What fraction with a denominator of 60 equals $\frac{3}{12}$? $\frac{15}{60}$

15 What fraction with a denominator of 30 equals $\frac{3}{5}$? $\frac{18}{30}$

Copyright © SRA/McGraw-Hill. Permission is granted to reproduce this page for classroom use.

52 • *Math Explorations and Applications* Level 4

LESSON 133

Student Edition pages 448–451

Mixed Numbers

LESSON PLANNER

Objectives

- to introduce students to mixed numbers
- to provide practice with writing mixed numbers and improper fractions
- to provide practice with rewriting mixed numbers as improper fractions and improper fractions as mixed numbers

Context of the Lesson This is the eighth of 12 lessons on understanding and using fractions and mixed numbers. So far in the program, students have worked only informally with mixed numbers. However, they are familiar with noninteger quantities greater than 1 from their work with decimals.

MANIPULATIVES

counters*

Program Resources

"Fracto 1" and "Fracto 2" Game Mats

Reteaching Master

Practice Master 133

Enrichment Master 133

For additional math integration: Math Throughout the Day*

For extra practice: CD-ROM* Lesson 133

1 Warm-Up 5 MINUTES

Problem of the Day Present the following problem on the chalkboard: Fill in the boxes, using the digits 1, 2, 3, and 4 to form as many true fraction statements as you can. ($\frac{3}{4} > \frac{1}{2}$; $\frac{2}{4} > \frac{1}{3}$; $\frac{2}{3} > \frac{1}{4}$)

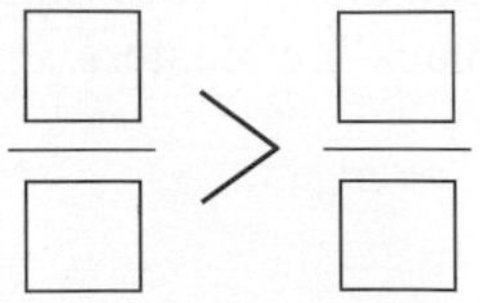

Problem-Solving Strategies Ask students who have solved the Problem of the Day to share how they solved it and any strategies they used.

EXPLORE

LESSON 133

Mixed Numbers

Mr. Cheng baked four loaves of bread. His children ate half of one loaf. Mr. Cheng had three and one-half loaves left.

Before **After**

We can write three and one half as $3\frac{1}{2}$.

Evan is slicing cucumbers for a salad. He started with six cucumbers. He had sliced four whole cucumbers and one third of another when the doorbell rang. He had one and two-thirds cucumbers left to slice when he returned to the kitchen.

Before **After**

We can write one and two thirds as $1\frac{2}{3}$.

Miss Batra bought five bags of popcorn for her movie theater. Last night she used three whole bags and three fourths of another. Miss Batra had one and one-fourth bags left.

Before **After**

◆ How would you write the number of bags she has left? $1\frac{1}{4}$

FANTASTIC FACT

An albatross is a huge seabird that can fly up to 25 miles per hour, and can even sleep while flying!

448 • Fractions and Decimals

Technology Connection Refer students to the software *Fraction Munchers* from MECC (Apple, Mac, for grades 3–12) for further practice with proper and improper fractions, mixed and whole numbers, numerators and denominators, reduced and unreduced fractions, equivalent fractions, and fractions greater than or less than $\frac{1}{2}$.

*available separately

Write a mixed number to show how many.

1. 

$3\frac{1}{4}$ ■ pizzas

2. 

$2\frac{3}{4}$ ■ dollars

3. 

$2\frac{1}{2}$ ■ apples

4. 

$4\frac{1}{2}$ ■ glasses of juice

In each case write *yes* if the last sentence is true. Write *no* if it isn't true and explain why.

5. Dustin has a guitar lesson at 5:30 P.M. At 3:00 P.M. he said, "My guitar lesson starts in $2\frac{1}{2}$ hours." **yes**

6. A can of frozen orange juice makes enough juice for six glasses. Deborah used one can to make a pitcher of orange juice. She drank $3\frac{1}{2}$ glasses for breakfast. There are $3\frac{1}{2}$ glasses of orange juice left. **no; this is one glass more than six**

7. DeDe works $3\frac{3}{4}$ hours every day at a hardware store. Today she could have worked two hours before dinner and $1\frac{3}{4}$ hours after dinner. **yes**

8. Sonia told Jay to meet her in $1\frac{1}{2}$ hours. Jay showed up on time 90 minutes later. **yes**

MENTAL MATH Present simple addition problems with common fractions. Students show thumbs up if the sum is greater than 1, thumbs down if the sum is less than 1, and stand up if the sum equals 1.

a. $\frac{1}{2} + \frac{1}{4}$ (thumbs down) **b.** $\frac{3}{4} + \frac{2}{3}$ (thumbs up)

c. $\frac{1}{3} + \frac{1}{8}$ (thumbs down) **d.** $\frac{7}{8} + \frac{2}{3}$ (thumbs up)

2 Teach

Using the Student Pages Review the rules for the "Fracto 1" and "Fracto 2" Game Mats as needed so that students can play when they finish their work on pages 448–451. These games were introduced in Lesson 20, and they provide practice with recognizing fractional areas of circles and rectangles.

Go over page 448 with the class. Be sure everyone knows what a mixed number is and how to write mixed numbers. Then have students complete page 449 on their own. When everyone has finished, discuss problems 5–8. Although some of the problems involve adding and subtracting mixed numbers, the contexts and numbers have been chosen so that students can do them without needing to know algorithms. Therefore, discuss the problems using diagrams and concrete objects rather than teaching a general step-by-step procedure.

Games . . . offer excellent problem-solving opportunities. One of the benefits of such games is that some pupils will simply be practicing necessary skills while others will have proceeded on to some serious problem solving. Two children playing such a game together may be thinking on very different levels. However, it is likely that the player who is solving some serious problems will influence the other player after a while either by action or by word.

—Stephen S. Willoughby, *Mathematics Education for a Changing World*

◆ LESSON 133 Mixed Numbers

Teach

Using the Student Pages Go over the material on these pages with the class. Be sure students realize that the term *improper fraction* refers to any fraction whose numerator is greater than its denominator. Do several examples with students to demonstrate how to convert an improper fraction to a mixed number and a mixed number to an improper fraction. Use diagrams or **counters*** to model the relationship between improper fractions and mixed numbers. Then have students complete these pages on their own or in pairs.

Using the "Fracto 1" and "Fracto 2" Game Mats Have students play "Fracto 1" and "Fracto 2," which provide practice with recognizing fractional areas of circles and rectangles. Complete instructions for playing can be found on the Game Mats. A copy of these Game Mats can also be found on pages 592–593 of this Teacher's Guide.

◆ **LESSON 133 Mixed Numbers**

A fraction with a numerator greater than its denominator is called an **improper fraction.** For example, $\frac{13}{6}$ is an improper fraction.

Sometimes a mixed number is easier to work with than an improper fraction. Sometimes an improper fraction is easier to work with than a mixed number.

To change $\frac{13}{6}$ to a mixed number, ask how many whole units there are in $\frac{13}{6}$. (How many times does 6 go into 13?) The answer is 2. What's left over? 1 is left over. So $\frac{13}{6}$ and $2\frac{1}{6}$ are the same number.

How many sixths are shaded in the picture below? From the picture, can you see that $\frac{13}{6}$ and $2\frac{1}{6}$ are the same number?

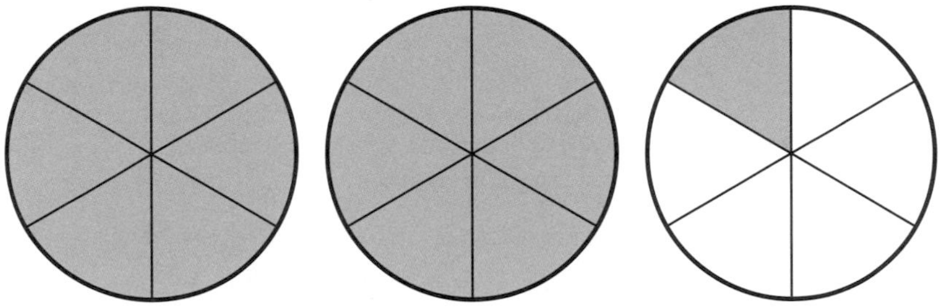

Change each improper fraction to a mixed number, or, if possible, to a whole number.

9. $\frac{5}{2}$ $\mathbf{2\frac{1}{2}}$
10. $\frac{5}{4}$ $\mathbf{1\frac{1}{4}}$
11. $\frac{8}{6}$ $\mathbf{1\frac{1}{3}}$
12. $\frac{7}{5}$ $\mathbf{1\frac{2}{5}}$
13. $\frac{15}{7}$ $\mathbf{2\frac{1}{7}}$
14. $\frac{29}{3}$ $\mathbf{9\frac{2}{3}}$
15. $\frac{8}{7}$ $\mathbf{1\frac{1}{7}}$
16. $\frac{7}{4}$ $\mathbf{1\frac{3}{4}}$
17. $\frac{11}{6}$ $\mathbf{1\frac{5}{6}}$
18. $\frac{28}{5}$ $\mathbf{5\frac{3}{5}}$
19. $\frac{17}{8}$ $\mathbf{2\frac{1}{8}}$
20. $\frac{21}{3}$ **7**
21. $\frac{20}{5}$ **4**
22. $\frac{13}{4}$ $\mathbf{3\frac{1}{4}}$
23. $\frac{4}{3}$ $\mathbf{1\frac{1}{3}}$
24. $\frac{7}{6}$ $\mathbf{1\frac{1}{6}}$
25. $\frac{24}{8}$ **3**
26. $\frac{16}{5}$ $\mathbf{3\frac{1}{5}}$
27. $\frac{17}{3}$ $\mathbf{5\frac{2}{3}}$
28. $\frac{11}{5}$ $\mathbf{2\frac{1}{5}}$
29. $\frac{12}{3}$ **4**
30. $\frac{21}{6}$ $\mathbf{3\frac{1}{2}}$
31. $\frac{25}{8}$ $\mathbf{3\frac{1}{8}}$
32. $\frac{26}{8}$ $\mathbf{3\frac{1}{4}}$

450 • Fractions and Decimals

Literature Connection Read *Thundercake* by Patricia Polacco, or excerpts from it, to students. Have them work in groups to decide how much of each ingredient they would need if they doubled, tripled, or quadrupled the recipe for thundercake.

RETEACHING p. 40

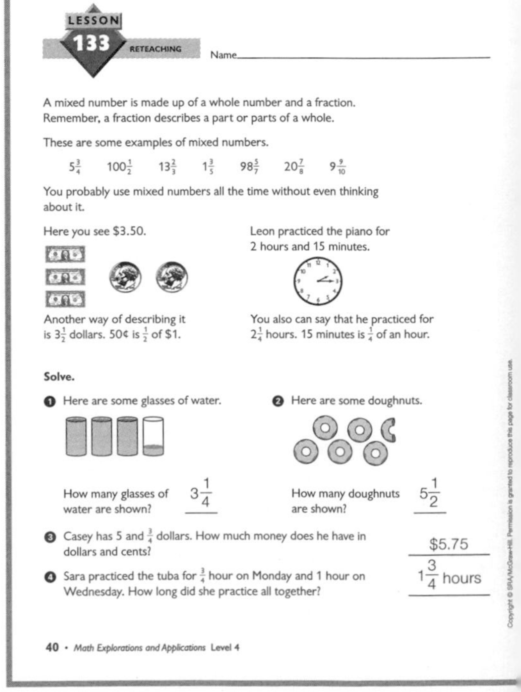

LESSON 133 RETEACHING Name________________

A mixed number is made up of a whole number and a fraction. Remember, a fraction describes a part or parts of a whole.

These are some examples of mixed numbers.

$5\frac{3}{4}$ $100\frac{1}{2}$ $13\frac{2}{3}$ $1\frac{3}{5}$ $98\frac{5}{7}$ $20\frac{7}{8}$ $9\frac{9}{10}$

You probably use mixed numbers all the time without even thinking about it.

Here you see \$3.50.

Another way of describing it is $3\frac{1}{2}$ dollars. 50¢ is $\frac{1}{2}$ of \$1.

Leon practiced the piano for 2 hours and 15 minutes.

You also can say that he practiced for $2\frac{1}{4}$ hours. 15 minutes is $\frac{1}{4}$ of an hour.

Solve.

1. Here are some glasses of water. How many glasses of water are shown? $3\frac{1}{4}$
2. Here are some doughnuts. How many doughnuts are shown? $5\frac{1}{2}$
3. Casey has 5 and $\frac{3}{4}$ dollars. How much money does he have in dollars and cents? \$5.75
4. Sara practiced the tuba for $\frac{3}{4}$ hour on Monday and 1 hour on Wednesday. How long did she practice all together? $1\frac{3}{4}$ hours

40 • *Math Explorations and Applications* Level 4

Copyright © SRA/McGraw-Hill. Permission is granted to reproduce this page for classroom use.

*available separately

If you wish to change a mixed number to an improper fraction, you reverse the process.

To change $2\frac{1}{6}$ to an improper fraction, ask how many sixths there are in 2 (you can count on the figure on the previous page, or just multiply 2 by 6). The answer is 12. So $2\frac{1}{6}$ is the same as $\frac{12}{6}$ plus $\frac{1}{6}$, or $\frac{13}{6}$.

Change each mixed number to an improper fraction.

33 $2\frac{5}{6}$ **$\frac{17}{6}$**	34 $4\frac{1}{3}$ **$\frac{13}{3}$**	35 $3\frac{1}{6}$ **$\frac{19}{6}$**	36 $4\frac{3}{5}$ **$\frac{23}{5}$**	37 $6\frac{5}{9}$ **$\frac{59}{9}$**
38 $2\frac{5}{7}$ **$\frac{19}{7}$**	39 $3\frac{1}{4}$ **$\frac{13}{4}$**	40 $3\frac{5}{6}$ **$\frac{23}{6}$**	41 $5\frac{3}{8}$ **$\frac{43}{8}$**	42 $2\frac{3}{8}$ **$\frac{19}{8}$**
43 $4\frac{3}{4}$ **$\frac{19}{4}$**	44 $1\frac{2}{5}$ **$\frac{7}{5}$**	45 $2\frac{1}{7}$ **$\frac{15}{7}$**	46 $8\frac{3}{5}$ **$\frac{43}{5}$**	47 $4\frac{5}{6}$ **$\frac{29}{6}$**
48 $1\frac{1}{2}$ **$\frac{3}{2}$**	49 $1\frac{3}{5}$ **$\frac{8}{5}$**	50 $7\frac{1}{2}$ **$\frac{15}{2}$**	51 $6\frac{5}{8}$ **$\frac{53}{8}$**	52 $1\frac{3}{5}$ **$\frac{8}{5}$**
53 $3\frac{2}{3}$ **$\frac{11}{3}$**	54 $1\frac{4}{5}$ **$\frac{9}{5}$**	55 $5\frac{3}{4}$ **$\frac{23}{4}$**	56 $8\frac{5}{6}$ **$\frac{53}{6}$**	57 $2\frac{1}{9}$ **$\frac{19}{9}$**

PROBLEM SOLVING

Solve these problems.

58 Kendra has four red markers and one green marker. What fraction of her markers are red? **$\frac{4}{5}$**

59 Tony used two eggs to make his breakfast. What part of one dozen eggs did he use? **$\frac{2}{12}$ or $\frac{1}{6}$**

60 The ski club has 36 members. Some members rent skis, but $\frac{3}{4}$ of the members own skis. How many members own skis? **27**

61 Caroline drank 8 ounces of juice at breakfast. What part of a 64-ounce pitcher of juice did she drink? **$\frac{8}{64}$ or $\frac{1}{8}$**

62 Christine has 12 rosebushes in her flower garden. Eight of the bushes have yellow roses. What fraction of the rosebushes have yellow roses? **$\frac{8}{12}$ or $\frac{2}{3}$**

3 Wrap-Up 5 MINUTES

In Closing Have students summarize the lesson by explaining the relationship between $\frac{7}{3}$ and $2\frac{1}{3}$.

SELF ASSESSMENT Have students write a brief statement that evaluates their understanding of mixed numbers and improper fractions. Encourage them to explain how to change one to the other. Have them give several real-life examples of mixed numbers.

Assessment Criteria

Did the student . . .

- ✓ contribute to the discussion of mixed numbers and improper fractions?
- ✓ communicate strategies used to convert from a mixed number to an improper fraction and vice versa?
- ✓ correctly answer at least 75% of the conversion problems?

Homework Have students find the ages, to the month, of four different people they know, including themselves. Have them consider how years can be divided and then express the ages as mixed numbers and as improper fractions.

ESL

Meeting Individual Needs

Students with limited English proficiency may be confused by the term *improper fraction.* They may think it means incorrect, wrong, or indecent. Help them understand that, in a mathematical context, an improper fraction is the opposite of a proper, or common, fraction because its numerator is greater than its denominator.

PRACTICE p. 133

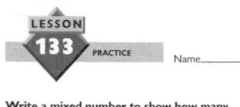

LESSON 133 PRACTICE Name_____

Write a mixed number to show how many.

1 $2\frac{1}{2}$ bars of soap

2 $3\frac{3}{4}$ circles

3 $3\frac{1}{3}$ pies

Change each improper fraction to a mixed number or whole number.

4 $\frac{27}{6}$ = $4\frac{3}{6}$ or $4\frac{1}{2}$　5 $\frac{7}{2}$ = $3\frac{1}{2}$　6 $\frac{18}{9}$ = 2

7 $\frac{8}{3}$ = $2\frac{2}{3}$　8 $\frac{7}{4}$ = $1\frac{3}{4}$　9 $\frac{13}{6}$ = $2\frac{1}{6}$

10 $\frac{35}{7}$ = 5　11 $\frac{16}{5}$ = $3\frac{1}{5}$　12 $\frac{19}{4}$ = $4\frac{3}{4}$

Change each mixed number to an improper fraction.

13 $3\frac{1}{5}$ = $\frac{16}{5}$　14 $9\frac{2}{7}$ = $\frac{65}{7}$　15 $5\frac{2}{3}$ = $\frac{17}{3}$

16 $16\frac{1}{2}$ = $\frac{33}{2}$　17 $11\frac{3}{4}$ = $\frac{47}{4}$　18 $6\frac{7}{10}$ = $\frac{67}{10}$

19 $1\frac{4}{9}$ = $\frac{13}{9}$　20 $2\frac{7}{8}$ = $\frac{23}{8}$　21 $6\frac{1}{3}$ = $\frac{19}{3}$

Copyright © SRA/McGraw-Hill. Permission is granted to reproduce this page for classroom use.

Math Explorations and Applications Level 4 • 133

ENRICHMENT p. 133

LESSON 133 ENRICHMENT Name_____

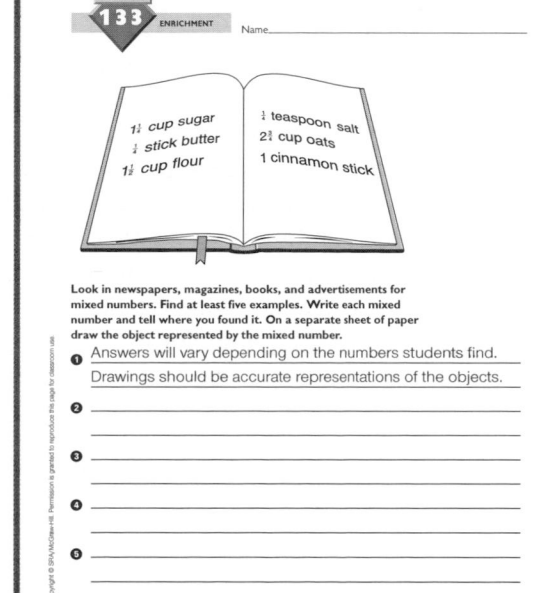

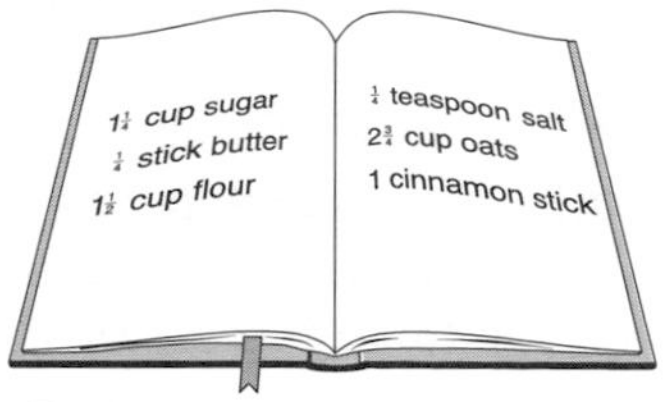

Look in newspapers, magazines, books, and advertisements for mixed numbers. Find at least five examples. Write each mixed number and tell where you found it. On a separate sheet of paper draw the object represented by the mixed number.

1 Answers will vary depending on the numbers students find. Drawings should be accurate representations of the objects.

2 _____

3 _____

4 _____

5 _____

Copyright © SRA/McGraw-Hill. Permission is granted to reproduce this page for classroom use.

Math Explorations and Applications Level 4 • 133

LESSON 134

Student Edition pages 452–453

Inches, Feet, and Yards

LESSON PLANNER

Objectives

- to review the inch, foot, and yard as customary units for measuring length
- to provide practice in estimating length and in measuring objects using customary units
- to provide practice using mixed numbers

Context of the Lesson This is the ninth of 12 lessons on understanding and using fractions and mixed numbers.

MANIPULATIVES

rulers* or tape measures

objects to be measured

Program Resources

Practice Master 134

Enrichment Master 134

For extra practice:
CD-ROM* Lesson 134

1 Warm-Up 5 MINUTES

Problem of the Day Draw the following figure on the chalkboard. Ask students how many parallelograms they can find. (13)

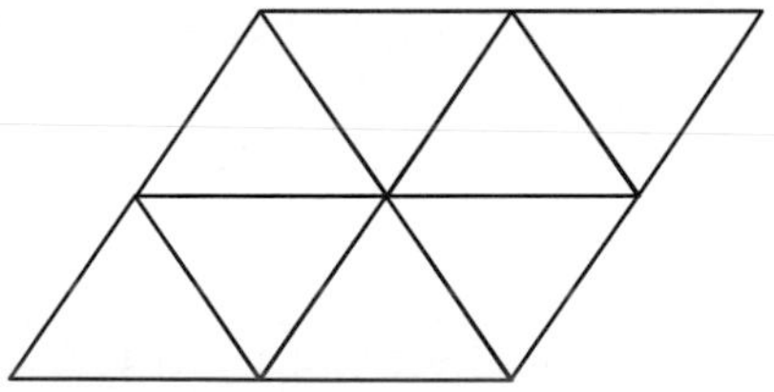

Problem-Solving Strategies Ask students who have solved the Problem of the Day to share how they solved it and any strategies they used.

MENTAL MATH MANIPULATIVES Hold up the following objects and challenge students to estimate their length using customary units of measure. After each estimate, have students use **rulers*** to measure to check for accuracy. (Estimates should improve after each object is measured.)

a. a videocassette

b. a keyboard

c. a poster

d. the height of a door

MIXED PRACTICE

LESSON 134

Inches, Feet, and Yards

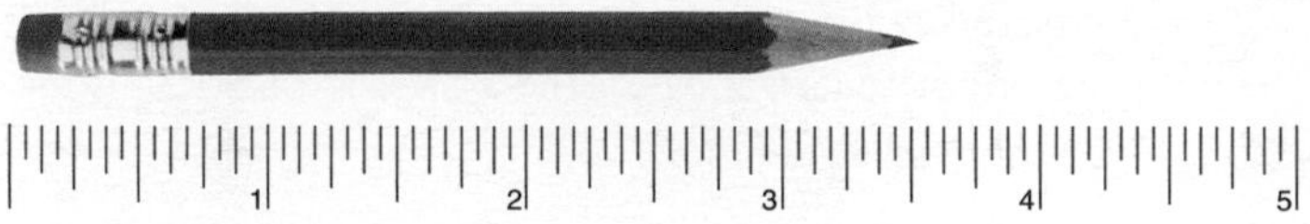

This pencil is between 3 and 4 inches long.

It is almost halfway between 3 and 4 inches. It is about $3\frac{1}{2}$ inches long.

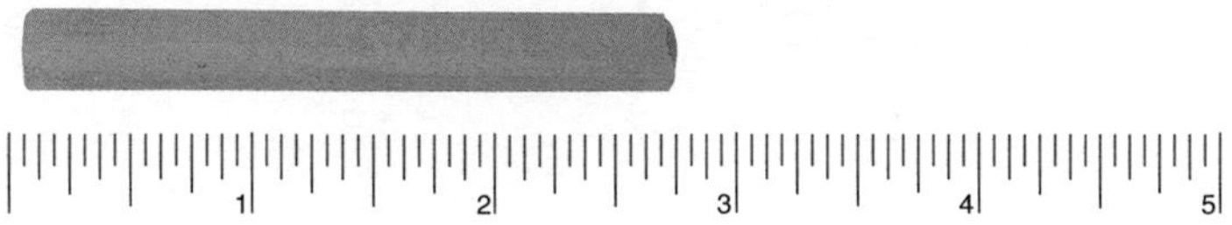

This piece of chalk is between 2 and 3 inches long. It is about $2\frac{3}{4}$ inches long.

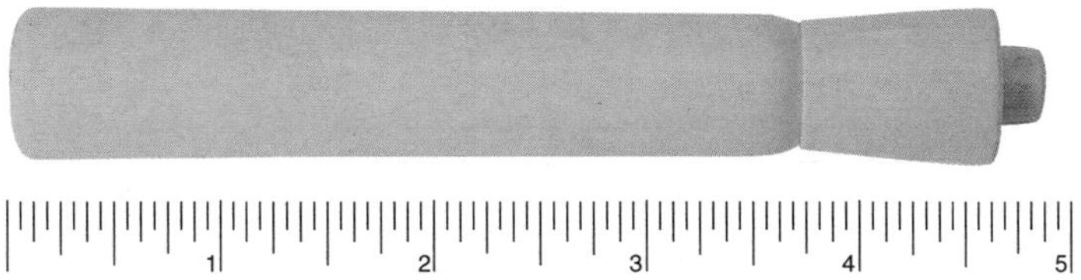

This marker is between 4 and 5 inches long. It is about $4\frac{7}{8}$ inches long.

Remember: 12 inches = 1 foot

36 inches = 3 feet = 1 yard

Answer these questions.

1. How many inches are there in 16 yards? **576**
2. How many inches are there in 10 feet? **120**
3. How many feet are there in 84 inches? **7**

Literature Connection Have small groups of students select a measurement experiment, puzzle, or game from the book *Measuring Up* by Sandra Markle to explore customary units of length. Groups can report their activities and findings to the class orally or in written form.

RETEACHING

Provide additional opportunities for students to estimate and measure lengths in the classroom, on the playground, or at home and to express these lengths in inches, feet, and yards.

*available separately

Estimate the length. Then measure to the nearest $\frac{1}{8}$ inch.

Answers $\frac{1}{8}$ greater or lesser should be considered correct.

❹ **$2\frac{7}{8}$ in.**

❺

$1\frac{7}{8}$ in.

❻ **$3\frac{3}{4}$ in.**

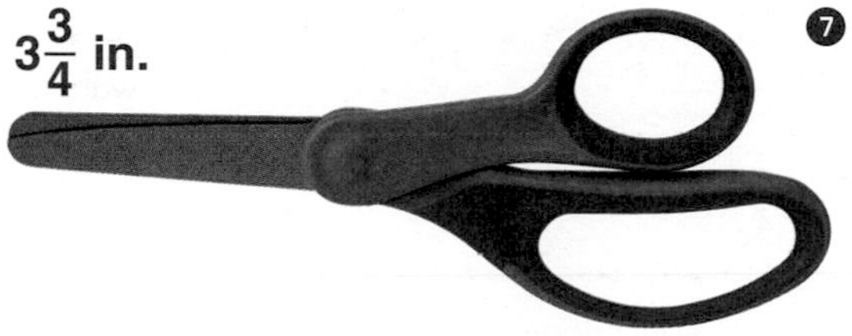

❼

1 in.

❽

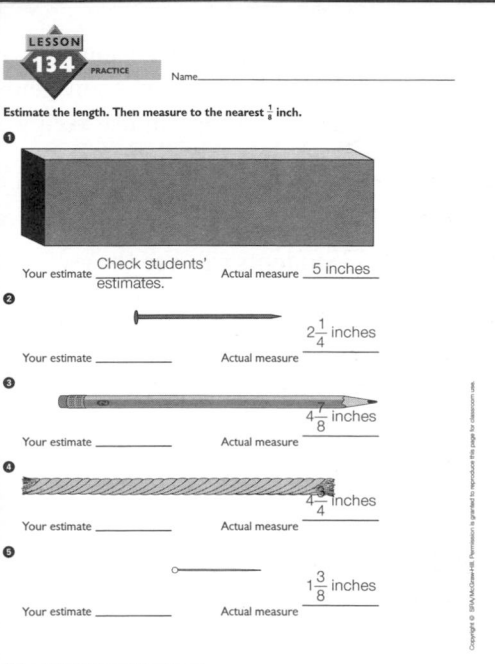

4 in.

❾

$5\frac{3}{8}$ in.

Measure. **Answers to the first four questions will vary based on the measurements of each classroom.**

- How long is your classroom in yards and feet? In feet only?
- How wide is your classroom in yards and feet? In feet only?
- How long is your desk in feet and inches? In inches only?
- How wide is your desk in feet and inches? In inches only?
- How long is the cover of your mathematics book in inches? **11 inches**
- How wide is the cover of your mathematics book in inches? **$8\frac{1}{2}$ inches**

❷ Teach

Using the Student Pages Work through page 452 with the class. Point out the equivalent relationships among customary units of length near the bottom of the page. Ask students if they notice anything about inches, feet, and yards that would make it easy to convert yards to inches or inches to feet. Remind them about the decimal nature of the metric system, and discuss the ease of conversion in the metric system versus conversion in the customary system.

COOPERATIVE LEARNING MANIPULATIVES Have students work independently on the six problems on page 453. Then have them work in small groups on the measuring activity at the bottom of the page. Tell them to estimate the dimensions of each object before measuring. Estimates that are within $\frac{1}{8}$ inch may be considered correct. Have **rulers*** and **tape measures*** available.

❸ Wrap-Up

5 MINUTES

In Closing Have students express the length 2 yards in two different ways. (72 in. or 6 ft)

ALTERNATIVE ASSESSMENT **Performance Assessment** Observe students as they complete the measuring activities on page 453. To assess their ability to measure accurately and to use mixed numbers, have students find the lengths of various other classroom objects. They should express the lengths in whole or mixed numbers of feet, inches, or yards.

PRACTICE p. 134

LESSON 134 PRACTICE Name________

Estimate the length. Then measure to the nearest $\frac{1}{8}$ inch.

❶

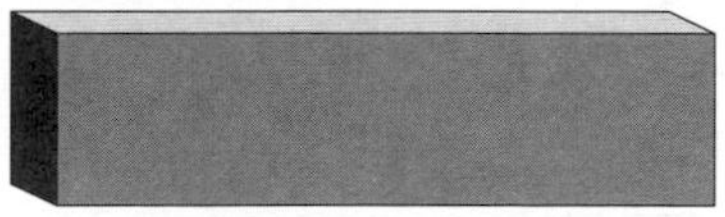

Your estimate Check students' estimates. Actual measure 5 inches

❷

Your estimate ______ Actual measure $2\frac{1}{4}$ inches

❸

Your estimate ______ Actual measure $4\frac{7}{8}$ inches

❹

Your estimate ______ Actual measure $4\frac{3}{4}$ inches

❺

Your estimate ______ Actual measure $1\frac{3}{8}$ inches

134 • *Math Explorations and Applications* Level 4

Copyright © SRA/McGraw-Hill. Permission is granted to reproduce this page for classroom use.

ENRICHMENT p. 134

LESSON 134 ENRICHMENT Name________

There are many ways to measure length, width, or height, even if you don't have a ruler or other standard tool of measurement.

Each of the following can be used as a measuring device by multiplying its length by the number of times it is used to measure an object or area. With a ruler, measure each item in the list and write the measurement in inches. Round when necessary.

Your shoelace ______ A belt ______ Your index finger ______

Use one of the nonstandard units listed above to answer the following questions. Then use a standard tool, like a ruler or yardstick, to find the actual measurements.

❶ What is the length and width of a table in your home? ______

❷ Which device did you use to measure it? ______

❸ What are the measurements using a standard tool? ______

❹ How tall is your teacher's desk? ______

❺ How long is it? ______

❻ How wide is it? ______

❼ Which device did you use to measure it? ______

❽ What are the measurements using a standard tool? ______

❾ What are the advantages of using standard tools and forms of measurement?
Answers will vary depending on the nonstandard unit each student chooses. You can measure anything using an item you already know the measure of. Most paper, for example, is $8\frac{1}{2}$" by 11". You could use a sheet of paper as a measuring tool. The advantage of using standard forms is that we can all communicate using common terms.

134 • *Math Explorations and Applications* Level 4

Copyright © SRA/McGraw-Hill. Permission is granted to reproduce this page for classroom use.

Assessment Criteria

Did the student . . .

✓ accurately estimate the lengths of objects?

✓ demonstrate an ability to measure objects to the nearest $\frac{1}{8}$ inch?

✓ express measurements in whole or mixed numbers, as appropriate?

Homework Have students estimate and then measure five objects in their homes to the nearest $\frac{1}{8}$ inch. Students should express the measurements in whole or mixed numbers.

*available separately

LESSON 135

Student Edition pages 454–455

Adding and Subtracting Fractions of Inches

LESSON PLANNER

Objectives

- ▶ to introduce and provide practice with addition and subtraction of simple fractions and mixed numbers
- ▶ to provide practice in solving word problems involving addition and subtraction of simple fractions and mixed numbers

Context of the Lesson This is the tenth of 12 lessons on understanding and using fractions and mixed numbers.

MANIPULATIVES

dual dial scale*

objects to be measured

strips of paper (optional)

Program Resources

"Fracto 1" and "Fracto 2" Game Mats

Practice Master 135

Enrichment Master 135

For additional math integration: Math Throughout the Day*

For extra practice: CD-ROM* Lesson 135

1 Warm-Up (5 MINUTES)

Problem of the Day Present this problem: Miyoshi has two fast-growing plants. When she bought them, both were $\frac{1}{2}$ foot tall. One plant grows 3 inches per week, and the other grows 5 inches per week. In what amount of time will one plant be a foot taller than the other? (After six weeks, one plant will be 24 in. tall, the other will be 36 in. tall.)

Problem-Solving Strategies Ask students who have solved the Problem of the Day to share how they solved it and any strategies they used.

MENTAL MATH / MANIPULATIVES Have students use customary units of measure to estimate the weight of the objects below. After each estimate, have students use a **scale*** to measure to check for accuracy. (Estimates should improve after each object is measured.)

a. a paintbrush **b.** a bottle of paint

c. a chalkboard eraser **d.** a stapler

EXPLORE

LESSON 135

Adding and Subtracting Fractions of Inches

Corey is putting a bulletin board on his wall. The bulletin board is $\frac{1}{4}$ inch thick. He wants the screws to go through the bulletin board and about $\frac{1}{2}$ inch into the wall. How long a screw should he use? **$\frac{3}{4}$ in.**

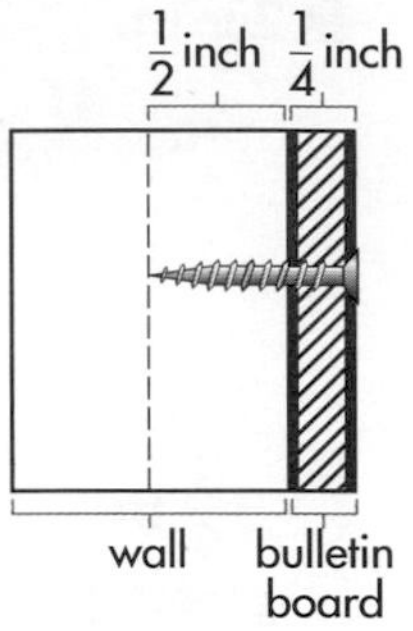

Measure to check.

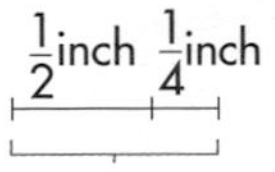

Is this $\frac{3}{4}$ inch long? **yes**

Corey has a $\frac{3}{4}$-inch wooden plug to fill a hole $\frac{1}{2}$ inch deep. How much must be cut off so that no wood sticks out of the hole? **$\frac{1}{4}$ in.**

Measure to check.

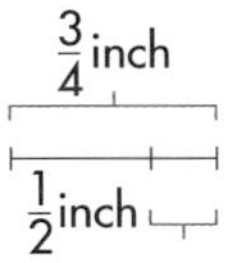

Is this $\frac{1}{4}$ inch? **yes**

FANTASTIC FACT **A person uses 72 different muscles in order to talk.**

Why teach it this way?

In this lesson students add and subtract fractions without formal algorithms for these operations. At this stage it is important to develop students' familiarity with simple fractions and their ability to solve practical problems involving fractions.

RETEACHING

MANIPULATIVES Have students make a model that shows common equivalent fractions. They can use **strips of paper** of equal length that they fold or mark off to show halves, thirds, fourths, sixths, eighths, twelfths, and sixteenths. Students can use these models to help them add and subtract fractions and to recognize common equivalent fractions.

*available separately

Figure out each answer. Then draw line segments and measure to check.

1. $\frac{1}{4}$ inch + $\frac{1}{4}$ inch **$\frac{1}{2}$ in.**
2. $\frac{3}{8}$ inch + $\frac{3}{8}$ inch **$\frac{3}{4}$ in.**
3. 2 inches − $\frac{1}{4}$ inch **$1\frac{3}{4}$ in.**
4. 1 inch − $\frac{5}{8}$ inch **$\frac{3}{8}$ in.**
5. $1\frac{1}{2}$ inches + $1\frac{1}{8}$ inches **$2\frac{5}{8}$ in.**
6. $\frac{3}{4}$ inch + $\frac{1}{2}$ inch **$1\frac{1}{4}$ in.**
7. $\frac{3}{4}$ inch − $\frac{1}{2}$ inch **$\frac{1}{4}$ in.**

Solve these problems.

8. Kurt rode his horse for two hours yesterday and $\frac{3}{4}$ hour today. How many hours did he ride during the past two days? **$2\frac{3}{4}$**
9. Dinah placed a box that is $\frac{3}{4}$ foot tall on another box that is $\frac{1}{4}$ foot tall. How tall are the two boxes together? **1 ft**
10. Cathy had $2\frac{1}{2}$ dollars. She gave a quarter to Brad. How much money does Cathy have now? **$2\frac{1}{4}$ dollars or $2.25**
11. Pauline had $1\frac{1}{2}$ pounds of trail mix. She gave her sister $\frac{1}{4}$ pound. How much does she have left? **$1\frac{1}{4}$ pound**
12. Ben had 4 dollars. He spent $\frac{1}{2}$ dollar for a soda and 2 dollars for a bumper sticker. How much did he have then? **$1\frac{1}{2}$ dollars or $1.50**
13. Andrea ran 2 miles on Monday and $2\frac{1}{2}$ miles on Wednesday. How many miles did she run in those two days? **$4\frac{1}{2}$**

2 Teach

Using the Student Pages You may wish to briefly review the "Fracto" Game Mats so students can play them as they finish pages 454 and 455. These games provide practice with recognizing fractional areas of circles and rectangles. Go over page 454 carefully with the class. Help students see how to add and subtract fractions, using fractions of an inch as a model. Have them work independently on page 455.

Using the "Fracto 1" and "Fracto 2" Game Mats Encourage students to play these games for further practice in recognizing fractional areas using circles and rectangles.

3 Wrap-Up

5 MINUTES

In Closing Have students explain and model how they would subtract $\frac{1}{4}$ from $2\frac{1}{2}$ and how they would add $\frac{1}{4}$ to $2\frac{1}{2}$.

SELF ASSESSMENT

Have students write brief statements in their Math Journals explaining their understanding of adding and subtracting fractions and mixed numbers to solve problems.

PRACTICE p. 135

LESSON 135 PRACTICE Name__________

Figure out the answer. Then draw line segments and measure to check.

1. $\frac{3}{4}$ inch + $\frac{1}{8}$ inch = $\frac{7}{8}$ inch
2. $1\frac{1}{4}$ inch + $\frac{1}{2}$ inch = $1\frac{3}{4}$ inches
3. $2\frac{1}{2}$ inches − $\frac{1}{4}$ inch = $2\frac{1}{4}$ inches
4. $\frac{3}{8}$ inch + $\frac{1}{4}$ inch = $\frac{5}{8}$ inch
5. 1 inch − $\frac{1}{4}$ inch = $\frac{3}{4}$ inch
6. $1\frac{3}{8}$ inch + $1\frac{1}{2}$ inch = $2\frac{7}{8}$ inches
7. $2\frac{1}{4}$ inches − $\frac{3}{4}$ inch = $1\frac{1}{2}$ inches
8. 3 inches − $\frac{7}{8}$ inch = $2\frac{1}{8}$ inches

Solve these problems.

9. Betsy placed a book that is $\frac{1}{2}$ inch thick on a book that is $\frac{3}{4}$ inch thick. How thick is the stack of two books? $1\frac{1}{4}$ inches
10. Corey swam $2\frac{1}{4}$ miles on Saturday and $2\frac{3}{4}$ miles on Sunday. How many miles did he swim in those two days? 5
11. Simona bought $1\frac{1}{2}$ pounds of bananas and $2\frac{1}{4}$ pounds of apples. How many pounds of fruit did she buy all together? $3\frac{3}{4}$
12. Mr. Grossman had a 4-foot long piece of wood. He cut off $\frac{1}{2}$ foot. How long was the remaining piece of wood? $3\frac{1}{2}$ feet
13. Jenny had five dollars. She spent a quarter on a pencil and two dollars on a notebook. How much did she have left? $2.75
14. Alex bought $\frac{3}{4}$ of a pound of candy. He ate $\frac{1}{8}$ of a pound of the candy. How much candy does Alex have left? $\frac{5}{8}$ pound

Copyright © SRA/McGraw-Hill. Permission is granted to reproduce this page for classroom use.

Math Explorations and Applications Level 4 • 135

ENRICHMENT p. 135

LESSON 135 ENRICHMENT Name__________

Recipes are often designed to serve four or six people. So what happens when you want to serve 10? 20? 100? 100,000? **The Cruncher: *Recipe Converter*** project can help you convert any recipe to serve any number of people.

Look at The Cruncher recipe for blueberry muffins. Follow the directions for increasing and decreasing the serving sizes.

Bring a favorite recipe from home and type it into the spreadsheet. Try changing it to serve more or fewer people. Try changing it to serve your entire class.

Answers will vary depending on the recipes students choose.

Copyright © SRA/McGraw-Hill. Permission is granted to reproduce this page for classroom use.

Math Explorations and Applications Level 4 • 135

Assessment Criteria

Did the student . . .

- ✓ contribute to the discussion of the problems?
- ✓ understand how to add and subtract fractions?
- ✓ communicate strategies used to add and subtract fractions?
- ✓ correctly answer at least 75% of the computation problems?

Homework Have students draw four line segments of different lengths. They should label the segments *A–D* and measure each one to the nearest $\frac{1}{4}$ inch. Then have them create and solve three addition and three subtraction problems based on their line segments.

LESSON 136

Student Edition pages 456–457

Adding and Subtracting Fractions

LESSON PLANNER

Objectives

- ▶ to demonstrate how to use equivalent fractions to add fractions with unlike denominators
- ▶ to demonstrate how to use equivalent fractions to subtract fractions with unlike denominators

Context of the Lesson This is the 11th of 12 lessons on understanding and using fractions and mixed numbers.

MANIPULATIVES

fraction tower cubes*

Program Resources

Reteaching Master

Practice Master 136

Enrichment Master 136

For extra practice:

CD-ROM* Lesson 136

Cumulative Review, page 564

1 Warm-Up

5 MINUTES

Problem of the Day Present the following problem to the class and suggest that students draw a picture to solve it: The floor of Mr. Gill's tool shed is a square. He covered it with 81 square paving stones. What fraction of the stones forms the border of the floor? ($\frac{32}{81}$)

Problem-Solving Strategies Ask students who have solved the Problem of the Day to share how they solved it and any strategies they used.

MENTAL MATH Provide practice with mixed numbers by having students convert these improper fractions to mixed numbers. Encourage students to respond quickly.

a. $\frac{5}{4}$ ($1\frac{1}{4}$)

b. $\frac{7}{5}$ ($1\frac{2}{5}$)

c. $\frac{10}{7}$ ($1\frac{3}{7}$)

d. $\frac{11}{6}$ ($1\frac{5}{6}$)

e. $\frac{10}{3}$ ($3\frac{1}{3}$)

f. $\frac{9}{2}$ ($4\frac{1}{2}$)

g. $\frac{17}{5}$ ($3\frac{2}{5}$)

h. $\frac{22}{7}$ ($3\frac{1}{7}$)

i. $\frac{29}{8}$ ($3\frac{5}{8}$)

j. $\frac{40}{6}$ ($6\frac{4}{6}$ or $6\frac{2}{3}$)

k. $\frac{64}{9}$ ($7\frac{1}{9}$)

l. $\frac{100}{3}$ ($33\frac{1}{3}$)

EXPLORE

LESSON 136

Adding and Subtracting Fractions

To add or subtract fractions with the same denominator, all we need to do is add or subtract the numerators. The denominator will stay the same. For instance, $\frac{5}{8} - \frac{3}{8} = \frac{2}{8}$. If we like, we can reduce $\frac{2}{8}$. So we could say $\frac{5}{8} - \frac{3}{8} = \frac{2}{8} = \frac{1}{4}$.

Most fractions come from measuring things. Most measurements are made using the same measuring instruments. Therefore, we usually add and subtract fractions that have the same denominator.

Sometimes, however, a person who measures with a ruler that is marked in sixteenths of an inch reports the measure in eighths, fourths, or halves. So we might want to add two fractions in which one denominator is a multiple of the other.

Occasionally we want to add fractions with different denominators that aren't multiples of each other. In these cases we convert the fractions to fractions with the same denominator. We then add or subtract the numerators.

$\frac{1}{3}$

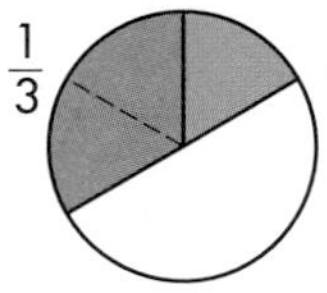

$\frac{1}{6}$

What is $\frac{1}{3} + \frac{1}{6}$? In the figure, $\frac{1}{6}$ of the circle has been shaded, and $\frac{1}{3}$ of the circle has been shaded. If you divide the $\frac{1}{3}$ into two equal parts, each is $\frac{1}{6}$. So we know that $\frac{1}{3}$ is the same as $\frac{2}{6}$. Is that a surprise? How many sixths are shaded in the circle all together?

$$\frac{1}{3} + \frac{1}{6} = \frac{3}{6} \text{ (or } \frac{1}{2}\text{)}$$

Music Connection Western musical notation involves the use of fractions to describe relative note lengths. For instance, students who read music distinguish among whole notes, half notes, quarter notes, eighth notes, and sixteenth notes. Work with the music teacher to present a collaborative lesson in which students add and subtract note lengths based on the standard system of musical notation. Students who study music can help those who do not.

RETEACHING p. 41

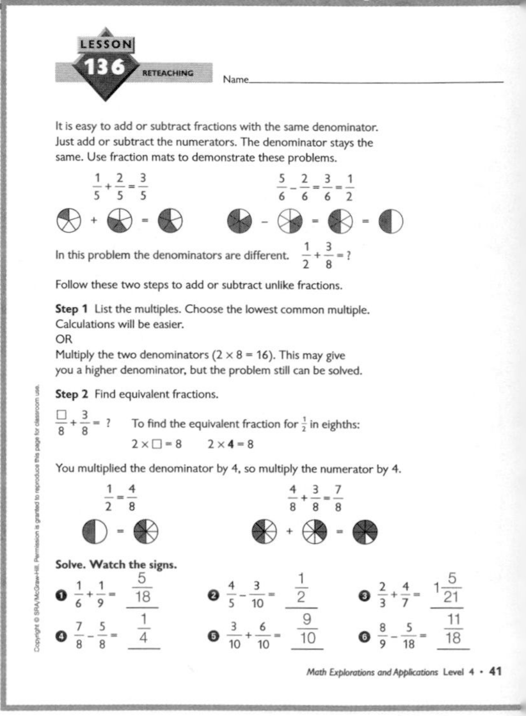

LESSON 136 RETEACHING

Name________________

It is easy to add or subtract fractions with the same denominator. Just add or subtract the numerators. The denominator stays the same. Use fraction mats to demonstrate these problems.

$\frac{1}{5} + \frac{2}{5} = \frac{3}{5}$ $\frac{5}{6} - \frac{2}{6} = \frac{3}{6} = \frac{1}{2}$

In this problem the denominators are different. $\frac{1}{2} + \frac{3}{8} = ?$

Follow these two steps to add or subtract unlike fractions.

Step 1 List the multiples. Choose the lowest common multiple. Calculations will be easier.

OR

Multiply the two denominators ($2 \times 8 = 16$). This may give you a higher denominator, but the problem still can be solved.

Step 2 Find equivalent fractions.

$\frac{\square}{8} + \frac{3}{8} = ?$ To find the equivalent fraction for $\frac{1}{2}$ in eighths:

$2 \times \square = 8$ $2 \times \mathbf{4} = 8$

You multiplied the denominator by 4, so multiply the numerator by 4.

$\frac{1}{2} = \frac{4}{8}$ $\frac{4}{8} + \frac{3}{8} = \frac{7}{8}$

Solve. Watch the signs.

1. $\frac{1}{6} + \frac{1}{9} =$ $\frac{5}{18}$
2. $\frac{4}{5} - \frac{3}{10} =$ $\frac{1}{2}$
3. $\frac{2}{3} + \frac{4}{7} =$ $1\frac{5}{21}$
4. $\frac{7}{8} - \frac{5}{8} =$ $\frac{1}{4}$
5. $\frac{3}{10} + \frac{6}{10} =$ $\frac{9}{10}$
6. $\frac{8}{9} - \frac{5}{18} =$ $\frac{11}{18}$

Copyright © SRA/McGraw-Hill. Permission is granted to reproduce this page for classroom use.

*available separately

If we had wanted to subtract $\frac{1}{4}$ from $\frac{2}{3}$ we would proceed in the same way.

FIGURE 1

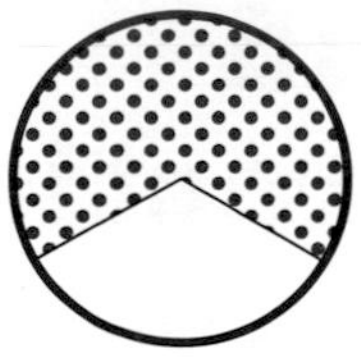

FIGURE 2

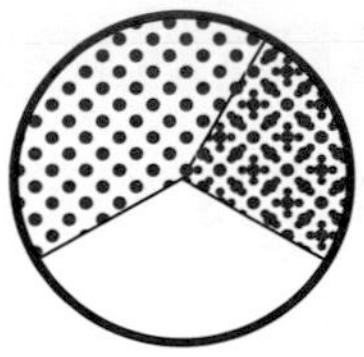

In Figure 1, $\frac{2}{3}$ of the circle has blue dots. In Figure 2, $\frac{1}{4}$ of the circle has blue and red dots. To subtract $\frac{1}{4}$ from $\frac{2}{3}$, notice the part of the circle that has blue dots but not red dots.

FIGURE 3

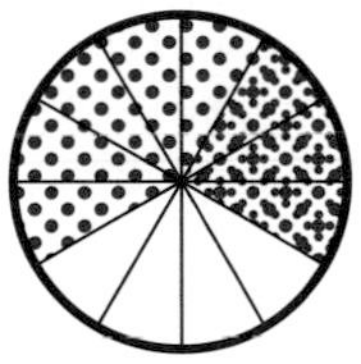

From Figure 2, it is hard to decide what part of the circle has only blue dots. However, if we divide Figure 2 into twelve equal parts as shown in Figure 3, then we see that $\frac{2}{3}$ is equivalent to $\frac{8}{12}$, and $\frac{1}{4}$ is equivalent to $\frac{3}{12}$. When we subtract we get $\frac{5}{12}$. Does $\frac{5}{12}$ of Figure 3 have blue dots but not red dots?

Instead of drawing pictures, you can convert fractions to equivalent fractions with a common denominator. If you multiply a number by 1, does its value change?

Another way to write 1 is $\frac{4}{4}$. Another way to write 1 is $\frac{3}{3}$.

$\frac{2}{3} \times \frac{4}{4} = \frac{8}{12}$ $\frac{1}{4} \times \frac{3}{3} = \frac{3}{12}$

So, $\frac{2}{3} - \frac{1}{4} = \frac{8}{12} - \frac{3}{12} = \frac{5}{12}$

Solve the following problems.

1. $\frac{1}{8} + \frac{3}{8} = n$ **$\frac{4}{8}$ or $\frac{1}{2}$**
2. $\frac{5}{16} + \frac{1}{4} = n$ **$\frac{9}{16}$**
3. $\frac{3}{8} + \frac{5}{8} = n$ **$\frac{8}{8}$ or 1**
4. $\frac{3}{4} - \frac{1}{2} = n$ **$\frac{1}{4}$**
5. $\frac{1}{3} + \frac{1}{8} = n$ **$\frac{11}{24}$**
6. $\frac{1}{2} - \frac{3}{8} = n$ **$\frac{1}{8}$**
7. $\frac{7}{16} - \frac{3}{16} = n$ **$\frac{4}{16}$ or $\frac{1}{4}$**
8. $\frac{3}{4} - \frac{2}{3} = n$ **$\frac{1}{12}$**
9. $\frac{5}{6} - \frac{1}{4} = n$ **$\frac{7}{12}$**

Use the Cumulative Review on page 564 after this lesson.

Unit 6 Lesson 136 • **457**

❷ Teach

Using the Student Pages Discuss with students how to add and subtract fractions with denominators that are not multiples of each other. Explain that another way of solving these kinds of problems is by asking "Into what number will the two denominators divide evenly?" Explain how that number becomes the denominator and that they should divide each denominator into it. Remind them to multiply the numerator by that number and follow through with the operation. Have them reduce if necessary. Then have students complete problems 1–9 on page 457 on their own.

❸ Wrap-Up

5 MINUTES

In Closing Have students explain how to add $\frac{1}{4} + \frac{1}{2}$ and how to subtract $\frac{7}{8} - \frac{3}{4}$.

ALTERNATIVE ASSESSMENT

MANIPULATIVES

Informal Assessment Observe students as they work through the problems in this lesson. Encourage them to draw pictures or use **fraction tower cubes*** to help them add or subtract fractions with unlike denominators.

Assessment Criteria

Did the student . . .

- ✓ contribute to the discussion of adding and subtracting fractions with unlike denominators?
- ✓ communicate strategies for using equivalent fractions to add and subtract fractions with unlike denominators?
- ✓ correctly answer at least seven of the nine problems on page 457?

Homework Have students write a detailed explanation of how to find the sum of $\frac{1}{6} + \frac{2}{3}$, as if they were going to teach this idea to someone who missed today's math lesson.

PRACTICE p. 136

LESSON 136 PRACTICE Name________

Answer these questions.

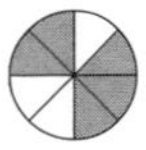

1. What is $\frac{1}{4} + \frac{3}{8}$? $\frac{5}{8}$
2. How many eighths are shaded in the circle all together? 5
3. What is $\frac{1}{2} + \frac{1}{5}$? $\frac{7}{10}$
4. How many tenths are shaded in the circle all together? 7

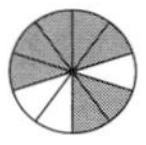

Solve. Watch the signs.

5. $\frac{1}{5} + \frac{2}{5} =$ $\frac{3}{5}$
6. $\frac{4}{5} - \frac{2}{5} =$ $\frac{2}{5}$
7. $\frac{1}{2} - \frac{1}{6} =$ $\frac{2}{6}$ or $\frac{1}{3}$
8. $\frac{3}{4} - \frac{1}{6} =$ $\frac{7}{12}$
9. $\frac{1}{2} + \frac{3}{10} =$ $\frac{8}{10}$ or $\frac{4}{5}$
10. $\frac{4}{5} + \frac{1}{10} =$ $\frac{9}{10}$
11. $\frac{7}{8} - \frac{1}{8} =$ $\frac{6}{8}$ or $\frac{3}{4}$
12. $\frac{1}{2} + \frac{3}{8} =$ $\frac{7}{8}$
13. $\frac{1}{3} + \frac{1}{4} =$ $\frac{7}{12}$
14. $\frac{2}{3} - \frac{7}{12} =$ $\frac{1}{12}$
15. $\frac{1}{8} + \frac{3}{16} =$ $\frac{5}{16}$
16. $\frac{11}{16} - \frac{1}{4} =$ $\frac{7}{16}$
17. $\frac{8}{9} - \frac{2}{9} =$ $\frac{6}{9}$ or $\frac{2}{3}$
18. $\frac{3}{7} + \frac{4}{7} =$ $\frac{7}{7}$ or 1
19. $\frac{7}{16} - \frac{3}{8} =$ $\frac{1}{16}$
20. $\frac{1}{3} + \frac{1}{6} =$ $\frac{3}{6}$ or $\frac{1}{2}$
21. $\frac{5}{6} - \frac{1}{6} =$ $\frac{4}{6}$ or $\frac{2}{3}$
22. $\frac{1}{3} + \frac{5}{12} =$ $\frac{9}{12}$ or $\frac{3}{4}$

Copyright © SRA/McGraw-Hill. Permission is granted to reproduce this page for classroom use.

136 • *Math Explorations and Applications* Level 4

ENRICHMENT p. 136

LESSON 136 ENRICHMENT Name________

These marbles are arranged to look like an arrowhead pointing to the right.

Make the arrowhead point to the left—by moving only three marbles!

Draw the new arrowhead in the space below, and show which marbles you moved where to make the arrowhead point to the left.

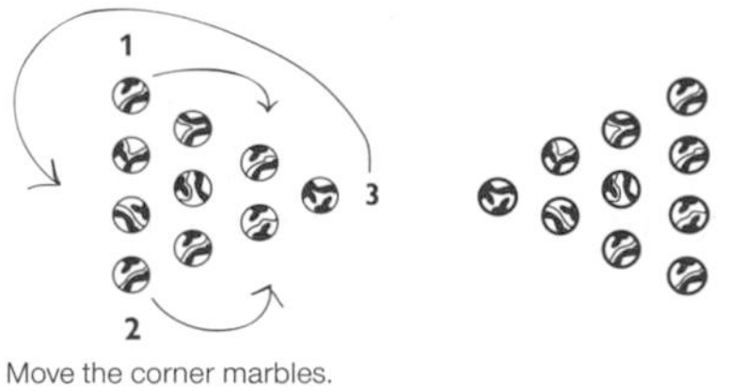

Move the corner marbles.

Copyright © SRA/McGraw-Hill. Permission is granted to reproduce this page for classroom use.

136 • *Math Explorations and Applications* Level 4

*available separately

LESSON 137

Student Edition pages 458–459

Adding and Subtracting Mixed Numbers and Improper Fractions

LESSON PLANNER

Objective

- ▶ to demonstrate how to use equivalent improper fractions to add and subtract mixed numbers with unlike denominators

Context of the Lesson This is the last of 12 lessons on understanding and using fractions and mixed numbers.

MANIPULATIVES

newspapers, magazines, flyers, and catalogs (optional)

index cards (optional)

Program Resources

Reteaching Master

Practice Master 137

Enrichment Master 137

For extra practice:
CD-ROM* Lesson 137

1 Warm-Up (5 MINUTES)

Problem of the Day Present the following problem on the chalkboard: Find the rules that fit all fractions inside the rectangle, triangle, and circle. Then add one more fraction to each shape that follows the rules you found. (All fractions in the rectangle are equivalent to $\frac{1}{2}$; all fractions in the triangle are improper and their numerators are 1 more than their denominators; all fractions in the circle are in eighths.)

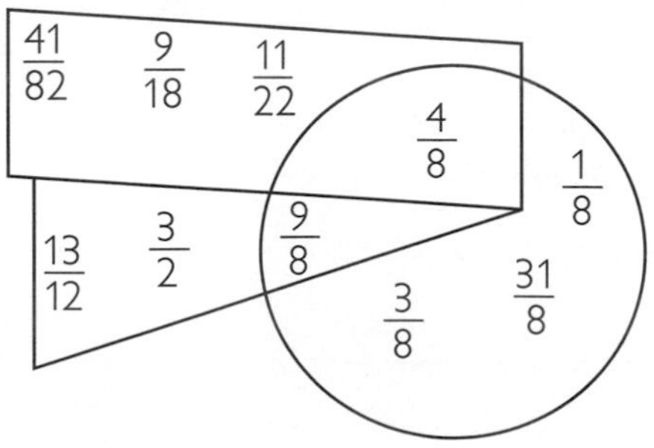

Problem-Solving Strategies Ask students who have solved the Problem of the Day to share how they solved it and any strategies they used.

EXPLORE

LESSON 137

Adding and Subtracting Mixed Numbers and Improper Fractions

You can add or subtract mixed numbers and improper fractions the same way you add and subtract other fractions. You may want to convert mixed numbers to improper fractions.

For example, $3\frac{1}{7} - 2\frac{2}{3}$ can be changed to $\frac{22}{7} - \frac{8}{3}$. We can rewrite this as $\frac{66}{21} - \frac{56}{21} = \frac{10}{21}$. There are other possible ways you could solve this. Choose whichever one makes the most sense.

Solve the following addition and subtraction problems. Write your answers as mixed numbers, fractions, or whole numbers.

1. $\frac{1}{3} + \frac{5}{3} = n$ **2**
2. $n = 6\frac{2}{3} - 4\frac{1}{7}$ **$2\frac{11}{21}$**
3. $n = 7\frac{5}{32} - 2\frac{1}{4}$ **$4\frac{29}{32}$**
4. $\frac{1}{3} + 1\frac{2}{3} = n$ **2**
5. $4\frac{1}{5} + 2\frac{3}{10} = n$ **$6\frac{1}{2}$**
6. $n = 4\frac{4}{16} - 3\frac{1}{4}$ **1**
7. $\frac{5}{4} + 7\frac{1}{4} = n$ **$8\frac{1}{2}$**
8. $3\frac{5}{16} - 1\frac{1}{4} = n$ **$2\frac{1}{16}$**
9. $2\frac{1}{2} + 7\frac{5}{8} = n$ **$10\frac{1}{8}$**
10. $2 + 1\frac{3}{7} = n$ **$3\frac{3}{7}$**
11. $n = 2\frac{7}{15} + 3\frac{8}{15}$ **6**
12. $3\frac{5}{12} - 2\frac{1}{6} = n$ **$1\frac{1}{4}$**
13. $\frac{1}{2} - \frac{1}{3} = n$ **$\frac{1}{6}$**
14. $4\frac{13}{16} - 3\frac{3}{4} = n$ **$1\frac{1}{16}$**
15. $n = 4\frac{19}{32} + 3\frac{7}{8}$ **$8\frac{15}{32}$**
16. $7\frac{1}{2} - 2\frac{1}{3} = n$ **$5\frac{1}{6}$**
17. $5\frac{5}{8} - 3\frac{1}{2} = n$ **$2\frac{1}{8}$**
18. $3\frac{12}{32} + 6\frac{5}{8} = n$ **10**
19. $n = 7\frac{1}{2} - 4\frac{1}{4}$ **$3\frac{1}{4}$**
20. $n = 5\frac{7}{8} + 2\frac{3}{4}$ **$8\frac{5}{8}$**
21. $3\frac{1}{2} + 7\frac{3}{8} = n$ **$10\frac{7}{8}$**

Real-World Connection (MANIPULATIVES) Have students look through **newspapers, magazines, store flyers,** and **catalogs** for examples of mixed numbers in everyday situations. Have them display their examples on a class bulletin board and write an improper fraction on an **index card** or self-stick note for each mixed number on display. Students can use the bulletin board interactively by trying to match each mixed number with its improper fraction.

RETEACHING p. 42

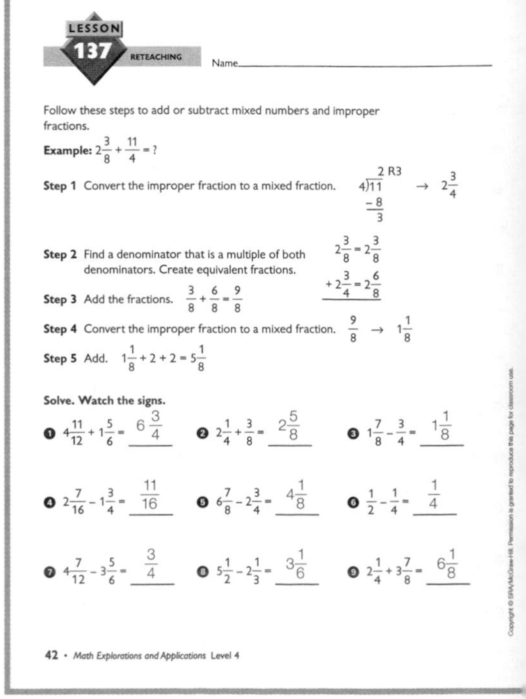
LESSON 137 RETEACHING Name______________

Follow these steps to add or subtract mixed numbers and improper fractions.

Example: $2\frac{3}{8} + \frac{11}{4} = ?$

Step 1 Convert the improper fraction to a mixed fraction. $4\overline{)11}$ = 2 R3, -8, 3 → $2\frac{3}{4}$

Step 2 Find a denominator that is a multiple of both denominators. Create equivalent fractions. $2\frac{3}{8} = 2\frac{3}{8}$; $+2\frac{3}{4} = 2\frac{6}{8}$

Step 3 Add the fractions. $\frac{3}{8} + \frac{6}{8} = \frac{9}{8}$

Step 4 Convert the improper fraction to a mixed fraction. $\frac{9}{8} \rightarrow 1\frac{1}{8}$

Step 5 Add. $1\frac{1}{8} + 2 + 2 = 5\frac{1}{8}$

Solve. Watch the signs.

1. $4\frac{11}{12} + 1\frac{5}{6} =$ $6\frac{3}{4}$
2. $2\frac{1}{4} + \frac{3}{8} =$ $2\frac{5}{8}$
3. $1\frac{7}{8} - \frac{3}{4} =$ $1\frac{1}{8}$
4. $2\frac{7}{16} - 1\frac{3}{4} =$ $\frac{11}{16}$
5. $6\frac{7}{8} - 2\frac{3}{4} =$ $4\frac{1}{8}$
6. $\frac{1}{2} - \frac{1}{4} =$ $\frac{1}{4}$
7. $4\frac{7}{12} - 3\frac{5}{6} =$ $\frac{3}{4}$
8. $5\frac{1}{2} - 2\frac{1}{3} =$ $3\frac{1}{6}$
9. $2\frac{1}{4} + 3\frac{7}{8} =$ $6\frac{1}{8}$

42 • *Math Explorations and Applications* Level 4

Copyright © SRA/McGraw-Hill. Permission is granted to reproduce this page for classroom use.

*available separately

Solve these problems.

Wendy is making a cabinet with five drawers. Each drawer of the cabinet will be $3\frac{3}{4}$ inches tall. The base will be $1\frac{1}{2}$ inches tall, and the section above the drawers will be $\frac{7}{8}$ inches tall.

22. How much room is needed for the five drawers? **$18\frac{3}{4}$ in.**
23. How much room is needed for the base and top section together? **$2\frac{3}{8}$ in.**
24. How much room is needed for the five drawers, the base, and the top section combined? **$21\frac{1}{8}$ in.**

Peter made a cake. The recipe for the frosting called for $1\frac{1}{2}$ cups of sugar. The recipe for the cake itself called for $1\frac{2}{3}$ cups of sugar. He wanted to know how much sugar was in the cake, including the frosting.

25. How much sugar was needed all together? **$3\frac{1}{6}$ cups**

Peter decided the cake and frosting were too sweet, so the next time he put only $\frac{3}{4}$ cup of sugar in the frosting and $1\frac{2}{3}$ cups of sugar in the cake.

26. How much less sugar was in the frosting than before? **$\frac{3}{4}$ cup**
27. How much less sugar was in only the cake than before? **0**
28. How much less sugar was in the combined cake and frosting? **$\frac{3}{4}$ cup**

Peter decided that the second cake didn't taste as good as he would have liked. He decided to use a sugar substitute. One teaspoon of the substitute $= \frac{1}{3}$ cup of sugar. The next time he made a cake he went back to the original recipe but used the substitute in place of some of the sugar. This was the best cake yet!

29. If Peter uses 3 teaspoons of the substitute in the frosting, how much less sugar should he use? How much regular sugar will he use in the frosting? **1 cup; $\frac{1}{2}$ cup**
30. If he uses 2 teaspoons of the substitute in the cake, how much sugar should he use? **1 cup**
31. With 5 teaspoons of sugar substitute, how much less sugar will he need to use in the cake? How much sugar will be used in the cake and the frosting all together? **$\frac{2}{3}$ cup; $1\frac{1}{2}$ cup**

PRACTICE p. 137

LESSON 137 PRACTICE Name__________

Solve. Write your answers as either mixed numbers or proper fractions (or whole numbers if possible).

1. $3\frac{1}{8} + \frac{7}{8} =$ 4
2. $4\frac{5}{32} - 3\frac{1}{8} =$ $1\frac{1}{32}$
3. $3 + 1\frac{5}{6} =$ $4\frac{5}{6}$
4. $\frac{1}{4} - \frac{1}{8} =$ $\frac{1}{8}$
5. $5\frac{1}{2} - 2\frac{1}{4} =$ $3\frac{1}{4}$
6. $5\frac{10}{32} + 1\frac{3}{8} =$ $6\frac{22}{32}$ or $6\frac{11}{16}$
7. $6\frac{3}{4} - 2\frac{6}{8} =$ 4
8. $3\frac{2}{5} + 4\frac{3}{5} =$ 8
9. $5\frac{3}{5} - 2\frac{1}{10} =$ $3\frac{5}{10}$ or $3\frac{1}{2}$
10. $4\frac{2}{3} - 1\frac{1}{8} =$ $3\frac{13}{24}$
11. $9\frac{1}{16} + 4\frac{1}{4} =$ $13\frac{5}{16}$
12. $\frac{3}{2} + 6\frac{1}{2} =$ 8
13. $4\frac{8}{32} - 2\frac{1}{8} =$ $2\frac{1}{8}$
14. $1\frac{5}{16} + 3\frac{3}{8} =$ $4\frac{11}{16}$

Solve these problems.

15. Cathy ran $2\frac{1}{2}$ miles on Monday and $3\frac{1}{8}$ miles on Tuesday. How far did she run over the two days? $5\frac{5}{8}$ miles
16. Mr. Walters worked $6\frac{1}{4}$ hours on Thursday and $8\frac{3}{4}$ hours on Friday. How many hours did he work over the two days? 15
17. Sam caught a $3\frac{5}{16}$-pound fish. The record for that lake was an $11\frac{1}{2}$-pound fish. How much less did Sam's fish weigh? $8\frac{3}{16}$ pounds
18. Mia has $1\frac{3}{8}$ cups of flour. She needs $4\frac{3}{4}$ cups of flour for baking. How much more flour does Mia need? $3\frac{3}{8}$ cups

Copyright © SRA/McGraw-Hill. Permission is granted to reproduce this page for classroom use.

Math Explorations and Applications Level 4 • 137

ENRICHMENT p. 137

LESSON 137 ENRICHMENT Name__________

Choose four numbers that use three steps to get to a common difference and write them in a square, like this.

3 6

7 1

Connect two numbers using a straight line (no diagonals). Find the difference between the two numbers and write it above or beside the center of the line you just drew.

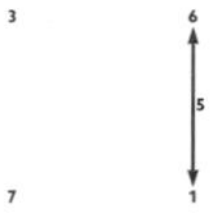

Do the same with the other pairs.

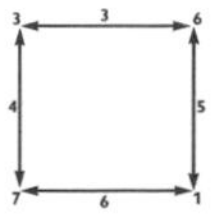

Connect your new numbers with straight lines and find and write their differences. Do it a third time to reach a common difference.

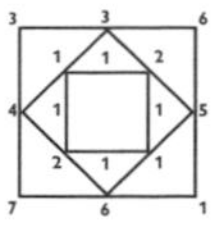

Pick four numbers that need four steps to reach a common difference, using the same method as above.
To use four steps, three of the numbers must be 0.

Copyright © SRA/McGraw-Hill. Permission is granted to reproduce this page for classroom use.

Math Explorations and Applications Level 4 • 137

MENTAL MATH Have students convert these mixed numbers to improper fractions. Encourage quick responses.

a. $3\frac{1}{2}$ $(\frac{7}{2})$ **b.** $4\frac{1}{4}$ $(\frac{17}{4})$
c. $5\frac{1}{3}$ $(\frac{16}{3})$ **d.** $6\frac{1}{5}$ $(\frac{31}{5})$

2 Teach

Using the Student Pages Review how to convert a mixed number to an improper fraction. Explain that the process of adding and subtracting improper fractions is the same as it is for proper fractions. Do several examples with the class. Then have students complete the problems on pages 458 and 459 individually. Talk about students' solutions when everyone has finished.

3 Wrap-Up 5 MINUTES

In Closing Ask students why it is useful to know how to change mixed numbers to improper fractions in order to add and subtract.

ALTERNATIVE ASSESSMENT

Informal Assessment Observe students as they work through the problems in this lesson. Provide assistance as necessary.

Assessment Criteria

Did the student . . .

- ✓ contribute to the discussion of adding and subtracting mixed numbers and improper fractions?
- ✓ apply skills from previous lessons to compute with mixed numbers and improper fractions?
- ✓ correctly answer at least 75% of the computation problems?

Homework Have students make up two problems that involve adding mixed numbers and two that involve subtracting mixed numbers. Ask them to solve the problems and be prepared to explain their solution methods.

UNIT 6

Student Edition pages 460–463

Mid-Unit Review

The Mid-Unit Review pinpoints troublesome skill areas for students, allowing time for additional practice and reteaching before the unit ends. If students did not do well on the Mid-Unit Review and have completed additional practice, you may want to use the Mid-Unit Review provided on Assessment Blackline Masters pages 54–55.

Using the Student Pages Have students complete problems 1–75 on pages 460–463 on their own. You might treat this review as a formal assessment of students' skills and have students complete this review as a timed test. See suggestions on page 51.

UNIT 6

ASSESSMENT

Mid-Unit Review

What fraction of each of the following figures has been shaded?

1. 
$\frac{5}{6}$

2. 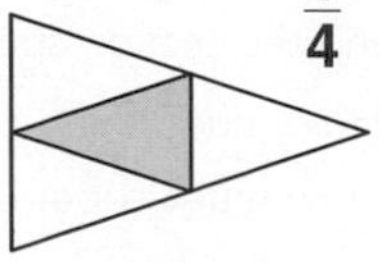
$\frac{1}{4}$

What fraction of each of the following sets has a ring around it?

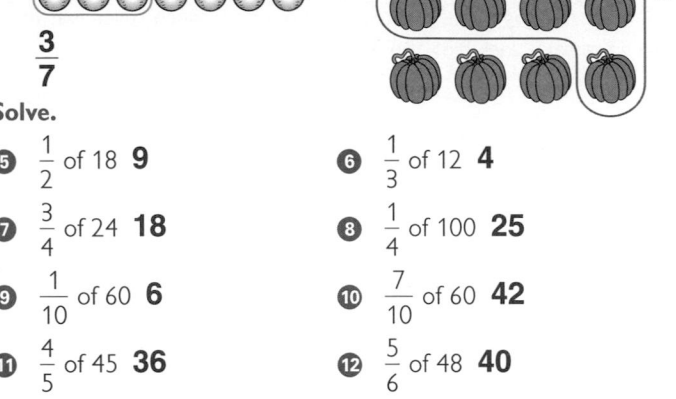

3. 
$\frac{3}{7}$

4. 
$\frac{5}{8}$

Solve.

5. $\frac{1}{2}$ of 18 **9**
6. $\frac{1}{3}$ of 12 **4**
7. $\frac{3}{4}$ of 24 **18**
8. $\frac{1}{4}$ of 100 **25**
9. $\frac{1}{10}$ of 60 **6**
10. $\frac{7}{10}$ of 60 **42**
11. $\frac{4}{5}$ of 45 **36**
12. $\frac{5}{6}$ of 48 **40**

For each of the following spinners, give the probability that the pointer will stop on red.

13. 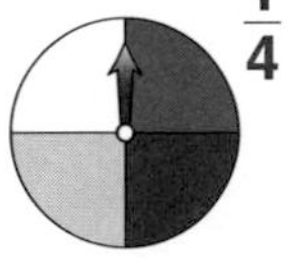
$\frac{1}{4}$

14. 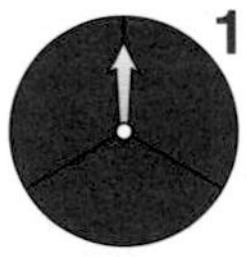
1

PROBLEM SOLVING

Use your understanding of finding fractions of numbers to solve these problems.

15. An election in the camera club only counts if at least $\frac{2}{3}$ of the members vote. The camera club has 30 members. How many members must vote for an election to count? **20**

16 About $\frac{6}{7}$ of the total population is right-handed. There are 35 students in Rico's class. About how many students in his class might be right-handed? **30**

17 The in-line skates Jessica wants cost $75. Starting next week, the skates will go on sale for $\frac{1}{3}$ off the regular price. How much will Jessica pay for the skates if she buys them on sale? **$50**

18 About $\frac{4}{5}$ of the people who come to Dr. Lieder's dental office each week are there for check-ups. If Dr. Lieder sees 50 patients a week, about how many are there for check-ups? **about 40**

What fraction of the circle is shaded?

19 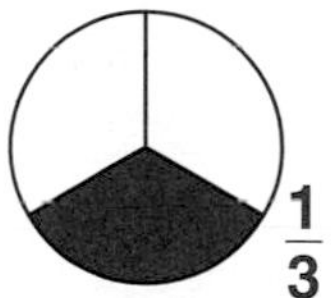 **$\frac{1}{3}$**

20 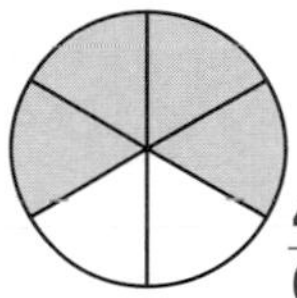 **$\frac{4}{6}$ $(\frac{2}{3})$**

21 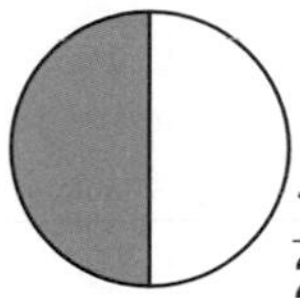 **$\frac{1}{2}$**

Answer these questions.

22 Which is greater, $\frac{1}{3}$ of the circle or $\frac{1}{6}$ of the circle? **$\frac{1}{3}$**

23 Which is greater, $\frac{2}{6}$ of the circle or $\frac{2}{3}$ of the circle? **$\frac{2}{3}$**

24 Which is greater, $\frac{3}{6}$ of the circle or $\frac{1}{2}$ of the circle? **They are the same.**

Convert each fraction to a fraction that is equivalent but has a denominator of 16.

25 $\frac{1}{2}$ **$\frac{8}{16}$**
26 $\frac{1}{4}$ **$\frac{4}{16}$**
27 $\frac{1}{8}$ **$\frac{2}{16}$**
28 $\frac{2}{4}$ **$\frac{8}{16}$**
29 $\frac{3}{4}$ **$\frac{12}{16}$**
30 $\frac{3}{8}$ **$\frac{6}{16}$**
31 $\frac{5}{8}$ **$\frac{10}{16}$**
32 $\frac{6}{8}$ **$\frac{12}{16}$**

Show which fraction of the circle is larger or whether they are the same. Replace ● with <, >, or =.

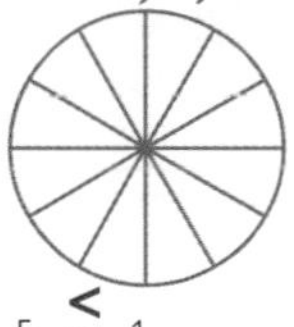

33 $\frac{1}{4}$ ● $\frac{1}{6}$ **>**
34 $\frac{5}{12}$ ● $\frac{1}{2}$ **<**
35 $\frac{1}{3}$ ● $\frac{4}{12}$ **=**

Unit 6 Mid-Unit Review • **461**

Home Connections You may want to send home the Home Connections Blackline Masters letter on pages 54–55 to provide additional activities that families can complete together. These activities apply the skills presented in this unit.

ALTERNATIVE ASSESSMENT

Portfolio Assessment The Portfolio Assessment task provided on Assessment Blackline Masters page 98 can be used at this time to evaluate students' ability to use fractions to alter a recipe for various numbers of servings.

ALTERNATIVE ASSESSMENT

Performance Assessment Performance Assessment Task 1, provided on Assessment Blackline Masters pages 87–88, can be used at this time to evaluate students' proficiency with fractional notation. You may want to administer this assessment to individual students or small groups of students.

Unit Project This would be a good time to assign the "Fairlawn School Buys a Computer" project on pages 532 and 533. Students can begin working on the project in cooperative groups in their free time as they work through the unit. The Unit Project is a good opportunity for students to analyze and design a fund-raising event and consider notions of "fairness" with respect to pricing, advertising, and raising funds for a useful cause.

◆ UNIT 6 Mid-Unit Review

◆ Unit 6 Mid-Unit Review

Solve.

36. Marty and Marcia share a pizza that is sliced into eight equal pieces. If Marcia eats three pieces, will she have eaten more or less than $\frac{1}{2}$ of the pizza? **less**

37. Kazumi read $\frac{3}{4}$ of a 240-page book, and Ken read $\frac{1}{2}$ of a 210-page book.
    - **a.** Who read more pages? **Kazumi**
    - **b.** Who read more sentences? **can't tell**

38. Gabriel saves $5 each week. How much can he save in 40 weeks? **$200**

39. Dawn has $20.00. She wants to buy a scarf for $7.98 and a pair of slippers for $13.44. Does she have enough money? **no**

40. Frida has 30 feet of chicken wire. If she builds a pen with an area of 32 square feet, is it possible that she has enough chicken wire to enclose it? **yes**

41. A movie lasts 2 hours and 20 minutes. If the movie begins at 3:45 P.M., what time will it end? **6:05 P.M.**

42. Jason is $9\frac{1}{2}$ years old. In how many years will he be 18 years old? **$8\frac{1}{2}$**

Write a mixed number to represent how many are shown.

43. 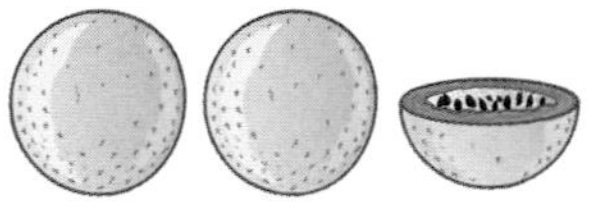 **$2\frac{1}{2}$ melons**

44.  **$1\frac{1}{4}$ dollars**

Change each improper fraction to a mixed number, or to a whole number, if possible.

45. $\frac{7}{2}$ $\mathbf{3\frac{1}{2}}$ 46. $\frac{4}{3}$ $\mathbf{1\frac{1}{3}}$ 47. $\frac{9}{6}$ $\mathbf{1\frac{1}{2}}$ 48. $\frac{12}{4}$ **3**

49. $\frac{27}{5}$ $\mathbf{5\frac{2}{5}}$ 50. $\frac{33}{8}$ $\mathbf{4\frac{1}{8}}$ 51. $\frac{15}{5}$ **3** 52. $\frac{23}{5}$ $\mathbf{4\frac{3}{5}}$

53. $\frac{30}{8}$ $\mathbf{3\frac{3}{4}}$ 54. $\frac{10}{4}$ $\mathbf{2\frac{1}{2}}$ 55. $\frac{16}{3}$ $\mathbf{5\frac{1}{3}}$ 56. $\frac{16}{4}$ **4**

Change each mixed number to an improper fraction.

57. $4\frac{1}{2}$ $\mathbf{\frac{9}{2}}$ 58. $1\frac{5}{6}$ $\mathbf{\frac{11}{6}}$ 59. $3\frac{3}{4}$ $\mathbf{\frac{15}{4}}$ 60. $2\frac{1}{3}$ $\mathbf{\frac{7}{3}}$

61. $5\frac{5}{6}$ $\mathbf{\frac{35}{6}}$ 62. $6\frac{7}{8}$ $\mathbf{\frac{55}{8}}$ 63. $1\frac{3}{10}$ $\mathbf{\frac{13}{10}}$ 64. $2\frac{4}{7}$ $\mathbf{\frac{18}{7}}$

65. $4\frac{4}{9}$ $\mathbf{\frac{40}{9}}$ 66. $9\frac{3}{5}$ $\mathbf{\frac{48}{5}}$ 67. $2\frac{3}{4}$ $\mathbf{\frac{11}{4}}$ 68. $3\frac{2}{3}$ $\mathbf{\frac{11}{3}}$

Estimate the length. Then measure to the nearest $\frac{1}{8}$ inch.

69. |————————| $\mathbf{1\frac{5}{16}}$ **in.**

Solve. Write your answers as mixed numbers, fractions, or whole numbers, if possible.

70. $\frac{9}{16} - \frac{3}{16}$ $\mathbf{\frac{6}{16}}$ **(or $\mathbf{\frac{3}{8}}$)**

71. $\frac{5}{6} + \frac{1}{4}$ $\mathbf{\frac{13}{12}}$ **(or $\mathbf{1\frac{1}{12}}$)**

72. $\frac{2}{3} + 3\frac{1}{3}$ **4**

73. $6\frac{3}{4} - 2\frac{1}{2}$ $\mathbf{\frac{17}{4}}$ **(or $\mathbf{4\frac{1}{4}}$)**

74. $4\frac{1}{3} + 3\frac{11}{12}$ $\mathbf{\frac{99}{12}}$ **(or $\mathbf{8\frac{1}{4}}$)**

75. $3\frac{15}{16} - 1\frac{1}{4}$ $\mathbf{\frac{43}{16}}$ **(or $\mathbf{2\frac{11}{16}}$)**

ASSESSMENT p. 54

UNIT 6 **Mid-Unit Review** (Use after Lesson 137.) Page 1 of 2

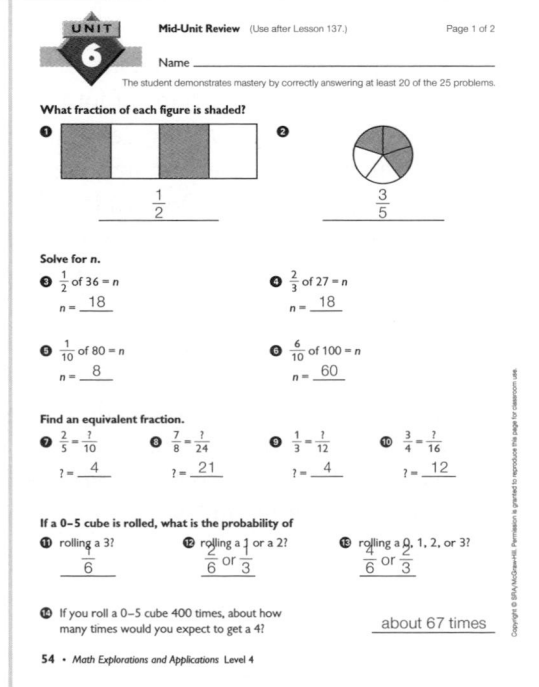

Name ________________

The student demonstrates mastery by correctly answering at least 20 of the 25 problems.

What fraction of each figure is shaded?

1. $\frac{1}{2}$
2. $\frac{3}{5}$

Solve for *n*.

3. $\frac{1}{2}$ of $36 = n$ $n =$ 18
4. $\frac{2}{3}$ of $27 = n$ $n =$ 18
5. $\frac{1}{10}$ of $80 = n$ $n =$ 8
6. $\frac{6}{10}$ of $100 = n$ $n =$ 60

Find an equivalent fraction.

7. $\frac{2}{5} = \frac{?}{10}$? = 4
8. $\frac{7}{8} = \frac{?}{24}$? = 21
9. $\frac{1}{3} = \frac{?}{12}$? = 4
10. $\frac{3}{4} = \frac{?}{16}$? = 12

If a 0–5 cube is rolled, what is the probability of

11. rolling a 3? $\frac{1}{6}$
12. rolling a 1 or a 2? $\frac{2}{6}$ or $\frac{1}{3}$
13. rolling a 0, 1, 2, or 3? $\frac{4}{6}$ or $\frac{2}{3}$
14. If you roll a 0–5 cube 400 times, about how many times would you expect to get a 4? about 67 times

Copyright © SRA/McGraw-Hill. Permission is granted to reproduce this page for classroom use.

54 • *Math Explorations and Applications* Level 4

LESSON 138

Student Edition pages 464–467

Parts of a Whole

LESSON PLANNER

Objectives

- ▶ to reintroduce the meaning of standard notation for decimals
- ▶ to demonstrate the relationship of decimals to corresponding fractions
- ▶ to review the concept of decimal place value

Context of the Lesson This is the first of 16 lessons on decimals. Students have worked with decimals used to represent monetary amounts throughout the year. The first five lessons in this sequence provide opportunities to build an understanding of decimals before going on to metric measurement and arithmetic with decimals.

MANIPULATIVES

decimal place-value pad*

play money*

magazines, newspapers, and ads (optional)

Program Resources

Reteaching Master

Practice Master 138

Enrichment Master 138

For extra practice:
CD-ROM* Lesson 138

1 Warm-Up (5 MINUTES)

Problem of the Day Present this problem: Franny and Karen are twins. They began earning money by baby-sitting when they were 12 years old. Franny started out charging \$2.50 per hour and got a raise of 40¢ per hour on her birthday each year. Karen began charging \$2.90 per hour and got a raise of 30¢ per hour on her birthday each year. How old were the twins when both charged the same hourly rate? What was that amount? (When they were 16, each charged \$4.10 per hour.)

Problem-Solving Strategies Ask students who have solved the Problem of the Day to share how they solved it and any strategies they used.

MENTAL MATH Write the number 4 on the chalkboard. Then read the following series of decimals aloud. Students respond by showing thumbs up if the decimal you say is greater than 4, showing thumbs down if it is less than 4, and standing if the decimal is equal to 4.

(continued on page 465)

PRACTICE

LESSON 138

Parts of a Whole

"I just made up a game," said June. "What's the least number greater than 0 that you can make?"

"I know," shouted Andy. "It's 1."

"I can do better than that," said Rico. "I say $\frac{1}{2}$."

"That's not fair," said Andy. "We can't use that kind of number."

"It's my game," said June. "Any kind of number is all right. And I'm going to say $\frac{1}{10}$."

"Well," said Andy, "I can make a number that's even less."

◆ Can you make a number less than $\frac{1}{10}$? **yes; for example, $\frac{1}{100}$**

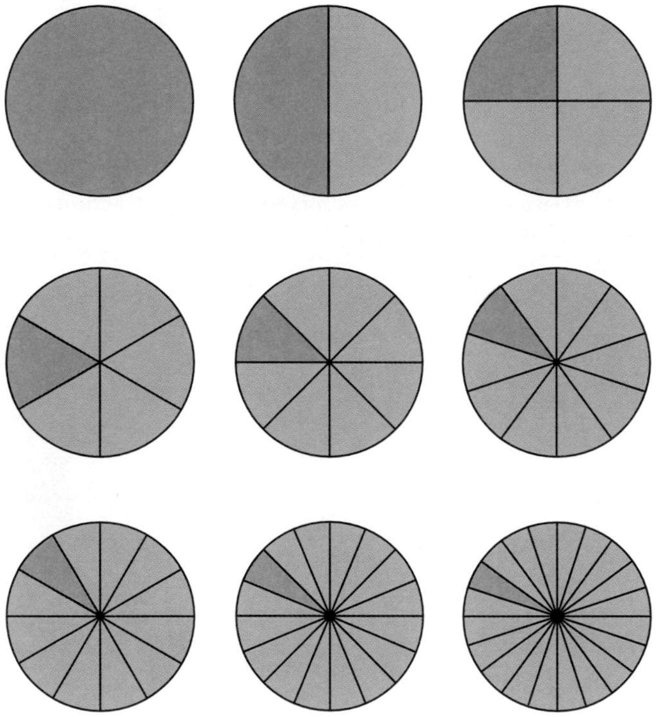

COOPERATIVE LEARNING Have students work in groups of four to practice reading and writing decimals and to make the connection between fractions and decimals. One student says a decimal, such as "four point zero six." Another student writes it in standard decimal form, another student reads it in standard form, ("four and six hundredths"), and another student writes the fraction or mixed number equivalent to it. Students rotate tasks so that everyone has the opportunity to try each role.

*available separately

If you divide a whole into ten equal parts, each part is one tenth of the whole.

We can write one tenth in two ways:

As a fraction: $\frac{1}{10}$ $\frac{1}{10} = 0.1$

As a decimal: 0.1

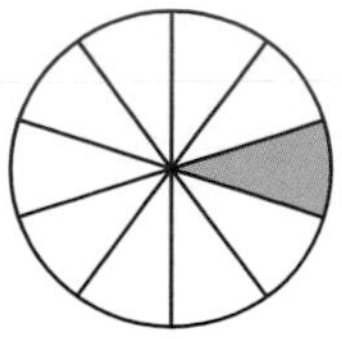

When you read 0.1, you say "one tenth" or "zero point one."

If you divide a whole into 100 equal parts, each part is one hundredth of the whole.

We can write one hundredth in two ways:

As a fraction: $\frac{1}{100}$ $\frac{1}{100} = 0.01$

As a decimal: 0.01

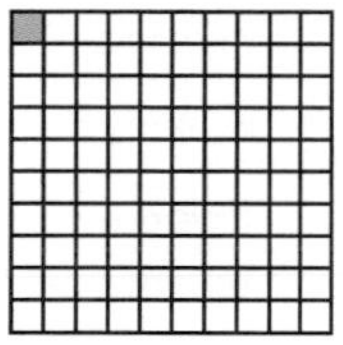

When you read 0.01, you say "one hundredth" or "zero point zero one."

Answer these questions.

1. Suppose you divide something into 1000 equal parts. What would each part be? Write it in two ways. **$\frac{1}{1000}$, 0.001**
2. Suppose you divide something into 10,000 equal parts. Show two ways to write what each part would be. **$\frac{1}{10{,}000}$, 0.0001**
3. Suppose you divide something into 100,000 equal parts. Show two ways to write what each part would be. **$\frac{1}{100{,}000}$, 0.00001**
4. Suppose you divide something into 1,000,000 equal parts. Show two ways to write what each part would be. **$\frac{1}{1{,}000{,}000}$, 0.000001**
5. Which is greater, $\frac{1}{10}$ or $\frac{1}{100}$? **$\frac{1}{10}$**
6. Which is greater, 0.1 or 0.01? **0.1**
7. Which is greater, 0.1 or 0.001? **0.1**

Mental Math (continued)

a. 7.00 (thumbs up) **b.** 5.0 (thumbs up)
c. 0.6 (thumbs down) **d.** 8.0 (thumbs up)
e. 4.00 (stand up) **f.** 0.73 (thumbs down)
g. 4.1 (thumbs up) **h.** 0.0958 (thumbs down)
i. 3.09 (thumbs down) **j.** 4.001 (thumbs up)

❷ Teach

Using the Student Pages Read the story on page 464 with the class and then discuss the question. Students may give successively lesser answers, such as one thousandth, one millionth, and so on. Guide students to realize that there are many very low numbers that are greater than 0. Proceed to page 465, which deals with the meaning of, and ways to write, lesser decimal numbers. Review the top of page 465 with the class. If most students have a solid understanding of this material, encourage them to solve problems 1–7 on their own. Otherwise, solve the problems as a class and have students verbalize their answers.

Note: This program follows the convention of writing a 0 in the ones place for decimals less than 1, except in cases where it might be confusing. However, written answers and oral responses that omit the 0 should be accepted.

CULTURAL DIVERSITY Some cultures follow the convention of using a comma rather than a decimal point to indicate the break between whole and fractional parts of a decimal number. You might point out this variation, especially if some students in your class may have seen or used this form.

LANGUAGE ARTS CONNECTION **Language Arts Connection** Help students recognize the spelling and pronunciation distinctions between the terms *tens* and *tenths, hundreds* and *hundredths,* and *thousands* and *thousandths.* Emphasize the importance of making these distinctions clear to avoid math misunderstandings.

PRACTICE

◆ LESSON 138 Parts of a Whole

Teach

Using the Student Pages When discussing page 466 with the class, draw a chart on the chalkboard similar to the one in the Student Edition. Use **play money*** for clarification as needed. For example, ask students whether they would rather have three dollars or 0.3 dollars. Next, discuss "going to the right." Emphasize the importance of the decimal point as an indication of the break between the whole number part and the fractional part of the decimal. You may want to use a **place-value pad*** to demonstrate this relationship. Proceed to page 467 and review the material at the top of the page with the class. Have students solve problems 8–37 on their own or in pairs. Then go over the problems together, having volunteers write their answers on the chalkboard and say them aloud.

◆ LESSON 138 Parts of a Whole

Our system of writing numbers is based on 10. Look at the number 3333.

thousands	hundreds	tens	ones
3	3	3	3

The red 3 stands for 3 ones.

What does the orange 3 stand for? **3 tens**

What does the green 3 stand for? **3 hundreds**

What does the blue 3 stand for? **3 thousands**

As we move to the left, each place is worth ten times as much.

A 3 in the tens place is ten times the value of a 3 in the ones place.

A 3 in the hundreds place is ten times a 3 in the tens place.

If you move to the right, it's just the opposite. Each place is worth one tenth as much.

A 3 in the tens place is one tenth of a 3 in the hundreds place.

A 3 in the ones place is one tenth of a 3 in the tens place.

Thousands	Hundreds	Tens	Ones

◆ What happens if you keep going to the right?

The next place is one tenth of 1. That's the tenths place.

Thousands	Hundreds	Tens	Ones	Tenths	?

◆ What happens if you keep going?

The next place is one tenth of one tenth. That's the hundredths place.

Thousands	Hundreds	Tens	Ones	Tenths	Hundredths

◆ How do you know what place you are in?

Real-World Connection Have students look through **magazines, newspapers, advertisements, product packaging,** or other real-world materials to find examples of the use of decimal notation. Encourage students to bring in examples to display on a poster or bulletin board. Use the display for students to practice reading and comparing decimals.

RETEACHING p. 43

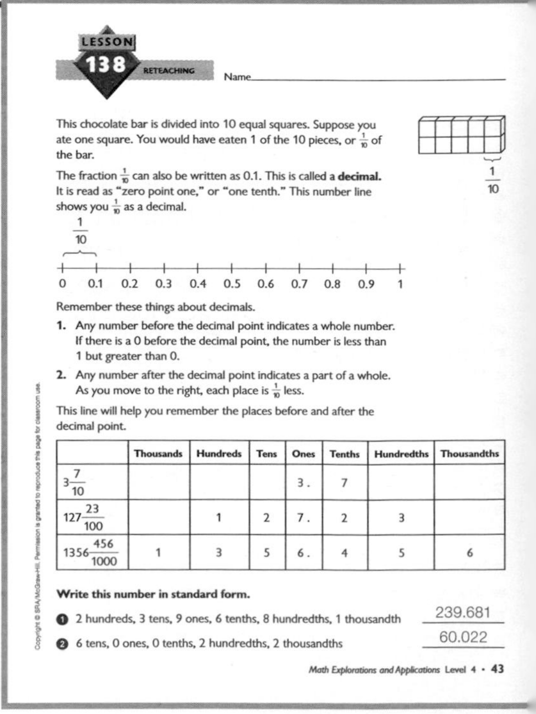
LESSON 138 RETEACHING Name

This chocolate bar is divided into 10 equal squares. Suppose you ate one square. You would have eaten 1 of the 10 pieces, or $\frac{1}{10}$ of the bar.

The fraction $\frac{1}{10}$ can also be written as 0.1. This is called a **decimal.** It is read as "zero point one," or "one tenth." This number line shows you $\frac{1}{10}$ as a decimal.

$\frac{1}{10}$

0 0.1 0.2 0.3 0.4 0.5 0.6 0.7 0.8 0.9 1

Remember these things about decimals.

1. Any number before the decimal point indicates a whole number. If there is a 0 before the decimal point, the number is less than 1 but greater than 0.
2. Any number after the decimal point indicates a part of a whole. As you move to the right, each place is $\frac{1}{10}$ less.

This line will help you remember the places before and after the decimal point.

	Thousands	Hundreds	Tens	Ones	Tenths	Hundredths	Thousandths
$3\frac{7}{10}$				3 .	7		
$127\frac{23}{100}$		1	2	7 .	2	3	
$1356\frac{456}{1000}$	1	3	5	6 .	4	5	6

Write this number in standard form.

1. 2 hundreds, 3 tens, 9 ones, 6 tenths, 8 hundredths, 1 thousandth 239.681
2. 6 tens, 0 ones, 0 tenths, 2 hundredths, 2 thousandths 60.022

Copyright © SRA/McGraw-Hill. Permission is granted to reproduce this page for classroom use.

*available separately

Use a dot between the ones place and the tenths place. The dot is called a **decimal point.**

Suppose you want to write 4 tens, 3 ones, 5 tenths, and 4 hundredths.

You would write it like this: 43.54

When you read it, you would say "forty-three and fifty-four hundredths" or "forty-three point five four."

Tell the value of the blue digit in each of the following numbers.

8. 0.05 **5 hundredths**
9. 1.63 **6 tenths**
10. 20.37 **2 tens**
11. 62.76 **7 tenths**
12. 74.35 **5 hundredths**
13. 0.57 **5 tenths**
14. 2.59 **2 ones**
15. 91.35 **5 hundredths**
16. 53.47 **5 tens**
17. 22.22 **2 tenths**
18. 1.6 **1 one**
19. 83.56 **6 hundredths**
20. 21.42 **4 tenths**
21. 17.52 **7 ones**
22. 15.06 **0 tenths**

Write each number in standard form.

23. 5 ones, 2 tenths, 4 hundredths **5.24**
24. 7 hundreds, 2 tens, 6 ones, 3 tenths **726.3**
25. 3 tens, 3 ones, 3 tenths, 3 hundredths **33.33**
26. 9 hundreds, 0 tens, 3 ones, 4 tenths, 5 hundredths **903.45**
27. 4 tens, 9 ones, 0 tenths, 7 hundredths **49.07**

Write each number in standard form. The first one has been done for you.

28. 30 + 4 + 0.6 + 0.04 **34.64**
29. 60 + 0 + 0.7 + 0.03 **60.73**
30. 50 + 9 + 0.3 + 0.07 **59.37**
31. 10 + 3 + 0.9 + 0.06 **13.96**
32. 16 + 0.8 + 0.05 **16.85**
33. 80 + 2 + 0.06 **82.06**
34. 90 + 1 + 0.7 + 0.02 **91.72**
35. 20 + 4 + 0.8 + 0.06 **24.86**
36. 4 + 0.6 + 0.09 **4.69**
37. 10 + 7 + 0.2 + 0.04 **17.24**

3 Wrap-Up (5 MINUTES)

In Closing Have students explain the purpose of the decimal point in decimal numbers. Then have them explain the differences in the value of the 6 in 46, 4.6, and 4.06. (6 ones in 46, 6 tenths of 1 in 4.6, 6 hundredths of 1 in 4.06)

ALTERNATIVE ASSESSMENT

Informal Assessment Circulate throughout the class and observe students as they work through this lesson. Encourage students to say the decimals aloud as they write them and to name the places in a decimal place-value chart.

Assessment Criteria

Did the student . . .

- ✓ contribute to the discussion of decimals, decimal notation, and comparison decimals?
- ✓ read and write decimals accurately?
- ✓ demonstrate understanding of the relationship between fractions and decimals?
- ✓ identify values of digits in decimals?
- ✓ correctly write decimals in standard form?

PRACTICE p. 138

LESSON 138 PRACTICE Name__________

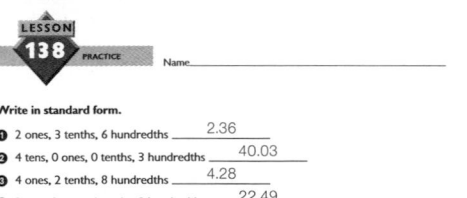

Write in standard form.

1. 2 ones, 3 tenths, 6 hundredths 2.36
2. 4 tens, 0 ones, 0 tenths, 3 hundredths 40.03
3. 4 ones, 2 tenths, 8 hundredths 4.28
4. 2 tens, 2 ones, 4 tenths, 9 hundredths 22.49
5. 2 hundreds, 4 tens, 3 ones, 9 tenths, 2 hundredths 243.92
6. 6 tens, 0 ones, 4 tenths, 5 hundredths 60.45
7. 5 ones, 3 tenths, 7 hundredths 5.37
8. 9 hundreds, 9 tens, 9 ones, 9 tenths 999.9
9. 1 hundred, 0 tens, 1 one, 0 tenths, 1 hundredth 101.01
10. 9 tens, 4 ones, 6 tenths, 3 hundredths 94.63
11. 50 + 8 + 0.6 + 0.05 58.65
12. 30 + 0 + 0.8 + 0.04 30.84
13. 90 + 0 + 0.7 + 0.02 90.72
14. 20 + 1 + 0 + 0.02 21.02
15. 10 + 9 + 0.6 + 0.08 19.68
16. 40 + 2 + 0.3 + 0.04 42.34
17. 60 + 9 + 0.0 + 0.06 69.06

Answer these questions.

18. Which is greater, 0.01 or 0.001? 0.01
19. Which is greater, $\frac{1}{1000}$ or $\frac{1}{10,000}$? $\frac{1}{1000}$
20. Which is greater, 000.1 or 0.001? 000.1

Copyright © SRA/McGraw-Hill. Permission is granted to reproduce this page for classroom use.

138 • *Math Explorations and Applications* Level 4

ENRICHMENT p. 138

LESSON 138 ENRICHMENT Name__________

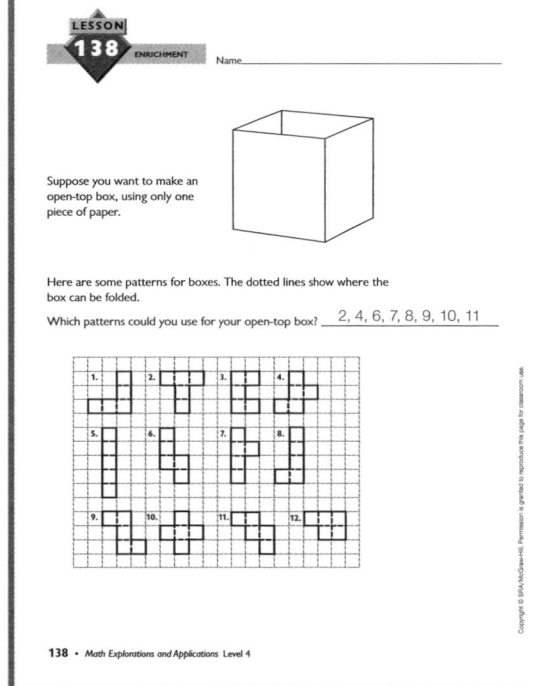

Suppose you want to make an open-top box, using only one piece of paper.

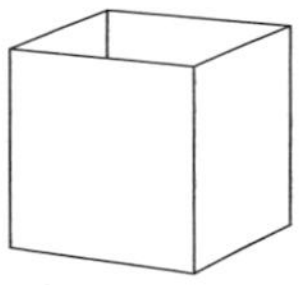

Here are some patterns for boxes. The dotted lines show where the box can be folded.

Which patterns could you use for your open-top box? 2, 4, 6, 7, 8, 9, 10, 11

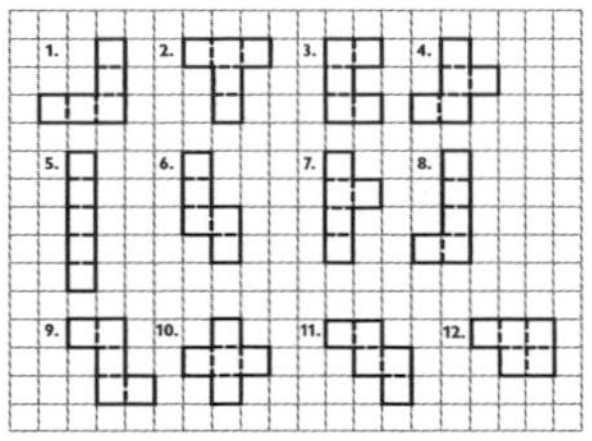

Copyright © SRA/McGraw-Hill. Permission is granted to reproduce this page for classroom use.

138 • *Math Explorations and Applications* Level 4

Homework Have students each create a place-value chart that identifies all the places from thousands to thousandths. Then have them use the charts as a reference in making the greatest possible decimal, the least possible decimal, and a decimal that represents about one half with the digits 0, 1, 3, and 5. They should use all four digits only once in forming each decimal.

Student Edition pages 468–471

Decimals and Fractions

LESSON PLANNER

Objectives

- ▶ to develop students' understanding of the relationship among tenths, hundredths, and thousandths
- ▶ to review and practice comparing decimals and using relation signs
- ▶ to explain the relationship of decimals to corresponding fractions

Context of the Lesson This is the second of 16 lessons on understanding and using decimals.

MANIPULATIVES

dual dial scale*
play money*
base-10 blocks*
objects to be measured

Program Resources

Practice Master 139
Enrichment Master 139
For extra practice:
CD-ROM* Lesson 139

1 Warm-Up

5 MINUTES

Problem of the Day Present the following problem: Use each of the digits 5, 3, 1, and 0 to form the greatest and least possible decimal numbers. Then use any of the same four digits to form two decimals with the same value. (5310.0; 0.0135; one pair of equivalent decimals is 15.30 = 15.3.)

Problem-Solving Strategies Ask students who have solved the Problem of the Day to share how they solved it and any strategies they used.

MENTAL MATH / MANIPULATIVES Have students estimate the weight in metric units of each object around the classroom to prepare for the work with decimals in this lesson sequence. After each estimate, have students use a **scale*** to measure to check for accuracy. (Estimates should improve after each object is measured.)

a. scissors

b. a calculator

c. a notebook

d. a textbook

PRACTICE

LESSON 139

Decimals and Fractions

Remember, if a whole is divided into 10 equal parts, 1 part would be $\frac{1}{10}$, or 0.1.

3 parts would be $\frac{3}{10}$, or 0.3.

$\frac{1}{10} = 0.1$

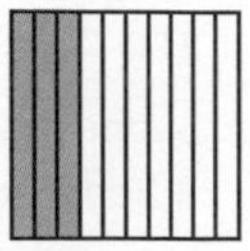

$\frac{3}{10} = 0.3$

If a whole is divided into 100 equal parts, 1 part would be $\frac{1}{100}$, or 0.01.

3 parts would be $\frac{3}{100}$, or 0.03.

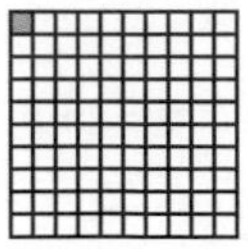

$\frac{1}{100} = 0.01$

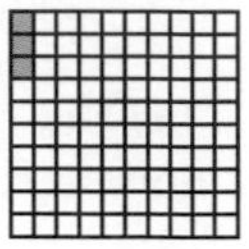

$\frac{3}{100} = 0.03$

Suppose you divided a whole into 1000 equal parts.

- ◆ What would 1 part be? **$\frac{1}{1000}$ or 0.001**
- ◆ What would 3 parts be? **$\frac{3}{1000}$ or 0.003**
- ◆ What would 7 parts be? **$\frac{7}{1000}$ or 0.007**

Remember, a dime is $\frac{1}{10}$ of a dollar and a cent is $\frac{1}{100}$ of a dollar. Ten cents is the same as 1 dime. So 1 dime is greater than 9 cents, and 3 cents is less than 1 dime.

Here's how to compare the decimals 0.007 and 0.03:

- ◆ Write a zero so the numbers have the same number of digits to the right of the decimal point.
- ◆ Line up the decimal points 0.007
  0.03**0** So 0.007 < 0.03

Replace the ● with <, >, or =.

1. 0.1 ● 0.3 **<**	2. 0.03 ● 0.1 **<**	3. 0.007 ● 0.08 **<**
4. 0.01 ● 0.03 **<**	5. 0.7 ● 0.08 **>**	6. 0.2 ● 0.09 **>**
7. 0.01 ● 0.07 **<**	8. 0.1 ● 0.001 **>**	9. 0.3 ● 0.03 **>**
10. 0.07 ● 0.03 **>**	11. 0.01 ● 0.001 **>**	12. 0.04 ● 0.04 **=**
13. 0.1 ● 0.01 **>**	14. 0.001 ● 0.003 **<**	15. 0.04 ● 0.004 **>**

468 • Fractions and Decimals

Why teach it this way?

This lesson and the previous one involve only decimals less than 1 to focus students on the places to the right of the decimal point. Beginning in the next lesson, students will work with decimals greater than 1.

*available separately

◆ Which is greater, 0.1 or 0.10?
same

$\frac{1}{10} = 0.1$  $\frac{10}{100} = 0.10$ 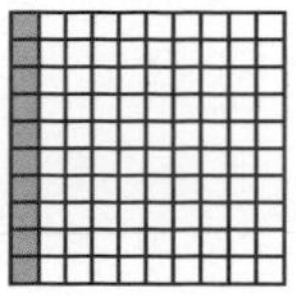

◆ Which is greater, 0.3 or 0.30?
same

$\frac{3}{10} = 0.3$ 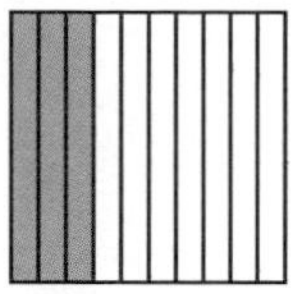 $\frac{30}{100} = 0.30$ 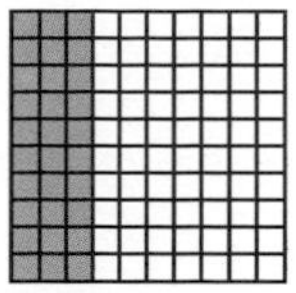

◆ Which is greater, 0.2 or 0.27?
0.27

$\frac{2}{10} = 0.2$ 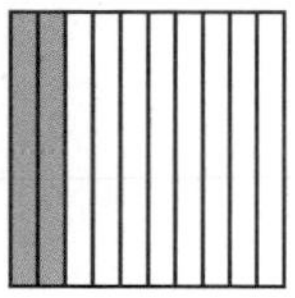 $\frac{27}{100} = 0.27$ 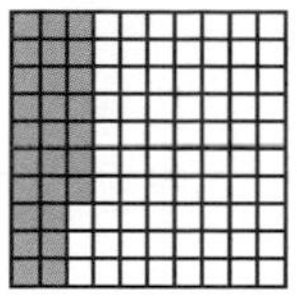

In each case, tell which is more money or whether they are the same amount.

16. 3 dimes or (33 cents?)
17. 6 cents or (1 dime?)
18. (11 cents) or 1 dime?
19. 8 dimes or 80 cents? **same**
20. 10 cents or 1 dime? **same**
21. (7 dimes) or 8 cents?

Write each amount as a decimal. The first one has been done for you.

22. 3 dimes and 7 cents = **$0.37**
23. 9 dimes and 8 cents = ■ **$0.98**
24. 6 dimes and 4 cents = ■ **$0.64**
25. 64 cents = ■ **$0.64**
26. 0 dimes and 8 cents = ■ **$0.08**
27. 7 dimes and 3 cents = ■ **$0.73**
28. 2 dimes and 9 cents = ■ **$0.29**
29. 6 cents = ■ **$0.06**
30. 8 dimes and 0 cents = ■ **$0.80**
31. 5 dimes and 9 cents = ■ **$0.59**

Technology Connection Refer students to the software *Math Power Series: Balancing Act* from Ventura Educational Systems (Mac, for grades K–8) for practice with whole numbers, integers, fractions, and decimals.

2 Teach

Using the Student Pages Go over the top of page 468 with the class. Discuss the questions together. Stress the importance of using a 0 as a place holder to the right of the decimal point when writing decimals in hundredths or thousandths. Remind students that they may write extra 0s to the right of numbers with decimal points without changing their value. Do one or two problems with the class. Quickly review the meaning of the relation signs. Use **base-10 blocks*** as an example and explain to students that they can look at the divided squares on the page or draw and shade their own squares to get a sense of the relative size of decimals. Then have students complete the page.

Go over the first three questions on page 469 as you refer to the divided squares. Review the meaning of the numerator and denominator of a fraction. Have students practice saying the answers to decimal problems, such as "zero point two seven." After discussing the questions, have students do problems 16–31 on page 469 independently. Provide **play money*** they can use for problems 22–31.

LEARNING STYLES

Meeting Individual Needs
Students who are kinesthetic learners may better understand decimals from working with concrete **base-10 materials***. You can use **play money*** (dollar bills, dimes, pennies) or standard **place-value materials*** in which the hundred flat block represents a whole, the ten long block represents tenths, and the unit cube represents hundredths. Create a decimal place-value chart to familiarize students with standard decimal notation.

*available separately

◆ LESSON 139 Decimals and Fractions

Teach

Using the Student Pages Go over one or more of the problems on page 470 with the class. Have students check both their decimal and fraction answers for each problem to be sure that they make sense.

Have students complete the problems on page 471 on their own. Remind them to count places carefully, particularly in decimals with thousandths and ten thousandths. To make it easier to compare decimals, students might use 0s to equate the number of digits both numbers in the pair have to the right of the decimal point.

Note: Except with money amounts, such as $5 and $3.75, there is generally no need to compare, add, or subtract decimals reported to different degrees of precision; that is, with different numbers of decimal places.

AT RISK **Meeting Individual Needs**

Explain to students that decimal notation is quite common. Help students identify the use of decimal notation in the world around them: for example, decimals are used in sports statistics such as batting averages and win-loss percentages; in competitive scoring for gymnastics and ice skating; and in timing auto races and track events to hundredths or thousandths of seconds. Automobiles also use decimal notation for some digital speedometers and most odometers. Encourage students to identify examples of the use of decimals in their environment.

◆ LESSON 139 Decimals and Fractions

For each figure, show what portion is shaded by writing a fraction and a decimal. The first one has been done for you.

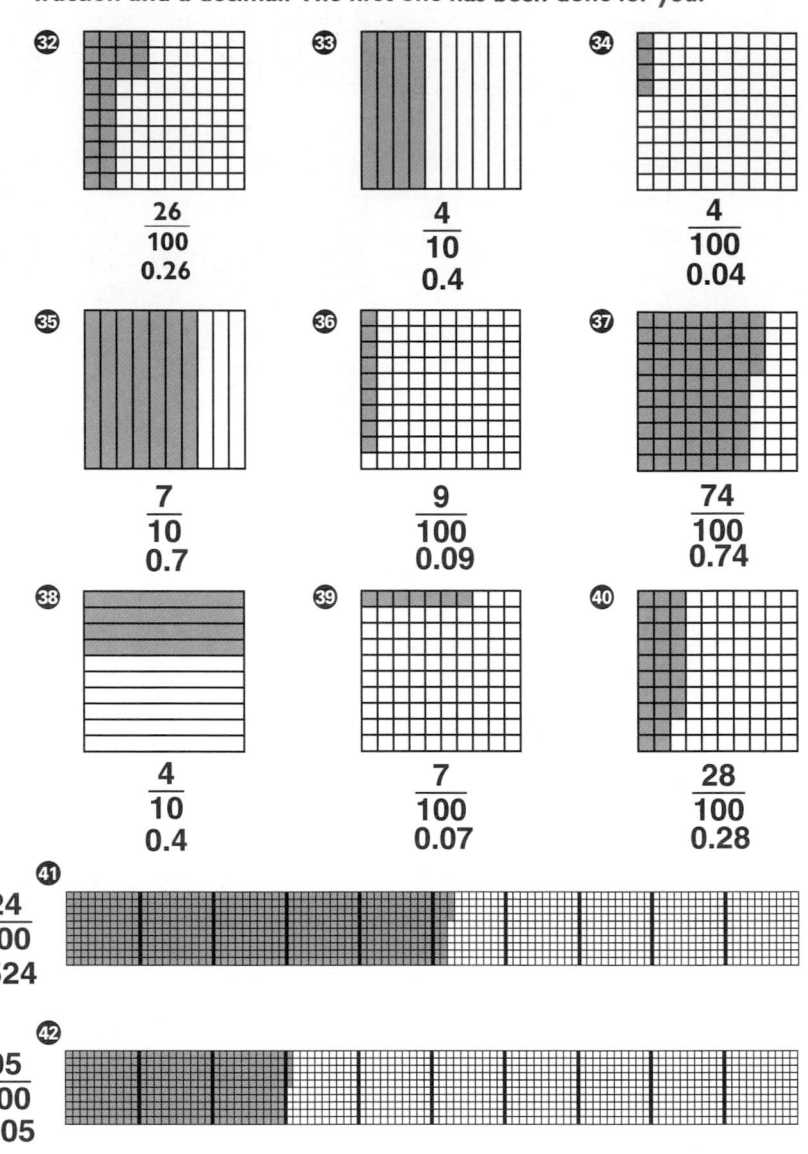

32. 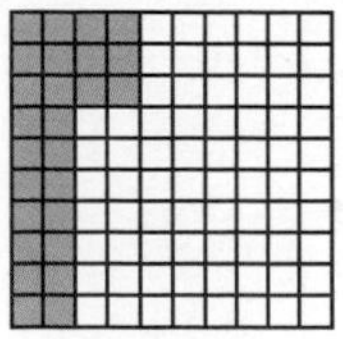
$\frac{26}{100}$ 0.26

33. 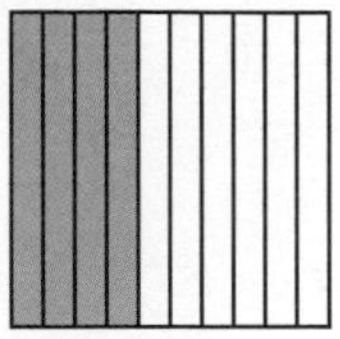
$\frac{4}{10}$ 0.4

34. 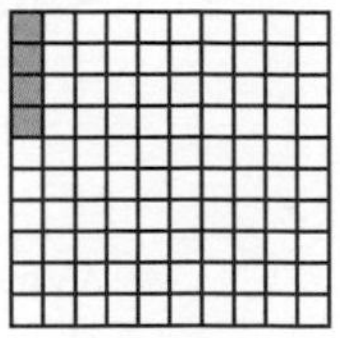
$\frac{4}{100}$ 0.04

35. 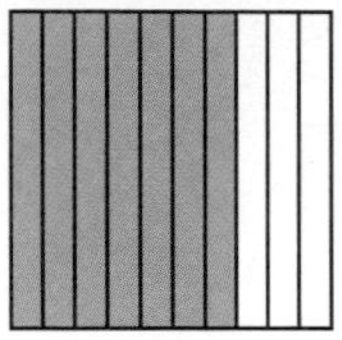
$\frac{7}{10}$ 0.7

36. 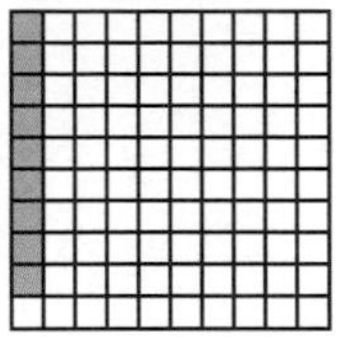
$\frac{9}{100}$ 0.09

37. 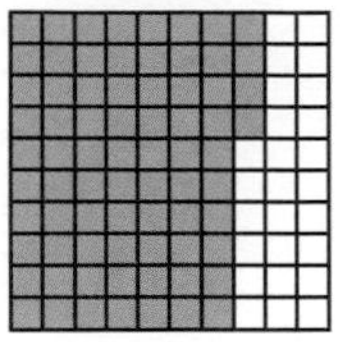
$\frac{74}{100}$ 0.74

38. 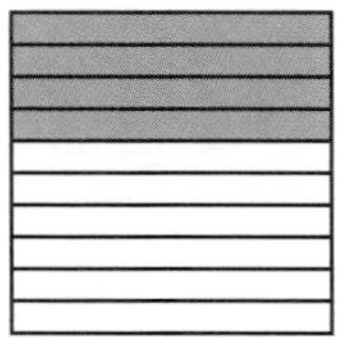
$\frac{4}{10}$ 0.4

39. 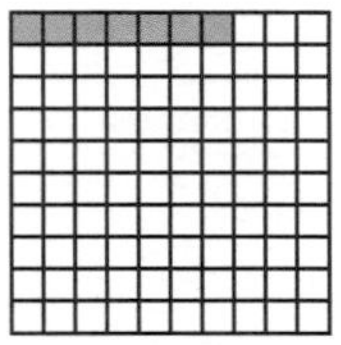
$\frac{7}{100}$ 0.07

40. 
$\frac{28}{100}$ 0.28

41. $\frac{524}{1000}$ 0.524 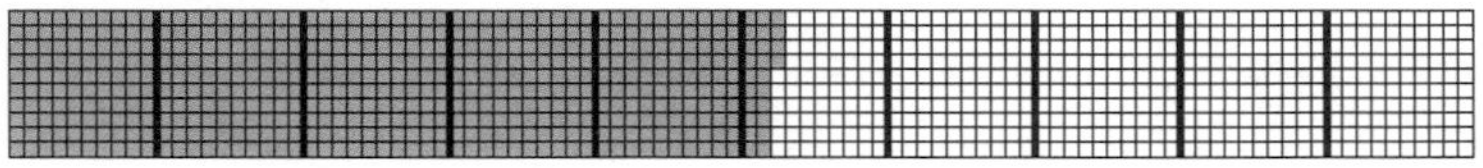

42. $\frac{305}{1000}$ 0.305 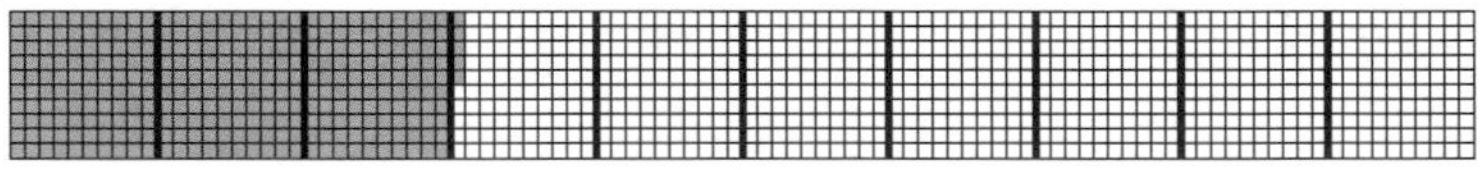

COOPERATIVE LEARNING You might have students work in trios to complete problems that require writing a fraction and a decimal for a diagram. For such problems, one student would be responsible for the fraction, another for the decimal, and the third student would be the judge. Students could rotate roles for subsequent problems so that each would have a chance to perform each task.

RETEACHING

Specific reteaching for decimals is not essential at this time. Because the next several lessons involve further work with decimals, students will have more opportunities to develop and demonstrate their understanding of this topic. You may want to assign Enrichment Master 139.

Write each of these fractions as a decimal.

Examples: $\frac{3}{100} = 0.03$ $\quad \frac{7}{10{,}000} = 0.0007$

43 $\frac{2}{10}$ = **0.2**	44 $\frac{478}{10{,}000}$ = **0.0478**	45 $\frac{10}{100}$ = **0.1**	46 $\frac{70}{1000}$ = **0.070**
47 $\frac{7}{10}$ = **0.7**	48 $\frac{4{,}783}{10{,}000}$ = **0.4783**	49 $\frac{11}{100}$ = **0.11**	50 $\frac{700}{1000}$ = **0.700**
51 $\frac{4}{100}$ = **0.04**	52 $\frac{74}{100}$ = **0.74**	53 $\frac{6}{10}$ = **0.6**	54 $\frac{78}{1000}$ = **0.078**
55 $\frac{40}{100}$ = **0.40**	56 $\frac{6}{100}$ = **0.06**	57 $\frac{1}{10}$ = **0.1**	58 $\frac{843}{1000}$ = **0.843**
59 $\frac{4}{1000}$ = **0.004**	60 $\frac{6}{1000}$ = **0.006**	61 $\frac{8}{10}$ = **0.8**	62 $\frac{6{,}286}{10{,}000}$ = **0.6286**
63 $\frac{47}{100}$ = **0.47**	64 $\frac{5}{100}$ = **0.05**	65 $\frac{9}{10}$ = **0.9**	66 $\frac{66}{100}$ = **0.66**
67 $\frac{478}{1000}$ = **0.478**	68 $\frac{8}{100}$ = **0.08**	69 $\frac{7}{1000}$ = **0.007**	70 $\frac{543}{1000}$ = **0.543**

Copy each pair of numbers. Replace the ● with <, >, or =.

71 0.02 **<** 0.3	72 0.47 **<** 0.53	73 0.406 **<** 0.407
74 0.83 **>** 0.80	75 0.8 **=** 0.80	76 0.8 **<** 0.83
77 0.62 **<** 0.90	78 0.9 **=** 0.90	79 0.62 **<** 0.9
80 0.48 **<** 0.70	81 0.48 **<** 0.7	82 0.100 **=** 0.1
83 0.230 **=** 0.23	84 0.230 **>** 0.023	85 0.010 **<** 0.1

PROBLEM SOLVING

Solve these problems.

86 Eric correctly answered eight out of ten questions on his English quiz. Write a fraction to show what part of the quiz he got right. **$\frac{8}{10}$ or $\frac{4}{5}$**

87 Jessica spent $16 for a CD and $4 for a pair of earrings. Write a fraction to show the cost of the earrings compared to that of the CD. **$\frac{4}{16}$ or $\frac{1}{4}$**

88 Tom cleaned his bedroom in $\frac{1}{3}$ of an hour. His sister spent $\frac{2}{5}$ of an hour cleaning her bedroom. Who spent less time cleaning? **Tom**

❸ Wrap-Up (5 MINUTES)

In Closing Have students explain how they would compare the decimals 0.24 and 0.3 to determine which is greater. (0.24 < 0.3)

ALTERNATIVE ASSESSMENT

Informal Assessment Observe students as they work through the problems in this lesson. Ask them to verbalize their understanding of decimals, fractions, and their relationship, as well as how to analyze two decimals to determine which is greater. Note whether students read, write, and say decimal numbers accurately.

Assessment Criteria

Did the student . . .

- ✓ contribute to the discussion of decimal notation and values?
- ✓ communicate strategies used to compare decimals?
- ✓ explain the relationship between fractions and decimals?
- ✓ correctly answer at least 75% of the problems?

Homework Have students look through magazines or newspapers to find three examples of decimal numbers. Have them write an equivalent fraction for each one.

PRACTICE p. 139

LESSON 139 PRACTICE Name__________

Draw <, >, or = to make each statement true.

1 0.5 (>) 0.2	2 0.6 (<) 0.8	3 0.6 (>) 0.09	4 0.08 (>) 0.03
5 0.2 (<) 0.6	6 0.09 (<) 0.1	7 0.020 (<) 0.2	8 0.76 (<) 0.8
9 0.09 (>) 0.04	10 0.6 (>) 0.06	11 0.087 (=) 0.087	12 0.83 (<) 0.9
13 0.6 (>) 0.49	14 0.408 (<) 0.532	15 0.268 (<) 0.8	16 0.039 (<) 0.53

Write each amount as a decimal.

17 7 dimes = $0.70 18 23 cents = $0.23

19 4 dimes and 6 cents = $0.46 20 9 dimes and 0 cents = $0.90

For each figure show what portion is shaded by writing a fraction and a decimal.

21 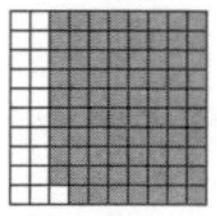
$\frac{79}{100}$; 0.79

22 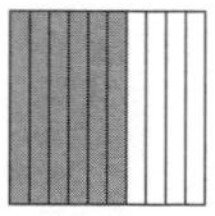
$\frac{6}{10}$; 0.6

23 
$\frac{45}{100}$; 0.45

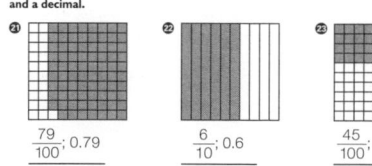

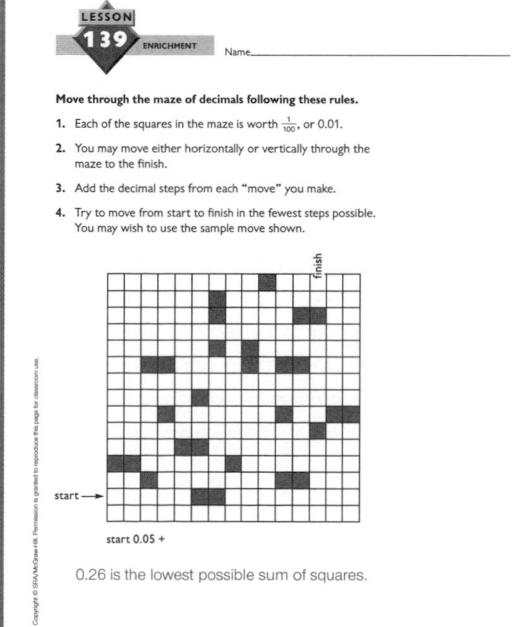

Write each fraction as a decimal.

24 $\frac{18}{100}$ = 0.18 25 $\frac{35}{100}$ = 0.35 26 $\frac{3428}{10{,}000}$ = 0.3428

27 $\frac{432}{1000}$ = 0.432 28 $\frac{5}{10}$ = 0.5 29 $\frac{87}{100}$ = 0.87

Copyright © SRA/McGraw-Hill. Permission is granted to reproduce this page for classroom use.

ENRICHMENT p. 139

LESSON 139 ENRICHMENT Name__________

Move through the maze of decimals following these rules.

1. Each of the squares in the maze is worth $\frac{1}{100}$, or 0.01.
2. You may move either horizontally or vertically through the maze to the finish.
3. Add the decimal steps from each "move" you make.
4. Try to move from start to finish in the fewest steps possible. You may wish to use the sample move shown.

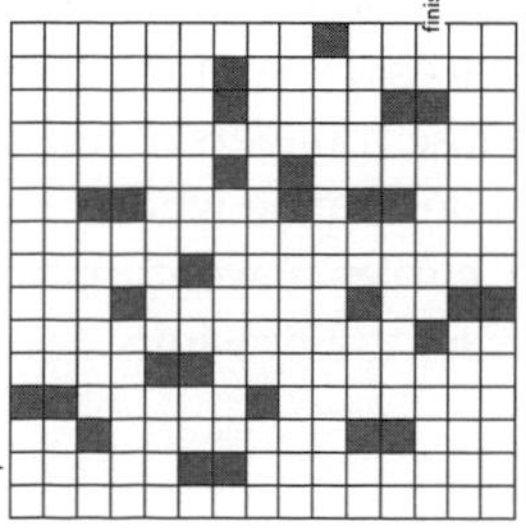

start 0.05 +

0.26 is the lowest possible sum of squares.

Copyright © SRA/McGraw-Hill. Permission is granted to reproduce this page for classroom use.

LESSON 140

Student Edition pages 472–475

Ordering Decimals

LESSON PLANNER

Objectives

- ▶ to demonstrate how to annex 0s to compare decimal amounts with different numbers of digits to the right of the decimal point
- ▶ to demonstrate that there is always another number between any two given numbers, no matter how close they are
- ▶ to demonstrate the use of decimals to calibrate a number line

Context of the Lesson This is the third of 16 lessons on understanding and using decimals.

MANIPULATIVES

calculators*
place-value pad*
financial section of a newspaper (optional)
paper squares (optional)

Program Resources

Number Cubes (0–5 and 5–10)
Reteaching Master
Practice Master 140
Enrichment Master 140
For extra practice:
CD-ROM* Lesson 140
Cumulative Review, page 565

1 Warm-Up

5 MINUTES

Problem of the Day Present the following problem and provide **calculators*** for students to use: Suppose you want to display 43.012 on your calculator, but you may press only the 0, the 1, the decimal point, and + keys. How can you do this? (Enter 10 + 10 + 10 + 10 + 1 + 1 + 1 + 0.01 + 0.001 + 0.001.)

Problem-Solving Strategies Ask students who have solved the Problem of the Day to share how they solved it and any strategies they used.

MENTAL MATH Provide practice comparing decimals less than 1. Have students use their hands to make each statement true by showing <, >, or =.

a.	0.02 ❑ 0.05 (<)	**b.**	0.02 ❑ 0.001 (>)
c.	0.05 ❑ 0.02 (>)	**d.**	0.4 ❑ 0.04 (>)
e.	0.70 ❑ 0.7 (=)	**f.**	0.2 ❑ 0.05 (>)
g.	0.8 ❑ 0.09 (>)	**h.**	0.09 ❑ 0.03 (>)
i.	0.09 ❑ 0.1 (<)	**j.**	0.09 ❑ 0.03 (>)
k.	0.45 ❑ 0.4 (>)	**l.**	0.06 ❑ 0.06 (=)
m.	0.06 ❑ 0.6 (<)	**n.**	0.06 ❑ 0.9 (<)

PRACTICE

LESSON 140

Ordering Decimals

Ordinarily, decimals that you compare should have the same number of digits to the right of the decimal point. However, when people measure they sometimes neglect to write the extra zeros at the end of the number.

For example, if you measure the length of a table to the nearest centimeter, you could report it as 1.34 meters. If the measurement came out to be 2.00 meters you should report it as 2.00 meters. This would show how much precision you believe is in your measurement. But some people will report this as just 2 meters.

If you assume the measurements are as precise as necessary, you can simply write extra zeros after a number to make comparison (and addition and subtraction) easier.

◆ List the following numbers in order from least to greatest. Insert a < symbol between each pair to make the statements true.

3, 3.5, 3.4073, 3.48, 3.408, 3.02, 3.40729
3 < 3.02 < 3.40729 < 3.4073 < 3.408 < 3.48 < 3.5

Rewrite each of the following sets of numbers from least to greatest with a < symbol between each pair.

1. 24, 19, 20, 23.9, 20.7, 23.97
   19 < 20 < 20.7 < 23.9 < 23.97 < 24
2. 2.4, 1.9, 2, 2.39, 2.07, 2.397
   1.9 < 2 < 2.07 < 2.39 < 2.397 < 24
3. 0.0024, 0.0019, 0.002, 0.00239, 0.00207, 0.002397
   0.0019 < 0.002 < 0.00207 < 0.00239 < 0.002397 < 0.0024
4. 2.0034, 1.99937, 2, 1.99, 2.01, 2.009
   1.99 < 1.99937 < 2 < 2.0034 < 2.009 < 2.01
5. 0.1, 0.02, 0.003, 0.0004, 0.00005, 0.000006
   0.000006 < 0.00005 < 0.0004 < 0.003 < 0.02 < 0.1
6. 8.82, 8.12, 8.0, 8.01, 8.6, 8.10
   8.0 < 8.01 < 8.10 < 8.12 < 8.6 < 8.82

Real-World Connection Obtain a table of foreign exchange rates from the **financial section of a newspaper**. Show students that the money equivalences are presented in decimal notation extended to many decimal places. Have students read some of these numbers, compare them, and determine whether a particular currency went up or down in value from the previous day.

*available separately

Mel asked, "Could there be two numbers so close together that there is no number in between them?" "I don't think so," said June. "Why don't you try to find out?"

Mel tried 0.001 and 0.002. Alia said, "I can find a number between them. I can think of those numbers as 0.0010 and 0.0020. Then 0.0015 must be exactly halfway between them."

"And 0.0014, 0.0013, and a lot of other numbers are between them too, but those numbers are closer to 0.001 than to 0.002," said Mel.

"We can also find lots of numbers between the two original numbers that are closer to 0.002, like 0.0016 and 0.0017," said June. "I think we can always find a lot of numbers between any two numbers."

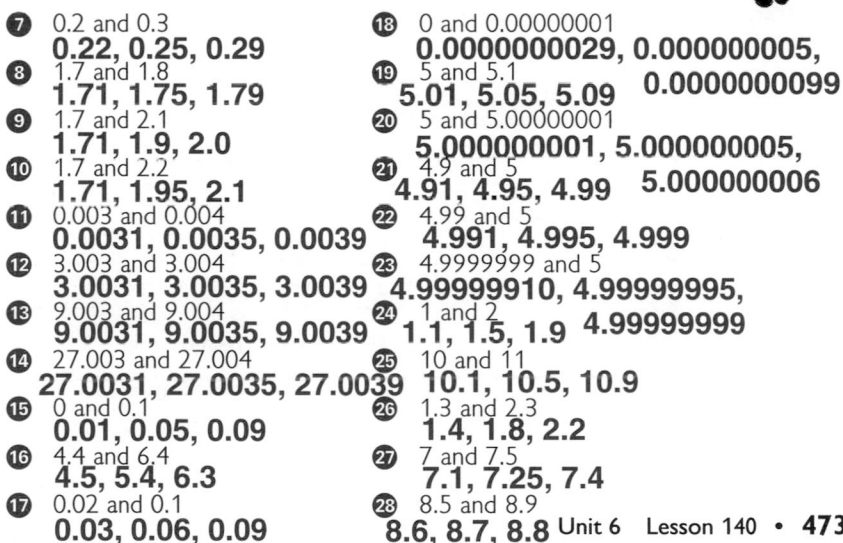

For each of the following pairs of numbers:

a. find a number that is exactly halfway between
b. find a number that is closer to the lesser number
c. find a number that is closer to the greater number
d. write the three numbers in order from least to greatest

Watch your numbering.

7. 0.2 and 0.3 **0.22, 0.25, 0.29**
8. 1.7 and 1.8 **1.71, 1.75, 1.79**
9. 1.7 and 2.1 **1.71, 1.9, 2.0**
10. 1.7 and 2.2 **1.71, 1.95, 2.1**
11. 0.003 and 0.004 **0.0031, 0.0035, 0.0039**
12. 3.003 and 3.004 **3.0031, 3.0035, 3.0039**
13. 9.003 and 9.004 **9.0031, 9.0035, 9.0039**
14. 27.003 and 27.004 **27.0031, 27.0035, 27.0039**
15. 0 and 0.1 **0.01, 0.05, 0.09**
16. 4.4 and 6.4 **4.5, 5.4, 6.3**
17. 0.02 and 0.1 **0.03, 0.06, 0.09**
18. 0 and 0.00000001 **0.0000000029, 0.000000005, 0.0000000099**
19. 5 and 5.1 **5.01, 5.05, 5.09**
20. 5 and 5.00000001 **5.000000001, 5.000000005, 5.000000006**
21. 4.9 and 5 **4.91, 4.95, 4.99**
22. 4.99 and 5 **4.991, 4.995, 4.999**
23. 4.9999999 and 5 **4.99999910, 4.99999995, 4.99999999**
24. 1 and 2 **1.1, 1.5, 1.9**
25. 10 and 11 **10.1, 10.5, 10.9**
26. 1.3 and 2.3 **1.4, 1.8, 2.2**
27. 7 and 7.5 **7.1, 7.25, 7.4**
28. 8.5 and 8.9 **8.6, 8.7, 8.8**

❷ Teach

Using the Student Pages Before beginning the lesson, demonstrate the "Roll a Decimal" game on page 474, which focuses on using place value and comparing decimals. Students can play it when they finish pages 472–473.

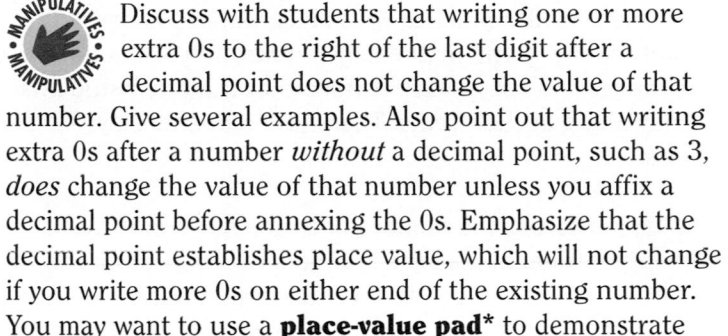

Discuss with students that writing one or more extra 0s to the right of the last digit after a decimal point does not change the value of that number. Give several examples. Also point out that writing extra 0s after a number *without* a decimal point, such as 3, *does* change the value of that number unless you affix a decimal point before annexing the 0s. Emphasize that the decimal point establishes place value, which will not change if you write more 0s on either end of the existing number. You may want to use a **place-value pad*** to demonstrate this point. Do exercises 1–6 with the class, or have small groups work on them and present their answers to the class.

Read the story on page 473 with the class. Discuss Alia's method for finding a number between two numbers. Ask students if they think her method will always work. (yes) Solve several problems with the class. Then have students complete the page on their own.

Technology Connection Refer students to the software *Math Shop Spotlight: Fractions and Decimals* from Scholastic (Mac, IBM for grades 4–8) for practice with adding and subtracting fractions, multiplying fractions by whole numbers, converting decimals to fractions, and adding decimals.

*available separately

◆ LESSON 140 Ordering Decimals

Teach

Using the Student Pages Demonstrate the "Roll a Decimal" game two or three times by having two students play it in front of the class. This game provides practice with place value, comparing, decimal numbers, and mathematical reasoning. Announce what the players roll at each turn so that the other students can play along at their seats. Then have students play in pairs.

Discuss the number line on page 475. Have students read the numbers that appear on the line. Then go over the discussion questions with the class. Ask students to explain their reasoning. Then have them complete the page on their own.

SPECIAL NEEDS · MANIPULATIVES

Meeting Individual Needs

Students with spatial or organizational difficulties, or those who have a limited grasp of the concept of decimal numbers, may have trouble finding a decimal between other decimals. You might modify the task to have them find numbers between decimals that are in tenths. Use **paper squares** divided into tenths and hundredths to model the solutions.

Observation of game-playing activity resembles observation of real-life-out-of-school activities as closely as anything we are likely to see in school. Such observation will often give greater insight into a child's thought patterns than anything else the teacher can do.

—Stephen S. Willoughby, *Mathematics Education for a Changing World*

◆ LESSON 140 Ordering Decimals

COOPERATIVE LEARNING

Roll a Decimal Game

GAME

Players: Two
Materials: One 0–5 cube, one 5–10 cube
Object: To make the greater decimal
Math Focus: Place value, comparing decimal numbers, and mathematical reasoning

RULES

1. Roll the 0–5 cube. If you roll a 0, roll that cube again.
2. Write a decimal point followed by as many blanks as the number rolled. If you rolled a 3, you would write: .___ ___ ___
3. Roll the 5–10 cube as many times as there are blanks in your decimal. If you roll a 10, roll that cube again.
4. Each time you roll the cube, write that number in one of your blanks.
5. The player with the greater decimal is the winner.

SAMPLE GAME

Sara rolled:	Sara wrote:	David rolled:	David wrote:
0 — rolled again		3	.___ ___ ___
2	.___ ___	6	.___ 6 ___
6	.___ 6	9	. 9 6 ___
7	. 7 6	10 — rolled again	
		10 — rolled again	
		6	. 9 6 6

David was the winner.

RETEACHING p. 44

LESSON 140 RETEACHING Name__________

When ordering decimals, each number should have the same number of digits after the decimal point. If a number doesn't, write in zeros to help make ordering easier.

This exercise will help you see the relationships between whole numbers, fractions, and decimals, making it easier to order decimals.

Study the grid below.

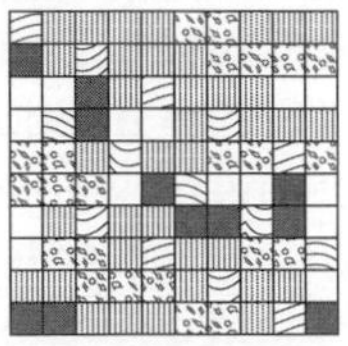

1. How many squares of each pattern are in this grid?
   14 37 11 23 15
2. Write the fraction describing each pattern.
   $\frac{14}{100}$ $\frac{37}{100}$ $\frac{11}{100}$ $\frac{23}{100}$ $\frac{15}{100}$
3. Write the decimal describing each pattern.
   0.14 0.37 0.11 0.23 0.15
4. Draw the pattern that shows up the most in the grid.
5. Draw the pattern that shows up the least in the grid.
6. Write the decimals in order from least to greatest.
   0.11 < 0.14 < 0.15 < 0.23 < 0.37

44 • *Math Explorations and Applications* Level 4

Copyright © SRA/McGraw-Hill. Permission is granted to reproduce this page for classroom use.

Look at the number line shown below.

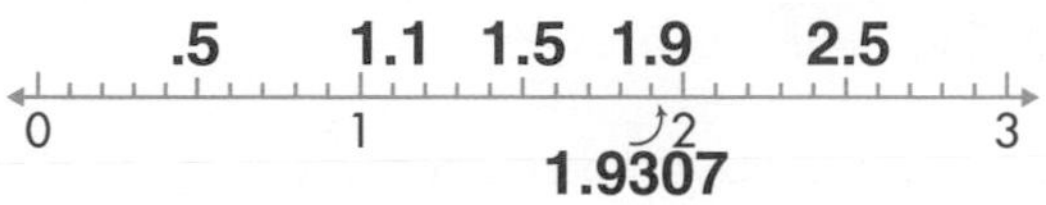

- Where would you put the number 1.5 so that it would be in the proper place?
- Where would you place 0.5 (or .5)?
- Where would you place 2.5?
- Where would you place 1.1?
- Where would you place 1.9?
- Where would you place 1.9307?

For each of the following sets of numbers, draw a number line and write the given numbers where they belong. Be sure to draw your number line so that all the numbers listed in the problem will fit. **Check students' work.**

29 0.01, 0.1, 2.06, 2.6, 1.704, 1.11111

30 2.11111, 2.01, 2.1, 3.704, 4.06, 4.6

31 0.73, 1.8, 0.099, 0.99, 2.05, 2.1

32 1.8, 2.1, 1.9, 2.01, 1.79, 2.001

For each of the following number lines, tell what number should be placed where a letter is shown.

33 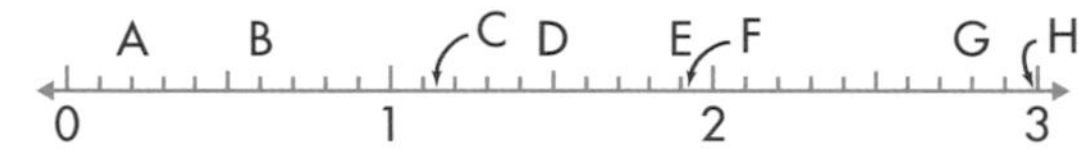

A 0.2 E 1.9
B 0.6 F 1.92
C 1.14 G 2.8
D 1.5 H 2.99

34 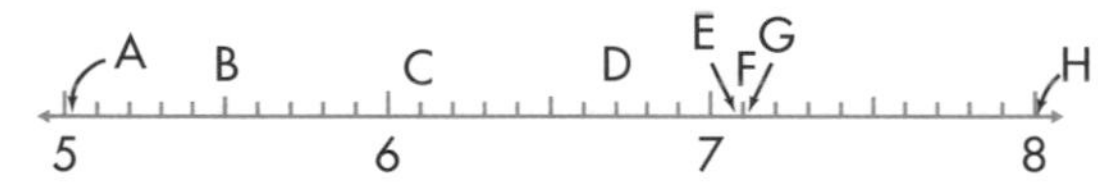

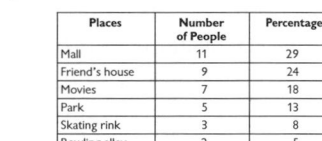

A 5.03 E 7.08
B 5.5 F 7.1
C 6.1 G 7.12
D 6.7 H 8.01

Use the Cumulative Review on page 565 after this lesson.

❸ Wrap-Up

5 MINUTES

In Closing Have students explain why extra 0s can be written to the right of some numbers without changing their value, but the 0s will change the value of other numbers.

SELF ASSESSMENT

Have each student write a statement summarizing what he or she knows about comparing and ordering decimals and about finding a number between two given numbers.

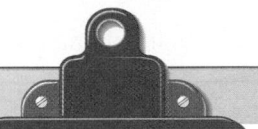

Assessment Criteria

Did the student . . .

- ✓ contribute to the discussion of annexing 0s to decimals?
- ✓ communicate strategies used to compare and order decimals?
- ✓ demonstrate how to find a number between any two given numbers?
- ✓ correctly place decimals on a number line?
- ✓ correctly answer at least 75% of the problems on the student pages?

PRACTICE p. 140

LESSON 140 PRACTICE Name__________

Rewrite each set of numbers from least to greatest with a < symbol between each pair to make the statement true.

1. 7.8, 8.1, 6.9, 7.79, 8.05, 6.945
   6.9 < 6.945 < 7.79 < 7.8 < 8.05 < 8.1
2. 0.078, 0.081, 0.779, 0.0805, 0.06945, 0.69
   0.06945 < 0.078 < 0.0805 < 0.081 < 0.69 < 0.779
3. 4.002, 4.03, 3.98, 2.999967, 3, 3.00056
   2.999967 < 3 < 3.00056 < 3.98 < 4.002 < 4.03

For each of the following pairs of numbers:
a. Find a number that is exactly halfway between.
b. Find a number that is closer to the lesser number.
c. Find a number that is closer to the greater number.
d. Write the three numbers in order from least to greatest.

Answers will vary. Sample answers are given.

4. 8.4 and 9.3
   a. 8.85 **b.** 8.41 **c.** 9.25 **d.** 8.41 < 8.85 < 9.25
5. 7 and 8
   a. 7.5 **b.** 7.1 **c.** 7.9 **d.** 7.1 < 7.5 < 7.9
6. 4.003 and 4.004
   a. 4.0035 **b.** 4.0031 **c.** 4.0039 **d.** 4.0031 < 4.0035 < 4.0039

Copyright © SRA/McGraw-Hill. Permission is granted to reproduce this page for classroom use.

ENRICHMENT p. 140

LESSON 140 ENRICHMENT Name__________

You can use **The Cruncher: *Go for Fun Survey*** project to collect information about where your friends like to go after school. Look at the information collected below.

Places	Number of People	Percentage
Mall	11	29
Friend's house	9	24
Movies	7	18
Park	5	13
Skating rink	3	8
Bowling alley	2	5
Swimming pool	1	3
Total Surveyed	38	

Tell how the percentage figures were found.
Each fraction of the total number of people surveyed is expressed as a percent.

Conduct your own survey of your friends' favorite places.

After you have collected the information, enter it into the table in The Cruncher to find out the percentages of people surveyed who liked each place on your list. What was the most popular place? What was the least popular?
Answers will vary.

Copyright © SRA/McGraw-Hill. Permission is granted to reproduce this page for classroom use.

Homework Have students play the "Roll a Decimal" game with a family member for further practice with place value and comparing decimals. A copy of this game can also be found on page 24 of the Home Connections Blackline Masters.

LESSON 141

Student Edition pages 476–479

Comparing Decimals Review

LESSON PLANNER

Objectives

- ✓ to assess students' understanding of the relative magnitude of decimals
- ▶ to provide problems involving coin combinations
- ▶ to facilitate students' development of the broad ability to use mathematical common sense

Context of the Lesson This lesson, the fourth of 16 lessons on understanding and using decimals, includes a checkpoint for assessing understanding of the relative magnitude of decimals. This lesson also contains Part 1 of "Iron and Gold," a five-part Thinking Story.

MANIPULATIVES

play coins*

base-10 blocks* (optional)

reference books, newspapers (optional)

foreign coins (optional)

pennies, dimes, and dollars (optional)

Program Resources

Practice Master 141

Enrichment Master 141

Assessment Master

For career connections: Careers and Math*

For extra practice: CD-ROM* Lesson 141

MIXED PRACTICE

LESSON 141

Comparing Decimals Review

In this lesson you'll practice comparing decimals.

Replace the ● with <, >, or =.

1 0.32 < 3.2	2 1.01 > 1.001	3 0.07 < 0.3
4 26.37 > 2.84	5 0.5 < 1.0	6 1.28 = 1.280
7 0.06 < 0.2	8 0.6 > 0.02	9 3.89 > 3.809
10 0.73 > 0.073	11 0.215 = 0.215	12 21.2 > 18.0
13 0.973 > 0.839	14 0.973 < 8.39	15 51.24 < 204.1
16 9.7 > 6.8	17 5.5555 < 40.7	18 1.4 > 0.8
19 0.0104 < 0.104	20 4.083 > 4.07	21 209.74 > 142.857
22 52.0 < 56.0	23 0.38 = 0.38	24 80.42 > 30.42
25 21.63 = 21.630	26 4.8 < 32.7	27 0.27 > 0.05
28 1.815 > 1.158	29 3.6 > 2.1	30 92.9 > 92.009

Order from least to greatest. Insert a < symbol between each pair of numbers to make true statements.

31 0.7, 1.2, 0.3, 0.002, 10.06, 10.1
0.002 < 0.3 < 0.7 < 1.2 < 10.06 < 10.1

32 0.005, 0.0002, 0.0001, 0.006, 0.01, 0.001
0.0001 < 0.0002 < 0.001 < 0.005 < 0.006 < 0.01

33 12.76, 12.75, 12.39, 12.93, 12.40, 12.04
12.04 < 12.39 < 12.40 < 12.75 < 12.76 < 12.93

34 1.1, 1.5, 1.05, 1.01, 1.2, 1.002
1.002 < 1.01 < 1.05 < 1.1 < 1.2 < 1.5

Use cents, nickels, dimes, quarters, and half-dollars to form each amount. Try to use as few coins as possible. The first one has been done for you.

35 $0.57 (50)(5)(1)(1)	36 $0.80 (50)(25)(5)
37 $0.35 (25)(10)	38 $0.74 (50)(10)(10)(1)(1)(1)(1)
39 $1.05 (50)(50)(5)	40 $0.17 (10)(5)(1)(1)

1 Warm-Up 5 MINUTES

Problem of the Day Write the following sentence on the chalkboard: TINA IS AT ANITRA'S HOUSE. Then present this problem: The five-word sentence contains exactly 20 letters. Tally them to find out which letter represents the largest part of the sentence and which letters represent equal parts of the sentence. Express the size of the parts in decimal form. (A = 0.2, which is the greatest decimal part of the sentence; N = 0.2; T, I, and S each represent 0.15; and R, H, O, U, and E each represent 0.05 of the whole sentence.)

Problem-Solving Strategies Ask students who have solved the Problem of the Day to share how they solved it and any strategies they used.

Social Studies Connection Provide **reference books** and **newspapers** to help students learn about monetary systems in other countries. Ask students who have **foreign coins** to bring them to class. Help students to understand the meaning of the foreign exchange rate table that appears in the financial pages of many daily newspapers. It gives the value of the dollar compared to other major foreign currencies, which changes daily. Students might list the various coins and bills used in different countries or estimate about how many *pesos, yen, francs,* or other kinds of money equal $1.

*available separately

Which of the following are possible? For those that are possible, write the coins needed. For those that are not possible, explain why.

41 Make 35 cents with three coins. **1 quarter, 2 nickels**

42 Make 54 cents with four coins. **not possible, need at least 5 coins**

43 Make 87 cents with 11 coins. **8 dimes, 1 nickel, 2 pennies or 3 quarters, 1 nickel, 7 pennies**

44 Make 86 cents with ten coins. **same as above with one fewer penny**

45 Make 75 cents with three coins. **3 quarters**

COOPERATIVE LEARNING **Work in groups to solve the next four problems.**

46 How many different coin combinations can you use to make 25 cents? Write six different combinations. **Answers may vary. Sample answers: 1 quarter; 2 dimes, one nickel; 1 dime, three nickels; 1 dime, 2 nickels, 5 pennies; 1 dime, 15 pennies; 5 nickels**

Hint: You can make 25 cents with 0 pennies, 5 pennies, 10 pennies, 15 pennies, 20 pennies, or 25 pennies. Make a chart to help you.

47 Eva had 50 coins that were worth $1.00. What coins could Eva have? How many answers are possible? Write or explain why you think no other answers are possible. **See margin.**

48 Paul has 40 coins whose total value is $1.00. What are the coins? **See margin.**

49 David has four coins. They are worth 46¢. Tell which of the following statements are reasonable and explain your answer.

a. David has two dimes. **reasonable; 10¢ + 10¢ + 25¢ + 1¢ = 46¢**

b. David has two quarters. **not reasonable; 25¢ + 25¢ = 50¢**

c. David has six pennies. **not reasonable; he has only four coins**

MENTAL MATH Write the decimal 0.60 on the chalkboard. As you say aloud these numbers, students respond by showing thumbs up if the number is greater than 0.60, thumbs down if the number is less than 0.60, and standing if the number is equivalent to 0.60:

a. 0.081 (thumbs down) **b.** 0.80 (thumbs up)
c. 0.091 (thumbs down) **d.** 0.600 (stand up)
e. 1.0 (thumbs up) **f.** 0.08 (thumbs down)
g. 0.066 (thumbs down) **h.** 1.06 (thumbs up)
i. 0.009 (thumbs down) **j.** 0.57 (thumbs down)

2 Teach

COOPERATIVE LEARNING · MANIPULATIVES

Using the Student Pages

Have students work independently on page 476. Have students work in pairs or small groups to solve the coin problems on page 477. Provide **play coins*** to help them solve the problems. Encourage students to try all the possibilities they can think of before deciding that a problem is impossible.

In problem 47 on page 477, there are two possible combinations: 45 pennies, 1 quarter, 2 dimes, and 2 nickels or 40 pennies, 2 dimes, and 8 nickels. Eva couldn't have 50 pennies because that totals only 50¢; she couldn't have 35 pennies because she would need an additional 15 coins to total 65¢. Using nickels, Eva would need 13, which is two short. Fewer than 35 pennies is also not possible for the same reason.

In problem 48, there are three possible combinations: 35 pennies, 2 quarters, and 3 nickels; 30 pennies, 4 dimes, and 6 nickels; and 25 pennies and 15 nickels.

LITERATURE CONNECTION

Literature Connection

Invite students to browse through *Money* by Joe Cribb to learn about the history of money, money from other parts of the world, and interesting alternatives to coins and bills.

GIFTED & TALENTED · MANIPULATIVES

Meeting Individual Needs

You might present more challenging coin problems to your gifted and talented students. An algebra or prealgebra book would include such problems. Although most students cannot yet solve these problems algebraically, they can use other strategies, such as modeling with **play coins*** or estimating and checking to find the solutions.

*available separately

◆ LESSON 141 Comparing Decimals Review

Teach

Using the Thinking Story "Iron and Gold (Part 1)" begins the five-part Thinking Story for this unit. Part 1 explores the importance of gathering data before making a decision.

Answers to Thinking Story Questions:

1. Gold is much more valuable than iron.
2. Highlight two relevant points in your discussion: (a) there is no reason to suppose that the majority's choice will be a good one, and (b) voting is seldom useful as a way to establish truth, and in this case the issue is one of fact: which bag contains the most gold.
3. Many answers are possible, but all should include some way of gaining information about the contents of the bags.

MATH JOURNAL In their Math Journals have students write their ideas for how the children should decide which bag to choose.

◆ LESSON 141 Comparing Decimals Review

THINKING STORY

Iron and Gold

Part 1

The queen of Addonia did not forget that Manolita, Marcus, Ferdie, and Portia helped find her treasure on Mugg Island.

"I am very pleased," said the queen. "You helped me get the Royal Treasure back. I will give you a reward."

She called her steward and said to him, "Give these children a bag of money."

The steward sniffed. "A whole bag of money for these children? Well, all right."

"And see that it has some gold in it," said the queen.

Marcus, Portia, Ferdie, and Manolita followed the steward. He set out three bags of money. One bag was red, one bag was blue, and one was green. "Pick the bag you want and be gone," he said.

"May we look inside?" Manolita asked.

"No," said the steward. "But you may reach in and pick up some coins to see what they are like. I will tell you this. Every bag has some iron coins and some gold coins. And some bags have more gold coins than others."

RETEACHING

MANIPULATIVES Students who do not have a firm grasp of the relative magnitude of decimals may benefit from working with concrete materials, such as **pennies*, dimes*, dollars*,** or **base-10 blocks***. Focus on relating the concrete materials to the standard decimal notation.

PRACTICE p. 141

LESSON 141 PRACTICE Name________________

Draw <, >, or = to make each statement true.

1. 6.8 (<) 8.6	2. 0.91 (>) 0.893	3. 42.6 (>) 4.26
4. 18.31 (=) 18.310	5. 462.5 (<) 465.2	6. 0.834 (<) 8.1
7. 7.76 (<) 77.6	8. 92.3 (>) 8.14	9. 10.62 (>) 10.0
10. 6.4 (>) 5.9	11. 8.3 (=) 8.300	12. 1.037 (>) 1.03
13. 9.11 (>) 8.10	14. 77.36 (>) 7.367	15. 402.0 (>) 386.9
16. 100.0 (<) 100.001	17. 1.5 (>) 0.92	18. 8.8 (>) 7.31
19. 20.003 (<) 21.0	20. 38.090 (=) 38.09	21. 17.282 (>) 15.91
22. 5.6 (>) 3.8	23. 2.0 (<) 3.14	24. 0.7 (>) 0.05
25. 1.09 (<) 2.0	26. 0.518 (=) 0.518	27. 9.091 (>) 9.087

Which of the following are possible? If possible, draw or write the coins needed. If not possible, tell why.

28. Make 65 cents with eight coins.
25, 25, 10, 1, 1, 1, 1, 1

29. Make 45 cents with five coins.
Sample answer: 25, 5, 5, 5, 5

30. Make 33 cents with four coins.
not possible, because you need 3 pennies plus at least 2 other coins

Copyright © SRA/McGraw-Hill. Permission is granted to reproduce this page for classroom use.

*available separately

"We'll take the bag with the most gold coins," said Ferdie. "Which one is that?"

"That's for you to figure out–if you can," said the steward, with a mean smile.

"I know," said Portia. "Let's vote! We'll each vote for the bag that we think has the most gold in it. We'll take the one that wins."

. . . to be continued

Work in groups. Discuss your answers and how you figured them out. Then compare your answers with those of other groups. **Answers are in margin.**

1. Why would the children want the bag that has the most gold coins in it? Why wouldn't they want the bag with the most iron coins?
2. Is voting a good way to decide which bag to take? Why or why not?
3. What would be a good way to choose which bag to take?

ENRICHMENT p. 141

LESSON 141 ENRICHMENT Name__________

Basketball players' records are expressed as shooting percentages. The number of shots a player made is compared to the number he or she tried to make. That fraction is expressed as a decimal, or percentage. For example, if a player made 5 shots out of 10, or $\frac{5}{10}$, the shooting percentage would be 0.500.

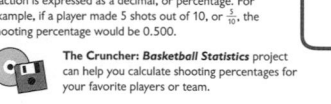

The Cruncher: *Basketball Statistics* project can help you calculate shooting percentages for your favorite players or team.

Answer these questions.

1. If a player made 3 out of 4 attempted shots, what would her shooting percentage be? 0.75
2. If a player made 1 out of 10 attempted shots, what would his shooting percentage be? 0.1
3. If a player made 20 out of 20 attempted shots, what would her shooting percentage be? 1.000

Set up the table with information for your favorite players or team and figure out their shooting percentages. Give it your best shot!

Copyright © SRA/McGraw-Hill. Permission is granted to reproduce this page for classroom use.

ASSESSMENT p. 53

UNIT 6 **Mastery Checkpoint 20** Understanding decimals (Lesson 141)

Name __________

The student demonstrates mastery by correctly answering at least 28 of the 35 problems.

Draw <, >, or = to make each statement true.

1. 0.2 (>) 0.1	2. 0.35 (<) 0.53	3. 36.1 (>) 15.3
4. 0.02 (>) 0.01	5. 0.4 (=) 0.40	6. 0.832 (<) 0.947
7. 1.0 (>) 0.1	8. 8.72 (<) 87.2	9. 0.947 (<) 8.32
10. 0.03 (<) 0.30	11. 12.3 (=) 12.300	12. 63.72 (<) 437.6
13. 0.1 (>) 0.001	14. 14.7 (<) 47.1	15. 82.1 (=) 82.100
16. 0.2 (>) 0.01	17. 0.81 (<) 8.01	18. 32.75 (=) 32.750
19. 0.05 (<) 0.3	20. 95.1 (=) 95.100	21. 8.5 (<) 26.5
22. 0.62 (<) 0.7	23. 73.2 (<) 703.2	24. 3.924 (>) 3.294
25. 4.703 (<) 4.73	26. 83.01 (<) 93.0	27. 4.9 (<) 5.16
28. 0.82 (>) 0.082	29. 50.63 (<) 60.63	30. 83.7 (>) 83.007

Solve these problems.

31. Use six coins to make 34¢. List the coins. 25¢, 5¢, 1¢ × 4
32. Can you make 67¢ using six coins? yes, 2 × 25¢, 1 × 10¢, 1 × 5¢, 2 × 1¢
33. How would you make 75¢ using five coins? 2 × 25¢, 2 × 10¢, 1 × 5¢
34. How would you make 58¢ with six coins? 2 × 25¢, 1 × 5¢, 3 × 1¢
35. Make 37¢ using four coins. 1 × 25¢, 1 × 10¢, 2 × 1¢

Copyright © SRA/McGraw-Hill. Permission is granted to reproduce this page for classroom use.

3 Wrap-Up 5 MINUTES

In Closing Discuss with students possible methods of gathering information to resolve dilemmas like the one discussed in the Thinking Story.

ANALYZING ANSWERS Determine the nature of the difficulty for students whose work on page 476 falls short of the desired level of mastery. If the trouble lies with confusion over the meaning of the relation signs, work with these students individually. Remind them that the two unequal relations signs always open toward the greater number and point toward the lesser number. Check to see if students are reading mathematical equations from left to right. Provide practice with problems similar to those on page 476. Have them point to the greater number and then insert the relation sign that will make the number sentence true when read from left to right.

Mastery Checkpoint 20

At this time most students should demonstrate mastery of the relative magnitude of decimals by correctly answering at least 80% of the problems on page 476 or a similar page. You may also wish to assign Assessment Blackline Masters page 53 to determine mastery. Record the results of this assessment on the Mastery Checkpoint Chart.

Assessment Criteria

Did the student . . .

- ✓ correctly answer at least 80% of the decimal relationship problems on page 476?
- ✓ communicate strategies used to solve the coin combination problems?
- ✓ contribute to the Thinking Story discussion?

Homework Have students create five problems like the ones on page 476 that involve comparing decimals. Also have them create two coin combination problems. Have students exchange and solve each other's problems.

Student Edition pages 480–481

Rounding Decimals

LESSON PLANNER

Objectives

- ▶ to provide practice with rounding numbers to a specified degree of precision
- ▶ to help students develop judgment about rounding numbers in specific realistic situations

Context of the Lesson This is the fifth of 16 lessons on understanding and using decimals.

MANIPULATIVES

none

Program Resources

Reteaching Master

Practice Master 142

Enrichment Master 142

For extra practice:
CD-ROM* Lesson 142

1 Warm-Up

5 MINUTES

Problem of the Day Present the following problem: Keisha and her dad have the same birthday. This year, Keisha's dad is five times older than Keisha. Three years from now, Keisha's dad will be only four times older than she is. How old are Keisha and her dad now, and how old will they be in three years? (9 and 45; 12 and 48)

Problem-Solving Strategies Ask students who have solved the Problem of the Day to share how they solved it and any strategies they used.

MENTAL MATH Write the decimal 4.07 on the chalkboard. As you say other numbers, students show thumbs up if the number is greater than 4.07 and thumbs down if the number is less than 4.07. They stand up if the number is equivalent to 4.07.

a. 4.008 (thumbs down)	**b.** 4.08 (thumbs up)
c. 4.073 (thumbs up)	**d.** 4.0089 (thumbs down)
e. 7 (thumbs up)	**f.** 4.070 (stand up)
g. 4.707 (thumbs up)	**h.** 4.069 (thumbs down)
i. 4.05889 (thumbs down)	**j.** 4.7 (thumbs up)

***MIXED* PRACTICE**

LESSON 142

Rounding Decimals

Suppose seven people went out to eat. The total bill was $36.77, and each person wants to pay the same amount.

If you divide 36.77 by 7, you get 5.2528571. But people cannot pay part of a penny. If we round to the nearest penny we will get an answer of $5.25 for each person. But 7 times 5.25 is 36.75, which is 2 cents short. In this case, we could either round up, or ask two people to pay an extra penny.

In real situations you must use your judgment about the best way to round numbers.

To round 3.5943295 to the nearest hundredth, we look at the digit to the right of the hundredths place. Because 4 is less than 5, the number is closer to 3.59 than to 3.60, so we round to 3.59.

If the next digit is 5, we usually round up if we know there are more nonzero digits. But what if the last digit is a 5 and we have no further information, or we know that is the last nonzero digit? Then there is no reason to round in either direction.

If we are working with a group of numbers, we should probably round such numbers up half the time and down half the time.

See how each of the following numbers is rounded to the nearest thousandth.

2.03450012 rounds to 2.035

2.0345 can be rounded to either 2.034 or 2.035

FANTASTIC FACT **The Statue of Liberty measures 151 feet tall and weighs 450,000 pounds. Her index finger is 8 feet long, taller than professional basketball players, and her big toe is about the size of a small car.**

480 • Fractions and Decimals

RETEACHING p. 45

LESSON 142 RETEACHING

Name________________

Rounding decimals is much like rounding whole numbers. Sometimes you might round up to the nearest multiple above. Sometimes you might round down to the nearest multiple below.

Example:
If you round 6.1747:

To the nearest tenth → 6.2. Round up.
Look at the digit to the right of the tens place. 7 is greater than 5, so 6.17 is closer to 6.20 than to 6.10.

6.10 6.11 6.12 6.13 6.14 6.15 6.16 6.17 6.18 6.19 6.20

To the nearest hundredth → 6.17. Round down.
To the right of the hundredths place is a 4. Because 4 is less than 5, the number 6.174 is closer to 6.170 than to 6.180.

6.170 .171 .172 .173 .174 .175 .176 .177 .178 .179 6.180

To the nearest thousandth → 6.175. Round up.
To the right of the thousandths place is a 7. Because 7 is greater than 5, 6.1747 is closer to 6.1750 than to 6.1740.

6.1740 6.1745 6.1750

When rounding decimals, remember:

- If you have a group of numbers, round up half the numbers and round down the other half.
- Round up if the next digit is a 5 and there are more nonzero digits.
- If the last nonzero digit is a 5, there is no reason to round up or down.

Round to the nearest tenth, hundredth, and thousandth.

1. 4.5678 4.6 4.57 4.568
2. 99.7899 99.8 99.79 99.790
3. 14.0096 14.0 14.01 14.010

Copyright © SRA/McGraw-Hill. Permission is granted to reproduce this page for classroom use.

Math Explorations and Applications Level 4 • 45

*available separately

25 no; averages cannot be used to calculate an exact quantity
26 no; He should report 82 as the average because his test scores consist of only 2 digits

Round each of the numbers to the nearest hundredth. Watch your numbering.

1. 4.7380389 **4.74**
2. 4.73501001 **4.74**
3. 4.735 **4.73 or 4.74**
4. 0.007 **0.01**
5. 1.003 **1.00**
6. 0.003 **0.00**
7. 45.928 **45.93**
8. 45.92800003 **45.93**
9. 3.451 **3.45**
10. 3.451999999 **3.45**
11. 0.051 **0.05**
12. 1.294 **1.29**
13. 3.481 **3.48**
14. 10.609 **10.61**
15. 8.543 **8.54**

Round each of the numbers to the nearest thousandth. Watch your numbering.

16. 1.23456 **1.235**
17. 1.2345 **1.234 or 1.235**
18. 1.234500001 **1.235**
19. 1.234499999 **1.234**
20. 0.0075 **0.007 or 0.008**
21. 0.148762 **0.149**
22. 19.417023 **19.417**
23. 4.0012 **4.001**
24. 2.71152 **2.712**

For each of the following, round in a way that makes sense.

25. Konala saved $7.00 last week, $8.50 the week before, and $5.20 the week before that. She decided the average amount she saves is $6.90 each week. She multiplied 52 by 6.90, getting 358.8, and announced that she will have exactly $358.80 in the bank in a year. Do you agree? Explain. **See above.**
26. Philip has taken three tests. On the first one he got a score of 92, on the second he scored 73, and on the third he scored 82. He finds the average to be 82.33333333333. Is that the average you would report? Why? **See above.**
27. Bonita needs one bag of fertilizer to fertilize each 200 square feet of her garden. She has measured the length of the garden to be 73.5 feet and the width to be 19 feet. How many bags of fertilizer should she buy? **7, the total area of her yard is 1396.5 sq. ft.**
28. Ms. Goldberg runs a bus company. Her buses can each carry 48 people. She has been asked to supply buses to take 500 people to a conference. She divides 500 by 48 and gets 10.416667. How many buses does she need? **11**

PRACTICE p. 142

LESSON 142 PRACTICE Name__________

Round to the nearest hundredth.

1. 2.675 2.68
2. 4.1245 4.12
3. 0.0016 0
4. 62.3290002 62.33
5. 6.213 6.21
6. 4.61739999 4.62
7. 2.4623001 2.46
8. 1.817405006 1.82
9. 5.652 5.65

Round to the nearest thousandth.

10. 4.315621 4.316
11. 4.3156 4.316
12. 2.13590004 2.136
13. 0.00115 0.001
14. 6.3078 6.308
15. 1.90350003 1.904

Solve these problems. Round the answers in a way that makes sense.

16. Roman bought a basketball for $16.99. He paid sales tax, which was $1.10435. How much did the basketball cost, including tax? $18.09
17. Missy is on the diving team. Her scores for a dive are 7.9, 6.9, 7.2, and 7.3. Her average score is 7.325. How should her average score be recorded? 7.3
18. The fourth-grade classes are going on a field trip. There are 648 people who need to be transported by buses that will carry 52 people each. How many buses are needed for the fourth-grade field trip? 13
19. Sandy has taken six math tests. These are her scores: 75, 86, 91, 78, 87, and 82. She finds her average to be 83.1666667. What score will Sandy get on her report card? 83

Copyright © SRA/McGraw-Hill. Permission is granted to reproduce this page for classroom use.

142 • *Math Explorations and Applications* Level 4

ENRICHMENT p. 142

LESSON 142 ENRICHMENT Name__________

Answer these questions.

1. Have you ever noticed that stores and car dealers often post prices as $3.99, $29.99, or $9999? Why do you think prices are often posted this way? Answers will vary; students should note that prices appear less expensive.
2. If you had $13 to spend and saw the following prices, how would you round them to add them easily in your head?
   six cans of juice for $2.49 $2.50
   one model airplane for $5.98 $6.00
   1 yard of fabric for $3.54 $3.50
   Will $13 be enough to buy everything? yes
3. Look through a catalog or visit a store to do a price study. Find 30 items and list their prices in a table on a separate sheet of paper. Describe any patterns you see. Answers will vary.

Copyright © SRA/McGraw-Hill. Permission is granted to reproduce this page for classroom use.

142 • *Math Explorations and Applications* Level 4

2 Teach

Using the Student Pages Discuss the material on page 480 with the class. Review how to round a number that ends in 5. Place special emphasis on the fact that in practical situations people apply their judgment about how to round. Ask students to suggest examples of realistic situations in which they might have to round decimal numbers. Then have students complete page 481 independently. Discuss the answers to questions 25–28 with the whole class when everyone has finished.

3 Wrap-Up

5 MINUTES

In Closing Have students explain how to round 5.805 to the nearest whole number, to the nearest tenth, and to the nearest hundredth. (6; 5.8; 5.81)

ALTERNATIVE ASSESSMENT

Informal Assessment Observe students as they work on the problems in this lesson. Encourage them to share their thinking. Note whether they read and write decimals accurately, and evaluate their grasp of the situations in the word problems.

Assessment Criteria

Did the student . . .

- ✓ contribute to the discussion of rounding decimals?
- ✓ demonstrate good judgment in rounding for realistic situations?
- ✓ correctly answer at least 75% of the rounding problems?

Homework For further practice with rounding decimals, assign Practice Master 142.

LESSON 143

Student Edition pages 482–485

Decimals: Multiplying and Dividing by Powers of 10

LESSON PLANNER

Objectives

- ▶ to introduce procedures for multiplying and dividing decimals by 10, 100, and 1000
- ▶ to provide practice in multiplying and dividing metric measurements by 10, 100, and 1000

Context of the Lesson This is the sixth of 16 lessons on understanding and using decimals. Students have multiplied and divided whole numbers by powers of 10 in various contexts this year.

MANIPULATIVES

two boxes (optional)

slips of paper (optional)

Program Resources

Number Wheels

Reteaching Master

Practice Master 143

Enrichment Master 143

The Cruncher*

For extra practice: CD-ROM* Lesson 143

1 Warm-Up

5 MINUTES

Problem of the Day Present the following problem. Tell students there are many possible answers: Using the digits 2, 3, 4, and all the 0s you want, create a division problem with a quotient of 800. (One possible answer is 2400 ÷ 3 = 800.)

Problem-Solving Strategies Ask students who have solved the Problem of the Day to share how they solved it and any strategies they used.

MENTAL MATH Provide problems involving multiplying and dividing whole numbers by powers of 10. Have students use Number Wheels to respond quickly.

a. 900 ÷ 10 = (90) **b.** 90 × 100 = (9000)

c. 9 × 10 = (90) **d.** 450 ÷ 10 = (45)

(continued on page 483)

EXPLORE

LESSON 143

Decimals: Multiplying and Dividing by Powers of 10

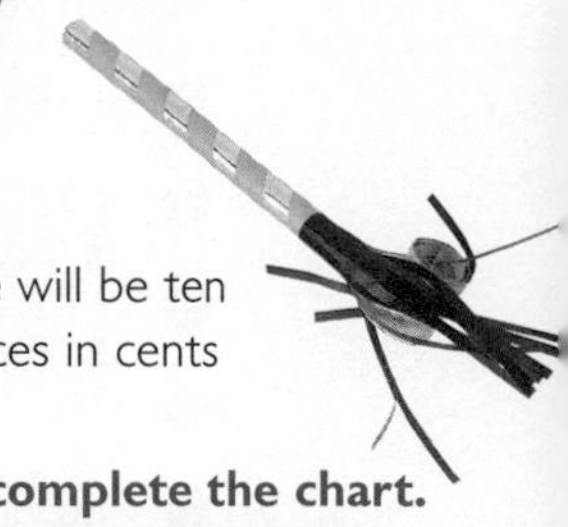

Olivia is buying supplies for a birthday party. There will be ten people at the party. She made a chart to show prices in cents and in dollars and cents.

Use a computer or other means to draw and complete the chart.

Item	Cents: Price for 1	Cents: Price for 10	Dollars and Cents: Price for 1	Dollars and Cents: Price for 10
Balloon	7¢	70¢	$0.07	$0.70
Noisemaker	29¢	290¢	$0.29	$2.90
Kazoo	45¢	450¢	$0.45	$4.50
Hat	63¢	630¢	$0.63	$6.30
Sticker	37¢	370¢	$0.37	$3.70

◆ Compare the two dollars-and-cents columns. What do you notice about the decimal point?

It shifts one place to the right across the columns.

Ten people are sharing the cost of the food for Olivia's birthday party. They made a chart to show the prices in cents and in dollars. Copy and complete the chart.

Item	Cents: Total Cost	Cents: Cost for Each Person	Dollars and Cents: Total Cost	Dollars and Cents: Cost for Each Person
Cupcakes	380¢	38¢	$3.80	$0.38
Ice cream	980¢	98¢	$9.80	$0.98
Cookies	470¢	47¢	$4.70	$0.47
Milk	260¢	26¢	$2.60	$0.26

◆ Compare the two dollars-and-cents columns. What do you notice about the decimal point?

It shifts one place to the left across the columns.

482 • Fractions and Decimals

Math Connection Remind students that they previously learned to multiply and divide whole numbers by powers of 10. Help them to see that the skills in this lesson are extensions of skills they previously used. You might work through an example such as 3800 ÷ 10, then ÷ 100, ÷ 1000, and ÷ 10,000 to show the progressive movement of the decimal point to the left in division. Also, provide an example such as 0.123 × 10, then × 100, × 1000, and × 10,000 to show the progressive movement of the decimal point to the right in multiplication.

*available separately

The value of a digit in its place in a number is ten times as great as in the place to its right. So you can multiply by 10 by moving the decimal point one place to the right.

Remember, the decimal point always comes after the ones place, even if it isn't written there.

Examples: 10 × 4.5 = ? 4.5. 10 × 4.5 = 45

3.06 × 10 = ? 3.0.6 3.06 × 10 = 30.6

Sometimes you need to write in a 0.

8 × 10 = ? 8.0. 8 × 10 = 80

Multiply.

1. 10 × 7 **70**
2. 12 × 10 **120**
3. 10 × 60 **600**
4. 10 × 59 **590**
5. 10 × 7.2 **72**
6. 10 × 81.34 **813.4**
7. 86.29 × 10 **862.9**
8. 47.28 × 10 **472.8**

To multiply by 100, move the decimal point two places to the right.

Examples: 100 × 17.15 = ? 17.1.5. 100 × 17.15 = 1715

6.7 × 100 = ? 6.7.0. 6.7 × 100 = 670

Multiply.

9. 100 × 7 **700**
10. 12 × 100 **1200**
11. 60 × 100 **6000**
12. 100 × 59 **5900**
13. 100 × 7.2 **720**
14. 100 × 81.34 **8134**
15. 100 × 86.29 **8629**
16. 100 × 47.28 **4728**

To multiply by 1000, move the decimal point three places to the right.

Examples: 1.9396 × 1000 = ? 1.9.3.9.6 1.9396 × 1000 = 1939.6

1.07 × 1000 = ? 1.0.7.0. 1.07 × 1000 = 1070

Multiply.

17. 1000 × 8 **8000**
18. 1000 × 0.798 **798**
19. 1000 × 73 **73,000**
20. 1000 × 7.23 **7230**
21. 50 × 1000 **50,000**
22. 1000 × 74.82 **74,820**
23. 42 × 1000 **42,000**
24. 1000 × 68.92 **68,920**
25. 479.26 × 100 **47,926**

Mental Math (continued)

e.	45 x 100 = (4500)	**f.**	4500 ÷ 100 = (45)
g.	4500 ÷ 10 = (450)	**h.**	45 x 10 = (450)
i.	6600 ÷ 10 = (660)	**j.**	660 x 10 = (6600)
k.	660 x 100 = (66,000)	**l.**	6600 ÷ 100 = (66)

2 Teach

Using the Student Pages Complete page 482 with the class. You may want to copy the chart onto the chalkboard and have volunteers fill in the answers. As you discuss the first question, be sure students notice that the decimal point moves one place to the right in multiplication by 10. In the second question, be sure they notice that the decimal point moves one place to the left in division by 10. Discuss the inverse relationship between multiplication and division to explain the opposing movements of the decimal point. On page 483, go through the examples under each rule for multiplying by 10, 100, and 1000. If students demonstrate that they understand the work, have them complete the page on their own. Otherwise, complete the page with the class. Go over the answers before moving on to page 484. Students can use a blank **Cruncher*** spreadsheet to prepare for multiplying and dividing by powers of 10.

Technology Connection Refer students to the software *Math Skills Collection* from Hartley (Mac, IBM, for grades 4–6) for practice with whole numbers, fractions, decimals and percents, measurement, shapes, and figures.

*available separately

◆ LESSON 143 Decimals: Multiplying and Dividing by Powers of 10

Teach

Using the Student Pages On page 484, go through the examples under each rule for dividing by 10, 100, and 1000. Again, discuss how the reverse movement for division makes sense because division is the inverse of multiplication. Have students complete the page independently, unless you think it would be more effective to work with the whole class. Then go through the information at the top of page 485 with the class. Solve problems 54–63 together. Then have students complete problems 64–68 on their own.

LEARNING STYLES · MANIPULATIVES

Meeting Individual Needs

Students who are kinesthetic or logical learners may benefit from using a function machine analogy to grasp the skills in this lesson. Simulate two function machines with **boxes, slips of paper,** or arrow notation. Make one machine multiply by 10 and the other follow the rule "move the decimal point one place to the right." Put some whole numbers into each function machine so students can see that the outputs are identical. Then put in some decimals. Use successively more complex numbers. Do a similar activity for × 100, then × 1000, then ÷ 10, and so on.

◆ LESSON 143 Decimals: Multiplying and Dividing by Powers of 10

The value of a digit in its place in a number is one tenth the value it would have in the place to its left. So you can divide by 10 by moving the decimal point one place to the left.

Examples:

47 ÷ 10 = ?	4.7.	47 ÷ 10 = 4.7
0.7 ÷ 10 = ?	.0.7	0.7 ÷ 10 = 0.07
38.6 ÷ 10 = ?	3.8.6	38.6 ÷ 10 = 3.86

Divide.

26. 38 ÷ 10 **3.8**
27. 0.8 ÷ 10 **0.08**
28. 0.9 ÷ 10 **0.09**
29. 5.9 ÷ 10 **0.59**
30. 3.8 ÷ 10 **0.38**
31. 43.2 ÷ 10 **4.32**
32. 0.78 ÷ 10 **0.078**
33. 48.27 ÷ 10 **4.827**

To divide by 100, move the decimal point two places to the left.

Examples:

545 ÷ 100 = ?	5.45.	545 ÷ 100 = 5.45
65 ÷ 100 = ?	.6 5.	65 ÷ 100 = 0.65

Sometimes you need to write in a 0.

0.73 ÷ 100 = ?	.0 0.73	0.73 ÷ 100 = 0.0073

Divide.

34. 75 ÷ 100 **0.75**
35. 8390 ÷ 100 **83.90**
36. 7.5 ÷ 100 **0.075**
37. 0.98 ÷ 100 **0.0098**
38. 6.8 ÷ 100 **0.068**
39. 183 ÷ 100 **1.83**
40. 1116 ÷ 100 **11.16**
41. 0.756 ÷ 100 **0.00756**

To divide by 1000, move the decimal point three places to the left.

Examples:

45 ÷ 1000 = ?	.0 4 5.	45 ÷ 1000 = 0.045
22 ÷ 1000 = ?	.0 2 2.	22 ÷ 1000 = 0.022

Divide.

42. 2500 ÷ 1000 **2.5**
43. 351 ÷ 1000 **0.351**
44. 14.76 ÷ 1000 **0.01476**
45. 16 ÷ 1000 **0.016**
46. 8 ÷ 1000 **0.008**
47. 125.7 ÷ 1000 **0.1257**
48. 147.6 ÷ 1000 **0.1476**
49. 279 ÷ 1000 **0.279**
50. 51 ÷ 1000 **0.051**
51. 327 ÷ 1000 **0.32**
52. 1476 ÷ 1000 **1.476**
53. 390 ÷ 1000 **0.39**

484 • Fractions and Decimals

LITERATURE CONNECTION

Literature Connection Have students read Part 7, "Thinking Big," of *Math for Smarty Pants* by Marilyn Burns to learn about powers of 10 and other ways to express "big" numbers.

RETEACHING p. 46

LESSON 143 RETEACHING Name__________

Multiplying and dividing with decimals is like working with whole numbers. You just need to remember to move the decimal points.

Multiplying
When you multiply a number, it becomes greater. Move the decimal point to the right.

14.5 × 10   1 4 . 5 = 145

3.75 × 100   3 . 7 5 = 375

Dividing
When you divide a number, it becomes less. Move the decimal point to the left.

14.5 ÷ 10   1 4 . 5 = 1.45

3.75 ÷ 100   0 0 3 . 7 5 = 0.0375

Study these tips for multiplying and dividing decimals by 10, 100, and 1000.

Multiplying
Use the number of 0s in the multiplier to tell you how many places to move the decimal point to the right.

When multiplying by. . .
10 (1 zero) – move 1 place right.
100 (2 zeros) – move 2 places right.
1000 (3 zeros) – move 3 places right.

Dividing
Use the number of 0s in the divisor to tell you how many places to move the decimal point to the left.

When dividing by. . .
10 (1 zero) – move 1 place left.
100 (2 zeros) – move 2 places left.
1000 (3 zeros) – move 3 places left.

Solve. Watch the signs.

1. 15.99 × 100 = 1599
2. 3000 ÷ 1000 = 3
3. 2.2 × 1000 = 2200
4. 399.9 × 10 = 3999
5. 5.6789 × 1000 = 5678.9
6. 85 ÷ 10 = 8.5
7. 9.9 × 100 = 990
8. 0.47 ÷ 100 = 0.0047
9. 11.1 × 10 = 111
10. 767 ÷ 100 = 7.67
11. 20.1 ÷ 1000 = 0.0201
12. 23.4 ÷ 10 = 2.34
13. 2.1 × 1000 = 2100
14. 545.63 ÷ 10 = 54.563

46 • *Math Explorations and Applications* Level 4

Copyright © SRA/McGraw-Hill. Permission is granted to reproduce this page for classroom use.

In general, to divide by a number that is written as a 1 with some number of 0s after it, you move the decimal point that number of places to the left. To multiply by such a number, you move the decimal point that many places to the right. Write extra 0s when necessary.

Examples:

11.76 × 10 ⟶ 11.7.6 ⟶ 117.6

135.6 ÷ 100 ⟶ 1.3 5.6 ⟶ 1.356

21.4 × 100 ⟶ 21.4.0. ⟶ 2140

Solve the following problems. Watch the signs. Watch your numbering.

54. 765.4321 × 10 **7654.321**
55. 765.4321 ÷ 10 **76.54321**
56. 765.4321 ÷ 100 **7.654321**
57. 765.4321 ÷ 1000 **).7654321**
58. 765.4321 × 1000 **765,432.1**
59. 765.4321 ÷ 100,000 **0.007654321**
60. 765.4321 × 100,000 **76,543,210**
61. 2 ÷ 1000 **0.002**
62. 2 × 1000 **2000**
63. 2 ÷ 10,000 **0.0002**

You know that there are 100 centimeters in a meter and 1000 meters in a kilometer. So, to find out how many centimeters there are in 73.2 meters, you multiply 73.2 by 100, getting 7320 (moving the decimal point two places to the right, after writing the extra 0).

Solve the following problems.

64. How many centimeters are there in 56.24 meters? **5624**
65. How many meters are there in 7.24 kilometers? **7240**
66. How many centimeters are there in 7.24 kilometers? **724,000**
67. How many meters are there in 2435 centimeters? **24.35**
68. How many kilometers are there in 2435 centimeters? **0.02435**

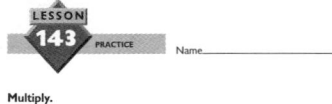

❸ Wrap-Up (5 MINUTES)

In Closing Ask students how to multiply 78.2 by 100 and how to divide 78.2 by 100.

ALTERNATIVE ASSESSMENT

Informal Assessment Observe students as they work through the problems in this lesson. Have them verbalize their reasoning and defend their answers. Note students who have trouble multiplying or dividing by 10, 100, and 1000. First have them decide whether the answer will be greater or lesser than the number they are multiplying or dividing. Then call their attention to the fact that the number of 0s—one in 10, two in 100, three in 1000—tells how far to move the decimal point.

Assessment Criteria

Did the student . . .

- ✓ contribute to the discussion of multiplying and dividing decimals by powers of 10?
- ✓ accurately apply the rules for multiplying and dividing by powers of 10?
- ✓ correctly answer at least 75% of the computation problems on pages 483–485?

Homework Assign Practice Master 143 for further practice with multiplying and dividing by powers of 10 using decimals.

PRACTICE p. 143

LESSON 143 PRACTICE Name____________

Multiply.

1. 6.3 × 100 = 630
2. 0.41 × 10 = 4.1
3. 42.61 × 100 = 4261
4. 903.1 × 10 = 9031
5. 28.418 × 100 = 2841.8
6. 10 × 3.034 = 30.34
7. 1000 × 51.073 = 51,073
8. 204.12 × 100 = 20,412
9. 600.3 × 1000 = 600,300
10. 10 × 1.091 = 10.91
11. 0.001 × 1000 = 1
12. 10 × 87.32 = 873.2
13. 4.386 × 100 = 438.6
14. 28.26 × 10 = 282.6
15. 100 × 37.3 = 3730
16. 47.5 × 1000 = 47,500
17. 132.6 × 10 = 1326
18. 45.32 × 100 = 4532
19. 10 × 9.5 = 95
20. 1000 × 8.76 = 8760

Solve. Watch the signs.

21. 1000 × 0.54 = 540
22. 1000 × 0.867 = 867
23. 4.37 × 10 = 43.7
24. 9.7 ÷ 10 = 0.97
25. 6.86 ÷ 100 = 0.0686
26. 11.2 ÷ 100 = 0.112
27. 52.5 ÷ 10 = 5.25
28. 100 × 1.45 = 145
29. 10 × 11.25 = 112.5
30. 1.234 ÷ 1000 = 0.001234

Solve these problems.

31. How many cents are there in $32.09? 3209¢
32. How many dollars are there in 4360 cents? $43.60
33. How many meters are there in 1235 centimeters? 12.35

Copyright © SRA/McGraw-Hill. Permission is granted to reproduce this page for classroom use.

ENRICHMENT p. 143

LESSON 143 ENRICHMENT Name____________

Most telephone numbers in the United States have seven digits, not including the area code.

Make a survey of the telephone numbers of the students in your school. Try to get a sample of about 100 telephone numbers. Make a list of the telephone numbers. Then on one copy of this activity sheet fill in the chart. Write "Last" in the blank at the top of the first column. Record with tally marks how many times the last digit is 0, how many times it is 1, and so on through 9.

On another copy of this sheet write "First" in the blank on the chart. Use tally marks to record how many times the first digit is 0, how many times it is 1, and so on through 9.

______ Digit	Tallies	Total
0	Answers will vary.	
1		
2		
3		
4		
5		
6		
7		
8		
9		

Keep this page in your Math Portfolio. You will use it again in Lesson 145.

Copyright © SRA/McGraw-Hill. Permission is granted to reproduce this page for classroom use.

LESSON 144

Student Edition pages 486–489

Approximating Errors Using Decimals

LESSON PLANNER

Objectives

- ✓ to provide practice with and assess mastery of multiplying and dividing decimals by powers of 10
- ▶ to facilitate the investigation of the effects of adding numbers with estimation errors and provide practice with approximating products
- ▶ to assist in the development of the broad ability to use mathematical common sense

Context of the Lesson This lesson, the seventh of 16 lessons on understanding and using decimals, includes a checkpoint for assessing mastery of multiplying and dividing decimals by powers of 10. It also contains Part 2 of "Iron and Gold," a five-part Thinking Story.

MANIPULATIVES

counters* (optional)

play money* (optional)

base-10 blocks* (optional)

three containers or bags (optional)

Program Resources

Practice Master 144

Enrichment Master 144

Assessment Master

For career connections: Careers and Math*

For extra practice: CD-ROM* Lesson 144; Cumulative Review, page 566

PROBLEM SOLVING

LESSON 144

Approximating Errors Using Decimals

When you round or approximate, it is useful to know how far from the exact number your approximation could be. The difference depends on how much you round each number.

Solve these problems.

1. Bill always "rounds off" the entries in his checkbook by dropping the cents. Thus, he writes $43 for $43.98, $57 for $57.26, and $97 for $97.01. Because he does this both for deposits to his account and for checks he writes, he thinks that his account should balance out in the end. Do you think it should? Why or why not? **no; it is not likely that the amount he rounds up will be identical to the amount he rounds down**

2. One month Bill made deposits in the following amounts: $416.20, $416.20, and $98.80.

   He also wrote checks in the following amounts: $7.83, $59.46, $12.50, $25.00, $241.10, $17.69, $50.00, $28.54, $25.00, $16.58, $57.43, $247.56, $73.12, $57.34, and $10.00.

   Assume Bill started with a balance of $100 in his checkbook.

   a. What should his balance be at the end of the month? **$102.05**

   b. What would Bill think his balance is? **$106.00**

   c. Can you devise a method for estimating how much difference there is likely to be between the exact balance and Bill's estimated balance? **Accept reasonable answers.**

3. Erin estimated each of ten distances to the nearest mile. When she added the distances, she got an estimated total of 473 miles. If her original estimates were correct to the nearest mile (no more than $\frac{1}{2}$ mile off), what are the greatest and least possible exact values for the total? **478 and 468**

486 • Fractions and Decimals

1 Warm-Up

5 MINUTES

Problem of the Day Present this problem: The band at Oneida High School is giving a concert. The program can last only 30 minutes. The band has six favorite songs that last five minutes each. Can they perform them and keep to the time limit? Explain. (6 × 5 = 30, but this leaves no time for introductions, applause, or other nonmusical parts of the concert. The band might perform five of the songs to allow time for other aspects of the concert.)

Problem-Solving Strategies Ask students who have solved the Problem of the Day to share how they solved it and any strategies they used.

Literature Connection Use the picture book *Is the Blue Whale the Biggest Thing There Is?* by Robert E. Wells to have students compare the size of Earth's largest mammal to the tallest mountain, the sun, and so on. Help them use decimal notation and multiplying and dividing by powers of 10 to represent the sizes of different objects relative to the blue whale.

*available separately

Multiply.

4 100 × 8.3 **830**	5 401.1 × 10 **4011**	6 10 × 88.34 **883.4**
7 10 × 90.0 **900**	8 77 × 1000 **77,000**	9 110.1 × 100 **11,010**
10 421.02 × 10 **4210.2**	11 8.06 × 10 **80.6**	12 384.71 × 100 **38,471**
13 10 × 59.3 **593**	14 100 × 91.011 **9101.1**	15 1000 × 62.073 **62,073**
16 816.41 × 100 **81,641**	17 100 × 910.11 **91,011**	18 10 × 93.74 **937.4**

Divide.

19 61.6 ÷ 10 **6.16**	20 8971.1 ÷ 10 **897.11**	21 0.7 ÷ 100 **0.007**
22 70.04 ÷ 100 **0.7004**	23 652.36 ÷ 100 **6.5236**	24 962.1 ÷ 10 **96.21**
25 8.23 ÷ 10 **0.823**	26 0.06 ÷ 100 **0.0006**	27 475 ÷ 100 **4.75**
28 0.43 ÷ 10 **0.043**	29 1.003 ÷ 10 **0.1003**	30 0.67 ÷ 100 **0.0067**
31 7.342 ÷ 1000 **0.007342**	32 900.1 ÷ 100 **9.001**	33 8.08 ÷ 1000 **0.00808**

Multiply or divide. Watch the signs.

34 29.03 × 100 **2903**	35 2.601 × 10 **26.01**	36 98.03 ÷ 10 **9.803**
37 0.507 ÷ 10 **0.0507**	38 0.04 ÷ 10 **0.004**	39 437.2 × 100 **43,720**
40 1000 × 0.301 **301**	41 3.45 ÷ 100 **0.0345**	42 1000 × 0.062 **62**
43 10 × 8.06 **80.6**	44 8.066 ÷ 100 **0.08066**	45 100 × 1.304 **130.4**
46 482.1 ÷ 100 **4.821**	47 32 × 1000 **32,000**	48 3.421 ÷ 100 **0.03421**

Challenge: A stack of 1000 sheets of paper is 9.5 centimeters thick. How many centimeters thick is each sheet? **0.0095**

MENTAL MATH Provide practice in approximating products. Encourage students to respond quickly to the following problems:

a. 476 x 24 = (11,000)	**b.** 520 x 31 = (16,000)
c. 789 x 49 = (40,000)	**d.** 312 x 77 = (24,000)
e. 981 x 18 = (17,000)	**f.** 623 x 88 = (55,000)
g. 223 x 32 = (7000)	**h.** 445 x 54 = (24,000)

2 Teach

PROBLEM SOLVING **Using the Student Pages** Discuss the problems on page 486. Read problem 1 and be sure to highlight the following points:

1. The number of checks written usually exceeds the number of deposits. Therefore, dropping the cents on each entry would probably mean that more is dropped from withdrawals than from deposits. Thus the real balance would probably be less than the approximated one.
2. The kinds and amounts of bills paid and the number of deposits made can substantially alter the results.

After students complete the exercises, discuss problem 3 with the class. You might have students think of ten numbers that total 473. Next, have them add 0.5 to each number and add the ten new numbers (478). Then have them subtract 0.5 from each of the original ten numbers and add them (468). Help students understand that since each of the original ten measurements may have been as much as $\frac{1}{2}$ mile too low or too high, the resulting sum may have been as much as 10 times $\frac{1}{2}$, or 5 miles, too low or too high.

Before students begin page 487, review the rules they learned for multiplying and dividing by powers of 10. Then have them complete the page independently.

TECHNOLOGY CONNECTION **Technology Connection** For practice with addition, subtraction, multiplication, and division of fractions and decimals, refer students to the software *Math Keys: Unlocking Fractions and Decimals* from MECC (Mac, IBM, for grades 3–6). Manipulatives like counters, bars, circles, and decimal blocks are used for solving problems.

SPECIAL NEEDS **Meeting Individual Needs**

Some students confuse the rules for multiplying and dividing by powers of 10. It may help them to develop a mnemonic code, such as "Multiply right, divide left." This simple phrase can serve to remind them that when they multiply by a power of 10, the decimal point moves the proper number of places to the right, and when they divide by a power of 10, the decimal point moves the correct number of places to the left.

◆ LESSON 144 Approximating Errors Using Decimals

Teach

Using the Thinking Story "Iron and Gold (Part 2)" explores sampling procedures and highlights the problems of choosing a sample that is too small or nonrepresentative.

Answers to Thinking Story Questions:

1. Marcus found that the blue bag yielded the most gold coins, the green bag yielded the next most, and the red bag the fewest. Manolita had found that the red bag yielded the most gold coins.
2. After seeing Marcus's results, most people would change their vote because Marcus's conclusion is based on more information.
3. Because Marcus took more coins from each bag, his results are more reliable. But he could still, by chance, have drawn more gold coins from the blue bag even if the red bag, for example, had the most gold coins. It is also possible that someone could have arranged the coins in a special way to deceive a person who would take a random sample by simply removing a handful from the top of each bag.
4. You could take a larger sample from each bag, especially from different parts of each bag—do not skim coins off the top, as Marcus did. You might thoroughly mix the coins in each bag before taking a sample.

MATH JOURNAL Have students write in their Math Journals what they would say to Manolita to convince her that she might want to reconsider her original decision.

LEARNING STYLES · MANIPULATIVES

Meeting Individual Needs

Visual, kinesthetic, and logical learners may better understand the concept of representative samples if they act out the Thinking Story. Provide **three containers** or **bags,** each of which holds a different assortment of red and blue **counters***. Let students draw one counter from each bag, as Manolita did, and then try to decide which bag has the most red counters. Then have them draw a handful as Marcus did and, if necessary, adjust their decision. Have them repeat this experiment enough times to get a sense of the importance of using a representative sample.

◆ LESSON 144 Approximating Errors Using Decimals

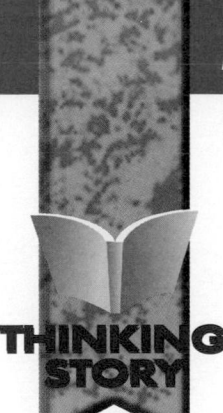

THINKING STORY

Iron and Gold

Part 2

You may want to refer to the first part of this Thinking Story on pages 478–479.

"Before I vote on which bag to take," said Manolita, "I want to find out what kind of coins are in them."

She reached into the red bag and drew out a gold coin. Then she reached into the blue bag and drew out an iron coin. She also drew an iron coin from the green bag.

"That settles it," said Manolita. "I vote for the red bag."

"Before I vote," said Marcus, "I want to take a big handful of coins from every bag."

Marcus scooped a handful of coins from the red bag. He got one gold coin, and all the rest were iron. Next he took a handful of coins from the blue bag. They were all gold except for one! Then he took a handful of coins from the green bag. He got four gold coins and eight iron ones.

"I'm glad I did that," Marcus said. "If we'd followed Manolita, we would have picked the wrong bag."

. . . to be continued

RETEACHING

MANIPULATIVES Continue to provide practice for students who have difficulty multiplying and dividing by powers of 10. Use **play money*** or **base-10 blocks*** to model the computations.

PRACTICE p. 144

LESSON 144 PRACTICE Name______________

Multiply or divide. Watch the signs.

1. 6.12 ÷ 100 = 0.0612
2. 96.8 ÷ 10 = 9.68
3. 3.004 × 1000 = 3004
4. 96.8 × 100 = 9680
5. 10 × 91 = 910
6. 100 × 7.1 = 710
7. 100 × 46.03 = 4603
8. 3.7 ÷ 10 = 0.37
9. 7.32 ÷ 1000 = 0.00732
10. 6321 ÷ 1000 = 6.321
11. 613.1 × 100 = 61,310
12. 43 ÷ 100 = 0.43
13. 54.210 ÷ 10 = 5.4210
14. 10 × 7.9 = 79
15. 100 × 2.301 = 230.1
16. 83 ÷ 100 = 0.83
17. 60 ÷ 100 = 0.60
18. 0.65 × 1000 = 650

PROBLEM SOLVING **Solve these problems.**

19. One month Mrs. Jones made deposits of the following amounts: $346.19, $89.25, and $179.76. She also wrote checks for the following amounts: $20.00, $2.45, $38.23, $171.16, $42.14, $12.39, $9.00, $27.53, and $97.98. Assume Mrs. Jones started with a balance of $250 in her checkbook.
   a. What would her balance be at the end of the month? $444.32
   b. What would her balance be if she "rounds off" the amounts each time by dropping the cents? $446.00
   c. What is the difference between the two balances? $1.68

Copyright © SRA/McGraw-Hill. Permission is granted to reproduce this page for classroom use.

*available separately

Work in groups. Discuss your answers and how you figured them out. Then compare your answers with those of other groups. Answers are in margin.

1. How is what Marcus found out different from what Manolita found out?
2. If you were Manolita, would you have changed your vote after seeing Marcus's results?
3. Can we be sure that Manolita voted for the wrong bag? Explain.
4. How could you be even more sure than Marcus about which bag to pick?

Use the Cumulative Review on page 566 after this lesson.

3 Wrap-Up (5 MINUTES)

In Closing Ask students why the size of a sample makes a difference when gathering information. Also ask why it is important for a sample to adequately represent the situation.

Mastery Checkpoint 21

By this time most students should be proficient with multiplying and dividing decimals by powers of 10. You can assess this ability by using page 487 or a similar page. To demonstrate mastery, students should correctly answer at least 80% of the problems. You may also wish to assign Assessment Blackline Masters page 56 to determine mastery. Record the results of this assessment on the Mastery Checkpoint Chart.

Assessment Criteria

Did the student . . .

- ✓ communicate strategies used to evaluate the approximation problems?
- ✓ correctly answer at least 80% of the computation problems on page 487?
- ✓ contribute to the Thinking Story discussion?

Homework Have students choose three groups of items in their home, such as socks in a drawer, glasses in a cupboard, or books on a shelf, to approximate. Have them record their approximation of the number of items, and then count the items and compare the actual number with their approximations.

ENRICHMENT p. 144

LESSON 144 ENRICHMENT Name________

SCIENCE CONNECTION **Answer these questions.**

Space shuttle astronauts orbit Earth at about 18,000 miles per hour. They circle the planet about 17 times per day. At 100 miles above Earth, each orbit is about 25,625 miles.

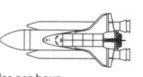

1. Use approximation to calculate how far you would go as an astronaut on a mission that lasted five days. Check your answer with a calculator.
   85 orbits × 25,625 miles each = 2,178,125 miles
   Approximations will vary. Possible approximation:
   $8 \times 10^1 \times 25 \times 10^3 = 200 \times 10^4$ (2,000,000 miles)
2. Suppose you are traveling at 25,000 miles per hour to Mars and back again. The trip through space takes 3840 hours. How far away is Mars? Use approximation.
   25,000 miles per hour × 3840 hours = 96,000,000 miles round-trip; Approximations will vary. Possible approximation:
   $25 \times 10^3 \times 4 \times 10^3 = 100 \times 10^6 = 100{,}000{,}000$ miles
   Mars is half the total distance, or approximately 50,000,000 miles.
3. You have invented a spacecraft that can travel at the speed of light (186,000 miles per second). To test it, you will fly to the star Sirius and back. The trip will take you 18 Earth years. Use multiplication and approximation to figure out how far you will travel.
   186,000 miles per second × 60 seconds × 60 minutes × 24 hours × 365 days × 18 years ≈ $186 \times 10^3 \times 6 \times 10^1 \times 6 \times 10^1 \times 2 \times 10^1 \times 4 \times 10^2 \times 2 \times 10^1 \approx 107{,}136 \times 10^9 \approx 107{,}136{,}000{,}000{,}000$ miles

Copyright © SRA/McGraw-Hill. Permission is granted to reproduce this page for classroom use.

ASSESSMENT p. 56

UNIT 6 **Mastery Checkpoint 21** Multiplying and dividing decimals by powers of 10 (Lesson 144)

Name ________

The student demonstrates mastery by correctly answering at least 32 of the 40 problems.

Multiply.

1. 7.2 × 10 = 72	2. 100 × 902.3 = 90,230
3. 100 × 80 = 8000	4. 88 × 1000 = 88,000
5. 10 × 376.05 = 3760.5	6. 473.01 × 100 = 47,301
7. 1000 × 49.6 = 49,600	8. 28.1 × 100 = 2810
9. 7.9 × 1000 = 7900	10. 79.3 × 1000 = 79,300

Divide.

11. 52.5 ÷ 10 = 5.25	12. 2.007 ÷ 10 = 0.2007
13. 80.05 ÷ 100 = 0.8005	14. 4387.2 ÷ 10 = 438.72
15. 7.36 ÷ 10 = 0.736	16. 563.71 ÷ 100 = 5.6371
17. 487.3 ÷ 100 = 4.873	18. 291.43 ÷ 10 = 29.143
19. 79.5 ÷ 1000 = 0.0795	20. 64.8 ÷ 1000 = 0.0648

Multiply or divide.

21. 92.1 ÷ 10 = 9.21	22. 632 ÷ 1000 = 0.632
23. 0.801 ÷ 10 = 0.0801	24. 100 × 0.903 = 90.3
25. 0.801 × 10 = 8.01	26. 10 × 0.0105 = 0.105
27. 100 × 72.835 = 7283.5	28. 63.4 ÷ 10 = 6.34
29. 0.43 × 100 = 43	30. 649 × 10 = 6490
31. 0.64 ÷ 1000 = 0.00064	32. 905.7 × 1000 = 905,700
33. 8.42 × 10 = 84.2	34. 10 × 4.82 = 48.2
35. 0.59 × 1000 = 590	36. 100 × 750 = 75,000
37. 2.45 × 100 = 245	38. 2.49 ÷ 1000 = 0.00249
39. 1.59 × 1000 = 1590	40. 34.8 ÷ 100 = 0.348

Copyright © SRA/McGraw-Hill. Permission is granted to reproduce this page for classroom use.

LESSON 145

Student Edition pages 490–491

Metric Units: Multiply and Divide by Powers of 10

LESSON PLANNER

Objectives

- to review measuring length with metric units
- to introduce the relationship among metric units of length and to provide practice converting from one to another
- to provide practical applications of decimals

Context of the Lesson This is the eighth of 16 lessons on understanding and using decimals. Students have worked with the metric system in previous lessons this year, and they measured length in nonstandard units in Level 1 and in meters and centimeters in Levels 2 and 3. Later lessons will review metric units of weight and volume.

MANIPULATIVES	Program Resources
base-10 cubes*	Reteaching Master
metersticks	Practice Master 145
metric rulers*	Enrichment Master 145
objects to be measured	For extra practice: CD-ROM* Lesson 145

1 Warm-Up

5 MINUTES

Problem of the Day Present this problem: Henri wrote down each decimal as he counted aloud by tenths from 3.3 to 6.6. How many times did he write the digit 5? (14 times)

Problem-Solving Strategies Ask students who have solved the Problem of the Day to share how they solved it and any strategies they used.

MENTAL MATH · MANIPULATIVES Have students first estimate and then use a **ruler*** to measure each object's length using metric units. (Estimates should improve after each measure.)

a. line segments drawn on a chalkboard

b. a tissue box

c. a paper bag

d. distance from a doorknob to the floor

e. a hallway

EXPLORE

LESSON 145

Metric Units: Multiply and Divide by Powers of 10

When this ruler is unfolded, it is 1 meter long.

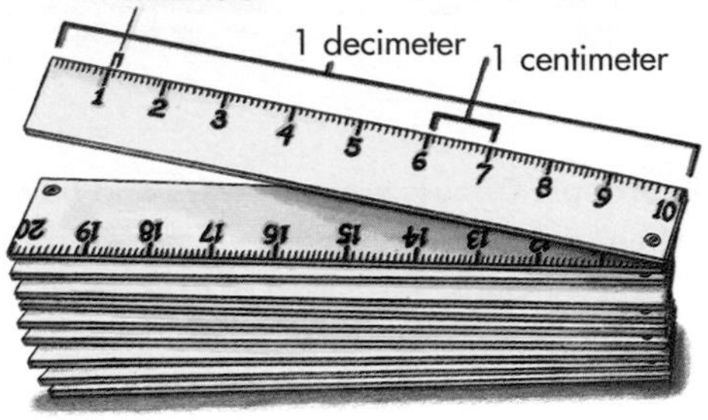

1 meter = 10 decimeters = 100 centimeters = 1000 millimeters

About how long is a meter? Most doors are about 2 meters high. A meterstick is 1 meter long. Most classroom doors are a little less than 1 meter wide.

If a meter is divided into ten equal parts, each part is 0.1 meter. That's also called 1 decimeter (dm).

1 dm = 0.1 m

Two of the parts (2 dm) would be 0.2 meter. 2 dm = 0.2 m

To convert between metric units, you multiply or divide by a power of 10.

To convert from a smaller unit to a larger unit, divide.

To convert from a larger unit to a smaller unit, multiply.

dm ⟶ m ÷10

m ⟶ dm ×10

cm ⟶ m ÷100

m ⟶ cm ×100

COOPERATIVE LEARNING Have students work in pairs or small groups to measure the dimensions of the classroom, their desks, or other objects. Encourage students to keep careful records, and have group members check each other's work by repeating the measuring. You can use these data throughout the unit to make up problems and activities, such as making a scale drawing of the classroom and its furniture.

RETEACHING p. 47

LESSON 145 RETEACHING Name__________

The metric system is based on units of 10. Each unit of measure is 10 times less or 10 times greater than the next unit.

This chart shows the relationships among units of length in the metric system. Notice that each unit is greater or less than another by 10 or a multiple of 10.

Metric Units of Length

1 meter (m) = 1000 millimeters (mm); 1 millimeter = $\frac{1}{1000}$ meter
1 meter = 100 centimeters (cm); 1 centimeter = $\frac{1}{100}$ meter
1 meter = 10 decimeters (dm); 1 decimeter = $\frac{1}{10}$ meter

Parts of a meter can also be expressed as decimals. One way to understand this is to use money as an example.

$1.00 = 100 pennies
One penny can be expressed as:
- $\frac{1}{100}$ of $1 • 0.01 of $1

1 meter = 100 centimeters
One centimeter can be expressed as:
- $\frac{1}{100}$ of 1 meter • 0.01 meter

$1 = 10 dimes
One dime can be expressed as:
- $\frac{1}{10}$ of $1 • 0.1 of $1

1 meter = 10 decimeters
One decimeter can be expressed as:
- $\frac{1}{10}$ of 1 meter • 0.1 meter

Here are some hints to help convert greater units of length to lesser units.

- To convert meters to **decimeters,** multiply by **10.** 3 m × 10 = 30 dm
- To convert meters to **centimeters,** multiply by **100.** 4 m × 100 = 400 cm
- To convert meters to **millimeters,** multiply by **1000.** 2 m × 1000 = 2000 mm

To find the reverse, simply divide. 200 mm ÷ 1000 = 0.2 m

Answers will vary. Possible answers:

Measure these items. Write each measurement two ways.

1. Length of foot 18 cm = 1.8 dm
2. Length of desk 32 cm = 320 mm
3. Length of pencil 14 cm = 0.14 m

Copyright © SRA/McGraw-Hill. Permission is granted to reproduce this page for classroom use.

*available separately

Find the value of the missing number.

❶ 3 dm = ■ m **0.3** ❷ 8 dm = ■ m **0.8** ❸ ■ dm = 6 m **60**

❹ 5 dm = ■ m **0.5** ❺ ■ dm = 9 m **90** ❻ ■ dm = 1.0 m **10**

If a meter is divided into 100 equal parts, each part is 0.01 meter. That's also called 1 centimeter (cm). 1 cm = 0.01 m

Two of the parts (2 cm) would be 0.02 meter. 2 cm = 0.02 m

Find the value of the missing number.

❼ 7 cm = ■ m **0.07** ❽ 8 cm = ■ m **0.08** ❾ ■ cm = 0.04 m **4**

❿ 27 cm = ■ m **0.27** ⓫ ■ cm = 0.31 m **31** ⓬ ■ cm = 1.00 m **100**

If a meter is divided into 1000 equal parts, each part is 0.001 meter. That's also called 1 millimeter (mm).

1 mm = 0.001 m

Two of the parts (2 mm) would be 0.002 meter. 2 mm = 0.002 m

Find the value of the missing number.

⓭ 6 mm = ■ m **0.006** ⓮ 709 mm = ■ m **0.709** ⓯ ■ mm = 0.300 m **300**

⓰ 66 mm = ■ m **0.066** ⓱ ■ mm = 0.004 m **4** ⓲ ■ mm = 0.305 m **305**

⓳ 347 mm = ■ m **0.347** ⓴ ■ mm = 0.76 m **760** ㉑ ■ mm = 1.000 m **1000**

Measure. Write each measurement in two ways. **Answers will vary according to measurements of each classroom.**

㉒ Classroom
Length: ■ cm = ■ m
Width: ■ cm = ■ m

㉓ Top of desk
Length: ■ mm = ■ cm
Width: ■ mm = ■ cm

FANTASTIC FACT

There are about 1500 different kinds of butterflies living in one square mile in the Amazon rain forest. There are only about 750 different kinds in all of the United States and Canada.

❷ Teach

Using the Student Pages If possible, use a **meterstick** during the opening discussion, or refer to the illustration of a folded meterstick on page 490. Go over the information about metric equivalences. Remind students that if you divide something into ten equal parts, one of those parts is $\frac{1}{10}$, or 0.1 of the whole. Do the first few problems as a class before having students complete the lesson on their own, using a meterstick or the illustrations of it as needed.

❸ Wrap-Up

5 MINUTES

In Closing Have students express 4 millimeters in terms of centimeters (0.4), 4 centimeters in terms of meters (0.04), and 4 centimeters in terms of millimeters (40).

ANALYZING ANSWERS / MANIPULATIVES

When students are converting from one unit to another in the metric system, make sure they understand that many small units make one big unit. Use concrete materials, such as **metersticks** or **base-10 blocks*** to reinforce this principle.

ALTERNATIVE ASSESSMENT

Performance Assessment Have students measure several dimensions you have measured in advance and present each measurement in two ways, such as in meters and centimeters or in centimeters and millimeters. Look for accuracy within 1 centimeter or 10 millimeters.

Assessment Criteria

Did the student . . .

- ✓ contribute to the discussion of relationships among metric units of length?
- ✓ correctly use measuring tools?
- ✓ explain how to decide whether to multiply or divide to convert between metric units?
- ✓ correctly answer at least 75% of the conversion problems?

Homework Have students make five different metric measurements at home, using the dimensions of a room and some of its contents. Have them present each metric measurement in two different units.

PRACTICE p. 145

LESSON 145 PRACTICE Name________

Find the value of the missing number.

❶ 6 dm = 0.6 m ❷ 4 dm = 0.4 m
❸ 7 m = 70 dm ❹ 90 dm = 9 m
❺ 1 m = 10 dm ❻ 6 m = 60 dm
❼ 70 m = 700 dm ❽ 21 cm = 0.21 m
❾ 9 cm = 0.09 m ❿ 0.42 m = 42 cm
⓫ 9 cm = 0.09 m ⓬ 100 cm = 1 m
⓭ 4 mm = 0.004 m ⓮ 127 mm = 0.127 m
⓯ 37 mm = 0.037 m ⓰ 1000 mm = 1 m
⓱ 810 mm = 0.810 m ⓲ 0.7 m = 700 mm
⓳ 2 km = 2000 m ⓴ 12 km = 12,000 m
㉑ 60 m = 0.06 km ㉒ 910 m = 0.91 km
㉓ 1000 m = 1 km ㉔ 3200 m = 3.2 km
㉕ 9 m = 90 dm ㉖ 850 m = 0.85 km
㉗ 2300 m = 2.3 km ㉘ 13 cm = 0.13 m
㉙ 0.34 m = 34 cm ㉚ 40 cm = 0.4 m
㉛ 15 km = 15,000 m ㉜ 11 dm = 1.1 m
㉝ 18 mm = 0.018 m ㉞ 0.135 m = 135 mm
㉟ 30 dm = 3 m ㊱ 7 km = 7000 m
㊲ 120 cm = 1.2 m ㊳ 234 mm = 0.234 m
㊴ 3.40 m = 340 cm ㊵ 3 m = 30 dm
㊶ 1700 m = 1.7 km ㊷ 0.642 m = 642 mm
㊸ 2000 mm = 2 m ㊹ 100 dm = 10 m

Copyright © SRA/McGraw-Hill. Permission is granted to reproduce this page for classroom use.

Math Explorations and Applications Level 4 • **145**

ENRICHMENT p. 145

LESSON 145 ENRICHMENT Name________

Use the list of telephone numbers from the survey you made in Lesson 143. Create a new chart. Write "Sum of Last Two Digits" in the blank at the top of the first column. Use tally marks to record how many times the sum of the last two digits is 0, how many times it is 1, and so on through 18.

Create another chart. Write "Sum of First Two Digits" in the blank. Use tally marks to record how many times the sum of the first two digits is 0, how many times it is 1, and so on through 18.

Look for patterns in the charts you have made. Discuss the patterns with a friend. Are the patterns the same in both charts?

Sum of ____ Two Digits	Tallies	Total
0	Answers will vary.	
1		
2		
3		
4		
5		
6		
7		
8		
9		
10		
11		
12		

Copyright © SRA/McGraw-Hill. Permission is granted to reproduce this page for classroom use.

Math Explorations and Applications Level 4 • **145**

*available separately

LESSON 146

Student Edition pages 492–495

Metric Measurements of Length

LESSON PLANNER

Objectives

- to provide practice with measuring
- to demonstrate how to express metric measures as decimals with one unit
- to provide map-reading practice
- to review methods of organizing data and making a bar graph

Context of the Lesson This is the ninth of 16 lessons on understanding and using decimals. Students have worked with maps and bar graphs in earlier grade levels and in previous lessons.

MANIPULATIVES	Program Resources
calculators* (optional)	"Find the Distance 1" and "Find the Distance 2" Game Mats
chart paper	Practice Master 146
graph paper	Enrichment Master 146
metric rulers*	**The Cruncher***
photograph or poster (optional)	For additional math integration: Math Throughout the Day*
	For extra practice: CD-ROM* Lesson 146

Note: This lesson may take more than one day.

MIXED PRACTICE

LESSON 146

Metric Measurements of Length

Angel measured a table and found it was 2 meters, 3 decimeters, 8 centimeters, and 5 millimeters long. There is a shorter way to report this measurement.

Change each unit to meters	Then add
2 m = 2 m	2.**000** m
3 dm = 0.3 m	0.3**00** m
8 cm = 0.08 m	0.08**0** m
5 mm = 0.005 m	0.005 m
	2.385 m

2 m, 3 dm, 8 cm, 5 mm = 2.385 m

Write each measurement in meters only.

1. 6 m, 3 dm, 8 cm, 5 mm **6.385 m**
2. 3 cm, 6 mm, 9 m **9.036 m**
3. 4 m, 0 dm, 2 cm, 6 mm **4.026 m**
4. 5 mm, 2 dm, 3 m **3.205 m**
5. 4 m, 2 cm, 6 mm **4.026 m**
6. 7 m, 4 cm, 1 dm, 0 mm **7.14 m**
7. 8 mm, 9 cm, 0 dm, 2 m **2.098 m**
8. 1 dm, 7 m, 4 cm **7.14 m**

1000 meters is called a kilometer (km). 1000 m = 1 km

It takes about 12 minutes to walk 1 kilometer.

1 meter is 0.001 kilometer. 1 m = 0.001 km

The distance from the library to the fire house was measured. It was 2 kilometers, 415 meters. Write that in kilometers only.

2 km = 2 km	2.**000** km	
415 m = 0.415 km	0.415 km	
	2.415 km	2 km, 415 m = 2.415 km

Write these measurements in kilometers only.

9. 1 km, 210 m **1.21 km**
10. 4 km, 50 m **4.05 km**
11. 4 km, 500 m **4.5 km**
12. 2200 m **2.2 km**

492 • Fractions and Decimals

1 Warm-Up (5 MINUTES)

Problem of the Day Present this problem: Use the digits 0, 1, 4, and 8 to create a decimal that fits each description without repeating digits in the same number.

a. This decimal is more than half of 1. (Possible answers include 0.8, 0.81, 0.814, and 0.84.)

b. This decimal is between 1 and 2. (Possible answers include 1.4, 1.8, and 1.048.)

Why teach it this way?

It is not necessary for students to do the conversion problems the way they are shown in the example on page 492. The addition procedure is fully shown only to help students understand why this simple method of conversion works; for example, 6 m, 3 dm, 8 cm, and 5 mm can be converted to meters using the given digits with a decimal point after the meters digit (6.385).

*available separately

Tell the length or diameter of each object in millimeters, then in centimeters. **Answers 1 mm greater or lesser should be accepted as correct.**

13. 
21 mm, 2.1 cm

14. 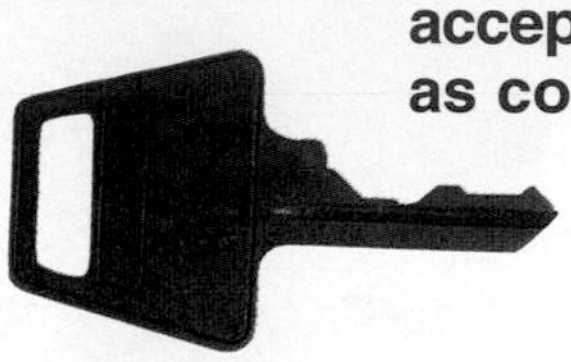
50 mm, 5.0 cm

15. 
33 mm, 3.3 cm

16. 
23 mm, 2.3 cm

17. 
50 mm, 5.0 cm

18. 
17 mm, 1.7 cm

19. 
46 mm, 4.6 cm

20. 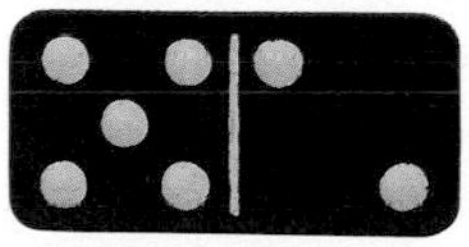
41 mm, 4.1 cm

21. 

40 mm, 4 cm

22. 
98 mm, 9.8 cm

AT RISK

Meeting Individual Needs

Tell students that measuring with accuracy is an important skill, particularly in such trades as carpentry, tile setting, auto mechanics, and picture framing. Measurements must be precise and expressed clearly. Have students make measurements to the nearest millimeter of a favorite **photograph** or **poster**, as if they were getting it framed, and express the measurements in centimeters.

c. This decimal is less than 0.5 but more than 0.1. (Possible answers include 0.14, 0.148, and 0.418.)

d. This decimal is close to 5. (Possible answers include 4.8, 4.81, and 4.801.)

Problem-Solving Strategies Ask students who have solved the Problem of the Day to share how they solved it and any strategies they used.

MENTAL MATH Present the following practice problems involving the basic facts in all four operations, emphasizing speedy recall:

a. 4 + 7 = (11)	**b.** 8 + 6 = (14)	**c.** 7 × 7 = (49)
d. 15 − 10 = (5)	**e.** 28 ÷ 7 = (4)	**f.** 12 − 9 = (3)
g. 72 ÷ 8 = (9)	**h.** 4 × 8 = (32)	**i.** 40 ÷ 10 = (4)
j. 5 × 8 = (40)	**k.** 3 + 7 = (10)	**l.** 9 × 7 = (63)
m. 10 − 5 = (5)	**n.** 10 × 10 = (100)	**o.** 32 ÷ 4 = (8)
p. 6 + 6 = (12)	**q.** 27 ÷ 9 = (3)	**r.** 8 + 5 = (13)

❷ Teach

Using the Student Pages You may wish to demonstrate the "Find the Distance" Game Mats before beginning these pages so that students can play them as they finish pages 492–495. These games provide practice with estimating distances and comparing line lengths.

Discuss the material at the top of page 492. Help students express some of the measurements they made in the preceding lesson using just one unit of length. After students complete problems 1–8, discuss how long a kilometer is. Relate a kilometer to other metric units, such as 1000 m, and also to actual distances in your community. Have students complete problems 9–12.

MANIPULATIVES Before assigning page 493, check that students can read a **metric ruler***. Do the first measurement as a class. Then have students finish the page on their own. Accept answers that are 1 mm too great or 1 mm too little as correct.

*available separately

◆ LESSON 146 Metric Measurements of Length

Teach

GEOGRAPHY CONNECTION

Using the Student Pages Discuss the map on page 494 to familiarize students with it. Go over the first problem with the class. Then have students complete the page on their own. Challenge students to write and solve additional problems based on this map. Students can use a blank **Cruncher*** spreadsheet to make a distance table that shows the relationship between cities and the patterns of the table.

COOPERATIVE LEARNING

Have students work on page 495 in small groups. Help two students demonstrate the measuring procedure, as described, for the class. When everyone has measured and checked their heights, have students share their results and list the measurements on the chalkboard. Then have each student organize the data into a frequency chart using **chart paper** like the one shown on page 495. Next, provide **graph paper** so students can display the data as a bar graph. Remind students that the horizontal scale must include numbers from the least to the greatest heights in the class. Students can use a blank **Cruncher*** spreadsheet to create a table and bar graph to tally and display the frequency of students' heights.

GAME

Introducing the "Find the Distance 1" and "Find the Distance 2" Game Mats These Game Mats provide practice with estimating distances, comparing line lengths, and multiplying by 2. Have students play the "Find the Distance 1" game in groups of two or three. Ask several volunteers to play a demonstration game as others watch to be sure everyone understands the rules. After students play the game once or twice, encourage them to try the harder version, which appears on the reverse side of the mat. Complete instructions can be found on the Game Mats. A copy of these Game Mats can also be found on pages 590-591 of this Teacher's Guide.

◆ LESSON 146 Metric Measurements of Length

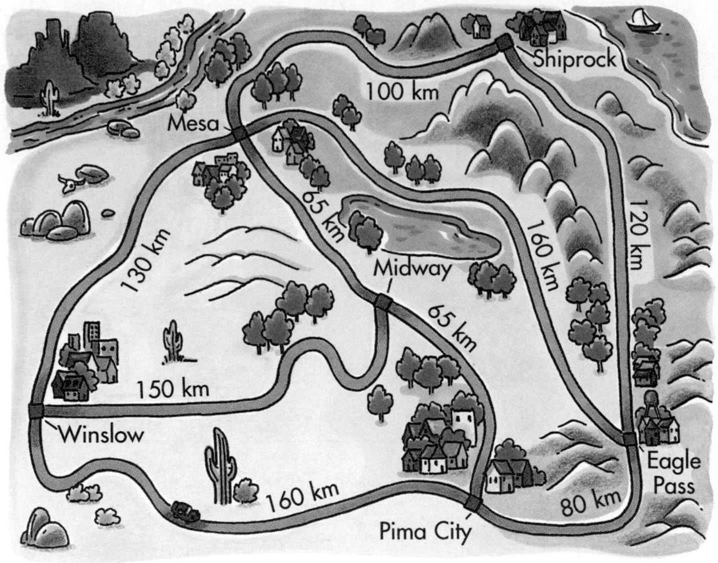

Use the map to answer these questions.

GEOGRAPHY CONNECTION

23. How many kilometers is it from Eagle Pass to Shiprock? **120**
24. How many kilometers is it from Eagle Pass to Mesa if you go through Shiprock? **220**
25. If you were going from Winslow to Eagle Pass, how much farther would it be to go through Mesa? **50 km**
26. Suppose you were going from Eagle Pass to Winslow and wanted to visit Pima City and Mesa on the way.
    a. Would it be shorter to visit Pima City first or Mesa first? **Pima City**
    b. How much shorter? **110 km**
27. Which town is closest to Eagle Pass? **Pima City**

LITERATURE CONNECTION

Literature Connection Provide a copy of *Measure* by Ivan Bulloch. Have students select from the book an activity or project that involves metric length measurement.

RETEACHING

Provide extra measuring practice by taking advantage of regular classroom situations that lend themselves to measuring, such as construction or crafts projects, athletic contests that involve distance, and so on.

*available separately

How tall are you?

COOPERATIVE LEARNING **Work in groups. Measure the height of each person in your group.**

Stand up straight.
Back to wall.
Put book on head.

Walk away.
Make a mark.

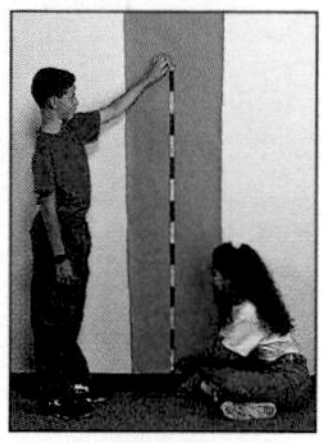

Measure in centimeters.

Ramona measured the height of each student in her class. She made a chart to show the height of each person.

28. What is the most common height of the students in Ramona's class? **123 cm**

Height (cm)	Number of People
118	||
119	
120	||
121	|||
122	~~||||~~ |
123	~~||||~~ ||
124	||||
125	
126	||
127	|

Then Ramona made a bar graph so people could see the results more easily.

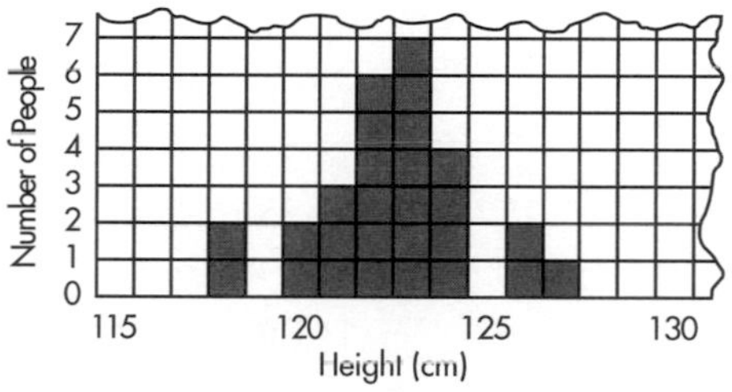

Use a computer or other means to make a chart and a bar graph to show the results for your class.

PRACTICE p. 146

LESSON 146 PRACTICE Name__________

Write the length of each object in millimeters and then in centimeters. Accept all reasonable answers.

1. 

80 mm 8.0 cm

2. 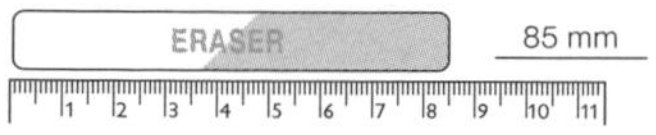

85 mm 8.5 cm

PROBLEM SOLVING **Solve these problems.**

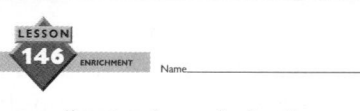

3. How many kilometers is it from Byestown to Peachtree Grove? 110
4. Which town is closest to Thomastown? Carsonville
5. How many kilometers is it from Carsonville to Peachtree Grove if you go through Thomastown? 140
6. If you were going from Smith City to Thomastown, how much shorter is it to go through Byestown? 75 km
7. Which town is farthest from Smith City? Knightsville

146 • *Math Explorations and Applications* Level 4

Copyright © SRA/McGraw-Hill. Permission is granted to reproduce this page for classroom use.

ENRICHMENT p. 146

LESSON 146 ENRICHMENT Name__________

GEOGRAPHY CONNECTION **Use a map, an atlas, an encyclopedia, or other reference book to find the distance from your city or town to the following places. Write your answers in miles.**

The distance from [your city or town] to

1. the capital of [your state] is Answers will depend on your location.
2. the nation's capital is Answers will depend on your location.
3. the southern border of [your state] is Answers will depend on your location.
4. the capital of the fiftieth state admitted to the United States is distance from your location to Honolulu, Hawaii.
5. the city at the mouth of the Mississippi River is distance from your location to New Orleans, Louisiana.
6. the capital of the state with the tallest mountain in the United States is distance from your location to Juneau, Alaska.
7. the capital of the only state that has a unicameral body of government is distance from your location to Lincoln, Nebraska.
8. the capital of the most populous state is distance from your location to Sacramento, California.
9. the capital of the home state of the nation's first president is distance from your location to Richmond, Virginia.

146 • *Math Explorations and Applications* Level 4

Copyright © SRA/McGraw-Hill. Permission is granted to reproduce this page for classroom use.

*available separately

3 Wrap-Up

5 MINUTES

In Closing Discuss the results of the height activity using the charts students made. Have students identify the most common height among students in the class, heights that two people share, and so on.

ALTERNATIVE ASSESSMENT

Performance Assessment You may wish to use the activities on page 495 for performance asssessment to check mastery of measuring in centimeters, organizing data into a chart, and making a bar graph from actual data.

Assessment Criteria

Did the student . . .

- ✓ contribute to the discussion of metric conversions?
- ✓ demonstrate skill and accuracy in measuring to the nearest millimeter and centimeter?
- ✓ correctly express measurements in millimeters and centimeters?
- ✓ apply map-reading skills to solve the problems on page 494?
- ✓ actively participate in the measuring and graphing activities on page 495?
- ✓ create an accurate chart and bar graph of the class data?

Homework Have students find the heights of all family members in their household and express the measurements in centimeters and meters. Alternatively, they can find the heights of four different chairs, plants, or doors in their homes.

GIFTED & TALENTED

Meeting Individual Needs

Encourage gifted and talented students to determine the average height of students in the class. Provide **calculators*** to help with the computations. Then have students analyze how many students, if any, are the average height, how many are taller, and how many are shorter.

LESSON 147

Student Edition pages 496–499

Adding and Subtracting Decimals

LESSON PLANNER

Objectives

✓ to provide practice for and assess mastery of adding and subtracting decimals by relating these skills to adding and subtracting monetary amounts

▶ to provide practice in solving word problems that involve adding and subtracting decimals

Context of the Lesson This is the tenth of 16 lessons on understanding and using decimals. Although this is the first lesson in Level 4 to focus on adding and subtracting decimals, it includes a Mastery Checkpoint for this skill because adding and subtracting decimals was taught in Level 3. The next two lessons provide practice in adding and subtracting decimals to solve practical problems.

MANIPULATIVES

play money* (optional)

graph paper (optional)

Program Resources

Reteaching Master

Practice Master 147

Enrichment Master 147

Assessment Master

The Cruncher*

For extra practice: CD-ROM* Lesson 147

LESSON 147

Adding and Subtracting Decimals

Linda has $0.97. If she earns $3.75 for washing Mr. Lomaki's dog, how much money will she have?

Do you remember how to add amounts of money?

$3.75 + 0.97 $4.72	Line up the decimal points so you can add cents to cents, dimes to dimes, dollars to dollars, and so on.

Felipe has $4.72. He needs $10 to buy a flashlight. How much more does he need?

Do you remember how to subtract amounts of money?

$10.00 − 4.72 $5.28	Line up the decimal points so you subtract cents from cents, dimes from dimes, dollars from dollars, and so on.

When you add or subtract decimals, line up the decimal points.

Example: 14.8 + 2.35 = ?

14.8 + 2.35	Line up the decimal points.
14.8**0** + 2.35	If it helps, put in a 0 (because 14.8 and 14.80 have the same value).
14.80 + 2.35 **17.15**	Add.

1 Warm-Up

5 MINUTES

Problem of the Day Present this problem: Find a decimal number that is equally greater than 1.7 and less than 7.1. (4.4)

Problem-Solving Strategies Ask students who have solved the Problem of the Day to share how they solved it and any strategies they used.

MENTAL MATH Present decimal addition and subtraction problems. Have students show thumbs up if the answer falls between 10 and 20 and thumbs down if the answer falls outside that range. Write these problems on the chalkboard:

a. 30 – 20.03 (thumbs down)

b. 50.56 – 0.38 (thumbs down)

(continued on page 497)

COOPERATIVE LEARNING Have students work in small groups to reinforce the steps of adding or subtracting decimals. One student records a decimal computation as the other group members take turns giving directions. For instance, group members might say, "First write the problem so that the decimal points are lined up. Begin with hundredths. Add (or subtract). Now do the tenths, then the ones. Place the decimal point in the answer directly below its position in the problem. Check that the answer makes sense."

*available separately

Example: 8.6 − 3.25

8.6
− 3.25

Line up the decimal points.

8.6**0**
− 3.25

If it helps, put in a 0 (because 8.6 and 8.60 have the same value).

8.60
− 3.25
5.35

Subtract.

Add or subtract.

1. 6.72 + 11.09 = **17.81**
2. 9.5 + 8.63 = **18.13**
3. 5.2 − 3.15 = **2.05**
4. 8.2 + 3.01 = **11.21**
5. 1.7 − 0.9 = **0.8**
6. 8.03 − 7.04 = **0.99**
7. 3.07 + 0.96 = **4.03**
8. 4.07 − 3.10 = **0.97**
9. 5.33 − 4.03 = **1.30**
10. 8.4 + 2.7 = **11.1**
11. 2.96 − 1.09 = **1.87**
12. 7.43 + 2.99 = **10.42**
13. 6.40 − 0.05 = **6.35**
14. 8.92 − 2.39 = **6.53**
15. 7.04 − 2.06 = **4.98**

Solve for *n*.

16. 2.36 + 6.5 = *n* **8.86**
17. 6.07 + 3.03 = *n* **9.10**
18. 10.9 − 9.01 = *n* **1.89**
19. 5.4 − 3.3 = *n* **2.1**
20. 2.34 − 2.09 = *n* **0.25**
21. 4.64 + 6 = *n* **10.64**
22. 8.26 − 8.19 = *n* **0.07**
23. 13.3 + 4.11 = *n* **17.41**
24. 25.01 + 0.6 = *n* **25.61**

PROBLEM SOLVING

Solve.

25. Kendra lives 1.25 kilometers from the library. She has walked 0.6 kilometers toward the library. How much farther does she have to walk to the library? **0.65 km**

Mental Math (continued)

c. 19.1 + 0.19 (thumbs up)

d. 15.49 – 10.05 (thumbs down)

e. 15 + 5.5 (thumbs down)

f. 32.9 – 20.8 (thumbs up)

g. 23.2 – 9.02 (thumbs up)

h. 40.55 – 25.50 (thumbs up)

i. 14.08 + 8.99 (thumbs down)

j. 6.89 + 9.04 (thumbs up)

2 Teach

Using the Student Pages Go over page 496 and the top of page 497 with the class. Emphasize the importance of lining up the decimal points. Then have students do problems 1–25 on page 497 independently. As students finish, they can go on to pages 498–499. Students can use a blank **Cruncher*** spreadsheet to create a table or chart that they can use to answer questions about the relationships among decimals.

> *The connections between mathematics and the real world, between mathematics and the various sciences, between mathematics and the social studies, between mathematics and languages, and between mathematics and the arts should be constantly emphasized, not obscured. Beyond that, the connections between various parts of mathematics should be made clearer than they now are.*
>
> —Stephen S. Willoughby, *Mathematics Education for a Changing World*

Physical Education Connection Record the times of the place finishers in different events. Hold a metric Olympics with the class and ask the physical education teacher for help. Plan several events, such as a 50-meter dash, a 100-meter dash, and a 200-meter run, and have students use the results to make up word problems like those on pages 498–499.

Literature Connection Have students read *Penelope Gets Wheels* by Esther Allen Peterson. Challenge them to determine the difference in the cost of the bicycles Penelope likes and the amount of money she has.

*available separately

◆ LESSON 147 Adding and Subtracting Decimals

Teach

Using the Student Pages The problems on these pages provide realistic applications for adding and subtracting decimals. Students can do them on their own and discuss them afterwards as a class. Encourage students who have trouble with the problems to draw sketches or diagrams of each situation described.

LEARNING STYLES · MANIPULATIVES

Meeting Individual Needs

Visual and kinesthetic learners may misalign decimal numbers when they add or subtract. Illustrate the importance of aligning decimals by having students add and subtract amounts of **play money***. Point out that the answers won't make sense unless the decimal points are lined up. It may also help these students to do their work on **graph paper,** using the squares to help them align the numbers and decimal points properly.

◆ LESSON 147 Adding and Subtracting Decimals

PHYSICAL EDUCATION CONNECTION

Solve these problems.

26. In the 1900 Olympics, Irving Baxter jumped 1.90 meters in the running high jump. In 1996, Charles Austin jumped 2.39 meters in the running high jump.
    a. Which man jumped higher? **Charles Austin**
    b. How much higher? **0.49 m**

27. In the 1996 Olympics, Gail Devers ran 100 meters in 10.94 seconds. In the same Olympics, four American women ran the 400-meter relay in 41.95 seconds. Was the average time for each runner in the relay faster or slower than Gail Devers's time? **faster**

28. In the 1896 Olympic games, Thomas Burke ran 100 meters in 12 seconds. In the 1900 Olympic games, Francis W. Jarvis ran 100 meters in 10.8 seconds.
    a. What was the difference in their times? **1.2 seconds**
    b. Who ran faster? **Francis W. Jarvis**

29. In the 1996 Olympics, Donovan Bailey ran 100 meters in 9.84 seconds. By how much time did he beat 10 seconds? **0.16 seconds**

30. In the 1996 Olympics, Gail Devers ran 100 meters in 10.94 seconds. If she ran that fast for 200 meters, how long would it take her to run 200 meters? **21.88 seconds**

31. In the 1996 Olympics, Merlene Ottey ran 200 meters in 22.24 seconds. She ran 100 meters in 10.94 seconds. Was her average speed for the 200-meter run faster or slower than for the 100-meter run? Why do you think there was this difference? **slower; she averaged a slower speed t conserve her energy for the longer rac**

RETEACHING p. 48

LESSON 147 RETEACHING Name__________

Adding and subtracting money and numbers written as decimals is like adding and subtracting whole numbers. Just remember to line up the decimal points.

Example 1: \$3.74 + \$1.97 = ?
Use play money to show how to add these amounts. Regroup when needed.

```
  $3.74    Line up the ones, tens, and hundreds.
+  1.97    Add.
  $5.71
```

Use grid paper to help you if you have trouble lining up the columns of numbers.

Example 2: 97.4 – 45.97 = ?
When subtracting decimals, follow the same rule of lining up the decimal points.

Step 1

```
  97.4     Line up the decimal points.
– 45.97
```

Step 2

```
   6 3 10
  97.40    Add a 0 to hold the place.
– 45.97    Subtract.
  51.43
```

Solve these problems.

1. A 1991 model electric car traveled 69.21 miles per hour. A 1991 Jaguar model XJ 220 traveled 212.3 miles per hour. How much faster did the Jaguar travel than the electric car? 143.09 mi/hr
2. Lena and Josie drove 100.5 kilometers on Monday and 200.7 kilometers on Tuesday. How far did they drive all together? 301.2 km

Solve. Watch the signs.

3. 24.5 + 11.79 = 36.29
4. 63.79 – 2.5 = 61.29
5. 987.12 + 256.02 = 1243.14
6. 63.915 – 14.729 = 49.186

Copyright © SRA/McGraw-Hill. Permission is granted to reproduce this page for classroom use.

PRACTICE p. 147

LESSON 147 PRACTICE Name__________

Add or subtract.

1. 4.12 + 3.77 = 7.89	2. 1.8 + 2.72 = 4.52	3. 6.84 – 2.43 = 4.41	4. 11.64 + 7.30 = 18.94	5. 19.07 – 2.78 = 16.29
6. 9.91 – 2.38 = 7.53	7. 4.03 – 2.75 = 1.28	8. 5.09 + 4.91 = 10.00	9. 2.4 – 1.27 = 1.13	10. 3.9 – 1.06 = 2.84
11. 10.3 – 2.94 = 7.36	12. 4.77 + 3.53 = 8.30	13. 6.07 – 4.31 = 1.76	14. 5.04 + 3.19 = 8.23	15. 7.98 + 5.02 = 13.00

Add or subtract.

16. 1.72 + 3.14 = 4.86
17. 3.5 + 7.5 = 11.0
18. 6.29 – 4.24 = 2.05
19. 8.12 – 4.37 = 3.75
20. 9.65 + 2.7 = 12.35
21. 5.09 + 5.09 = 10.18
22. 3.04 – 2.07 = 0.97
23. 14.72 – 11.1 = 3.62

Solve these problems.

24. Stella swam 200 meters in 1 minute and 49.7 seconds. Janice swam 200 meters in 2 minutes and 3.1 seconds. By how much did Stella beat Janice? 13.4 seconds
25. Roger swam 400 meters in 3 minutes and 47.2 seconds. Was his average speed for his swim more than 2 meters per second? no
26. Rita swam 100 meters in 52.8 seconds. By how much time did she beat 1 minute? 7.2 seconds

Copyright © SRA/McGraw-Hill. Permission is granted to reproduce this page for classroom use.

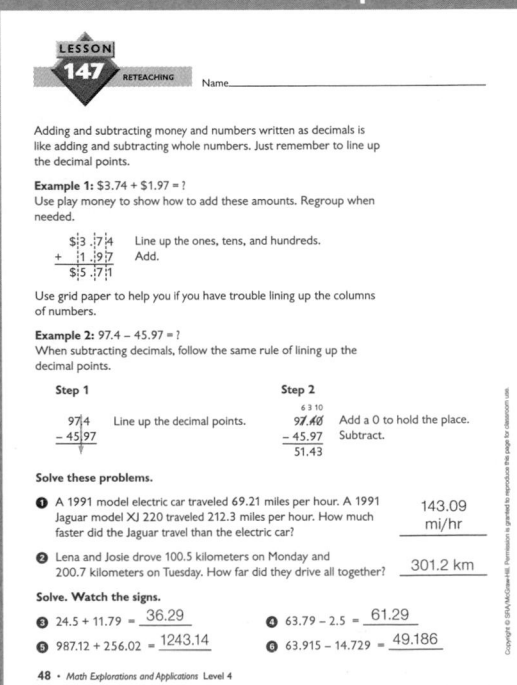

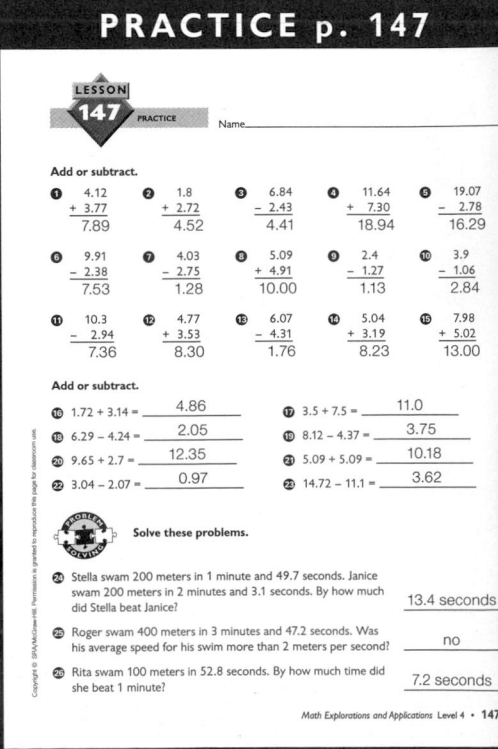

*available separately

32 In the 1900 Olympics, J. W. B. Tewksbury ran the 400-meter hurdle in 57.6 seconds. In 1996 Derek Adkins had a time of 47.54 seconds in the same event. How much faster was Adkins? **10.06 seconds**

33 The 10,000-meter run is an Olympic event. How many kilometers is 10,000 meters? **10**

34 In the 1996 Olympics, Michelle Smith swam 400 meters in 4 minutes and 7.25 seconds. In the 1924 Olympics, Johnny Weismuller swam 400 meters in 5 minutes and 4.8 seconds. By how much did Michelle Smith beat Johnny Weismuller's time? **57.55 seconds**

35 In the 1964 Olympics, Abebe Bikila ran the marathon barefoot in 2 hours, 12 minutes, and 11.2 seconds. In the 1948 Olympics, Delfo Cabrera ran the marathon in 2 hours, 34 minutes, and 51.6 seconds. In how much less time did Abebe Bikila run the marathon? **22 minutes and 40.4 seconds**

36 In the 1960 Olympics, Wilma Rudolph ran 100 meters in 11.0 seconds. Was her average speed for the race more than 10 meters per second? **no**

37 In the 1932 Olympics, Volmari Iso-Hollo ran an extra lap by mistake in the 3000-meter steeplechase. His time for the race was 10 minutes and 33.4 seconds. In the 1936 Olympics, he ran the same race in 9 minutes and 3.8 seconds. About how long do you think it took Iso-Hollo to run the extra lap? **A reasonable estimate is about 90 seconds.**

Unit 6 Lesson 147 • **499**

3 Wrap-Up (5 minutes)

In Closing Have students explain how to add 8.2 and 0.07 and how to subtract the same two numbers.

ANALYZING ANSWERS Check the work of students who fall short of the mastery objective to determine the nature of the difficulty. If the trouble lies with multidigit addition or subtraction of whole numbers that involves regrouping, provide additional review. If the problem is specific to decimal numbers, try some of the strategies described in Cooperative Learning and Meeting Individual Needs.

Mastery Checkpoint 22

At about this time most students should demonstrate mastery of the addition and subtraction of decimals by correctly answering at least 80% of the problems on page 497 and by using correct procedures in at least ten of the word problems on pages 498–499. You may also wish to assign Assessment Blackline Masters page 57 to determine mastery. Results of this assessment may be recorded on the Mastery Checkpoint Chart.

Assessment Criteria

Did the student . . .

- ✓ align numbers correctly to add and subtract decimals?
- ✓ communicate strategies used to solve the word problems?
- ✓ explain how to solve for *n*?
- ✓ correctly answer at least 80% of the computation problems on pages 497–499?

Homework Have students consult an almanac or browse the Internet to find other Olympic records reported in decimals. Challenge them to create two addition and two subtraction problems based on the data they find.

ENRICHMENT p. 147

LESSON 147 ENRICHMENT Name______

You can use **The Cruncher: *Can We Get a Pet?*** project to help you find the costs of taking care of an animal for a year. Then, on your own or using a calculator, you can figure out the cost per day.

First, write the type of pet you would like to have.

Then, think of all the possible costs involved. Make a list of as many as you can think of. (**The Cruncher** gives you some ideas.)

Research to find out the actual costs of the items on your list. Enter them into the spreadsheet. What is the total cost of taking care of the pet for one year? Answers will vary.

What is the cost per day? Show how you found out. the annual cost divided by 365

Is cost the only thing to think about when getting a pet? What are some others?

Other considerations may include the pet's disposition, whether family members are allergic, or whether there is enough space for the pet.

Copyright © SRA/McGraw-Hill. Permission is granted to reproduce this page for classroom use.

Math Explorations and Applications Level 4 • **147**

ASSESSMENT p. 57

UNIT 6 **Mastery Checkpoint 22** Addition and subtraction of decimal numbers (Lesson 147)

Name______

The student demonstrates mastery by correctly answering at least 16 of the 20 problems.

Solve for *n*.

1. $7.5 - 4.2 = n$ $n =$ 3.3
2. $9.4 + 6.7 = n$ $n =$ 16.1
3. $3.6 + 4.8 = n$ $n =$ 8.4
4. $3.25 + 5.4 = n$ $n =$ 8.65
5. $16.3 - 10 = n$ $n =$ 6.3
6. $12.2 - 6.3 = n$ $n =$ 5.9
7. $6.7 + 2.43 = n$ $n =$ 9.13
8. $23.9 - 17.7 = n$ $n =$ 6.2
9. $13.8 - 6.3 = n$ $n =$ 7.5

Add or subtract.

10. $5.2 - 3.15 =$ 2.05
11. $6.81 - 4.32 =$ 2.49
12. $8.96 + 1.43 =$ 10.39
13. $9.82 - 6.34 =$ 3.48
14. $7.89 + 6.30 =$ 14.19
15. $4.5 - 1.75 =$ 2.75
16. $8.31 - 4.58 =$ 3.73
17. $7.18 - 2.64 =$ 4.54
18. $5.43 - 2.83 =$ 2.60
19. $9.86 + 2.53 =$ 12.39

Solve.

20. In 1994 James's gym class ran the mile. The first group ran it in 7.30 minutes. Another group of runners averaged 8.2 minutes. A third group ran at 10.2 minutes. Could the first group run the mile two times before the third group finished once? no

Copyright © SRA/McGraw-Hill. Permission is granted to reproduce this page for classroom use.

Math Explorations and Applications Level 4 • **57**

LESSON 148

Student Edition pages 500–501

Addition and Subtraction of Decimals: Applications

LESSON PLANNER

Objectives

- to provide practice in solving word problems that involve adding and subtracting decimals
- to provide practice in adding and subtracting decimals

Context of the Lesson This is the 11th of 16 lessons on understanding and using decimals.

MANIPULATIVES

none

Program Resources

Number Cubes (0–5 and 5–10)

Practice Master 148

Enrichment Master 148

For extra practice:

CD-ROM* Lesson 148

Cumulative Review, page 567

1 Warm-Up

5 MINUTES

Problem of the Day Present this problem: Find the pattern in the following series of numbers. Then determine the next four numbers to continue the pattern: 1.2, 1.45, 1.15, 1.4, 1.1, 1.35, 1.05, . . . (The pattern alternates adding 0.25, then subtracting 0.3; the next four numbers are 1.3, 1.0, 1.25, and 0.95.)

Problem-Solving Strategies Ask students who have solved the Problem of the Day to share how they solved it and any strategies they used.

MENTAL MATH Write the numbers 0–2 on the chalkboard. Present problems in which students show thumbs up when answers fall within these boundaries and thumbs down when answers fall outside these boundaries:

a. 0.05 + 1.9 (thumbs up)

b. 8.66 – 3.04 (thumbs down)

c. 3.01 – 1.02 (thumbs up)

d. 0.15 + 0.98 (thumbs up)

e. 8.6 – 7.3 (thumbs up)

f. 0.11 + 0.09 (thumbs down)

g. 6.67 – 5.07 (thumbs up)

h. 3.12 – 2.05 (thumbs up)

LESSON 148

Addition and Subtraction of Decimals: Applications

Many situations involve decimal numbers. Use your skills at working with decimals to solve the following problems.

1. A year ago Jake bought a used car that had traveled 48,927.8 miles. Now the car has traveled 75,485.2 miles. How many miles has the car traveled in the past year? **26,557.4**
2. Donna wants to ride her bike at least 50 miles every week. At the beginning of the week the odometer on her bike showed 143.6 miles. Now it shows 184.8 miles. How many more miles does she have to ride this week to meet her goal? **8.8**
3. Steve had $25.81. Last week he spent $7.50 and earned $12.75 washing cars. How much money does he have now? **$31.06**
4. A movie ticket costs $6.25.
   - **a.** How much will two tickets cost? **$12.50**
   - **b.** How much will four tickets cost? **$25.00**
5. Melissa needs 6 pounds of cheese to make sandwiches for her party. She bought packages of cheese that weigh 2.2 pounds and 2.6 pounds.
   - **a.** How many more pounds of cheese does she need? **1.2**
   - **b.** If she buys another package of cheese and it weighs 2.1 pounds, how much will be left over? **0.9 pounds**

Language Arts Connection Have students make up their own word problems involving the addition and subtraction of decimals. Students can exchange and solve each other's problems. Compile the problems in a file or put them on display in an interactive bulletin board.

RETEACHING

Have students turn notebook paper sideways so that the lines form columns. Students can use these columns to help them align decimal numbers properly before they add or subtract them.

COOPERATIVE LEARNING

GAME

Harder Roll a Decimal Game

Players: Two
Materials: One 0–5 cube, one 5–10 cube
Object: To get the greater total score
Math Focus: Place value, subtracting decimal numbers, and mathematical reasoning

RULES

1. Follow rules 1 through 4 for the "Roll a Decimal" game on page 474.
2. Subtract the lesser decimal from the greater decimal and award the difference to the player with the greater decimal.
3. After an agreed-upon number of rounds, add your scores.
4. The player with the greater total is the winner.

SAMPLE GAME

Round	Sara	David	Sara's Score	David's Score
1	0.76	0.966		0.206
2	0.957	0.676	0.281	
3	0.97775	0.9665	0.01125	
4	0.8	0.9576		0.1576
5	0.99	0.866	0.124	
6	0.86855	0.8875		0.01895
Total			0.41625	0.38255

After six rounds, Sara was the winner.

Use the Cumulative Review on page 567 after this lesson.

2 Teach

Using the Student Pages Demonstrate the "Harder Roll a Decimal" game on page 501, which focuses on place value and subtracting decimal numbers. Have students work independently on the problems on page 500 and then play the game in pairs when they finish.

Model the "Harder Roll a Decimal" game by having two students play two or three rounds in front of the class. This game provides practice with place value, subtracting and adding decimal numbers, and mathematical reasoning. At first, suggest that games last three rounds. Students may play longer games later on, if they wish.

3 Wrap-Up

5 MINUTES

In Closing Have students explain how to add 4.8 and 6.43.

ALTERNATIVE ASSESSMENT

Informal Assessment Observe students as they play the "Harder Roll a Decimal" game to determine their skill in adding and subtracting decimals.

Assessment Criteria

Did the student . . .

- ✓ correctly solve the word problems involving decimals?
- ✓ explain his or her solution methods?
- ✓ actively participate in playing the game?

Homework Have students play the "Harder Roll a Decimal" game with family members for further practice with place value and adding and subtracting decimals. A copy of this game can be found on page 25 of the Home Connections Blackline Masters.

LOOKING AHEAD Sample checks, check stubs, check registers, and checking account statements might be helpful to show students in the next lesson.

PRACTICE p. 148

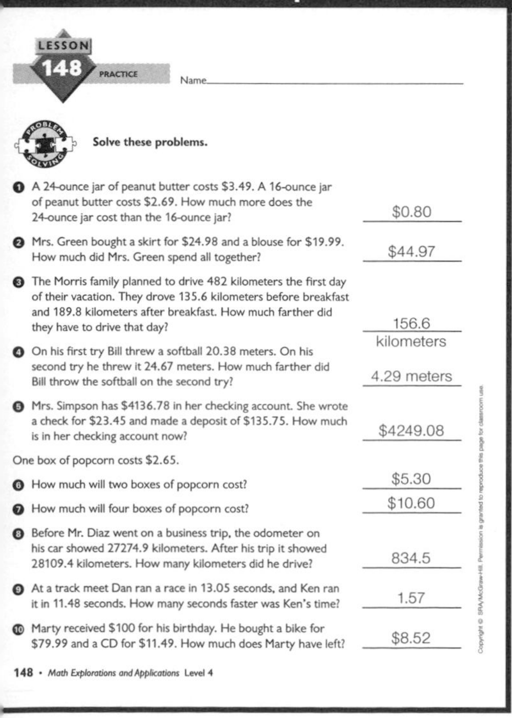

LESSON 148 PRACTICE Name________

Solve these problems.

1. A 24-ounce jar of peanut butter costs \$3.49. A 16-ounce jar of peanut butter costs \$2.69. How much more does the 24-ounce jar cost than the 16-ounce jar? \$0.80
2. Mrs. Green bought a skirt for \$24.98 and a blouse for \$19.99. How much did Mrs. Green spend all together? \$44.97
3. The Morris family planned to drive 482 kilometers the first day of their vacation. They drove 135.6 kilometers before breakfast and 189.8 kilometers after breakfast. How much farther did they have to drive that day? 156.6 kilometers
4. On his first try Bill threw a softball 20.38 meters. On his second try he threw it 24.67 meters. How much farther did Bill throw the softball on the second try? 4.29 meters
5. Mrs. Simpson has \$4136.78 in her checking account. She wrote a check for \$23.45 and made a deposit of \$135.75. How much is in her checking account now? \$4249.08

One box of popcorn costs \$2.65.

6. How much will two boxes of popcorn cost? \$5.30
7. How much will four boxes of popcorn cost? \$10.60
8. Before Mr. Diaz went on a business trip, the odometer on his car showed 27274.9 kilometers. After his trip it showed 28109.4 kilometers. How many kilometers did he drive? 834.5
9. At a track meet Dan ran a race in 13.05 seconds, and Ken ran it in 11.48 seconds. How many seconds faster was Ken's time? 1.57
10. Marty received \$100 for his birthday. He bought a bike for \$79.99 and a CD for \$11.49. How much does Marty have left? \$8.52

Copyright © SRA/McGraw-Hill. Permission is granted to reproduce this page for classroom use.

148 • *Math Explorations and Applications* Level 4

ENRICHMENT p. 148

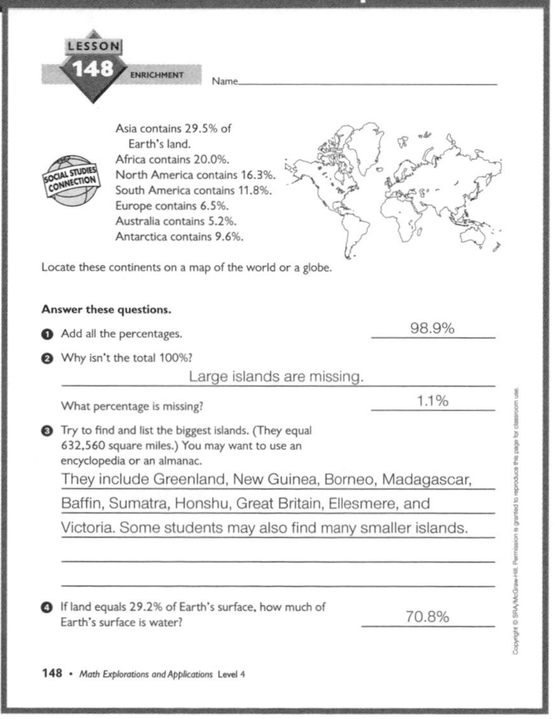

LESSON 148 ENRICHMENT Name________

SOCIAL STUDIES CONNECTION

Asia contains 29.5% of Earth's land.
Africa contains 20.0%.
North America contains 16.3%.
South America contains 11.8%.
Europe contains 6.5%.
Australia contains 5.2%.
Antarctica contains 9.6%.

Locate these continents on a map of the world or a globe.

Answer these questions.

1. Add all the percentages. 98.9%
2. Why isn't the total 100%? Large islands are missing.
   What percentage is missing? 1.1%
3. Try to find and list the biggest islands. (They equal 632,560 square miles.) You may want to use an encyclopedia or an almanac.
   They include Greenland, New Guinea, Borneo, Madagascar, Baffin, Sumatra, Honshu, Great Britain, Ellesmere, and Victoria. Some students may also find many smaller islands.
4. If land equals 29.2% of Earth's surface, how much of Earth's surface is water? 70.8%

Copyright © SRA/McGraw-Hill. Permission is granted to reproduce this page for classroom use.

148 • *Math Explorations and Applications* Level 4

LESSON 149

Student Edition pages 502–505

Adding and Subtracting Decimals: Balancing a Checkbook

LESSON PLANNER

Objectives

- ▶ to introduce the basic skills of maintaining and balancing a checkbook
- ▶ to provide realistic problems and practice in adding and subtracting money amounts
- ▶ to assist in the development of the broad ability to use mathematical common sense

Context of the Lesson This lesson, the 12th of 16 lessons on understanding and using decimals, includes Part 3 of "Iron and Gold," a five-part Thinking Story.

MANIPULATIVES

sample check stubs, check registers, or checking account statements

play money* (optional)

Program Resources

"Checkbook" and "Harder Checkbook" Game Mats

Practice Master 149

Enrichment Master 149

For career connections: Careers and Math*

For additional math integration: Math Throughout the Day*

For extra practice: CD-ROM* Lesson 149

EXPLORE

LESSON 149

Adding and Subtracting Decimals: Balancing a Checkbook

Many people use a checking account for their money. They use addition and subtraction to record how much money they have in their account after each transaction.

Whenever Ms. Taylor pays someone with a check, she keeps a record of it in her checkbook. That way she can keep track of how much money she has in her checking account.

Ms. Taylor keeps the record of each check in a check register. Look at this check register to see what information is on it.

CHECK #	DATE	TRANSACTION	DEBIT		CREDIT		BALANCE	
							907	13
D	1-3-97	Deposit			649	39	649	39
							1556	52
109	1-3	Star Realty Co.	470	85			470	85
		Rent					1085	67

Every month Ms. Taylor gets a statement from her bank. The statement shows the bank's records of her account.

The statement for January said that Ms. Taylor had $907.13 in her account on January 3 and $1349.76 at the end of the month. This did not agree with her records.

Look at Ms. Taylor's checkbook on page 503. Did she make an error in her calculations? If she did, correct the error so that her records show the same balance at the end of the month as the bank statement shows.

Check #111 has the error.

1 Warm-Up

5 MINUTES

Problem of the Day Present the following problem: In the problem $4.AB + A.99 = 1B.A2$, A and B stand for different digits. Find the value of A and B so that the addition works. ($A = 8$, $B = 3$)

Problem-Solving Strategies Ask students who have solved the Problem of the Day to share how they solved it and any strategies they used.

CULTURAL DIVERSITY Economic exchange does not always involve cash. In some cultures bartering, or exchanging one good or service for another, is common. Ask students who come from countries or cultures that have barter systems to discuss their experiences. Have the class consider the benefits and drawbacks of bartered transactions and cash transactions. Discuss bartering in which students might engage, such as doing yard work for a neighbor in return for guitar lessons.

Ms. Taylor's Checkbook

CHECK #	DATE	TRANSACTION	DEBIT	CREDIT	BALANCE
					907 13
D	1-3-97	Deposit		649 39	649 39
					1556 52
109	1-3	Star Realty Co.	470 85		470 85
		Rent			1085 67
110	1-8	CASH	50 00		50 00
					1035 67
111	1-12	Watts Power Co.	83 19		83 19
		electricity			1052 52
112	1-14	Betty's Boutique	34 26		34 26
		Pants			1022 26
113	1-16	Clothing Mart	110 85		110 85
		Jacket			911 41
114	1-28	Terrific Travel Agency	107 00		107 00
		bus tickets			804 41
D	1-30	Deposit		649 39	649 39
					1453 80

1. Dr. Xiang had $507.08 in her checking account. She made a deposit of $325.00 and then wrote a check for $106.88 and another check for $75. What is her new balance? **$650.20**
2. Karen opened a new checking account with $100. She wrote a check for $27.14 to pay her cable television bill. Then she wrote a check for $37.09 to pay for groceries. Does she have enough money in her checking account to write a check for $40 in cash? **no**
3. Michael made a deposit of $215.81 to his checking account. That gave him a balance of $403.05. How much money did Michael have in his account before he made that deposit? **$187.24**
4. Jared wrote a check in the amount of $28.46 for two CDs. He wrote another check for $42.69 to pay for a new sweatshirt. Jared's original balance was $116.39. What is his new balance? **$45.24**

Real-World Connection Many people today use on-line banking services, which eliminates the need for paper checks, check registers, and account statements. You might invite someone familiar with one of these services to provide a demonstration for the class. Or, ask a local software store to lend you a sample program to share with students. Help students make the connections between what they see on pages 502 and 503 and the data that appear on the computer screen.

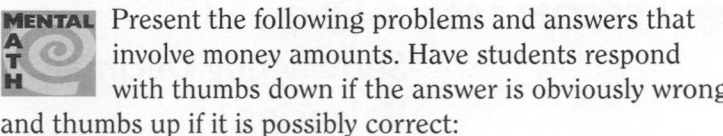

MENTAL MATH Present the following problems and answers that involve money amounts. Have students respond with thumbs down if the answer is obviously wrong and thumbs up if it is possibly correct:

a. $3.16 + $4.37 = $8.53 (thumbs down)
b. $4.99 – $2.49 = $2.50 (thumbs up)
c. $2.08 + $0.83 = $10.15 (thumbs down)
d. $3.98 + $2.00 = $5.98 (thumbs up)
e. $4.16 – $0.45 = $1.03 (thumbs down)
f. $8.64 – $3.22 = $11.17 (thumbs down)

2 Teach

Using the Student Pages Demonstrate the "Checkbook" and "Harder Checkbook" Game Mats with two or three students in front of the class. These games provide practice with adding and subtracting multidigit numbers and maintaining a record of money transactions. Students may play these games when they have completed pages 502–505.

Discuss page 502 with the class. Confirm that students understand what a checking account is and how it works. Go over the meaning of each entry and have students verify that each calculation on the sample stub is correct. Explain that the bank also keeps records of Ms. Taylor's account and sends her a summary or statement of these records each month. Show students **sample statements, check stubs,** and **check registers**, if possible. Have students find the difference in the end-of-month balances between the bank's records and Ms. Taylor's records. Ask if the error is in the number of dollars or cents, if it is necessary to check all the arithmetic, and if anyone can think of a shortcut.

Have students find the error in Ms. Taylor's checkbook on page 503, reminding them that they can use addition to check subtraction.

LEARNING STYLES · MANIPULATIVES

Meeting Individual Needs Kinesthetic and visual learners may benefit from using **play money*** when discussing checking accounts. Have them start with the same amount of play money as Ms. Taylor's balance and model her transactions to better understand how a checking account works. Students may also want to use sample checks, or make their own checks to fill out and model their own purchases.

*available separately

◆ LESSON 149 Adding and Subtracting Decimals: Balancing a Checkbook

Teach

Using the Thinking Story "Iron and Gold (Part 3)" explores the pitfalls of using a sample that does not represent a whole set. You may wish to review the earlier parts of the Thinking Story, which appear on pages 478–479 and 488–489. Then have students read Part 3 of the story and discuss the questions in groups.

Answers to Thinking Story Questions:

1. Manolita thinks she was right because Ferdie's result agrees with hers: the red bag yields the most gold coins.
2. If the blue bag had mostly gold coins on the top (as Marcus found) and none on the bottom, it seems the steward may have tried to fool them by sprinkling a few gold coins on top of a bag filled with iron coins.
3. Ferdie and Marcus could have gotten different results just by chance. But it's also possible, as suggested above, that the mix of coins was different at the top and bottom of each bag.

MATH JOURNAL Have students write in their Math Journals from the point of view of the steward, explaining how he is trying to fool the children and why.

GAME **Introducing the "Checkbook" and "Harder Checkbook" Game Mats** The "Checkbook" Game Mat provides practice with adding and subtracting multidigit numbers using dollar amounts. The "Harder Checkbook" Game Mat provides the same type of practice using dollars and cents. Both games focus on maintaining a record of money transactions. Instructions can be found on the Game Mats. A copy of these Game Mats can also be found on pages 586-587 of this Teacher's Guide.

◆ LESSON 149 Adding and Subtracting Decimals: Balancing a Checkbook

THINKING STORY

Iron and Gold

Part 3

You may want to refer to the earlier parts of this Thinking Story on pages 478–479 and 488–489.

"Have you decided now which bag to take?" the steward asked, with his mean grin.

"Yes," said Marcus, "we'll take the blue bag. It has the most gold coins in it."

"Wait a minute," said Ferdie. Then he whispered to the other children. "I think the man is trying to trick us. He doesn't want us to get much gold. Let me try something different."

Ferdie took a handful of coins from each bag, but he didn't do it the way Marcus did. Instead of scooping the coins from the top of the bag, he reached all the way to the bottom of each bag and took the coins from there.

From the bottom of the red bag Ferdie got five gold coins and three iron ones. From the bottom of the blue bag he got only iron coins. And from the bottom of the green bag he got four gold coins and four iron ones.

"I was right," said Manolita. "The red bag is best."

LITERATURE CONNECTION **Literature Connection** Help students consult *Jobs for Kids* by Carol Barkin and Elizabeth James to learn about jobs that fit their interests, experiences, and abilities. Help them use the suggestions in the book to make a budget based on their potential earnings.

RETEACHING

No reteaching is recommended on checkbooks and checking accounts. You may want to assign Enrichment Master 149.

"I think something funny is going on here," said Marcus.

"I told you," Ferdie said. "The steward was trying to trick us."

. . . to be continued

Work in groups. Discuss your answers and how you figured them out. Then compare your answers with those of other groups. **Answers are in margin.**

1. Why does Manolita think she was right?
2. What reason does Ferdie have to say the steward was trying to trick them?
3. How could Ferdie and Marcus get such different results?

❸ Wrap-Up (5 MINUTES)

In Closing Ask students to explain the benefit of taking a large sampling from the bags before making a decision on which one to choose.

ALTERNATIVE ASSESSMENT

Portfolio Assessment Have students write about the possibility of having their own checking accounts. Encourage them to discuss advantages and disadvantages of maintaining a checking account and to identify problems they might encounter if they were fully responsible for the account.

Assessment Criteria

Did the student . . .

✓ demonstrate understanding of how a checking account works?

✓ communicate strategies used to find and fix the error in the checking account?

✓ contribute to the Thinking Story discussion?

Homework Have students create an imaginary checking account statement for themselves. Let them "open" the account with $500, and then show at least four checks they might write and one deposit they might make. For example, two checks might be for $26.00 for two compact discs and $55.00 worth of music lessons. The same student might deposit the money he or she earned from a paper route or from doing chores for neighbors. The students should keep a running balance.

PRACTICE p. 149

LESSON 149 PRACTICE

Name____________________

Every month Mrs. Joyner gets a statement from her bank. The statement for May showed she had $321.46 in her account on May 4 and $159.36 at the end of the month. This did not agree with her records.

Look at Mrs. Joyner's checkbook. Did she make an error in her calculations? If she did, correct the error so that her records show the same balance at the end of the month as the statement shows.

NUMBER	DATE	DESCRIPTION OF TRANSACTION	PAYMENT	DEPOSIT	BALANCE $ 321.46
211	May 5	Roger's Jewelers	−179.35	$	−179.35 142.11
212	May 11	Carson's Fashions	−42.37		−42.37 184.48
213	May 17	Lander's Service Station	−68.23		−68.23 116.25
214	May 22	Noteworthy News	−22.15		−22.15 94.10
	May 24	deposit		+150.00	+150.00 244.10

Error: The Carson's Fashions transaction was added instead of subtracted.

321.46
−179.35
142.11
− 42.37
99.74
− 68.23
31.51
− 22.15
9.36
+ 150.00
159.36

Copyright © SRA/McGraw-Hill. Permission is granted to reproduce this page for classroom use.

ENRICHMENT p. 149

LESSON 149 ENRICHMENT

Name____________________

COOPERATIVE LEARNING

With this experiment you can measure your reaction time. You will need a centimeter ruler, a partner, and the chart of distances and times shown below.

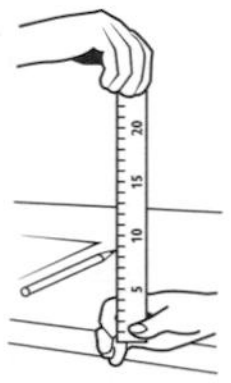

Have your partner hold the ruler so that the 0 end hangs down. (See picture at right.) Put your thumb and forefinger just below the end of the ruler and be ready to catch the ruler when it falls. Put your arm on the edge of a table so that your arm does not move up or down. When you're ready, your partner should let go of the ruler without letting you know exactly when it is going to happen.

Look at the ruler to see where you caught it. Then find that number of centimeters in the table below to see what your reaction time is.

Distance Ruler Falls (centimeters)	Reaction Time (seconds)	Distance Ruler Falls (centimeters)	Reaction Time (seconds)
2	0.06	14	0.17
4	0.09	16	0.18
6	0.11	18	0.19
8	0.13	20	0.20
10	0.14	22	0.21
12	0.16	24	0.22

If your reaction time is as quick as 0.06 second, you probably guessed when the ruler was going to drop. To get a better idea of your real reaction time, repeat the experiment several times and find your average reaction time.

Now trade places and find your partner's reaction time.

Copyright © SRA/McGraw-Hill. Permission is granted to reproduce this page for classroom use.

LESSON 150

Student Edition pages 506–509

Multiplying a Decimal by a Whole Number

LESSON PLANNER

Objectives

- ▶ to demonstrate how to find the product of a decimal and a whole number
- ▶ to provide practice with multiplying a decimal by a whole number
- ▶ to demonstrate the use of a calculator to explore multiplying two decimals

Context of the Lesson This is the 13th of 16 lessons on understanding and using decimals. The next lesson provides more practice in multiplying decimals and whole numbers.

MANIPULATIVES	Program Resources
calculators*	Reteaching Master
graph paper (optional)	Practice Master 150
	Enrichment Master 150
	For extra practice: CD-ROM* Lesson 150

1 Warm-Up (5 MINUTES)

Problem of the Day Present the following problem: Sara, Molly, and Rose are sisters. Molly, the middle sister, is the only one whose age is an even number. Sara is the oldest. The girls' age range is eight years. Their mean age is 12, but no sister is that age this year. Use the clues to find the age of each sister. (Sara is 17, Molly is 10, Rose is 9.)

Problem-Solving Strategies Ask students who have solved the Problem of the Day to share how they solved it and any strategies they used.

MENTAL MATH Write the bounds 40–50 on the chalkboard. Say, for example, "I am thinking of a number between 6 and 7. I will multiply it by 3." Students show thumbs up if the answer definitely falls within the bounds, show thumbs down if the answer is definitely out of range, and stand up if the answer may or may not fall within the bounds.

(continued on page 507)

EXPLORE

LESSON 150

Multiplying a Decimal by a Whole Number

Jenny is making 21 banners for her school play. Each banner takes 1.3 meters of cloth. What is the total length of cloth Jenny needs?

To find out, you would multiply 1.3 by 21.

Chad told Jenny that 21 × 1.3 was 27.3.

Can that be right? Why or why not?

You could do the problem in decimeters. Multiply 13 by 21.

$$\begin{array}{r} 13 \\ \times\ 21 \\ \hline 13 \\ 26\ \\ \hline 273 \end{array} \qquad 273 \text{ dm} = 27.3 \text{ m}$$

So Jenny needs 27.3 meters of cloth.

Chad was right. 21 × 1.3 = 27.3

Let's look at the two multiplications side by side.

$$\begin{array}{r} 13 \\ \times\ 21 \\ \hline 13 \\ 26\ \\ \hline 273 \end{array} \qquad \begin{array}{r} 1.3 \\ \times\ 21 \\ \hline 13 \\ 26\ \\ \hline 27.3 \end{array}$$

The problems and the answers are the same, except for the decimal point.

◆ Can you figure out a simple rule for deciding where to put the decimal point in the answer? **Put the decimal point in the answer as many places from the right as it is in the decimal factor.**

Literature Connection Read *Benjamin's 365 Birthdays* by Judi Barrett to the class, and have students determine how many birthdays Benjamin would celebrate in 0.25 years, in 0.5 years, in 1.5 years, and so on.

*available separately

To multiply a decimal by a whole number:

A. Multiply as you would with two whole numbers.

B. Put the decimal point in the answer as many places from the right as it is in the decimal factor.

Example A: 2.3 × 514

```
   5 1 4      Multiply as you would with two whole numbers.
 ×   2.3
   154 2
  1028
  1182.2  — Then place the point in the answer.
```

```
   5 1 4
 ×   2.3  — The point is one place from the right.
   154 2
  1028
  1182.2  — So put the point one place from the right in the answer.
```

Example B: 73 × 0.375

```
   0.375      Multiply as you would with two whole numbers.
 ×  73
   1 125
  26 25
  27.375  — Then place the point in the answer.
```

```
   0.375  — The point is three places from the right.
 ×  73
   1 125
  26 25
  27.375  — So put the point three places from the right in the answer.
```

Technology Connection Refer students to the software *Whole Numbers, Decimals, and Fractions/Decimals: Multiplication and Division* from Gamco (Apple, IBM for grades 3–10) for further practice with the multiplication and division of decimals.

Mental Math (continued)

	Number between	Multiply by
a.	3 and 4	5 (thumbs down)
b.	10 and 11	3 (thumbs down)
c.	6 and 7	8 (stand up)
d.	20 and 21	2 (thumbs up)
e.	10 and 11	3 (thumbs down)
f.	5 and 6	8 (stand up)
g.	8 and 9	6 (stand up)
h.	3 and 4	8 (thumbs down)

2 Teach

Using the Student Pages Go over pages 506 and 507 carefully with the class. Discuss the banner problem, emphasizing that the procedure for multiplying 1.3 by 21 is the same as for multiplying 13 by 21. The only difference is that in 1.3 x 21, the product has a decimal point. Have students use their own words to state a rule for deciding where to place the decimal point in the product. Be sure that everyone grasps the rule. Work through examples A and B on page 507 with the class. Move your finger along each product from right to left as students count off in unison the number of places to determine where the decimal point belongs.

Meeting Individual Needs
Students who are concrete learners or who grasp concepts better when they apply to real life may benefit from doing multiplication problems that involve whole-number and decimal monetary amounts. This application may help students intuitively see why the algorithm works. Also, logical learners can check their work for reasonableness by asking questions. Suppose a student multiplies 35.6 x 2 and gets a product of 7.12. Guide the student to estimate the answer by finding 35 x 2. Ask, "Should the exact product be around 7 or around 70? What do you notice about your answer?"

◆ LESSON 150 Multiplying a Decimal by a Whole Number

Teach

Using the Student Pages Have students work independently on page 508. Students who finish early can play a game of their choice, such as the "Harder Roll a Decimal" game on page 501, which focuses on using place value and subtracting decimals. Next work through page 509 with the class, or have students work in pairs or small groups. Students may hypothesize that the number of the digits to the right of the decimal point in the product is the same as the total number of digits to the right of the points in the two factors. Provide enough **calculators*** so that each student or group can actively explore. Be aware that different calculators have different-sized displays and different algorithms for truncating numbers that may be too great to fit in the display. Therefore, if you use a variety of calculators, results may vary.

SPECIAL NEEDS

Meeting Individual Needs

Students with organizational or spatial weaknesses may benefit from doing the multiplication on **graph paper.** They write each digit in its own box, which helps them keep the partial products in order and may eliminate the kinds of errors that result from misalignment.

◆ LESSON 150 Multiplying a Decimal by a Whole Number

Remember:

$$\begin{array}{r} 4.07 \\ \times\ 12 \\ \hline 814 \\ 407\ \\ \hline 48.84 \end{array}$$

—The point is two places from the right.

—Place the point two places from the right.

$$\begin{array}{r} 357 \\ \times 0.006 \\ \hline 2.142 \end{array}$$

The point is three places from the right.

Place the point three places from the right.

Multiply.

1. 3.07 × 11 **33.77**
2. 7198 × 0.09 **647.82**
3. 71.3 × 85.2 **6074.7**
4. 82 × 0.03 **2.46**
5. 6.8 × 13 **88.4**
6. 2.306 × 1528 **3523.56**
7. 127 × 0.007 **0.889**
8. 5.23 × 0.1 **0.523**
9. 0.83 × 22 **18.26**
10. 385 × 1.2 **462**
11. 1.05 × 0.06 **0.063**
12. 97.8 × 79 **7726.2**
13. 39 × 2.25 **87.75**
14. 256 × 1.2 **307.2**
15. 451 × 82.3 **37,117.**
16. 1008 × 0.009 **9.072**
17. 8.2 × 7.9 **64.78**
18. 19.84 × 17.76 **352.358**
19. 673 × 5.6 **3768.8**
20. 617 × 2.5 **1542.5**
21. 268.4 × 1.26 **338.184**
22. 27.9 × 1.83 **51.057**
23. 112 × 4.92 **551.04**
24. 6.4 × 2.83 **18.112**

PROBLEM SOLVING

Solve these problems.

25. Bart is the manager of a baseball team. His team needs 13 new shirts. Each shirt costs $7.29. Bart has $75. Does he have enough money? **no**
26. Myrna wants to buy two shelves. One is 3 meters long and the other is 4 meters long. A shelf costs $4.05 per meter. How much will the two shelves cost? **$28.35**
27. Mr. Washington is building a house. He needs 27 electrical outlets. Each outlet costs $2.71. Will the 27 outlets cost more than $100? **no**
28. The Omega Publishing Company ships an average of 751 books a week. It costs 48¢ to mail each book. How much does mailing cost, on the average, for the week? **$360.48**
29. Eric needs to buy stamps to send 18 party invitations. Each stamp costs 32¢. Eric has $5.75. Does he have enough money to buy stamps for all of the invitations? **no; he needs 1¢ more**

508 • Fractions and Decimals

RETEACHING p. 49

LESSON 150 RETEACHING Name________________

Multiplying a decimal by a whole number is easy once you know the rules.

Example:
Four friends split a pizza. Each friend owed $1.64. How can you find out how much the pizza cost?

To solve, multiply $1.64 by 4.

You can think of $1.64 as 164¢ and multiply it this way.

$$\begin{array}{r} 164 \\ \times\ \ 4 \\ \hline 656¢ \end{array} \rightarrow \$6.56$$

Or you can multiply it this way.

$$\begin{array}{r} \$1.64 \\ \times\ \ 4 \\ \hline \$6.56 \end{array}$$

The decimal point is two places from the right in the decimal factor. Put it two places from the right in the answer.

Because 656¢ is equal to 6 dollars, 5 dimes, and 6 pennies, it doesn't matter which way you multiplied. The answer is the same.

When multiplying decimals by whole numbers, remember these steps:

Step 1 Multiply as you would any whole numbers.

Step 2 Put the decimal point in the answer the same number of places from the right as it is in the decimal factor.

Look at this example:

$$\begin{array}{r} 649.72 \\ \times\ \ 2.48 \\ \hline \end{array}$$

a.
$$\begin{array}{r} 649.72 \\ \times\ \ 2.48 \\ \hline 519776 \\ 259888\ \\ 129944\ \ \\ \hline 16113056 \end{array}$$

b.
$$\begin{array}{r} 649.72 \\ \times\ \ 2.48 \\ \hline 519776 \\ 259888\ \\ 129944\ \ \\ \hline 1611.3056 \end{array}$$

How many numbers are to the right of the decimal point? (four)

Move the decimal point to the left four places.

Solve.

1. 208 × 0.17 = 35.36
2. 1.234 × 24 = 29.616
3. 84 × 1.5 = 126
4. 5.55 × 9 = 49.95

Copyright © SRA/McGraw-Hill. Permission is granted to reproduce this page for classroom use.

Math Explorations and Applications Level 4 • 49

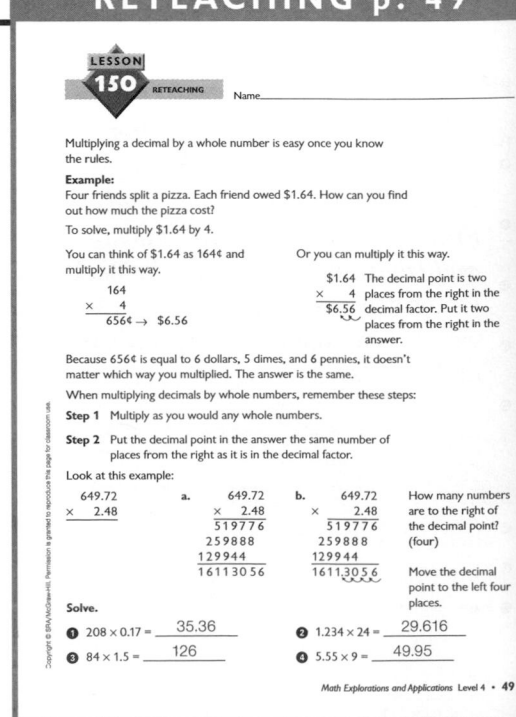

*available separately

six; it is
e same as
e sum of
e number
digits to
e right of
e decimal
int in
ch factor

41 Answers will vary depending on calculators being used; the end; the accuracy of the product is not affected as much by omitting fractional amounts from the end.

Use your calculator to solve these problems.

30. Multiply 1.234 by 56.789. **70.077626**

31. The answer should be between 1 × 56 and 2 × 57. Did the calculator give an answer between 56 and 114? **yes**

32. How many digits are there to the right of the decimal point in your answer? Can you see any relationship between the number of digits to the right of the decimal point and the original factors?

33. What is 4.32 × 8.714? Between what numbers would the answer be? How many digits are going to be to the right of the decimal point? Did the calculator give a reasonable answer? **37.64448; between 32 and 45; five; yes**

◆ Do you have a hypothesis about the number of digits to the right of the decimal point in the product when you multiply two decimal numbers? If so, what is it? **See margin.**

Check your hypothesis with the following products. If your hypothesis doesn't seem to work, see if you can figure out why.

34. 3.452 × 0.0034 **0.0117368**
35. 53.1 × 1.8745 **99.53595**
36. 3.45 × 1.2 **4.14**
37. 1.25 × 1.04 **1.3**
38. 547.682 × 934.86 **512,005.99452**
39. 73.56 × 4.709 **346.39404**

40. Look at problems 36 and 37. Answer these questions.

a. Why is the number of digits to the right of the decimal point in the product not the same as the total number of digits to the right of the points in the two factors? Does the calculator drop all zeros to the right of the last nonzero number after the decimal point? **If the product ends in zero, the zero can be dropped; yes**

b. If you multiply 345 by 12, the product is 4140. Does that explain your answer for problem 36? What is the product of 125 and 104? Can you explain what happened in problem 37? **yes; 13,000; the three zeros were dropped**

41. See if you can explain what happened in problem 38. How many digits can your calculator display? If your calculator has to leave off some digits from a product, does it make more sense that it omits digits at the beginning of the number or the end of the number? Why?

PRACTICE p. 150

LESSON 150 PRACTICE Name________________

Multiply.

1. 1.8 × 6 = 10.8	2. 3.04 × 5 = 15.2	3. 7.18 × 7 = 50.26	4. 2.83 × 3 = 8.49	5. 2.19 × 2 = 4.38
6. 9.4 × 8 = 75.2	7. 4.12 × 6 = 24.72	8. 5.45 × 5 = 27.25	9. 6.9 × 9 = 62.1	10. 4.74 × 4 = 18.96
11. 4.003 × 12 = 48.036	12. 1.07 × 24 = 25.68	13. 8.14 × 27 = 219.78	14. 4.5 × 16 = 72.0	15. 2.4 × 41 = 98.4
16. 3.18 × 36 = 114.48	17. 7.4 × 34 = 251.6	18. 9.2 × 57 = 524.4	19. 2.64 × 29 = 76.56	20. 3.80 × 63 = 239.40
21. 4.21 × 311 = 1309.31	22. 9.75 × 406 = 3958.5	23. 6.02 × 832 = 5008.64	24. 3.21 × 645 = 2070.45	25. 1.72 × 98 = 168.56

PROBLEM SOLVING **Solve these problems.**

26. Marvin buys 312 pencils. Each pencil costs 16¢. How much will the pencils cost? $49.92

27. Janice buys eight packages of party favors. Each package costs $2.79. Janice has $20. Does she have enough money? no

28. Joshua needs five shirts for school. Each shirt costs $12.75. Will the shirts cost more than $65? no

Copyright © SRA/McGraw-Hill. Permission is granted to reproduce this page for classroom use.

150 • *Math Explorations and Applications* Level 4

ENRICHMENT p. 150

LESSON 150 ENRICHMENT Name________________

What would you do if you had some money of your own to invest? Would you put it in the bank to earn interest, or would you buy something that is expected to increase in value? You can use **The Cruncher: *Put Your Money to Work*** project to explore some options.

Suppose you have $50 to invest. You could put it into a bank account where it earns interest every day, or you could buy comic books that may increase in value every year.

1. Before you figure out which method earns the most money, write about which method you think is the best choice. Why do you think so?
Answers will vary. Students may prefer the bank because they are assured of a return. They may prefer the comic books because it is possible to get a greater return.

2. Which is the safest choice? Does that mean it is the best choice, too? Explain.
The bank is the safest choice. (It is unlikely you will lose money.); answers will vary.

3. Now find out what happens to a $50 investment. Which earns the most after five years?
Both earn the same ($75, or $25 profit) after five years.

4. Now which investment would you choose? Why?
Answers will vary depending on students' preferences.

Copyright © SRA/McGraw-Hill. Permission is granted to reproduce this page for classroom use.

150 • *Math Explorations and Applications* Level 4

3 Wrap-Up 5 MINUTES

In Closing Have students state a rule for multiplying a decimal number by a whole number.

ANALYZING ANSWERS If students make errors, determine whether the problem stems from lack of recall of multiplication facts, difficulty with the multiplication algorithm, or misplacement of the decimal place in the product. Provide extra practice with the appropriate skills.

ALTERNATIVE ASSESSMENT **Performance Assessment** You may wish to use students' work on page 508 as an assessment of their ability to multiply decimals by whole numbers and to solve word problems with mixed operations. If so, have students work independently, and allow adequate time for them to finish.

Assessment Criteria

Did the student . . .

✓ contribute to the discussion of the algorithm for multiplying a decimal by a whole number?

✓ demonstrate understanding of the rule for placing the decimal point in the product?

✓ actively participate in the calculator exploration?

✓ correctly answer at least 75% of the computation problems on page 508?

Homework Have students look through print ads to select five items, each of which has a decimal price over $1 but under $100. Then have students determine the cost of buying three of each item they select.

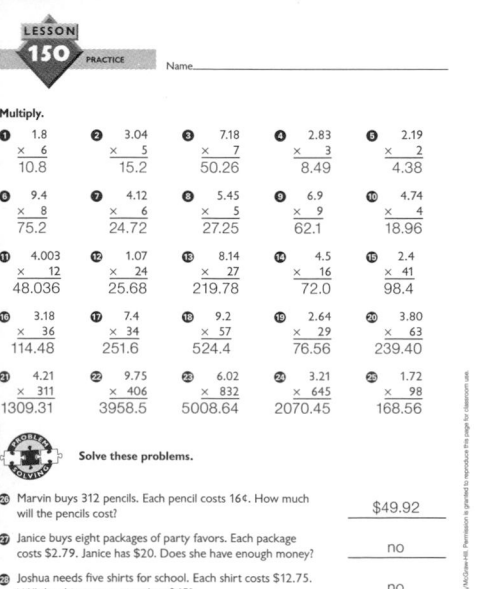

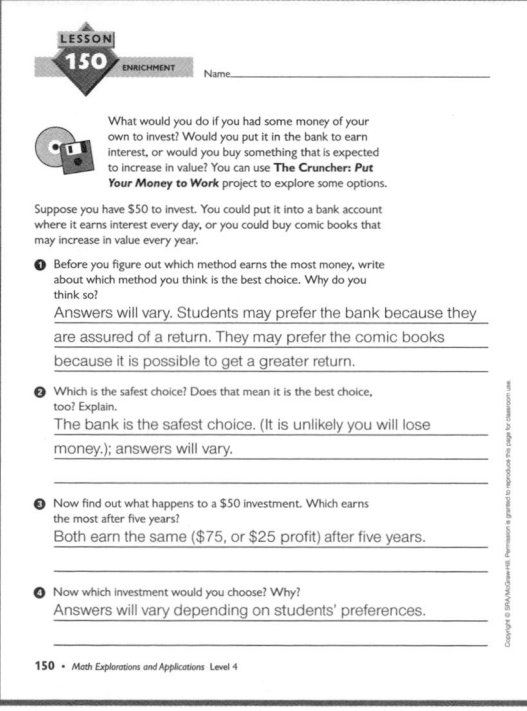

LESSON 151

Student Edition pages 510–513

Practicing Multiplication of Decimals and Whole Numbers

LESSON PLANNER

Objectives

- ▶ to provide practice with estimating products to solve problems that involve multiplying decimals and whole numbers
- ▶ to provide practice with applying function rules and graphing to decimals and fractions
- ▶ to assist in the development of the broad ability to use mathematical common sense

Context of the Lesson This is the 14th of 16 lessons on understanding and using decimals. This lesson includes Part 4 of "Iron and Gold," a five-part Thinking Story. The next two lessons cover applying decimals to measuring metric weight and volume.

MANIPULATIVES

calculators*
graph paper
play money* (optional)

Program Resources

Practice Master 151
Enrichment Master 151
For career connections: Careers and Math*
For extra practice: CD-ROM* Lesson 151

LESSON 151

Practicing Multiplication of Decimals and Whole Numbers

Use your knowledge of multiplication and decimals to solve the following problems.

1. If a snail can crawl 0.6 meter a day, how far can it crawl in a week? In a month (31 days)? In a year (365 days)? **4.2 m; 18.6 m; 219 m**
2. Ahmad wants to tile his kitchen floor. Each tile covers 0.34 square meter. Ahmad ordered 60 tiles. Each tile cost $1.46. How much did he pay for the tiles? **$87.60**
3. Mrs. Khan bought 15 bags of pretzels for a party. Each bag cost $4.89. How much did she pay? **$73.35**
4. Alberto wants to call his mother long distance. He has only $4 in change. Each minute costs 31¢. Can he talk for 15 minutes? **no**

In each problem, two of the answers are clearly wrong and one is correct. Choose the correct answer.

5	8 × 1.7	**a.** 19.6	(**b.**) 13.6	**c.** 7.6
6	6 × 2.4	**a.** 10.4	**b.** 22.4	(**c.**) 14.4
7	4.9 × 5	**a.** 28.67	**b.** 259.7	(**c.**) 24.5
8	0.5 × 9	**a.** 34.5	(**b.**) 4.5	**c.** 45
9	8.73 × 9	**a.** 71.07	(**b.**) 78.57	**c.** 83.67
10	20 × 5.1	(**a.**) 102	**b.** 94.2	**c.** 98.2
11	16 × 3.28	(**a.**) 52.48	**b.** 42.48	**c.** 72.48
12	33.51 × 2	(**a.**) 67.02	**b.** 47.14	**c.** 105.2
13	70 × 67.3	**a.** 4971.0	**b.** 47,111	(**c.**) 4711.0

510 • Fractions and Decimals

1 Warm-Up (5 MINUTES)

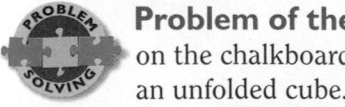

Problem of the Day Present this problem on the chalkboard: The pattern below represents an unfolded cube. If you fold it into a cube, which pair of opposite faces would have the greatest sum? (5.6 + 8.4 = 14.0 is greater than either 3.2 + 6.5 or 2.3 + 4.8.)

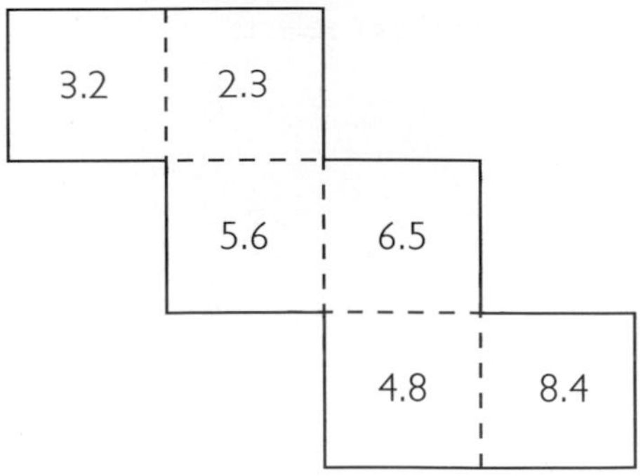

Literature Connection Read *Kid Power* by Susan Beth Pfeffer, or excerpts from it, with the class. Tell students that in Janie's "odd jobs" business she gets ten percent of the pay that her friends make. Explain that 10% is the same as $\frac{10}{100}$ or 0.10. Have students use their skills in multiplying decimals and whole numbers to determine Janie's actual profit from the various jobs.

*available separately

Solve these problems. Use a computer or other means to draw and complete the charts. You may want to use graphing software to graph your data.

14 Use the function rule to complete the chart.

x —(×3)→ n —(−2)→ y

x	1	2	3	4	5
y	1	4	**7**	**10**	**13**

15 Now plot the points on a graph.

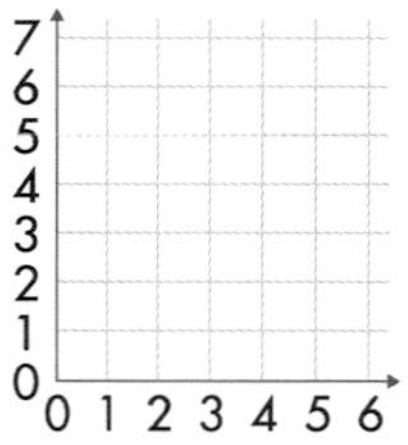

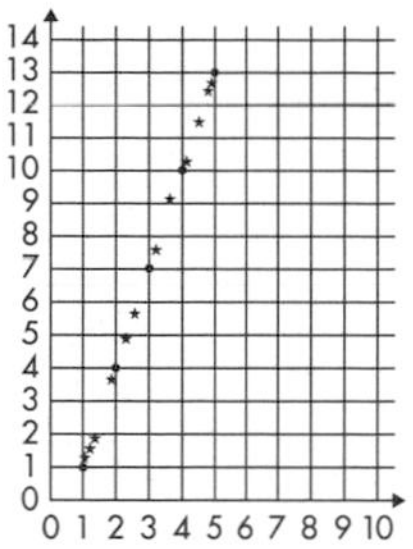

16 Do all five points seem to be on the same straight line? **yes**

17 Use your calculator to help you fill out the following chart for the function rule of problem 14. Then plot all of these points on the same graph you used for problem 15. Do these points also seem to lie on the same straight line? **yes**

x	1.1	1.2	1.3	1.9	2.3	2.6	3.2	3.7	4.1	4.5	4.8	4.9
y	1.3	1.6	**1.9**	**3.7**	**4.9**	**5.8**	**7.6**	**9.1**	**10.3**	**11.5**	**12.4**	**12.7**

Solve.

18 Mr. Becker bought 12.2 gallons of gasoline on Sunday. On Thursday he bought 8.3 gallons of gasoline.

a. How much gasoline did Mr. Becker buy all together? **20.5 gallons**

b. How much more gasoline did he buy on Sunday than he bought on Thursday? **3.9 gallons**

Unit 6 Lesson 151 • **511**

Science Connection

Many scientific measurements are given as decimals. For instance, Earth orbits the sun at a speed of 18.51 miles per second. Have students find facts given in decimal form that pertain to the solar system, geology, or other areas of science that they may be studying. Invite them to use the data to create and solve multiplication problems that involve decimals and whole numbers.

Problem-Solving Strategies Ask students who have solved the Problem of the Day to share how they solved it and any strategies they used.

MENTAL MATH Write the bounds 30–40 on the chalkboard. Provide problems in which students approximate the product of any decimal that falls between the first two numbers multiplied by the third number. Students show thumbs up if the product is definitely within the bounds, show thumbs down if it is definitely out of range, and stand if the product is not obviously in or out of bounds.

	Number between	Multiply by
a.	7 and 8	5 (thumbs up)
b.	3 and 4	9 (stand up)
c.	6 and 7	2 (thumbs down)
d.	8 and 9	7 (thumbs down)
e.	5 and 6	6 (thumbs up)
f.	15 and 16	2 (thumbs up)
g.	9 and 10	3 (stand up)
h.	2 and 3	9 (thumbs down)
i.	3 and 4	8 (stand up)
j.	10 and 11	3 (thumbs up)

2 Teach

Using the Student Pages Have students work independently on page 510. Discuss the word problems as a class after students finish them. Have volunteers give answers for problems 5–13 and explain how they decided to eliminate the other choices.

Proceed to page 511. If necessary, review function rules and graphing ordered pairs. Explain that the same rules apply to functions and graphs of decimals as to whole numbers. You may need to tell students to look ahead so that they select a scale that will accommodate the decimal numbers for the graph in problem 15. Have **graph paper** for problem 15 and **calculators*** for problem 17.

*available separately

◆ LESSON 151 Practicing Multiplication of Decimals and Whole Numbers

Teach

Using the Thinking Story "Iron and Gold (Part 4)" explores choosing samples that better represent the population from which they come and making inferences based on these samples. The children gather more evidence to help them choose the best bag. Ask students to summarize what has happened in the story so far. Then have them read Part 4 of the story and discuss the questions in groups.

Answers to Thinking Story Questions:

1. From the evidence, the green bag is best. In every handful taken from it, about half the coins are gold. The other bags have shown mixed results, but after the contents were mixed, it appeared that fewer than half of the coins in each bag were gold.
2. Samples taken from the green bag have been about half gold and half iron.
3. Mixing up the coins is a way to overcome any trickery and to get a sample that gives an unbiased estimate of what the contents of the whole bag are like.
4. The steward apparently put gold coins on top of the blue bag to fool the children if they only sampled the top. It seems he also put some gold coins on the bottom of the red bag to fool them if, as Ferdie did, they became suspicious and dug to the bottom.

MATH JOURNAL In their Math Journals have students tell what they think the steward meant by saying "Oh well, democracy wins again!"

THINKING STORY

◆ LESSON 151 Practicing Multiplication of Decimals and Whole Numbers

Iron and Gold

Part 4

You may want to review earlier parts of this Thinking Story on pages 478–479, 488–489, and 504–505.

"The blue bag has the most gold on the top, and the red bag has the most gold on the bottom," said Marcus. "Portia, why don't you take coins from the middle of each bag? That way we can find out which has the most gold there."

"I have a different idea," said Portia. She reached into each bag and stirred and stirred until the coins were all mixed up. Then she took a big handful from each bag. From the red bag she got three gold coins and 13 iron ones. From the blue bag she got four gold coins and 11 iron ones. From the green bag she got nine gold coins and seven iron ones.

"Oh, no!" said Manolita. "First the red bag wins. Then the blue bag wins. Then the red bag wins again, and now the green bag wins! How can we ever tell which bag to take?"

"I guess we'd better take the red bag," said Ferdie. "It won twice."

512 • Fractions and Decimals

CULTURAL DIVERSITY Students who have lived in nondemocratic nations may not understand the steward's remark at the end of the Thinking Story. If necessary, explain that in a democracy people are free to express their ideas and to make decisions together, even if there is disagreement. They can express their opinions through voting, as the children did. In some other governmental systems, one person or committee may make all the decisions, which people must follow without question.

RETEACHING

MANIPULATIVES Students may benefit from solving multiplication problems with **play money***, which may help them grasp multiplication with decimals and whole numbers.

*available separately

"I say the blue bag," said Marcus. "I got almost all gold coins when I took a handful from it."

"I vote for the green bag," said Portia.

"Me too," said Manolita.

"Oh, well," said the steward. "Democracy wins again!"

. . . to be continued

Work in groups. Discuss your answers and how you figured them out. Then compare your answers with those of other groups. **Answers are in margin.**

1. Which bag do you think is the best choice? Why?
2. About what fraction of the coins in the green bag do you think are gold?
3. What would be a reason for mixing up the coins in each bag, the way Portia did?
4. What do you think the steward did to trick the children two ways?

3 Wrap-Up

5 MINUTES

In Closing Ask students which sampling technique provided the children in the Thinking Story with the best information.

ALTERNATIVE ASSESSMENT

Informal Assessment Observe students as they solve the problems on page 510, make the graphs for page 511, and discuss the Thinking Story. Ask them to verbalize their thinking so you can determine how they solved the various problems.

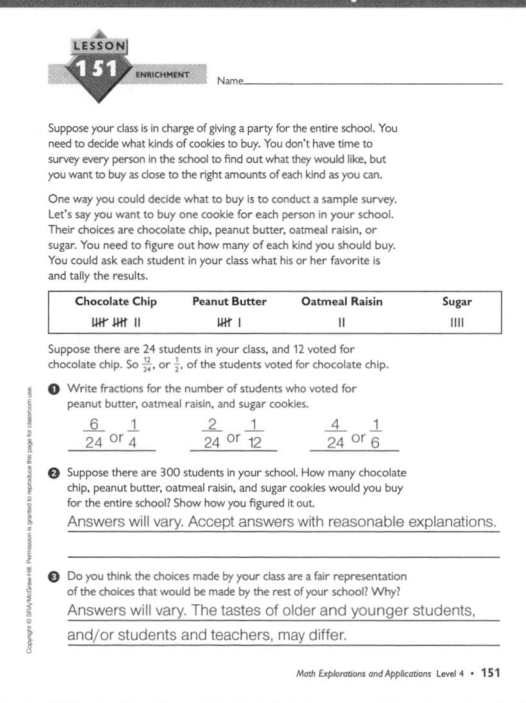

Assessment Criteria

Did the student . . .

- ✓ communicate strategies used to solve the word problems?
- ✓ correctly answer at least 75% of the approximation problems on page 510?
- ✓ demonstrate understanding of functions and graphs that involve decimals?
- ✓ contribute to the Thinking Story discussion?

PRACTICE p. 151

LESSON 151 PRACTICE Name________________

In each problem two of the answers are clearly wrong and one is correct. Choose the correct answer.

1	$6 \times 2.3 =$ b	a. 10.6	b. 13.8	c. 3.4
2	$5 \times 1.7 =$ c	a. 4.5	b. 12.5	c. 8.5
3	$3.4 \times 8 =$ b	a. 22.0	b. 27.2	c. 41.4
4	$0.9 \times 9 =$ a	a. 8.1	b. 81	c. 0.81
5	$3 \times 0.43 =$ a	a. 1.29	b. 3.71	c. 6.83
6	$4.6 \times 4 =$ b	a. 192	b. 18.4	c. 1.62
7	$9.13 \times 5 =$ c	a. 456.5	b. 4.565	c. 45.65
8	$0.02 \times 8 =$ a	a. 0.16	b. 2.18	c. 16.02
9	$60 \times 41.4 =$ c	a. 54.94	b. 347.4	c. 2484.0
10	$7.6 \times 14 =$ a	a. 106.4	b. 100.64	c. 10,064

11. Use the function rule $x \xrightarrow{\times 2} n \xrightarrow{+1} y$ to complete this chart.

x	1.1	2.1	3.1	4.1	5.1
y	3.2	5.2	7.2	9.2	11.2

12. Plot the points on the graph.

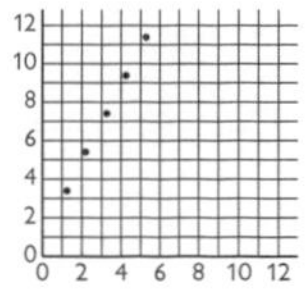

13. Do the five points seem to be on the same straight line? yes

Copyright © SRA/McGraw-Hill. Permission is granted to reproduce this page for classroom use.

Math Explorations and Applications Level 4 • **151**

ENRICHMENT p. 151

LESSON 151 ENRICHMENT Name________________

Suppose your class is in charge of giving a party for the entire school. You need to decide what kinds of cookies to buy. You don't have time to survey every person in the school to find out what they would like, but you want to buy as close to the right amounts of each kind as you can.

One way you could decide what to buy is to conduct a sample survey. Let's say you want to buy one cookie for each person in your school. Their choices are chocolate chip, peanut butter, oatmeal raisin, or sugar. You need to figure out how many of each kind you should buy. You could ask each student in your class what his or her favorite is and tally the results.

Chocolate Chip	Peanut Butter	Oatmeal Raisin	Sugar
卌 卌 II	卌 I	II	IIII

Suppose there are 24 students in your class, and 12 voted for chocolate chip. So $\frac{12}{24}$, or $\frac{1}{2}$, of the students voted for chocolate chip.

1. Write fractions for the number of students who voted for peanut butter, oatmeal raisin, and sugar cookies.

   $\frac{6}{24}$ or $\frac{1}{4}$ $\frac{2}{24}$ or $\frac{1}{12}$ $\frac{4}{24}$ or $\frac{1}{6}$

2. Suppose there are 300 students in your school. How many chocolate chip, peanut butter, oatmeal raisin, and sugar cookies would you buy for the entire school? Show how you figured it out.

   Answers will vary. Accept answers with reasonable explanations.

3. Do you think the choices made by your class are a fair representation of the choices that would be made by the rest of your school? Why?

   Answers will vary. The tastes of older and younger students, and/or students and teachers, may differ.

Copyright © SRA/McGraw-Hill. Permission is granted to reproduce this page for classroom use.

Math Explorations and Applications Level 4 • **151**

Homework Assign Practice Master 151 to reinforce the skill of multiplying decimals or Enrichment Master 151.

LOOKING AHEAD Obtain **metric weights***, **liter containers***, and a **metric scale** or **balance*** to measure metric weight and volume for Lesson 152.

*available separately

LESSON 152

Student Edition pages 514–515

Using Decimals: Weight and Volume

LESSON PLANNER

Objectives

✓ to assess understanding of measuring and converting metric units

▶ to provide experience in measuring with metric units of weight and volume and practice in converting one metric unit to another

▶ to provide experience in plotting data and creating a line graph

Context of the Lesson This lesson, the 15th of 16 lessons on understanding and using decimals, contains a Mastery Checkpoint on measuring and converting metric units.

MANIPULATIVES

graph paper

liter containers*

metric scale or balance* and metric weights

index cards (optional)

Program Resources

Number Wheels

Practice Master 152

Enrichment Master 152

Assessment Master

For extra practice:

CD-ROM* Lesson 152

1 Warm-Up (5 MINUTES)

Problem of the Day Present this problem: Make a magic square out of the digits 2–10 so that the sum of each row and diagonal is 18. (first row: 7, 8, 3; second row: 2, 6, 10; third row: 9, 4, 5)

Problem-Solving Strategies Ask students who have solved the Problem of the Day to share how they solved it and any strategies they used.

MENTAL MATH Present problems involving multiplication and division of decimals by powers of 10. Have students use Number Wheels, indicating the position of the decimal point with their index fingers. Write these problems on the chalkboard:

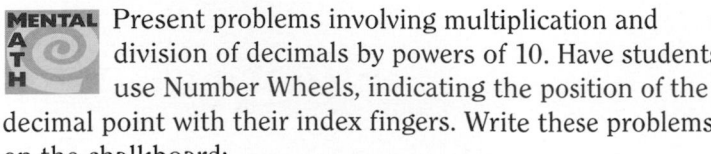

a. 35 ÷ 10 = (3.5) **b.** 350 ÷ 100 = (3.5)

c. 350 ÷ 1000 = (0.35) **d.** 55 ÷ 100 = (0.55)

MIXED **PRACTICE**

LESSON 152

Using Decimals: Weight and Volume

You have measured objects to find their length. You can also measure objects to find their weight or volume. **Weight** describes how heavy something is.

The gram and the kilogram are metric units of weight.

Two paper clips weigh about 1 gram (1 g).

A marble weighs about 5 grams (5 g).

A man's shoe weighs about 500 grams (500 g).

1 kilogram is 1000 grams. 1 kg = 1000 g

1 gram is one thousandth of a kilogram. 1 g = 0.001 kg

Solve.

1. 2 g = ■ kg **0.002**
2. 805 g = ■ kg **0.805**
3. 0.05 kg = ■ g **50**
4. 40 g = ■ kg **0.040**
5. 900 g = ■ kg **0.900**
6. 0.005 kg = ■ g **5**
7. 88 g = ■ kg **0.088**
8. 0.3 kg = ■ g **300**
9. 25 kg = ■ g **25,000**
10. 620 g = ■ kg **0.620**
11. 8 kg = ■ g **8000**
12. 2.5 kg = ■ g **2500**

Volume is the number of cubic units that will fill an object.

The liter and milliliter are metric units of volume.

About how much is 1 liter?

Each container holds about 1 liter (1 L).

There are 1000 milliliters in 1 liter. 1000 mL = 1 L

1 milliliter is one thousandth of a liter. 1 mL = 0.001 L

Solve.

13. 3 mL = ■ L **0.003**
14. 500 mL = ■ L **0.500**
15. 0.025 L = ■ mL **25**
16. 63 mL = ■ L **0.063**
17. 758 mL = ■ L **0.758**
18. 0.725 L = ■ mL **725**
19. 40 mL = ■ L **0.040**
20. 0.002 L = ■ mL **2**
21. 2.5 L = ■ mL **2500**
22. 409 mL = ■ L **0.409**
23. 0.02 L = ■ mL **20**
24. 5 L = ■ mL **5000**

RETEACHING

MANIPULATIVES To help students remember metric units, have them write common metric units on blank **index cards**: m, dm, cm, mm, kg, g, L, and mL. Then present measurements without the unit, saying, for example, "The classroom is 8 _____ long." Have students display the card that indicates the correct unit; in this case it is meters.

PRACTICE p. 152

LESSON 152 PRACTICE Name_______________

Solve.

Remember: 1 kg = 1000 g.

1. 4 g = 0.004 kg
2. 65 g = 0.065 kg
3. 70 g = 0.070 kg
4. 280 g = 0.280 kg
5. 921 g = 0.921 kg
6. 3 g = 0.003 kg
7. 6 kg = 6000 g
8. 0.1 kg = 100 g
9. 41 kg = 41,000 g
10. 0.007 kg = 7 g

Remember: 1000 mL = 1 L, and 1 mL = 0.001 L.

11. 7 mL = 0.007 L
12. 28 mL = 0.028 L
13. 80 mL = 0.080 L
14. 206 mL = 0.206 L
15. 900 mL = 0.900 L
16. 0.003 L = 3 mL
17. 0.04 L = 40 mL
18. 6 L = 6000 mL
19. 0.725 L = 725 mL
20. 4.6 L = 4600 mL
21. 10 g = 0.01 kg
22. 0.5 kg = 500 g
23. 3500 m = 3.5 km
24. 0.3 km = 300 m
25. 3 km = 3000 m
26. 70 m = 0.07 km
27. 125 g = 0.125 kg
28. 0.25 kg = 250 g
29. 660 m = 0.66 km
30. 10 kg = 10,000 g
31. 1.5 m = 1500 mm
32. 0.5 L = 500 mL
33. 7500 mm = 7.5 m
34. 375 mL = 0.375 L
35. 850 mm = 0.850 m
36. 6.2 L = 6200 mL
37. 11.4 m = 11,400 mm
38. 0.8 L = 800 mL

152 • *Math Explorations and Applications* Level 4

Copyright © SRA/McGraw-Hill. Permission is granted to reproduce this page for classroom use.

*available separately

COOPERATIVE LEARNING **Work in groups with a set of containers and a balance. Measure the weights of various volumes of water in grams.**

Luisa made a chart to show the weight of each volume of water.

Use a computer or other means to make a chart to show your results, or copy and complete Luisa's chart.

	Volume of Water in Container (milliliters)	Weight of Empty Container (grams)	Weight of Container with Water (grams)	Weight of Water (grams)	
25	0	8	8	0	
26	10	8	18	■	10
27	20	8	27	■	19
28	40	8	47	■	39
29	50	8	57	■	49
30	0	10	10	■	0
31	60	10	71	■	61
32	80	10	91	■	81
33	100	10	110	■	100
34	0	21	21	■	0
35	120	21	141	■	120
36	140	21	163	■	142
37	160	21	185	■	164

Luisa made a line graph to show her results. You might want to use graphing software to graph your results. If you haven't done the experiment, make a graph of Luisa's results.

MATH JOURNAL **In your Math Journal explain how kilograms and grams are like kilometers and meters. How are liters and milliliters like meters and millimeters?**

ENRICHMENT p. 152

LESSON 152 ENRICHMENT Name______

SOCIAL STUDIES CONNECTION

In the United States we use the same number system for both customary and metric units of weight and measure. Other civilizations developed their number systems, which were very different from ours.

Choose one of these number systems to investigate: Roman, Babylonian, Egyptian, or Mayan. Use an encyclopedia or other reference materials for your research. Write a summary of the system and how it works.

Answers will vary depending on the system each student chooses.

Try writing the following numbers using the system you chose.

Your age ______

The year you were born ______

The current year ______

The number of students in your class ______

The number of students in your school ______

Is the system you chose easy or difficult to use? Why? What are its advantages and disadvantages?

Write what you think about this number system.

Copyright © SRA/McGraw-Hill. Permission is granted to reproduce this page for classroom use.

ASSESSMENT p. 58

UNIT 6 **Mastery Checkpoint 23** Measuring length, weight, and volume (Lesson 152)

Name ______

The student demonstrates mastery by correctly answering at least 16 of the 20 problems.

Ring the better estimate.

1. A glass of milk holds about **(a.)** 250 mL **b.** 250 L
2. Ten paper clips weigh about **a.** 5 kg **(b.)** 5 g
3. Your shoe might weigh about **(a.)** 300 g **b.** 300 kg
4. A carton of milk holds about **(a.)** 1000 mL **b.** 1000 L
5. A book measures about **a.** 20 m **(b.)** 20 cm
6. A broom measures about **a.** 140 cm **(b.)** 140 mm

Write the equivalent measure.

7. 4 mL = 0.004 L
8. 7200 mL = 7.2 L
9. 0.85 L = 850 mL
10. 650 g = 0.65 kg
11. 3.8 kg = 3800 g
12. 4.2 kg = 4200 g
13. 532 cm = 5.32 m
14. 8 cm = 0.08 m
15. 2.4 km = 2400 m
16. 2700 mL = 2.7 L
17. 13 km = 13,000 m
18. 280 g = 0.28 kg

Solve these problems.

19. Melanie bought a package that has 40 pieces of string cheese. She found out that each piece weighs 28 grams. How many kilograms of cheese did she buy? 1.12
20. Jill bought a 2-liter bottle of soda. How many 250-mL servings can she make? 8

Copyright © SRA/McGraw-Hill. Permission is granted to reproduce this page for classroom use.

*available separately

2 Teach

Using the Student Pages Go over page 514, discussing each metric unit. Do one or two problems in each set. Let students examine the gram and kilogram **weights** and handle the **liter containers***. Point out the milliliter calibrations and show the difference between 1 milliliter of water and 1 liter of water.

COOPERATIVE LEARNING Have students work in small groups to do the experiment described on page 515. Do the experiment and graph as a whole class if there is only one **balance***. Have **graph paper** available.

3 Wrap-Up

5 MINUTES

In Closing Have students explain the difference between weight and volume and which units are used for each.

Mastery Checkpoint 23

Students should demonstrate mastery of these skills by correctly answering at least 80% of the problems on page 514 or on Assessment Blackline Masters page 58.

Assessment Criteria

Did the student . . .

- ✓ contribute to the discussion of weight and volume?
- ✓ actively participate in the measuring and graphing activity?
- ✓ correctly answer at least 80% of the conversion problems on page 514?
- ✓ prepare and present reasonably accurate charts and graphs?

Homework For further practice with the metric system assign Practice Master 152.

LESSON 153

Student Edition pages 516–517

Cubic Centimeters

LESSON PLANNER

Objectives

- ▶ to review volume as measured in cubic units
- ▶ to review the cubic centimeter as a standard unit of volume
- ▶ to provide practice in solving word problems that involve metric units

Context of the Lesson This is the last of 16 lessons on understanding and using decimals. The cubic centimeter was introduced in Level 3.

MANIPULATIVES

play money* (optional)

measuring tools* (optional)

Program Resources

"Metric Unit" Game Mat

Practice Master 153

Enrichment Master 153

For additional math integration:
Math Throughout the Day*

For extra practice:
CD-ROM* 153
Cumulative Review, page 568

1 Warm-Up

5 MINUTES

Problem of the Day Present students with the following problem: Figure out how many 1-inch cubes are required to build a cube that is 1 foot long on each side. (1728)

Problem-Solving Strategies Ask students who have solved the Problem of the Day to share how they solved it and any strategies they used.

MENTAL MATH Review fraction notation by writing the following fractions on the chalkboard and having students respond in unison with the correct name:

a. $\frac{1}{2}$ (one half) **b.** $\frac{4}{5}$ (four fifths)

c. $\frac{1}{5}$ (one fifth) **d.** $\frac{1}{6}$ (one sixth)

e. $\frac{1}{4}$ (one fourth) **f.** $\frac{5}{6}$ (five sixths)

g. $\frac{3}{10}$ (three tenths) **h.** $\frac{3}{8}$ (three eighths)

i. $\frac{2}{9}$ (two ninths) **j.** $\frac{3}{4}$ (three fourths)

PRACTICE

LESSON 153

Cubic Centimeters

Volume measures the space inside an object.

The cubic centimeter is a metric unit of volume.

This cube has a volume of 1 cubic centimeter.

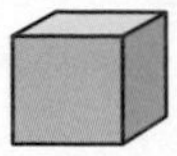

1 cubic centimeter is about the same volume as 1 milliliter.

Find the volume of each box in cubic centimeters by figuring out how many cubes there are.

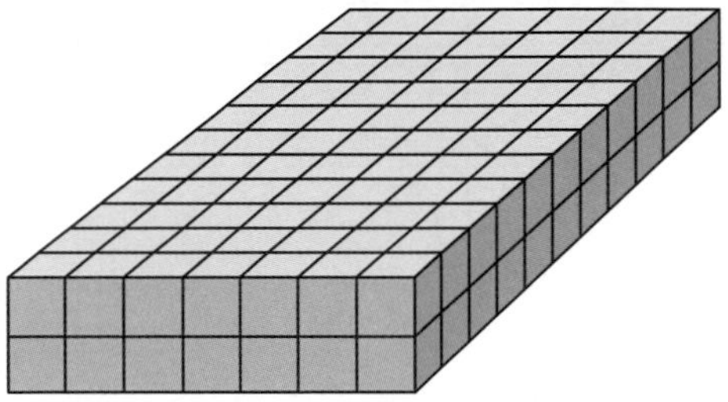

1 154 cm^3

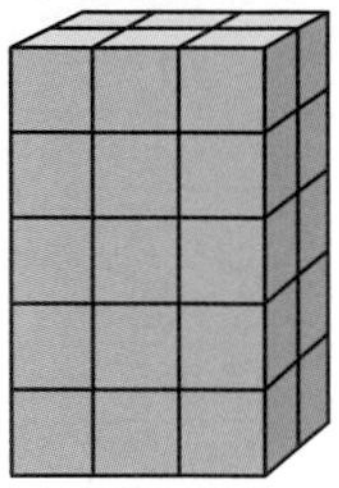

2 30 cm^3

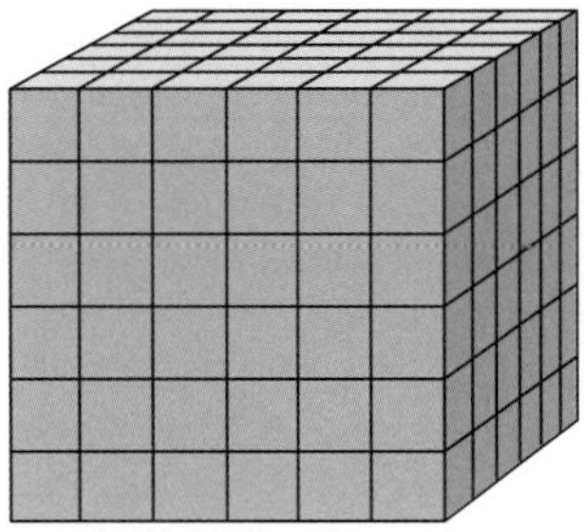

3 216 cm^3

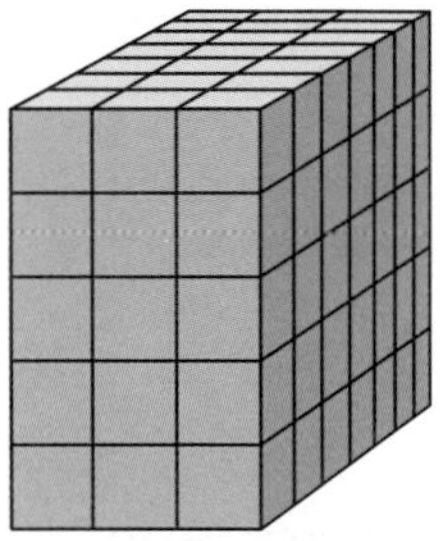

4 105 cm^3

Why teach it this way?

The symbol for cubic centimeter is cm^3. To avoid confusing students with superscript notation, *Math Explorations and Applications* does not ask them to use this symbol. However, it is used in the Teacher's Guides to annotate answers as a way of saving space.

RETEACHING

MANIPULATIVES Help students who have trouble with the word problems on page 517 by providing them with concrete objects, **play money***, and **metric measuring tools*** so they can model the problems. In each case, have students check to see that their solutions make sense in the context of the problems.

*available separately

Solve these problems.

5. A 1-liter container is half-filled with water. How many milliliters of water are in the container? **500**
6. Which is a better buy, a 1.5-liter can of apple juice for \$2.40 or two 700-milliliter cans of the same juice for \$1.20 each? **the 1.5-liter can**
7. A liter of water weighs 1.00 kg. How much do each of these weigh?
   - **a.** one half liter of water **0.5 kg**
   - **b.** 0.5 liter of water **0.5 kg**
   - **c.** 100 milliliters of water **0.1 kg**
   - **d.** 0.1 liter of water **0.1 kg**
8. An empty jar weighs 100 grams. When filled with water, the jar weighs 500 grams.
   - **a.** How much does the water in the jar weigh? **400 g**
   - **b.** How many milliliters of water does the jar contain? (Remember, 1 liter of water weighs 1 kilogram.) **400**
9. Seth weighed 100 marbles. They weighed 490 grams all together. On the average, how much does each marble weigh? **4.9 g**
10. Pam wants to buy a sweater that costs \$26.99 and a denim skirt that costs \$34.99. She has \$70.00. Does she have enough money to buy both items? **yes; the items cost \$61.98**
11. Lina wants to go fishing. She has \$4. Worms cost 73¢ each. Does she have enough money to buy four worms? **yes**

Use the Cumulative Review on page 568 after this lesson.

❷ Teach

Using the Student Pages You may wish to begin by demonstrating the "Metric Unit" Game Mat, so that students who finish the problems on pages 516–517 early can begin playing. This game provides practice with determining metric units of weight and length. Go over the first problem on page 516 with the class. Have students complete the page independently. Have students complete page 517 on their own or in small groups. Help students read and understand the problems as needed.

Using the "Metric Unit" Game Mat Have students play this game in groups of two, three, or four. This game provides practice with various units of metric measure involving weight and length. Complete instructions can be found on the Game Mat. A copy of "Metric Unit" can also be found on page 589 of this Teacher's Guide.

❸ Wrap-Up

5 MINUTES

In Closing Have students explain the use of cubic centimeters to report volume.

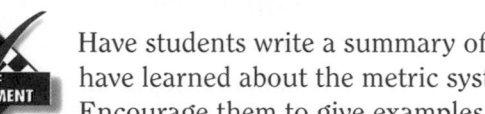

SELF ASSESSMENT

Have students write a summary of what they have learned about the metric system. Encourage them to give examples of units used for each kind of measurement: length, weight, and volume (liquid and solid). They should date their statements and add them to their Math Portfolios.

PRACTICE p. 153

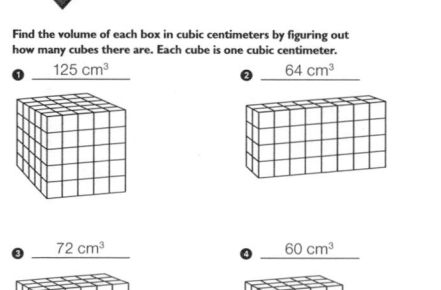

LESSON 153 PRACTICE Name__________

Find the volume of each box in cubic centimeters by figuring out how many cubes there are. Each cube is one cubic centimeter.

1. 125 cm^3

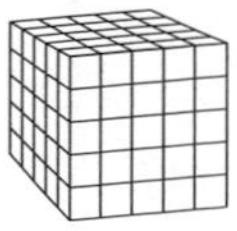

2. 64 cm^3

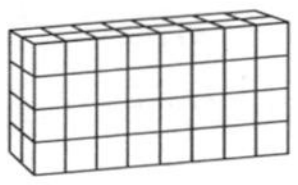

3. 72 cm^3

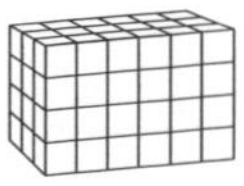

4. 60 cm^3

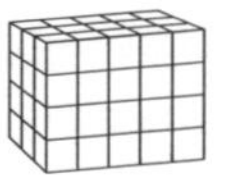

Solve these problems.

5. Which is a better buy—a 1.8-liter bottle of tomato juice for \$1.29 or three 500-milliliter bottles of the same juice for \$0.45 each? the 1.8-liter bottle
6. Steven is making a batch of cookies. He has a recipe that makes two dozen cookies but wants to make six dozen. The recipe calls for 250 grams of sugar. How much sugar should he use to make six dozen cookies? 750 grams

Copyright © SRA/McGraw-Hill. Permission is granted to reproduce this page for classroom use.

Math Explorations and Applications Level 4 • 153

ENRICHMENT p. 153

LESSON 153 ENRICHMENT Name__________

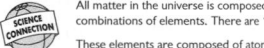

SCIENCE CONNECTION

All matter in the universe is composed of elements or combinations of elements. There are 109 elements.

These elements are composed of atoms of only one kind. When atoms of different kinds of elements are combined into molecules, the result is called a compound.

Water is an example of a compound. The smallest possible portion of water is one molecule made up of two hydrogen atoms and one oxygen atom. So, water is a compound composed of two elements. Gold is an example of an element; it is made up of only one kind of atom.

The elements were organized by scientists into the Periodic Table of the Elements. Look it up in an encyclopedia. The table lists the atomic weight for the atoms of each element.

Scientists use the idea of atomic weight to compare the weights of different elements or combinations of elements.

Water has an atomic weight of about 18. Silver has an atomic weight of 108; gold, 197; lead, 207; and copper, 64.

Suppose that you weigh a liter of water and find it weighs 1 kilogram.

1. Based on what you know about atomic weights, can you predict about how much 1 liter of melted gold would weigh? Gold is almost 11 times heavier than water, so 1 liter of gold would weigh about 11 kilograms.
2. Predict about how much 1 liter of melted silver would weigh. 6 kilograms
3. Predict about how much 1 liter of melted lead would weigh. 11.5 kilograms
4. Predict about how much 1 liter of melted copper would weigh. 3.5 kilograms
5. Alchemists were people who used to try to make gold out of other metals. Why do you think they often tried to use lead? Gold and lead weigh about the same.

Copyright © SRA/McGraw-Hill. Permission is granted to reproduce this page for classroom use.

Math Explorations and Applications Level 4 • 153

Assessment Criteria

Did the student . . .

- ✓ correctly calculate and label volume in cubic centimeters?
- ✓ communicate strategies used to determine the volume of each box?
- ✓ accurately solve at least five of the seven word problems on page 517?

Homework For further practice with the metric system, assign Practice Master 153.

LESSON 154

Student Edition pages 518–521

Keep in Shape: Fractions and Decimals

LESSON PLANNER

Objectives

✓ to assess students' proficiency at adding and subtracting simple fractions

▶ to provide practice with multiplying and dividing decimals by powers of 10 and with multiplying decimals and whole numbers

▶ to assist in developing the broad ability to use mathematical common sense

Context of the Lesson This lesson includes a checkpoint for assessing mastery of adding and subtracting simple fractions. It also contains Part 5 of "Iron and Gold," a five-part Thinking Story. The next lesson begins the end-of-unit sequence of review, practice, and testing.

MANIPULATIVES

fraction tower cubes* (optional)

counters* (optional)

play money* (optional)

world map or globe (optional)

egg cartons (optional)

paper squares (optional)

cardboard rulers (optional)

Program Resources

"Fracto 1" and "Fracto 2" Game Mats

Number Cubes (0–5)

Number Wheels

Practice Master 154

Enrichment Master 154

Assessment Masters

For career connections: Careers and Math*

For additional math integration: Math Throughout the Day*

For extra practice: CD-ROM* Lesson 154

1 Warm-Up 5 MINUTES

Problem of the Day Present this problem: Use only the digits 1, 2, 4, and 8 to create two fractions. Their sum must equal 1. ($\frac{1}{2} + \frac{4}{8} = 1$)

Problem-Solving Strategies Ask students who have solved the Problem of the Day to share how they solved it and any strategies they used.

PROBLEM SOLVING

LESSON 154

Keep in Shape: Fractions and Decimals

Keep in shape by solving problems that involve fractions.

Solve these problems.

1. The road repair crew used $\frac{1}{4}$ truckload of cement yesterday and $\frac{1}{2}$ truckload today. How many truckloads did they use all together? **$\frac{3}{4}$**

2. Mr. Moore drove from his home to Durango. When he left home, he had about $\frac{3}{4}$ of a tank of gasoline in his car. When he arrived in Durango, he had only $\frac{1}{4}$ of a tank.
   - **a.** What fraction of a tank of gas did Mr. Moore use on the trip to Durango? **about $\frac{1}{2}$**
   - **b.** Can Mr. Moore drive back home without getting more gasoline? **no**
   - **c.** What fraction of a tank of gasoline does Mr. Moore need to fill his tank in Durango? **about $\frac{3}{4}$**
   - **d.** If Mr. Moore fills his tank in Durango, about how full will it be when he gets home? **about $\frac{1}{2}$**
   - **e.** How many tanks of gasoline does Mr. Moore use on a trip to Durango and back? **about 1**
   - **f.** Can you make a good estimate of how many miles it might be from Mr. Moore's home to Durango? **Reasonable estimates range from 100 to 140 miles.**

518 • Fractions and Decimals

Geography Connection Most of the world's rubies come from the Asian countries of Myanmar (Burma), Thailand, Cambodia, and Sri Lanka, as well as North Carolina in the United States. Have students locate the four countries and the American state on a **world map** or **globe**.

SPECIAL NEEDS · MANIPULATIVES

Meeting Individual Needs

Some students may still need to use manipulative materials to add and subtract fractions. Provide them with an assortment of fraction pieces, **egg cartons**, **paper squares** they can fold, or **cardboard rulers** calibrated in eighths or twelfths to model the fractions in the word problems.

*available separately

Keep in shape by practicing multiplying and dividing with decimals. Remember to place the decimal point in the correct position in each answer.

3. 100 × 3.5 **350**
4. 100,000 × 394.565 **39,456,500**
5. 5.7 ÷ 1000 **0.0057**
6. 10 × 36.237 **362.37**
7. 14.3 ÷ 10,000 **0.00143**
8. 101.6761 × 1,000,000 **101,676,100**
9. 10 × 15.576 **155.76**
10. 55.107 ÷ 100 **0.55107**
11. 1,000,000 × 6.5591 **6,559,100**
12. 1000 × 53.45 **53,450**
13. 56.227 ÷ 100,000 **0.00056227**
14. 10,000 × 89,065.339 **890,653,390**
15. 100 × 323.75 **32,375**
16. 84.6 ÷ 100 **0.846**
17. 10,000 × 46.5 **465,000**
18. 60.273 ÷ 10,000 **0.0060273**
19. 237.39 ÷ 1000 **0.23739**
20. 10 × 9.78 **97.8**

Multiply.

21. 4 × 3.5 **14**
22. 76.39 × 91 **6951.49**
23. 17.95 × 6 **107.7**
24. 327 × 9.37 **3063.99**
25. 7 × 59.106 **413.742**
26. 3.1 × 872 **2703.2**
27. 53 × 5.467 **289.751**
28. 124 × 0.47 **58.28**
29. 37 × 4.86 **179.82**
30. 53.15 × 79 **4198.85**
31. 40.5 × 67 **2713.5**
32. 102 × 9.14 **932.28**
33. 82.7 × 17 **1405.9**
34. 2.208 × 7129 **15,740.832**
35. 36 × 67.3 **2422.8**
36. 32.153 × 6.15 **197,740.95**
37. 76.3 × 325 **24,797.5**
38. 15.08 × 717 **10,812.36**
39. 63 × 36.7 **2312.1**
40. 2585 × 7.12 **18,405.2**

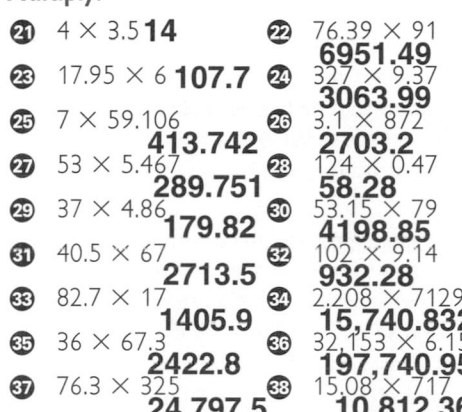

Solve.

41. Toshio wants to buy three new books that cost $6.25 each. To raise money, he is selling some of his old books for $0.49 each.
    a. If he sells 35 of his old books, how much money will he take in? **$17.15**
    b. Will that be enough to pay for the new books? **no**

MENTAL MATH Provide problems that involve adding and subtracting simple fractions. Students can use Number Wheels to show the numerator with the two left wheels and the denominator with the two right wheels. For example, students would show 0104 for $\frac{1}{4}$.

a. $\frac{1}{2} + \frac{1}{4} = (\frac{3}{4})$ **b.** $\frac{1}{3} + \frac{2}{3} = (1)$

c. $\frac{1}{5} + \frac{3}{5} = (\frac{4}{5})$ **d.** $\frac{5}{6} - \frac{4}{6} = (\frac{1}{6})$

e. $\frac{1}{2} + \frac{1}{8} = (\frac{5}{8})$ **f.** $1 - \frac{3}{4} = (\frac{1}{4})$

g. $\frac{3}{8} - \frac{1}{8} = (\frac{2}{8}$ or $\frac{1}{4})$ **h.** $\frac{1}{2} - \frac{1}{4} = (\frac{1}{4})$

i. $\frac{5}{6} - \frac{2}{6} = (\frac{3}{6}$ or $\frac{1}{2})$ **j.** $\frac{7}{8} + \frac{1}{8} = (1)$

2 Teach

Using the Student Pages Have students work on page 518 in groups or individually. Provide help as needed and encourage them to draw diagrams or use manipulatives such as **fraction tower cubes***, if necessary. When students finish, discuss the problems with the class. Note that the answers given for problem 2 assume that Mr. Moore did not buy any gasoline on the way to Durango.

Have students work independently on page 519. Those who finish early can play either version of "Fracto" for practice with recognizing fractional areas of circles and rectangles, or "Fractions of 60" (page 435), which reinforces the skill of finding fractions of a number.

GIFTED & TALENTED **Meeting Individual Needs** Have students create an experiment similar to the situation in the Thinking Story. For example, students might put various numbers of red and green **counters*** in different containers, predict which color they are likely to draw from each one, and then try it to see what really happens. Challenge students to explain the difference between what *should* happen, based on mathematical probability, and what *does* happen in the actual event.

Technology Connection Refer students to the software *Math Football: Fractions* or *Touchdown Math: Fractions* from Gamco (Apple, IBM, Mac, for grades 4–12) for practice with adding, subtracting, multiplying, and dividing fractions and mixed numbers and with mixed operations.

*available separately

◆ LESSON 154 Keep in Shape: Fractions and Decimals

Teach

Using the Thinking Story "Iron and Gold" (Part 5) is the last part of the Thinking Story for this unit. It explores how the relative numbers of rubies and pieces of glass in a jar affect the likelihood of picking a specific one. If you wish, review the previous four parts of the Thinking Story, which appear on pages 478–479, 488–489, 504–505, and 512–513.

Answers to Thinking Story Questions:

1. Ferdie chose the wrong jar. It contained more rubies but also more glass jewels—about equal numbers of each. The other jar contained more rubies than glass jewels, so there was a greater chance of drawing a ruby from it.
2. Both jars held as many glass jewels as rubies. No matter which jar Portia chose, she had only one chance out of two. The probability that Portia would draw a ruby is $\frac{1}{2}$, no matter which jar she chose.
3. If Marcus chose the jar on the right, he would have seven chances of drawing a ruby and only one chance of drawing a glass bead. Or, all but one of the jewels in that jar were rubies.
4. Marcus had one chance in eight of failing, and he was evidently just unlucky. Point out that in a class of 24 to 32 students, if everyone took a turn with a probability of success similar to Marcus's, you would expect three or four to draw glass jewels and the rest to draw rubies. Thus the less fortunate outcome is not "impossible."
5. If Manolita took the jar on the right, she was sure to get a ruby because that was the only thing in the jar. The probability of drawing a ruby was 1.
6. Manolita had the best chance: one out of one. Marcus had the next best chance: seven out of eight. Portia had only one chance out of two. Ferdie had the same chance, choosing the full jar. However, if he had chosen the other jar, he would have had a better chance than Portia: about six out of ten, which is better than half.

MATH JOURNAL Have students write in their Math Journals a summary of the entire Thinking Story for this unit and describe something they learned from it.

◆ LESSON 154 Keep in Shape: Fractions and Decimals

THINKING STORY

Iron and Gold

Part 5

You may want to review earlier parts of this Thinking Story on pages 478–479, 488–489, 504–505, and 512–513.

"I was hiding behind the door," said the queen. "And I saw what the steward did. He was trying to cheat you. Now I know that he has been cheating me, too, and stealing money from the Royal Treasury. I will see that he pays for his crimes. But now I want to give you another reward."

The queen set out some glass jars filled with jewels. "The red jewels are rubies and the yellow ones are worthless glass," said the queen. "You may each choose one jewel, but you will be blindfolded so that you can't tell if you are taking a ruby or a piece of glass. I will shake up the jar before you draw, so that you can't remember where a ruby is and reach for it."

These are the first two jars she showed them:

RETEACHING

MANIPULATIVES Provide manipulative materials such as **fraction tower cubes*** that students can use to help them add and subtract simple fractions. Students can also use **play money*** to practice multiplying decimals.

PRACTICE p. 154

LESSON 154 PRACTICE Name__________

Multiply or divide.

1. 1000 × 25.62 = 25,620
2. 1,000,000 × 4.2931 = 4,293,100
3. 10 × 3.85 = 38.5
4. 34.61 ÷ 100 = 0.3461
5. 10,000 × 35.9801 = 359,801
6. 42.34 × 10 = 423.4
7. 476.12 ÷ 1000 = 0.47612
8. 31.8872 ÷ 10,000 = 0.00318872

Multiply.

9. 34.1 × 7 = 238.7
10. 1.305 × 5208 = 6796.44
11. 54.27 × 74 = 4015.98
12. 25.81 × 9 = 232.29
13. 70.2 × 45 = 3159
14. 38 × 12.7 = 482.6

PROBLEM SOLVING **Solve these problems.**

15. Mrs. Ming was baking a cake. She needed $1\frac{3}{4}$ cups sugar for the cake and $2\frac{1}{2}$ cups sugar for the frosting. How much sugar did she need all together? $4\frac{1}{4}$ cups
16. Marco walked $1\frac{3}{8}$ miles from his friend's house. How many miles will Marco walk if he walks to his friend's house and back home? $2\frac{3}{4}$
17. Mr. Hayden bought $3\frac{1}{2}$ feet of rope. He cut off a piece $1\frac{1}{3}$ feet long. How long was the remaining piece of rope? $2\frac{1}{6}$ feet

154 • *Math Explorations and Applications* Level 4

Copyright © SRA/McGraw-Hill. Permission is granted to reproduce this page for classroom use.

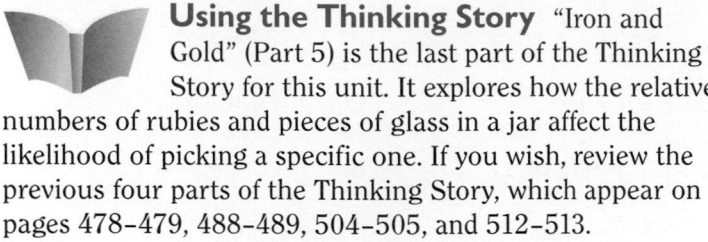

*available separately

Ferdie got the first turn. "I want to draw from the full jar," he said, "because it has the most rubies in it." Ferdie wasn't so lucky, however. He drew a piece of glass.

These are the jars that Portia could choose from:

"I don't think it matters which jar I draw from," Portia said. She drew from the jar that had only two jewels in it, and she got the worthless yellow jewel.

These are the jars Marcus got to draw from:

"I know for sure which jar to choose from," Marcus said. "I'm sure to get a ruby." He picked the jar with only eight jewels. The queen blindfolded him. Then she shook the jar. Marcus reached into it–and got a yellow jewel. "Impossible," he said.

These are the jars Manolita got to choose from:

"Don't feel bad," said Manolita. "When I sell my ruby, I'll share the money with all of you."

. . . the end

Work in groups. Discuss your answers and how you figured them out. Then compare your answers with those of other groups. **Answers are in margin.**

1. Did Ferdie choose the right jar to draw from? Why or why not?
2. Why would Portia say it didn't matter which jar she drew from?
3. Why might Marcus be so sure he would get a ruby?
4. If Marcus chose the right jar, how could he fail to get a ruby?
5. Could Manolita be sure she would get a ruby? How?
6. Of all the children, who had the best chance of getting a ruby? Who had the next best chance? Who had the poorest chance?

ENRICHMENT p. 154

LESSON 154 ENRICHMENT Name________________

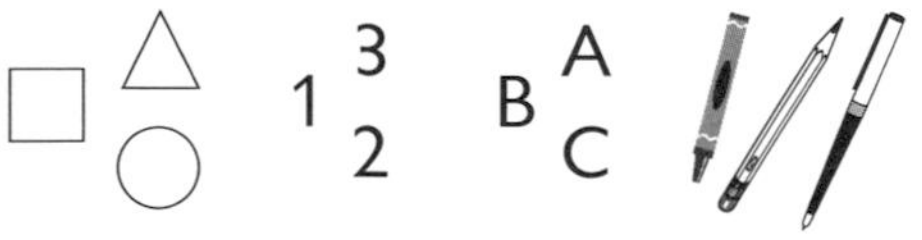

Each box should contain a shape, a letter, a number, and a writing instrument. The shapes have been done for you. Draw the other objects in the correct boxes, using the following clues to decide which box each object goes in.

The crayon is not between the pen and the pencil.

The pencil is not with the square or the triangle.

A is in the box to the left of the circle.

3 is in the box to the right of 2.

1 is in the box with B to the right of the pen.

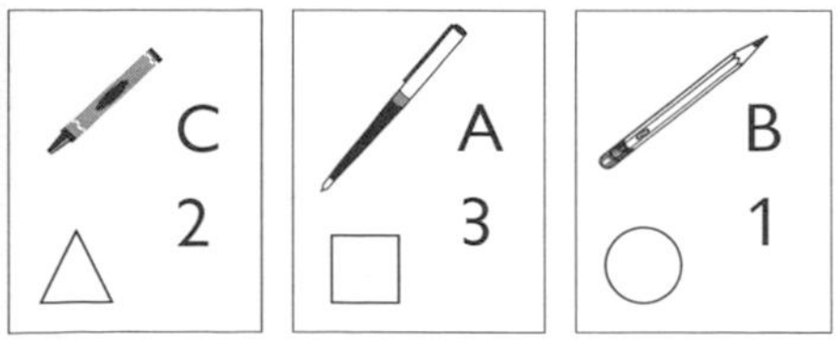

154 • *Math Explorations and Applications* Level 4

Copyright © SRA/McGraw-Hill. Permission is granted to reproduce this page for classroom use.

ASSESSMENT p. 59

UNIT 6 **Mastery Checkpoint 24** Adding and subtracting simple fractions (Lesson 154)

Name ________________

The student demonstrates mastery by correctly answering at least 8 of the 10 problems.

Solve these problems.

1. Martin lives $\frac{3}{4}$ mile from school. Seth lives $\frac{1}{4}$ mile from school. How much farther from school does Martin live? $\frac{1}{2}$ mile
2. Ruth's mother wants to build some bookshelves for Ruth. One will be $3\frac{1}{3}$ feet long and the other will be $2\frac{1}{3}$ feet long. How long of a board does she need for both shelves? $5\frac{2}{3}$ ft.
3. Marie lives $\frac{1}{2}$ mile from school. Chris lives $\frac{1}{2}$ mile beyond Marie. How far from school does Chris live? 1 mile
4. Mr. Carver made three bean salad. He used $\frac{1}{4}$ pound black beans, $\frac{1}{4}$ pound pinto beans, and $\frac{1}{4}$ pound navy beans. How many pounds of beans did he use in all? $\frac{3}{4}$ lb
5. The O'Brien family had $\frac{3}{4}$ dozen eggs. They used $\frac{1}{4}$ dozen for breakfast. How many eggs do they have left? $\frac{1}{2}$ dozen

Copyright © SRA/McGraw-Hill. Permission is granted to reproduce this page for classroom use.

Math Explorations and Applications Level 4 • 59

3 Wrap-Up (5 MINUTES)

In Closing Ask students to contrast a probability of 0 with a probability of 1.

Mastery Checkpoint 24

By this time most students should be able to add and subtract simple fractions. Students should correctly answer at least 5 of the 7 problems on page 518. You may also assign Assessment Blackline Masters pages 59–60 to determine mastery. Record the results of this assessment on the Mastery Checkpoint Chart.

Assessment Criteria

Did the student . . .

✓ communicate strategies used to solve the word problems?

✓ correctly answer at least 5 of the 7 word problems on page 518?

✓ contribute to the Thinking Story discussion?

Homework Have students play the "Fractions of 60" game with a family member. This game provides practice with finding fractions of a number. A copy of this game can also be found on page 26 of the Home Connections Blackline Masters.

LESSON 155 Unit 6 Review

Student Edition pages 522–525

Using the Student Pages Use this Unit 6 Review as a preliminary unit test to indicate areas in which each student is having difficulty or in which the entire class may need help. If students do not do well on the Unit 6 Review, you may spend a day or so helping students overcome their individual difficulties before they take the Unit Test.

Next to each set of problems is a list of the lessons in the unit covered in those problems. Students can refer to a specific lesson for additional instruction if they need help. You can also use this information to make additional assignments based on the previous lesson concepts.

Problems 1–9 If students miss more than one of these comparing-decimals problems, show how 0s can be written to the right of a decimal number without changing its value. When two numbers to be compared do not have the same number of digits to the right of the decimal point, have students write enough 0s to make the number of digits the same. Then have students compare the numbers as though there were no decimal point.

Problems 10–18 Students who miss more than one of these problems on multiplying and dividing decimals by powers of 10 should be assessed to determine the nature of the difficulty. If the trouble is with moving the decimal point in the wrong direction, have the students work with simple problems using **play money*** so that they can easily check whether their answers make sense. If the trouble is moving the decimal point the wrong number of places, give students simple problems for further practice.

Problems 19–24 If students miss more than one of these problems about converting metric units, give extra help as suggested in the appropriate lessons.

Problems 25–26 If students miss either of these problems about measuring with metric units, pair them with students who can measure correctly. Have them measure objects in the room. The students who need help should do the measuring while the other students record the results and check to see that the work is being done correctly. Have **rulers*** available.

ASSESSMENT

LESSON 155 Unit 6 Review

Lessons 139, 141

Replace each ● with <, >, or =.

1. 0.7 ● 0.07 **>**
2. 0.2 ● 0.09 **>**
3. 0.40 ● 1.22 **<**
4. 0.14 ● 0.32 **<**
5. 0.325 ● 0.096 **>**
6. 0.0005 ● 0.008 **<**
7. 0.68 ● 0.86 **<**
8. 0.49 ● 0.049 **>**
9. 1.28 ● 10.28 **<**

Lessons 143, 144

Multiply or divide.

10. 1000 × 1.257 **1257**
11. 100 × 0.037 **3.7**
12. 3.996 ÷ 10 **0.3996**
13. 35.298 × 10 **352.98**
14. 4.73 × 1000 **4730**
15. 100,000 ÷ 10 **10,000**
16. 1000 × 1.87 **1870**
17. 16.49 × 100 **1649**
18. 2.93 ÷ 10,000 **0.000293**

Lesson 145

Solve.

19. 3 dm = ■ m **0.3**
20. 6 dm, 3 cm, 9 mm = ■ m **0.639**
21. 100 cm = ■ m **1**
22. ■ mm = 0.650 m **650**
23. 35 mm = ■ m **0.035**
24. ■ cm = 0.45 m **45**

Lesson 146

Give the length of each object to the nearest centimeter.

25. ■ cm **11**

26. ■ cm **14**

*available separately

Add or subtract.

Lessons 147, 149

(27) 3.6 + 1.5 **5.1** (28) 15.17 − 13.29 **1.88** (29) 6.2 − 2.7 **3.5**

(30) 90.528 − 18.016 **72.512** (31) 12.2 − 8.9 **3.3** (32) 0.03 + 0.31 **0.34**

(33) 20.13 + 9.18 **29.31** (34) 24.26 − 24.01 **0.25** (35) 3.11 + 20.26 **23.37**

Multiply.

Lessons 150, 151

(36) 6 × 3.5 **21** (37) 7 × 0.152 **1.064** (38) 60 × 3.5 **210**

(39) 400 × 1.8 **720** (40) 0.37 × 8 **2.96** (41) 5.316 × 90 **478.44**

(42) 5.41 × 300 **1623** (43) 63.587 × 2 **127.174** (44) 3.425 × 50 **171.25**

Order the following decimals from least to greatest. Insert a < symbol between each pair of numbers to make true statements.

Lesson 140

(45) **0.041 < 0.39 < 0.47 < 0.63 < 1.6 < 2.0**

(45) 1.6, 2.0, 0.47, 0.63, 0.041, 0.39 (46) 0.10, 0.21, 0.008, 0.06, 0.50, 0.49

(46) **0.008 < 0.06 < 0.10 < 0.21 < 0.49 < 0.50**

Change each improper fraction to a mixed number or a whole number.

Lesson 133

(47) $\frac{14}{8}$ $\mathbf{1\frac{3}{4}}$ (48) $\frac{16}{5}$ $\mathbf{3\frac{1}{5}}$ (49) $\frac{12}{3}$ **4** (50) $\frac{10}{9}$ $\mathbf{1\frac{1}{9}}$ (51) $\frac{16}{7}$ $\mathbf{2\frac{2}{7}}$

What fraction of each figure is shaded?

Lesson 126

(52) 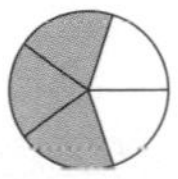 $\mathbf{\frac{3}{5}}$ (53) 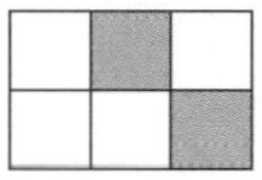 $\mathbf{\frac{2}{6}}$ **or** $\mathbf{\frac{1}{3}}$ (54) 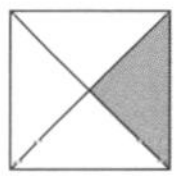 $\mathbf{\frac{1}{4}}$

Solve for *n*.

Lesson 127

(55) $\frac{4}{5}$ of 20 = *n* **16** (56) $\frac{6}{6}$ of 180 = *n* **180** (57) $\frac{4}{10}$ of 100 = *n* **40**

Solve.

If a 0–5 cube is rolled, what is the probability of

Lessons 128, 129, 131

(58) rolling a 2? $\mathbf{\frac{1}{6}}$ (59) rolling a 0 or a 1? $\mathbf{\frac{2}{6}}$ **or** $\mathbf{\frac{1}{3}}$

(60) rolling a 0, 1, 2, 3, 4, or 5? $\mathbf{\frac{6}{6}}$ **or 1** (61) rolling an even number? $\mathbf{\frac{3}{6}}$ **or** $\mathbf{\frac{1}{2}}$

Unit 6 Review • **523**

Problems 27–35 If students miss more than two of these problems on adding and subtracting decimals, check to determine the difficulty. Reteach as necessary, pointing out to students the similarity to whole-number addition problems. Emphasize the importance of lining up the decimals correctly, and explain that 0s can be written to the right of the decimal without changing the number's value.

Problems 36–44 If students miss more than two of these problems on multiplying whole numbers and decimals, check to determine the nature of the trouble. Reteach using an appropriate strategy.

Problems 45–46 If students miss any of the decimal-ordering problems, point out that 0s can be written to the right of each number so that relationships can be seen. Reteach if necessary.

Problems 47–51 If students miss one of these problems on changing improper fractions to a mixed or a whole number, check to see whether the difficulty is with the arithmetic or the conversion steps. Provide reteaching from Lesson 133.

GAME **Problems 52–54** If students miss any of these problems about fractions of geometric figures, check to see whether the errors are from carelessness or whether the students don't understand the concept of a fraction of a shape. Students who do not understand may require special help and might benefit from playing the "Fracto" Game Mats, which provide practice with recognizing fractions of circles and rectangles.

GAME **Problems 55–57** If students miss more than one of these problems about fractions of numbers, first check to be sure that they understand the process. If students are making mistakes in division or multiplication, give extra practice with the facts. The "Four Cube Multiplication" game on page 305 provides practice with multidigit multiplication and place value. The multiplication version of the "Roll a Problem" game on page 325 also reinforces the skill of using multidigit multiplication and place value. The "Diviso" game on page 367 provides further practice with division and mental factorization, along with the "Four Cube Division" game on page 374.

Problems 58–61 If students miss one or more of these probability problems because they don't understand the concept, provide extra help. Explain the fractions of probability using a Number Cube (0–5), and, if necessary, demonstrate by rolling a cube.

◆ LESSON 155 Unit 6 Review

Problems 62–70 Provide extra teaching to students who miss more than two of these word problems. Allow students to use drawings to solve the problems.

Problems 71–90 Provide additional help for students who have difficulty adding and subtracting fractions and mixed numbers. Check to see whether the difficulty is with simple arithmetic or the process.

Problems 91–96 If students miss more than one of the rounding problems, provide reteaching. If necessary, have students draw number lines so that they can see the relationships.

Problems 97–100 Provide extra teaching for students who miss one or more of the word problems involving fractions and mixed numbers. Allow students to draw illustrations that may help them with solving these problems.

◆ LESSON 155 Unit 6 Review

Answer the following questions.

Lesson 134

62. How many inches are there in 7 feet? **84**
63. How many feet are there in 19 yards? **57**

Solve these problems.

Lessons 130, 132, 148, 149, 151, 154

64. Mark bought 2 pounds of popcorn. He popped half of it last week. How much popcorn is left? **1 pound**
65. Wayne had $342.38 in his checking account. He wrote a check for $37.49. How much did he then have in his account? **$304.89**
66. Priscilla bought some nails and screws at the hardware store. The bill came to $2.47. How much change should she get if she gives the clerk a $5 bill? **$2.53**
67. Which has more juice, a 1.4-liter can of juice or two 750-milliliter cans of juice? **two 750-mL cans**
68. Ten copies of a book weigh 45 kilograms. How much does each copy of the book weigh? **4.5 kg**
69. Terry had the flu, and his temperature was 102.3°F. The next day his temperature was 99.4°F. How much did his temperature drop? **2.9°F**
70. Rebecca took 36 foul shots and made 20 of them. Did she miss more than $\frac{1}{4}$ of the shots? **yes**

RETEACHING

Students who have difficulty with this Unit Review should have further opportunity to review and to practice the skills before they proceed. For each set of problems there are specific suggestions for reteaching. These suggestions can be found in the margins.

Add or subtract the following fractions and mixed numbers. Show answers as whole numbers, or as mixed numbers or proper fractions reduced to lowest terms.

Lessons 133, 136, 137

71. $\frac{3}{5} + \frac{1}{5}$ $\mathbf{\frac{4}{5}}$ 72. $8\frac{5}{12} - 3\frac{1}{12}$ $\mathbf{5\frac{1}{3}}$ 73. $9\frac{5}{16} - 7\frac{3}{4}$ $\mathbf{1\frac{9}{16}}$ 74. $5\frac{1}{2} + 2\frac{2}{3}$ $\mathbf{8\frac{1}{6}}$
75. $\frac{1}{3} + \frac{2}{3}$ **1** 76. $4\frac{5}{16} - 3\frac{1}{8}$ $\mathbf{1\frac{3}{16}}$ 77. $9\frac{5}{16} + 7\frac{3}{4}$ $\mathbf{17\frac{1}{16}}$ 78. $2\frac{2}{5} + 1\frac{1}{2}$ $\mathbf{3\frac{9}{10}}$
79. $1\frac{2}{3} + 2\frac{2}{3}$ $\mathbf{4\frac{1}{3}}$ 80. $5\frac{3}{16} - 2\frac{3}{4}$ $\mathbf{2\frac{7}{16}}$ 81. $1\frac{2}{3} + 3\frac{1}{4}$ $\mathbf{4\frac{11}{12}}$ 82. $2\frac{2}{5} - 1\frac{1}{2}$ $\mathbf{\frac{9}{10}}$
83. $3\frac{1}{16} + 5\frac{1}{4}$ $\mathbf{8\frac{5}{16}}$ 84. $2\frac{4}{5} + 1\frac{9}{10}$ $\mathbf{4\frac{7}{10}}$ 85. $3\frac{1}{4} - 1\frac{2}{3}$ $\mathbf{1\frac{7}{12}}$ 86. $3\frac{1}{10} - 2\frac{1}{2}$ $\mathbf{\frac{3}{5}}$
87. $10\frac{4}{5} - 7\frac{3}{5}$ $\mathbf{3\frac{1}{5}}$ 88. $2\frac{4}{5} - 1\frac{9}{10}$ $\mathbf{\frac{9}{10}}$ 89. $5\frac{1}{2} - 2\frac{2}{3}$ $\mathbf{2\frac{5}{6}}$ 90. $3\frac{1}{10} + 2\frac{1}{2}$ $\mathbf{5\frac{3}{5}}$

Round each number to the nearest hundredth.

Lesson 142

91. 4.8352 **4.84** 92. 0.0031 **0.00** 93. 2.394 **2.39**

Round each number to the nearest thousandth.

94. 0.0072 **0.007** 95. 4.0013 **4.001** 96. 1.2345 **1.234 or 1.235**

PROBLEM SOLVING

Solve these problems.

Lessons 133, 136, 137

97. A cake recipe calls for $2\frac{2}{3}$ cups of sugar. The recipe for the frosting to go with the cake calls for $1\frac{1}{2}$ cups of sugar. How much sugar is that all together? $\mathbf{4\frac{1}{6}}$ **cups**

98. One teaspoon of sugar substitute can replace $\frac{1}{3}$ cup of sugar. If 2 teaspoons of the substitute are used in the cake, how much sugar should be used? **2 cups**

99. If 2 teaspoons of the substitute are also used in the frosting, how much sugar should be used in the frosting? $\mathbf{\frac{5}{6}}$ **cups**

100. If you make the substitutions suggested in problems 98 and 99, how much regular sugar will be in the combined cake and frosting? $\mathbf{2\frac{5}{6}}$ **cups**

ALTERNATIVE ASSESSMENT

Portfolio Assessment If you have not already completed the Portfolio Assessment task provided on Assessment Blackline Masters page 98, it can be used at this time to evaluate students' ability to use fractions to alter a recipe for various numbers of servings.

ALTERNATIVE ASSESSMENT

Performance Assessment Performance Assessment Task 2, provided on Assessment Blackline Masters pages 89–90, can be used at this time to evaluate students' proficiency with understanding decimals. You may want to administer this assessment to individual students or small groups of students.

Unit Project If you have not already assigned the "Fairlawn School Buys a Computer" project on pages 532 and 533, you may want to do so at this time. This project is a good opportunity for students to analyze and design a fund-raising event and consider notions of "fairness" with respect to pricing, advertising, and raising funds for a useful cause.

PRACTICE p. 155

LESSON 155 PRACTICE Name________

Add or subtract.

1. 1.45 + 6.92 = 8.37
2. 0.04 + 5.83 = 5.87
3. 75.408 − 13.716 = 61.692
4. 40.34 + 23.67 = 64.01
5. 12.78 − 3.89 = 8.89
6. 5.3 − 2.8 = 2.5

Multiply or divide.

7. 10,000 × 45.702 = 457,020
8. 5.23 × 10 = 52.3
9. 76.2309 ÷ 1000 = 0.0762309
10. 125.06 ÷ 10 = 12.506
11. 1,000,000 × 8.28076 = 8,280,760
12. 10,000 ÷ 100 = 100

Multiply.

13. 6.24 × 400 = 2496
14. 2.915 × 8 = 23.32
15. 6 × 0.109 = 0.654
16. 48.27 × 3 = 144.81
17. 5 × 0.067 = 0.335
18. 70 × 4.38 = 306.6

Add or subtract. Write your answer as a whole number, if possible, or as a mixed number or proper fraction reduced to lowest terms.

19. $\frac{2}{3} + 3\frac{1}{3} =$ 4
20. $7\frac{1}{16} + 2\frac{1}{4} =$ $9\frac{5}{16}$
21. $4\frac{1}{2} + 1\frac{3}{10} =$ $5\frac{4}{5}$
22. $4\frac{1}{2} - 1\frac{3}{10} =$ $3\frac{1}{5}$
23. $3\frac{3}{8} - 1\frac{3}{16} =$ $2\frac{3}{16}$
24. $3\frac{3}{8} + 1\frac{3}{16} =$ $4\frac{9}{16}$

Copyright © SRA/McGraw-Hill. Permission is granted to reproduce this page for classroom use.

Math Explorations and Applications Level 4 • 155

ENRICHMENT p. 155

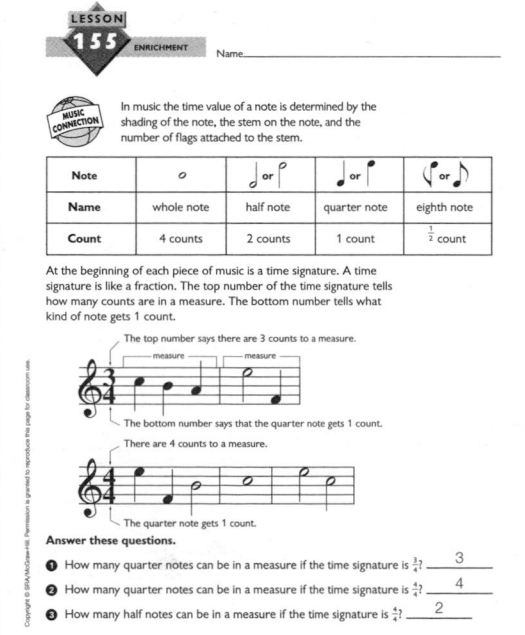

LESSON 155 ENRICHMENT Name________

MUSIC CONNECTION

In music the time value of a note is determined by the shading of the note, the stem on the note, and the number of flags attached to the stem.

Note	𝅝	𝅗𝅥 or 𝅗𝅥	♩ or ♩	♪ or ♪
Name	whole note	half note	quarter note	eighth note
Count	4 counts	2 counts	1 count	$\frac{1}{2}$ count

At the beginning of each piece of music is a time signature. A time signature is like a fraction. The top number of the time signature tells how many counts are in a measure. The bottom number tells what kind of note gets 1 count.

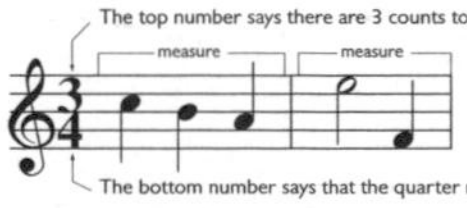
The top number says there are 3 counts to a measure.
measure
measure
The bottom number says that the quarter note gets 1 count.

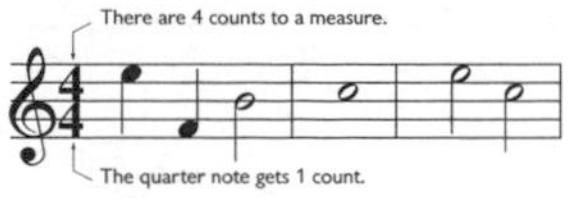
There are 4 counts to a measure.
The quarter note gets 1 count.

Answer these questions.

1. How many quarter notes can be in a measure if the time signature is $\frac{3}{4}$? 3
2. How many quarter notes can be in a measure if the time signature is $\frac{4}{4}$? 4
3. How many half notes can be in a measure if the time signature is $\frac{4}{4}$? 2

Copyright © SRA/McGraw-Hill. Permission is granted to reproduce this page for classroom use.

Math Explorations and Applications Level 4 • 155

LESSON 156

Student Edition pages 526–529

Unit 6 Practice

Using the Student Pages The purpose of these pages is to provide additional practice for those students who demonstrated a need for it on the Unit Review. You may wish to assign only the specific exercises in this Unit Practice in which students need further reinforcement. Listed in the margin beside each instruction line are the lessons covered in the unit so that you or the students can refer to the specific lesson for additional review and instruction.

GAME Students who do not require additional practice on specific concepts may enjoy playing any of the games you have played so far, such as the "Fractions of 60" game on page 435. This game provides practice with finding fractions of a number and addition. These students may also help by practicing flash card drills and playing appropriate games with students who need remedial practice or by actually teaching certain procedures to other students.

You may want to use Cumulative Review page 569 after this lesson.

MIXED PRACTICE

LESSON 156

Unit 6 Practice

Replace each ● with <, >, or =.

Lessons 139, 141

1. 0.3 ● 0.4 **<**
2. 0.65 ● 0.6 **>**
3. 0.67 ● 0.33 **>**
4. 0.2 ● 0.02 **>**
5. 0.55 ● 0.60 **<**
6. 0.305 ● 0.810 **<**
7. 0.2 ● 0.003 **>**
8. 0.15 ● 0.07 **>**
9. 0.265 ● 0.260 **>**
10. 0.07 ● 0.007 **>**
11. 0.9 ● 0.99 **<**
12. 0.5 ● 0.050 **>**

Solve.

Lesson 145

13. 100 cm = ■ m **1**
14. ■ mm = 1 cm **10**
15. 3 dm, 2 cm, 5 mm = ■ m **0.32**
16. 400 cm = ■ m **4**
17. ■ cm = 1 dm **10**
18. 2 dm, 0 cm, 6 mm = ■ m **0.206**
19. 1 dm = ■ m **0.1**
20. ■ dm = 1 m **10**
21. 6 dm, 5 mm = ■ m **0.605**
22. 5 dm = ■ m **0.5**
23. 45 mm = ■ m **0.045**
24. 8 cm, 5 mm = ■ m **0.085**

Follow the directions and answer the questions.

Lessons 126, 133

25. Draw a circle. Shade $\frac{2}{4}$ of it. Then shade another $\frac{1}{4}$ of it.
26. Draw another circle the same size as the one you drew in problem 25. Shade $\frac{3}{4}$ of it.
27. What is $\frac{1}{4} + \frac{2}{4}$? **$\frac{3}{4}$**
28. Draw a rectangle. Shade $\frac{3}{4}$ of it. What fraction is **not** shaded? **$\frac{1}{4}$**
29. What is $\frac{4}{4} - \frac{3}{4}$? **$\frac{1}{4}$**

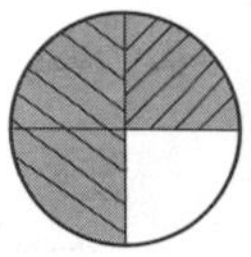

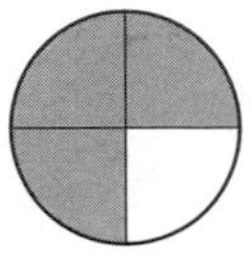

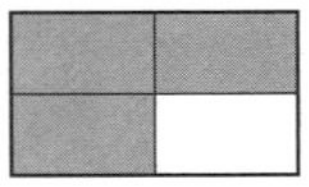

Solve for *n*.

Lesson 127

30. $n = \frac{1}{2}$ of 24 **12**
31. $n = \frac{1}{8}$ of 32 **4**
32. $n = \frac{2}{6}$ of 30 **10**
33. $n = \frac{3}{4}$ of 24 **18**
34. $n = \frac{1}{3}$ of 30 **10**
35. $n = \frac{2}{4}$ of 24 **12**
36. $n = \frac{3}{8}$ of 24 **9**
37. $n = \frac{2}{3}$ of 60 **40**
38. $n = \frac{6}{8}$ of 24 **18**
39. $n = \frac{1}{4}$ of 32 **8**
40. $n = \frac{1}{6}$ of 30 **5**
41. $n = \frac{2}{4}$ of 32 **16**

Solve these problems.

Lessons 130, 132, 148, 149, 151, 154

42 Selena had $65.00 in her checking account.

a. She deposited $25.00. How much did she have then in her account? **$90.00**

b. She wrote a check for $38.00. How much does she now have in her account? **$52.00**

c. Does she have enough money to buy a sweater that costs $16.99 and a pair of shoes that costs $34.99? **yes**

43 Bruce had two quarters and two dimes. Then he found a $1 bill. How much money does he have? **$1.70**

44 Maya bought some vegetables. The grocer charged her $1.74. If Maya paid with a $5 bill, how much change did she get? **$3.26**

45 It is 1.4 kilometers from Ethan's house to the museum. How far is it there and back? **2.8 km**

46 The doorway in Makio's classroom is 85 centimeters wide. Can a table that is 1 meter wide fit through the doorway without being tilted? **no**

47 Janis says she is 140 centimeters tall. Grace says she is 1.35 meters tall.

a. Who is taller? **Janis**

b. By how much? **5 cm**

48 Callie wants to find out the weight of a paper clip. She weighs 100 clips and finds out that they weigh 50 grams. How much does one paper clip weigh? **0.5 g**

49 In the running broad jump, Bennett jumped 6.21 meters. His opponent, Judd, jumped 6.16 meters.

a. Who won? **Bennett**

b. By how many centimeters? **5**

◆ LESSON 156 Unit 6 Practice

◆ LESSON 156 Unit 6 Practice

New City has 150 parking meters in its downtown shopping area.

People must pay 10 cents per hour if they park their cars from 8 A.M. to 6 P.M., Monday through Saturday. Parking is free on Sunday. The chief of police estimates that each meter is in use about half of the time.

COOPERATIVE LEARNING **Work in groups to solve these problems. Be sure to explain how you get your answers.**

Lessons 127, 130, 147, 150

50. About how much money do the parking meters take in during one week? **$450**
51. The monthly cost to repair the meters and collect the money is about $500. About how much profit does New City get from its parking meters each year? **$17,400**
52. If New City raises parking fees to 20 cents per hour, the chief of police estimates that the meters will be in use only $\frac{1}{3}$ of the time. Will the meters produce more profit at the new rate or the old rate? Explain your reasoning. **the new rate; $600 > $450**

Round each number to the nearest hundredth.

Lesson 142

53. 1.48721 **1.49**
54. 6.489 **6.49**
55. 241.7911 **241.79**

Round each number to the nearest thousandth.

56. 61.00213 **61.002**
57. 8.54762 **8.548**
58. 21.3981 **21.398**

RETEACHING

Students who have difficulty with this Unit Practice should have further opportunity to review and to practice the skills before they proceed. Beside each set of problems is a reference to the lesson or lessons from which the problems were taken. You may want to review the individual lessons with students who are having difficulty with them.

Students can use a blank **Cruncher*** spreadsheet to create a table for recording the results of a coin toss and comparing the actual results with the predicted outcome.

COOPERATIVE LEARNING

Perform the following experiments with two friends. One of you keeps records, one flips the coins or rolls the cubes, and the third person keeps track of the total number of rolls or flips.

Lessons 128, 129, 131

59. Flip a coin 100 times. How often did it land heads up? About what fraction of the time did it land heads up? (Pick the answer that's closest to your result.)
   a. None of the time **b.** $\frac{1}{4}$ of the time **c.** $\frac{1}{2}$ of the time
   d. $\frac{3}{4}$ of the time **e.** All the time
   The answer should be about $\frac{1}{2}$ of the time.

60. If you flip a coin once, what is the probability that it will land heads up? **$\frac{1}{2}$**

Roll a 0–5 cube 120 times. Keep track of the number of times you get each number. Answer these questions.

Lessons 128, 129, 131

61. About what fraction of the time did you roll a 0? A 5?
   a. $\frac{0}{6}$ **b.** $\frac{1}{6}$ **c.** $\frac{2}{6}$ **d.** $\frac{3}{6}$ **e.** $\frac{4}{6}$ **f.** $\frac{5}{6}$
   The answer should be close to $\frac{1}{6}$.

62. How many times did you roll an even number?
   The answer should be close to 60.

Answer these questions.

63. If you flip a penny and a nickel (or any two coins) together 100 times, how many times do you think you'll get zero heads? One head? Two heads? Then put your predictions on a chart like the one shown.

64. Now try it. Keep a tally. You can change your predictions after a few flips.

65. Were your predictions close?

Heads	How Many Times in 100 Flips: Predicted	How Many Times in 100 Flips: Actual
0	**25**	**Answers**
1	**50**	**will**
2	**25**	**vary.**

Use the Cumulative Review on page 569 after this lesson.

PRACTICE p. 156

LESSON 156 PRACTICE Name____________

Draw <, >, or = to make each statement true.

1. 0.345 (>) 0.340
2. 0.23 (>) 0.023
3. 0.004 (<) 0.4
4. 0.01 (=) 0.010
5. 0.75 (>) 0.70
6. 0.412 (<) 0.634
7. 0.8 (<) 0.88
8. 0.35 (>) 0.04
9. 0.9 (>) 0.83

Find the value of the missing number.

1 meter = 10 decimeters = 100 centimeters = 1000 millimeters
1 m = 10 dm = 100 cm = 1000 mm

10. __40__ dm = 4 m
11. 1 dm = __100__ mm
12. 200 cm = __2__ m
13. 50 dm = __5__ m
14. __3__ dm = 300 mm
15. 2 dm, 6 cm, 7 mm = __0.267__ m
16. 9 dm, 4 mm = __0.904__ m
17. 38 m = __38,000__ mm

Draw a circle. Then shade the appropriate fraction.

18. Shade $\frac{3}{6}$ of it. Then shade another $\frac{1}{6}$ of it.

Check students' drawings.

19. Shade $\frac{2}{3}$ of it.

Copyright © SRA/McGraw-Hill. Permission is granted to reproduce this page for classroom use.

ENRICHMENT p. 156

LESSON 156 ENRICHMENT Name____________

MUSIC CONNECTION

In each case fill in the time signature ($\frac{4}{4}$, $\frac{3}{4}$, or $\frac{2}{4}$).

4/4
Two or more eighth notes next to each other can be written with the flags connected.
3/4
2/4

Answer these questions.

1. If the time signature is $\frac{4}{4}$, how many quarter notes can be in a measure that has only quarter notes? __4__
2. If the time signature is $\frac{4}{4}$, how many eighth notes can be in a measure that has only eighth notes? __8__
3. If the time signature is $\frac{4}{4}$, how many half notes can be in a measure that has only half notes? __2__
4. If the time signature is $\frac{4}{4}$, how many whole notes can be in a measure? __1__
5. If the time signature is $\frac{3}{4}$, how many quarter notes can be in a measure that has only quarter notes? __3__

Copyright © SRA/McGraw-Hill. Permission is granted to reproduce this page for classroom use.

*available separately

UNIT 6

Student Edition pages 530–531

Unit Test

Using the Student Pages The Unit 6 Test on Student Edition pages 530 and 531 provides an opportunity to formally evaluate your students' proficiency with concepts developed in this unit. It is similar in content and format to the Unit 6 Review. Students who did well on the Unit 6 Review may not need to take this test. Students who did not do well on the Unit 6 Review should be provided with additional practice opportunities, such as the Unit 6 Practice pages, before taking the Unit 6 Test. For further evaluation, you may wish to have these students also take the Unit 6 Test in standardized format, provided on Assessment Blackline Masters pages 149–158 or the Unit 6 Test on Assessment Blackline Masters pages 61–64.

Unit Test

Replace each ● with <, >, or =.

1. 0.04 ● 0.3 **<**
2. 1.5 ● 1.06 **>**
3. 0.025 ● 0.007 **>**
4. 0.08 ● 0.003 **>**
5. 0.75 ● 0.80 **<**
6. 0.750 ● 1.000 **<**
7. 7.82 ● 7.082 **>**
8. 2.49 ● 2.491 **<**
9. 0.840 ● 0.084 **>**

Multiply or divide.

10. 1.652 × 100 **165.2**
11. 12.4 ÷ 1000 **0.0124**
12. 10 × 0.18 **1.8**
13. 10 × 1.3 **13**
14. 1000 × 1.3 **1300**
15. 100 × 0.14 **14**
16. 12.07 ÷ 10 **1.207**
17. 3.821 ÷ 100 **0.03821**
18. 5.329 × 10,000 **53,290**
19. 16.5 ÷ 100 **0.165**
20. 2.93 × 1000 **2930**
21. 862.7 × 10 **8627**

Solve.

22. ■ dm = 0.3 m **3**
23. ■ cm = 0.4 m **40**
24. 65 mm = ■ m **0.065**
25. 2 dm, 5 cm = ■ m **0.25**

Round each number to the nearest hundredth.

26. 241.612 **241.61**
27. 81.356 **81.36**
28. 1.0042 **1.00**
29. 17.43111 **17.43**
30. 21.1172 **21.12**
31. 4.0163 **4.02**

Round each number to the nearest thousandth.

32. 1643.21891 **1643.219**
33. 17.00129 **17.001**
34. 1.0041 **1.004**
35. 2.48163 **2.482**
36. 19.8122 **19.812**
37. 7.9116 **7.912**

Add or subtract.

38. 40.53 + 40.85 **81.38**
39. 30.0 − 0.0345 **29.9655**
40. 1.57 + 63.97 **68.5**
41. 26.47 − 16.18 **10.29**
42. 16.774 + 28.845 **45.619**
43. 15.62 − 1.80 **13.8**
44. 0.051 + 27.754 **27.805**
45. 8.5 − 7.9 **0.6**
46. 83.79 − 72.91 **10.**
47. 2.91 − 1.62 **1.29**
48. 29.01 + 15.42 **44.43**
49. 16.8 − 15.2 **1.6**

Multiply.

50. 2 × 7.2 **14.4**
51. 40 × 2.3 **92**
52. 40,000 × 8.73 **349,200**
53. 0.241 × 70 **16.87**
54. 27.38 × 600 **16,428**
55. 7.49 × 30 **224.7**
56. 300 × 5.11 **1533**
57. 4.0 × 10 **40**
58. 65.25 × 2.82 **184.005**

What fraction of each figure is shaded?

59. 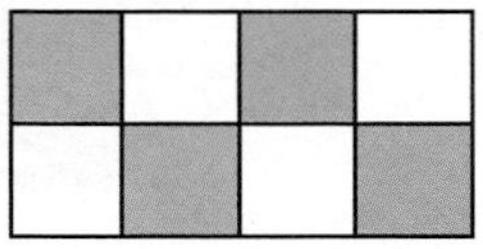 **$\frac{4}{8}$ or $\frac{1}{2}$**

60. 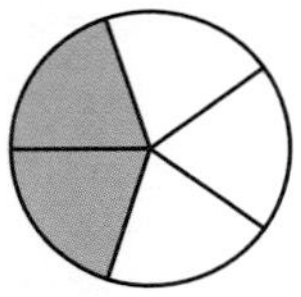 **$\frac{2}{5}$**

Solve for *n*.

61. $\frac{1}{2}$ of 62 = n **31**
62. $\frac{5}{6}$ of 42 = n **35**
63. $n = \frac{1}{4} + \frac{2}{4}$ **$\frac{3}{4}$**
64. $\frac{2}{3}$ of 45 = n **30**
65. $\frac{1}{3}$ of 90 = n **30**
66. $n = \frac{5}{8} - \frac{2}{8}$ **$\frac{3}{8}$**
67. $\frac{3}{10}$ of 1000 = n **300**
68. $\frac{1}{10}$ of 50 = n **5**
69. $n = \frac{3}{6} + \frac{3}{6}$ **$\frac{6}{6}$ or 1**

PROBLEM SOLVING

Solve these problems.

70. If you roll a 5–10 cube one time, what is the probability of rolling an odd number? **$\frac{3}{6}$ or $\frac{1}{2}$**
71. If you roll a 0–5 cube 600 times, how many times would you expect to roll a 4? **about 100**
72. Tasha has three quarters and three dimes. How much more money does she need to buy a notebook that costs $1.25 with tax included? **20¢**
73. Rodney lives on a block that is rectangular. It is 0.25 kilometer long and 0.10 kilometer wide. How far does Rodney jog when he jogs around the block once? **0.7 km**
74. It takes Amy one-half hour to walk home from school. If she leaves school at 3:30 P.M., when will she get home? **4:00 P.M.**
75. Joe needs 20 more minutes to finish his homework. It is now 4:55 P.M. What time will he finish? **5:15 P.M.**

ASSESSMENT p. 61

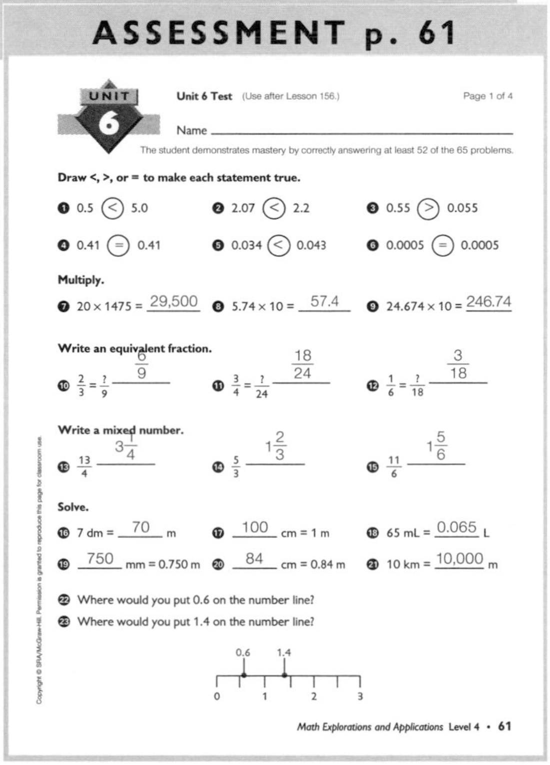

UNIT 6 Unit 6 Test (Use after Lesson 156.) Page 1 of 4

Name ____________

The student demonstrates mastery by correctly answering at least 52 of the 65 problems.

Draw <, >, or = to make each statement true.

1. 0.5 (<) 5.0
2. 2.07 (<) 2.2
3. 0.55 (>) 0.055
4. 0.41 (=) 0.41
5. 0.034 (<) 0.043
6. 0.0005 (=) 0.0005

Multiply.

7. 20 × 1475 = 29,500
8. 5.74 × 10 = 57.4
9. 24.674 × 10 = 246.74

Write an equivalent fraction.

10. $\frac{2}{3} = \frac{?}{9}$ $\frac{6}{9}$
11. $\frac{3}{4} = \frac{?}{24}$ $\frac{18}{24}$
12. $\frac{1}{6} = \frac{?}{18}$ $\frac{3}{18}$

Write a mixed number.

13. $\frac{13}{4}$ $3\frac{1}{4}$
14. $\frac{5}{3}$ $1\frac{2}{3}$
15. $\frac{11}{6}$ $1\frac{5}{6}$

Solve.

16. 7 dm = 70 m
17. 100 cm = 1 m
18. 65 mL = 0.065 L
19. 750 mm = 0.750 m
20. 84 cm = 0.84 m
21. 10 km = 10,000 m

22. Where would you put 0.6 on the number line?
23. Where would you put 1.4 on the number line?

0.6 1.4
0 1 2 3

Copyright © SRA/McGraw-Hill. Permission is granted to reproduce this page for classroom use.

UNIT 6

Student Edition pages 532–533

Wrap-Up

PRESENTING THE PROJECT

Project Objectives

- ▶ to provide experience in analyzing and designing a fund-raising event
- ▶ to introduce notions of "fairness" with respect to pricing, advertising, and raising funds for a useful cause

Discuss as a class the questions and answers on pages 532 and 533. If appropriate, allow students to embark on a long-term project to raise funds for a local charity or to purchase materials for their classroom. Use a blank **Cruncher*** spreadsheet to help answer the project questions.

COOPERATIVE LEARNING **Minds on Math** SRA's *Minds on Math* is a series of units covering Problem Solving, Data Collection, Number Sense, Measurement, Money, and Geometry and Spatial Relations. Each unit provides a series of open-ended projects for individuals or small groups. These projects develop problem-solving and critical-thinking skills, utilize real-world materials, emphasize language, and integrate cross-curricular connections. Use projects from *Measuring* to investigate a variety of nonstandard and standard units.

UNIT 6 WRAP-UP

PROJECT

Fairlawn School Buys a Computer

The 25 students in the fourth grade at Fairlawn School are raising $800 to buy a computer. They decided to sell apples to pay for the computer. They can purchase a bushel of apples for $15. They found that there are, on the average, 100 apples in a bushel.

1. What is a fair price at which the children should resell the apples? Remember, they have to make enough money to pay for the apples *and* to buy the computer. **Accept reasonable answers. The resale price must be more than 15¢ pe app**
2. What other information will help the class set a fair price? **knowing what other suppliers charge for a bushel of apples**

Pricing the Apples

The children visited neighborhood stores and found that the price of apples was as low as 18 cents each in one store and as high as 28 cents each in another store. After much discussion, the children decided to charge 25¢ for each apple.

3. Based on 100 apples in a bushel, by how much did they mark up the price of an apple? **10¢**
4. How many apples will they have to sell to make $800? **8000**
5. How many apples should each child be expected to sell? **320**
6. How much money will the class have to invest to purchase the apples? **$1200**

*available separately

Advertising the Apples

The principal of Fairlawn School said the class could have free advertising space in the school-parent newsletter if the students would write their own advertisement. The class couldn't agree on which of the following three advertisements would be most useful.

COOPERATIVE LEARNING

Discuss the following questions in small groups.

7. Which advertisement is the fairest? Which is the most unfair? **the second; the third**
8. Which advertisement will most likely produce the most sales? **the second**
9. Write a fair advertisement for the Fairlawn School's fourth-grade class. Decorate the advertisement so it will attract attention. **Check students' advertisements.**
10. Besides selling apples, what are some other ways for a fourth-grade class to raise money? **bake sale, flower sale**
11. Could your classroom benefit from a computer or other equipment that will improve your education?
12. About how much money will it cost? If you don't know, where would you go to find the price?

Costs will vary depending on model, equipment, etc.

Develop a plan to raise the needed money. Be sure your plan is fair.

What Is a Math Project? If this is the first time you have used math projects in your classroom, you may want to refer to pages 96–97 in this Teacher's Guide for more detailed information about effectively implementing and assessing projects.

Homework Have students write a plan for a fund-raising event for a cause of their choice. Ask them to specify the cause, how the money raised would be used, and their fund-raising goals and strategies.

Wrapping Up the Project Allow students to come up with their own ideas for improving the fund-raising project on pages 532 and 533.

Assessing the Project Note those students who were most involved in the project and the project discussions, and also note those who did not participate as much. Try to persuade those students who did not to brainstorm reasons why it might be good to participate in a project.

Real-World Connection Invite interested students to watch public television or listen to a public radio station during a fund-raising drive. How do the stations raise the money? Why do they need to raise the money? How much do they raise?

Why teach it at this time?

Although this project could be done at any time, it is included here because this unit includes considerable work with money.

Cumulative Review

Use after Lesson 4.

Write the numbers in standard form.

1. 40 + 7 **47**
2. 800 + 20 + 7 **827**
3. 3000 + 600 + 50 + 1 **3651**
4. 6000 + 100 + 0 + 0 **6100**
5. 40,000 + 500 + 70 + 2 **40,572**
6. 5 + 600 + 80,000 + 100,000 **180,605**
7. 300,000 + 4,000 + 70 **304,070**
8. 2,000,000 + 40,000 + 6,000 + 800 + 10 **2,046,810**
9. 500,000 + 200 **500,200**
10. 3 + 80 + 200 + 40,000 + 90,000,000 **90,040,283**
11. 20,000,000 + 500,000 + 80,000 + 100 + 9 **20,580,109**

Count up or down. Write the missing numbers.

12. 15, 16, 17, ■, ■, ■, ■, ■, 23 **18, 19, 20, 21, 22**
13. 97, 98, 99, ■, ■, ■, ■, 104 **100, 101, 102, 103**
14. 403, 402, 401, ■, ■, ■, ■, ■, 395 **400, 399, 398, 397, 396**
15. 45,677; 45,678; 45,679; ■; ■; ■; ■; 45,684 **45,680; 45,681; 45,682; 45,683**
16. 1,000,204; 1,000,203; 1,000,202; ■; ■; ■; ■; 1,000,197 **1,000,201; 1,000,200; 1,000,199; 1,000,198**

Write the greatest number and the least number.

17. Use the digits 4, 2, 8, and 5. **greatest = 8542; least = 2458**
18. Use the digits 3, 9, 1, 0, and 6. **greatest = 96,310; least = 10,369**

Write six different numbers in order from greatest to least.

19. Use the digits 5, 7, and 9. **975, 957, 795, 759, 597, 579**
20. Use the digits 1, 4, and 8. **841, 814, 481, 418, 184, 148**

Cumulative Review

Use after Lesson 9.

Add or subtract to solve for *n*.

1. 7 + 6 = *n* **13**
2. 4 + 9 = *n* **13**
3. 14 − 9 = *n* **5**
4. 8 − 7 = *n* **1**
5. 13 − 8 = *n* **5**
6. *n* = 16 − 8 **8**
7. 8 + 9 = *n* **17**
8. *n* = 5 + 6 **11**
9. 8 + 3 = *n* **11**
10. *n* = 4 + 8 **12**
11. 12 − 6 = *n* **6**
12. *n* = 15 − 6 **9**

Add or subtract.

13. 17 − 9 = **8**
14. 6 + 5 + 1 + 3 = **15**
15. 5 + 3 + 2 + 3 + 2 = **15**
16. 10 − 4 = **6**
17. 8 − 7 = **1**
18. 6 − 0 = **6**

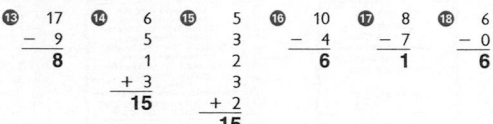

Use a computer or other means to copy and complete each chart. Watch the function rule.

19. −7

In	Out
19	■ **12**
16	■ **9**
14	■ **7**
11	■ **4**

20. +10

In	Out
0	■ **10**
3	■ **13**
8	■ **18**
10	■ **20**

ALGEBRA READINESS

Solve for *n*.

21. *n* + 4 = 9 **5**
22. 7 − *n* = 2 **5**
23. 18 + *n* = 25 **7**

PROBLEM SOLVING

Solve these problems.

24. Clem owns seven horses. He needs 12 horses to open a riding stable. How many more horses does he need? **5**
25. Daria had $9. Then she did chores and earned $8. Does she have enough money to buy a CD that costs $14? **yes**

Cumulative Review

Use after Lesson 13.

Use the chart to answer questions 1–5.

Population Growth of Four States

State	1970	1980	1990
Colorado	2,209,596	2,889,735	3,294,394
Iowa	2,825,368	2,913,808	2,776,755
Kentucky	3,220,711	3,660,324	3,685,296
Nevada	488,738	800,508	1,201,833

1. Which state had the greatest population in 1970? In 1980? In 1990? **Kentucky had the greatest population in all three decades.**
2. Name the state or states that had a greater population in 1990 than in 1980. **Colorado, Kentucky, Nevada**
3. Which state nearly doubled in population between 1970 and 1980? **Nevada**
4. Which state, if any, gained in population between 1970 and 1980 and lost in population between 1980 and 1990? **Iowa**
5. Which state had close to a million people in 1980? **Nevada**

Add or subtract.

6. 45 + 34 = **79**
7. 73 + 18 = **91**
8. 84 − 54 = **30**
9. 50 − 26 = **24**
10. 269 + 407 = **676**
11. 784 − 512 = **272**
12. 472 − 385 = **87**
13. 8592 + 3714 = **12,306**
14. 2003 + 5458 = **7461**
15. 269 − 182 = **87**
16. 660 + 299 = **959**
17. 750 + 250 = **1000**
18. 481 − 101 = **380**
19. 357 + 728 = **1085**
20. 1000 − 545 = **455**

Cumulative Review

Use after Lesson 17.

Replace ● with <, >, or = to make each statement true.

1. 37 ● 29 **>**
2. 71 ● 21 + 50 **=**
3. 70 ● 81 **<**
4. 11 ● 77 − 55 **<**
5. 5 + 8 ● 8 + 5 **=**
6. 54 ● 34 + 10 **>**
7. 6 ● 16 − 6 **<**
8. 6 + 7 ● 20 − 8 **>**
9. 100 ● 84 + 20 **<**
10. 50 ● 33 + 22 **<**
11. 62 + 6 ● 62 + 3 **>**
12. 91 − 19 ● 82 − 28 **>**
13. 76 − 21 ● 15 − 4 **>**
14. 21 ● 17 + 4 **=**

PROBLEM SOLVING

Solve these problems.

15. Mrs. Moran bought 11 apples, 13 oranges, 17 bananas, and 26 carrots. How many more pieces of fruit than vegetables did she buy? **15**
16. Matt had $6.76. He bought a pen for 75¢ and a book for $2.96. How much money does he have left? **$3.05**
17. Karen and her family are driving to their favorite amusement park. The park is 50 kilometers from their house. So far, they have driven 13 kilometers. How much farther do they have to drive to reach the park? **37 km**

Choose the correct answer.

18. 70[illegible] + 3[illegible]5 — a. 917 **(b.) 1076** c. 1194
19. 47[illegible] − [illegible] — a. 504 b. 484 **(c.) 319**

Solve for *n*. Watch the signs.

20. 2 + *n* = 11 **9**
21. *n* + 6 = 40 **34**
22. *n* − 8 = 41 **49**
23. 25 − *n* = 5 **20**
24. *n* − 7 = 7 **14**
25. *n* + 10 = 17 **7**

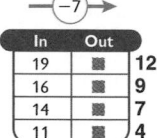

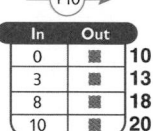

Cumulative Review

Use after Lesson 21.

Which statements do not make sense?

1. One half of Chan-Ho's cousins are boys and $\frac{3}{4}$ are girls. **does not make sense**
2. Ruby took 30 foul shots and made 25 of them. She made $\frac{1}{2}$ of the foul shots. **does not make sense**
3. There are 12 eggs in a dozen. If Robert uses six eggs for breakfast, $\frac{1}{2}$ of the dozen will remain. **makes sense**
4. The top half of the brick is bigger than the bottom half. **does not make sense**

Solve these problems.

5. Kelli is in a walk-a-thon to raise money for charity. She has walked 12 of the 20 kilometers. Is she halfway there? **yes**
6. The Math Club has 24 members. Two thirds of them are boys. Are there more boys or girls in the club? **boys**
7. Skates that usually sell for \$100 are on sale for \$68. Is that more or less than $\frac{1}{4}$ off the regular price? **more**
8. Rege has six dollars and eight dimes. Write the amount in dollars and cents. **$6.80**
9. The largest audience ever to see a circus was 52,385 people. They saw the circus inside the Superdome in New Orleans, Louisiana, in 1975. The largest audience for a circus inside a tent was 16,702 people. They saw it in Concordia, Kansas, in 1924. About how much larger was the Superdome audience than the tent audience?

   (a.) About 35,000 **b.** About 3500 **c.** About 350,000

Add or subtract.

10. 45,710 − 9,804 **35,906**
11. 465 + 9102 + 66 + 3 **9639**
12. 381,840 + 77,096 **458,936**
13. 123,456,789 + 234,567 **123,691,356**
14. 50,000 − 41,072 **8928**
15. 4307 − 906 **3401**

Cumulative Review

Use after Lesson 25.

Write the amount in dollars and cents.

1. 1 cent **$0.01**
2. 4 dimes **$0.40**
3. 5 dimes and 3 cents **$0.53**
4. 9 dimes and 9 cents **$0.99**
5. 1 dollar and 1 dime **$1.10**
6. 4 dollars and 7 dimes **$4.70**
7. 7 dollars and 3 cents **$7.03**
8. 8 dollars, 4 dimes, and 6 cents **$8.46**

Replace ● with <, >, or = to make each statement true.

9. $2.00 ● $1.79 **>**
10. $0.63 ● $6.03 **<**
11. $4.77 ● $4.68 **>**
12. $0.80 ● $0.08 **>**
13. $52 ● $52.00 **=**
14. $48.92 ● $50 **<**
15. $54.39 ● $54.93 **<**
16. $4.89 ● $4.87 **>**

Add or subtract. Use shortcuts when you can.

17. $14 + $2.33 **$16.33**
18. $20.00 − $4.75 **$15.25**
19. $0.50 + $0.25 **$0.75**
20. $6.48 − $1.04 **$5.44**
21. $39.88 − $9.88 **$30.00**
22. $4.63 + $31 **$35.63**

Use the menu to answer the questions.

Benjy's Breakfast Barn (All prices include tax!)

Breads		Drinks		Fruits	
Muffin	65¢	Juice	81¢	Melon	96¢
Bagel	90¢	Milk	33¢	Grapefruit	68¢
Toast	52¢	Hot Cocoa	77¢	Banana	44¢

23. How much will it cost for a muffin, a milk, and two bananas? **$1.86**
24. Tara has $1.50 to spend on breakfast. If she orders a bagel, what drink can she afford to get with it? **milk**
25. Leon orders melon, hot cocoa, and toast. How much change will he get back from $5? **$2.75**

Cumulative Review

Use after Lesson 27.

Use the table to choose the best answer.

Distances from Washington, D.C.

City	Distance (in miles)
Atlanta, Georgia	632
Boise, Idaho	2397
Cleveland, Ohio	380
Houston, Texas	1414
Orlando, Florida	842
Seattle, Washington	2788

1. About how far is it from Washington, D.C., to Houston?

   a. About 2000 miles (b.) About 1400 miles **c.** About 140 miles
2. About how much farther is it from Washington, D.C., to Boise than from Washington, D.C., to Orlando?

   (a.) About 1600 miles **b.** About 3000 miles **c.** About 1000 miles
3. About how far is it from Cleveland to Washington, D.C., to Atlanta?

   a. About 250 miles (b.) About 1000 miles **c.** About 700 miles
4. About how far is it from Seattle to Washington, D.C., and back?

   a. About 2800 miles **b.** About 4000 miles (c.) About 5600 miles

Add or subtract.

5. $5.08 − $3.26 **$1.82**
6. $0.75 + $2.13 **$2.88**
7. $25.87 + $44.50 **$70.37**
8. $5 − $0.88 **$4.12**
9. $30.00 − $17.49 **$12.51**
10. $1.23 + $4.56 + $7.89 **$13.68**

Cumulative Review

Use after Lesson 32.

Multiply to solve for *n*.

1. $4 \times 0 = n$ **0**
2. $4 \times 5 = n$ **20**
3. $0 \times 8 = n$ **0**
4. $1 \times 7 = n$ **7**
5. $4 \times 4 = n$ **16**
6. $6 \times 6 = n$ **36**
7. $9 \times 6 = n$ **54**
8. $2 \times 5 = n$ **10**
9. $8 \times 4 = n$ **32**
10. $7 \times 3 = n$ **21**
11. $3 \times 6 = n$ **18**
12. $8 \times 3 = n$ **24**

Multiply.

13. 8×7 = **56**
14. 9×4 = **36**
15. 7×7 = **49**
16. 6×8 = **48**
17. 4×3 = **12**
18. 5×9 = **45**
19. 4×7 = **28**
20. 3×9 = **27**
21. 2×4 = **8**
22. 9×2 = **18**

Complete the chart.

	Length of Side	Area of Square	
23	1 cm	■	**1 square cm**
24	3 cm	■	**9 square cm**
25	5 cm	■	**25 square cm**
26	7 cm	■	**49 square cm**
27	9 cm	■	**81 square cm**

Solve for *n*.

28. $16 - n = 4$ **12**
29. $25 + n = 34$ **9**
30. $18 - n = 7$ **11**

Cumulative Review

Use after Lesson 37.

Copy and complete the price chart.

Beads at 8¢ Each

1

0	1	2	3	4	5	6	7	8	9	10
0	8	■ 16	■ 24	■ 32	■ 40	■ 48	■ 56	■ 64	■ 72	■ 80

Use the price chart to answer these questions.

2. Siri buys six beads and pays with a $1 bill. How much change should she get back? **52¢**
3. The Bead Shop has a sale. For every two beads Siri buys, she gets one free. How much will she spend for six beads on sale? **32¢**

What time is it?

4. 20 minutes after 4:45 P.M.? **5:05 P.M.**
5. 45 minutes after 12:30 A.M.? **1:15 A.M.**
6. 10 minutes after 1:05 P.M.? **1:15 P.M.**
7. 5 minutes before noon? **11:55 A.M.**

How long is each event?

8. A play that has a 55-minute first act, a 15-minute intermission, and a 50-minute second act. **2 hours**
9. A football game that has four 15-minute quarters, two 5-minute intermissions, and one 12-minute half-time. **1 hour and 22 minutes**
10. A school day that has seven 50-minute class periods, six 10-minute breaks, and one 35-minute lunch period. **7 hours and 25 minutes**
11. Making cookies that take 35 minutes to mix the batter, 12 minutes to bake, and 25 minutes to cool. **1 hour and 12 minutes**

Multiply.

12. 7 × 8 **56**
13. 7 × 7 **49**
14. 8 × 9 **72**
15. 9 × 6 **54**

Cumulative Review

Use after Lesson 42.

Solve these problems. Simplify each answer.

1. 2 weeks 5 days + 4 weeks 4 days = ■ **7 weeks 2 days**
2. 3 hours 50 minutes + 2 hours 45 minutes = ■ **6 hours 35 minutes**
3. 6 weeks 2 days − 4 weeks 6 days = ■ **1 week 3 days**
4. 4 days 10 hours − 20 hours = ■ **3 days 14 hours**
5. 5 days 18 hours + 1 week 9 hours = ■ **13 days 3 hours**
6. 3 days 11 hours 36 minutes − 1 day 20 hours 5 minutes = ■ **1 day 15 hours 31 minutes**

Use a computer or other means to copy and complete this chart about rectangular swimming pools.

	Whose Pool	Length (meters) At Least	Length (meters) No More Than	Width (meters) At Least	Width (meters) No More Than	Area (square meters) At Least	Area (square meters) No More Than
7	Ellie's	9	10	8	9	■ **72**	■ **90**
8	Jacob's	4	5	6	7	■ **24**	■ **35**
9	Nora's	5	6	5	6	■ **25**	■ **36**
10	Van's	7	8	9	10	■ **63**	■ **80**

Multiply to solve for *n*.

11. 2 × 8 = *n* **16**
12. 4 × 9 = *n* **36**
13. 6 × 8 = *n* **48**
14. 3 × 4 = *n* **12**
15. 8 × 8 = *n* **64**
16. 3 × 9 = *n* **27**
17. 5 × 0 = *n* **0**
18. 6 × 4 = *n* **24**
19. 2 × 6 = *n* **12**
20. 6 × 7 = *n* **42**
21. 7 × 8 = *n* **56**
22. 5 × 7 = *n* **35**
23. 9 × 8 = *n* **72**
24. 4 × 4 = *n* **16**
25. 1 × 1 = *n* **1**

Cumulative Review

Use after Lesson 47.

ALGEBRA READINESS

Solve for *n*.

1. 2 × *n* = 14 **7**
2. 6 × *n* = 24 **4**
3. 3 × *n* = 21 **7**
4. *n* × 4 = 20 **5**
5. *n* × 8 = 56 **7**
6. *n* × 6 = 30 **5**
7. 50 = *n* × 5 **10**
8. 45 = *n* × 5 **9**
9. 63 = *n* × 9 **7**
10. 36 = *n* × 4 **9**
11. 72 = *n* × 8 **9**
12. 42 = *n* × 6 **7**

PROBLEM SOLVING

Solve these problems.

13. Each day, Mara feeds 4 cups of dry food to her cats. A bag of cat food has 40 cups. How many days can Mara feed her cats from one bag of cat food? **10**
14. Jess has to make 30 posters for the school fair. If he makes four posters each day, will he finish in a week? **no**
15. Mr. Freed bought 65 new books for the library. So far he has shelved 47 of them. How many more books must be shelved? **18**
16. Stacy has a limit of three hours a week of Internet time. If she spends 20 minutes a day on the Internet, will she be over or under her limit? By how much? **under; 40 minutes**

Divide. Watch for remainders.

17. 8 ÷ 8 = *n* **1**
18. 27 ÷ 9 = *n* **3**
19. *n* = 16 ÷ 4 **4**
20. 42 ÷ 7 = *n* **6**
21. 6 ÷ 1 = *n* **6**
22. *n* = 36 ÷ 6 **6**
23. 18 ÷ 3 = *n* **6**
24. 70 ÷ 10 = *n* **7**
25. *n* = 28 ÷ 4 **7**
26. $10\overline{)62}$ **6 R2**
27. $6\overline{)30}$ **5**
28. $3\overline{)14}$ **4 R2**
29. $5\overline{)40}$ **8**
30. $9\overline{)62}$ **6 R8**
31. $8\overline{)32}$ **4**
32. $7\overline{)50}$ **7 R1**
33. $4\overline{)28}$ **7**
34. $2\overline{)7}$ **3 R1**
35. $1\overline{)3}$ **3**

Cumulative Review

Use after Lesson 50.

Divide. Watch for remainders.

1. $10\overline{)36}$ **3 R6**
2. $6\overline{)35}$ **5 R5**
3. $3\overline{)16}$ **5 R1**
4. $5\overline{)44}$ **8 R4**
5. $9\overline{)13}$ **1 R4**
6. $8\overline{)30}$ **3 R6**
7. $7\overline{)47}$ **6 R5**
8. $4\overline{)28}$ **7**
9. $2\overline{)13}$ **6 R1**
10. $6\overline{)40}$ **6 R4**
11. $9\overline{)60}$ **6 R6**
12. $6\overline{)16}$ **2 R4**
13. $3\overline{)15}$ **5**
14. $5\overline{)21}$ **4 R1**
15. $9\overline{)42}$ **4 R6**

PROBLEM SOLVING

Solve.

16. Raymond baked 24 muffins. He gave the same number of muffins to each of three friends. How many muffins did each friend get? How many muffins were left over? **8; none**
17. A van holds eight students. Thirty students are going on a field trip by van. How many vans are needed to carry everyone? **4**
18. Lucy is buying party invitations. The invitations she likes come eight to a package. She needs to send 20 invitations. How many packages of invitations should she buy? **3**

Solve for *n*. Watch the signs.

19. 27 ÷ (9 ÷ 3) = *n* **9**
20. 11 − (4 × 2) = *n* **3**
21. (6 × 5) + (21 ÷ 3) = *n* **37**
22. (32 ÷ 8) × (10 − 6) = *n* **16**
23. (3 × 6) ÷ 2 = *n* **9**
24. 15 − (5 × 2) = *n* **5**

Solve this problem.

25. Jason bought three oranges. He cut each orange into six slices. He put half of the slices in his lunch box and the rest in his brother's lunch box. How many slices of orange did Jason take for his lunch? **9**

ASSESSMENT

Cumulative Review

Use after Lesson 54.

Use the coordinate grid.

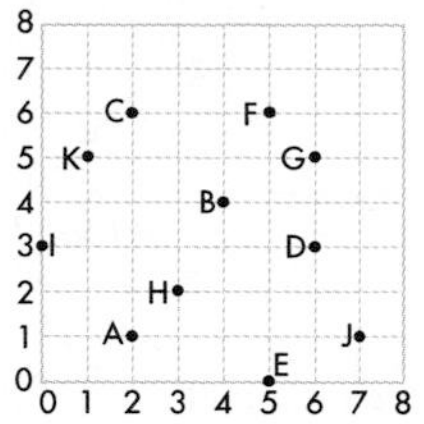

1. What are the coordinates of point *H*? **(3, 2)**
2. What are the coordinates of point *K*? **(1, 5)**
3. What are the coordinates of point *A*? **(2, 1)**
4. What are the coordinates of point *E*? **(5, 0)**
5. What are the coordinates of point *D*? **(6, 3)**
6. What is the letter at (5, 6)? **F**
7. What is the letter at (6, 5)? **G**
8. What is the letter at (0, 3)? **I**
9. What is the letter at (7, 1)? **J**

In each case, tell what *y* is.

10. 9 → (+3) → *y* **12**
11. 9 → (÷3) → *y* **3**
12. 9 → (×3) → *y* **27**
13. 11 → (−8) → *y* **3**
14. 35 → (−8) → *y* **27**
15. 15 → (×2) → *y* **30**

ASSESSMENT

Cumulative Review

Use after Lesson 59.

Write the numbers in standard form.

1. 8000 + 300 + 50 + 2 **8352**
2. 9000 + 20 + 6 **9026**
3. 30,000 + 4,000 + 8 **34,008**
4. 10,000 + 4,000 + 500 + 70 + 1 **14,571**
5. 400,000 + 20,000 + 8,000 + 500 + 70 + 9 **428,579**
6. 600,000 + 80,000 + 7,000 + 900 + 30 + 1 **687,931**

Find the perimeter.

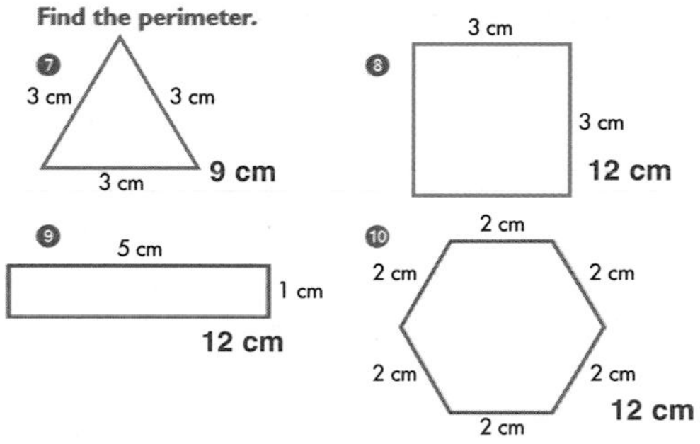

7. **9 cm**
8. **12 cm**
9. **12 cm**
10. **12 cm**

Add or subtract.

11. 847 − 598 = **249**
12. 612 − 377 = **235**
13. 9827 + 3878 = **13,705**
14. 2314 + 5986 = **8300**
15. 36 + 43 = **79**
16. 700 − 472 = **228**
17. 650 + 199 = **849**
18. 721 − 201 = **520**
19. 3000 − 875 = **2125**
20. 29 − 17 = **12**

ASSESSMENT

Cumulative Review

Use after Lesson 63.

Write the amount in dollars and cents.

1. 4 dimes and 3 cents **$0.43**
2. 2 quarters and 6 cents **$0.56**
3. 3 dollars, 7 dimes, and 2 cents **$3.72**
4. 7 dollars and 3 quarters **$7.75**
5. 8 dollars and 9 cents **$8.09**
6. 5 dollars, 3 dimes, and 2 cents **$5.32**
7. 5 dollars, 1 dime, and 6 cents **$5.16**
8. 1 dollar and 3 cents **$1.03**

Subtract.

9. 508 − 329 = **179**
10. 634 − 367 = **267**
11. 320 − 78 = **242**
12. 544 − 479 = **65**

Copy each list of ordered pairs. Replace the *x* or *y* with the correct number.

13. *x* → (÷3) → *y* (6, *y*) **2**, (9, *y*) **3**, (21, *y*) **7**, (*x*, 5) **15**, (*x*, 4) **12**
14. *x* → (×6) → *y* (9, *y*) **54**, (7, *y*) **42**, (5, *y*) **30**, (*x*, 24) **4**, (*x*, 42) **7**

Copy and complete these charts.

15. *x* → (×4) → *y*

x	*y*
0	**0**
4	**16**
5	20
8	32

16. *x* → (÷7) → *y*

x	*y*
70	**10**
56	**8**
49	7
35	5

Multiply or divide.

17. 7 × 8 **56**
18. 45 ÷ 5 **9**
19. 48 ÷ 6 **8**
20. 4 × 9 **36**

ASSESSMENT

Cumulative Review

Use after Lesson 68.

Divide. Watch for remainders.

1. 9)31 **3 R4**
2. 2)9 **4 R1**
3. 8)36 **4 R4**
4. 3)32 **10 R2**
5. 4)20 **5**
6. 6)46 **7 R4**
7. 5)19 **3 R4**
8. 1)8 **8**

PROBLEM SOLVING

Solve these problems.

9. Nia has to read 35 pages for homework. She has seven more pages to go. How many pages has she already read? **28**
10. Andre took $53.90 from his bank account to buy a skateboard. Now his balance is $136.45. How much money did he have in the bank before he bought the skateboard? **$190.35**
11. In 1984, 37,290,870 American households got cable television. By 1994, 60,483,600 households had cable television. About how many more households had cable TV in 1994 than in 1984? **about 23 million**
12. The Millers went to Ocean World. They bought two adult tickets at $7 each and three children's tickets at $4 each. They paid $3 to park their car, $10 for snacks, and $5 for a toy shark. How much did they spend at Ocean World? **$44**
13. Priscilla makes clown puppets. Each puppet needs seven buttons. If Priscilla has 32 buttons, how many clown puppets can she make? **4**
14. Felipe bought six pairs of socks. Each pair cost $3, including tax. He gave the clerk $20. How much change should he receive? **$2**
15. Darren ordered concert tickets over the phone. Tickets cost $9 each. Darren paid a service charge of $3 to cover the cost of mailing the tickets to his home. He spent a total of $30. How many tickets did he order? **3**

Cumulative Review

Use after Lesson 73.

Copy the list of ordered pairs, but replace each *x* or *y* with the correct number. Then graph each set of ordered pairs.

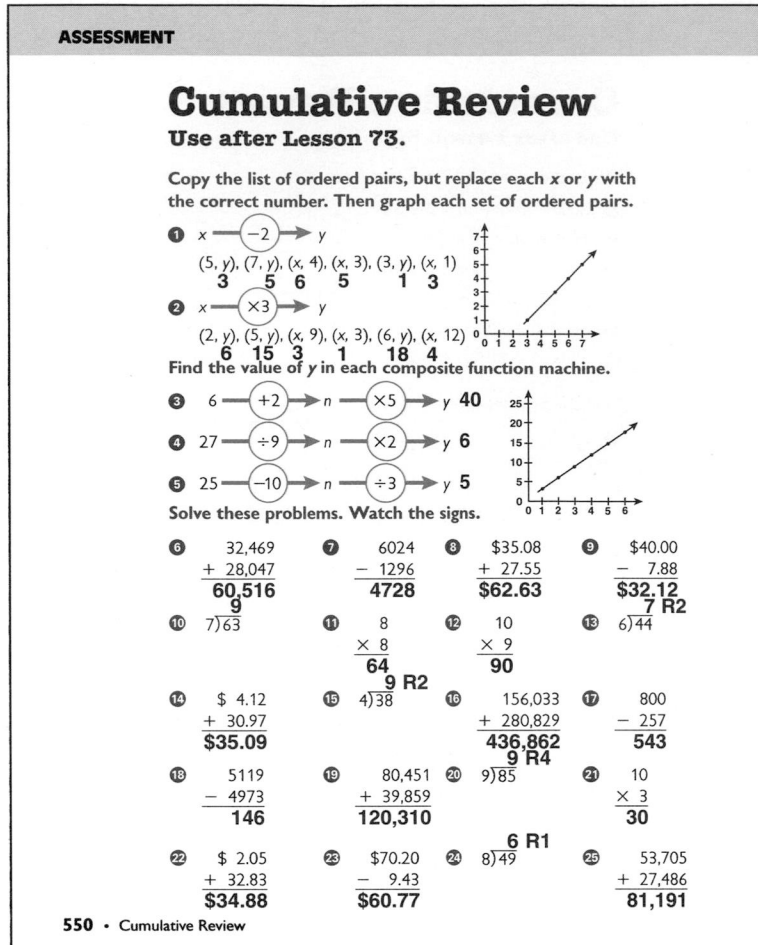

1. $x \rightarrow (-2) \rightarrow y$
(5, *y*), (7, *y*), (*x*, 4), (*x*, 3), (3, *y*), (*x*, 1) **3 5 6 5 1 3**

2. $x \rightarrow (\times 3) \rightarrow y$
(2, *y*), (5, *y*), (*x*, 9), (*x*, 3), (6, *y*), (*x*, 12) **6 15 3 1 18 4**

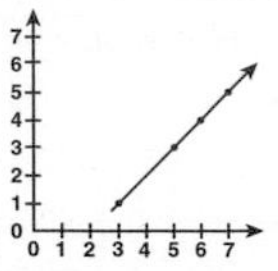

Find the value of *y* in each composite function machine.

3. $6 \rightarrow (+2) \rightarrow n \rightarrow (\times 5) \rightarrow y$ **40**
4. $27 \rightarrow (\div 9) \rightarrow n \rightarrow (\times 2) \rightarrow y$ **6**
5. $25 \rightarrow (-10) \rightarrow n \rightarrow (\div 3) \rightarrow y$ **5**

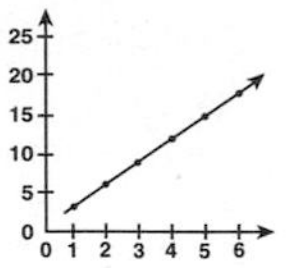

Solve these problems. Watch the signs.

6. 32,469 + 28,047 = **60,516**
7. 6024 − 1296 = **4728**
8. $35.08 + 27.55 = **$62.63**
9. $40.00 − 7.88 = **$32.12**
10. 7)63 **9**
11. 8 × 8 = **64**
12. 10 × 9 = **90**
13. 6)44 **7 R2**
14. $ 4.12 + 30.97 = **$35.09**
15. 4)38 **9 R2**
16. 156,033 + 280,829 = **436,862**
17. 800 − 257 = **543**
18. 5119 − 4973 = **146**
19. 80,451 + 39,859 = **120,310**
20. 9)85 **9 R4**
21. 10 × 3 = **30**
22. $ 2.05 + 32.83 = **$34.88**
23. $70.20 − 9.43 = **$60.77**
24. 8)49 **6 R1**
25. 53,705 + 27,486 = **81,191**

Cumulative Review

Use after Lesson 77.

In each case, tell whether the lines are *parallel*, *perpendicular*, or *neither*.

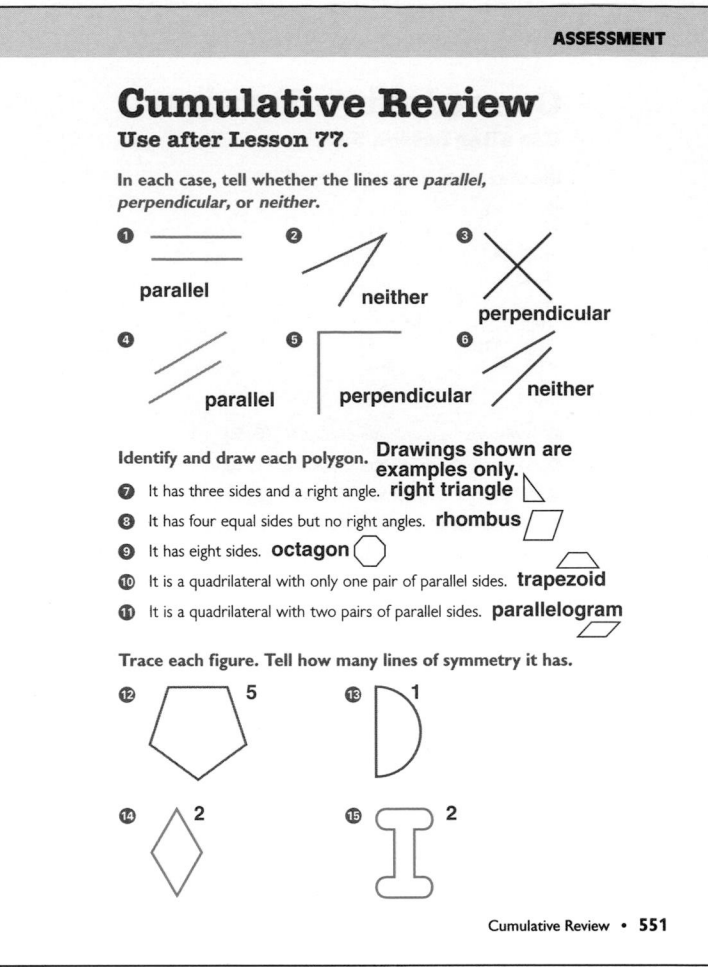

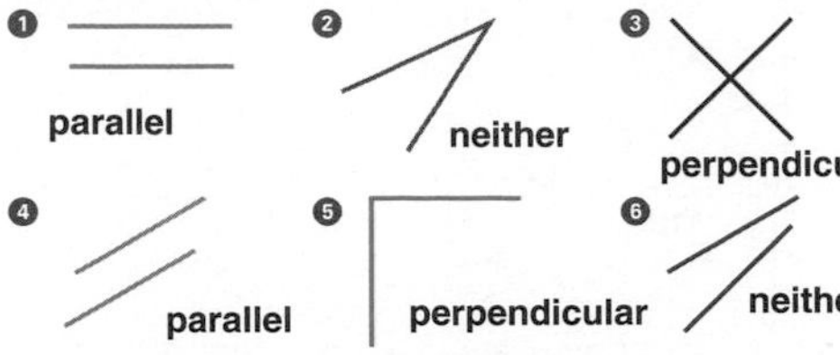

1. **parallel**
2. **neither**
3. **perpendicular**
4. **parallel**
5. **perpendicular**
6. **neither**

Identify and draw each polygon. **Drawings shown are examples only.**

7. It has three sides and a right angle. **right triangle**
8. It has four equal sides but no right angles. **rhombus**
9. It has eight sides. **octagon**
10. It is a quadrilateral with only one pair of parallel sides. **trapezoid**
11. It is a quadrilateral with two pairs of parallel sides. **parallelogram**

Trace each figure. Tell how many lines of symmetry it has.

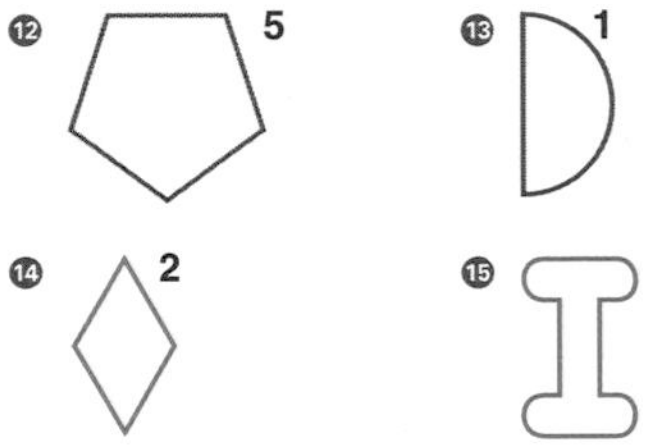

12. **5**
13. **1**
14. **2**
15. **2**

Cumulative Review

Use after Lesson 82.

Tell whether the figures are *congruent*, *similar*, or *neither*.

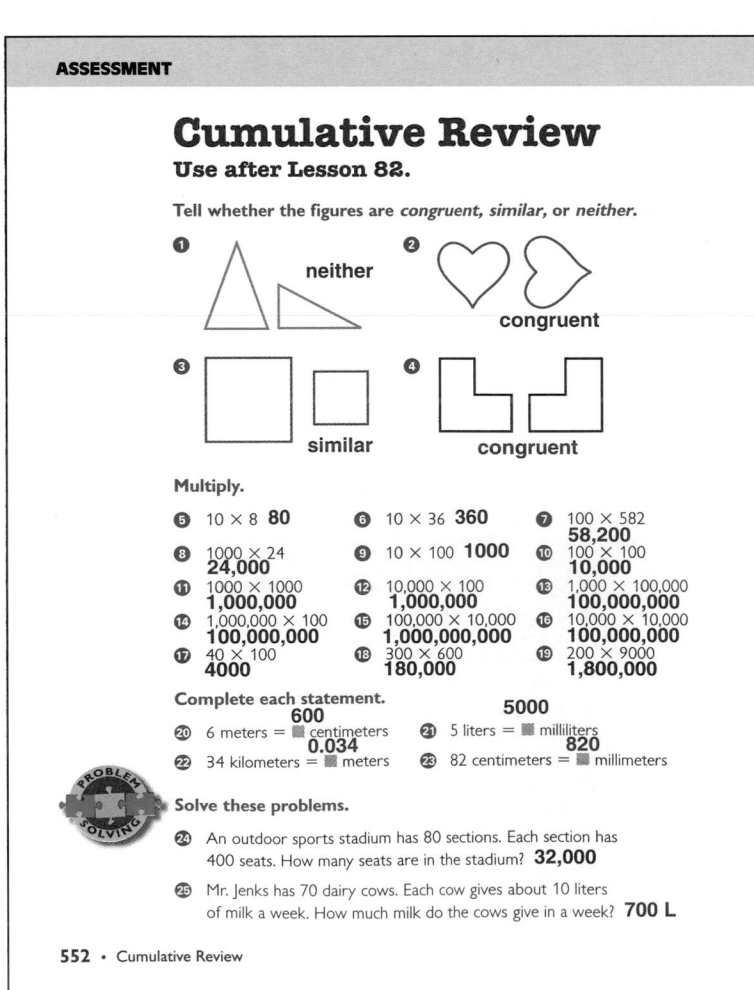

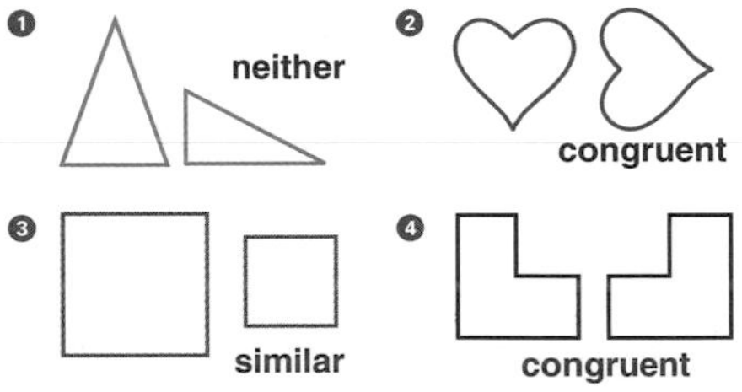

1. **neither**
2. **congruent**
3. **similar**
4. **congruent**

Multiply.

5. 10 × 8 **80**
6. 10 × 36 **360**
7. 100 × 582 **58,200**
8. 1000 × 24 **24,000**
9. 10 × 100 **1000**
10. 100 × 100 **10,000**
11. 1000 × 1000 **1,000,000**
12. 10,000 × 100 **1,000,000**
13. 1,000 × 100,000 **100,000,000**
14. 1,000,000 × 100 **100,000,000**
15. 100,000 × 10,000 **1,000,000,000**
16. 10,000 × 10,000 **100,000,000**
17. 40 × 100 **4000**
18. 300 × 600 **180,000**
19. 200 × 9000 **1,800,000**

Complete each statement.

20. 6 meters = ■ centimeters **600**
21. 5 liters = ■ milliliters **5000**
22. 34 kilometers = ■ meters **0.034**
23. 82 centimeters = ■ millimeters **820**

PROBLEM SOLVING

Solve these problems.

24. An outdoor sports stadium has 80 sections. Each section has 400 seats. How many seats are in the stadium? **32,000**
25. Mr. Jenks has 70 dairy cows. Each cow gives about 10 liters of milk a week. How much milk do the cows give in a week? **700 L**

Cumulative Review

Use after Lesson 88.

Multiply. Solve for *n*.

1. 800 × 50 = *n* **40,000**
2. 1,000 × 10,000 = *n* **10,000,000**
3. 300 × 600 = *n* **180,000**
4. 10 × 47 = *n* **470**
5. 90 × 7000 = *n* **630,000**
6. 100 × 5142 = *n* **514,200**
7. 6 × 70,000 = *n* **420,000**
8. 62 × 100 = *n* **6200**
9. 2000 × 100 = *n* **200,000**
10. 100 × 449 = *n* **44,900**
11. 7000 × 8000 = *n* **56,000,000**
12. 703 × 1000 = *n* **703,000**
13. 10,000 × 30 = *n* **300,000**
14. 123 × 100 = *n* **12,300**
15. 900 × 90,000 = *n* **81,000,000**
16. 500 × 20,000 = *n* **10,000,000**

Round to the nearest ten.

17. 71 **70**
18. 36 **40**
19. 55 **50 or 60**
20. 322 **320**

Round to the nearest hundred.

21. 739 **700**
22. 260 **300**
23. 1296 **1300**
24. 650 **600 or 700**

Round to the nearest thousand.

25. 4867 **5000**
26. 2075 **2000**
27. 34,624 **35,000**
28. 8554 **9000**

Approximate to solve these problems.

29. Tariq wants to buy four blocks of modeling clay for $2.77 (277 cents) each. He has $15. Does he have enough money for the clay? **yes**
30. Drew's heart beats about 76 times every minute. He says that his heart beats over 100,000 times a day. Is he right? (There are 60 minutes in one hour and 24 hours in one day.) **yes**

Cumulative Review

Use after Lesson 91.

Approximate to choose the correct answer.

1. 43 × 29 — a. 927 b. 1657 (c.) 1247
2. 84 × 76 — a. 56,724 (b.) 6384 c. 7204
3. 196 × 88 — a. 153,618 (b.) 17,248 c. 1948
4. 408 × 61 — (a.) 24,888 b. 30,608 c. 20,758

Multiply.

5. 33 × 3 = **99**
6. 81 × 3 = **243**
7. 17 × 9 = **153**
8. 16 × 8 = **128**
9. 52 × 6 = **312**
10. 96 × 4 = **384**
11. 77 × 2 = **154**
12. 23 × 7 = **161**
13. 68 × 8 = **544**
14. 82 × 7 = **574**
15. 60 × 9 = **540**
16. 18 × 4 = **72**
17. 43 × 5 = **215**
18. 462 × 4 = **1848**
19. 751 × 8 = **6008**
20. 119 × 8 = **952**
21. 309 × 2 = **618**
22. 284 × 5 = **1420**
23. 518 × 3 = **1554**
24. 841 × 5 = **4205**
25. 676 × 7 = **4732**
26. 934 × 9 = **8406**
27. 604 × 6 = **3624**
28. 953 × 3 = **2859**

Solve these problems.

29. How many pounds in 38 tons? **76,000**
30. How many feet in 5 miles? **26,400**

Cumulative Review

Use after Lesson 95.

Multiply.

1. 53 × 36 = **1908**
2. 81 × 93 = **7533**
3. 57 × 42 = **2394**
4. 29 × 15 = **435**
5. 86 × 70 = **6020**
6. 44 × 54 = **2376**
7. 73 × 12 = **876**
8. 85 × 31 = **2635**
9. 60 × 58 = **3480**
10. 48 × 67 = **3216**
11. 423 × 29 = **12,267**
12. 621 × 14 = **8694**
13. 167 × 15 = **2505**
14. 218 × 50 = **10,900**
15. 505 × 49 = **24,745**
16. 209 × 12 = **2508**
17. 843 × 37 = **31,191**
18. 600 × 89 = **53,400**
19. 430 × 70 = **30,100**
20. 891 × 15 = **13,365**

Solve these problems.

21. A rectangle is 73 meters long and 51 meters wide.
    a. What is the area of the rectangle? **3723 sq. m**
    b. What is the perimeter of the rectangle? **248 m**
22. A square is 25 centimeters on a side. What is the area of the square? **625 sq. cm**
23. A case of cat food has six rows with nine cans in each row. How many cans are in 12 cases? **648**
24. A National Basketball Association (NBA) professional team has 12 players. How many players are there on the 29 teams that make up the NBA? **348**
25. Fourteen buses each took 52 people to a baseball game. How many people rode the buses all together? **728**

Cumulative Review

Use after Lesson 100.

Multiply.

1. 435 × 531 = **230,985**
2. 618 × 420 = **259,560**
3. 792 × 300 = **237,600**
4. 636 × 859 = **546,324**
5. 307 × 370 = **113,590**
6. 742 × 802 = **595,084**
7. 210 × 448 = **94,080**
8. 1272 × 3086 = **3,925,392**
9. 5419 × 8672 = **46,993,568**
10. 54,073 × 209 = **11,301,257**

Solve for *n*. Watch the signs.

11. $8 + 5 = n$ **13**
12. $11 - n = 4$ **7**
13. $7 \div 7 = n$ **1**
14. $7 + n = 15$ **8**
15. $24 \div 3 = n$ **8**
16. $17 - n = 9$ **8**
17. $n = 3 \times 10$ **30**
18. $30 \div n = 5$ **6**
19. $8 \times 0 = n$ **0**
20. $7 + n = 13$ **6**
21. $n = 13 - 5$ **8**
22. $48 \div 6 = n$ **8**

Use the menu to answer the questions.

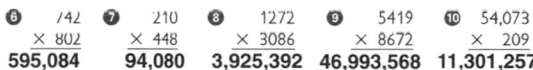

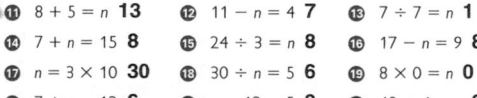

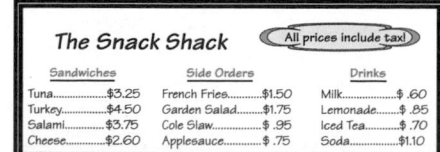

The Snack Shack — All prices include tax!

Sandwiches		Side Orders		Drinks	
Tuna	$3.25	French Fries	$1.50	Milk	$ .60
Turkey	$4.50	Garden Salad	$1.75	Lemonade	$ .85
Salami	$3.75	Cole Slaw	$ .95	Iced Tea	$ .70
Cheese	$2.60	Applesauce	$ .75	Soda	$1.10

23. What is the most money you can spend on a sandwich, a side order, and a drink? **$7.35**
24. What is the least money you can spend on a sandwich, a side order, and a drink? **$3.95**
25. RaeLynn has $4.80 to spend on lunch. If she orders a tuna sandwich, what side order and drink can she also get? **cole slaw or apple sauce and milk**

Cumulative Review

Use after Lesson 103.

Solve these problems.

On the highway, Alex travels about 60 miles in one hour. His car can go about 27 miles on 1 gallon of gasoline. The tank holds 18 gallons.

1. About how far can Alex travel on one tankful of gasoline? **486 miles**
2. About how far does he travel in four hours on the highway? **240 miles**
3. Alex is planning a trip. He estimates that it will take 18 hours of driving time. About how many miles long is the trip? **1080 miles**
4. Can Alex make it there on two tankfuls of gasoline? **no**
5. A gallon of paint covers about 400 square feet. Dan is going to paint a wall that is 36 feet long and 11 feet high. He wants to put on two coats. Will 1 gallon of paint be enough for the job? **no**
6. A jar of pickles costs $2.67. How much will eight jars of pickles cost? **$21.36**
7. Paper comes in packs of 500 sheets. How many sheets of paper will Lina have if she buys 20 packs? **10,000**
8. All 475 students from Bell Top School are going on a field trip. They are traveling by bus. Each bus can seat 45 students. It costs $98 to rent each bus for the day.
    a. Will 11 buses be too few, just enough, or too many? **just enough**
    b. How many extra seats, or how many seats too few, will there be? **20 extra seats**
    c. How much will it cost to rent 11 buses for the day? **$1078**

Find the area and the perimeter.

9. A rectangle has a length of 5 cm and a width of 2 cm. **area = 10 sq. cm, perimeter = 14 cm**
10. A square has a side of 4 cm. **area = 16 sq. cm, perimeter = 16 cm**

Page 558

Cumulative Review

Use after Lesson 107.

Divide. Watch for remainders.

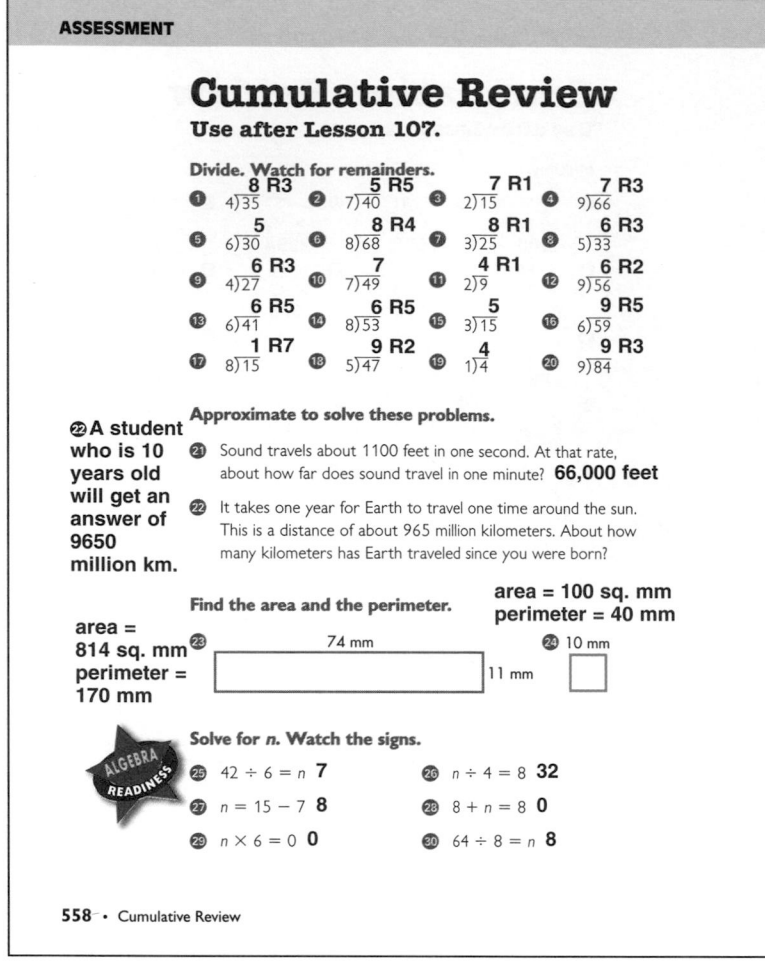

1. 4)35 **8 R3**
2. 7)40 **5 R5**
3. 2)15 **7 R1**
4. 9)66 **7 R3**
5. 6)30 **5**
6. 8)68 **8 R4**
7. 3)25 **8 R1**
8. 5)33 **6 R3**
9. 4)27 **6 R3**
10. 7)49 **7**
11. 2)9 **4 R1**
12. 9)56 **6 R2**
13. 6)41 **6 R5**
14. 8)53 **6 R5**
15. 3)15 **5**
16. 6)59 **9 R5**
17. 8)15 **1 R7**
18. 5)47 **9 R2**
19. 1)4 **4**
20. 9)84 **9 R3**

Approximate to solve these problems.

21. Sound travels about 1100 feet in one second. At that rate, about how far does sound travel in one minute? **66,000 feet**
22. It takes one year for Earth to travel one time around the sun. This is a distance of about 965 million kilometers. About how many kilometers has Earth traveled since you were born?

22 A student who is 10 years old will get an answer of 9650 million km.

Find the area and the perimeter.

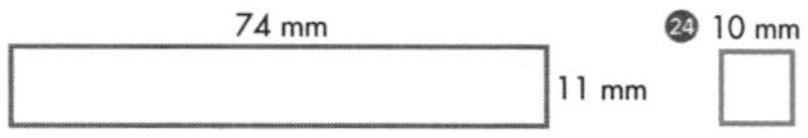

23. **area = 814 sq. mm perimeter = 170 mm**
24. **area = 100 sq. mm perimeter = 40 mm**

Solve for *n*. Watch the signs.

ALGEBRA READINESS

25. $42 \div 6 = n$ **7**
26. $n \div 4 = 8$ **32**
27. $n = 15 - 7$ **8**
28. $8 + n = 8$ **0**
29. $n \times 6 = 0$ **0**
30. $64 \div 8 = n$ **8**

Page 559

Cumulative Review

Use after Lesson 112.

Solve for *n*. Watch the signs.

1. $32 \div n = 8$ **4**
2. $n \div 7 = 6$ **42**
3. $n = 21 \div 7$ **3**
4. $63 \div 9 = n$ **7**
5. $54 \div 6 = n$ **9**
6. $18 \div n = 6$ **3**
7. $n \div 3 = 3$ **9**
8. $n = 36 \div 6$ **6**
9. $12 \div n = 3$ **4**
10. $n \div 5 = 8$ **40**
11. $n = 5 \div 5$ **1**
12. $16 \div 2 = n$ **8**

Add or subtract.

13. 699 + 431 = **1130**
14. 296 − 154 = **142**
15. 10,281 − 8,479 = **1,802**
16. 21,649 + 14,298 = **35,947**
17. 15,829 − 12,969 = **2,860**

Divide. Check your answers.

18. 165 ÷ 5 **33**
19. 728 ÷ 7 **104**
20. 303 ÷ 4 **75 R3**
21. 961 ÷ 6 **160 R1**
22. 994 ÷ 9 **110 R4**
23. 305 ÷ 5 **61**
24. 453 ÷ 2 **226 R1**
25. 288 ÷ 3 **96**
26. 842 ÷ 7 **120 R2**
27. 791 ÷ 8 **98 R7**
28. 297 ÷ 4 **74 R1**
29. 490 ÷ 5 **98**

PROBLEM SOLVING

Solve these problems.

30. Six lemons cost 90¢. How much is one lemon? **15¢**
31. Three stamps cost 96¢. How much is that per stamp? **32¢**
32. Four jugs of cider cost $7.56 (756¢). How much is that per jug? **$1.89**
33. Two T-shirts cost $18. How much is one T-shirt? **$9**
34. An 8-ounce jar of olives costs $3.28 (328¢). How much is that per ounce? **41¢**
35. A 5-pound bag of rice costs $1.25 (125¢). A 9-pound bag of rice costs $1.98 (198¢). Which bag is the better buy? Why? **the 9-pound bag; it costs only 22¢ per pound, and the 5-pound bag costs 25¢ per pound**

Page 560

Cumulative Review

Use after Lesson 116.

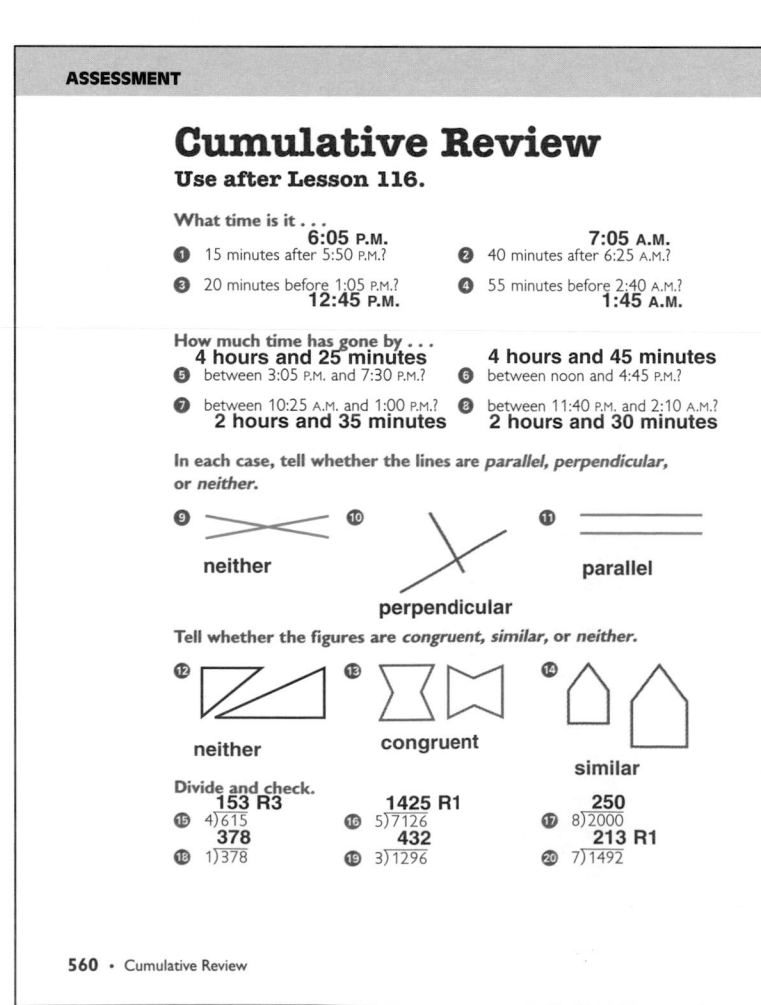

What time is it . . .

1. 15 minutes after 5:50 P.M.? **6:05 P.M.**
2. 40 minutes after 6:25 A.M.? **7:05 A.M.**
3. 20 minutes before 1:05 P.M.? **12:45 P.M.**
4. 55 minutes before 2:40 A.M.? **1:45 A.M.**

How much time has gone by . . .

5. between 3:05 P.M. and 7:30 P.M.? **4 hours and 25 minutes**
6. between noon and 4:45 P.M.? **4 hours and 45 minutes**
7. between 10:25 A.M. and 1:00 P.M.? **2 hours and 35 minutes**
8. between 11:40 P.M. and 2:10 A.M.? **2 hours and 30 minutes**

In each case, tell whether the lines are *parallel, perpendicular,* or *neither.*

9. **neither**
10. **perpendicular**
11. **parallel**

Tell whether the figures are *congruent, similar,* or *neither.*

12. **neither**
13. **congruent**
14. **similar**

Divide and check.

15. 4)615 **153 R3**
16. 5)7126 **1425 R1**
17. 8)2000 **250**
18. 1)378 **378**
19. 3)1296 **432**
20. 7)1492 **213 R1**

Page 561

Cumulative Review

Use after Lesson 122.

Look at the graph. What are the coordinates of these points?

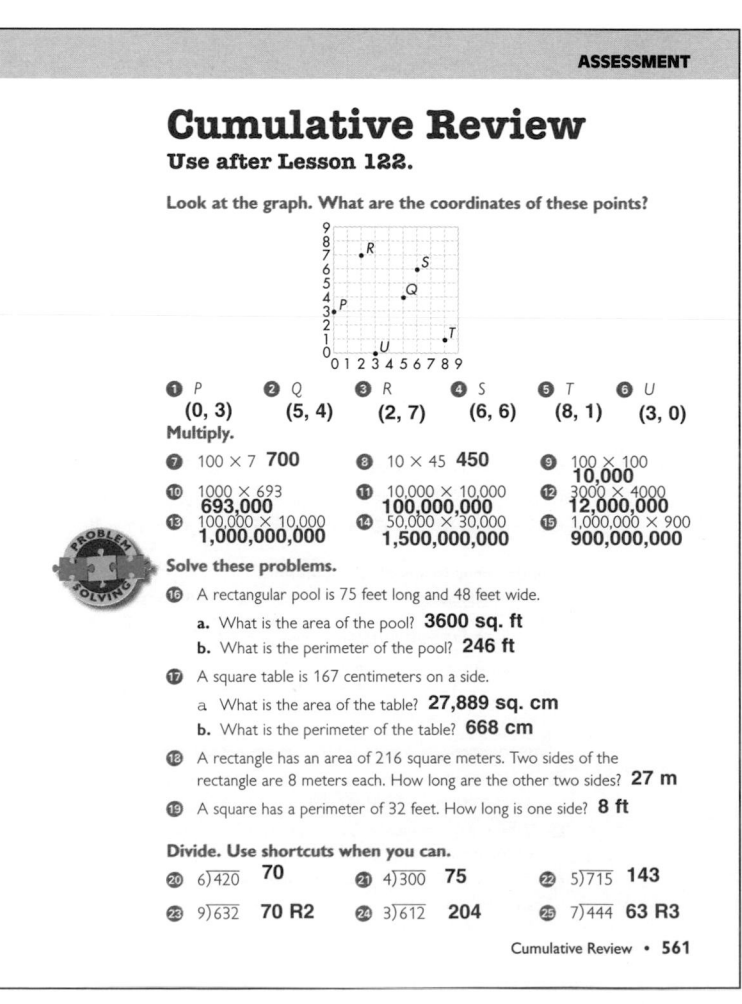

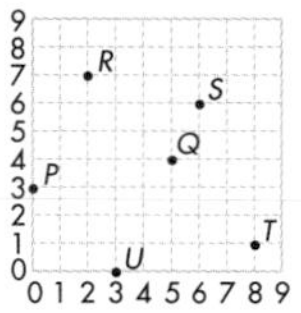

1. *P* **(0, 3)**
2. *Q* **(5, 4)**
3. *R* **(2, 7)**
4. *S* **(6, 6)**
5. *T* **(8, 1)**
6. *U* **(3, 0)**

Multiply.

7. 100 × 7 **700**
8. 10 × 45 **450**
9. 100 × 100 **10,000**
10. 1000 × 693 **693,000**
11. 10,000 × 10,000 **100,000,000**
12. 3000 × 4000 **12,000,000**
13. 100,000 × 10,000 **1,000,000,000**
14. 50,000 × 30,000 **1,500,000,000**
15. 1,000,000 × 900 **900,000,000**

PROBLEM SOLVING

Solve these problems.

16. A rectangular pool is 75 feet long and 48 feet wide.
    - **a.** What is the area of the pool? **3600 sq. ft**
    - **b.** What is the perimeter of the pool? **246 ft**
17. A square table is 167 centimeters on a side.
    - a. What is the area of the table? **27,889 sq. cm**
    - **b.** What is the perimeter of the table? **668 cm**
18. A rectangle has an area of 216 square meters. Two sides of the rectangle are 8 meters each. How long are the other two sides? **27 m**
19. A square has a perimeter of 32 feet. How long is one side? **8 ft**

Divide. Use shortcuts when you can.

20. 6)420 **70**
21. 4)300 **75**
22. 5)715 **143**
23. 9)632 **70 R2**
24. 3)612 **204**
25. 7)444 **63 R3**

Cumulative Review
Use after Lesson 125.

Solve these problems.

1. Dana paid $2.45 (245¢) for seven postcards. How much did each postcard cost? **35¢**
2. Simon bought four tortillas for 72¢. How much should six tortillas cost? **$1.08 (or 108¢)**
3. Adam needs 46 candles for his father's birthday cake. Candles come in packages of ten.
   a. How many packages should he buy? **5**
   b. How many extra candles will he have? **4**
4. Felice bowled three games. Her scores were 87, 106, and 128. What was her average score for the three games? **107**
5. Mr. Glazer drove 310 miles in five hours. What was the average number of miles he drove each hour? **62**

Find the mean of each set of numbers.

6. 14, 16, 18, 13, 24 **17**
7. 55, 66, 33, 88, 22, 77, 44 **55**
8. 3253, 3542, 3425, 3244, 3526 **3398**

Solve for *n*.

9. $90 \div 9 = n$ **10**
10. $54 \div 6 = n$ **9**
11. $0 \times 1 = n$ **0**
12. $5 + n = 13$ **8**
13. $n \times 4 = 24$ **6**
14. $n \div 7 = 6$ **42**
15. $27 + n = 54$ **27**
16. $18 \div n = 3$ **6**
17. $81 \div n = 9$ **9**
18. $59 - n = 21$ **38**
19. $49 \div n = 7$ **7**
20. $8 \times n = 64$ **8**

Cumulative Review
Use after Lesson 131.

Solve these problems without dividing. Use the information to the right to help you.

1. 24)576 **24**
2. 61)3965 **65**
3. 150)900 **6**
4. 98)8722 **89**
5. 43)2365 **55**
6. 34)578 **17**
7. 6)900 **150**
8. 89)8722 **98**

$61 \times 65 = 3965$	$89 \times 98 = 8722$
$55 \times 43 = 2365$	$24 \times 24 = 576$
$17 \times 34 = 578$	$6 \times 150 = 900$

Choose the correct answer without dividing.

9. 13)65 a. 3 b. 4 **(c.) 5** d. 6 e. 7
10. 22)484 a. 10 b. 15 c. 20 **(d.) 22** e. 25
11. 250)2000 **(a.) 8** b. 10 c. 12 d. 14 e. 16
12. 18)288 a. 15 **(b.) 16** c. 17 d. 18 e. 19

Solve.

13. List five prime numbers between 1 and 20. **2, 3, 5, 7, 11, 13, 17, 19**
14. List five composite numbers between 20 and 30. **21, 22, 24, 25, 26, 27, 28**
15. List five numbers between 1 and 20 that have exactly two factors. **1, 2, 3, 5, 7, 11, 13, 17, 19**
16. List five numbers between 20 and 30 that have more than two factors. **20, 21, 22, 24, 25, 26, 27, 28, 30**

List all the factors of each number.

17. 8 **1, 2, 4, 8**
18. 9 **1, 3, 9**
19. 12 **1, 2, 3, 4, 6, 12**
20. 27 **1, 3, 9, 27**

Cumulative Review
Use after Lesson 136.

Find the mean for each set of numbers.

1. 11, 11, 11, 11, 11 **11**
2. 4, 8, 12, 16, 20, 24, 28 **16**
3. 100, 200, 300, 400 **250**
4. 37, 44, 27, 39, 43 **38**

Complete each statement.

5. If something cannot happen, the probability is ■. **0**
6. If something is certain to happen, the probability is ■. **1**
7. If you flip a coin, the probability of getting heads is ■. $\mathbf{\frac{1}{2}}$
8. If you roll a 0–5 cube, the probability of getting a 4 is ■. $\mathbf{\frac{1}{6}}$

What fraction of the set is shaded?

9.  $\mathbf{\frac{1}{5}}$
10.  $\mathbf{\frac{5}{7}}$
11.  $\mathbf{\frac{5}{9}}$
12.  $\mathbf{\frac{1}{2}}$

Solve.

13. $\frac{1}{2}$ of 14 **7**
14. $\frac{1}{3}$ of 15 **5**
15. $\frac{1}{4}$ of 28 **7**
16. $\frac{2}{3}$ of 15 **10**
17. $\frac{1}{5}$ of 50 **10**
18. $\frac{1}{8}$ of 32 **4**
19. $\frac{3}{10}$ of 50 **15**
20. $\frac{7}{8}$ of 32 **28**

Cumulative Review
Use after Lesson 140.

Complete each equivalent fraction.

1. $\frac{1}{2} = \frac{■}{8}$ **4**
2. $\frac{■}{5} = \frac{4}{20}$ **1**
3. $\frac{2}{3} = \frac{6}{■}$ **9**
4. $\frac{5}{■} = \frac{25}{35}$ **7**
5. $\frac{3}{10} = \frac{■}{100}$ **30**
6. $\frac{3}{8} = \frac{■}{56}$ **21**
7. $\frac{3}{4} = \frac{21}{■}$ **28**
8. $\frac{4}{7} = \frac{400}{■}$ **700**

Replace ● with <, >, or =.

9. $\frac{1}{2}$ ● $\frac{1}{3}$ **>**
10. $\frac{2}{3}$ ● $\frac{10}{12}$ **<**
11. $\frac{2}{3}$ ● $\frac{6}{9}$ **=**
12. $\frac{5}{10}$ ● $\frac{4}{8}$ **=**
13. $\frac{3}{10}$ ● $\frac{3}{5}$ **<**
14. $\frac{1}{6}$ ● $\frac{1}{4}$ **<**
15. $\frac{3}{4}$ ● $\frac{7}{8}$ **<**
16. $\frac{11}{12}$ ● $\frac{1}{2}$ **>**

Write a mixed number to show how many.

17.  $\mathbf{2\frac{1}{2}}$
18.  $\mathbf{3\frac{1}{3}}$
19.  $\mathbf{4\frac{3}{4}}$
20.  $\mathbf{3\frac{3}{4}}$

Rewrite each mixed number as an improper fraction.

21. $3\frac{1}{3}$ $\mathbf{\frac{10}{3}}$
22. $4\frac{4}{7}$ $\mathbf{\frac{32}{7}}$
23. $1\frac{5}{8}$ $\mathbf{\frac{13}{8}}$
24. $2\frac{5}{6}$ $\mathbf{\frac{17}{6}}$
25. $6\frac{7}{10}$ $\mathbf{\frac{67}{10}}$

Rewrite each improper fraction as a mixed number.

26. $\frac{11}{5}$ $\mathbf{2\frac{1}{5}}$
27. $\frac{17}{3}$ $\mathbf{5\frac{2}{3}}$
28. $\frac{14}{9}$ $\mathbf{1\frac{5}{9}}$
29. $\frac{13}{2}$ $\mathbf{6\frac{1}{2}}$
30. $\frac{15}{4}$ $\mathbf{3\frac{3}{4}}$

ASSESSMENT

Cumulative Review

Use after Lesson 144.

Estimate the length. Then measure to the nearest $\frac{1}{8}$ inch.

1.  $3\frac{3}{8}$ **in.**
2.  $2\frac{7}{8}$ **in.**
3.  $5\frac{5}{8}$ **in.**
4.  $4\frac{3}{4}$ **in.**

Add or subtract.

5. $\frac{1}{3} + \frac{1}{3}$ $\mathbf{\frac{2}{3}}$
6. $\frac{3}{8} + \frac{4}{8}$ $\mathbf{\frac{7}{8}}$
7. $\frac{3}{10} + \frac{4}{10}$ $\mathbf{\frac{7}{10}}$
8. $\frac{9}{12} - \frac{4}{12}$ $\mathbf{\frac{5}{12}}$
9. $\frac{7}{8} - \frac{6}{8}$ $\mathbf{\frac{1}{8}}$
10. $\frac{9}{10} - \frac{6}{10}$ $\mathbf{\frac{3}{10}}$
11. $\frac{3}{5} - \frac{1}{5}$ $\mathbf{\frac{2}{5}}$
12. $\frac{4}{9} + \frac{4}{9}$ $\mathbf{\frac{8}{9}}$

Write in standard form.

13. 4 ones, 3 tenths, and 9 hundredths **4.39**
14. 8 tens, 2 ones, and 6 tenths **82.6**
15. 9 hundreds, 4 tens, 0 ones, 7 tenths, and 8 hundredths **940.78**
16. 7 thousands, 5 tens, 1 tenth, and 8 hundredths **7050.18**

Add.

17. 20 + 5 + 0.3 + 0.09 **25.39**
18. 70 + 1 + 0.6 + 0.02 **71.62**
19. 10 + 4 + 0.6 + 0.01 **14.61**
20. 50 + 4 + 0.9 + 0.07 **54.97**

ASSESSMENT

Cumulative Review

Use after Lesson 148.

Write each amount as a decimal.

1. 4 dimes and 5 cents **$0.45**
2. 9 cents **$0.09**
3. 7 dimes **$0.70**
4. 0 dimes and 3 cents **$0.03**
5. 60 cents **$0.60**
6. 1 cent **$0.01**

Order the decimals from least to greatest.

7. 0.12, 2.01, 1.02, 0.21 **0.12< 0.21< 1.02< 2.01**
8. 0.473, 0.309, 0.2, 0.07 **0.07<0.2<0.309<0.473**
9. 1.083, 0.854, 0.9, 1.6, 0.44 **0.44<0.854<0.9<1.083<1.6**
10. 0.926, 0.6, 0.29, 0.602, 0.91 **0.29<0.6<0.602<0.91<0.926**

Solve. Watch the signs.

11. 468 + 694 **1162**
12. 5591 ÷ 8 **698 R7**
13. $12.00 − $9.52 **$2.48**
14. 84 × 57 **4788**
15. 62,057 + 8,409 **70,466**
16. 7124 − 5806 **1318**
17. 428 × 63 **26,964**
18. 907 ÷ 4 **226 R3**
19. 40,000 × 90 **3,600,000**

PROBLEM SOLVING

Solve these problems.

20. Guy has $418.91 in his checking account. He writes a check for $39.74 to buy a telephone. How much money does he have left in his account? **$379.17**
21. Zola spent $30 for six pairs of tights. If she bought two more pairs of tights, how much would she spend all together? **$40**
22. Randy has 15 cousins. Two thirds of them live in Maine. How many of his cousins live in Maine? **10**
23. A play lasts 2 hours and 55 minutes. If it begins at 2:30 P.M., what time will it end? **5:25 P.M.**
24. Alyssa had $1\frac{1}{2}$ pounds of clay. She used $\frac{1}{4}$ pound to make beads. How much clay is left? $\mathbf{1\frac{1}{4}}$ **pounds**
25. Mrs. Bellini wants to buy three magazines for $2.50 each. How much change should she receive from a $10 bill? **$2.50**

ASSESSMENT

Cumulative Review

Use after Lesson 153.

Copy and complete the chart.

	Item	Cents		Dollars and Cents	
		Price for 1	Price for 10	Price for 1	Price for 10
1	bolt	49¢	■ **490¢**	■ **$0.49**	■ **$4.90**
2	tack	13¢	■ **130¢**	■ **$0.13**	■ **$1.30**
3	nail	8¢	■ **80¢**	■ **$0.08**	■ **$0.80**
4	screw	24¢	■ **240¢**	■ **$0.24**	■ **$2.40**
5	hook	77¢	■ **770¢**	■ **$0.77**	■ **$7.70**
6	washer	11¢	■ **110¢**	■ **$0.11**	■ **$1.10**

Multiply.

7. 10 × 6.7 **67**
8. 100 × 0.45 **45**
9. 10 × 63.08 **630.8**
10. 100 × 1.085 **108.5**
11. 10 × 3.27 **32.7**
12. 1000 × 7.9 **7900**
13. 100 × 71 **7100**
14. 1000 × 32.61 **32,610**
15. 100 × 8.4 **840**
16. 1000 × 2.852 **2852**
17. 100 × 7.43 **743**
18. 1000 × 0.104 **104**

Divide.

19. 34 ÷ 10 **3.4**
20. 3.4 ÷ 10 **0.34**
21. 0.34 ÷ 10 **0.034**
22. 4.17 ÷ 10 **0.417**
23. 19 ÷ 100 **0.19**
24. 2.8 ÷ 100 **0.028**
25. 0.56 ÷ 100 **0.0056**
26. 2065 ÷ 100 **20.65**
27. 4 ÷ 1000 **0.004**
28. 62 ÷ 1000 **0.062**
29. 7.35 ÷ 1000 **0.00735**
30. 4307 ÷ 1000 **4.307**

Rewrite each mixed number as an improper fraction.

31. $2\frac{1}{3}$ $\mathbf{\frac{7}{3}}$
32. $3\frac{3}{5}$ $\mathbf{\frac{18}{5}}$
33. $1\frac{4}{7}$ $\mathbf{\frac{11}{7}}$
34. $8\frac{1}{6}$ $\mathbf{\frac{49}{6}}$
35. $5\frac{7}{10}$ $\mathbf{\frac{57}{10}}$

Rewrite each improper fraction as a mixed number.

36. $\frac{19}{5}$ $\mathbf{3\frac{4}{5}}$
37. $\frac{22}{3}$ $\mathbf{7\frac{1}{3}}$
38. $\frac{16}{9}$ $\mathbf{1\frac{7}{9}}$
39. $\frac{17}{2}$ $\mathbf{8\frac{1}{2}}$
40. $\frac{21}{4}$ $\mathbf{5\frac{1}{4}}$

ASSESSMENT

Cumulative Review

Use after Lesson 156.

Tell the length of each object in millimeters, then in centimeters.

1.  **21 mm 2.1 cm**
2.  **9 mm 0.9 cm**
3. **33 mm 3.3 cm**
4.  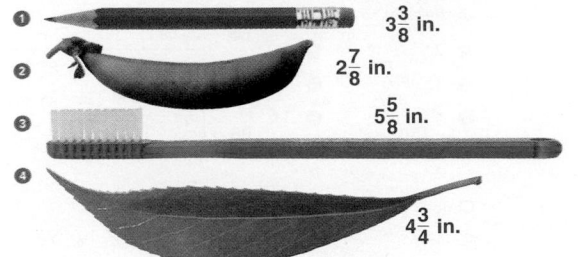 **14 mm 1.4 cm**

Add or subtract.

5. 5.24 + 69.4 = **74.64**
6. 6.7 − 0.81 = **5.89**
7. 8.14 − 6.932 = **1.208**
8. 21.05 + 7.85 = **28.90**
9. 11 − 3.4 = **7.6**

Solve for *n*.

10. 3.15 + 8.2 = *n* **11.35**
11. 43.06 − 9.7 = *n* **33.36**
12. 0.64 + 1.7 = *n* **2.34**
13. 10.4 − 0.7 = *n* **9.7**
14. 10 − 6.254 = *n* **3.746**
15. 0.7 − 0.13 = *n* **0.57**
16. 5.48 + 23 = *n* **28.48**
17. 32.62 + 9.09 = *n* **41.71**
18. 6.8 + 4.32 = *n* **11.12**

Multiply or divide.

19. 4.05 × 13 **52.65**
20. 8.2 × 5.03 **41.246**
21. 0.61 × 45 **27.45**
22. 69.2 ÷ 100 **0.692**
23. 1.25 ÷ 10 **0.125**
24. 17.84 ÷ 1000 **0.01784**

Complete each statement.

25. 4 g = ■ kg **0.004**
26. 52 g = ■ kg **0.052**
27. 7.8 kg = ■ g **7800**
28. 6 mL = ■ L **0.006**
29. 0.05 L = ■ mL **50**
30. 750 mL = ■ L **0.750**

Metric System

Length		Weight (mass)		Liquid Volume (capacity)	
millimeter (mm)	0.001 m	milligram (mg)	0.001 g	milliliter (mL)	0.001 L
centimeter (cm)	0.01 m	centigram (cg)	0.01 g	centiliter (cL)	0.01 L
decimeter (dm)	0.1 m	decigram (dg)	0.1 g	deciliter (dL)	0.1 L
meter (m)	1 m	gram (g)	1 g	liter (L)	1 L
dekameter (dam)	10 m	dekagram (dag)	10 g	dekaliter (daL)	10 L
hectometer (hm)	100 m	hectogram (hg)	100 g	hectoliter (hL)	100 L
kilometer (km)	1000 m	kilogram (kg)	1000 g	kiloliter (kL)	1000 L

◆ **Meaning of Metric Prefixes**

milli	one thousandth	A millimeter is one thousandth of a meter.
centi	one hundredth	A centiliter is one hundredth of a liter.
deci	one tenth	A decigram is one tenth of a gram.
deka	ten	A dekaliter is ten liters.
hecto	one hundred	A hectometer is one hundred meters.
kilo	one thousand	A kilogram is one thousand grams.

◆ **Units of area are derived from units of length.**

square centimeter (cm^2)	$1\ cm^2 = 0.0001\ m^2$
square meter (m^2)	$1\ m^2 = 10{,}000\ cm^2$
hectare (ha)	$1\ ha = 10{,}000\ m^2$
square kilometer (km^2)	$1\ km^2 = 1{,}000{,}000\ m^2$

Examples:

The area of this square is 1 square centimeter.

A square 1 meter long on a side has an area of 1 square meter.

A square 100 meters long on a side has an area of 1 hectare.

A square 1 kilometer long on a side has an area of 1 square kilometer.

◆ **Units of volume can also be derived from units of length.**

cubic centimeter (cm^3)

cubic meter (m^3) $1\ m^3 = 1{,}000{,}000\ cm^3$

Examples:

The volume of this cube is 1 cubic centimeter.

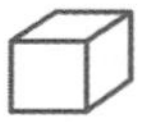

A cube 1 meter long on a side has a volume of 1 cubic meter.

◆ **Descriptions of some common units:**

kilometer	*You can walk a kilometer in about 12 minutes.*
meter	*Most classroom doors are about 1 meter wide.*
centimeter	*This line segment is 1 centimeter long.*
millimeter	*This line segment is 1 millimeter long.*
liter	*Four average-sized glasses hold about 1 liter of liquid all together.*
milliliter	*This cube holds about 1 milliliter of liquid.* 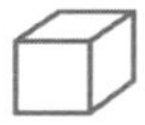
kilogram	*A pair of size-10 men's shoes weighs about 1 kilogram.*
gram	*A nickel weighs about 5 grams.*

Customary System

◆ **Length**

inch (in.)	1 in. =	$\frac{1}{12}$ ft
		$\frac{1}{36}$ yd
foot (ft)	1 ft =	12 in.
		$\frac{1}{3}$ yd
yard (yd)	1 yd =	36 in.
		3 ft
mile (mi)	1 mi =	5280 ft
		1760 yd

◆ **Area**

square inch (sq in. or $in.^2$)	
square foot (sq ft or ft^2)	$1\ ft^2 = 144\ in.^2$
square yard (sq yd or yd^2)	$1\ yd^2 = 9\ ft^2$
acre (A)	$1\ A = 4840\ yd^2$
square mile (sq mi or mi^2)	$1\ mi^2 = 640\ A$

◆ **Weight**

ounce (oz)	1 oz =	$\frac{1}{16}$ lb
pound (lb)	1 lb =	16 oz
ton (T)	1 T =	2000 lb

◆ **Volume**

cubic inch (cu in. or $in.^3$)	
cubic foot (cu ft or ft^3)	$1\ ft^3 = 1728\ in.^3$
cubic yard (cu yd or yd^3)	$1\ yd^3 = 27\ ft^3$

◆ **Liquid Volume (capacity)**

fluid ounce (fl oz)	1 fl oz =	$\frac{1}{8}$ cup
cup (c)	1 c =	8 fl oz
		$\frac{1}{2}$ pt
pint (pt)	1 pt =	16 fl oz
		2 c
		$\frac{1}{2}$ qt
quart (qt)	1 qt =	32 fl oz
		4 c
		$\frac{1}{4}$ gal
gallon (gal)	1 gal =	128 fl oz
		16 c
		8 pt
		4 qt

◆ **Descriptions of some common units:**

mile *You can walk a mile in about 30 minutes.*

yard *Most classroom doors are about 1 yard wide.*

foot *This book is about 1 foot long.*

inch *This line segment is 1 inch long.*

gallon **quart** **pint**

You can buy milk, orange juice, and other drinks in several sizes of containers.

cup *One average-sized glass holds about 1 cup of liquid.*

ton *A small car weighs about 1 ton.*

pound *Three apples weigh about 1 pound.*

ounce *A marble weighs about 1 ounce.*

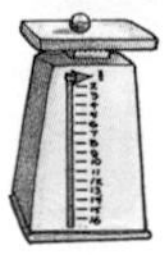

A

addend A number that is added to another number to make a sum. For example:

35 — addend
+ 48 — addend
83 — sum

7 + 8 = 15 — sum (7 — addend, 8 — addend)

algorithm A step-by-step way to solve a certain type of problem.

approximation An answer to a mathematical problem that is not precise but is close enough for the purpose. Sometimes an approximate answer is more useful than a precise answer. (See *estimate*.)

area The number of square units inside a figure. The area of this rectangle is 6 square centimeters:

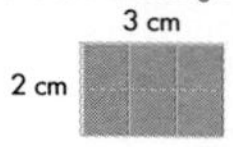

arrow operation A way to show an action of a function machine. In 7 —(×8)→ 56, 7 goes in and is multiplied by 8 to give 56. The function rule in this case is ×8. In the operation 6 ←(−5)— 11, 11 goes in and 5 is subtracted from it to give 6. The function rule in this case is −5.

average A number that can sometimes be used to describe a group of numbers. To find the average of a set of numbers, add the numbers and divide the sum by how many numbers were added. The average of 5, 6, 6, 8, and 10 is 7 (5 + 6 + 6 + 8 + 10 = 35, and 35 ÷ 5 = 7). (Also called *mean*.)

axes (of a graph) The two zero lines of a graph that give the coordinates of points. The horizontal axis is the *x*-axis. The vertical axis is the *y*-axis.

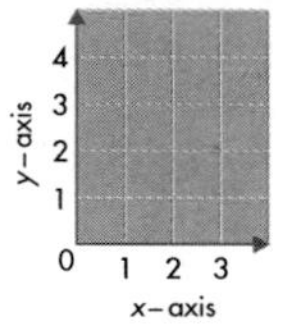

B

balance 1. The amount of money remaining in an account. 2. A double-pan balance is an instrument used to measure weight.

bound A number that an answer must be greater than or less than. For example, 36 × 21 must be less than 40 × 30, or 1200. So 1200 is an upper bound. The answer to 36 × 21 must be greater than 30 × 20, or 600. So 600 is a lower bound.

C

circle A figure (in a plane) in which all points are the same distance from a point called the *center*. In this figure, for example, points *A*, *B*, and *C* are the same distance from point *O*, the center of the circle:

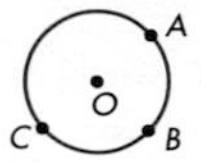

common multiple A number that is a multiple of two or more numbers.

composite function A function with two or more operations.

For example:

x —(×3)→ *n* —(+5)→ *y*

composite number A whole number having factors other than 1 and itself.

congruent Figures that are the same size and shape; that is, they fit perfectly when placed on top of each other. These triangles are congruent:

These triangles are not congruent:

coordinates Numbers that give the position of a point on a graph. In the figure shown, for example, the

coordinates of point *A* are (2, 3). 2 is the *x*-coordinate. 3 is the *y*-coordinate.

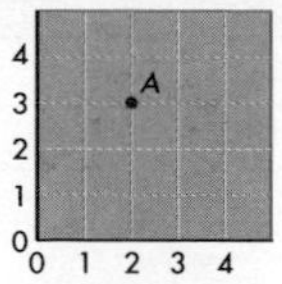

cylinder A space figure with two faces that are circles.

D

decimal point A dot used to separate the ones digit from the tenths digit.

denominator The part of a fraction written below the line. The part written above the line is called the *numerator*. The denominator tells how many equal parts something is divided into; the numerator tells how many of those parts are being referred to. In the fraction $\frac{3}{4}$ the denominator (4) indicates that something is divided into four equal parts. The numerator (3) says to consider three of those parts.

diameter A line segment, going through the center of a circle, that starts at one point on the circle and ends at the opposite point on the circle. (Also, the length of that line segment.) *AB* is a diameter of this circle.

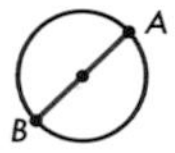

difference The amount by which one number is greater or less than another. For example:

43 — minuend
− 16 — subtrahend
27 — difference

10 − 7 = 3 — difference (7 — subtrahend, 10 — minuend)

digit Any of the numbers 0, 1, 2, 3, 4, 5, 6, 7, 8, and 9. The two digits in 15 are 1 and 5.

dividend A number that is divided by a divisor. For example:

6 ÷ 3 = 2 — quotient (3 — divisor, 6 — dividend)

divisor — 8)347 — dividend, 43 — quotient
32
27
24
3

divisor A number that a dividend is divided by. (See *dividend*.)

E

edge The segment where two faces of a space figure meet.

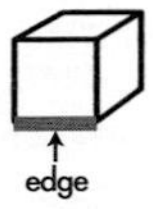

equilateral triangle A triangle with all three sides the same length. For example:

equivalent fractions Fractions that have the same value. For example, $\frac{2}{6}$, $\frac{4}{12}$, and $\frac{1}{3}$ are equivalent fractions.

estimate A judgment about the size or quantity of something. (Also, to make such a judgment.) Sometimes it is more useful to make an estimate than to measure or count precisely. (See *approximation*.)

even number Any multiple of 2. The numbers 0, 2, 4, 6, 8, and so on are even numbers.

F

face A flat surface of a space figure.

factor A number that is multiplied by another number. (See *multiplicand*.)

fraction Examples of fractions are $\frac{1}{2}$, $\frac{3}{4}$, and $\frac{7}{8}$. The

fraction $\frac{3}{4}$ means that something is divided into four equal parts and that we are considering three of those parts. (See *denominator* and *numerator*.)

function machine A machine (sometimes imaginary) that does the same thing to every number that is put into it. (See *arrow operation*.)

function rule See *arrow operation*.

half line See *ray*.

heptagon A polygon with seven sides.

hexagon A polygon with six sides.

hundredth If a whole is divided into 100 equal parts, each part is one hundredth of the whole.

I

improper fraction A fraction whose numerator is greater than or equal to its denominator.

inequality A statement that tells which of two numbers is greater. For example, 4 > 3 is read "4 is greater than 3," and 3 + 6 < 10 is read "3 plus 6 is less than 10."

intersecting lines Lines that meet. In this figure, lines *AB* and *CD* intersect at point *E*:

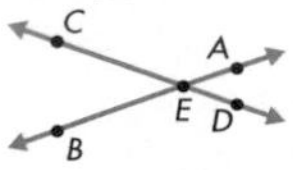

inverse operation An operation that undoes the results of another operation. Multiplication and division are inverse operations; addition and subtraction are inverse operations.

—(× 3)→ is the inverse of —(÷ 3)→

—(− 6)→ is the inverse of —(+ 6)→

isosceles triangle A triangle with two equal sides. These are isosceles triangles:

L

line of symmetry A line on which a figure can be folded into two congruent parts.

line segment A part of a line with two endpoints. For example, *AB* is a line segment; points *A* and *B* are its endpoints.

M

mean See *average*.

median The middle number in a group of numbers when they are listed in order from least to greatest. If there are two numbers in the middle, their average is the median. The median of 2, 3, 4, 5, and 6 is 4.

minuend A number from which another number is subtracted. (See *difference*.)

mixed number A number made up of a whole number and a fraction. The numbers $1\frac{1}{2}$, $2\frac{3}{4}$, and $7\frac{7}{8}$ are mixed numbers.

mode The number that occurs most often in a set of numbers. The mode of 1, 2, 3, 1, 4, and 1 is 1.

multiple A number that is some whole number of times another number. 12 is a multiple of 3 because 3 × 4 = 12.

multiplicand A number that is multiplied by another number, the multiplier. For example:

5 — multiplicand
× 3 — multiplier
15 — product

3 × 5 = 15 — product (5 — multiplicand, 3 — multiplier)

The multiplier and multiplicand are also called the factors of the product.

multiplier See *multiplicand*.

N

numerator The part of a fraction written above the line. (See *denominator*.)

O

octagon A polygon with eight sides.

odd number A whole number that is not a multiple of 2. All whole numbers that are not even are odd. The numbers 1, 3, 5, 7, 9, 11, and so on are odd numbers.

ordered pair Two numbers written so that one is considered before the other. Coordinates of points are written as ordered pairs, with the *x*-coordinate written first, then the *y*-coordinate. For example: (3, 4). (See *coordinates*.)

P

parallel lines Lines in a plane that do not intersect.

Lines *AB* and *CD* are parallel:

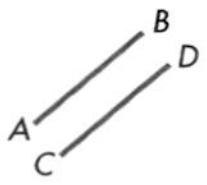

Lines *EF* and *GH* are not parallel:

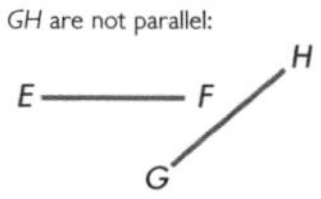

parallelogram A quadrilateral with opposite sides parallel and congruent.

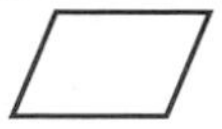

parentheses A pair of symbols (   ) used to show in which order operations should be done. For example, (3 × 5) + 7 says to multiply 5 by 3 and then add 7. 3 × (5 + 7) says to add 5 and 7 and then multiply by 3.

partial product The product that comes from multiplying the multiplicand by one of the digits of the multiplier. For example:

36
× 12
72 — This partial product comes from multiplying 36 by 2 ones.
36 — This partial product comes from multiplying 36 by 1 ten.
432 — The product comes from adding the partial products.

pentagon A polygon with five sides.

perimeter The distance around a figure. The perimeter of this rectangle is 6 cm:

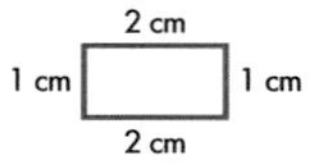

perpendicular lines Lines that intersect at right angles.

These lines are perpendicular:

So are these:

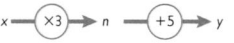

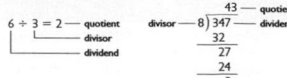

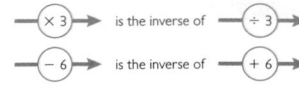

But these are not:

place value The value of a digit in a number. The value of 7 in 27 is 7 ones; in 74 its value is 70, or 7 tens; and in 726 its value is 700, or 7 hundreds.

polygon A certain kind of figure with straight sides. These figures are polygons:

These are not:

Here are the names of some common polygons and the number of their sides:

Number of Sides	Name
3	triangle
4	quadrilateral
5	pentagon—a regular pentagon has five equal sides:

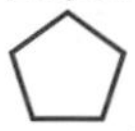

6 hexagon—a regular hexagon has six equal sides:

8 octagon—a regular octagon has eight equal sides:

prime number A whole number divisible only by 1 and itself.

prism A space figure with two parallel, congruent faces, called bases. These are prisms:

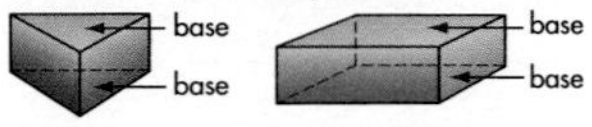

probability How likely it is that something will happen. The probability that a certain thing will happen is a fraction. The denominator is the total number of possible things that can happen, and the numerator is the number of ways this particular thing can happen. The probability that an ordinary coin will land on heads when it is flipped is about $\frac{1}{2}$.

product The result of multiplying two numbers together. (See *multiplicand.*)

profit In a business, the money that is left after all expenses have been paid.

pyramid A space figure formed by connecting points of a polygon to a point not in the plane of the polygon. These are pyramids:

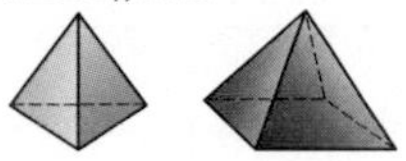

Q

quadrilateral A polygon with four sides.

quotient The result (other than the remainder) of dividing one number by another number. (See *dividend.*)

R

radius A line segment that goes from the center of a circle to a point on the circle. (Also, the length of such a segment.) *OA* is a radius of the circle shown here. The radius of this circle is 1 centimeter.

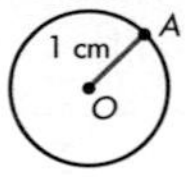

ray A set of points that has one endpoint and extends without end in one direction. In the figure below, *OA* and *OB* are rays.

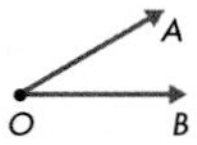

rectangle A quadrilateral in which all four angles are right angles.

reflection A change in the location of a figure when it is flipped over a line.

regroup To rename a number to make adding and subtracting easier.

Example of regrouping in subtraction:

$$\begin{array}{r} \scriptstyle 1\ 15 \\ \not{2}\not{5} \\ -17 \\ \hline 8 \end{array}$$

(To subtract in the ones column, 2 tens and 5 is regrouped as 1 ten and 15.)

Example of regrouping in addition:

$$\begin{array}{r} \scriptstyle 1\ \ \ \\ 296 \\ +\ 442 \\ \hline 738 \end{array}$$

(After the tens column is added, 13 tens is regrouped as 1 hundred and 3 tens.)

relation signs The three basic relation signs are > (greater than), < (less than), and = (equal to). (See *inequality.*)

remainder A number less than the divisor that remains after the dividend has been divided by the divisor as many times as possible. For example, when

you divide 25 by 4, the quotient is 6 with a remainder of 1:

$$\begin{array}{r} 6 \ \mathbf{R1} \\ 4\overline{)25} \\ \underline{24} \\ 1 \end{array}$$

right angle An angle that forms a square corner.

These are right angles:

These are not:

rotation A change in the location of a figure when it is turned in a circle around a point.

rounding Changing a number to another number that is easier to work with and that is close enough for the purpose. (See *approximation.*)

S

sphere A space figure with all points the same distance from a point called the *center.*

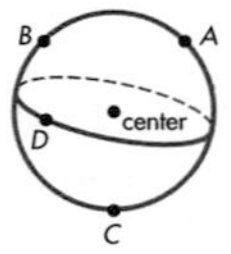

square A quadrilateral with four equal sides and four equal angles.

subtrahend A number that is subtracted from another number. (See *difference.*)

sum The result of adding two or more numbers. (See *addend.*)

symmetrical figure A figure that can be divided in half so that each half looks exactly like the other. (See *line of symmetry.*)

T

tenth If a whole is divided into ten equal parts, each part is one tenth of the whole.

translation A change in the location of a figure when it is placed on top of another figure.

trapezoid A quadrilateral with exactly one pair of parallel sides. This is a trapezoid:

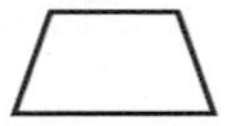

triangle A polygon that has three sides.

U

unit cost The cost of one item or one specified amount of an item. If 20 pencils cost 40¢, then the unit cost is 2¢ for each pencil. If dog food costs $9 for 3 kilograms, then the unit cost is $3 per kilogram.

V

vertex 1. The point where two rays meet. 2. The point of intersection of two sides of a polygon. 3. The point of intersection of three edges of a space figure.

volume The number of cubic units that fit inside a space figure.

W

whole number The numbers that we use to show how many (0, 1, 2, 3, and so on). The number 3 is a whole number, but $3\frac{1}{2}$ and 4.5 are not whole numbers.

Z

zero The number that tells how many things there are when there aren't any. Any number times 0 is 0 and any number plus 0 is that number: $0 \times 3 = 0$ and $0 + 3 = 3$.

GAME DIRECTORY

Game	Principal Skills	Begin Using* Student's Edition	Begin Using* Teacher's Guide
Roll a Number	Using place value (distinguishing the value of each digit in multidigit numbers); using intuitive notions of probability	page 11	Lesson 2
Order	Using place value; using intuitive notions of probability	page 13	Lesson 3
Roll a 15	Addition, subtraction, and mathematical reasoning	page 15	Lesson 4
Don't Go Over 1000	Adding two three-digit numbers; approximating sums	page 41	Lesson 12
Roll a Problem	Adding and subtracting multidigit numbers; using place value; using intuitive notions of probability	page 45	Lesson 13
Transaction	Adding and subtracting money (dollars); maintaining a record of money transactions; using place value		Lesson 13
Inequality	Recognizing true and false inequality statements; mathematical reasoning	page 55	Lesson 16
Fracto 1	Recognizing fractional areas of a circle; recognizing which fraction areas, when combined, are more than half the area of a circle		Lesson 20
Fracto 2	Recognizing fractional areas of a rectangle; recognizing which fraction areas, when combined, are more than half the area of a rectangle		Lesson 20
Store	Forming amounts of money; making change		Lesson 21
Harder Store	Forming amounts of money; making change		Lesson 21
Money Roll	Using place value; using decimal and money notation; using intuitive notions of probability	page 75	Lesson 22
Harder Transaction	Adding and subtracting money (dollars and cents); maintaining a record of money transactions		Lesson 23
Multiple Crossing	Practicing basic facts; using factors up to 10; using mathematical reasoning		Lesson 29
Multiplication Table	Using a multiplication table; multiplying with two factors of 5 or less		Lesson 30
Harder Multiplication Table	Using two multiplication tables; multiplying with two factors of 10 or less		Lesson 30
Shopping	Multiplying with factors up to 9; forming amounts of money; making change		Lesson 31
Harder Shopping	Multiplying two-digit numbers by one-digit numbers; forming amounts of money; making change		Lesson 31

GAME DIRECTORY

Game	Principal Skills	Begin Using* Student Edition	Begin Using* Teacher's Guide
Add the Products	Multiplication and addition	page 110	Lesson 32
Minutes	Telling time to five-minute intervals		Lesson 35
Harder Minutes	Telling time to the nearest minute		Lesson 35
Customary Unit	Determining which customary units of weight and length make sense with given numbers to describe given objects		Lesson 36
Metric Unit	Determining which metric units of weight and length make sense with given numbers to describe given objects		Lesson 37
Multigo 1	Solving missing-factor problems related to the multiplication facts; using mathematical reasoning		Lesson 41
Multigo 2	Solving missing-factor problems related to the multiplication facts; using mathematical reasoning		Lesson 41
Cubo	Using mental arithmetic with all four operations	page 163	Lesson 48
Animal Data	Collecting and displaying data on a graph; using compass directions and mathematical reasoning		Lesson 51
Baseball	Locating coordinates on a graph; using mathematical reasoning		Lesson 52
Snake	Solving missing-term problems; using mental arithmetic; using mathematical reasoning		Lesson 53
Function	Using mental arithmetic; using mathematical reasoning	page 194	Lesson 57
Cubo Challenge	Using mental arithmetic with all four operations; using mathematical reasoning	page 261	Lesson 77
Cube 100	Multiplying one-digit and two-digit numbers by one-digit numbers; adding one-digit and two-digit numbers; using mathematical reasoning	page 293	Lesson 87
Four Cube Multiplication	Using multidigit multiplication; using place value; using mathematical reasoning	page 305	Lesson 89
(Multiplication) Roll a Problem	Using multidigit multiplication; using place value; using intuitive notions of probability	page 325	Lesson 95
More or Less Game	Multiplying two-digit numbers; working with inequality relationships; using intuitive notions of probability	page 339	Lesson 100
Diviso	Dividing by one-digit divisors; using mental factorization	page 367	Lesson 107

GAME DIRECTORY

GAME	PRINCIPAL SKILLS	BEGIN USING* Student's Edition	Teacher's Guide
Four Cube Division	Dividing by one-digit divisors; using place value	page 374	Lesson 110
Harder Snake	Finding multiplication and division function rules		Lesson 120
Fractions of 60	Finding fractions of whole numbers; using addition	page 435	Lesson 127
Anything but 10	Mental addition; practicing addition; applying intuitive notions of probability	page 441	Lesson 130
Roll a Decimal	Using place value; comparing decimal numbers; using mathematical reasoning	page 474	Lesson 140
Find the Distance 1	Estimating straight distance to nearest centimeter; comparing line lengths; practicing basic facts		Lesson 146
Find the Distance 2	Estimating straight distance to the nearest centimeter; comparing line lengths; practicing basic facts		Lesson 146
Harder Roll a Decimal	Using place value; subtracting decimals; using mathematical reasoning	page 501	Lesson 148
Checkbook	Adding and subtracting multidigit numbers; maintaining a record of money transactions		Lesson 149
Harder Checkbook	Adding and subtracting multidigit numbers involving dollars and cents; maintaining a record of money transactions		Lesson 149

***These games and their variations should be used many times throughout the year. Feel free to use them again any time after they are introduced.**
****Games in red are from the Game Mat set.**

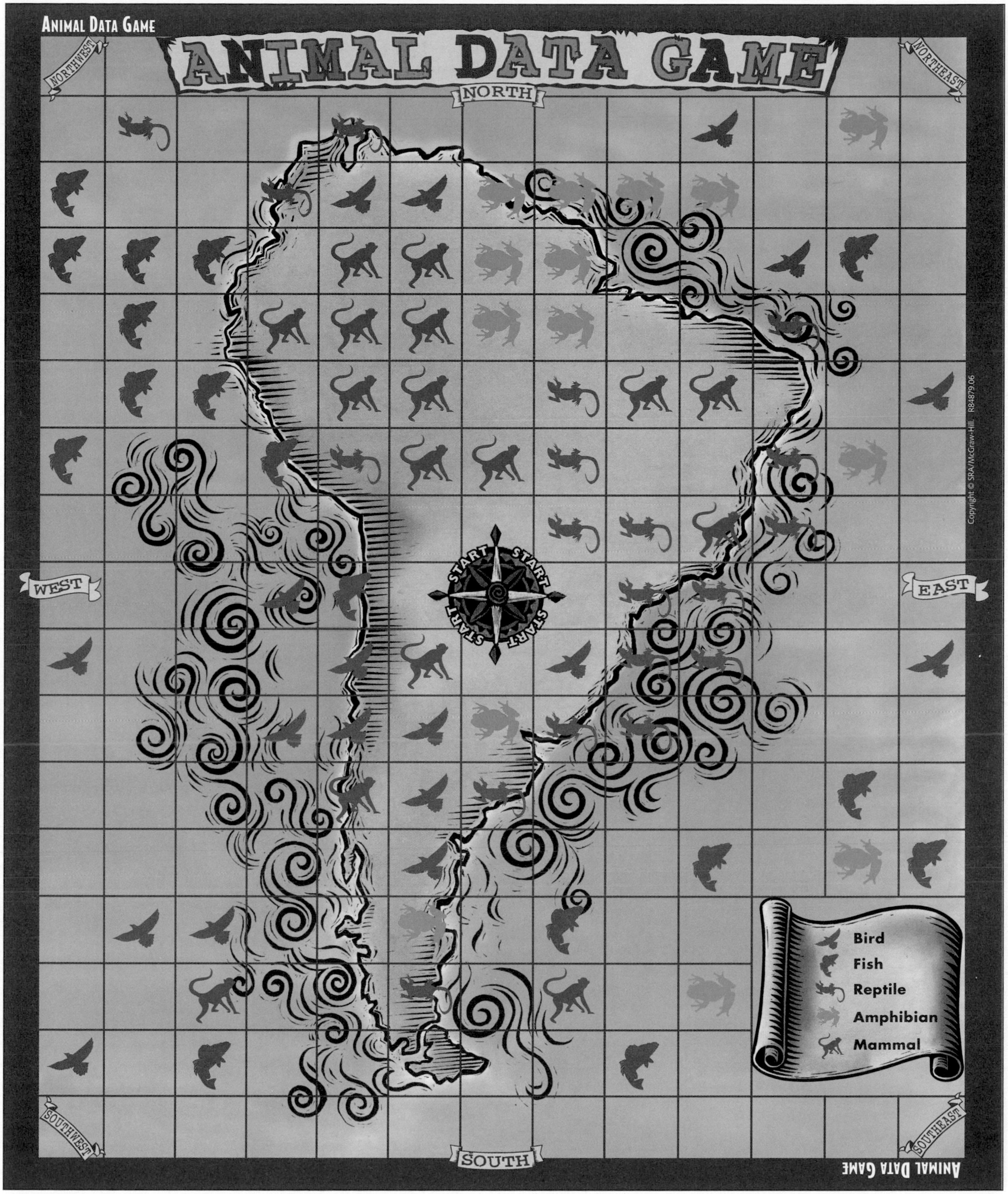

Copyright © SRA/McGraw-Hill. All rights reserved.

How to Play Animal Data

Math Focus:

- Collecting and displaying data on a graph
- Using compass directions and mathematical reasoning

Object of the Game: To be the first to complete a graph

Players: Two, three, or four

MATERIALS

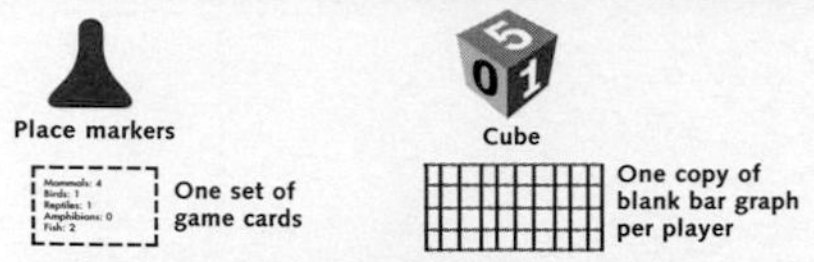

SET UP

- For each group, make one copy of the game cards and cut them out.
- Shuffle the cards and place them face down next to the game mat.
- Make one copy of the blank bar graph for each player and distribute the copies.
- Review the different animal groups and their characteristics.
- Players roll the 0-5 number cube. The person who rolls the highest number goes first.
- Players put their place markers on the compass in the center of the board.

HOW TO PLAY

1. All players draw a game card, which tells each player how many of each animal group he or she must graph.
2. Players take turns announcing a direction, rolling the number cube, and moving the number of spaces indicated. Players must announce a direction *before* rolling.
3. Each time players land on an animal group listed on their game card, they fill in one more box on their graphs. Players who land on a group that they do not need or have already filled in on their graphs must wait until the next turn to roll again.

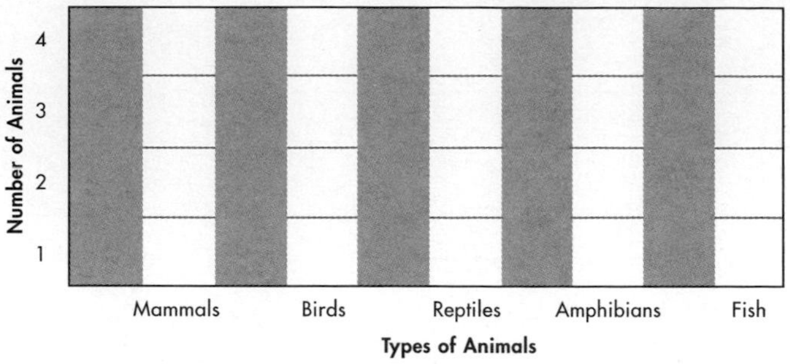

4. Players whose roll would land them on an occupied square or take them off the board cannot move that turn.
5. Players who roll a 0 cannot move that turn, but they can record another animal if there is one on their space.
6. The player who fills in his or her graph first is the winner.

Animal Data Game

Mammals: 2 Birds: 2 Reptiles: 1 Amphibians: 1 Fish: 2	Mammals: 1 Birds: 1 Reptiles: 1 Amphibians: 2 Fish: 3	Mammals: 1 Birds: 1 Reptiles: 3 Amphibians: 1 Fish: 2	Mammals: 1 Birds: 4 Reptiles: 1 Amphibians: 1 Fish: 1	Mammals: 2 Birds: 3 Reptiles: 1 Amphibians: 1 Fish: 1	Mammals: 4 Birds: 0 Reptiles: 1 Amphibians: 3 Fish: 0
Mammals: 3 Birds: 1 Reptiles: 1 Amphibians: 2 Fish: 1	Mammals: 1 Birds: 2 Reptiles: 1 Amphibians: 1 Fish: 3	Mammals: 0 Birds: 2 Reptiles: 2 Amphibians: 1 Fish: 3	Mammals: 3 Birds: 1 Reptiles: 1 Amphibians: 1 Fish: 2	Mammals: 1 Birds: 1 Reptiles: 1 Amphibians: 1 Fish: 4	Mammals: 0 Birds: 4 Reptiles: 1 Amphibians: 1 Fish: 2
Mammals: 4 Birds: 1 Reptiles: 1 Amphibians: 0 Fish: 2	Mammals: 3 Birds: 3 Reptiles: 1 Amphibians: 0 Fish: 1	Mammals: 1 Birds: 2 Reptiles: 0 Amphibians: 2 Fish: 3	Mammals: 3 Birds: 2 Reptiles: 1 Amphibians: 1 Fish: 1	Mammals: 2 Birds: 2 Reptiles: 2 Amphibians: 2 Fish: 0	Mammals: 2 Birds: 0 Reptiles: 3 Amphibians: 1 Fish: 2

Copyright © SRA/McGraw-Hill. Permission is granted to reproduce this page for classroom use only.

Copyright © SRA/McGraw-Hill. All rights reserved.

Math Focus: Locating coordinates on a graph
Object of the Game: To score more runs
Players: Two

MATERIALS

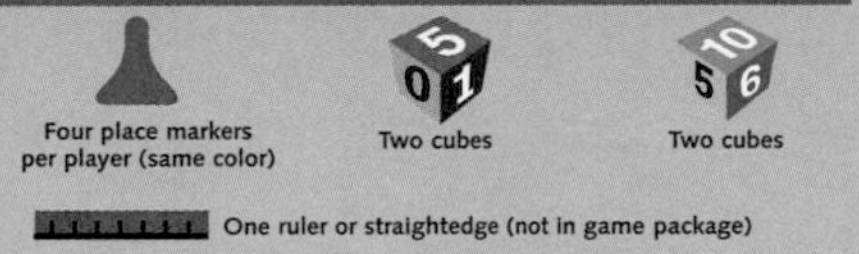

SET UP

- Decide how many full innings will be played.
- Each player rolls the 0-5 number cube. The player who rolls the higher number goes first.

HOW TO PLAY

1. When you bat, you make an ordered pair by rolling any cube to get the first number and another cube to get the second number. You must roll one cube at a time and use the numbers in order.
2. Place the straightedge through (0, 0) and through the point corresponding to the ordered pair that you rolled. For example, if you roll 9 and 5, the straightedge starts at (0, 0) and passes through (9, 5).
3. If the straightedge crosses **OUT**, it's an out.
4. If the straightedge crosses **HIT**, it's a hit. Move a marker to the appropriate base. On a hit, runners on base may also advance the same number of bases. For example, a runner on second can go to third during a single.
5. If you roll (0, 0), it is a bunt. You are out, but if there are runners on base, they may advance one base.
6. Write down the numbers you roll and all outs, hits, and runs.
7. Each player gets three outs per inning. The player with more runs at the end of the game wins.

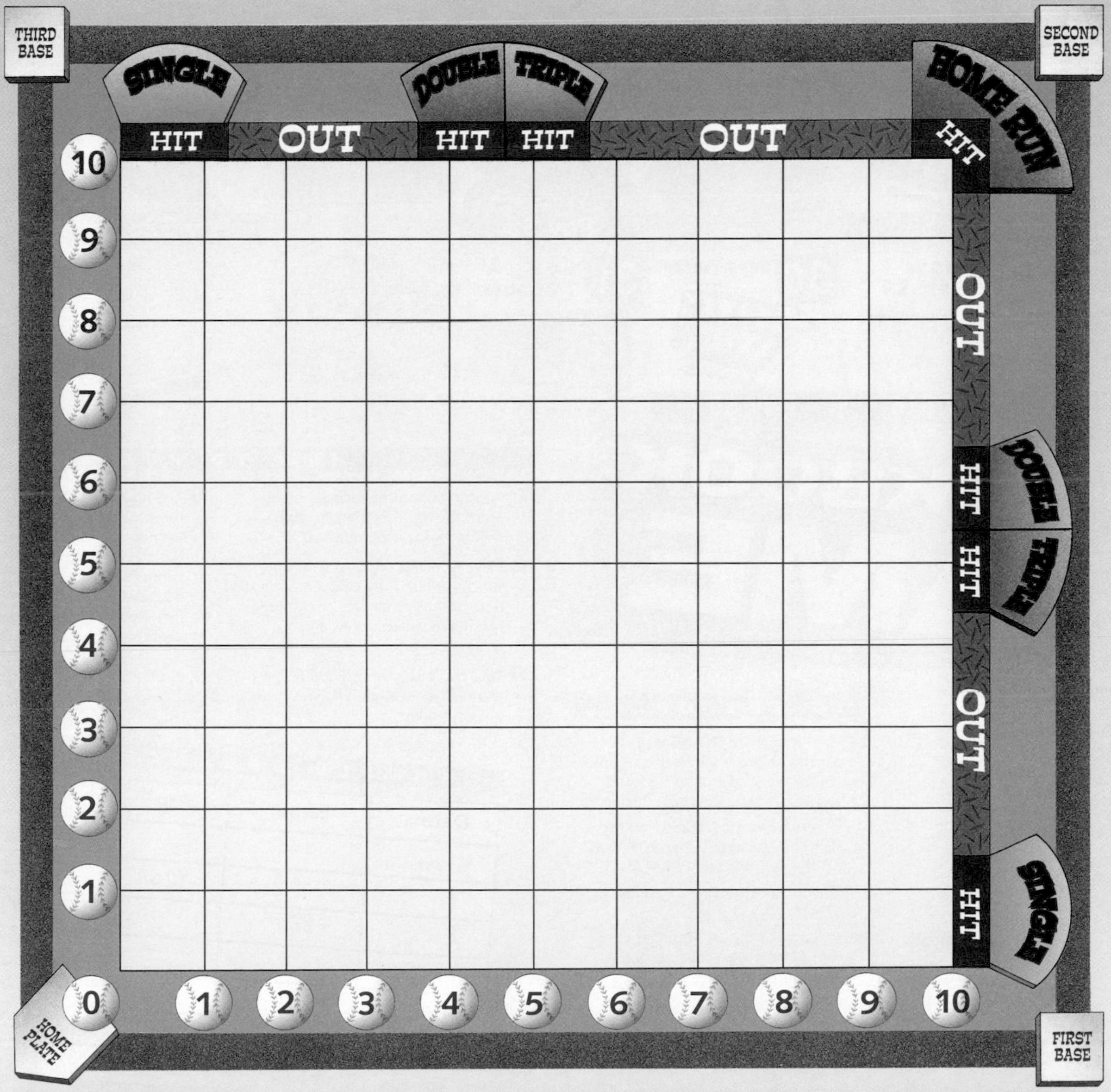

BASEBALL GAME

Copyright © SRA/McGraw-Hill R84887.04

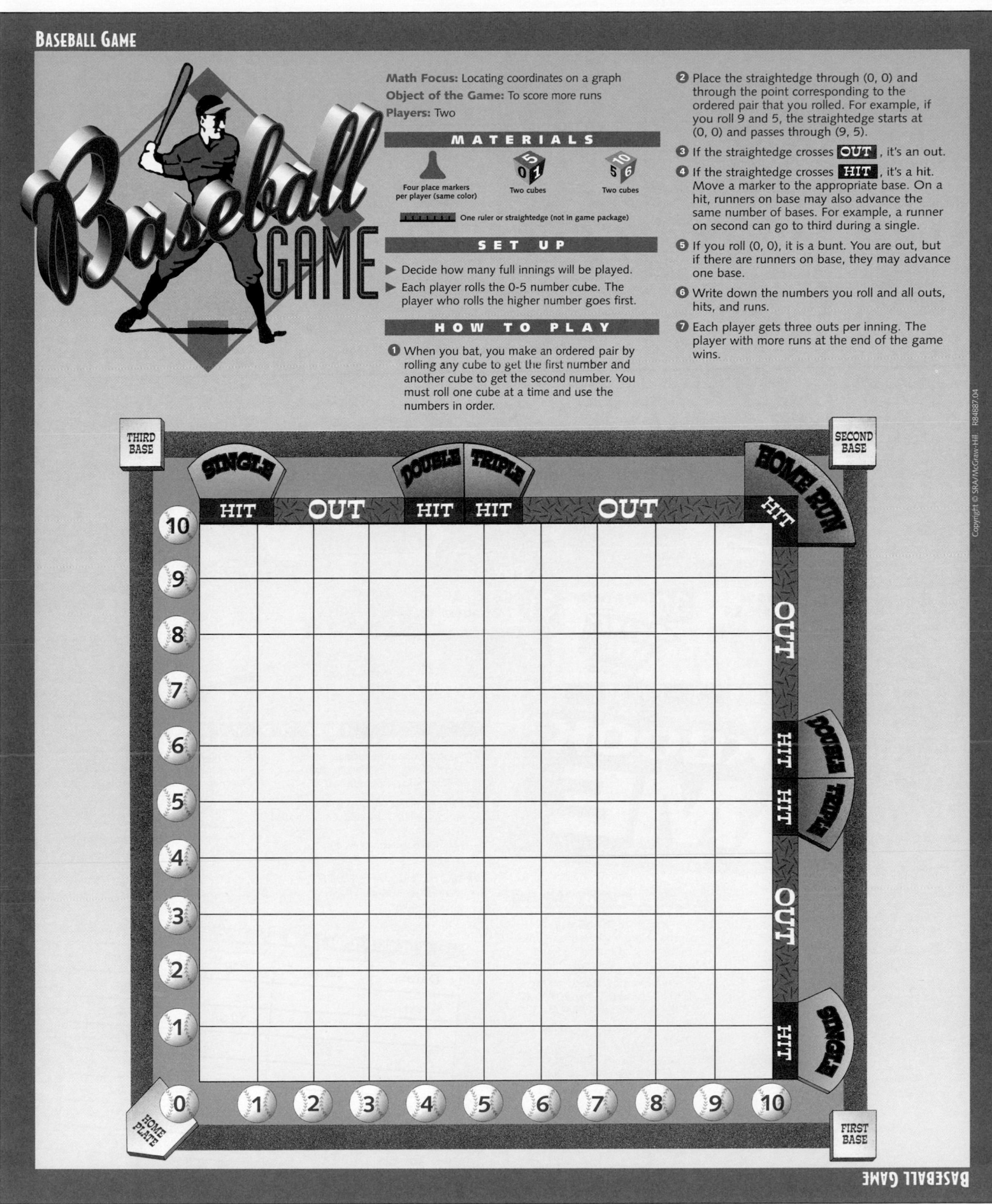

Copyright © SRA/McGraw-Hill. All rights reserved.

Copyright © SRA/McGraw-Hill. R84860.06

CHECKBOOK GAME

Math Focus:
- Adding and subtracting two-digit and three-digit numbers
- Maintaining a record of money transactions

Object of the Game: To have the largest balance at the end of the month

Players: Two or three

MATERIALS

Place markers
Cube
One balance sheet per player

SET UP

- Photocopies of the balance sheet for the "Harder Checkbook Game" can be handed out to students.
- Players prepare their balance sheets by writing "Start" on the first line under DATE and "$1000" on the first line under BALANCE.
- Players put their place markers on START.
- Players roll the 0-5 number cube. The person who rolls the highest number goes first.

HOW TO PLAY

1. Players take turns rolling the cube and moving their markers the number of spaces indicated.
2. Players follow the directions on the spaces where they land, entering the date and all payments or earnings on their balance sheets and recalculating their balances.
3. Play continues until all the players have either reached FINISH or run out of money.
4. The player with the largest balance at the end of the game is declared the winner. The other players then check the addition and subtraction in the winner's balance sheet. If the balance does not check, the player with the highest correct balance becomes the winner.

SAMPLE BALANCE SHEET

Date	Earn	Pay	Balance
Start			$1000
3		-$26	$974
8	+$23		$997
11			
4	+$50		$1047
6		-$20	$1027
Totals	+$73	-$46	$1027

CHECKBOOK GAME

Copyright © SRA/McGraw-Hill. All rights reserved.

Sunday	Monday	Tuesday	Wednesday	Thursday	Friday	Saturday
Start Your Balance is $1000.00	1 Supermarket Pay $35.22	2 Dentist Bill Pay $50.00	3 Electric Bill Pay $26.14	4 STOCK DIVIDEND Earn $50.00	5 Insurance Bill Pay $38.17	6 THEATER TICKETS Pay $20.00
7 Eat in Restaurant Pay $20.82	8 WORK OVERTIME Earn $23.50	9 Supermarket Pay $51.62	10 United Fund Pay $100.00	11 Go Back 7 Spaces	12 Income TAX Pay $212.00	13 Go to Movies Pay $5.00
14 Visit Museum FREE	15 RENT Pay $150.00	16 Holiday! No bills today	17 Supermarket Pay $47.94	18 BUY BOOKS Pay $14.50	19 Telephone Bill Pay $17.36	20 WORK OVERTIME Earn $43.71
21 VISIT ZOO FREE	22 Supermarket Pay $35.61	23 Go Back 7 Spaces	24 Parking Ticket Pay $5.00	25 Go Ahead 2 Spaces	26 Automobile Repairs Pay $285.00	27 JOB BONUS Earn $250.00
28 Eat in Restaurant Pay $22.16	29 NEW SHOES Pay $15.45	30 Supermarket Pay $51.62	31 Go Back 7 Spaces	Finish Wait until all players finish		

HARDER CHECKBOOK GAME

Math Focus:
- Adding and subtracting two-digit, three-digit, and four-digit numbers
- Maintaining a record of money transactions

Object of the Game: To have the largest balance at the end of the month

Players: Two or three

MATERIALS

Place markers · Cube · One balance sheet per player

SET UP

- Photocopies of the sample balance sheet can be handed out to students.
- Players prepare their balance sheets by writing "Start" on the first line under DATE and "$1000" on the first line under BALANCE.
- Players put their place markers on START.
- Players roll the 0-5 number cube. The person who rolls the highest number goes first.

HOW TO PLAY

1. Players take turns rolling the cube and moving their markers the number of spaces indicated.
2. Players follow the directions on the spaces where they land, entering the date and all payments or earnings on their balance sheets and recalculating their balances.
3. Play continues until all the players have either reached FINISH or run out of money.
4. The player with the largest balance at the end of the game is declared the winner. The other players then check the addition and subtraction in the winner's balance sheet. If the balance does not check, the player with the highest correct balance becomes the winner.

SAMPLE BALANCE SHEET

Date	Earn	Pay	Balance

HARDER CHECKBOOK GAME

Copyright © SRA/McGraw-Hill. All rights reserved.

CUSTOMARY UNIT GAME

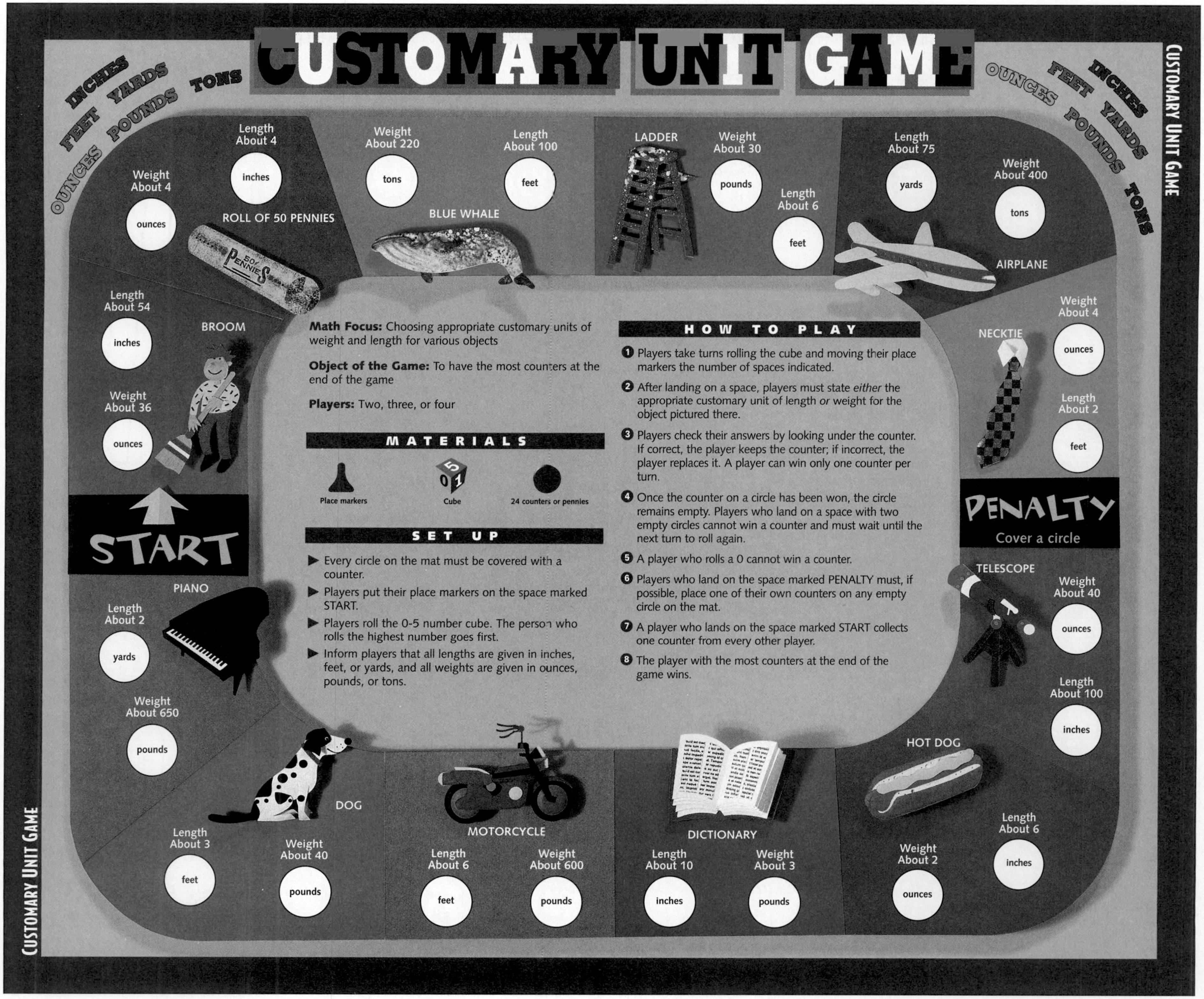

Math Focus: Choosing appropriate customary units of weight and length for various objects

Object of the Game: To have the most counters at the end of the game

Players: Two, three, or four

MATERIALS

Place markers, Cube, 24 counters or pennies

SET UP

- Every circle on the mat must be covered with a counter.
- Players put their place markers on the space marked START.
- Players roll the 0-5 number cube. The person who rolls the highest number goes first.
- Inform players that all lengths are given in inches, feet, or yards, and all weights are given in ounces, pounds, or tons.

HOW TO PLAY

1. Players take turns rolling the cube and moving their place markers the number of spaces indicated.
2. After landing on a space, players must state *either* the appropriate customary unit of length *or* weight for the object pictured there.
3. Players check their answers by looking under the counter. If correct, the player keeps the counter; if incorrect, the player replaces it. A player can win only one counter per turn.
4. Once the counter on a circle has been won, the circle remains empty. Players who land on a space with two empty circles cannot win a counter and must wait until the next turn to roll again.
5. A player who rolls a 0 cannot win a counter.
6. Players who land on the space marked PENALTY must, if possible, place one of their own counters on any empty circle on the mat.
7. A player who lands on the space marked START collects one counter from every other player.
8. The player with the most counters at the end of the game wins.

CUSTOMARY UNIT GAME

Copyright © SRA/McGraw-Hill. All rights reserved.

METRIC UNIT GAME

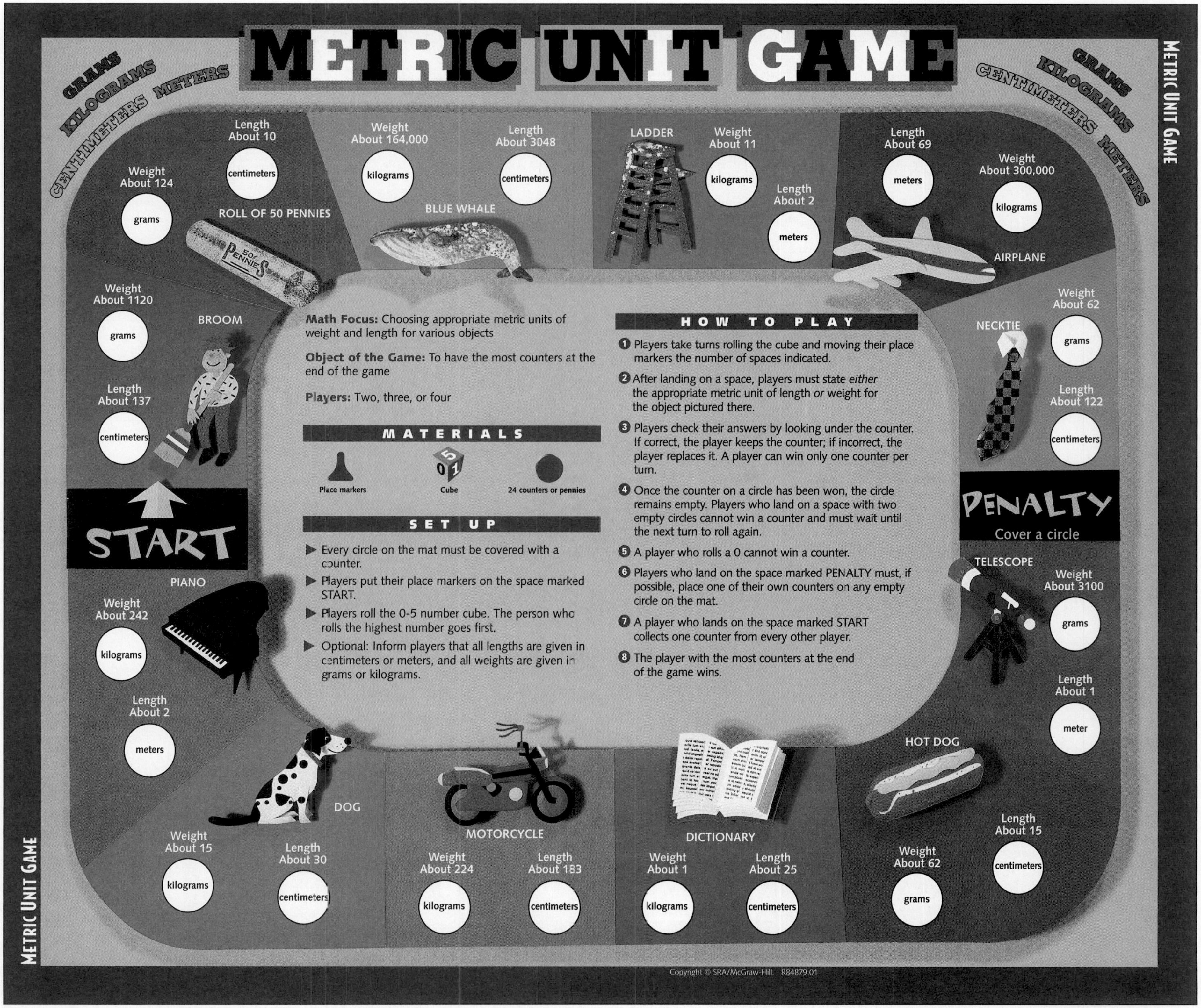

Math Focus: Choosing appropriate metric units of weight and length for various objects

Object of the Game: To have the most counters at the end of the game

Players: Two, three, or four

MATERIALS

Place markers — Cube — 24 counters or pennies

SET UP

- Every circle on the mat must be covered with a counter.
- Players put their place markers on the space marked START.
- Players roll the 0-5 number cube. The person who rolls the highest number goes first.
- Optional: Inform players that all lengths are given in centimeters or meters, and all weights are given in grams or kilograms.

HOW TO PLAY

1. Players take turns rolling the cube and moving their place markers the number of spaces indicated.
2. After landing on a space, players must state *either* the appropriate metric unit of length *or* weight for the object pictured there.
3. Players check their answers by looking under the counter. If correct, the player keeps the counter; if incorrect, the player replaces it. A player can win only one counter per turn.
4. Once the counter on a circle has been won, the circle remains empty. Players who land on a space with two empty circles cannot win a counter and must wait until the next turn to roll again.
5. A player who rolls a 0 cannot win a counter.
6. Players who land on the space marked PENALTY must, if possible, place one of their own counters on any empty circle on the mat.
7. A player who lands on the space marked START collects one counter from every other player.
8. The player with the most counters at the end of the game wins.

Copyright © SRA/McGraw-Hill. R84879.01

METRIC UNIT GAME

Copyright © SRA/McGraw-Hill. All rights reserved.

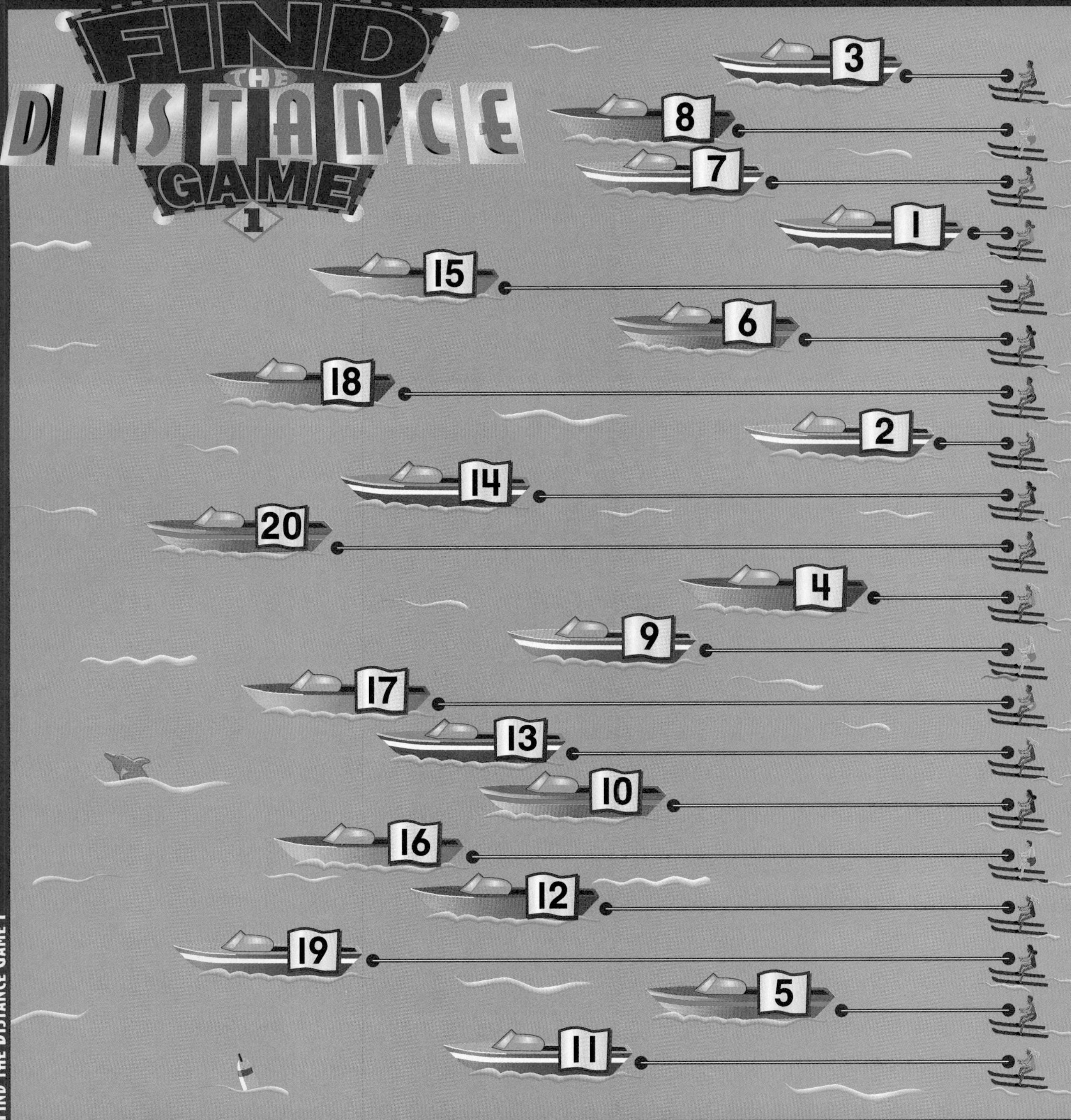

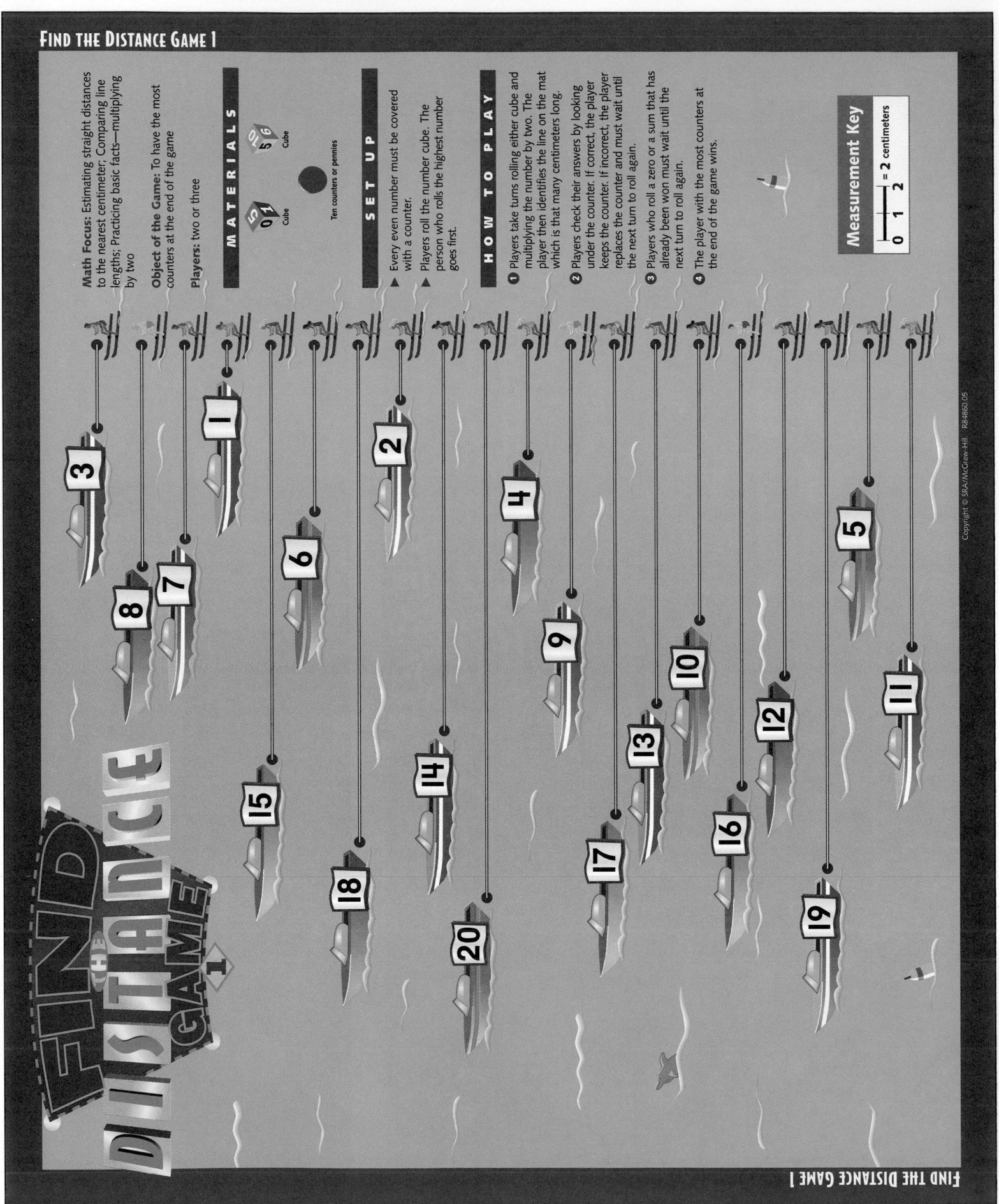

Math Focus: Estimating straight distances to the nearest centimeter; Comparing line lengths; Practicing basic facts—multiplying by two

Object of the Game: To have the most counters at the end of the game

Players: two or three

MATERIALS

Cube   Cube

Ten counters or pennies

SET UP

- Every even number must be covered with a counter.
- Players roll the number cube. The person who rolls the highest number goes first.

HOW TO PLAY

1. Players take turns rolling either cube and multiplying the number by two. The player then identifies the line on the mat which is that many centimeters long.
2. Players check their answers by looking under the counter. If correct, the player keeps the counter. If incorrect, the player replaces the counter and must wait until the next turn to roll again.
3. Players who roll a zero or a sum that has already been won must wait until the next turn to roll again.
4. The player with the most counters at the end of the game wins.

Measurement Key

0 1 2 = 2 centimeters

Copyright © SRA/McGraw-Hill. R84860.05

FIND THE DISTANCE GAME 1

Copyright © SRA/McGraw-Hill. All rights reserved.

Math Focus: Estimating straight distances to the nearest centimeter; Comparing line lengths; Practicing basic facts—multiplying by two

Object of the Game: To have the most counters at the end of the game

Players: two or three

MATERIALS

Cube | Cube | Ten counters or pennies

SET UP

- Every even-numbered circle must be covered with a counter.
- Players roll the number cube. The person who rolls the highest number goes first.

HOW TO PLAY

1. Players take turns rolling either cube and multiplying the number by two. The player then identifies the line on the mat which is that many centimeters long.
2. Players check their answers by looking under the counter. If correct, the player keeps the counter. If incorrect, the player replaces the counter and must wait until the next turn to roll again.
3. Players who roll a zero or a sum that has already been won must wait until the next turn to roll again.
3. The player with the most counters at the end of the game wins.

FIND THE DISTANCE GAME 2

Copyright © SRA/McGraw-Hill. All rights reserved.

FRACTO 1

Math Focus:

- Recognizing fractional areas of a circle from fifths to tenths
- Recognizing which common fractions equal more than 1/2 when added together

Object of the Game: To have more pies at the end of the game

Players: Two

MATERIALS

30 counters of the same color for each player, or 30 pennies and 30 dimes

SET UP

- The first player chooses his or her counters, and is followed by the second player.
- Everyone rolls the 0-5 number cube. The person who rolls the higher number goes first.

HOW TO PLAY

1. Take turns rolling the cubes to make proper fractions (equivalent to 1 or less). If you roll a 0 on either of the cubes, roll that cube again.
2. Cover an amount of pie equal to the fraction you rolled. For example, if you roll a 3 and a 7, cover 3/7 of a pie divided into sevenths. The sections you cover do not have to be in the same pie.
3. You can also cover sections of pies divided into different fractions, as long as the total amount you cover equals the fraction that you rolled. For example, if you roll a 3 and a 6, you could cover 4/8 of the pies divided into eighths, since 4/8 = 3/6. Or you could cover 3/9 of the ninths pies and 1/6 of the sixths pies, since 3/9 + 1/6 = 3/6.
4. If you cannot use the fraction you rolled, you must wait until your next turn to roll again.
5. You win a pie when you cover more than half of it. Place your counter in the center and return any of your opponent's counters.
6. If you cover half of a pie and your opponent covers the other half, neither of you can win that pie.
7. Keep playing until all the pies are either won or completely covered. The player who has more pies at the end of the game is the winner.

Copyright © SRA/McGraw-Hill. R84887.01

Copyright © SRA/McGraw-Hill. All rights reserved.

FRACTO 2

Math Focus:
- Recognizing fractional areas of a circle from fifths to tenths
- Recognizing which common fractions equal more than 1/2 when added together

Object of the Game: To have more loaves at the end of the game

Players: Two

MATERIALS

SET UP

- The first player chooses his or her counters and is followed by the second player.
- Players roll the 0-5 number cube. The person who rolls the higher number goes first.

HOW TO PLAY

1. Take turns rolling the cubes to make proper fractions (equivalent to 1 or less). If you roll a 0 on either of the cubes, roll that cube again.
2. Cover an amount of loaf equal to the fraction you rolled. For example, if you roll a 3 and a 7, cover 3/7 of a loaf divided into sevenths. The sections you cover do not have to be in the same loaf.
3. You may also cover sections of loaves divided into different fractions, as long as the total amount you cover equals the fraction that you rolled. For example, if you roll a 3 and a 6, you could cover 4/8 of the loaves divided into eighths, since 4/8 = 3/6. Or you could cover 3/9 of the ninths loaves and 1/6 of the sixths loaves, since 3/9 + 1/6 = 3/6.
4. If you cannot use the fraction you rolled, you must wait until your next turn to roll again.
5. You win a loaf when you cover more than half of it. Place your counter in the WINNER circle, and return any of your opponent's counters left on the loaf.
6. If you cover half of a loaf and your opponent covers the other half, neither of you can win that loaf.
7. Keep playing until all the loaves are either won or completely covered. The player who has more loaves at the end of the game is the winner.
8. In case of a tie, clear all the loaves and begin playing again. The first person to win a loaf is the winner

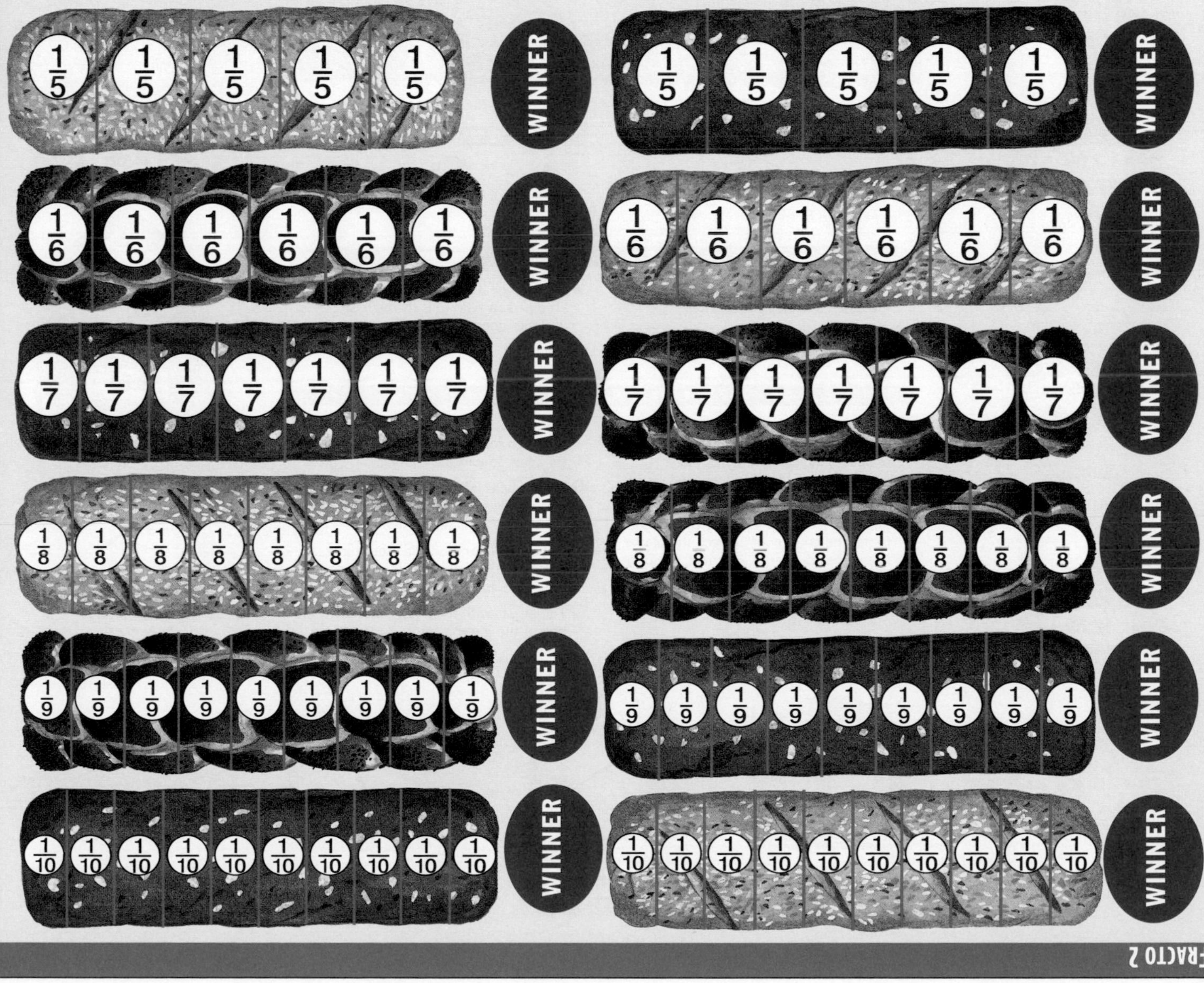

FRACTO 2

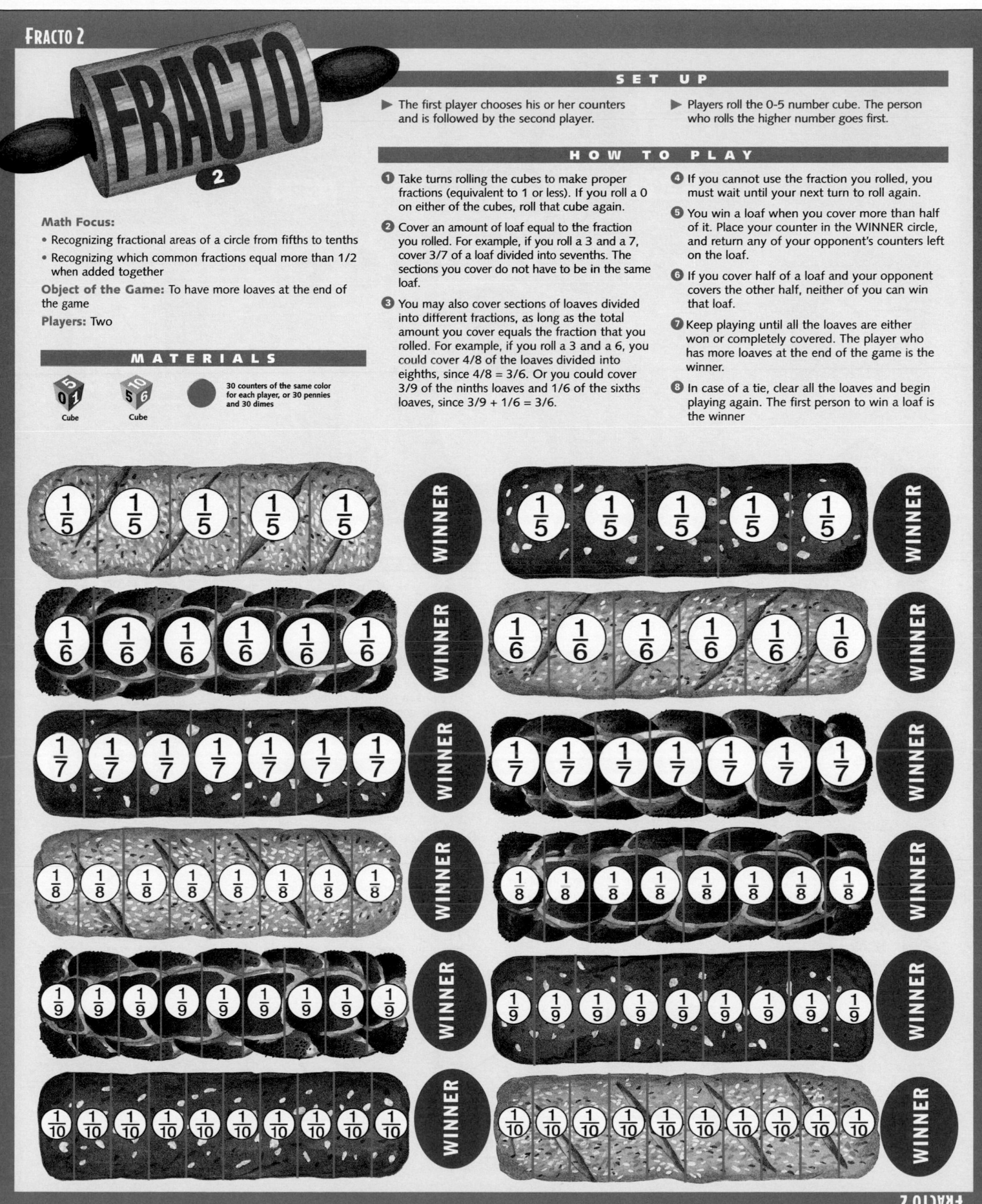

Copyright © SRA/McGraw-Hill. All rights reserved.

MINUTES

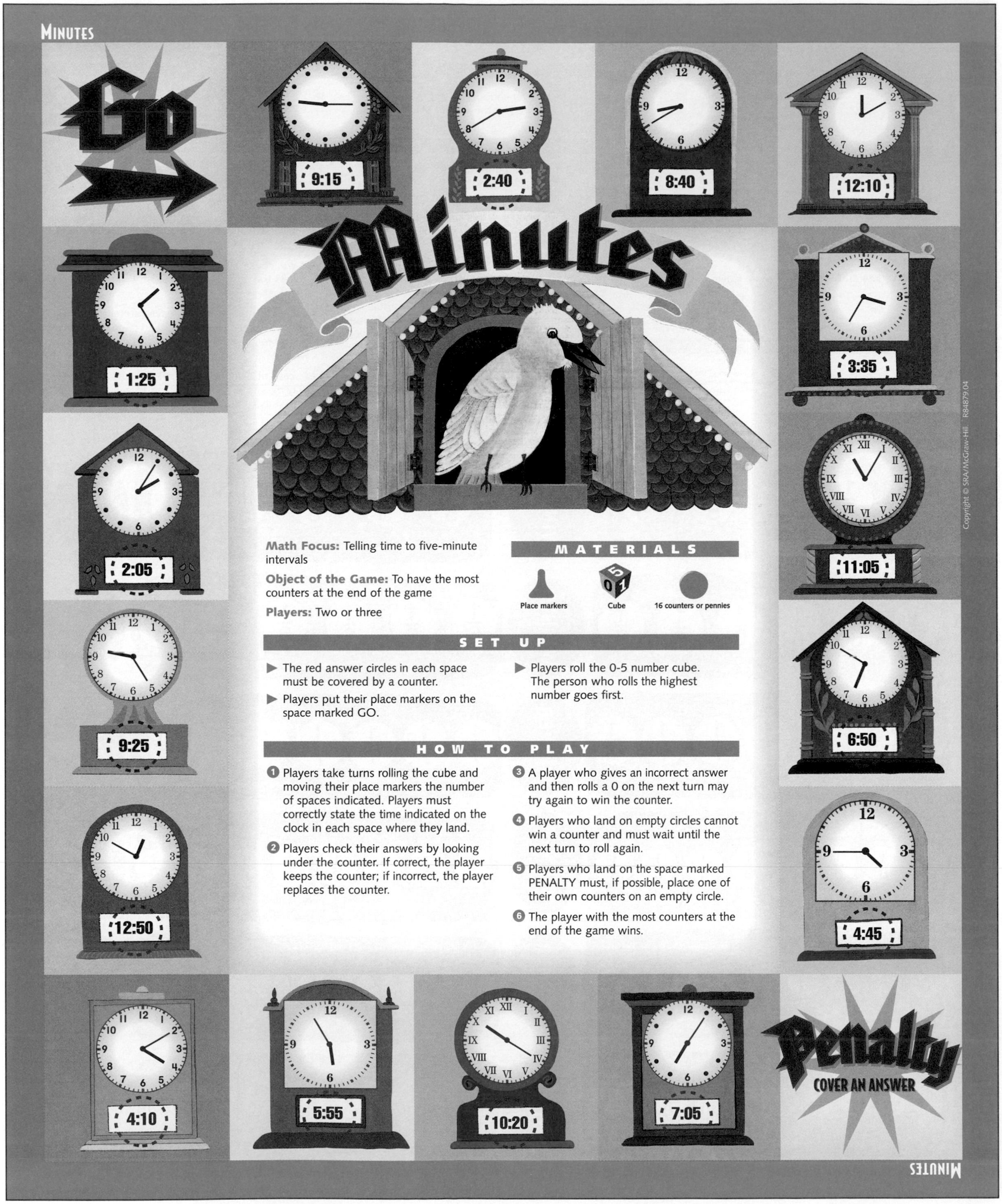

Minutes

Math Focus: Telling time to five-minute intervals

Object of the Game: To have the most counters at the end of the game

Players: Two or three

MATERIALS

Place markers, Cube, 16 counters or pennies

SET UP

- The red answer circles in each space must be covered by a counter.
- Players put their place markers on the space marked GO.
- Players roll the 0-5 number cube. The person who rolls the highest number goes first.

HOW TO PLAY

1. Players take turns rolling the cube and moving their place markers the number of spaces indicated. Players must correctly state the time indicated on the clock in each space where they land.
2. Players check their answers by looking under the counter. If correct, the player keeps the counter; if incorrect, the player replaces the counter.
3. A player who gives an incorrect answer and then rolls a 0 on the next turn may try again to win the counter.
4. Players who land on empty circles cannot win a counter and must wait until the next turn to roll again.
5. Players who land on the space marked PENALTY must, if possible, place one of their own counters on an empty circle.
6. The player with the most counters at the end of the game wins.

Copyright © SRA/McGraw-Hill. R84879.04

Copyright © SRA/McGraw-Hill. All rights reserved.

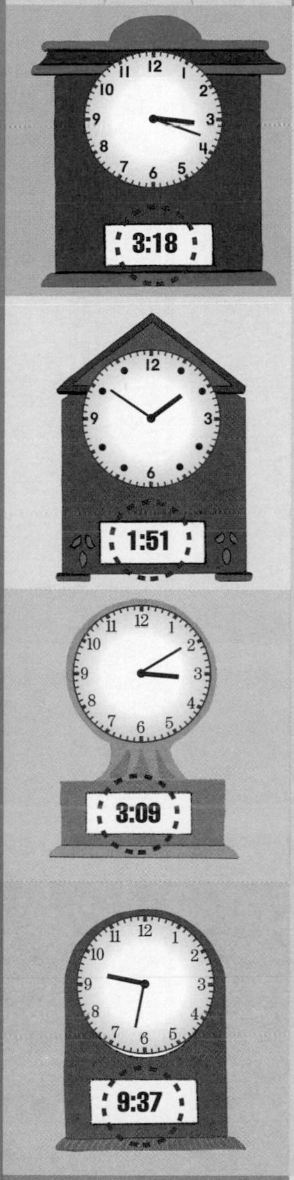

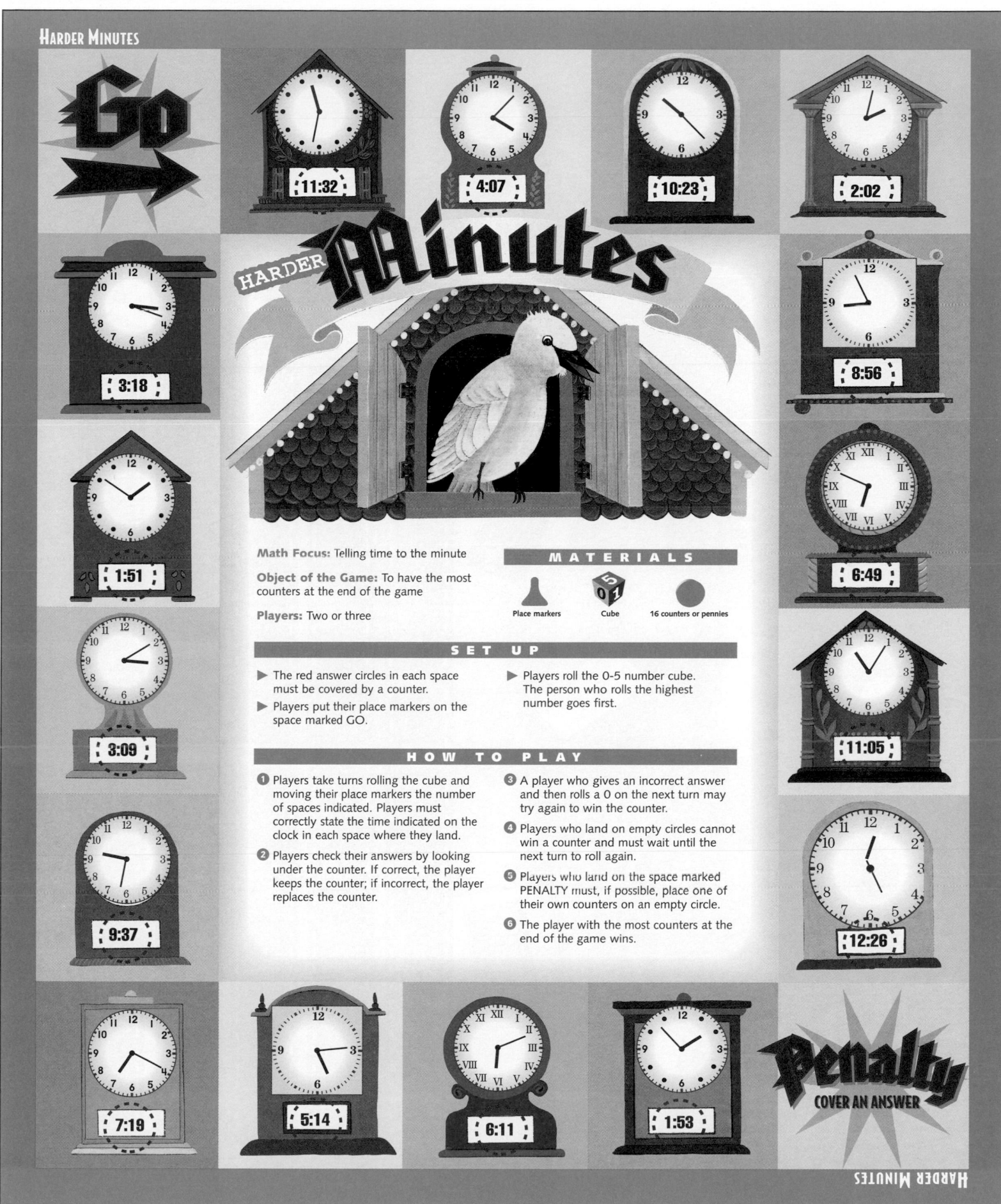

Math Focus: Telling time to the minute

Object of the Game: To have the most counters at the end of the game

Players: Two or three

MATERIALS

- Place markers
- Cube
- 16 counters or pennies

SET UP

- ▶ The red answer circles in each space must be covered by a counter.
- ▶ Players put their place markers on the space marked GO.
- ▶ Players roll the 0-5 number cube. The person who rolls the highest number goes first.

HOW TO PLAY

1. Players take turns rolling the cube and moving their place markers the number of spaces indicated. Players must correctly state the time indicated on the clock in each space where they land.
2. Players check their answers by looking under the counter. If correct, the player keeps the counter; if incorrect, the player replaces the counter.
3. A player who gives an incorrect answer and then rolls a 0 on the next turn may try again to win the counter.
4. Players who land on empty circles cannot win a counter and must wait until the next turn to roll again.
5. Players who land on the space marked PENALTY must, if possible, place one of their own counters on an empty circle.
6. The player with the most counters at the end of the game wins.

HARDER MINUTES

Copyright © SRA/McGraw-Hill. All rights reserved.

Math Focus: Solving missing-factor problems related to the multiplication facts

Object of the Game: To capture five squares in a straight line

Players: Two

MATERIALS

SET UP

Players roll the 0-5 number cube. The person who rolls the higher number goes first.

The first player chooses a card on the game mat to play and is followed by the second player.

HOW TO PLAY

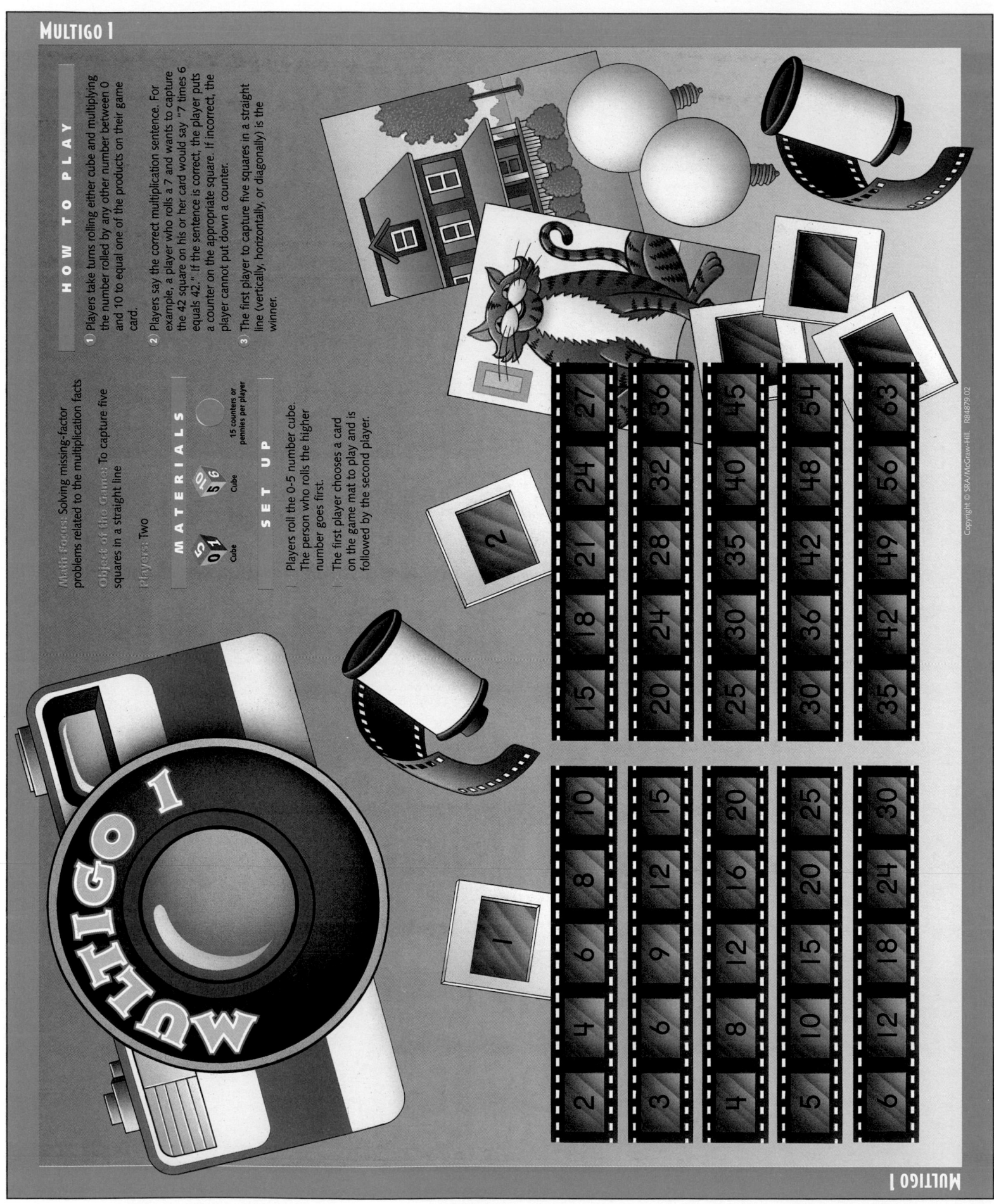

1. Players take turns rolling either cube and multiplying the number rolled by any other number between 0 and 10 to equal one of the products on their game card.
2. Players say the correct multiplication sentence. For example, a player who rolls a 7 and wants to capture the 42 square on his or her card would say "7 times 6 equals 42." If the sentence is correct, the player puts a counter on the appropriate square. If incorrect, the player cannot put down a counter.
3. The first player to capture five squares in a straight line (vertically, horizontally, or diagonally) is the winner.

2	4	6	8	10
3	6	9	12	15
4	8	12	16	20
5	10	15	20	25
6	12	18	24	30

15	18	21	24	27
20	24	28	32	36
25	30	35	40	45
30	36	42	48	54
35	42	49	56	63

Copyright © SRA/McGraw-Hill. R84879.02

Copyright © SRA/McGraw-Hill. All rights reserved.

Math Focus: Solving missing-factor problems related to the multiplication facts

Object of the Game: To capture five squares in a straight line

Players: Two

MATERIALS

- Cube (0–5)
- Cube (5–10)
- 15 counters or pennies per player

SET UP

- Players roll the 0-5 number cube. The person who rolls the higher number goes first.
- The first player chooses a card on the game mat to play and is followed by the second player.

HOW TO PLAY

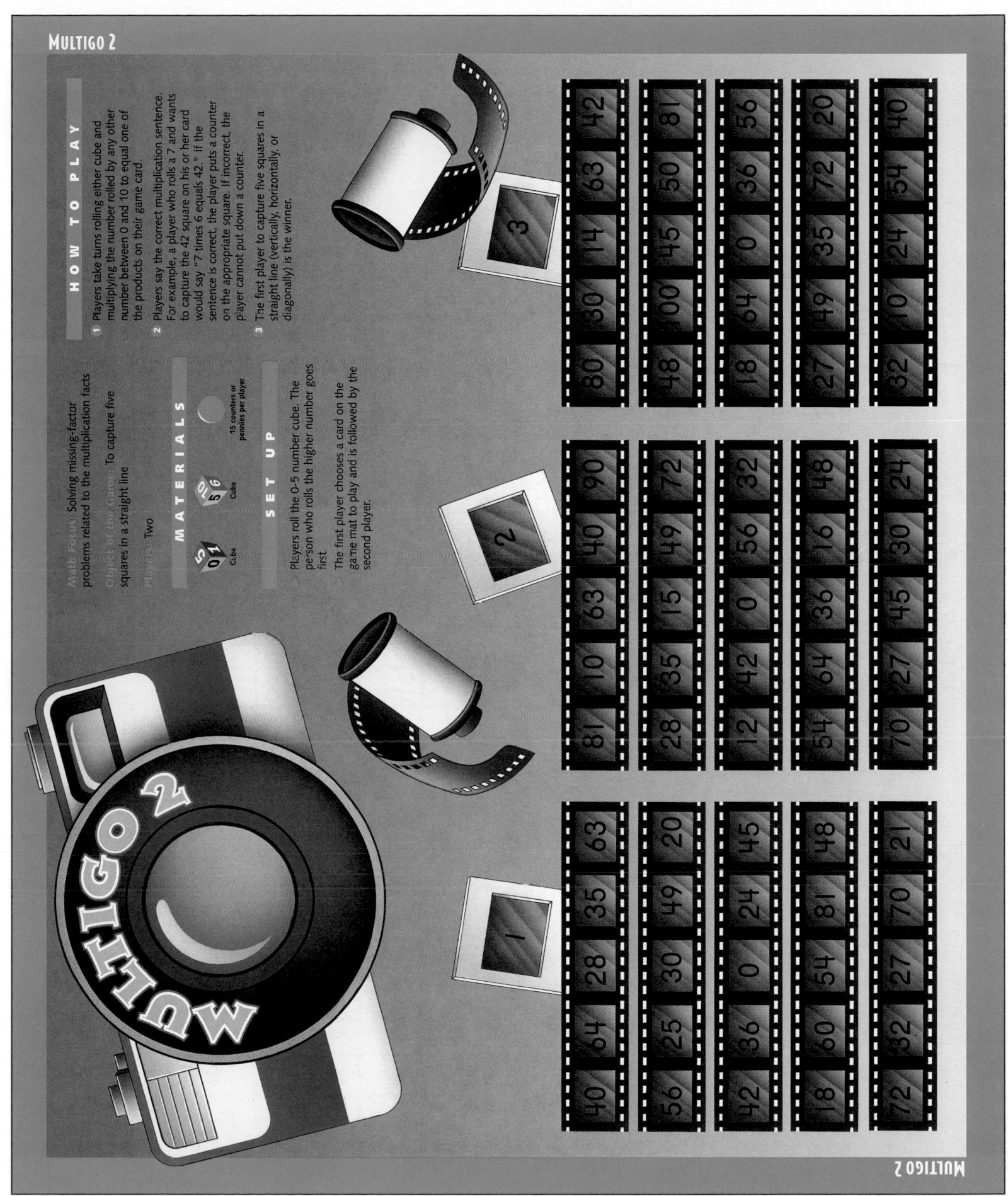

1. Players take turns rolling either cube and multiplying the number rolled by any other number between 0 and 10 to equal one of the products on their game card.
2. Players say the correct multiplication sentence. For example, a player who rolls a 7 and wants to capture the 42 square on his or her card would say "7 times 6 equals 42." If the sentence is correct, the player puts a counter on the appropriate square. If incorrect, the player cannot put down a counter.
3. The first player to capture five squares in a straight line (vertically, horizontally, or diagonally) is the winner.

1

40	64	28	35	63
56	25	30	49	20
42	36	0	24	45
18	60	54	81	48
72	32	27	70	21

2

81	10	63	40	90
28	35	15	49	72
12	42	0	56	32
54	64	36	16	48
70	27	45	30	24

3

80	30	14	63	42
48	00	45	50	81
18	64	0	36	56
27	49	35	72	20
32	10	24	54	40

MULTIGO 2

Copyright © SRA/McGraw-Hill. All rights reserved.

Multiple Crossing

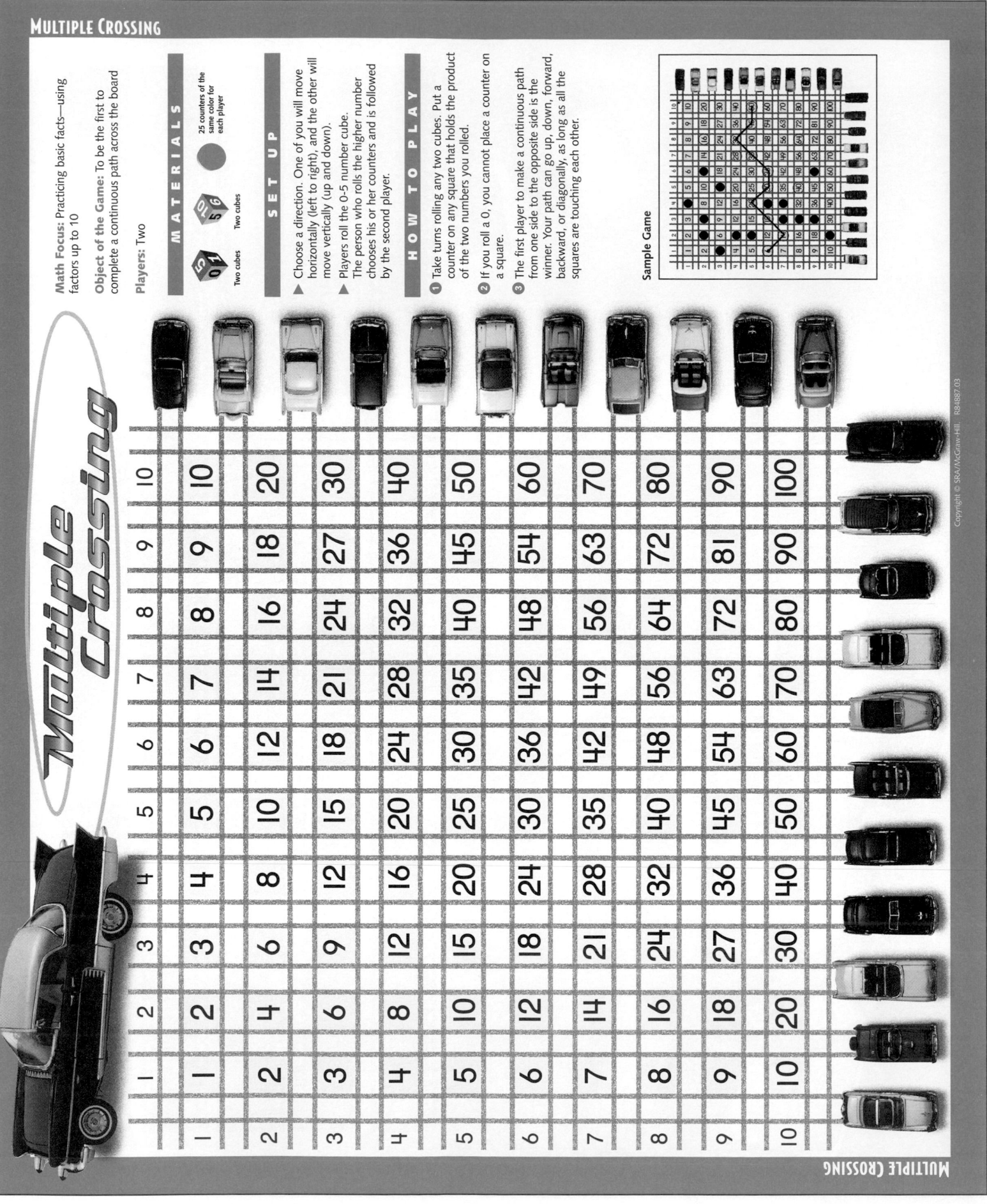

	1	2	3	4	5	6	7	8	9	10
1	1	2	3	4	5	6	7	8	9	10
2	2	4	6	8	10	12	14	16	18	20
3	3	6	9	12	15	18	21	24	27	30
4	4	8	12	16	20	24	28	32	36	40
5	5	10	15	20	25	30	35	40	45	50
6	6	12	18	24	30	36	42	48	54	60
7	7	14	21	28	35	42	49	56	63	70
8	8	16	24	32	40	48	56	64	72	80
9	9	18	27	36	45	54	63	72	81	90
10	10	20	30	40	50	60	70	80	90	100

Math Focus: Practicing basic facts—using factors up to 10

Object of the Game: To be the first to complete a continuous path across the board

Players: Two

MATERIALS

SET UP

- ▶ Choose a direction. One of you will move horizontally (left to right), and the other will move vertically (up and down).
- ▶ Players roll the 0-5 number cube. The person who rolls the higher number chooses his or her counters and is followed by the second player.

HOW TO PLAY

1. Take turns rolling any two cubes. Put a counter on any square that holds the product of the two numbers you rolled.
2. If you roll a 0, you cannot place a counter on a square.
3. The first player to make a continuous path from one side to the opposite side is the winner. Your path can go up, down, forward, backward, or diagonally, as long as all the squares are touching each other.

Sample Game

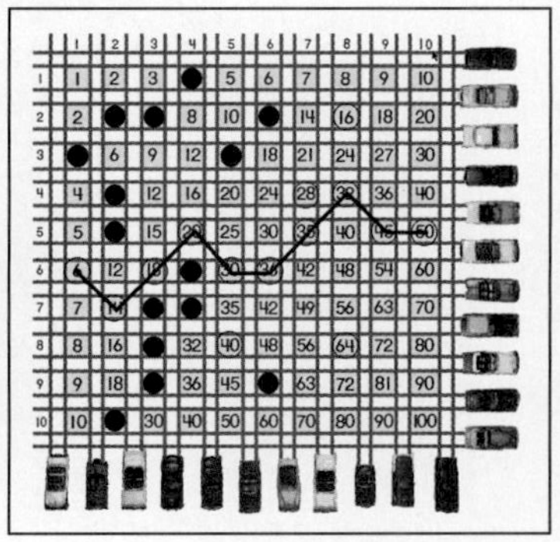

Copyright © SRA/McGraw-Hill. R84887.03

Copyright © SRA/McGraw-Hill. All rights reserved.

Multiplication Table Game

Math Focus:
- Practicing basic facts–multiplying two factors of 5 or less
- Using a multiplication table

Object of the Game: To have more counters at the end of the game

Players: Two

MATERIALS

Two cubes

36 counters or pennies

SET UP

- Every circle on the mat must be covered with a counter.
- Players roll the 0-5 number cube. The person who rolls the higher number goes first.

HOW TO PLAY

1. Players take turns rolling both cubes and making multiplication sentences out of the numbers. For example, if a 4 and a 2 are rolled, the player could say either "4 times 2 equals 8" or "2 times 4 equals 8."
2. After giving the multiplication sentence, players check their answers by looking under the appropriate counter. If correct, the player keeps the counter; if incorrect, the player replaces the counter.
3. Once the counter on a circle has been won, the circle remains empty. A player who cannot make a multiplication sentence that applies to a covered circle cannot win a counter that turn.
4. The player with more counters at the end of the game wins.

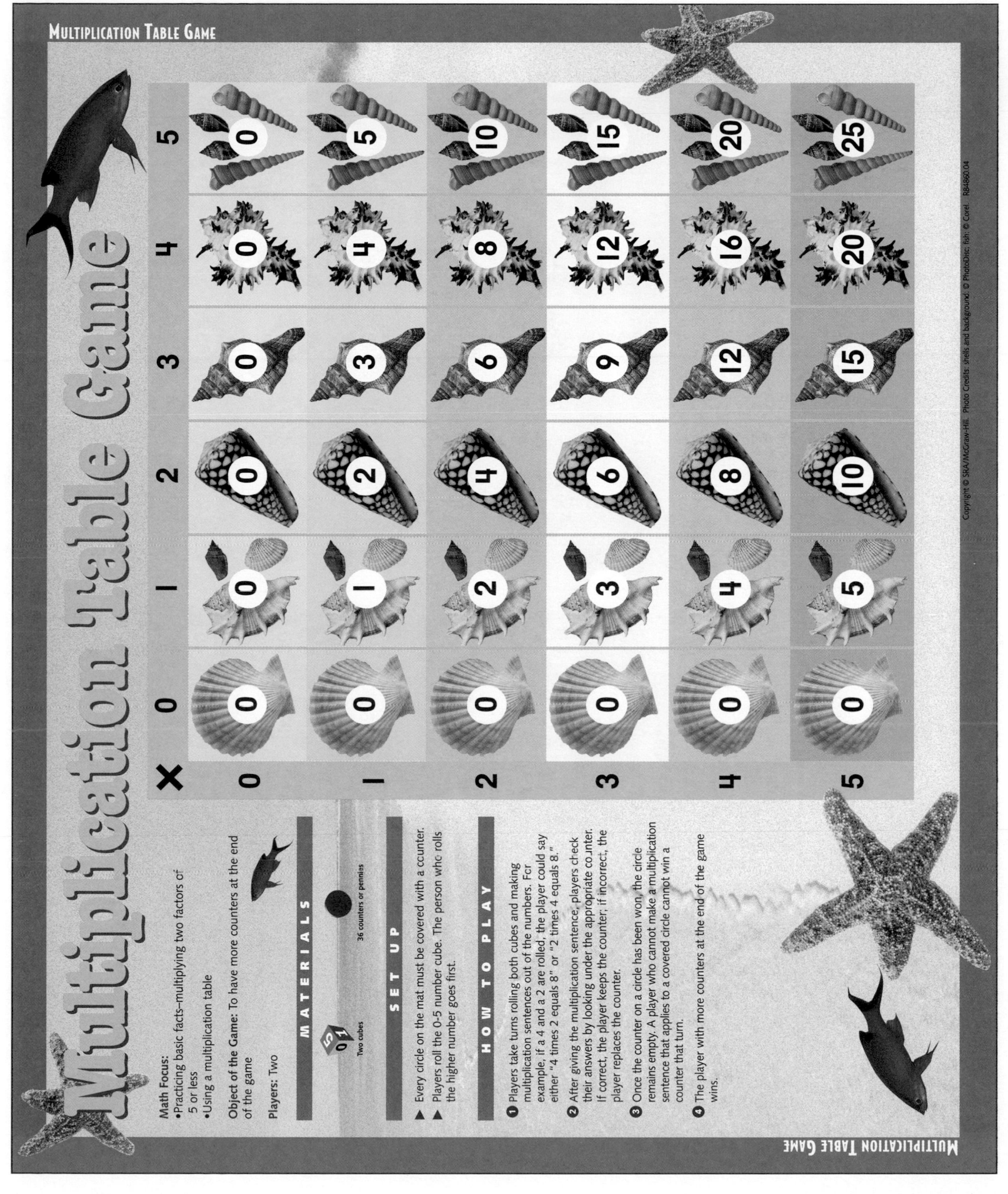

×	0	1	2	3	4	5
0	0	0	0	0	0	0
1	0	1	2	3	4	5
2	0	2	4	6	8	10
3	0	3	6	9	12	15
4	0	4	8	12	16	20
5	0	5	10	15	20	25

Copyright © SRA/McGraw-Hill. Photo Credits: shells and background: © PhotoDisc; fish: © Corel. R84860.04

MULTIPLICATION TABLE GAME

Copyright © SRA/McGraw-Hill. All rights reserved.

HARDER Multiplication Table Game

Math Focus:
- Practicing basic facts–multiplying two factors of 10 or less
- Using a multiplication table

Object of the Game: To have more counters at the end of the game

Players: Two

MATERIALS

Cube — Two cubes — 36 counters or pennies

SET UP

- ▶ Every circle on the mat must be covered with a counter.
- ▶ Players roll the 0-5 number cube. The person who rolls the higher number goes first.

HOW TO PLAY

1. There are actually two harder versions of this game. One game is played rolling one 0-5 and one 5-10 number cube. The second game is played with two 5-10 number cubes. Players take turns rolling both cubes and making multiplication sentences out of the numbers. For example, if a 4 and a 9 are rolled, the player could say either "4 times 9 equals 36" or "9 times 4 equals 36."
2. After giving the multiplication sentence, players check their answers by looking under the appropriate counter. If correct, the player keeps the counter; if incorrect, the player replaces the counter.
3. Once the counter on a circle has been won, the circle remains empty. A player who cannot make a multiplication sentence that applies to a covered circle cannot win a counter that turn.
4. The player with more counters at the end of the game wins.

×	5	6	7	8	9	10
0	0	0	0	0	0	0
1	5	6	7	8	9	10
2	10	12	14	16	18	20
3	15	18	21	24	27	30
4	20	24	28	32	36	40
5	25	30	35	40	45	50

×	5	6	7	8	9	10
5	25	30	35	40	45	50
6	30	36	42	48	54	60
7	35	42	49	56	63	70
8	40	48	56	64	72	80
9	45	54	63	72	81	90
10	50	60	70	80	90	100

HARDER MULTIPLICATION TABLE GAME

Copyright © SRA/McGraw-Hill. All rights reserved.

Shopping Game

Math Focus:
- Practicing basic facts—multiplying with factors up to 9
- Forming amounts of money and making change

Object of the Game: To be the first to have $250

Players: Two, three, or four

MATERIALS

Place markers

Cube

Per player:
one $50 bill
two $20 bills
three $10 bills
five $5 bills
five $1 bills

SET UP

- Players select stores to own. If two are playing, each player chooses two stores; if three are playing, one store will not be owned by anyone.
- Players put their place markers on the space marked START.
- Players roll the 0-5 number cube. The person who rolls the highest number goes first.

HOW TO PLAY

1. Players take turns rolling the cube and moving their place markers the number of spaces indicated.
2. After landing on a space, players roll the cube to see how many of the items pictured they must buy, and then they pay the store owner. For example, a player who lands on an item that costs $8 and then rolls a 3 must pay the owner $24 for three of the items.
3. Even if a player has already bought an item, the player must buy it again if he or she lands on that space again.
4. Players who roll a 0, land in their own stores, or land on stores that nobody owns buy nothing.
5. A player who lands on the space marked START collects $5 from every player.
6. The first player to have $250 wins.

Copyright © SRA/McGraw-Hill. R84879.03

Copyright © SRA/McGraw-Hill. All rights reserved.

HARDER Shopping Game

Math Focus:
- Practicing basic facts—multiplying with factors up to 9
- Forming amounts of money and making change

Object of the Game: To be the first to have $450

Players: Two, three, or four

MATERIALS

Place markers

Cube

Per player:
one $100 bill
two $50 bills
five $20 bills
three $10 bills
five $5 bills
five $1 bills

SET UP

- Players select stores to own. If two are playing, each player chooses two stores; if three are playing, one store will not be owned by anyone.
- Players put their place markers on the space marked START.
- Players roll the 0-5 number cube. The person who rolls the highest number goes first.

HOW TO PLAY

1. Players take turns rolling the cube and moving their place markers the number of spaces indicated.
2. After landing on a space, players roll the cube to see how many of the items pictured they must buy, and then they pay the store owner. For example, a player who lands on an item that costs $8 and then rolls a 4 must pay the owner $32 for four of the items.
3. Even if a player has already bought an item, the player must buy it again if he or she lands on that space again.
4. Players who roll a 0, land in their own stores, or land on stores that nobody owns buy nothing.
5. A player who lands on the space marked START collects $5 from every player.
6. The first player to have $450 wins.

HARDER SHOPPING GAME

Copyright © SRA/McGraw-Hill. All rights reserved.

SNAKE

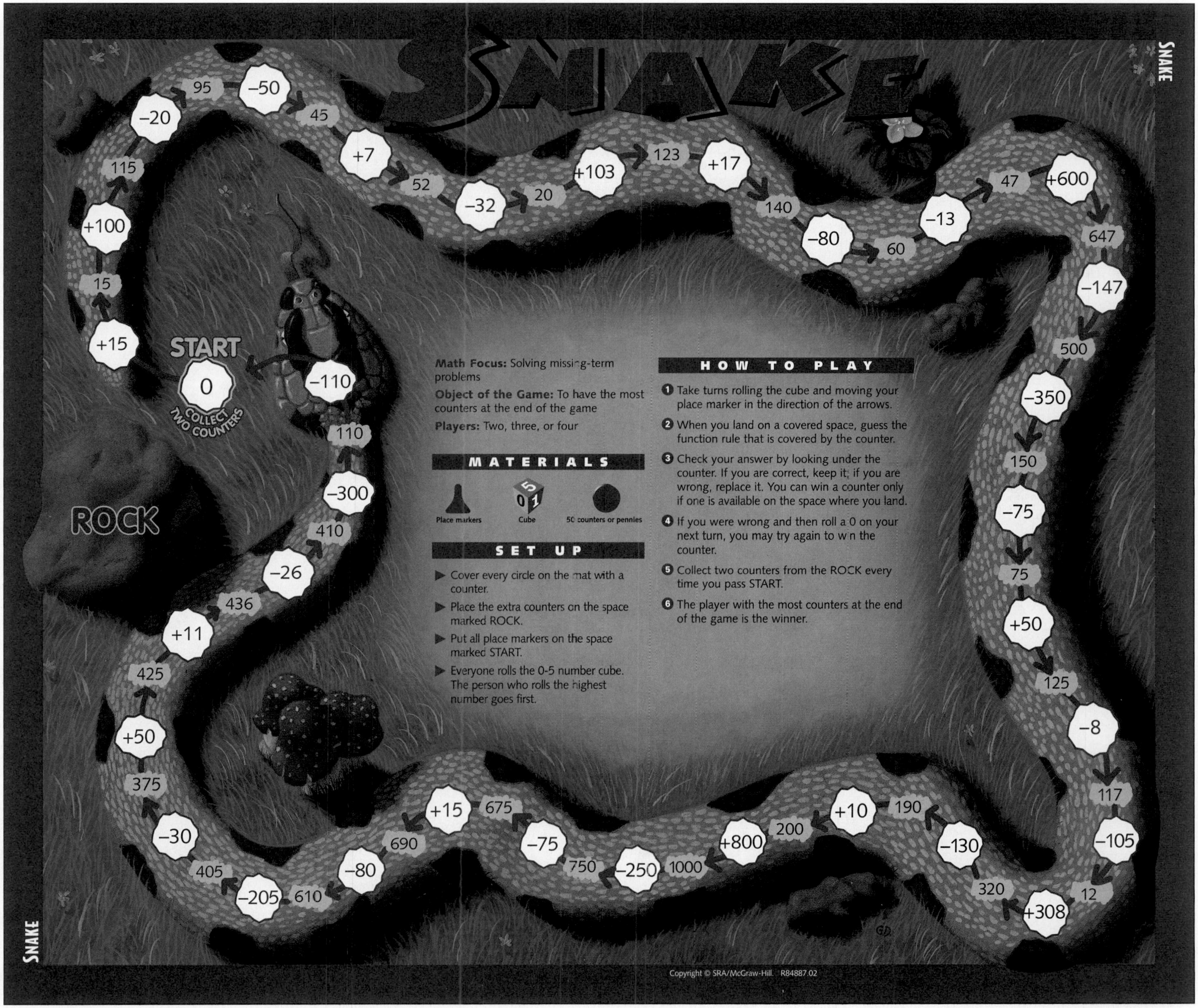

Math Focus: Solving missing-term problems

Object of the Game: To have the most counters at the end of the game

Players: Two, three, or four

MATERIALS

Place markers — Cube — 50 counters or pennies

SET UP

- Cover every circle on the mat with a counter.
- Place the extra counters on the space marked ROCK.
- Put all place markers on the space marked START.
- Everyone rolls the 0-5 number cube. The person who rolls the highest number goes first.

HOW TO PLAY

1. Take turns rolling the cube and moving your place marker in the direction of the arrows.
2. When you land on a covered space, guess the function rule that is covered by the counter.
3. Check your answer by looking under the counter. If you are correct, keep it; if you are wrong, replace it. You can win a counter only if one is available on the space where you land.
4. If you were wrong and then roll a 0 on your next turn, you may try again to win the counter.
5. Collect two counters from the ROCK every time you pass START.
6. The player with the most counters at the end of the game is the winner.

Copyright © SRA/McGraw-Hill. R84887.02

SNAKE

Copyright © SRA/McGraw-Hill. All rights reserved.

HARDER SNAKE

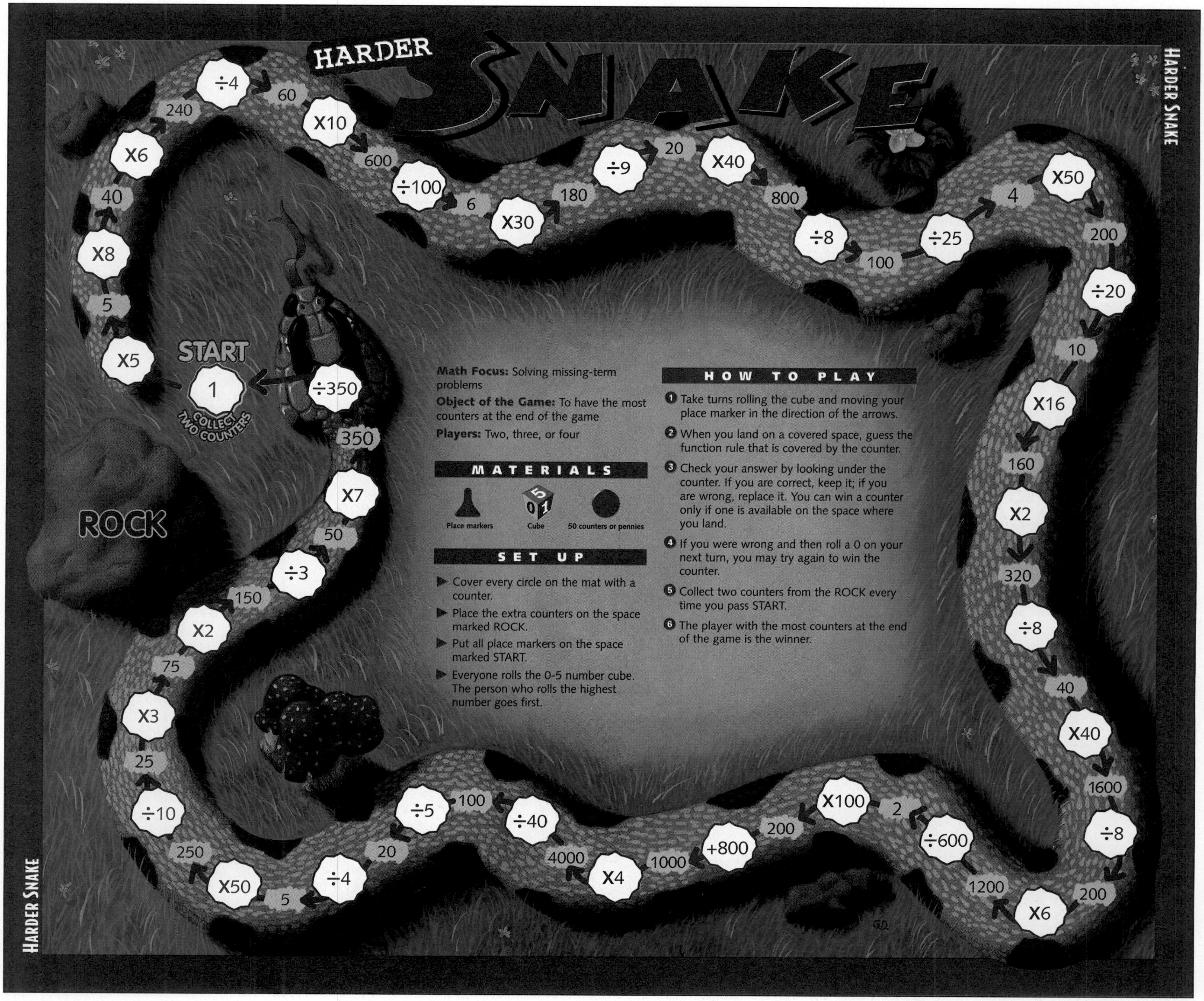

Math Focus: Solving missing-term problems

Object of the Game: To have the most counters at the end of the game

Players: Two, three, or four

MATERIALS

Place markers — Cube — 50 counters or pennies

SET UP

- Cover every circle on the mat with a counter.
- Place the extra counters on the space marked ROCK.
- Put all place markers on the space marked START.
- Everyone rolls the 0-5 number cube. The person who rolls the highest number goes first.

HOW TO PLAY

1. Take turns rolling the cube and moving your place marker in the direction of the arrows.
2. When you land on a covered space, guess the function rule that is covered by the counter.
3. Check your answer by looking under the counter. If you are correct, keep it; if you are wrong, replace it. You can win a counter only if one is available on the space where you land.
4. If you were wrong and then roll a 0 on your next turn, you may try again to win the counter.
5. Collect two counters from the ROCK every time you pass START.
6. The player with the most counters at the end of the game is the winner.

HARDER SNAKE

Copyright © SRA/McGraw-Hill. All rights reserved.

Math Focus:
- Forming amounts of money (multiples of 25¢)
- Making change

Object of the Game: To be the first to have $500

Players: Two, three, or four

MATERIALS

Place markers

Cube

Per player:
- one $100 bill
- one $50 bill
- two $20 bills
- three $10 bills
- four $5 bills
- eight $1 bills
- two half dollars
- four quarters

SET UP

- ▶ Players select departments in the store to manage. If two are playing, each can choose two departments; if three are playing, one department will not be managed by anyone.
- ▶ Players sort their money into piles in front of them.
- ▶ Players put their place markers on the space marked START.
- ▶ Players roll the 0-5 number cube. The person who rolls the highest number goes first.

HOW TO PLAY

1. Players take turns rolling the cube and moving their place markers the number of spaces indicated.
2. After landing on a space, the player says the price of the object pictured there and pays the amount shown to the player who manages the department. Players must count out the money as they pay, largest bills first.
3. Even if a player has already bought an item, the player must buy it again if she or he lands on that space again.
4. If a player lands in a department that he or she manages, or that nobody manages, no payment is made.
5. Players who land on the space marked START collect $10 from every other player.
6. A player who rolls a 0 does not move that turn but also does not have to buy the item again on that turn.
7. The first player to have $500 wins.

Copyright © SRA/McGraw-Hill. All rights reserved.

Math Focus:

- Forming amounts of money
- Making change

Object of the Game: To be the first to have $20

Players: Two, three, or four

MATERIALS

Place markers

Cube

Per player:
one $5 bill
seven $1 bills
two half dollars
four quarters
six dimes
six nickels
ten pennies

SET UP

- Players select departments in the store to manage. If two are playing, each can choose two departments; if three are playing, one department will not be managed by anyone.
- Players sort their money into piles in front of them.
- Players put their place markers on the space marked START.
- Players roll the 0-5 number cube. The person who rolls the highest number goes first.

HOW TO PLAY

1. Players take turns rolling the cube and moving their place markers the number of spaces indicated.
2. After landing on a space, the player says the price of the object pictured there and pays the amount shown to the player who manages the department. Players must count out the money as they pay, largest bills or coins first.
3. Even if a player has already bought an item, the player must buy it again if she or he lands on that space again.
4. If a player lands in a department that he or she manages, or that nobody manages, no payment is made.
5. Players who land on the space marked START collect $1 from every other player.
6. A player who rolls a 0 does not move that turn but also does not have to buy the item again on that turn.
7. The first player to have $20 wins.

Copyright © SRA/McGraw-Hill. All rights reserved.

Copyright © SRA/McGraw-Hill. R84887.05

Math Focus:

- Adding and subtracting amounts of money (dollars)
- Maintaining a record of money transactions

Object of the Game: To have the greatest balance at the end of the game

Players: Two or three

MATERIALS

- Place markers
- Two cubes (0-5)
- Two cubes (5-10)
- One score sheet per player

SET UP

- The blank balance sheet for "Harder Transaction" can be photocopied for students to use.
- Put your place markers on the space marked START.
- On your score sheet write "Start" under DATE and "$1000" under BALANCE.
- Everyone rolls one 0-5 number cube. The person who rolls the highest number goes first.

DATE	EARN	PAY	BALANCE
Start			$1000
3		–$24	$ 976
8	+$861		$1837
11			
4	+76		$1913
6		–$45	$1868

HOW TO PLAY

1. Take turns rolling one 0-5 cube and moving your place marker the correct number of spaces.
2. When you land on a space that says "Earn" or "Pay," roll one cube for each blank line in the amount. Arrange the digits in the best order. Try to earn the most and pay the least. For example, if you roll a 7, 0, and 2 and have to pay, make the amount $207. If you are earning, make the amount $720.
3. Zero cannot be used as the first digit of an amount. Also, 10 cannot be used. If you roll a 10, roll that cube again.
4. On every turn write down what you earn or pay under the correct column, then add what you earned or subtract what you paid in the BALANCE column. Also, write down the date of each transaction.
5. Keep playing until everyone reaches FINISH or runs out of money.
6. The player with the greatest correct balance wins. Players must check the winner's addition and subtraction. Add to find each total in the winner's PAY column and EARN column. Then add the EARN total to $1000 and subtract the PAY total. This balance should match the winner's final balance. If there is a mistake in the balance, the player with the greatest correct balance wins instead.

Reminder: If you land on a space that says "Pay $_ _," roll two 0-5 cubes and choose the lesser amount to pay. If you land on a space that says "Earn $_ _," roll two 5-10 cubes and choose the greater combination of digits.

TRANSACTION

Copyright © SRA/McGraw-Hill. All rights reserved.

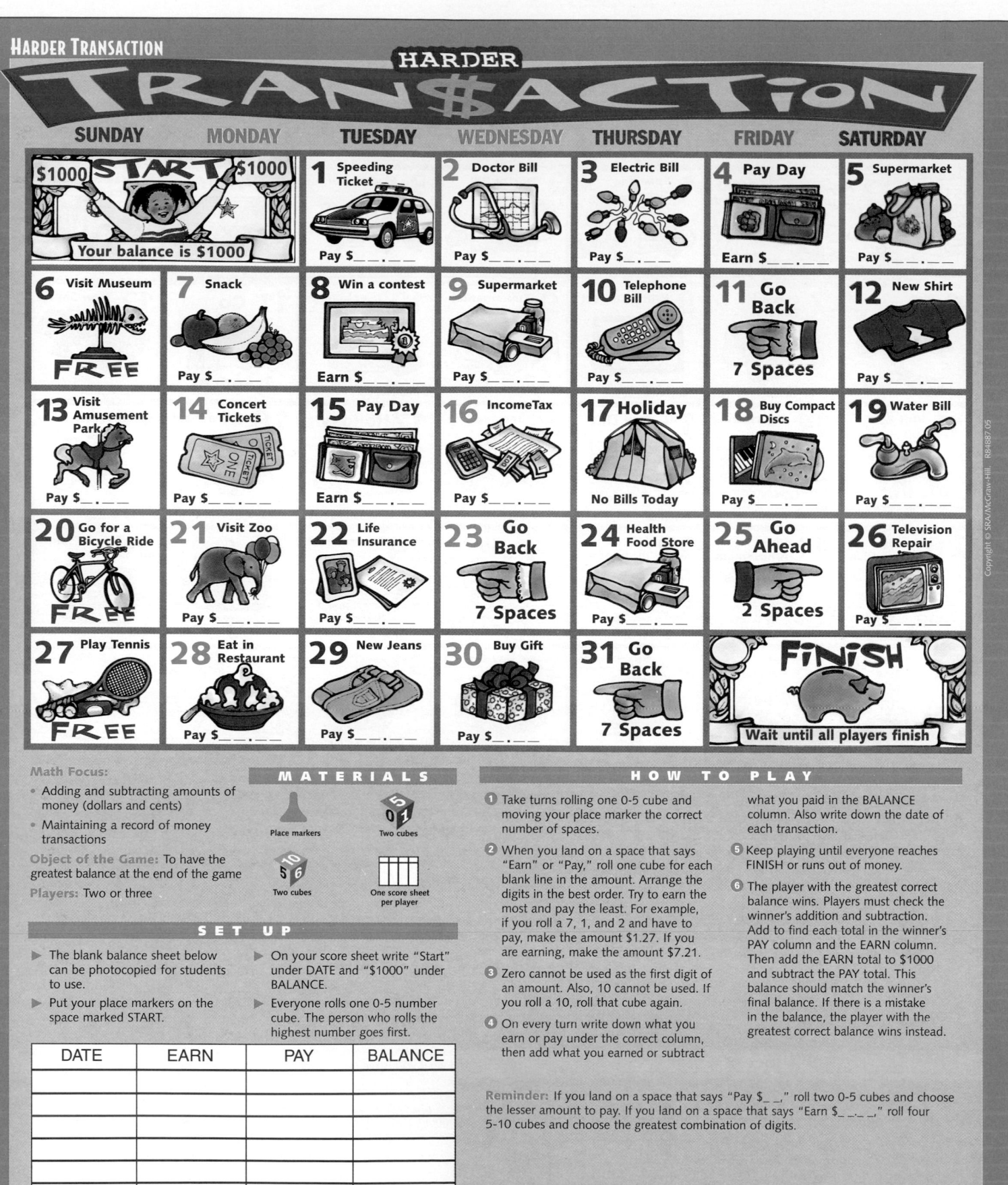

Copyright © SRA/McGraw-Hill. R84887.05

Math Focus:

- Adding and subtracting amounts of money (dollars and cents)
- Maintaining a record of money transactions

Object of the Game: To have the greatest balance at the end of the game

Players: Two or three

MATERIALS

Place markers

Two cubes

Two cubes

One score sheet per player

SET UP

- The blank balance sheet below can be photocopied for students to use.
- Put your place markers on the space marked START.
- On your score sheet write "Start" under DATE and "$1000" under BALANCE.
- Everyone rolls one 0-5 number cube. The person who rolls the highest number goes first.

DATE	EARN	PAY	BALANCE

HOW TO PLAY

1. Take turns rolling one 0-5 cube and moving your place marker the correct number of spaces.
2. When you land on a space that says "Earn" or "Pay," roll one cube for each blank line in the amount. Arrange the digits in the best order. Try to earn the most and pay the least. For example, if you roll a 7, 1, and 2 and have to pay, make the amount $1.27. If you are earning, make the amount $7.21.
3. Zero cannot be used as the first digit of an amount. Also, 10 cannot be used. If you roll a 10, roll that cube again.
4. On every turn write down what you earn or pay under the correct column, then add what you earned or subtract what you paid in the BALANCE column. Also write down the date of each transaction.
5. Keep playing until everyone reaches FINISH or runs out of money.
6. The player with the greatest correct balance wins. Players must check the winner's addition and subtraction. Add to find each total in the winner's PAY column and the EARN column. Then add the EARN total to $1000 and subtract the PAY total. This balance should match the winner's final balance. If there is a mistake in the balance, the player with the greatest correct balance wins instead.

Reminder: If you land on a space that says "Pay $_ _," roll two 0-5 cubes and choose the lesser amount to pay. If you land on a space that says "Earn $_ _._ _," roll four 5-10 cubes and choose the greatest combination of digits.

HARDER TRANSACTION

Copyright © SRA/McGraw-Hill. All rights reserved.

INDEX

D

E

F

G

N

T

U

V

W

Y

SCOPE & SEQUENCE

	K		Level 1				Level 2				Level 3				Level 4						Level 5						Level 6						Glencoe*		
Units	1	2	1	2	3	4	1	2	3	4	1	2	3	4	1	2	3	4	5	6	1	2	3	4	5	6	1	2	3	4	5	6	6	7	8
Addition (whole numbers)																																			
Meaning of addition	●	●	●																																
Basic facts		✓	✓	✓	●	✓	✓	●	●	●	✓	●	●	●	✓	●	✓	●	●	●	●	●	●	●		●	●	●	●	●	●				
Missing addend problems	●	●	●	✓	●	●	●	●	●	●	●	●	●		●	●	●	●	●		●	●		●	●	●	●	●	●		●	●			
Three or more addends		●	●		●	●	●		✓	●	✓	●	●	●	●	●	●	●	●	●	●	●	●	●	●	●	●	●	●	●	●	●	●	●	●
Two-digit numbers				●	✓	✓	●	✓	✓	●	✓	●	●	●	✓	●	●	●	●	●	✓	●	●	●	●	●	●	●		●	●	●	●	●	●
Three-digit numbers										✓	✓	●	●	●	✓	●	●	●	●	●	✓	●	●	●	●	●	✓	●	●	●	●	●	●	●	●
Greater numbers										●	✓	●	●	●	✓	●	●	●	●		✓	●	●	●		●	✓	●	●			●	●	●	●
Adding money	●	✓	●	✓	✓	●	●	●	●	●	●	●	●	●	●	●	●	●	●	●	✓	●		●			●	●	●	●			●	●	●
Estimating sums				●	●	●		●	●	●	✓			●	✓	●	●	●	●	●	✓	●	●		●	●	●	●		●			●	●	●
Algebra																																			
Properties of whole numbers			●	●		●	●	●				●		●		●					●	●		●			●							●	●
Integers (negative numbers)	●			●		●		●		●	●		●		●	●						●		●	●		●	●			●		●	●	●
Operations with integers											●				●	●						●		●			●	●			●		●	●	●
Missing term problems	●	●	●	✓	●	●	●	●	●	●	●	●	●		●	●	●	●	●	●	●	●	●	●	●	●	●	●	●	●	●	●	●	●	●
Make and solve number sentences and equations		●	●	●	●	●	●	●	●	●	●	●	●	●	●	●	●	●	●	●	●	●	●	●		●	●	●		●	●		●	●	●
Variables											●	●	●	●	●	●	●	●	●	●	●	●	●	●	●	●	●		●	●	●	●	●	●	●
Parentheses and order of operations											●	●	●			●	●		●		●	●	●		●						●		●	●	●
Inverse operations							●			●		✓			●	●	●		●		●	●	●						●	●	●				
Function machines/tables	●	●		●	●	●	●	●		●		●			●	●	●	●	●	●		✓		●						●	✓		●	●	●
Function rules	●	●		●	●	●				●		●			●	●	✓		●	●	●	✓	●	●						●	✓		●	●	●
Inverse functions								●		●		●					✓		●			✓	●							●	●				
Composite functions										●		●					✓			●		✓		●							●				
Coordinate graphing																																			
One quadrant													●	●			●	●	●			●		●							✓		●	●	●
Four quadrants																						✓		●	●						●		●	●	●
Graphing linear functions																	✓		●	●		✓		●							✓			●	●
Graphing nonlinear functions																															●				●
Using formulas														●		●					●	●		●	●						●	●	●	●	●
Square numbers												●				●		●	●		●		●			●		●				●	●	●	●
Square roots																															●	●	●	●	●
Decimals and money																																			
Place value										●		●	●	●	●	●		●		✓	●					●	●	●	●				●	●	●
Comparing and ordering											●	●	✓	●	●	●			●	✓	●	●	✓	●		●	●	●		●			●	●	●
Rounding														●	●		●	●	●	●	●	●					●	●	●			●	●	●	●
Relating decimals and fractions													●		●					✓			✓	●	●	●	●			●		●	●	●	●
Relating decimals and percents																				●						✓			●			●	●	●	●
Adding													✓	●	●	●	●	●	●	✓	✓	●	●	●	●	●		✓	●	●			●	●	●
Estimating sums															●	●	●		●	●	✓	●					●	●	●	●	●		●	●	●
Subtracting													✓	●	●	●	●	●	●	✓	✓	●	●	●	●	●		✓	●	●			●	●	●
Estimating differences															●	●		●	●	●	✓					●		●		●			●	●	●
Multiplying by powers of 10																				✓	✓	●	●	●	●	●		●	●		●	●	●	●	●
Multiplying by a whole number												●		●				●	●	●	✓	●	●	●	●	✓		●	●	●	●	●	●	●	●
Multiplying by a decimal																				●						✓		✓	●	●	●	●	●	●	●
Estimating products																		●		●	✓	●	●	●		●	●	●	●	●	●	●	●	●	●
Dividing by powers of 10																				✓	✓	●	●	●	●			●	●		●	●	●	●	●
Dividing by a whole number																			●	●	●	✓	●	✓	●	●		●		●			●	●	●
Dividing by a decimal																			●							●		✓	●				●	●	●
Estimating quotients																			●		●							●		●	●		●	●	●
Identifying and counting currency	●	✓	●	●	✓	✓	●			●	●	●	✓		●	●		●	●	●	●														
Exchanging money	●	●		●	✓	✓	●	●	●	✓	●	●	✓	●	●	●	●	●	●	●	●			●			●	●	●						
Making change				●	●	✓	●	●	●	●	●	●	●	●	●	●	●	●	●	✓	●	●						●							
Computing with money			●	✓	✓	✓	●	●	●	●	●	●	●	●	●	●	●	●	●	✓	●	●	●	●	●	●	●	●	●	●	●	●	●	●	●
Division (whole numbers)																																			
Meaning of division	●	●			●	●				●	●	●																							
Basic facts										●		✓	●	●	●	✓	✓	●	●	●	●	●	●	●		●	●	●	●	●	●				
Remainders												●	●			✓	●	●	✓		✓	✓	●			●	✓		●	●			●		
Missing term problems										●		●				●	●	●	●		●	●	●	●	●	●			●	●	●				
One-digit divisors												●	●			●	●	●	✓	●	✓	●	●	●	●	●	✓	●	●	●	●	●	●	●	●
Two-digit divisors																		●	●				●	✓	●	●	●	●	●	●	●	●	●	●	●
Greater divisors																							●	●		●	●	●			●		●	●	●
Dividing by multiples of 10												●	●				●	●	●	●	●	●	●	●	●	●	●	●	●		●	●	●	●	●
Dividing money										●		●				●	●	●	●		✓		●	●			●	●		●			●	●	●
Estimating quotients																●	●	●	●		●	●	✓	●	●	●	✓	●	●		●		●	●	●
Fractions																																			
Fractions of a whole	●	✓		●	●			✓	●			●	✓	●	●		●		●	●		●	✓				●				●	●			
Fractions of a set					●			●				●	✓	●	●					✓			✓							●					
Fractions of a number				●	●	●		●					●		●	●	●	●		●			✓			●				●	●	●			
Comparing/ordering					●			●					●				●			●			●	●	●					●	●		●	●	●
Equivalent fractions					●			●					●							●			●	●		●				●			●	●	●
Reduced form																				●				●						●		●	●	●	●
Mixed numbers and improper fractions												●	●	●						●				✓						●			●	●	●
Adding–like denominators															●					✓			●	✓		●				●	●	●	●	●	●

✓ indicates Mastery Checkpoints

**Mathematics: Applications and Connections* Courses 1–3, Levels 6–8 © 1999

	K		Level 1				Level 2				Level 3				Level 4						Level 5						Level 6						Glencoe*		
Units	1	2	1	2	3	4	1	2	3	4	1	2	3	4	1	2	3	4	5	6	1	2	3	4	5	6	1	2	3	4	5	6	6	7	8
Fractions (continued)																																			
Adding–unlike denominators															•					✓				✓	•	•				✓	•	•	•	•	•
Adding mixed numbers																				•				✓	•	•				✓	•		•	•	•
Subtracting–like denominators																				✓				✓	•	•				•	•	•	•	•	•
Subtracting–unlike denominators																				✓				✓	•	•				✓	•	•	•	•	•
Subtracting mixed numbers																				•				✓	•	•				✓	•		•	•	•
Multiplying by a whole number																									•	•				•	•	•	•	•	•
Multiplying by a fraction or mixed number																•								•		✓				✓	•	•	•	•	•
Reciprocals																														•			•	•	•
Dividing a fraction by a whole number																														•			•	•	•
Dividing by a fraction or mixed number																														✓	•		•	•	•
Geometry																																			
Identifying/drawing figures	•	•	•	•	•	•	•	•	•	•	•	•	•	•	•	•	•	•	•	•	•	•	•	•	•	•		•				•	•	•	•
Classifying figures	•	•	•	•	•	•		•						•			•	•		•					•							•	•	•	•
Classifying triangles																•								•	•							•	•	•	•
Classifying quadrilaterals				•				•						•			•	•		•					•							•	•	•	•
Solid figures		•		•		•		•						•			•				•		•	•	•		•	•				•	•	•	•
Spatial visualization																•	•		•	•	•		•	•			•	•				•	•	•	•
Congruence	•	•			•	•		✓						•			•								•						•	•	•	•	•
Similarity														•			•								•	•				•		•	•	•	•
Symmetry	•	•		•	•	•		•						•			•								•						•	•	•	•	•
Translation/reflection/rotation													•			•	•								•						•	•	•	•	•
Measuring and classifying angles														•		•	•				•			•	•	•						✓	•	•	•
Parallel and perpendicular lines														•			•	•							•							•	•	•	•
Relationships with parallel lines																																✓		•	•
Perimeter		•			•		•		•				•		•	•	•	•	•		•		•		•	•					•	•	•	•	•
Radius and diameter														•	•		•	•							•						•	•	•	•	•
Circumference																	•	•			•				•						•	•	•	•	•
Areas of triangles																									•							•	•	•	•
Areas of quadrilaterals										•		•		•		•	•	•	•	•	•	•		•	•	•	•	•	•	•	•	•	•	•	•
Surface area																																•	•	•	•
Volume														•			•			•				•	•						•	•	•	•	•
Pythagorean Theorem																																•	•	•	•
Manipulatives																																			
Used in concept development	•	•	•	•	•	•	•	•	•	•	•	•	•	•	•	•	•	•	•	•	•		•	•	•	•	•	•		•	•	•	•	•	•
Used in reteaching and individualized instruction	•	•	•	•	•	•	•	•	•	•	•	•	•	•	•	•	•	•	•	•	•	•	•	•	•	•	•	•	•	•	•	•	•	•	•
Measurement																																			
Length																																			
Estimate	✓		•	•	•	•	•				•	•	✓	•	•	•	•	•	•	•	✓	•	•	•	•	•	✓	•		•	•	•	•	•	•
Compare	✓		•	•	•	•	•	•		•	•	•	✓	•	•	•	•	•	•	•	•	•		•		•	•			•			•	•	•
Use nonstandard units	✓		•	•	•	•		•			•	•	•					•	•		•			•	•		•	•					•		
Use customary units			•	•	•	•	✓	•	•	•	•	•	•	•	•	•	•	•	•	•	•	•	•	•	•	•	•	•	•	•	•	•	•	•	•
Use metric units			•	•	•	•	✓	•	•	•	•	•	✓	•	•	•	•	•	•	•	✓	•	•	•	•	•	✓	•	•	•	•	•	•	•	•
Mass/Weight																																			
Estimate	✓	•	•		•	•	•		•					•	•	•	•	•		•	•	•		•		•	•	•		•		•			
Compare	✓	•	•		•	•		•	•	•	•		✓	•		•	•	•		•	•	•		•		•									
Use nonstandard units	✓	•			•	•					•																								
Use customary units					•	•			•	•	•	•	✓	•	•	•	•	•	•	•	•	•	•	•		•				•	•	•	•	•	•
Use metric units					•	•	•	•	•		•	•	✓	•	•	•	•	•	•	•	•	•	•	•	•	•	•	•	•	•	•	•	•	•	•
Capacity																																			
Estimate	•	•		•	•	•			•					•		•	•				•	•				•	•	•			•	•			
Compare					•	•			•			•	•				•			•	•	•				•						•			
Use nonstandard units				•	•	•								•																					
Use customary units					•	•			•		•		•	•	•	•	•	•	•	•	•	•	•	•	•	•				•	•	•	•	•	•
Use metric units					•				•			•		•	•	•		•	•	•	•	•	•	•		•		•		•		•	•	•	•
Temperature																																			
Estimate	•		•		•	•																										•	•		
Use degrees Fahrenheit						•		•		•	•		•		•		•		•		•	•	•	•						•	•		•	•	•
Use degrees Celsius																					•	•	•	•			•				•	•	•	•	•
Converting within customary system							•	•	•	•			•	•		•		•	•	•	•	•		•		•		•				•	•	•	•
Converting within metric system							•	•	•				•	•	•	•	•	•	•	•	•			•		•		•				•	•	•	•
Telling time																																			
To the hour		✓				•		•	✓	•	•				•	•		•																	
To the half hour		•				•		•	✓	•	•				•	•																			
To the quarter hour		•				•		•	✓	•	•				•	•																			
To the minute									✓	•	✓				•	•		•																	
Adding and subtracting time			•	•	•	•		•			•	•	•	•	•	•	•	•		•	•			•		•							•		
A.M. and P.M.										•	•				•	•	•	•	•	•		•	•			•									
Estimating time	•	•	•	•	•	•		•		•	•	•		•	•	•		•	•	•															
Calculating elapsed time			•	•	•	•	•		•	•	•			•	•	•	•	•	•	•	•		•	•	•	•	•			•	•	•	•		
Reading a calendar	•	•			•	•	•	•	•	•	•	•	•	•		•	•	•	•																
Reading a map		•		•			•	•	•	•	•	•	•	•	•	•	•	•	•	•	•	•	•	•	•	•	•	•		•		•	•	•	•

✓ indicates Mastery Checkpoints

**Mathematics: Applications and Connections* Courses 1–3, Levels 6–8 © 1999

	K		Level 1				Level 2				Level 3				Level 4						Level 5						Level 6						Glencoe*		
Units	1	2	1	2	3	4	1	2	3	4	1	2	3	4	1	2	3	4	5	6	1	2	3	4	5	6	1	2	3	4	5	6	6	7	8
Mental Arithmetic																																			
Basic fact strategies–addition and subtraction																																			
Use patterns		•	•	•	•	✓	•																										•	•	•
Count on	•	•	✓	✓	✓	✓	•																												
Count up or back		•	✓	✓	✓	✓	•																												
Use doubles				✓	•	✓	•			•	•																								
Use doubles plus 1				✓	•	✓	•				•																								
Make 10	•		•	•	•	•		•																											
Use properties			•	•		•	•																												
Use related facts			•	•		•	•								•																				
Basic fact strategies–multiplication and division																																			
Use patterns										•		•	•			•																	•	•	•
Use skip-counting				•	•	•				•		•			•	•																			
Use properties												•				•																			
Use related facts												✓			•	•			•		•														
Chain calculations		•	•	•	•	•	•	•	•	•	•	•	•	•	•	•	•		•	•	•	•	•		•		•	•		•	•		•	•	•
Multidigit addition and subtraction								•	•	•	•	•	•	•	•	•	•	•	•	•	•	•	•	•	•	•	•	•		•	•	•	•	•	•
Multidigit multiplication and division												•		•	•	•	•	•	•	•	•	•	•	•		•	•	•		•	•	•	•	•	•
Multiples and powers of 10					•	✓				•		✓	•	•	•	•	•	•	•	•	•	•	•	•	•	•	•	•	•	•	•	•	•	•	•
Using computational patterns			•	•	•	✓	•			•	•	•	•	•	•	•	•	•	•		•	•	•	•	•	•	•	•	•	•	•	•	•	•	•
Approximation			•	•	•	•				•	✓	•	•	•	✓	•	•	•	•	•	•	•	•	•	•	•	•	•	•	•	•	•			
Find a fraction of a number				•	•	•		•					•		•					•			•	•						•			•	•	•
Find a percent of a number																										•			•		•	•		•	•
Use divisibility rules																						•							•	•			•	•	•
Find equivalent fractions, decimals, and percents													•	•						•			•	•	•	•				•		•	•	•	•
Multiplication (whole numbers)																																			
Meaning of multiplication		•		•	•	•				•		•				•		•			•														
Basic facts						•				✓		✓	•	•	•	✓	•	•	•	•	•	•	•	•		•	•	•	•	•	•	•			
Missing factor problems										•		•	•			•	•	•	•		•	•	•	•	•	•	•		•	•	•	•			
One-digit multipliers										•				✓		•	•	✓	•	•	✓	•	•	•	•	•	✓	•	•	•	•	•	•	•	•
Two-digit multipliers														•	•	•	•	✓	•	•	✓	•	•	•	•	•	✓	•	•		•	•	•	•	•
Greater multipliers															•	•		✓	•		✓	•	•		•	•	✓	•	•			•	•	•	•
Multiplying by multiples of 10												✓	•	•	•	•	•	✓	•	•	✓	•	•	•	•	✓	•	•	•	•	•	•	•	•	•
Multiplying money										•		•				•	•	•	•	•	✓	•	•			•	•	•			•		•	•	•
Estimating products										•		•		•		•	•	•	•	•	✓	•	•		•	•	✓	•	•				•	•	•
Number and numeration																																			
Reading and writing numbers	✓	•	✓	✓	•	✓	✓			✓	✓			•	✓					•	✓						✓								
Number lines		•	✓	•	•	•	•			•	•		•		•			•		•			•	•		•	•						•	•	•
Counting	✓	•	✓	•	•	✓	✓			•	✓			•	✓	•					✓														
Skip counting		•		•	•	•		•		•	•	•			•	•																			
Ordinal numbers	•	•	•	•	•	•																													
Place value		•		•	•	•	•	•	•		•		•	•	•	•	•	•		•	✓		•		•		✓	•	•		•		•	•	
Roman numerals										•				•						•	•			•											
Comparing and ordering numbers	✓	•		•	•	✓	•	•		•	•	•	•	•	•	•			•	•	✓		•	•	•		✓	•		•	•		•	•	•
Rounding									•		•				•			•	•	•	•	•	•	•	•	•	•	•				•	•	•	
Estimation/Approximation		•	•	•	•	•	•				•		•	•	✓	•	•	•	•	•	•	•	•	•	•	•	✓	•	•	•	•	•	•	•	•
Integers (negative numbers)				•		•		•		•	•		•		•	•						•		•	•	•	•	•			•		•	•	•
Even/odd numbers				•	•		•		✓	•	•				•		•	•	•	•				•											
Prime and composite numbers																			•		•			•					•				•	•	•
Factors and prime factorization																•	•	•	•		•		•	•					•	•			•	•	•
Common factors																•								•					•	•		•			
Common multiples																•					•	•		•						•			•	•	•
Checking divisibility																						•	•						•	•			•	•	•
Exponents														•				•		•	•		•			•		•			•	•	•	•	•
Exponential notation and scientific notation																		•		•								•				•	•	•	•
Square roots																															•	•	•	•	•
Patterns, Relations, and Functions																																			
Classifying objects	✓	•	•	•																															
Number patterns	•	•	✓	•	•	•	•	•	•	•	•	•	•	•	•	•	•	•		•	•	•	•	•		•				•	•		•	•	•
Picture patterns	✓		•	•	•	•																													
Geometric patterns	✓	•	•	•	•			•	✓			•	•	•																			•	•	•
Ordered pairs																	•	•	•	•		✓		•	•						•		•	•	•
Graphing ordered pairs																	•		•	•		✓		•	•						✓		•	•	•
Inequalities	✓	•		•	•	✓	•	•	✓	•	✓		•	•	•			•		✓	•		•	•		•	•			•			•	•	•
Function machines/tables	•	•		•	•	•	•	•		•		•			•	•	•	•	•			✓		•						•	✓		•	•	•
Function rules	•	•		•	•	•		•		•		•	•		•	•	•	•	•	•	•	✓	•	•						•	✓		•	•	•
Graphing functions																	•			•		✓		•							✓		•	•	•
Probability																																			
Determining possible outcomes	•					•				•				•	•					•				•		•		•		•			•	•	•
Predicting outcomes	•	•	•			•				•			•	•	•					•	•	•				•		•		•			•	•	•
Conducting experiments	•	•				•				•				•	•					•		•		•		•				•			•	•	•
Experimental probability																				•						•				•			•	•	•
Theoretical probability																				•						•		•		•			•	•	•
Using probability to plan strategies			•	•	•	•	•	•			•	•	•	•	•	•	•	•	•	•	•		•	•	•	•	•	•	•	•	•		•	•	•

✓ indicates Mastery Checkpoints

**Mathematics: Applications and Connections* Courses 1–3, Levels 6–8 © 1999

	K		Level 1				Level 2				Level 3				Level 4						Level 5						Level 6						Glencoe*		
Units	1	2	1	2	3	4	1	2	3	4	1	2	3	4	1	2	3	4	5	6	1	2	3	4	5	6	1	2	3	4	5	6	6	7	8
Problem Solving																																			
Work with various problem types • Multi-step problems • Multiple solutions • No solutions	●	●	✓	●	●	●	●	●	●	●	●	✓	●	●	●	✓	●	●	●	●	●	●	●	●	●	●	●	●	●	●	●	●	●	●	●
Use logical reasoning, including: • Interpreting data • Checking reasonableness • Solving problems with too much information • Interpreting the quotient and remainder • Choosing the appropriate operation • Using estimation • Using guess and check	●	●	✓	●	●	●	●	✓	●	●	✓	✓	●	●	✓	✓	●	●	●	●	●	●	●	●	●	●	✓	●	●	●	●	●	●	●	●
Choose an appropriate strategy, including: • Solving a simpler problem • Eliminating possibilities • Acting it out • Using/finding a pattern • Using/making a table • Using/drawing a picture or diagram • Using manipulatives • Conducting an experiment	●	●	✓	●	●	●	●	●	●	●	●	✓	●	●	●	✓	●	●	●	●	●	●	●	●	●	●	●	●	●	●	●	●	●	●	●
Ratio and Proportion																																			
Meaning/use of ratio and proportion															●								●	✓	●	●				●	●		●	●	●
Rates																		●	●	●	●	●	●	✓			●	●		✓	●	●	●	●	●
Similar figures																		●							●					●		●	●	●	●
Map scales													●	●											●	●		●		●			●	●	●
Meaning of percent																										●			●				●	●	●
Percent of a number																				●						✓			✓	●	●	●	●	●	●
Percent discounts																										✓			✓		●		●	●	●
Sales tax															●				●	●						✓			✓		●			●	
Simple/compound interest																					●					●			●	●				●	●
Statistics and graphing																																			
Surveying	●	●	●			●				●			●		●		●			●			●			●	●				●		●	●	●
Tallying	●		●			●		●		●			●		●	●		●		●						●				●			●	●	●
Making tables with data	●	●	●	●	●	●	●	●		●	●	●	●	●	●	●	●	●	●	●	●		●	✓		●	●			●	●		●		
Real and picture graphs	●	●	●				●						●				●	●													●		●	●	●
Bar graphs	●	●	●		●		●			●	●		●	●		●	●		●	●	●		●	●							●		●	●	●
Line graphs													●	●			●	●	●	●	●	●	●			●					●		●	●	●
Circle graphs																	●						●						●		●	●	●	●	●
Finding the mean																			●	●			●	✓	●	●				✓	●		●	●	●
Finding the median																			●				●	●						●			●	●	●
Finding the mode																			●				●	●						●			●	●	●
Subtraction (whole numbers)																																			
Meaning of subtraction		●	●				●																												
Basic facts		●	✓	✓	●	●	✓	●	●	●	✓	●	●	●	✓	●	●	●	●		●	●	●	●		●	●	●	●	●	●				
Missing term problems				●	●	●	●			●	●				●	●	●	●	●		●	●	●	●	●	●	●		●		●				
Two-digit numbers				✓	✓	✓	●	✓	●	●	✓	●	●	●	✓	●	●	●	●	●	●	●	●	●	●	●	●	●		●	●	●	●	●	●
Three-digit numbers										✓	✓	●	●	●	✓	●	●	●	●	●	✓	●	●	●	●	●	✓	●	●	●	●	●	●	●	●
Greater numbers										●	✓	●	●	●	✓	●	●	●	●		✓	●	●	●		●	✓	●	●		●	●	●	●	●
Subtracting money			●	✓		●	●	●	●	●	●	●	●	●	●	●	●			●	✓	●					✓	●					●	●	●
Estimating differences					●	●				●	✓			●	✓	●	●	●	●	●	✓	●			●	●	✓	●	●				●	●	●
Technology																																			
Calculators																																			
Counting		●	●			●			●					●																					
Skip counting		●				●				●		●			●	●						✓													
Computation with whole numbers		●	●	●		●	●			●	●	●	●	●	●	●	●	●	●	●	●	✓	●	●	●	●	●	●		●	●	●	●	●	●
Computation with decimals													●			●				●	●	●	●	●	●	●		●	●	●	●	●	●	●	●
Computation with fractions																							●	●		●	●			●			●	●	●
Computation with integers (negative numbers)											●				●	●						●		●			●						●	●	●
Using function rules				●				●							●	●			●	●		●									●		●	●	●
Order of operations															●	●					●										●		●	●	●
Function keys																		●	●	●	●					●		●	●			●	●	●	●
Computers																																			
Spreadsheets														●			●	●	●	●	●	●	●	●	●	●	●	●	●	●	●	●	●	●	●
Functions												●	●		●	●	●	●		●		●									●				
Graphs											●		●				●	●	●	●	●	●	●	●							●	●			
Charts and tables											●	●	●	●	●	●	●	●	●	●	●	●	●	●	●	●		●	●	●	●	●			

✓ indicates Mastery Checkpoints

**Mathematics: Applications and Connections* Courses 1–3, Levels 6–8 © 1999